AZEOTROPIC DATA

Tables of azeotropes and nonazeotropes compiled by L. H. Horsley and coworkers at the Dow Chemical Co. Included are a formula index, a bibliography, and three articles, "Vapor-Liquid Equilibrium Diagrams of Alcohol-Ketone Azeotropes as a Function of Pressure," "Graphical Method for Predicting Effect of Pressure on Azeotropic Systems," and "Graphical Method for Predicting Azeotropism and Effect of Pressure on Azeotropic Constants."

Number six of the Advances in Chemistry Series
Edited by the staff of *Industrial and Engineering Chemistry*

Published June 1952 by
AMERICAN CHEMICAL SOCIETY
1155 Sixteenth Street, N.W.
Washington, D. C.

UNIVERSITY OF NOTTINGHAM
UNIVERSITY LIBRARY NOTTINGHAM
WITHDRAWN
FROM THE LIBRARY

CONTENTS

Table of Azeotropes and Nonazeotropes

L. H. HORSLEY

The Dow Chemical Co., Midland, Mich.

This table of azeotropes and nonazeotropes is a revision of the two previous tables published in *Analytical Chemistry*, August 1947 and July 1949 (*167*, *168*), together with approximately 6000 new systems, bringing the total number of systems to over 14,000.

The table is arranged in two parts: (1) table of binary systems and (2) table of ternary systems, followed by a formula index and bibliography. As in the previous tables, the individual systems are arranged according to empirical formula using the *Chemical Abstracts* system, except that inorganic compounds are listed first in alphabetical order, followed by organic systems in the order carbon, hydrogen, bromine, chlorine, fluorine, iodine, nitrogen, oxygen, sulfur.

For a given binary system the lower order compound according to formula is chosen as the A-component and under each A-component the B-components are likewise arranged according to empirical formula. For ternary systems the same arrangement is used, using the lowest order formula as A-component, the next lowest order as B-component, and the highest order formula as C-component.

To facilitate finding all systems containing a given component a formula index is included at the end of the tables listing the systems containing a given component.

The following abbreviations are used in the table:

Min. b.p. Minimum boiling point azeotrope with no data given
V-l. Vapor-liquid equilibrium data are given in the original reference
Vol. Azeotropic concentration is given in volume per cent. Unless so indicated, all concentrations are weight per cent
Mm. Pressure in mm. of mercury absolute
~ Approximate
> Greater than
< Less than

For systems for which more than one literature reference is available, an attempt has been made to select those data that are most reliable and complete. The auxiliary references for which no data have been given are listed with an asterisk. Where there is appreciable discrepancy in the data of two references, both sets of data have been included.

Because Lecat has published identical data on most of his systems in two or more journals, only his most recent reference is listed here, except where there are large discrepancies in his data, in which case both sets of data have been included.

Table I. Binary Systems

No	B-Component			Azeotropic Data		
No	Formula	Name	B.P., ° C.	B.P., ° C.	Wt. % A	Ref.
A =	**A**	**Argon**	**−186**			
1	N_2	Nitrogen, 500–1500 mm.	−195	Nonazeotrope, V-l.		164
A =	**AgCl**	**Silver Chloride**	**1550**			
2	Cl_2Pb	Lead chloride	954	Nonazeotrope		255
A =	$\mathbf{BCl_3}$	**Boron Chloride**	**11.5**			
3	B_2H_6	Boron hydride	−92.5	Nonazeotrope		263
A =	$\mathbf{BF_3}$	**Boron Fluoride**	**−100**			
4	B_2H_6	Boron hydride	−92	−106	77.2	263
5	H_2O	Water, 100 mm.	....	....	62	262
			100	....	60	262
		1 mm.	....	46	65	390
6	H_3N	Ammonia	−33	180	80	390
7	CH_2O_2	Formic acid, 11 mm.	....	43	42	390
8	CH_4O	Methanol, 4 mm.	....	58	52	390
9	C_2H_3N	Acetonitrile	81.6	101	62	390
10	$C_2H_4O_2$	Acetic acid, 15 mm	....	70	47	262
			118.1	150	36	262
		746 mm.	118	140	....	390
		13 mm.	....	59	36	390
11	$C_2H_4O_2$	Methyl formate	31.9	91	53	390
12	C_2H_5ClO	2-Chloroethanol, 2 mm.	....	59	30	387
13	C_2H_6O	Ethyl alcohol, 15 mm.	....	51	42	390
14	C_2H_6O	Methyl ether	−21	127	60	390
15	$C_3H_6O_2$	Ethyl formate	54.1	102	48	390
16	$C_3H_6O_2$	Methyl acetate	57.1	110	48	390
17	$C_3H_6O_2$	Propionic acid, 17 mm.	....	62	31	390
18	$C_3H_6O_3$	Methyl glycolate, 3 mm.	....	60	43	390
19	C_3H_8O	Ethyl methyl ether	10.8	127	53	390
20	C_3H_8O	Propyl alcohol, 2 mm.	....	56	36	390
21	C_3H_9N	Trimethylamine	3.5	230	53	390
22	$C_4H_6O_2$	Crotonic acid, 12.5 mm	....	81	28	390
23	$C_4H_8O_2$	Butyric acid, 11 mm.	....	64	28	390
24	$C_4H_8O_2$	Ethyl acetate	77.05	119	44	390
25	$C_4H_{10}O$	Butyl alcohol, 3 mm.	....	64.5	31	390
26	$C_4H_{10}O$	Ethyl ether	34.5	125	48	390
27	C_5H_5N	Pyridine	115.5	300	46	390
28	$C_5H_{10}O_2$	Ethyl propionate	99.15	116	40	390
29	$C_5H_{10}O_2$	Propyl acetate	101.6	127	40	390
30	$C_6H_{14}O$	Amyl methyl ether, 10 mm.	....	55	40	390
31	$C_6H_{14}O$	Isopropyl ether, 98 mm.	....	61	40	390
A =	$\mathbf{B_2H_6}$	**Boron Hydride**	**−92.5**			
31a	BrH	Hydrobromic acid	−67	Nonazeotrope		263
32	ClH	Hydrochloric acid	−85	−94	64	263
		205 mm.	−106	−115	68	263
33	C_2H_6	Ethane, 100–760 mm.	−88	Nonazeotrope		263
A =	**BrH**	**Hydrobromic Acid**	**−73**			
34	H_2O	Water	100	126	47.5	243
		100 mm.	....	74.12	49.80	32, 191*, 332*
		500 mm.	....	112.94	48.19	
		900 mm.	....	129.13	47.40	
		1200 mm.	....	137.34	47.03	
35	H_2S	Hydrogen sulfide	−70/480	−70/420	60.5 V-l.	378
36	SO_2	Sulfur dioxide	−10	Nonazeotrope, V-l.		378
A =	$\mathbf{Br_2}$	**Bromine**	**58.75**			
37	I_2	Iodine	185.3	Nonazeotrope		243
38	CCl_4	Carbon tetrachloride, 735 mm.	76	57.7	89 V-l.	375

No.	Formula	B-Component Name	B.P., ° C.	Azeotropic Data B.P., ° C.	Wt. % A	Ref.
A =	**Br_4Sn**	**Tin Bromide**	**206.7**			
39	I_4Sn	Tin iodide	346.0	Nonazeotrope, V-l.		*314*
40	$C_7H_{12}O_4$	Ethyl malonate	198.9	Reacts		*243*
41	$C_{10}H_8$	Naphthalene	218.1	Nonazeotrope		*243*
A =	**C**	**Graphite**	**2300/0.01**			
42	MnS	Manganese sulfide	....	1375/0.01mm.	....	*302*
				% graphite is inversely proportional to pressure		
A =	**CCl_2O**	**Phosgene**	**8.2**			
43	FH	Hydrofluoric acid, 3000 mm.	....	21	77	*21*
44	$C_2H_4Cl_2$	1,2-Dichloroethane	83.45	Nonazeotrope		*255*
A =	**CF_2O**	**Carbonyl Fluoride**	**....**			
45	CF_4O	Trifluoromethyl hypofluorite	−94.2	−97.0	10	*183*
A =	**CO_2**	**Carbon Dioxide**	**−79.1**			
46	ClH	Hydrochloric acid	−82	Nonazeotrope		*243*
47	Cl_2	Chlorine	−37.6	Nonazeotrope		*255*
48	H_2O	Water	100	Nonazeotrope		*243*
49	SO_2	Sulfur dioxide	−10	Nonazeotrope		*243*
50	CS_2	Carbon disulfide	46.2	Nonazeotrope		*243*
51	CH_3Cl	Chloromethane	−23.7	Nonazeotrope		*195*
52	C_2H_5Cl	Chloroethane	12.4	Nonazeotrope		*239*
53	C_2H_6	Ethane	−93	Max. v.p. mixture		*195*
54	C_2H_6O	Methyl ether	−23.65	Nonazeotrope		*255*
A =	**ClH**	**Hydrochloric Acid**	**−80**			
55	H_2O	Water, 50 mm.	....	48.724	23.42	*33*
		250 mm	....	81.205	21.883	*56**
		760 mm.	100	108.584	20.222	*191**
		1220 mm.	....	122.98	19.358	*333**
56	SO_2	Sulfur dioxide	−10	Nonazeotrope at −35° C.		*378*
57	C_2H_6	Ethane, 48 atm.	....	15	56	*243*
			....	25.4	59	*243*
58	C_2H_6O	Methyl ether	−22	−2	38	*124*
				Azeotropic to critical point		*196*
			−23.65	−1.5	60	*243*
59	C_6H_7N	Aniline	184.35	244.8	~27.5	*243*
A =	**$ClHO_4$**	**Perchloric Acid**	**110**			
60	H_2O	Water	100	203	71.6	*243*
A =	**Cl_2**	**Chlorine**	**−37.6**			
61	H_2O	Water	100	Nonazeotrope		*243*
62	SO_2	Sulfur dioxide	−9.7	−34.7	89	*68*
		7 atm.	....	18	80	*68*
		20 atm.	....	57.5	75.5	*68*
A =	**Cl_2Cu**	**Cupric Chloride**	**....**			
63	Cl_2Pb	Lead chloride	954	Min b.p.		*255*
64	Cl_2Zn	Zinc chloride	732	Min. b.p.		*255*
A =	**Cl_2O_2S**	**Thionyl Chloride**	**70.5**			
65	Cl_3OP	Phosphorus oxychloride	107.2	....	96.5/0° C.	*255*
A =	**Cl_2Pb**	**Lead Chloride**	**954**			
66	Cl_2Zn	Zinc chloride	732	Nonazeotrope		*255*
A =	**Cl_3Sb**	**Antimony Chloride**	**....**			
67	C_nH_{2n+2}	Paraffins	200–220	Min. b.p.		*89, 386*
68	....	Aromatics	200–220	Nonazeotrope		*89, 386*

No.	B-Component Formula	Name	B.P., ° C.	Azeotropic Data B.P., ° C.	Wt. % A	Ref.
A =	**Cl_4Si**	**Silicon Chloride**	**56.7**			
69	Cl_4Ti	Titanium chloride	136	Nonazeotrope		*255*
70	CCl_4	Carbon tetrachloride	76.75	Nonazeotrope		*425*
71	$CHCl_3$	Chloroform	61	55.6	70	*343*
72	CH_3NO_2	Nitromethane	101	53.8	94	*340*
73	C_2H_3N	Acetonitrile	82	49.0	90.6	*340, 342**
74	$C_2H_4Cl_2$	1,1-Dichloroethane	57.4	52.7	63.5	*343*
75	$C_2H_4Cl_2$	1,2-Dichloroethane	83.7	Azeotropic?		*343*
76	C_3H_3N	Acrylonitrile	79	51.2	89	*340, 342**
77	C_3H_5N	Propionitrile	97	55.6	92	*340*
78	C_3H_9SiCl	Chlorotrimethylsilane		Azeotrope composition independent of pressure		*339, 342**
			57.5	54.7	64.8	*340*
79	C_6H_{14}	3-Methylpentane	63.3	Nonazeotrope		*343*
80	C_6H_{14}	2-Methylpentane	60.4	Nonazeotrope		*343*
A =	**Cl_4Sn**	**Tin Chloride**	**113.85**			
81	Cl_4Ti	Titanium chloride	136	Nonazeotrope		*255*
82	C_3H_5ClO	Epichlorohydrin	116.45	Reacts		*243*
83	C_5H_5N	Pyridine	115.5	Reacts		*243*
84	C_6H_6	Benzene	80.2	Nonazeotrope		*243*
85	C_6H_{12}	Cyclohexane	80.75	Nonazeotrope		*255*
86	$C_6H_{12}O_2$	Ethylbutyrate	119.9	Reacts		*243*
87	C_7H_8	Toluene	110.7	109.15	52	*243*
88	C_7H_{14}	Methylcyclohexane	101.15	<100.8	>15	*242*
89	C_7H_{14}	Methylcyclohexane	101.1	Nonazeotrope		*225*
90	C_8H_{10}	Ethylbenzene	136.15	Nonazeotrope		*255*
91	C_8H_{16}	1,3-Dimethylcyclohexane	120.7	112.5	80	*242*
92	C_8H_{18}	2,5-Dimethylhexane	109.4	107.5	40	*228, 255*
93	C_8H_{18}	Octane	125.75	<113.2	>80	*225, 242*
A =	**Cl_4Ti**	**Titanium Chloride**	**136**			
94	CCl_4	Carbon tetrachloride	76.75	Nonazeotrope		*255*
A =	**Cu**	**Copper**	**2310**			
95	Pb	Lead	1525	Azeotropic		*255*
96	Sn	Tin	2275	Max. b.p.		*243*
A =	**FH**	**Hydrofluoric Acid**	**19.54**			
97	H_2O	Water	100	111.35	35.6	*121*
				B.p. curve		*332**
		750 mm.	100	112.0	38.26 V-l.	*275*
98	CCl_2F_2	Dichlorodifluoromethane	....	20	8	
				(Under pressure)		*21*
99	$CHClF_2$	Chlorodifluoromethane	....	....	1–2.2	*21*
100	C_4H_{10}	Butane	0	Min. b.p.		*122, 132*
101	C_4H_{10}	2-Methylpropane	−10	Min. b.p.		*122, 132*
102	$C_4H_{10}O$	Ethyl ether	34.5	74	40	*66*
A =	**F_3Sb**	**Antimony Fluoride**	**319**			
103	F_5Sb	Antimony pentafluoride	155	390	62	*243*
			155	384	80	*243*
A =	**HI**	**Hydriodic Acid**	**−34**			
104	H_2O	Water, 744 mm.	100	127	57	*191*, 332*
			....	18	60.5	*332*
			....	100	58.2	*332*
105	H_2S	Hydrogen sulfide	−63.5	Nonazeotrope/60° C., V-l.		*378*
A =	**HNO_3**	**Nitric Acid**	**86**			
106	H_2O	Water, 735 mm.	100	120.5	68	*332, 367**
		75 mm.	....	....	66.7	*332*
		1200 mm	....	....	68.7	*332*

	B-Component			Azeotropic Data		
No.	Formula	Name	B.P., ° C.	B.P., ° C.	Wt. % A	Ref.
A =	H_2O	**Water**	**100**			
107	HCN	Hydrocyanic acid	26	V.p. curve		243
108	H_2O_2	Hydrogen peroxide	152.1	Nonazeotrope, V-l.		133
109	H_2S	Hydrogen sulfide	−63.5	Nonazeotrope		243
110	H_3N	Ammonia	−33.5	Nonazeotrope		243
111	H_4N_2	Hydrazine	113.5	120	28.5	243
112	O_2S	Sulfur dioxide	−10	Nonazeotrope		243
113	O_3S	Sulfur trioxide	47	338	~19	243
			....	....	17.2	332
114	$O_{10}P_4$	Phosphorus pentoxide, 104 mm.	....	694	8.9	391
		753 mm.	....	869	7.9	391
115	CCl_4	Carbon tetrachloride	76.75	66	4.1	93, 279*
116	CS_2	Carbon disulfide	46.25	42.6	2.8	90, 268*
117	$CHCl_3$	Chloroform	61.2	56.12	2.8	323, 409*
118	CH_2Cl_2	Dichloromethane	41.5	38.1	1.5	15
119	CH_2O	Formaldehyde	−21	Nonazeotrope, V-l.		305
120	CH_2O_2	Formic acid	100.75	107.2	22.6	323
			....	....	22.5	109
		45 lb./sq. inch abs.	....	139	15	109
		175 mm.	....	63	35	109
		15 mm.	....	....	40	109
121	CH_3NO_2	Nitromethane	101.0–101.7	83.6	23.6 V-l.	120*, 353
122	CH_3NO_3	Methyl nitrate	64.8	<61.5	<16	240
123	CH_4O	Methanol, 0–150 lb./sq. inch gage		Nonazeotrope		290
				V-l. data		191*, 290, 433*
124	CH_5N	Methylamine	−6	Nonazeotrope		255
125	C_2HCl_3	Trichloroethylene	86.2–86.6	73.6	5.4	138*, 323
126	C_2HCl_3O	Chloral	97.75	95	7	328
127	C_2HCl_5	Pentachloroethane	162.0	95.9	....	255
128	$C_2H_2Cl_2$	*cis*-1,2-Dichloroethylene	60.2	55.3	3.35	71
129	$C_2H_2Cl_2$	*trans*-1,2-Dichloroethylene	48.35	45.3	1.9	71
130	C_2H_3N	Acetonitrile	81.5	76.0	14.2 V-l.	80*, 289, 258*, 309*, 394*
		300 mm.	54.4	51.1	10.5 V-l.	
		150 mm.	36.7	34.1	7.2 V-l.	
131	$C_2H_4Cl_2$	1,2-Dichloroethane	84	72	19.5	13, 148*
132	$C_2H_4Cl_2O$	Bis(chloromethyl) ether	106	Min. b.p.		286
133	C_2H_4O	Acetaldehyde	20.2	Nonazeotrope, V-l.		77
134	C_2H_4O	Ethylene oxide	10	Nonazeotrope, V-l.		77
135	$C_2H_4O_2$	Acetic acid	118	Nonazeotrope, V-l.		191*, 370
136	$C_2H_4O_2$	Methyl formate	31.9	Nonazeotrope		150
137	C_2H_5Br	Bromoethane	38.4	37	1.3 vol.	332
138	C_2H_5ClO	2-Chloroethanol, 748 mm.	128.7	97.75	58	16, 185, 36*
		50 mm.	....	35–36	60	16, 36*, 185
139	C_2H_5I	Iodoethane	70	66	3–4 vol.	303
140	C_2H_5IO	1-Iodo-2-ethanol	176	98.7	77	93
141	C_2H_5NO	Acetamide	221.2	Nonazeotrope		209
142	$C_2H_5NO_3$	Ethyl nitrate	87.68	74.35	22	218
143	C_2H_6O	Ethyl alcohol	78.3	78.174	4.0	14*, 64*, 138*, 282, 323*, 433
			Effect of pressure			189, 410
144	$C_2H_6O_2$	Glycol	197.4	Nonazeotrope		90,209
145	$C_2H_6SO_4$	Methyl sulfate	189.1	98.6	73	255
146	C_2H_7N	Dimethylamine	7.3	Nonazeotrope		255
147	C_2H_7N	Ethylamine	16.55	Nonazeotrope		255
148	$C_2H_8N_2$	Ethylenediamine	116	118	20–25	80
149	C_3H_3N	Acrylonitrile	....	70	13	394
			77.3	71	12	93
150	C_3H_4O	2-Propyn-1-ol	....	V-l.		364
151	C_3H_5ClO	1-Chloro-2-propanone	121	Min. b.p.		286
152	C_3H_5ClO	α-Chloropropionaldehyde	86	80.5–81	....	284

	B-Component			Azeotropic Data		
No.	Formula	Name	B.P., ° C.	B.P., ° C.	Wt. % A	Ref.
A =	H_2O	**Water** (*continued*)	**100**			
153	C_3H_5ClO	Epichlorohydrin	117	88	25	*112*
154	$C_3H_5ClO_2$	Methyl chloroacetate	131.4	92.7	36.15	*58*
155	C_3H_5I	3-Iodopropene	102.0	80.7	10?	*243*
156	C_3H_5N	Propionitrile	97	81.5–83	24	*394*
157	$C_3H_6Cl_2$	1,2-Dichloropropane	97	78	12	*137*
158	C_3H_6O	Acetone, 0–35 lb./sq. inch gage	....	Nonazeotrope		*155**, 290,*
		85 lb./sq. inch gage	125.1	124.1	3	*323**,*
		0–185 lb./sq. inch gage		V-l.		*351*
159	C_3H_6O	Allyl alcohol	96.90	88.89	27.7	*149**, 357,*
					V-l.	*412**, 422***
160	C_3H_6O	Propylene oxide	34.1	33.8	1.0	*255*
			35	Nonazeotrope		*93*
161	$C_3H_6O_2$	1,3-Dioxolane	75	70–73	6.7	*142*
162	$C_3H_6O_2$	Ethyl formate	54.1	Nonazeotrope		*150*
163	$C_3H_6O_2$	Methoxyacetaldehyde, 770 mm.	92.3	88.8	20	*94*
164	$C_3H_6O_2$	Methyl acetate	57	56.4	3.2–3.7	*127*
			57	Nonazeotrope		*150*
			57	56.5	V-l.	*271*
165	$C_3H_6O_2$	Propionic acid	141.4	99.1	82.2	*191**, 285*
					V-l.	*243***
166	$C_3H_6O_3$	Methyl carbonate	90.25	77.5	11	*255*
167	$C_3H_6O_3$	Trioxane	114.5	91.4	30	*411*
168	C_3H_7Cl	1-Chloropropane	46.4	43.4	1.0	*93*
169	C_3H_7Cl	2-Chloropropane	36.5	33.6	1.2	*93*
170	C_3H_7ClO	1-Chloro-2-propanol	127	....	49	*63*
			127.4	95.4	45.8	*61*
		743 mm.	...	96	50.9	*185*
171	C_3H_7ClO	2-Chloro-1-propanol	133.7	96	50.9	*255*
172	C_3H_7N	Allylamine	52.9	Nonazeotrope		*360*
173	C_3H_7NO	Propionamide	222.1	Nonazeotrope		*215*
174	$C_3H_7NO_2$	Isopropyl nitrite	40.1	Nonazeotrope		*255*
175	$C_3H_7NO_2$	Propyl nitrite	47.75	Nonazeotrope		*255*
176	C_3H_7NO	Propyl nitrate	110.5	84.8	25	*218, 240*
177	C_3H_8O	Isopropyl alcohol	82–82.3	80.3	12.6	*75**, 205**,*
					V-l.	*334**, 353,*
						*433***
178	C_3H_8O	Propyl alcohol, 740 mm.	97.3	87	28.3	*191**, 259,*
		1790 mm.	....	110	27.8	*307**,*
		2830 mm.	....	124	27.5	*433***
		3860 mm.	....	135	27.2	
		5930 mm.	....	151	26.7	
			97.3	87.76	29.1, V-l.	*120*
179	$C_3H_8O_2$	2-Methoxyethanol	124.5	99.9	77.8	*62, 236*
180	$C_3H_8O_2$	Methylal	42.3	42.05	1.4	*131*
			42.25	Nonazeotrope		*243*
181	$C_3H_8O_2$	1,2-Propanediol	187.8	Nonazeotrope		*255*
182	C_3H_9N	Trimethylamine	3.5	Nonazeotrope		*255*
183	$C_3H_{10}N_2$	1,2-Propanediamine	119.7	Nonazeotrope		*61*
184	C_4H_4O	Furan	31.7	Nonazeotrope		*255*
185	$C_4H_4N_2$	Pyrazine	114–115	95.5	40	*299*
186	C_4H_4O	1-Butyn-3-one	85	74	35	*371*
187	C_4H_4S	Thiophene	84	Min. b.p.		*418*
188	C_4H_5N	*cis-* and *trans*-crotononitrile	107.5–120.5	85	....	*67*
189	C_4H_5N	Pyrrol	129.8	93–93.5	....	*17*
190	C_4H_6O	3-Butyn-1-ol	128.9	Min. b.p.		*113*
191	$C_4H_6O_2$	Biacetyl	87–88	78.5	....	*57*
192	$C_4H_6O_2$	Methyl acrylate	80	71	7.2	*320*
193	C_4H_7Cl	1-Chloro-2-methyl-1-propene	68.1	61.9	7.5	*51*
194	C_4H_7ClO	α-3-Chloro-2-buten-1-ol	164	98.1	....	*154*
195	C_4H_7ClO	β-3-Chloro-2-buten-1-ol	166	98.8	....	*154*
196	$C_4H_7ClO_2$	4-Chloromethyl 1,3-dioxolane, 40 mm.	67	99	....	*355*
197	$C_4H_7ClO_2$	Ethyl chloroacetate	143.5	95.2	45.12	*58*
198	C_4H_7N	Butyronitrile	118	87.5	31	*394*
199	C_4H_7N	Isobutyronitrile	103	82.5	23	*394*

		B-Component		Azeotropic Data		
	[...]rmula	Name	B.P., ° C.	B.P., ° C.	Wt. % A	Ref.
A —	[...]O	**Water** (*continued*)	**100**			
200	$C_4H_8Cl_2O$	1,3-Dichloro-2-methyl-2-propanol	174	98.3	64.8	*51*
201	C_4H_8O	2-Butanone	79.6	73.41	11.3 V-l.	*232*, 271*, 358, 359**
		768–1243 mm.	Effect of pressure			*152*
202	C_4H_8O	1-Buten-3-ol	96–97	Azeotropic		*255*
203	C_4H_8O	Butyraldehyde	74	68	6	*204*
204	C_4H_8O	Crotonyl alcohol	119–120	....	60	*255*
205	$C_4H_8O_2$	Butyric acid	162.45	99.4	81.5	*191*, 225, 285, 306**
			....	....	80 V-l.	
206	$C_4H_8O_2$	Dioxane	101.32	87.82	18 V-l.	*61*, 90*, 368*
207	$C_4H_8O_2$	1,3-Dioxane	104–105	86.5	....	*355*
208	$C_4H_8O_2$	Ethyl acetate, 25 mm.	2.51	−1.90	3.60	*139*, 273, 359*, 427**
		250 mm.	46.87	42.55	6.28	
		760 mm.	77.15	70.38	8.47	
		1441 mm.	97.80	89.08	9.94	
209	$C_4H_8O_2$	Isobutyric acid	154.35	99.3	79	*243*
210	$C_4H_8O_2$	Isopropyl formate	68.8	65.0	3	*255*
211	$C_4H_8O_2$	Methyl propionate	79.85	71.4	3.9	*211*
212	$C_4H_8O_2$	Propyl formate	80.9	71.6	2.3	*150, 211*, 324**
213	$C_4H_8O_3$	Methyl lactate	144.8	99	80	*348*
214	C_4H_9Cl	1-Chlorobutane	77.9	68.1	6.6	*93*
215	C_4H_9Cl	1-Chloro-2-methylpropane	68.8	61.6	3.3	*93*
216	C_4H_9ClO	1-Chloro-2-methyl-2-propanol	126.7	93–94	34	*51*
217	C_4H_9I	1-Iodo-2-methylpropane	122.5	95–96	21 vol.	*303*
218	C_4H_9N	Methallylamine	78.7	78.4	4.1	*360*
219	$C_4H_9NO_2$	Butyl nitrite	78.2	70.0	~7	*255*
220	$C_4H_9NO_2$	Isobutyl nitrite	67.1	63.2	8	*255*
221	$C_4H_9NO_3$	Isobutyl nitrate	122.9	88.5	28	*239*
222	$C_4H_{10}O$	Butyl alcohol	117.4	92.7	42.5 V-l.	*52*, 61*, 215*, 304*, 359*, 367*, 387*
223	$C_4H_{10}O$	*sec*-Butyl alcohol	99.4	87.5	27.3	*75, 359**
			....	87.5	26, V-l.	*52*
224	$C_4H_{10}O$	*tert*-Butyl alcohol	82.5	79.9	11.76	*359*, 433*
225	$C_4H_{10}O$	Ethyl ether	34.5	34.15	1.26	*359*
		11 atm.	....	114	4.5	*312*
226	$C_4H_{10}O$	Isobutyl alcohol	107.0	89.8	33.0 V-l.	*191*, 313, 382, 433**
		100–130° C.	Effect of pressure			*55*
227	$C_4H_{10}O$	Methyl propyl ether	38.9	~38.7	~2	*243*
228	$C_4H_{10}O_2$	*l*-2,3-Butanediol, 14–75 lb./sq. inch gage	....	Nonazeotrope, V-l.		*398*
229	$C_4H_{10}O_2$	*meso*-2,4-Butanediol, 200–760 mm.	183–184	Nonazeotrope, V-l.		*293*
230	$C_4H_{10}O_2$	1,1-Dimethoxyethane	64.3	61.3	3.6	*20*
231	$C_4H_{10}O_2$	1,2-Dimethoxyethane	83	76	10.5	*62*, 174*
232	$C_4H_{10}O_2$	2-Ethoxyethanol	135.1	99.4	71.2	*62, 206**
			....	....	70.0 V-l.	*14, 92**
233	$C_4H_{10}O_2$	Ethoxymethoxymethane	65.91	61.25	4.4	*429*
234	$C_4H_{10}O_2$	1-Methoxy-2-propanol	118	96	~48.5	*93*
235	$C_4H_{10}O_2$	1-Methoxy-2-propanol	118	97.5	35	*317*
236	$C_4H_{10}O_2$	2-Methoxy-1-propanol	130	98	67	*317*
237	$C_4H_{10}O_3$	Diethylene glycol	245.5	Nonazeotrope		*236*
238	$C_4H_{11}NO$	3-Methoxypropylamine	116	....	~95	*4*
239	$C_5H_4O_2$	2-Furaldehyde	161.45	97.85	65	*236*
		100–200° F.	....	V-l.		*300*
240	C_5H_5N	Pyridine	115	94	57	*19, 233**
241	C_5H_6O	2-Methyl-3-butyn-2-ol	104.4	91.0	29 V-l.	*78*
242	C_5H_6O	2-Methylfuran	63.7	58.2	....	*310*
243	$C_5H_6O_2$	Furfuryl alcohol	169.35	98.5	80	*225*

No.	Formula	B-Component Name	B.P., ° C.	Azeotropic Data B.P., ° C.	Wt. % A	Ref.
A =	H_2O	**Water** (*continued*)	100			
244	C_5H_7NO	Furfurylamine	144	99	74	*381*
245	C_5H_8O	3-Methyl-3-buten-2-one, 735 mm.	98.5	82	....	*39*
		100 mm.	45–46	34–35	....	*39*
246	C_5H_8O	2-Methyl-3-butyne-2-ol, 100 mm.	....	Min. b.p.		*366*
247	$C_5H_8O_2$	Allyl acetate	105	Azeotropic		*286*
248	$C_5H_8O_2$	Ethyl acrylate	100	98.3	....	*324*
249	$C_5H_8O_2$	Methyl methacrylate, 200 mm.	....	49	11.6	*426*
			99.5	86–92	....	*426*
250	$C_5H_8O_2$	2,3-Pentanedione	109	86	....	*57*
251	$C_5H_9ClO_2$	Propyl chloroacetate	162.3	97.1	57.5	*58*
252	$C_5H_{10}O$	Cyclopentanol	140.85	96.25	58	*255*
253	$C_5H_{10}O$	Isovaleraldehyde	92.5	77	12	*93*
254	$C_5H_{10}O$	2-Methyltetrahydrofuran	77	Min. b.p.		*147*
255	$C_5H_{10}O$	3-Methyl-2-butanone	94	~79	~13	*243*
256	$C_5H_{10}O$	2-Pentanone	102.3	83.3	19.5	*232**, *359*
257	$C_5H_{10}O$	3-Pentanone	102.05	82.9	14	*232*
258	$C_5H_{10}O$	Tetrahydropyran	....	Min. b.p.		*40*
259	$C_5H_{10}O_2$	Butyl formate	106.6	83.8	16.5	*150*, *218*
260	$C_5H_{10}O_2$	4,5-Dimethyl-1,3-dioxolane	....	Min. b.p.		*355*
261	$C_5H_{10}O_2$	3-Ethoxy-1,2-epoxypropane	124–126	90–91	....	*112*
262	$C_5H_{10}O_2$	Ethyl propionate	99.15	81.2	10	*211*, *324**
263	$C_5H_{10}O_2$	3-Hydroxy-3-methyl-2-butanone	141.0	98.6	61.0 V-l.	*78*
264	$C_5H_{10}O_2$	Isobutyl formate	98.3	79.5	18.9	*150**, *428*
265	$C_5H_{10}O_2$	Isopropyl acetate	88.6	76.6	10.6	*211**, *359*
266	$C_5H_{10}O_2$	Isovaleric acid	176.5	99.5	81.6	*243*
267	$C_5H_{10}O_2$	Methyl butyrate	102.65	82.7	11.5	*211*
268	$C_5H_{10}O_2$	Methyl isobutyrate	92.3	77.7	6.8	*211*
269	$C_5H_{10}O_2$	Propyl acetate	101.6	82.4	14	*137**, *150*
270	$C_5H_{10}O_3$	Ethyl carbonate	126.5	91	30	*255*
271	$C_5H_{10}O_3$	2-Methoxyethyl acetate	144.6	97.0	51.5	*206*
272	$C_5H_{10}O_3$	Methyl β-methoxypropionate, 100 mm.	84	Azeotropic		*45*
273	$C_5H_{11}Cl$	1-Chloropentane	108.35	82	....	*171*, *286**
274	$C_5H_{11}N$	Piperidine	105.8	92.8	35	*377*
275	$C_5H_{11}NO$	Tetrahydrofurfurylamine	153	Nonazeotrope		*381*
276	$C_5H_{11}NO_2$	Isoamyl nitrite	97.15	<80.6	<15	*255*
277	$C_5H_{11}NO_3$	Isoamyl nitrate	149.75	95.0	40	*240*
278	$C_5H_{12}O$	*n*-Amyl alcohol	137.8	95.8	54.4	*131**, *150*, *225**, *271**, *304**
279	$C_5H_{12}O$	*tert*-Amyl alcohol	102.25	87.35	27.5	*225*
280	$C_5H_{12}O$	*tert*-Butyl methyl ether	55	52.6	4	*105*
281	C_5H_{12}	Pentane	36.15	34.9	....	*255*
282	$C_5H_{12}O$	Ethyl propyl ether	63.6	59.5	4	*218*
283	$C_5H_{12}O$	Isoamyl alcohol	132.05	95.15	49.60	*307**, *433*
284	$C_5H_{12}O$	3-Methyl-2-butanol	112.9	91.0	33	*256*
285	$C_5H_{12}O$	2-Pentanol	119.3	91.7	36.5	*225**, *359*
286	$C_5H_{12}O$	3-Pentanol	115.4	91.7	36.0	*225*
287	$C_5H_{12}O_2$	1,1-Diethoxymethane	87.5	75.2	10	*131*, *274**, *401**
288	$C_5H_{12}O_2$	1,2-Dimethoxypropane	92–93	80	....	*174*
289	$C_5H_{12}O_2$	2-Propoxyethanol	151.35	98.75	72	*236*
290	$C_5H_{12}O_3$	2-(2-Methoxyethoxy)ethanol	192.95	Nonazeotrope		*236*
291	$C_5H_{12}O_3$	1,1,2-Trimethoxyethane	126	93	30	*144*
292	$C_5H_{13}NO$	3-Ethoxypropylamine	....	....	80	*4*
293	C_6H_5Cl	Chlorobenzene	131.8	90.2	28.4	*308*
294	$C_6H_5NO_2$	Nitrobenzene	210.85	98.6	88 vol.	*279*
295	C_6H_6	Benzene	80.2	69.25	8.83	*279**, *359**, *430*
296	C_6H_6O	Phenol, 127 mm.	....	56.3	94.5	*350*
		294 mm.	....	75.0	92.8	*350*
		531 mm.	....	90.0	91.71	*350*
			182	99.52	90.79	*308*, *359**
297	C_6H_7N	Aniline	....	41	86.6, V-l.	*350*
			....	56.3	84, V-l.	*350*

No.	B-Component Formula	Name	B.P., ° C.	Azeotropic Data B.P., ° C.	Wt. % A	Ref.
A =	H_2O	**Water** (*continued*)	**100**			
297	C_6H_7N	Aniline (*continued*)	....	75	81.8, V-l.	*350*
			....	90	80.5, V-l.	*350*
298	C_6H_7N	2-Picoline	129.5	93.5	48	*17*, 18*
299	C_6H_7N	3-Picoline, 700 mm.	144/760	94.1	61.4	*17*, 70*, 82, 260**
300	C_6H_7N	4-Picoline, 700 mm.	145.3/760	94.6	63.5	*17*, 70*, 82, 260**
301	C_6H_8	1,4-Cyclohexadiene	85.6	71.3	....	*255*
302	C_6H_8	1,3-Cyclohexadiene	80.8	68.9	9	*243*
303	$C_6H_8N_2$	Phenylhydrazine	243	Nonazeotrope		*243*
304	$C_6H_8O_2$	Vinyl crotonate	132.7	91.0	24.2	*356*
305	$C_6H_8O_4$	Methyl fumarate	193.25	98.85	74.5	*255*
306	C_6H_{10}	Cyclohexane	82.75	70.8	10	*243*
307	C_6H_{10}	4-Methyl-1,3-pentadiene	....	67.0	7.5	*347*
308	$C_6H_{10}O$	1-Hexen-5-one	129	Min. b.p.		*286*
309	$C_6H_{10}O$	Mesityl oxide	129.5	91.8	34.8	*286*, 359*
310	$C_6H_{10}O$	Mesityl oxide	128	91.3	29 vol.	*287*
311	$C_6H_{10}O_2$	Crotonyl acetate	129	Min. b.p.		*286*
312	$C_6H_{11}ClO_2$	Butyl chloroacetate	181.9	98.12	75.49	*58*
313	$C_6H_{11}ClO_2$	Isobutyl chloroacetate	174.4	97.8	64.18	*58*
314	$C_6H_{11}N$	Diallylamine	110.4	87	22–23	*360*
315	C_6H_{12}	Cyclohexane	80.75	68.95	9	*243*
316	$C_6H_{12}O$	Cyclohexanol	160.65	~97.8	~80	*243*
317	$C_6H_{12}O$	2,2-Dimethyltetrahydrofuran	90	Min. b.p.		*147*
318	$C_6H_{12}O$	2-Hexanone	127	90.5	26 vol.	*232, 286*, 287, 359**
319	$C_6H_{12}O$	3-Hexanone	124	Min. b.p.		*286*
320	$C_6H_{12}O$	4-Methyl-2-pentanone	115.9	87.9	24.3	*359*
321	$C_6H_{12}O$	2-Methyl-2-pentene-4-ol	....	94.6	40.8	*347*
322	$C_6H_{12}O$	Pinacolone	106	~85	~14.5	*243*
323	$C_6H_{12}O_2$	Amyl formate	132	91.6	28.4	*150, 286**
324	$C_6H_{12}O_2$	Butyl acetate	126.2	90.2	28.7	*150, 286*, 359**
325	$C_6H_{12}O_2$	*sec*-Butyl acetate	112.4	87	22.5	*286*, 359*
326	$C_6H_{12}O_2$	Ethyl butyrate	120.1	87.9	21.5	*211*
327	$C_6H_{12}O_2$	Ethyl isobutyrate	110.1	85.2	15.2	*211*
328	$C_6H_{12}O_2$	4-Hydroxy-4-methylpentanone	166	98.8	87.3	*61*, 359*
329	$C_6H_{12}O_2$	Isoamyl formate	124.2	90.2	21	*150, 211*, 286**
330	$C_6H_{12}O_2$	Isobutyl acetate	117.2	87.4	16.5	*150*, 211*, 286**
331	$C_6H_{12}O_2$	Isopropyl propionate	110.3	85.2	19.9	*255*
332	$C_6H_{12}O_2$	Methyl isovalerate	116.3	87.2	19.2	*211*
333	$C_6H_{12}O_2$	Propyl propionate	122.1	88.9	23	*211, 286**
334	$C_6H_{12}O_3$	2,2-Dimethoxy-3-butanone	145	94	....	*57*
335	$C_6H_{12}O_3$	2-Ethoxyethyl acetate	156.8	97.4	45	*206*
336	$C_6H_{12}O_3$	Paraldehyde	124	90	28.5	*243, 403*
337	$C_6H_{12}O_3$	Trioxane	114.5	91.4	30	*411*
338	C_6H_{14}	Hexane	68.95	61.55	....	*243*
339	$C_6H_{14}O$	*tert*-Amyl methyl ether	86	73.8	9	*105*
340	$C_6H_{14}O$	*tert*-Butyl ethyl ether	73	65.2	6	*105*
341	$C_6H_{14}O$	2-Ethyl-1-butanol	148.9	96.7	58.7	*61*
342	$C_6H_{14}O$	Hexyl alcohol	157.85	97.8	75	*225*
343	$C_6H_{14}O$	Isopropyl ether	69	62.2	4.5	*89*, 359*
344	$C_6H_{14}O$	Propyl ether	90.7	75.4	....	*307*
345	$C_6H_{14}O_2$	Acetal	103.6	82.6	14.5	*20, 243*
346	$C_6H_{14}O_2$	2-Butoxyethanol	171.2	98.8	79.2	*62, 207*
347	$C_6H_{14}O_2$	1,2-Diethoxyethane	123	89.4	25	*62, 243*
348	$C_6H_{14}O_2$	Ethoxypropoxymethane	113.7	85.90	18.4	*429*
349	$C_6H_{14}O_2$	Pinacol	174.35	Nonazeotrope		*206*
350	$C_6H_{14}O_4$	Triethylene glycol	288.7	Nonazeotrope		*206*
351	$C_6H_{15}N$	Diisopropylamine	83.86	74.1	9.2	*360*
352	$C_6H_{15}N$	3,3-Dimethyl-1-butylamine	112.8	92.9	....	*170*
353	$C_6H_{15}N$	Triethylamine	89.4	75	10	*404*
354	$C_6H_{15}NO$	2-Diethylaminoethanol	162	Azeotropic		*8*
355	$C_6H_{15}NO$	3-Isopropoxypropylamine	147	....	67	*4*

No.	B-Component Formula	Name	B.P., ° C.	Azeotropic Data B.P., ° C.	Wt. % A	Ref.
A =	H_2O	**Water** (*continued*)	**100**			
356	C_7H_7Cl	*p*-Chlorotoluene	163.5	95	....	*49*
357	C_7H_8	Toluene	110.7	84.1	13.5	*243, 279*, 359*
358	C_7H_8O	Anisole	153.85	95.5	40.5	*211*
359	C_7H_8O	Benzyl alcohol	205.2	99.9	91	*215*
360	$C_7H_8O_2$	*m*-Methoxyphenol	214.7	99.25	80	*255*
361	C_7H_9N	2,6-Lutidine, 700 mm.	144/760	93.3	51.5	*17*, 70*, 82, 260**
362	$C_7H_{13}ClO_2$	Isoamyl chloroacetate	195.2	98.95	77.76	*58*
363	C_7H_{14}	Methylcyclohexane	101.15	81.0	....	*255*
364	$C_7H_{14}O$	2-Heptanone	149	95	48	*287, 288*
365	$C_7H_{14}O$	4-Heptanone	143	94	....	*286*, 287*
366	$C_7H_{14}O$	2-Methylcyclohexanol	168.5	98.4	80	*256*
367	$C_7H_{14}O_2$	Amyl acetate	148.8	95.2	41	*150, 286, 288**
368	$C_7H_{14}O_2$	*sec*-Amyl acetate	133.5	92.0	33.2	*359*
369	$C_7H_{14}O_2$	Butyl propionate	146.8	94.8	41	*255*
370	$C_7H_{14}O_2$	Butyl propionate	137	Min b.p.		*286*
371	$C_7H_{14}O_2$	Enanthic acid	222.0	Heteroazeotrope		*255*
372	$C_7H_{14}O_2$	Ethyl isovalerate	134.7	92.2	30.2	*211*
373	$C_7H_{14}O_2$	Ethyl valerate	145.45	94.5	40	*255*
374	$C_7H_{14}O_2$	Isoamyl acetate	142	93.8	36.3	*150, 211, 286**
375	$C_7H_{14}O_2$	Isobutyl propionate	136.85	92.75	52.2	*211*
376	$C_7H_{14}O_2$	Isopropyl isobutyrate	120.8	88.4	23	*255*
377	$C_7H_{14}O_2$	Methyl caproate	149.8	95.3	41	*255*
378	$C_7H_{14}O_2$	Propyl butyrate	142.8	94.1	36.4	*211, 286**
379	$C_7H_{14}O_2$	Propyl isobutyrate	133.9	92.15	30.8	*211*
380	$C_7H_{14}O_3$	1,3-Butanediol methyl ether acetate	171.75	97.8	60	*255*
381	$C_7H_{14}O_3$	2,2-Dimethoxy-3-pentanone	162.5	95.5	....	*57*
382	C_7H_{16}	Heptane	98.4	80.0	....	*255*
383	$C_7H_{16}O$	Amyl ethyl ether	120	Min. b.p.		*286*
384	$C_7H_{16}O$	*tert*-Amyl ethyl ether	101	81.2	13	*105*
385	$C_7H_{16}O$	Heptyl alcohol	176.15	98.7	83	*225*
386	$C_7H_{16}O_2$	Diisopropoxymethane	....	79–80	12	*401*
387	$C_7H_{16}O_2$	Dipropoxymethane	137.2	92.2	40.3	*131, 401**
388	C_8H_8	Styrene	145	93	....	*278*
389	$C_8H_8O_2$	Benzyl formate	202.3	99.2	80	*218*
390	$C_8H_8O_2$	Methyl benzoate	199.45	99.08	79.2	*211*
391	$C_8H_8O_2$	Phenyl acetate	195.7	98.9	75.1	*211*
392	C_8H_{10}	Ethylbenzene, 60 mm.	60.5	33.5	33	*26, 278**
393	C_8H_{10}	*m*-Xylene	139	92	35.8	*279*, 323*
394	$C_8H_{10}O$	Phenetole	170.4	97.3	59	*211*
395	$C_8H_{10}O_2$	Veratrole	205.5	99.0	76.5	*211*
396	$C_8H_{11}N$	*s*-Collidine	171	Min. b.p.		*328*
397	$C_8H_{12}O_4$	Ethyl maleate	223.3	99.65	88.2	*255*
398	C_8H_{14}	Diisobutylene	101	81	87	*359*
399	$C_8H_{14}O$	2-Methallyl ether	134.6	92.5	31.0	*361*
400	$C_8H_{15}N$	Dimethallylamine	149.0	94.1	40.3	*360*
401	$C_8H_{16}O$	Allyl isoamyl ether	120	Min. b.p.		*286*
402	$C_8H_{16}O$	2,2,5,5-Tetramethyltetrahydrofuran	115	Min. b.p.		*147*
403	$C_8H_{16}O_2$	Butyl butyrate	165.7	97.2	53	*218*
404	$C_8H_{16}O_2$	Ethyl caproate	166.8	97.15	54	*218*
405	$C_8H_{16}O_2$	Isoamyl propionate	160.3	96.55	48.5	*211*
406	$C_8H_{16}O_2$	Isobutyl butyrate	156.8	96.3	46	*211*
407	$C_8H_{16}O_2$	Isobutyl isobutyrate	147.3	95.5	39.4	*211*
408	$C_8H_{16}O_2$	Propyl isovalerate	155.8	96.2	45.2	*211*
409	$C_8H_{16}O_3$	2,2-Diethoxy-3-butanone	163.5	95–96	....	*57*
410	$C_8H_{16}O_4$	2-(2-Ethoxyethoxy)ethyl acetate	218.5	99.2	76	*255*
411	C_8H_{18}	Octane	124.75	89.4	....	*255*
412	$C_8H_{18}O$	Butyl ether	142.6	92.9	33	*286*, 288, 307**
413	$C_8H_{18}O$	*sec*-Butyl ether	121	Min. b.p.		*286*
414	$C_8H_{18}O$	2-Ethylhexanol	183.5	99.1	80	*61*
415	$C_8H_{18}O$	Ethyl hexyl ether	143–144	92.9	29 vol.	*287*

	B-Component			Azeotropic Data		
No.	Formula	Name	B.P., ° C.	B.P., ° C.	Wt. % A	Ref.
A =	H_2O	Water (*continued*)	100			
416	$C_8H_{18}O$	Isobutyl ether	122.2	88.6	23	*218, 286**
417	$C_8H_{18}O$	Octyl alcohol	195.15	99.4	90	*225*
418	$C_8H_{18}O$	*sec*-Octyl alcohol	178.7	98	73	*243*
419	$C_8H_{18}O_2$	Acetaldehyde dipropyl acetal	147.7	94.7	36.6	*20*
420	$C_8H_{18}O_3$	2-Ethoxyethyl ether	....	98.4	78.5	*62*
421	$C_8H_{19}N$	Dibutylamine	....	Min. b.p.		*190*
422	$C_8H_{19}N$	1,1,3,3-Tetramethylbutylamine	140	86	35	*330*
423	$C_9H_{10}O_2$	Benzyl acetate	214.9	99.60	87.5	*211*
424	$C_9H_{10}O_2$	Ethyl benzoate	212.4	99.40	84.0	*211, 279**
425	$C_9H_{10}O_2$	Methyl α-toluate	215.3	99.6	88	*255*
426	C_9H_{12}	Mesitylene	164.6	96.5	....	*255*
427	$C_9H_{12}O$	Phenyl propyl ether	190.2	98.5	66	*218*
428	$C_9H_{18}O_2$	Butyl isovalerate	177.6	98.0	63	*255*
429	$C_9H_{18}O_2$	Ethyl enanthate	188.7	98.5	72	*255*
430	$C_9H_{18}O_2$	Isoamyl butyrate	178.5	98.05	63.5	*211*
431	$C_9H_{18}O_2$	Isoamyl isobutyrate	168.9	97.35	56.0	*211*
432	$C_9H_{18}O_2$	Isobutyl isovalerate	168.7	97.4	55.8	*211*
433	$C_9H_{18}O_2$	Methyl caprylate	192.9	98.8	74	*255*
434	$C_9H_{18}O_3$	Isobutyl carbonate	190.3	98.6	74	*255*
435	$C_9H_{20}O_2$	Dibutoxy methane	181.8	98.2	62	*131*
436	$C_9H_{20}O_2$	Diisobutoxymethane	163.8	97.2	47.5	*131, 401**
437	$C_{10}H_8$	Naphthalene	218	98.8	84	*279*
438	$C_{10}H_{10}O_2$	Isosafrole	252.0	99.8	96.0	*218*
439	$C_{10}H_{10}O_2$	Methyl cinnamate	261.9	99.9	95.5	*218*
440	$C_{10}H_{10}O_2$	Safrol	235.9	99.72	92.3	*211*
441	$C_{10}H_{10}O_4$	Methyl phthalate	283.2	99.95	97.5	*255*
442	$C_{10}H_{12}O$	Anethole	235.7	99.7	92	*255*
443	$C_{10}H_{12}O$	Estragole	215.6	99.3	82	*218*
444	$C_{10}H_{12}O_2$	Ethyl α-toluate	228.75	99.73	91.3	*211*
445	$C_{10}H_{12}O_2$	Propyl benzoate	230.85	99.70	90.9	*211*
446	$C_{10}H_{14}N_2$	Nicotine	....	99.988	2.5	*365*
447	$C_{10}H_{14}O_2$	*m*-Diethoxybenzene	235.0	99.7	91	*218*
448	$C_{10}H_{16}$	Camphene	159.6	96.0	....	*255*
449	$C_{10}H_{18}O$	Cineol	176.35	99.55	57.0	*211*
450	$C_{10}H_{18}O$	Linalool	199	~99.7	....	*243*
451	$C_{10}H_{20}O_2$	Ethyl caprylate	208.35	99.25	82	*255*
452	$C_{10}H_{20}O_2$	Isoamyl isovalerate	193.5	98.8	74.1	*211*
453	$C_{10}H_{20}O_2$	Methyl pelargonate	213.8	99.45	85	*255*
454	$C_{10}H_{20}O_3$	2,2-Dipropoxy-3-butanone	196–7	98.5	....	*57*
455	$C_{10}H_{20}O_4$	2-(2-Butoxyethoxy)ethyl acetate	245.3	99.8	92	*255*
456	$C_{10}H_{22}$	Decane	173.3	97.2	....	*255*
457	$C_{10}H_{22}$	2,7-Dimethyloctane	160.1	96.1	....	*255*
458	$C_{10}H_{22}O$	Amyl ether	190	98.4	....	*307*
459	$C_{10}H_{22}O$	Isoamyl ether	172.6	97.4	54	*218, 307**
460	$C_{10}H_{22}O_2$	Acetaldehyde dibutyl acetal	188.8	98.7	66.3	*20, 366**
461	$C_{10}H_{22}O_2$	Acetaldehyde diisobutyl acetal	171.3	97.4	52.5	*20*
462	$C_{11}H_{12}O_2$	Ethyl cinnamate	272	99.93	97	*255*
463	$C_{11}H_{14}O_2$	1-Allyl-3,4-dimethoxybenzene	255.0	99.85	96.2	*218*
464	$C_{11}H_{14}O_2$	Butyl benzoate	249.8	99.88	94	*218*
465	$C_{11}H_{14}O_2$	1,2-Dimethoxy-4-propenylbenzene	270.5	99.95	98.8	*255*
466	$C_{11}H_{14}O_2$	Isobutyl benzoate	242.15	99.82	92.6	*211*
467	$C_{11}H_{20}O$	Isobornyl methyl ether	192.2	98.55	68	*218*
468	$C_{11}H_{20}O$	Methyl terpineol ether	216.2	99.3	83	*255*
469	$C_{11}H_{22}O_2$	Ethyl pelargonate	227	99.6	88	*255*
470	$C_{11}H_{22}O_3$	Isoamyl carbonate	232.2	99.75	91	*255*
471	$C_{11}H_{24}O_2$	Diamyloxymethane	221.6	99.2	93	*131*
472	$C_{11}H_{24}O_2$	Diisoamyloxymethane	207	99.3	78.8	*20, 401**
473	$C_{12}H_{10}O$	Phenyl ether	259.3	99.33	96.75	*211*
474	$C_{12}H_{14}O_4$	Ethyl phthalate	298.5	99.98	98	*255*
475	$C_{12}H_{16}O_2$	Isoamyl benzoate	262.3	99.9	95.6	*211*
476	$C_{12}H_{20}O_2$	Bornyl acetate	227.6	99.62	87.3	*211*
477	$C_{12}H_{22}O$	Ethyl isobornyl ether	203.8	98.9	75	*255*
478	$C_{12}H_{24}O_3$	2,2-Dibutoxy-3-butanone	228–230	97–8	....	*57*
479	$C_{12}H_{24}O_3$	2,2-Diisobutoxy-3-butanone	214–215	98	....	*57*
480	$C_{12}H_{26}O_2$	Acetaldehyde diamyl acetal	225.3	99.8	85.5	*20*
481	$C_{12}H_{26}O_2$	Acetaldehyde diisoamyl acetal	213.6	99.3	78.8	*20*

No.	Formula	B-Component Name	B.P., ° C.	Azeotropic Data B.P., ° C.	Wt. % A	Ref.
A =	H_3N	**Ammonia**	**−33.5**			
482	CH_5N	Methylamine	6.32	Nonazeotrope		*331*
483	C_2H_6O	Methyl ether	−23	−37	42.5	*158*
		11 atm.	....	25	56	*158*
484	C_2H_7N	Dimethylamine	6.88	Nonazeotrope		*331*
485	C_3H_4	Propyne	−23	−35	75	*93*
486	C_3H_6	Cyclopropane	−31.5	−44	20	*93*
487	C_3H_6	Propene, 1200 mm.	−34.2	−42	10–15	*93*
488	C_3H_8	Propane	−42	−44	5–10	*93*
489	C_3H_8O	Propyl alcohol	97.2	Nonazeotrope		*328*
490	C_3H_9N	Trimethylamine	2.87	−34	73	*6*, 331*
		210 lb./sq. inch gage	....	....	82	*331*
491	C_4H_6	1,3-Butadiene	−4.5	−37	55	*93*
492	C_4H_6	1-Butyne	7	Nonazeotrope		*93*
493	C_4H_8	1-Butene	−6	−37.5	45	*93*
494	C_4H_8	2-Methylpropene	−6	−38.5	45	*93*
495	C_4H_{10}	Butane	−0.5	−37.1	45	*93*
			....	−37.0	54	*158*
		375 lb./sq. inch gage	....	55.5	57	*88*
496	C_4H_{10}	2-Methylpropane	−10	−38.4	35	*93*
		12 atm.	....	25	45	*158*
497	C_5H_{12}	2-Methylbutane	27.6	−34.5	65	*93*
A =	NO	**Nitric Oxide**	**−153.6**			
498	NO_2	Nitrogen peroxide	26	Nonazeotrope		*255*
A =	N_2	**Nitrogen**	**−196**			
499	O_2	Oxygen	−183	Nonazeotrope		*328*
500	CH_4	Methane	−164	Nonazeotrope		*255*
A =	N_2O	**Nitrous Oxide**	**15**			
501	C_2H_6	Ethane, 45 atm.	28	12.8	80	*243*
				Min. b.p.	85.5	*195*
A =	O_2S	**Sulfur Dioxide**	**−10**			
502	CH_4S	Methanethiol	6.8	Nonazeotrope		*255*
503	C_2H_4	Ethylene	−103.9	Nonazeotrope		*146*
504	C_2H_6	Ethane	−83.3	Min. b.p.		*146*
505	C_2H_6O	Methyl ether, pressure in atm.	56.1/12.5	56.1/6.6	60	*41*
			77.1/20.3	77.1/12.1	60	*41*
			108.7/36.8	108.7/26.7	60	*41*
506	C_3H_6	Propene	−48	Nonazeotrope		*146*, 406*
507	C_3H_8	Propane, 7 kg./cm.$^{-2}$	....	....	22	*146*, 406*
			Azeotropic at all pressures			*406*
508	C_4H_8	1-Butene	−6.7	−16	61	*123, 272*
		2.37 atm.	....	3	62	*272*
509	C_4H_8	2-Methylpropene	−6.7	−14	59	*272*
		0.46 atm.	....	−30	57	*272*
		2.40 atm.	....	3	66	*272*
510	C_4H_8	*trans*-2-Butene	1.0	−14	71	*272*
		0.46 atm.	....	−29	70	*272*
		2.05 atm.	....	3	75	*272*
511	C_4H_8	*cis*-2-Butene	3.7	−13	72	*272*
		2.05 atm.	....	3	75	*272*
512	C_4H_{10}	Butane	−0.6	−18	63.3	*272*
		0.46 atm.	....	−35	62	*272*
		2.65 atm.	....	3	66	*272*
513	C_4H_{10}	2-Methylpropane	−12.4	−24	....	*272*
		3.17 atm.	....	3	57.4	*272*
514	C_5H_{10}	2-Methyl-1-butene	32.0	Min. b.p.		*123*
515	C_5H_{10}	3-Methyl-1-butene	21.2	Min. b.p.		*123*
516	C_5H_{10}	2-Methyl-2-butene	37.7	Min. b.p.		*123*
517	C_5H_{10}	1–Pentene	30.2	Min. b.p.		*123*
518	C_5H_{10}	2-Pentene	35.8	Min. b.p.		*123*
519	C_5H_{12}	2-Methylbutane	27.9	Min. b.p.		*123*
520	C_5H_{12}	Pentane	36.2	Min. b.p.		*123*

No.	B-Component Formula	Name	B.P., ° C.	Azeotropic Data B.P., ° C.	Wt. % A	Ref.
A =	**Pb**	**Lead**	**1525**			
521	Sn	Tin	2275	Nonazeotrope		*243*
A =	**CClN**	**Cyanogen Chloride**	**12.5**			
522	HCN	Hydrocyanic acid, 15 mm.	....	Nonazeotrope, V-l.		*136*
A =	**CCl_2F_2**	**Dichlorodifluoromethane**	**0/44.76**			
523	$C_2H_4F_2$	1,1-Difluoroethane, lb./sq. inch abs.	0/38.34	0/52.72	74, V-l.	*301*
A =	**CCl_3NO_2**	**Trichloronitromethane**	**111.9**			
524	$CHBrCl_2$	Bromodichloromethane	90.1	Nonazeotrope		*234*
525	CH_2Br_2	Dibromomethane	97.0	Nonazeotrope		*234*
526	CH_2O_2	Formic acid	100.75	91	....	*223*
527	CH_3NO_2	Nitromethane	101.2	<100.4	<15	*255*
528	CH_4O	Methanol	64.65	Nonazeotrope		*234*
529	C_2Cl_4	Tetrachloroethylene	121.1	Nonazeotrope		*234*
530	$C_2H_4O_2$	Acetic acid	118.1	107.65	80.5	*234*
531	C_2H_5ClO	2-Chloroethanol	128.6	108.9	85	*234*
532	C_2H_6O	Ethyl alcohol	78.32	77.5	34	*234*
533	C_3H_5ClO	Epichlorohydrin	116.45	~106	....	*243*
534	C_3H_5I	3-Iodopropene	101.8	Nonazeotrope		*234*
535	$C_3H_6Cl_2$	1,3-Dichloropropane	129.8	Nonazeotrope		*234*
536	C_3H_6O	Allyl alcohol	96.85	94.2	56	*234, 357**
537	$C_3H_6O_2$	Propionic acid	141.3	Nonazeotrope		*234*
538	C_3H_7ClO	1-Chloro-2-propanol	127.0	<110.8	<96	*234*
539	C_3H_7I	1-Iodopropane	102.4	Nonazeotrope		*234*
540	C_3H_8O	Isopropyl alcohol	82.4	81.95	35	*234*
541	C_3H_8O	Propyl alcohol	97.2	94.05	58.5	*234*
542	$C_3H_8O_2$	2-Methoxyethanol	124.5	<110.5	<82	*234*
543	$C_4H_8O_2$	Dioxane	101.35	Nonazeotrope		*234*
544	$C_4H_8O_2$	Isobutyric acid	154.6	Nonazeotrope		*234*
545	C_4H_8S	Tetrahydrothiophene	118.8	Nonazeotrope		*246*
546	C_4H_9Br	1-Bromobutane	101.5	Nonazeotrope		*234*
547	C_4H_9I	1-Iodo-2-methylpropane	120.8	Nonazeotrope		*234*
548	$C_4H_{10}O$	*n*-Butyl alcohol	117.8	106.65	80	*234*
549	$C_4H_{10}O$	*sec*-Butyl alcohol	99.5	96.1	60	*234*
550	$C_4H_{10}O$	*tert*-Butyl alcohol	82.45	82.25	37	*234*
551	$C_4H_{10}O$	Isobutyl alcohol	108.0	102.05	68	*234*
552	$C_4H_{10}S$	Butanethiol	97.5	Nonazeotrope		*255*
553	C_5H_5N	Pyridine	115.4	Nonazeotrope		*233*
554	$C_5H_{10}O$	Isovaleraldehyde	92.1	Nonazeotrope		*234*
555	$C_5H_{10}O$	3-Pentanone	102.05	Nonazeotrope		*255*
556	$C_5H_{10}O_2$	Ethyl propionate	99.1	Nonazeotrope		*234*
557	$C_5H_{10}O_2$	Methyl butyrate	102.65	Nonazeotrope		*234*
558	$C_5H_{10}O_2$	Propyl acetate	101.6	Nonazeotrope		*212*
559	$C_5H_{11}Br$	1-Bromo-3-methylbutane	120.65	Nonazeotrope		*234*
560	$C_5H_{11}Cl$	1-Chloro-3-methylbutane	99.4	Nonazeotrope		*234*
561	$C_5H_{12}O$	*tert*-Amyl alcohol	102.35	98.9	65	*234*
562	$C_5H_{12}O$	Isoamyl alcohol	131.9	111.15	93	*234*
563	$C_5H_{12}O$	3-Methyl-2-butanol	112.9	<106.5	<80	*234*
564	$C_5H_{12}O$	2-Pentanol	119.8	108.0	83	*234*
565	$C_5H_{12}O$	3-Pentanol	116.0	<107.3	<82	*234*
566	C_6H_6	Benzene	80.15	Nonazeotrope		*234*
567	C_6H_{10}	Cyclohexene	82.75	Nonazeotrope		*234*
568	C_6H_{12}	Cyclohexane	80.75	Nonazeotrope		*234*
569	$C_6H_{12}O$	Cyclohexanol	160.8	Nonazeotrope		*234*
570	$C_6H_{12}O$	3-Hexanone	123.3	Nonazeotrope		*255*
571	$C_6H_{12}O_2$	Ethyl isobutyrate	110.1	Nonazeotrope		*212*
572	$C_6H_{12}O_2$	Isobutyl acetate	117.4	Nonazeotrope		*234*
573	$C_6H_{12}O_2$	Methyl isovalerate	116.5	Nonazeotrope		*234*
574	$C_6H_{14}O$	*n*-Hexyl alcohol	157.85	Nonazeotrope		*234*
575	$C_6H_{14}O_2$	Acetal	103.55	Nonazeotrope		*234*
576	$C_6H_{14}S$	Isopropyl sulfide	120.5	Nonazeotrope		*246*
577	C_7H_8	Toluene	110.75	Nonazeotrope		*234*
578	C_7H_{14}	Methylcyclohexane	101.15	100.8	27	*234*
579	$C_7H_{14}O$	2-Methylcyclohexanol	168.5	Nonazeotrope		*234*

	B-Component			Azeotropic Data		
No.	Formula	Name	B.P., ° C.	B.P., ° C.	Wt. % A	Ref.
A =	**CCl_3NO_2**	**Trichloronitromethane** (*continued*)	**111.9**			
580	C_7H_{16}	*n*-Heptane	98.4	98.32	7	*234*
581	$C_7H_{16}O$	*n*-Heptyl alcohol	176.15	Nonazeotrope		*234*
582	C_8H_{10}	Ethylbenzene	136.15	Nonazeotrope		*234*
583	C_8H_{10}	*m*-Xylene	139.2	Nonazeotrope		*234*
584	C_8H_{16}	1,3-Dimethylcyclohexane	120.7	111.0	80	*234*
585	C_8H_{18}	2,5-Dimethylhexane	109.3	<107.5	<55	*234*
586	$C_8H_{18}O$	Isobutyl ether	122.3	Nonazeotrope		*234*
A =	**CCl_4**	**Carbon Tetrachloride**	**76.75**			
587	CS_2	Carbon disulfide	46.25	Nonazeotrope, V-l.		*295*
588	$CHCl_3$	Chloroform	61.2	Nonazeotrope, b.p. curve		*155*
589	CH_2O_2	Formic acid	100.7	66.65	81.5	*243*
590	CH_3NO_2	Nitromethane	101.2	71.3	83	*234*
591	CH_3NO_3	Methyl nitrate	64.8	<63.5	....	*240*
592	CH_4O	Methanol	64.7	55.7	79.44	*243, 372*, 432*
593	C_2Cl_4	Tetrachloroethylene	120.8	Nonazeotrope, V-l.		*265*
594	$C_2H_3Cl_3O_2$	Chloral hydrate	97.5	~76	....	*243*
595	C_2H_3N	Acetonitrile	81.6	65.1	83	*207*
596	$C_2H_4Br_2$	1,2-Dibromoethane	131.5	Nonazeotrope		*243*
597	$C_2H_4Cl_2$	1,1-Dichloroethane	57	V-l.		*180*
598	$C_2H_4Cl_2$	1,2-Dichloroethane	82.85	75.3	78.4, V-l.	*186*, 188*, 434*
599	$C_2H_4O_2$	Acetic acid	118.5	76.55	97	*222*
600	C_2H_5Br	1-Bromoethane	38.4	Nonazeotrope		*255*
601	C_2H_5ClO	Chloromethyl methyl ether	59.5	Nonazeotrope		*236*
602	C_2H_5I	Iodoethane	72.3	Nonazeotrope		*229*
			72.3	Min. b.p.		*329*
603	$C_2H_5NO_3$	Ethyl nitrate	87.68	74.95	84.5	*216*
604	C_2H_6O	Ethyl alcohol	78.3	65.08	84.15	*254*
		200 mm.	....	32.1	90	*155*, 161*,*
		380 mm.	....	47.0	85	*351, 352,*
		760 mm.	....	64.9	80	*405**
				Vapor pressure curves		
605	C_3H_3N	Acrylonitrile	77.3	66.2	79	*93*
606	C_3H_5ClO	Epichlorohydrin	116.4	Nonazeotrope		*236*
607	C_3H_6O	Acetone	56.15	56.08	11.5	*10*, 155*, 231*
608	C_3H_6O	Allyl alcohol	96.9	72.5	91.15	*149, 243, 357**
609	$C_3H_6O_2$	Methyl acetate	57.0	Nonazeotrope		*243*
610	$C_3H_6O_3$	Methyl carbonate	90.25	75.75	88	*207*
611	$C_3H_6O_3$	Methyl carbonate	90.35	Nonazeotrope		*227*
612	C_3H_7Br	1-Bromopropane	71.0	Nonazeotrope		*229*
613	C_3H_8O	Isopropyl alcohol	82.45	68.95	82	*252, 436**
614	C_3H_8O	Propyl alcohol	97.25	73.4	92.1, V-l.	*65, 163*, 254, 436**
615	C_3H_9SiCl	Chlorotrimethylsilane	57.5	Nonazeotrope		*343*
616	$C_3H_9BO_3$	Methyl borate	68.7	Nonazeotrope		*227*
617	C_4H_4S	Thiophene	84	Nonazeotrope		*207*
618	$C_4H_6O_2$	Allyl formate	80.0	74.3	66	*242*
619	C_4H_8O	2-Butanone	79.6	73.8	71	*10*, 232*
620	C_4H_8O	Isobutyraldehyde	63.5	Nonazeotrope		*255*
621	$C_4H_8O_2$	Butyric acid	163.5	Nonazeotrope		*277*
622	$C_4H_8O_2$	Dioxane	101.35	Nonazeotrope		*239*
623	$C_4H_8O_2$	Ethyl acetate, 789.2 mm.	....	76.15	68.7	*354*
		583.7 mm.	....	66.72	73.0	*354*
		484.5 mm.	....	61.32	75.4	*354*
		385.2 mm.	....	55.22	78.6	*354*
		285.7 mm.	....	47.36	82.2	*354*
		685.0 mm.	....	71.56	70.9, V-l.	*354, 405**
624	$C_4H_8O_2$	Isopropyl formate	68.8	68.0	12	*242*
625	$C_4H_8O_2$	Methyl propionate	79.85	76.0	~75	*253*
626	$C_4H_8O_2$	Propyl formate	80.8	74.6	60	*252*
627	C_4H_9Br	2-Bromo-2-methylpropane	73.3	Nonazeotrope		*243*

No.	Formula	B-Component Name	B.P., ° C.	Azeotropic Data B.P., ° C.	Wt. % A	Ref.
A =	CCl_4	**Carbon Tetrachloride** (*continued*)	**76.75**			
628	C_4H_9ClO	1-Chloroethyl ethyl ether	98.5	Nonazeotrope		*255*
629	$C_4H_9NO_2$	Butyl nitrite	78.2	75.3	70	*230*
630	$C_4H_9NO_2$	Isobutyl nitrite	67.1	Nonazeotrope		*230*
631	$C_4H_{10}O$	Butyl alcohol	117.75	76.55	97.5	*254*
632	$C_4H_{10}O$	*sec*-Butyl alcohol	99.5	74.6	92.4	*93*
633	$C_4H_{10}O$	*tert*-Butyl alcohol	82.55	71.1	83	*10*, 207*
634	$C_4H_{10}O$	Ethyl ether	34.6	Nonazeotrope, V-l.		*405*
635	$C_4H_{10}O$	Isobutyl alcohol	108	75.8	94.5	*243, 436**
636	$C_4H_{10}S$	Ethyl sulfide	92.2	Nonazeotrope		*212*
637	C_5H_5N	Pyridine	115.5	Nonazeotrope		*243*
638	$C_5H_{10}O$	Isovaleraldehyde	92.1	Nonazeotrope		*255*
639	$C_5H_{10}O$	3-Methyl-2-butanone	95.4	Nonazeotrope		*232*
640	$C_5H_{10}O_2$	Isobutyl formate	98.2	Nonazeotrope		*255*
641	$C_5H_{10}O_2$	Isopropyl acetate	90.8	Nonazeotrope		*227*
642	$C_5H_{10}O_2$	Methyl isobutyrate	92.3	Nonazeotrope		*243*
643	$C_5H_{11}NO_2$	Isoamyl nitrite	97.15	Nonazeotrope		*230*
644	$C_5H_{12}O$	*tert*-Amyl alcohol	102.25	76.57	95.5	*205*
645	$C_5H_{12}O$	Isoamyl alcohol	131.3	Nonazeotrope		*207*
646	$C_5H_{12}O$	2-Pentanol	119.8	Nonazeotrope		*255*
647	$C_5H_{12}O$	3-Pentanol	116.0	Nonazeotrope		*255*
648	C_6H_5Cl	Chlorobenzene	131.8	Nonazeotrope		*243*
649	$C_6H_5NO_2$	Nitrobenzene	210.75	Nonazeotrope		*234*
650	C_6H_6	Benzene, <280 mm.	80.1	Azeotropic		*54*
		100 mm.	....	51.93	99	*54*
651	C_6H_6	Benzene	80.12	Nonazeotrope, V-l.		*60, 163*, 352, 432**
652	C_6H_8	1,3-Cyclohexadiene	80.8	Azeotrope doubtful		*243*
653	C_6H_8	1,4-Cyclohexadiene	85.6	Nonazeotrope		*243*
654	C_6H_{10}	Cyclohexene	82.75	Nonazeotrope		*243*
655	C_6H_{12}	Cyclohexane, 40–70° C.	80.75	Nonazeotrope, V-l.		*345*
			80.75	76.5	....	*242*
656	C_6H_{12}	Methylcyclopentane	72.0	<71.6	<32	*242*
657	C_6H_{14}	Hexane	68.95	Azeotrope doubtful		*243*
658	$C_6H_{14}O$	Propyl ether	90.55	Nonazeotrope		*228*
659	$C_6H_{14}O_2$	Acetal	104.5	Nonazeotrope		*243*
660	C_7H_8	Toluene	110.3	Nonazeotrope		
				B.p. curve		*162*
661	C_7H_{16}	Heptane	98.4	Nonazeotrope		
				Vapor pressure data		*369*
662	C_8H_{18}	2,5-Dimethylhexane	109.4	Nonazeotrope		*255*
A =	CS_2	**Carbon Disulfide**	**46.25**			
663	$CHCl_3$	Chloroform	61.2	Nonazeotrope		*207*, 334*
664	CH_2Cl_2	Dichloromethane	40	35.7	35	*93*
665	CH_2O_2	Formic acid	100.75	42.55	83	*235*
666	CH_3I	Iodomethane	42.55	41.5	40	*207*
667	CH_3NO_2	Nitromethane	101.2	44.25	90	*235*
668	CH_3NO_3	Methyl nitrate	64.8	39.8	71	*240*
669	CH_4O	Methanol	64.7	37 65	86	*10*, 235*
670	C_2Cl_6	Hexachloroethane	184.8	Nonazeotrope		*328*
671	C_2H_3Br	1-Bromoethylene	15.8	Nonazeotrope		*246*
672	$C_2H_4Cl_2$	1,1-Dichloroethane	57.25	44.75	72	*207*
673	$C_2H_4Cl_2O$	Bis(chloromethyl) ether	104	43.1	75	*235*
			105.5	Nonazeotrope		*246*
674	$C_2H_4O_2$	Acetic acid	118.5	Nonazeotrope		*334*
675	$C_2H_4O_2$	Methyl formate	31.7	24.75	33	*235*
676	C_2H_5Br	Bromoethane	38.4	37.85	33	*243, 334**
677	C_2H_5Cl	Chloroethane	13	Nonazeotrope		*211*
678	C_2H_5ClO	Chloromethyl methyl ether	59.15	43.1	75	*235*
679	C_2H_5I	Iodoethane	72.3	Nonazeotrope		*334*
680	$C_2H_5NO_2$	Ethyl nitrite	17.4	16.5	~5	*218*
681	$C_2H_5NO_2$	Nitroethane	114.2	Nonazeotrope		*234*
682	$C_2H_5NO_3$	Ethyl nitrate	87.7	Nonazeotrope		*207*
683	C_2H_6O	Ethyl alcohol	78.3	42.6	91	*27*, 235, 334*
684	C_2H_6S	Methyl sulfide	37.4	Nonazeotrope		*255*
685	C_3H_4O	Acrolein	52.45	<42.5	<71	*246*

No.	B-Component Formula	Name	B.P., ° C.	Azeotropic Data B.P., ° C.	Wt. % A	Ref.
A =	CS_2	**Carbon Disulfide** (*continued*)	**46.25**			
686	C_3H_5Br	3-Bromopropene	70.5	Nonazeotrope		246
687	C_3H_5Cl	3-Chloropropene	45.15	41.2	50	246
688	C_3H_6O	Acetone	56.15	39.25	67	235, 387*
		1 kg./sq. cm.	....	....	66	334*, 397
		16.5 kg./sq. cm.	....	....	62.6	397
		32.5 kg./sq. cm.	....	....	59.4	397
		42 kg./sq. cm.	....	....	55.5	397
689	C_3H_6O	Allyl alcohol	96.95	Nonazeotrope		243
690	C_3H_6O	Allyl alcohol	96.85	45.25	93.5	207
691	C_3H_6O	Propionaldehyde	48.7	40.0	60	246
692	$C_3H_6O_2$	Ethyl formate	54.15	39.35	63	235
693	$C_3H_6O_2$	Methyl acetate	57	39.55	70	235, 334*
694	$C_3H_6O_2$	Propionic acid	141.3	Nonazeotrope		246
695	$C_3H_6O_3$	Methyl carbonate	90.25	45.72	91	207
696	C_3H_7Br	1-Bromopropane	71.0	Nonazeotrope		246
697	C_3H_7Br	2-Bromopropane	59.4	46.08	89.5	207
698	C_3H_7Cl	1-Chloropropane	46.65	42.05	55.5	207
699	C_3H_7Cl	2-Chloropropane	35.0	33.5	~20	228
700	$C_3H_7NO_2$	Isopropyl nitrite	40.1	35.5	42	207
701	$C_3H_7NO_2$	Propyl nitrite	47.75	40.15	62	207
702	C_3H_8O	Ethyl methyl ether	38.95	37.8	22	246
703	C_3H_8O	Isopropyl alcohol	62.45	44.22	92.4	235, 334*
704	C_3H_8O	Propyl alcohol	97.1	45.65	94.5	131*, 235
705	$C_3H_8O_2$	Methylal	42.25	37.25	46	235
706	$C_3H_9BO_3$	Methyl borate	68.7	Nonazeotrope		207
707	$C_3H_9BO_3$	Methyl borate	68.7	44.0	~84	228
708	C_4H_4O	Furan	31.7	Nonazeotrope		246
709	C_4H_5NS	Allylisothiocyanate	152.05	Nonazeotrope		255
710	$C_4H_6O_2$	Biacetyl	87.5	Nonazeotrope		243
711	C_4H_7N	Pyrroline	90.9	Nonazeotrope		255
712	C_4H_8O	2-Butanone	79.6	45.85	84	232
713	C_4H_8O	Butyraldehyde	75.2	Nonazeotrope		246
714	C_4H_8O	Isobutyraldehyde	63.5	44.7	86	250
715	$C_4H_8O_2$	Butyric acid	164.0	Nonazeotrope		246
716	$C_4H_8O_2$	Ethyl acetate	77.1	46.02	92.7	235, 334*
717	$C_4H_8O_2$	Isobutyric acid	164.6	Nonazeotrope		255
718	$C_4H_8O_2$	Isopropyl formate	68.8	43.0	~82	228
719	$C_4H_8O_2$	Methyl propionate	79.85	Nonazeotrope		207
720	$C_4H_8O_2$	Propyl formate	80.8	Nonazeotrope		207
721	C_4H_9Br	2-Bromo-2-methylpropane	73.25	Nonazeotrope		246
722	C_4H_9Cl	1-Chlorobutane	78.5	Nonazeotrope		246
723	C_4H_9Cl	2-Chlorobutane	68.25	Nonazeotrope		246
724	C_4H_9Cl	1-Chloro-2-methylpropane	68.85	Nonazeotrope		211
725	C_4H_9Cl	2-Chloro-2-methylpropane	50.8	43.5	62	207
726	C_4H_9ClO	2-Chloroethyl ethyl ether	98.5	Nonazeotrope		246
727	$C_4H_9NO_2$	Butyl nitrite	78.2	Nonazeotrope		207
728	$C_4H_9NO_2$	Isobutyl nitrite	67.1	45.55	86	235
729	$C_4H_{10}O$	Butyl alcohol	116.9	Nonazeotrope		207
730	$C_4H_{10}O$	Ethyl ether	34.6	34.5	13?	235, 334*
731	$C_4H_{10}O$	*tert*-Butyl alcohol	82.45	44.9	93	235
732	$C_4H_{10}O$	Isobutyl alcohol	107.85	Nonazeotrope		207
733	$C_4H_{10}O$	Methyl propyl ether	38.8	36.2	~18	243
734	$C_4H_{10}O_2$	Acetaldehyde dimethyl acetal	64.3	<45.9	....	255
735	$C_4H_{11}N$	Diethylamine	55.9	Nonazeotrope		211
736	C_5H_6O	2-Methylfuran	63.8	Nonazeotrope		246
737	C_5H_8	Isoprene	34.3	<34.15	<7	246
738	C_5H_{10}	Cyclopentane	49.4	44.0	67	246
739	C_5H_{10}	2-Methyl-2-butene	37.15	36.5	~17	243
740	C_5H_{10}	3-Methyl-1-butene	20.6	Nonazeotrope		246
741	$C_5H_{10}O$	Cyclopentanol	140.85	Nonazeotrope		255
742	$C_5H_{10}O$	3-Methyl-2-butanone	95.4	Nonazeotrope		232
743	$C_5H_{10}O$	2-Pentanone	102.35	Nonazeotrope		232
744	$C_5H_{10}O$	3-Pentanone	102.05	Nonazeotrope		232
745	$C_5H_{10}O_2$	Ethyl propionate	99.1	Nonazeotrope		246
746	$C_5H_{10}O_2$	Isobutyl formate	98.2	Nonazeotrope		246
747	$C_5H_{10}O_2$	Isopropyl acetate	89.5	Nonazeotrope		255

No.	B-Component Formula	Name	B.P., ° C.	Azeotropic Data B.P., ° C.	Wt. % A	Ref.
A =	**CS_2**	**Carbon Disulfide** *(continued)*	**46.25**			
748	$C_5H_{10}O_2$	Isovaleric acid	176.5	Vapor pressure data		*243*
749	$C_5H_{10}O_2$	Propyl acetate	101.6	Nonazeotrope		*246*
750	$C_5H_{11}NO_2$	Isoamyl nitrite	97.15	Nonazeotrope		*207*
751	C_5H_{12}	2-Methylbutane	27.95	Nonazeotrope		*218*
752	C_5H_{12}	Pentane	36.15	35.7	11	*235*
753	$C_5H_{12}O$	Amyl alcohol	138.2	Nonazeotrope		*246*
754	$C_5H_{12}O$	*tert*-Amyl alcohol	102.35	Nonazeotrope		*207*
755	$C_5H_{12}O$	Ethyl propyl ether	63.85	Nonazeotrope		*246*
756	$C_5H_{12}O$	Isoamyl alcohol	131.9	Nonazeotrope		*207*
757	$C_5H_{12}O$	3-Methyl-2-butanol	112.9	Nonazeotrope		*255*
758	$C_5H_{12}O$	2-Pentanol	119.8	Nonazeotrope		*255*
759	$C_5H_{12}O$	3-Pentanol	116.0	Nonazeotrope		*255*
760	$C_5H_{12}O_2$	Diethoxymethane	87.95	Nonazeotrope		*246*
761	C_6H_6	Benzene	80.2	Nonazeotrope, V-l.		*46, 334**
762	C_6H_8	1,3-Cyclohexadiene	80.4	Nonazeotrope		*255*
763	C_6H_{10}	Cyclohexene	82.75	Nonazeotrope		*246*
764	C_6H_{10}	Methylcyclopentene	75.85	Nonazeotrope		*255*
765	C_6H_{12}	Cyclohexane	80.75	Nonazeotrope		*243*
766	C_6H_{12}	Methylcyclopentane	72.0	Nonazeotrope		*246*
767	$C_6H_{12}O$	Pinacolone	106.2	Nonazeotrope		*246*
768	$C_6H_{12}O$	4-Methyl 2-pentanone	116.05	Nonazeotrope		*232*
769	C_6H_{14}	2,3-Dimethylbutane	58.0	<46.15	<97	*246*
770	C_6H_{14}	Hexane	68.95	Nonazeotrope		*243*
771	$C_6H_{15}N$	Triethylamine	89.35	Nonazeotrope		*255*
772	C_7H_8	Toluene	110.7	Nonazeotrope		*243*
773	C_7H_{14}	Methylcyclohexane	101.15	Nonazeotrope		*246*
774	C_7H_{16}	Heptane	98.45	Nonazeotrope		*255*
A =	**$CHBrCl_2$**	**Bromodichloromethane**	**90.2**			
775	CH_2O_2	Formic acid	100.7	78.15	~76	*243*
776	CH_3NO_2	Nitromethane	101.2	87.3	75	*234*
777	CH_3NO_3	Methyl nitrate	64.8	Nonazeotrope		*240*
778	CH_4O	Methanol	64.7	63.8	60	*243*
779	C_2HCl_3	Trichloroethylene	86.9	Nonazeotrope		*229*
780	C_2HCl_3	Trichloroethylene	86.95	86.7	22	*208*
781	C_2HCl_3O	Chloral	97.75	90.1	97.5	*252*
782	$C_2H_4O_2$	Acetic acid	118.5	Nonazeotrope		*243*
783	C_2H_5BrO	2-Bromoethanol	150.2	Nonazeotrope		*255*
784	C_2H_5ClO	2-Chloroethanol	128.6	Nonazeotrope		*244*
785	$C_2H_5NO_2$	Nitroethane	114.2	Nonazeotrope		*234*
786	$C_2H_5NO_3$	Ethyl nitrate	90.1	86.85	35	*207*
787	C_2H_6O	Ethyl alcohol	78.3	75.5	72	*243*
788	$C_2H_6O_2$	Glycol	197.4	Nonazeotrope		*253*
789	C_3H_6O	Acetone	56.15	Nonazeotrope		*232*
790	C_3H_6O	Allyl alcohol	96.95	85.85	82.5	*243*, 357*
791	$C_3H_6O_3$	Methyl carbonate	90.35	91.95	64.5	*252*
792	C_3H_7ClO	1-Chloro-2-propanol	127.0	Nonazeotrope		*255*
793	C_3H_7I	2-Iodopropane	89.45	90.7	<50	*229*
794	C_3H_8O	Isopropyl alcohol	82.45	79.4	62	*252*
795	C_3H_8O	Propyl alcohol	97.2	86.4	80.5	*243*
796	$C_3H_9BO_3$	Methyl borate	68.7	Nonazeotrope		*227*
797	C_4H_8O	2-Butanone	79.6	90.85	89.5	*250*
798	$C_4H_8O_2$	Ethyl acetate	77.1	90.55	88	*252*
799	$C_4H_8O_2$	Methyl propionate	79.85	91.2	~85	*218*
800	$C_4H_8O_2$	Propyl formate	80.85	90.9	82	*253*
801	C_4H_9Br	2-Bromobutane	91.2	91.65	45	*242*
802	C_4H_9Br	1-Bromo-2-methylpropane	91.4	91.8	45	*229*
803	$C_4H_9NO_2$	Butyl nitrite	78.2	Nonazeotrope		*230*
804	$C_4H_{10}O$	Butyl alcohol	117.75	Nonazeotrope		*207*
805	$C_4H_{10}O$	*sec*-Butyl alcohol	99.6	87.5	....	*243*
806	$C_4H_{10}O$	*tert*-Butyl alcohol	82.55	79.0	~65	*212*
807	$C_4H_{10}O$	Isobutyl alcohol	108	89.3	89	*243*
808	$C_4H_{10}O_2$	Acetaldehyde dimethyl acetal	64.3	Nonazeotrope		*239*
809	$C_4H_{10}S$	Ethyl sulfide	92.2	96.7	~58	*211*
810	$C_5H_{10}O$	3-Methyl-2-butanone	95.4	97.2	50	*232*
811	$C_5H_{10}O$	2-Pentanone	102.35	102.85	35	*232*

No.	Formula	B-Component Name	B.P., ° C.	Azeotropic Data B.P., ° C.	Wt. % A	Ref.
A =	**$CHBrCl_2$**	**Bromodichloromethane** (*continued*)	**90.2**			
812	$C_5H_{10}O$	3-Pentanone	102.05	102.65	36	*232*
813	$C_5H_{10}O_2$	Butyl formate	106.7	Nonazeotrope		*227*
814	$C_5H_{10}O_2$	Ethyl propionate	99.15	100–6	35	*218*
815	$C_5H_{10}O_2$	Isobutyl formate	97.9	98.7	40	*253*
816	$C_5H_{10}O_2$	Isopropyl acetate	90.8	96.0	55	*227*
817	$C_5H_{10}O_2$	Methyl butyrate	102.65	103.5	25	*218*
818	$C_5H_{10}O_2$	Methyl isobutyrate	92.3	93.8	58	*253*
819	$C_5H_{10}O_2$	Propyl acetate	101.6	102.3	29.5	*252*
820	$C_5H_{11}NO_2$	Isoamyl nitrite	97.15	Nonazeotrope		*230*
821	$C_5H_{12}O$	*tert*-Amyl alcohol	102.0	~88.8	~92	*215*
822	$C_5H_{12}O$	3-Methyl-2-butanol	112.6	Nonazeotrope		*255*
823	$C_5H_{12}O_2$	Diethoxymethane	87.9	94.05	74	*248*
824	C_6H_6	Benzene	80.2	Nonazeotrope		*208*
825	C_6H_{10}	Cyclohexene	82.75	82	..	*243*
826	C_6H_{12}	Cyclohexane	80.75	Nonazeotrope		*255*
827	C_6H_{12}	Methylcyclopentane	72.0	Nonazeotrope		*255*
828	$C_6H_{12}O$	4-Methyl-2-pentanone	116.05	Nonazeotrope		*207*
829	$C_6H_{12}O$	Pinacolone	106.2	Nonazeotrope		*232*
830	C_6H_{14}	Hexane	68.8	Nonazeotrope		*255*
831	$C_6H_{14}O$	Propyl ether	90.55	97.0	54	*239*
832	$C_6H_{14}O_2$	Acetal	103.55	Nonazeotrope		*252*
833	C_7H_{14}	Methylcyclohexane	101.15	Nonazeotrope		*255*
834	C_7H_{16}	Heptane	98.4	<90.0	....	*255*
A =	**$CHBr_2$**	**Bromoform**	**149.5**			
835	CH_2O_2	Formic acid	100.75	97.4	52	*248*
836	$C_2H_2Cl_4$	1,1,2,2-Tetrachloroethane	146.2	145.5	45	*229*
837	$C_2H_3BrO_2$	Bromoacetic acid	205.1	Nonazeotrope		*255*
838	$C_2H_3ClO_2$	Chloroacetic acid	189.35	148.5	96.9	*244*
839	$C_2H_4Br_2$	1,2-Dibromoethane	129.8	Nonazeotrope, b.p. curve		*162, 243**
840	$C_2H_4Cl_2O$	2,2-Dichloroethanol	146.2	<143.0	<55	*255*
841	$C_2H_4O_2$	Acetic acid	118.5	118.3	18	*222*
842	C_2H_5ClO	2-Chloroethanol	128.6	127.4	46	*244*
843	C_2H_5NO	Acetamide	221.15	Nonazeotrope		*207*
844	C_2H_5NO	Acetamide	221.2	149	98	*215*
845	$C_2H_6O_2$	Glycol	197.4	146.75	~93.5	*212*
846	C_2H_7NO	2-Aminoethanol	170.8	Reacts		*207*
847	$C_3H_5ClO_2$	Methyl chloroacetate	130.0	Nonazeotrope		*212*
848	$C_3H_6Cl_2O$	1,3-Dichloro-2-propanol	175.8	Nonazeotrope		*255*
849	C_3H_6O	Allyl alcohol	96.95	Nonazeotrope		*212*
850	$C_3H_6O_2$	Propionic acid	140.9	138.0	63	*207*
851	C_3H_7ClO	1-Chloro-2-propanol	127.0	Nonazeotrope		*255*
852	C_3H_7NO	Propionamide	222.2	Nonazeotrope		*207*
853	$C_3H_7NO_2$	Ethyl carbamate	185.25	149.25	97.5	*244*
854	C_3H_8O	Propyl alcohol	97.2	Nonazeotrope		*212*
855	$C_3H_8O_2$	2-Methoxyethanol	124.5	Nonazeotrope		*206*
856	$C_4H_6O_4$	Methyl oxalate	164.45	Nonazeotrope		*255*
857	$C_4H_7BrO_2$	Ethyl bromoacetate	~158.2	Nonazeotrope		*218*
858	$C_4H_7ClO_2$	Ethyl chloroacetate	143.55	143.52	4	*207*
859	$C_4H_7Cl_3O$	Ethyl 1,1,2-trichloroethyl ether	172.5	Nonazeotrope		*255*
860	$C_4H_8Cl_2O$	Bis(2-chloroethyl) ether	178.65	Nonazeotrope		*207*
861	$C_4H_8Cl_2O$	1,2-Dichloroethyl ethyl ether	145.5	151.3	91	*255*
862	$C_4H_8O_2$	Butyric acid	162.45	146.8	93.2	*163, 206**
863	$C_4H_8O_2$	Isobutyric acid	154.35	145.5	81	*221*
864	$C_4H_8O_3$	Methyl lactate	144.8	~152	....	*243*
865	C_4H_9I	1-Iodo-2-methylpropane	120.4	Nonazeotrope		*163*
866	$C_4H_{10}O$	Butyl alcohol	117.75	Nonazeotrope		*207*
867	$C_4H_{10}O$	Isobutyl alcohol	107.85	Nonazeotrope		*212*
868	$C_4H_{10}O_2$	2-Ethoxyethanol	135.3	Nonazeotrope		*236*
869	$C_5H_4O_2$	2-Furaldehyde	161.45	Nonazeotrope		*207*
870	$C_5H_9ClO_2$	Propyl chloroacetate	162.5	Nonazeotrope		*255*
871	$C_5H_{10}O_2$	Isovaleric acid	176.5	148.7	96	*207*
872	$C_5H_{10}O_2$	Isovaleric acid	176.5	Nonazeotrope		*222*
873	$C_5H_{10}O_2$	Valeric acid	186.35	Nonazeotrope		*255*
874	$C_5H_{11}I$	1-Iodo-3-methylbutane	147.65	Nonazeotrope		*211*

No.	Formula	B-Component Name	B.P., ° C.	Azeotropic Data B.P., ° C.	Wt. % A	Ref.
A =	**$CHBr_3$**	**Bromoform** (*continued*)	**149.5**			
875	$C_5H_{11}NO_3$	Isoamyl nitrate	149.75	144.8	57	*240*
876	$C_5H_{12}O$	Isoamyl alcohol	129	Nonazeotrope		*163*
			130.8	131.35	43	*207*
877	$C_5H_{12}O_2$	2-Propoxyethanol	151.35	147.15	84	*207*
878	C_6H_5Br	Bromobenzene	156.1	Nonazeotrope		*229*
879	C_6H_5Cl	Chlorobenzene	131.75	Nonazeotrope		*255*
880	C_6H_5ClO	*o*-Chlorophenol	176.8	Nonazeotrope		*255*
881	$C_6H_5NO_2$	Nitrobenzene	210.75	Nonazeotrope		*234*
882	C_6H_6O	Phenol	182.2	Nonazeotrope		*222*
883	C_6H_7N	Aniline	184.35	Nonazeotrope		*255*
884	$C_6H_{10}O$	Cyclohexanone	155.6	158.5	~52	*253*
885	$C_6H_{10}O$	Mesityl oxide	129.45	Nonazeotrope		*207*
886	$C_6H_{10}O_4$	Ethylidene diacetate	168.5	Nonazeotrope		*207*
887	$C_6H_{10}S$	Allyl sulfide	139.35	>150.5	....	*246*
888	$C_6H_{12}O$	Cyclohexanol	160.7	Nonazeotrope		*212*
			160.7	149.5?	95?	*225*
889	$C_6H_{14}O$	Hexyl alcohol	157.85	147.7	86	*222*
890	$C_6H_{14}O_2$	2-Butoxyethanol	171.15	Nonazeotrope		*236*
891	$C_6H_{14}S$	Propyl sulfide	140.8	151.5	90	*235*
892	C_7H_8	Toluene	110.65	Nonazeotrope		*243*
893	C_7H_8O	Anisole	153.85	Nonazeotrope		*243*
894	C_7H_8O	*o*-Cresol	191.1	Nonazeotrope		*255*
895	$C_7H_{14}O$	4-Heptanone	143.55	151.0	77	*232*
896	$C_6H_{14}O$	3-Methylcyclohexanol	168.5	Nonazeotrope		*255*
897	$C_7H_{14}O_2$	Amyl acetate	148.8	>154.0	<65	*242*
898	$C_7H_{14}O_2$	Ethyl isovalerate	134.7	Nonazeotrope		*227*
899	$C_7H_{14}O_2$	Ethyl valerate	145.45	>152.7	....	*255*
900	$C_7H_{14}O_2$	Isoamyl acetate	142.1	150.2	82	*163**, *253*
901	$C_7H_{14}O_2$	Isobutyl propionate	137.5	150.0	....	*255*
902	$C_7H_{16}O$	Heptyl alcohol	176.15	Nonazeotrope		*255*
903	$C_7H_{16}O_3$	Ethyl orthoformate	145.75	Nonazeotrope		*239*
904	C_8H_{10}	Ethylbenzene	136.15	Nonazeotrope		*255*
905	C_8H_{10}	*m*-Xylene	139.0	Nonazeotrope		*218*
906	$C_8H_{10}O$	Benzyl methyl ether	167.8	Nonazeotrope		*239*
907	$C_8H_{16}O_2$	Butyl butyrate	166.4	Nonazeotrope		*227*
908	$C_8H_{16}O_2$	Isoamyl propionate	160.7	>161.0	>18	*255*
909	$C_8H_{16}O_2$	Isobutyl butyrate	156.8	157.7	35	*253*
910	$C_8H_{16}O_2$	Isobutyl isobutyrate	147.3	151	75	*253*
911	$C_8H_{18}O$	Butyl ether	142.2	Nonazeotrope		*228*
912	$C_8H_{18}O$	Isobutyl ether	122.3	Nonazeotrope		*239*
913	C_9H_{12}	Propylbenzene	158.9	Nonazeotrope		*218*
914	$C_{10}H_{16}$	Camphene	159.6	~148.5	~95	*215*
915	$C_{10}H_{16}$	α-Pinene	155.8	146.5	75	*208*
916	$C_{10}H_{16}$	Nopinene	163.8	<149.0	>91	*255*
917	$C_{10}H_{22}$	2,7-Dimethyloctane	160.25	Nonazeotrope		*253*
A =	**$CHClF_2$**	**Chlorodifluoromethane**	**−40**			
918	C_3H_8	Propane, 86 lb./sq. inch gage	....	....	68	*316*
A =	**$CHCl_3$**	**Chloroform**	**61.2**			
919	CH_2Cl_2	Dichloromethane	41.5	Nonazeotrope		*110*
920	CH_2O_2	Formic acid	100.7	59.15	85	*217*
921	CH_3I	Iodomethane	42.5	Nonazeotrope		*255*
922	CH_3NO_2	Nitromethane	101.15	Nonazeotrope		*228*
923	CH_4O	Methanol	64.7	53.43	87.4, V-l.	*405*
			....	20	91.7	*155**, *187*,
			....	35	89.7	*243*,
			....	49	87.8	*334**
924	$C_2H_3Cl_3O_2$	Chloral hydrate	97.5	Nonazeotrope		*243*
925	$C_2H_4Cl_2$	1,1-Dichloroethane	57.3	V-l.		*180*
926	$C_2H_4Cl_2$	1,2-Dichloroethane	83.28	Nonazeotrope, V-l.		*186*
927	$C_2H_4Cl_2O$	Bis(chloromethyl) ether	59.15	>63.9	<80	*255*
928	$C_2H_4O_2$	Acetic acid	118.1	Nonazeotrope		*255*
929	$C_2H_4O_2$	Methyl formate	31.9	Nonazeotrope		*243*
930	C_2H_5Br	Bromoethane	38.4	Nonazeotrope		*334*
931	C_2H_5Cl	Chloroethane	13.3	Nonazeotrope		*243*

No.	Formula	Name	B.P., ° C.	B.P., ° C.	Wt. % A	Ref.
	B-Component			Azeotropic Data		
A =	$CHCl_3$	**Chloroform** (*continued*)	**61.2**			
932	C_2H_5I	Iodoethane	72.3	Nonazeotrope		*334*
933	C_2H_6O	Ethyl alcohol	78.3	59.35	93	*409*
			....	35	95.9, V-l.	*155*, 334*, 344, 395*
			....	45	94.8, V-l.	
			....	55	93.7, V-l.	
934	C_3H_6O	Acetone	56.10	64.43	78.5, V-l.	*322*
				64–65	80	*119*, 155*, 323, 334, 372*, 395*, 405**
935	C_3H_6O	Allyl alcohol	96.95	Nonazeotrope		*243*
936	C_3H_6O	Propionaldehyde	50	Max. b.p.		*111*
937	C_3H_6O	Propylene oxide	35	Nonazeotrope		*111*
938	$C_3H_6O_2$	Ethyl formate	54.15	62.7	87	*243*
939	$C_3H_6O_2$	Methyl acetate	57.05	64.8	77	*243*
			57	64–65	78	*334, 372**
			....	20	52.9	*329*
			....	40	50.3	*329*
			....	63.3	46.6	*329*
940	C_3H_7Br	1-Bromopropane	71.0	Nonazeotrope		*229*
941	C_3H_7Br	2-Bromopropane	59.4	62.2	65	*250*
942	$C_3H_7NO_2$	Isopropyl nitrite	40.1	Nonazeotrope		*230*
943	$C_3H_7NO_2$	Propyl nitrite	47.75	Nonazeotrope		*230*
944	C_3H_8O	Isopropyl alcohol	82.45	Nonazeotrope		*334*
			82.45	60.8	95.5	*243*
945	C_3H_8O	Propyl alcohol	97.2	Nonazeotrope		*243*
946	$C_3H_8O_2$	Methylal	42.3	61.8	92.5	*111*, 207*
947	C_3H_8S	Propanethiol	67.5	Nonazeotrope		*243*
948	$C_3H_9BO_3$	Methyl borate	68.7	>70	....	*255*
949	C_3H_9SiCl	Chlorotrimethylsilane	57.5	Nonazeotrope		*343*
950	C_4H_8O	2-Butanone	79.6	Nonazeotrope		*207, 423*
951	C_4H_8O	Butyraldehyde	76	Max. b.p.		*111*
			76	Nonazeotrope		*255*
952	C_4H_8O	Isobutyraldehyde	63	Max. b.p.		*111*
			63	Nonazeotrope		*255*
953	C_4H_8O	Isobutylene oxide	50	Max. b.p.		*111*
954	$C_4H_8O_2$	Dioxane	101	Nonazeotrope		*111*
955	$C_4H_8O_2$	Ethyl acetate	76	Nonazeotrope		*334*
956	$C_4H_8O_2$	Isopropyl formate	68.8	70.0	>14	*242*
957	$C_4H_8O_2$	Methyl propionate	79.85	Nonazeotrope		*255*
958	$C_4H_8O_2$	Propyl formate	80.85	Nonazeotrope		*255*
959	$C_4H_9NO_2$	Butyl nitrite	78.2	Nonazeotrope		*230*
960	$C_4H_9NO_2$	Isobutyl nitrite	67.1	Nonazeotrope		*230*
961	$C_4H_{10}O$	*sec*-Butyl alcohol	99.5	Nonazeotrope		*255*
962	$C_4H_{10}O$	*tert*-Butyl alcohol	82.55	Nonazeotrope		*211*
963	$C_4H_{10}O$	Ethyl ether	35	Nonazeotrope		*111, 334**
964	$C_4H_{10}O$	Isobutyl alcohol	108.0	Nonazeotrope		*255*
965	$C_4H_{10}O$	Methyl propyl ether	38.9	Nonazeotrope		*239*
966	$C_4H_{10}O_2$	Ethoxymethoxymethane	65.9	>67.5	20	*239*
967	$C_4H_{10}O_2$	Acetaldehyde dimethyl acetal	64.3	67.2	32	*239*
968	$C_4H_{10}S$	Ethyl sulfide	92.2	Nonazeotrope		*211*
969	C_5H_{10}	2-Methyl-2-butene	37.15	Nonazeotrope		*243*
970	C_5H_{12}	Pentane	36.15	Nonazeotrope		*243*
971	$C_5H_{12}O$	Ethyl propyl ether	63.85	>69.0	>35	*239*
972	C_6H_5Cl	Chlorobenzene	131.8	....	....	*243*
973	$C_6H_5NO_2$	Nitrobenzene	210.75	Nonazeotrope		*234*
974	C_6H_6	Benzene	79.90	Nonazeotrope, V-l.		*111*, 267*, 322, 334*, 405**
975	C_6H_8	1,3-Cyclohexadiene	80.8	Nonazeotrope		*243*
976	C_6H_{10}	Biallyl	60.2	~55	....	*243*
977	C_6H_{10}	Cyclohexene	82.75	Nonazeotrope		*243*
978	C_6H_{12}	Cyclohexane	80.75	Nonazeotrope		*243*
979	C_6H_{12}	Methylcyclopentane	72.0	60.5	80	*255*
980	C_6H_{12}	Methylcyclopentane	71.9	Azeotropic		*384*
981	C_6H_{14}	2,3-Dimethylbutane	58.0	55.5	47	*242*

No.	Formula	B-Component Name	B.P., ° C.	Azeotropic Data B.P., ° C.	Wt. % A	Ref.
A =	**$CHCl_3$**	**Chloroform** (*continued*)	**61.2**			
982	C_6H_{14}	Hexane	68.95	59.95	72	*243*
983	$C_6H_{14}O$	Isopropyl ether	68	70.5	36, V-l	*110*, 111*
984	$C_6H_{15}N$	Triethylamine	89	Nonazeotrope		*111*
985	C_7H_8	Toluene	110.65	Nonazeotrope		*243*
986	C_7H_{14}	Methylcyclohexane	101.15	Nonazeotrope		*255*
987	C_7H_{16}	Heptane	98.45	....	....	*243*
988	C_8H_{18}	2,5-Dimethylhexane	109.4	Nonazeotrope		*255*
A =	**CHN**	**Hydrocyanic Acid**	**26**			
989	CH_4O	Methanol	64.7	Nonazeotrope		*243*
990	$C_2H_5O_2$	Methyl formate	31.7	24.0	52	*255*
991	$C_2H_5NO_2$	Ethyl nitrite	17.4	16.5	15	*255*
A =	**CH_2Br_2**	**Dibromomethane**	**97.0**			
992	CH_4O	Methanol	64.65	64.25	52	*255*
993	CH_4O	Methanol	64.7	Azeotrope doubtful		*243*
994	$C_2H_4O_2$	Acetic acid	118.1	94.8	84	*242*
995	C_2H_5ClO	2-Chloroethanol	128.6	Nonazeotrope		*255*
996	$C_2H_5NO_3$	Ethyl nitrate	87.7	Nonazeotrope		*240*
997	C_2H_6O	Ethyl alcohol	78.3	76	62	*253*
998	C_3H_6O	Allyl alcohol	96.95	~86.5	~80	*243*
999	$C_3H_6O_2$	Propionic acid	141.3	Nonazeotrope		*255*
1000	$C_3H_6O_3$	Methyl carbonate	90.35	Nonazeotrope		*227*
1001	C_3H_7ClO	1-Chloro-2-propanol	127.0	Nonazeotrope		*255*
1002	C_3H_8O	Isopropyl alcohol	82.4	<81.0	>32	*255*
1003	C_3H_8O	Propyl alcohol	97.2	<90.5	>74	*247*
1004	C_4H_9Br	1-Bromobutane	101.5	Nonazeotrope		*255*
1005	C_4H_9ClO	1-Chloroethyl ethyl ether	98.5	<96.0	<72	*255*
1006	$C_4H_{10}O$	Isobutyl alcohol	108.0	94.8	82	*247*
1007	$C_4H_{10}S$	Butanethiol	97.5	<95.5	<72	*255*
1008	$C_5H_{10}O$	3-Methyl-2-butanone	95.4	98.0	70	*232*
1009	$C_5H_{10}O$	2-Pentanone	102.35	Nonazeotrope		*232*
1010	$C_5H_{10}O$	3-Pentanone	102.05	Nonazeotrope		*232*
1011	$C_5H_{10}O_2$	Isopropyl acetate	90.8	Nonazeotrope		*227*
1012	$C_5H_{10}O_2$	Methyl isobutyrate	92.3	92	....	*227*
1013	$C_5H_{10}O_2$	Propyl acetate	101.6	Nonazeotrope		*227*
1014	$C_5H_{11}NO_2$	Isoamyl nitrite	97.15	96.5	....	*230*
1015	$C_5H_{12}O$	Isoamyl alcohol	131.9	Nonazeotrope		*255*
1016	$C_5H_{12}O_2$	Diethoxymethane	87.95	Nonazeotrope		*207*
1017	C_6H_6	Benzene	80.15	Nonazeotrope		*255*
1018	$C_6H_{14}O$	Propyl ether	90.1	Nonazeotrope		*239*
1019	$C_6H_{14}O_2$	Acetal	103.55	Nonazeotrope		*239*
1020	C_7H_8	Toluene	110.75	Nonazeotrope		*255*
1021	C_7H_{14}	Methylcyclohexane	101.15	<96.4	<75	*255*
1022	C_7H_{16}	Heptane	98.4	<95.5	>58	*242*
A =	**CH_2ClNO_2**	**Chloronitromethane**	**122.5**			
1023	C_2Cl_4	Tetrachloroethylene	121.1	115.2	45	*242*
1024	C_5H_5N	Pyridine	115.4	Nonazeotrope		*233*
1025	$C_5H_{11}Br$	1-Bromo-3-methylbutane	120.65	115.5	40	*242*
1026	$C_5H_{11}Cl$	1-Chloro-3-methylbutane	99.4	Nonazeotrope		*255*
1027	$C_6H_{14}S$	Isopropyl sulfide	120.5	<119.7	20	*234*
1028	C_7H_8	Toluene	110.75	Nonazeotrope		*255*
1029	C_8H_{18}	Octane	125.75	<121.0	<80	*255*
A =	**CH_2Cl_2**	**Dichloromethane**	**40.0**			
1030	CH_3I	1-Iodomethane	42.5	39.8	79	*207*
1031	CH_3NO_3	Methyl nitrate	64.8	Nonazeotrope		*207*
1032	CH_4O	Methanol	64.65	37.8	92.7	*110*, 207*
1033	C_2H_3N	Acetonitrile	81.6	Nonazeotrope		*245*
1034	C_2H_4O	Acetaldehyde	20.65	Nonazeotrope		*255*
1035	$C_2H_4O_2$	Methyl formate	32	Nonazeotrope		*111*
			31.9	~30.8	~20	*243*
1036	C_2H_5Br	1-Bromoethane	38.4	38.1	20	*229*
1037	C_2H_5ClO	Chloromethyl methyl ether	59.15	Nonazeotrope		*335*
1038	C_2H_6O	Ethyl alcohol	78.3	<39.85	>95	*207*

No.	Formula	B-Component Name	B.P., ° C.	Azeotropic Data B.P., ° C.	Wt. % A	Ref.
A =	**CH_2Cl_2**	**Dichloromethane** (*continued*)	**40.0**			
1039	C_2H_6S	Ethanethiol	36.2	Nonazeotrope		*243*
1040	C_3H_6O	Acetone	56	Nonazeotrope		*110*, 111*
1041	C_3H_6O	Propionaldehyde	50	Max. b.p.		*111*
			50	Nonazeotrope		*255*
1042	C_3H_6O	Propylene oxide	34.1	40.6	77	*111*, 239*
1043	$C_3H_6O_2$	Ethyl formate	54	Nonazeotrope		*111*
			54.15	41	92	*227*
1044	$C_3H_6O_2$	Methyl acetate	57.0	Nonazeotrope		*207*
1045	$C_3H_7NO_2$	Isopropyl nitrite	40.1	39.45	53	*207*
1046	$C_3H_7NO_2$	Propyl nitrite	47.75	Nonazeotrope		*207*
1047	C_3H_8O	Isopropyl alcohol	82.4	Nonazeotrope		*207*
1048	$C_3H_8O_2$	Methylal	42.3	45.0	41	*111*, 239*
1049	C_4H_4O	Furan	31.7	Nonazeotrope		*207*
1050	C_4H_8O	Isobutylene oxide	50	Max. b.p.		*111*
1051	$C_4H_{10}O$	Ethyl ether	34.6	40.8	70	*111*, 207*
1052	$C_4H_{10}O$	Methyl propyl ether	38.9	44.8	57	*207*
1053	C_5H_{10}	Cyclopentane	49.3	38.0	70	*207*
1054	C_5H_{10}	2-Methyl-2-butene	37.1	<36.5	<52	*207*
1055	C_5H_{12}	2-Methylbutane	27.95	26.0	27	*207*
1056	C_5H_{12}	Pentane	36.15	<35.5	<49	*255*
1057	C_6H_{12}	Methylcyclopentane	72.0	Nonazeotrope		*207*
1058	C_6H_{14}	2,3-Dimethylbutane	58.0	39.0	83	*207*
1059	C_6H_{14}	*n*-Hexane	68.8	Nonazeotrope		*207*
1060	$C_2H_4O_2$	Acetic acid	118.1	Nonazeotrope		*245*
1061	$C_2H_6O_2$	Glycol	197.4	168.7	86	*249*
1062	C_2H_7NO	2-Aminoethanol	170.8	Reacts		*207*
1063	$C_3H_6O_2$	Propionic acid	141.3	140.65	27	*207*
1064	$C_3H_7NO_2$	Ethyl carbamate	185.25	169.35	75	*207*
1065	$C_4H_8O_2$	Butyric acid	164.0	159.1	60	*250*
1066	$C_4H_8O_2$	Isobutyric acid	154.6	151.8	47	*207*
1067	$C_4H_{10}O_2$	2-Ethoxyethanol	135.3	Nonazeotrope		*255*
1068	$C_5H_6O_2$	Furfuryl alcohol	169.35	165.8	55	*245*
1069	$C_5H_{10}O_2$	Isovaleric acid	176.5	168.5	75	*245*
1070	$C_5H_{12}O$	Isoamyl alcohol	131.9	Nonazeotrope		*245*
1071	$C_5H_{12}O_2$	2-Propoxyethanol	151.35	Nonazeotrope		*255*
1072	$C_6H_4Cl_2$	*p*-Dichlorobenzene	174.4	171.3	48	*229*
1073	C_6H_5Br	Bromobenzene	156.1	Nonazeotrope		*245*
1074	$C_6H_{10}O_4$	Ethylidene diacetate	168.5	164.15	44	*250*
1075	$C_6H_{12}O_3$	2-Ethoxyethyl acetate	156.8	Nonazeotrope		*255*
1076	$C_6H_{14}O_2$	2-Butoxyethanol	171.15	167.15	58	*207*
1077	C_7H_7Cl	*o*-Chlorotoluene	159.2	Nonazeotrope		*245*
1078	$C_7H_{14}O_2$	Butyl propionate	146.8	Nonazeotrope		*245*
1079	$C_7H_{16}O$	Heptyl alcohol	176.15	169.8	62	*207*
1080	C_8H_{10}	*m*-Xylene	139.2	Nonazeotrope		*255*
1081	$C_8H_{16}O_2$	Butyl butyrate	166.4	164.0	38	*245*
1082	$C_8H_{16}O_2$	Isoamyl propionate	160.7	159.5	22	*245*
1083	$C_8H_{18}O$	*sec*-Octyl alcohol	180.4	174.0	72	*245*
1084	$C_9H_{18}O_2$	Isobutyl isovalerate	171.2	167.9	52	*245*
1085	$C_{10}H_{18}O$	Cineole	176.35	169.6	60	*239*
1086	$C_{10}H_{22}O$	Isoamyl ether	173.2	166.5	55	*239*
A =	**CH_2O_2**	**Formic Acid**	**100.75**			
1087	CH_3I	Iodomethane	42.6	42.1	6	*207*, 221*
1088	CH_3NO_2	Nitromethane	101.22	97.05	45.5	*234*
1089	C_2Cl_4	Tetrachloroethylene	121.1	88.15	50.0	*218*
1090	C_2HCl_3	Trichloroethylene	86.95	74.1	25	*243*
1091	C_2HCl_5	Pentachloroethane	161.95	Nonazeotrope		*221*
1092	$C_2H_2Cl_4$	1,1,2,2-Tetrachloroethane	146.25	99.25	68	*218*
1093	C_2H_3Br	Bromoethylene	15.8	Nonazeotrope		*222*
1094	$C_2H_4Br_2$	1,2-Dibromoethane	131.65	94.65	51.5	*218*
1095	$C_2H_4Cl_2$	1,1-Dichloroethane	57.25	56.0	5	*222*
1096	$C_2H_4Cl_2$	1,2-Dichloroethane	83.7	77.4	14	*217*
1097	$C_2H_4O_2$	Acetic acid	118.1	Nonazeotrope, V-l.		*3*
1098	C_2H_5Br	Bromoethane	38.40	38.23	3	*218*
1099	C_2H_5Cl	Chloroethane	13.1	Nonazeotrope		*221*
1100	C_2H_5ClO	Chloromethyl methyl ether	59.5	Nonazeotrope		*243*

No.	Formula	B-Component Name	B.P., ° C.	Azeotropic Data B.P., ° C.	Wt. % A	Ref.
A =	**CH_2O_2**	**Formic Acid (*continued*)**	**100.75**			
1101	C_2H_5I	Iodoethane	72.3	65.6	22	*217*
1102	$C_2H_5NO_2$	Nitroethane	114.2	Nonazeotrope		*234*
1103	C_2H_6S	Methyl sulfide	37.4	Nonazeotrope		*246*
1104	C_3H_5Br	3-Bromopropene	70.5	64.5	~22	*242*
1105	C_3H_5Cl	2-Chloropropene	22.65	Nonazeotrope		*255*
1106	C_3H_5Cl	3-Chloropropene	45.7	45.0	7.5	*222*
1107	C_3H_5ClO	1-Chloro-2-propanone	119	Nonazeotrope		*243*
1108	C_3H_5Cl	Epichlorohydrin	116.45	Nonazeotrope		*243*
1109	C_3H_5I	3-Iodopropene	102	85	~35	*243*
1110	$C_3H_6Cl_2$	2,2-Dichloropropane	70.4	<66.0	<25	*255*
1111	C_3H_6O	Acetone	56.15	Nonazeotrope		*232*
1112	C_3H_7Br	1-Bromopropane	71.0	64.7	27	*217*
1113	C_3H_7Br	2-Bromopropane	59.35	56.0	14	*221*
1114	C_3H_7Cl	1-Chloropropane	54.1	45.7	8	*235*
1115	C_3H_7Cl	2-Chloropropane	34.8	34.7	1.5	*221*
1116	C_3H_7I	1-Iodopropane	102.4	82	36	*221*
1117	C_3H_7I	2-Iodopropane	89.45	75.2	29	*242*
1118	$C_3H_8O_2$	Methylal	42.15	Nonazeotrope		*236*
1119	C_3H_9N	Trimethylamine, azeotrope composition independent of pressure	9	179	~24.5	*243*
1120	C_4H_4S	Thiophene	84	Min. b.p.		*418*
1121	C_4H_6O	Crotonaldehyde	102.15	~95	....	*243*
1122	C_4H_8O	2-Butanone	79.6	Nonazeotrope		*206*
1123	$C_4H_8O_2$	Dioxane	101.35	113.35	43	*236*
1124	C_4H_8S	Tetrahydrothiophene	118.8	<94.5	<73	*246*
1125	C_4H_9Br	1-Bromobutane	101.5	81.4	35	*242*
1126	C_4H_9Br	1-Bromo-2-methylpropane	91.3	76.7	30	*235*
1127	C_4H_9Br	2-Bromo-2-methylpropane	73.3	66.2	22	*221*
1128	C_4H_9Cl	1-Chlorobutane	78.5	69.4	25	*242*
1129	C_4H_9Cl	1-Chloro-2-methylpropane	68.85	62.95	19	*243*
1130	C_4H_9Cl	2-Chloro-2-methylpropane	51.6	50.0	11.2	*221*
1131	C_4H_9I	1-Iodobutane	130.4	92.6	52	*242*
1132	C_4H_9I	1-Iodo-2-methylpropane	120.4	89.5	45	*222*
1133	$C_4H_{10}O$	Ethyl ether	34.6	Nonazeotrope		*243*
1134	$C_4H_{10}S$	Ethyl sulfide	92.2	82.2	35	*235*
1135	C_5H_5N	Pyridine	115.5	150–151	63.5	*151, 243*
1136	C_5H_{10}	Cyclopentane	49.3	46.0	16	*242*
1137	C_5H_{10}	2-Methyl-2-butene	37.15	35.0	10.5	*221*
1138	C_5H_{10}	3-Methyl-1-butene	22.5	~22.2	~2	*217*
1139	$C_5H_{10}O$	3-Methyl-2-butanone	95.4	>102.15	<85	*232*
1140	$C_5H_{10}O$	2-Pentanone	102.35	105.5	32	*232*
1141	$C_5H_{10}O$	3-Pentanone	102.05	105.25	33	*232*
1142	$C_5H_{10}O_2$	Isobutyl formate	98.3	Nonazeotrope		*421*
1143	$C_5H_{11}Br$	1-Bromo-3-methylbutane	120.3	90.5	47	*221*
1144	$C_5H_{11}Cl$	1-Chloro-3-methylbutane	99.4	80.0	33.5	*222*
1145	$C_5H_{11}I$	1-Iodo-3-methylbutane	147.65	97.0	62	*242*
1146	C_5H_{12}	2-Methylbutane	27.95	27.2	4	*217*
1147	C_5H_{12}	Pentane	36.15	34.2	10	*217*
1148	$C_5H_{12}O$	Ethyl propyl ether	63.6	Azeotrope doubtful		*243*
1149	$C_6H_4Cl_2$	*p*-Dichlorobenzene	174.6	Nonazeotrope		*222*
1150	C_6H_5Br	Bromobenzene	156.1	98.1	68	*248*
1151	C_6H_5Cl	Chlorobenzene	131.75	93.7	59	*248*
1152	C_6H_5F	Fluorobenzene	84.9	73.0	27	*242*
1153	C_6H_6	Benzene	80.2	71.05	31	*243*
1154	C_6H_7N	Aniline	184.35	Nonazeotrope		*243*
1155	C_6H_7N	2-Picoline	134	158	25	*243*
1156	C_6H_7N	3-Picoline, 200 mm.	....	100–125	....	*81*, 327*
		100 mm.	....	98–110	....	
1157	C_6H_7N	4-Picoline, 200 mm.	....	100–175	....	*81*, 327*
		100 mm.	....	98–110	....	
1158	C_6H_8	1,3-Cyclohexadiene	80.8	~71	30	*243*
1159	C_6H_{10}	Biallyl	60.2	~46	....	*221*
1160	C_6H_{10}	Cyclohexene	82.75	71.5	21	*243*
1161	$C_6H_{10}S$	Allyl sulfide	139.35	97.5	80	*246*
1162	C_6H_{12}	Cyclohexane	80.75	70.7	30	*243*
1163	C_6H_{12}	Methylcyclopentane	72.0	63.3	29	*242*

	B-Component			Azeotropic Data		
No.	Formula	Name	B.P., ° C.	B.P., ° C.	Wt. % A	Ref.
A =	**CH_2O_2**	**Formic Acid** (*continued*)	**100.75**			
1164	$C_6H_{12}O$	Pinacolone	106.2	>107.1	<24	*232*
1165	C_6H_{14}	2,3-Dimethylbutane	58.0	52.5	22	*242*
1166	C_6H_{14}	Hexane	68.95	60.6	28	*217*
1167	$C_6H_{14}S$	Isopropyl sulfide	120.5	93.5	62	*246*
1168	$C_6H_{14}S$	Propyl sulfide	141.5	98.0	83	*246*
1169	C_7H_7Cl	*o*-Chlorotoluene	159.3	100.2	83	*221*
1170	C_7H_7Cl	*p*-Chlorotoluene	162.4	100.5	88	*221*
1171	C_7H_8	Toluene	110.7	85.8	50	*243*
1172	C_7H_9N	2,6-Lutidine, 200 mm.	....	100–125	....	*81*, 327*
		100 mm.	....	98–110	....	
1173	C_7H_{14}	Methylcyclohexane	101.1	80.2	46.5	*221*
1174	C_7H_{16}	*n*-Heptane	98.45	78.2	56.5	*207, 324**
1175	C_8H_8	Styrene	145.8	95.75	73	*4*
1176	C_8H_{10}	Ethylbenzene	136.15	~94.0	68	*221*
		200 mm.	....	60	69	*26*
1177	C_8H_{10}	*m*-Xylene	139	92.8	71.8	*206*, 323*
1178	C_8H_{10}	*o*-Xylene	143.6	95.5	74	*221*
1179	C_8H_{10}	*p*-Xylene	138.4	~95	70.0	*221*
1180	$C_8H_{11}N$	Dimethylaniline	194.05	Nonazeotrope		*243*
1181	C_8H_{16}	1,3-Dimethylcyclohexane	120.7	89.0	51	*242*
1182	C_8H_{18}	2,5-Dimethylhexane	109.4	83.2	48	*242*
1183	C_8H_{18}	Octane	125.8	90.5	63	*221*
1184	$C_8H_{18}O$	Butyl ether	141	Nonazeotrope		*217*
1185	C_9H_7N	Quinoline	237.3	Nonazeotrope		*289*
1186	C_9H_8	Indene	182.4	Nonazeotrope		*223*
1187	C_9H_{12}	Cumene	152.8	97.2	<88	*242*
1188	C_9H_{12}	Mesitylene	164.6	<99.7	<96	*255*
1189	C_9H_{12}	Propylbenzene	159.3	<98.8	<93	*255*
1190	$C_{10}H_{16}$	Camphene	159.6	Nonazeotrope		*218*
1191	$C_{10}H_{16}$	*d*-Limonene	177.8	Nonazeotrope		*218*
1192	$C_{10}H_{16}$	Thymene	179.7	Reacts		*222*
1193	$C_{10}H_{22}$	2,7-Dimethyloctane	160.1	<98.5	<93	*255*
A =	**CH_3Br**	**Bromomethane**	**3.65**			
1194	CH_4O	Methanol	64.7	3.55	99.45	*423*
1195	C_2H_4O	Acetaldehyde	20.2	Nonazeotrope		*243*
1196	$C_2H_4O_2$	Methyl formate	31.75	Nonazeotrope		*227*
1197	$C_2H_5NO_2$	Ethyl nitrite	17.4	Nonazeotrope		*230*
1198	$C_3H_7NO_2$	Isopropyl nitrite	40.1	Nonazeotrope		*230*
1199	C_4H_6	Butadiene	−4.5	Nonazeotrope		*93*
1200	C_4H_8	1-Butene	−6.5	Nonazeotrope		*93*
1201	C_4H_{10}	Butane	−0.6	−4.4	57.3	*156*
A =	**CH_3Cl**	**Chloromethane**	**−23.7**			
1202	C_2H_6O	Methyl ether	−23.65	Azeotropic		*239*
1203	C_4H_{10}	2-Methylpropane	−10	Azeotropic		*73*
A =	**CH_3I**	**Iodomethane**	**42.5**			
1204	CH_3NO_3	Methyl nitrate	64.8	Nonazeotrope		*207*
1205	CH_4O	Methanol	64.7	37.8	95.5	*163*, 207*
1206	$C_2H_4O_2$	Methyl formate	31.9	31	~17	*243*
1207	C_2H_6O	Ethyl alcohol	78.3	41.2	96.8	*253*
1208	C_3H_6O	Acetone	56.15	42.4	95	*207*
1209	$C_3H_6O_2$	Ethyl formate	54.1	Nonazeotrope		*218*
1210	$C_3H_6O_2$	Methyl acetate	56.95	Nonazeotrope		*207*
1211	C_3H_7Cl	1-Chloropropane	46.65	42.1	85	*242*
1212	$C_3H_7NO_2$	Isopropyl nitrite	40.1	39.5	>30	*207*
1213	C_3H_8O	Isopropyl alcohol	82.4	42.4	98.2	*211*
1214	C_3H_8O	Propyl alcohol	97.2	Nonazeotrope		*155*
1215	$C_3H_8O_2$	Methylal	42.2	39.45	57	*207*
1216	$C_4H_8O_2$	Ethyl acetate	77.1	Nonazeotrope		*207*
1217	$C_4H_{10}O$	Ethyl ether	34.6	Nonazeotrope		*207*
1218	$C_4H_{10}O$	Methyl propyl ether	38.8	Nonazeotrope		*207*
1219	$C_4H_{12}Si$	Tetramethylsilane	26.64	26.1	28.8	*9*
1220	C_5H_{10}	Cyclopentane	49.3	<42.0	>66	*255*
1221	C_5H_{10}	2-Methyl-2-butene	37.1	<36.2	>40	*255*
1222	C_5H_{10}	2-Methyl-2-butene	37.15	Azeotrope doubtful		*243*

No.	Formula	B-Component Name	B.P., ° C.	Azeotropic Data B.P., ° C.	Wt. % A	Ref.
A =	**CH_3I**	**Iodomethane** (*continued*)	**42.5**			
1223	C_5H_{10}	3-Methyl-1-butene	37.1	<36.2	>40	*242*
1224	C_5H_{12}	2-Methylbutane	27.95	<25.0	>20	*242*
1225	C_5H_{12}	Pentane	36.2	<33.8	>38	*207*
1226	$C_6H_5NO_2$	Nitrobenzene	210.75	Nonazeotrope		*234*
1227	C_6H_{14}	Hexane	68.85	Nonazeotrope		*207*
A =	**CH_3NO_2**	**Methyl Nitrite**	**−16**			
1228	C_4H_6	Butadiene	−4.7	Nonazeotrope		*266*
1229	C_4H_8	1-Butene	−6	−16	....	*266*
1230	C_4H_8	2-Methylpropene	−6	−16	....	*266*
1231	C_4H_{10}	Butane	−0.6	−20	....	*266*
1232	C_4H_{10}	2-Methylpropane	−11	−20	....	*266*
A =	**CH_3NO_2**	**Nitromethane**	**101.2**			
1233	CH_4O	Methanol	64.65	64.5	8	*234*
1234	C_2Cl_4	Tetrachloroethylene	121.1	95.0	80?	*234*
1235	C_2HCl_3	Trichloroethylene	86.2	V-l		*435*
1236	C_2HCl_3	Trichloroethylene	86.9	81.4	20	*234*
1237	C_2HCl_3O	Chloral	97.75	93	35	*252*
1238	$C_2H_4O_2$	Acetic acid	118.1	101.2	96	*234*
1239	C_2H_4S	Ethylene sulfide	55.7	Nonazeotrope		*255*
1240	C_2H_5ClO	2-Chloroethanol	128.6	Nonazeotrope		*234*
1241	C_2H_5I	Iodoethane	72.3	71.2	10	*234*
1242	$C_2H_5NO_3$	Ethyl nitrate	87.70	87.68	1.2	*207*
1243	C_2H_6O	Ethyl alcohol	78.3	75.95	26.8	*234*
1244	$C_2H_6O_2$	Glycol	197.4	Nonazeotrope		*256*
1245	C_2H_6S	Ethanethiol	35.8	Nonazeotrope		*234*
1246	C_2H_6S	Methyl sulfide	37.4	Nonazeotrope		*234*
1247	C_2H_7NO	2-Aminoethanol	170.8	Nonazeotrope		*255*
1248	C_3H_5Br	3-Bromopropene	70.0	<69.8	>4	*234*
1249	C_3H_5I	3-Iodopropene	101.8	89.0	....	*228, 234*
1250	C_3H_6O	Allyl alcohol	96.85	89.3	43	*234*
1251	$C_3H_6O_2$	Propionic acid	141.3	Nonazeotrope		*234*
1252	C_3H_7Br	1-Bromopropane	71.0	70.6	7	*234*
1253	C_3H_7Br	2-Bromopropane	59.2	Nonazeotrope		*228*
1254	C_3H_7Cl	1-Chloropropane	46.4	Nonazeotrope		*235*
1255	C_3H_7ClO	1-Chloro-2-propanol	127.0	Nonazeotrope		*234*
1256	C_3H_7ClO	2-Chloro-1-propanol	133.7	Nonazeotrope		*234*
1257	C_3H_7I	1-Iodopropane	102.4	89.2	>42	*234*
1258	C_3H_7I	2-Iodopropane	89.45	82.0	33	*234*
1259	$C_3H_7NO_3$	Propyl nitrate	110.5	100.2	75	*234*
1260	C_3H_8O	Isopropyl alcohol	82.0	79.3	28.2 V-l.	*72*, 353*
1261	C_3H_8O	Propyl alcohol	97.2	89.3	47.5	*120, 234**
1262	C_3H_9SiCl	Chlorotrimethylsilane	57.7	Nonazeotrope		*340*
1263	C_4H_6O	Crotonaldehyde	102.15	99	....	*243*
1264	C_4H_8O	2-Butanone	79.6	Nonazeotrope		*232*
1265	$C_4H_8O_2$	Dioxane	101.35	100.55	56.5	*207*
1266	$C_4H_8O_2$	Ethyl acetate	77.1	Nonazeotrope		*234*
1267	$C_4H_8O_2$	Methyl propionate	79.85	Nonazeotrope		*234*
1268	$C_4H_8O_2$	Propyl formate	80.85	Nonazeotrope		*234*
1269	C_4H_9Br	1-Bromobutane	101.5	90.0	50	*234*
1270	C_4H_9Br	1-Bromo-2-methylpropane	91.4	84.0	34	*234*
1271	C_4H_9Br	2-Bromo-2-methylpropane	73.25	72.2	9	*234*
1272	C_4H_9Cl	1-Chlorobutane	78.5	75.5	16	*234*
1273	C_4H_9Cl	1-Chloro-2-methylpropane	68.85	68.35	6	*234*
1274	C_4H_9I	1-Iodobutane	130.4	99.8	~90	*228*, 234*
1275	C_4H_9I	1-Iodo-2-methylpropane	120.8	96.7	>60	*234*
1276	$C_4H_{10}O$	Butyl alcohol	117.8	97.8	70	*234*
1277	$C_4H_{10}O$	*sec*-Butyl alcohol	99.5	91.1	46	*234*
1278	$C_4H_{10}O$	*tert*-Butyl alcohol	82.45	79.4	32	*234*
1279	$C_4H_{10}O$	Isobutyl alcohol	108.0	94.6	56.5	*234*
1280	$C_4H_{10}O_2$	2-Ethoxyethanol	135.3	Nonazeotrope		*234*
1281	$C_4H_{10}S$	1-Butanethiol	97.5	<93.2	....	*234*
1282	$C_4H_{10}S$	Ethyl sulfide	92.1	85.0	30	*234*
1283	C_5H_5N	Pyridine	115.4	<100.5	>85	*255*

No.	B-Component Formula	Name	B.P., ° C.	Azeotropic Data B.P., ° C.	Wt. % A	Ref.
A =	CH_3NO_2	**Nitromethane** (*continued*)	**101.2**			
1284	C_5H_{10}	3-Methyl-1-butene	20.6	Nonazeotrope		*234*
1285	C_5H_{10}	Cyclopentane	49.3	<47.5	>9	*234*
1286	$C_5H_{10}O$	Cyclopentanol	140.85	Nonazeotrope		*234*
1287	$C_5H_{10}O$	3-Methyl-2-butanone	95.4	<94.8	....	*255*
1288	$C_5H_{10}O$	2-Pentanone	102.35	99.15	56	*232*
1289	$C_5H_{10}O$	3-Pentanone	102.05	99.1	55	*232*
1290	$C_5H_{10}O_2$	Butyl formate	106.8	<98.7	<60	*234*
1291	$C_5H_{10}O_2$	Ethyl propionate	99.1	96.0	35	*234*
1292	$C_5H_{10}O_2$	Isobutyl formate	98.2	94.7	32	*234*
1293	$C_5H_{10}O_2$	Isopropyl acetate	89.5	<89.3	....	*234*
1294	$C_5H_{10}O_2$	Methyl butyrate	102.65	97.95	50	*234*
1295	$C_5H_{10}O_2$	Methyl isobutyrate	92.5	91.2	....	*234*
1296	$C_5H_{10}O_2$	Propyl acetate	101.6	97.6	45	*234*
1297	$C_5H_{11}Br$	1-Bromo-3-methylbutane	120.65	97.5	....	*234*
1298	$C_5H_{11}Cl$	1-Chloro-3-methylbutane	99.4	88.2	48	*234*
1299	$C_5H_{11}NO_2$	Isoamyl nitrite	97.15	94.2	....	*234*
1300	C_5H_{12}	2-Methylbutane	27.95	Nonazeotrope		*234*
1301	$C_5H_{12}O$	*tert*-Amyl alcohol	102.35	93.1	49.5	*234*
1302	$C_5H_{12}O$	Isoamyl alcohol	131.9	100.6	88	*234*
1303	$C_5H_{12}O$	3-Methyl-2-butanol	112.9	96.4	63	*234*
1304	$C_5H_{12}O$	2-Pentanol	119.8	98.5	73	*234*
1305	$C_5H_{12}O$	3-Pentanol	116.0	97.4	68	*234*
1306	$C_5H_{12}O_2$	2-Propoxyethanol	151.35	Nonazeotrope		*234*
1307	C_6H_5Cl	Chlorobenzene	131.75	Nonazeotrope		*255*
1308	C_6H_6	Benzene	80.15	79.15	14	*234*
1309	C_6H_{10}	Cyclohexene	82.75	<74.5	<31	*234*
1310	C_6H_{10}	Biallyl	60.1	<57.5	<23	*234*
1311	$C_6H_{10}S$	Allyl sulfide	139.35	Nonazeotrope		*234*
1312	C_6H_{12}	Cyclohexane	80.75	70.2	28	*234*
1313	C_6H_{12}	Methylcyclopentane	72.0	64.2	23	*234*
1314	$C_6H_{12}O$	Cyclohexanol	160.8	Nonazeotrope		*234*
1315	$C_6H_{12}O$	4-Methyl-2-pentanone	116.05	Nonazeotrope		*232*
1316	$C_6H_{12}O$	Pinacolone	106.2	<100.5	....	*232*
1317	$C_6H_{12}O_2$	Ethyl butyrate	121.5	Nonazeotrope		*234*
1318	$C_6H_{12}O_2$	Ethyl isobutyrate	110.1	100.1	72	*234*
1319	$C_6H_{12}O_2$	Isobutyl acetate	117.2	Nonazeotrope		*228*
1320	$C_6H_{12}O_2$	Methyl isovalerate	116.5	Nonazeotrope		*228*
1321	C_6H_{14}	2,3-Dimethylbutane	58.0	<54.5	<26	*234*
1322	C_6H_{14}	*n*-Hexane	68.8	62.0	21	*234*
1323	$C_6H_{14}O$	*n*-Hexyl alcohol	157.85	Nonazeotrope		*234*
1324	$C_6H_{14}O_2$	Acetal	104.5	95	~65	*243*
1325	$C_6H_{14}S$	Isopropyl sulfide	120.5	<99.5	>85	*255*
1326	$C_6H_{14}S$	Propyl sulfide	141.5	Nonazeotrope		*246*
1327	$C_6H_{15}NO$	2-(Diethylamino)ethanol	162.2	Nonazeotrope		*255*
1328	C_7H_8	Toluene	110.75	96.5	55	*130**, *234*
1329	C_7H_{14}	Methyl cyclohexane	101.15	81.25	39.5	*234*
1330	C_7H_{16}	*n*-Heptane	98.4	80.2	37	*234*
1331	C_8H_8	Styrene	145.8	Nonazeotrope		*234*
1332	C_8H_{10}	Ethylbenzene	136.15	Nonazeotrope		*234*
1333	C_8H_{10}	*m*-Xylene	139.2	Nonazeotrope		*201*
1334	C_8H_{10}	*o*-Xylene	144.3	Nonazeotrope		*234*
1335	C_8H_{16}	1,3-Dimethylcyclohexane	120.7	90.2	50	*234*
1336	C_8H_{18}	2,5-Dimethylhexane	109.4	85.5	43	*234*
1337	C_8H_{18}	*n*-Octane	125.75	92.0	53	*234*
1338	$C_8H_{18}O$	Isobutyl ether	122.3	Nonazeotrope		*234*
1339	C_9H_{12}	Cumene	152.8	Nonazeotrope		*234*
1340	C_9H_{12}	Mesitylene	164.6	Nonazeotrope		*234*
1341	C_nH_{2n+2}	Paraffins	90–118	25–90	....	*130*
A =	CH_3NO_3	**Methyl Nitrate**	**64.8**			
1342	CH_4O	Methanol	64.65	52.5	73	*240*
1343	$C_2H_4Cl_2$	1,2-Dichloroethane	83.45	Nonazeotrope		*240*
1344	C_2H_5Br	Bromoethane	38.4	Nonazeotrope		*240*
1345	C_2H_5I	Iodoethane	72.3	<63.5	<72	*240*
1346	C_2H_6O	Ethyl alcohol	78.3	<59.5	>64	*240*
1347	C_3H_5Br	3-Bromopropene	70.5	62.8	68	*240*

No.	Formula	B-Component Name	B.P., ° C.	Azeotropic Data B.P., ° C.	Wt. % A	Ref.
A =	**CH_3NO_3**	**Methyl Nitrate** (*continued*)	**64.8**			
1348	C_3H_5Cl	3-Chloropropene	45.3	Nonazeotrope		*240*
1349	C_3H_7Br	1-Bromopropane	71.0	63.0	70	*240*
1350	C_3H_7Br	2-Bromopropane	59.4	57.3	32	*240*
1351	C_3H_7Cl	1-Chloropropane	46.65	Nonazeotrope		*240*
1352	C_3H_8O	Isopropyl alcohol	82.42	<62.5	>78	*240*
1353	$C_3H_8O_2$	Methylal	42.3	Nonazeotrope		*237*
1354	C_4H_4S	Thiophene	84.7	Nonazeotrope		*240*
1355	C_4H_9Br	2-Bromo-2-methylpropane	73.25	63.8	<80	*240*
1356	C_4H_9Cl	1-Chlorobutane	78.5	Nonazeotrope		*240*
1357	C_4H_9Cl	2-Chlorobutane	68.25	<62.0	<64	*240*
1358	C_4H_9Cl	1-Chloro-2-methylpropane	68.85	61.2	61	*240*
1359	$C_4H_{10}O$	*tert*-Butyl alcohol	82.45	63.2	84	*240*
1360	$C_4H_{10}O$	Ethyl ether	34.6	Nonazeotrope		*237*
1361	$C_4H_{10}O_2$	Ethoxymethoxymethane	65.8	<63.9	....	*237*
1362	C_5H_{10}	Cyclopentane	49.4	<47.2	>20	*240*
1363	C_5H_{12}	Pentane	36.15	<35.5	<10	*240*
1364	$C_5H_{12}O$	Ethyl propyl ether	63.85	<61.5	....	*237*
1365	C_6H_5F	Fluorobenzene	84.9	Nonazeotrope		*240*
1366	C_6H_6	Benzene	80.15	Nonazeotrope		*240*
1367	C_6H_{12}	Cyclohexane	80.75	61.0	77	*240*
1368	C_6H_{12}	Methylcyclopentane	72.0	57.8	60	*240*
1369	C_6H_{14}	2,3-Dimethylbutane	58.0	51.0	38	*240*
1370	C_6H_{14}	Hexane	68.8	56.0	56	*240*
1371	C_7H_{16}	Heptane	98.4	Nonazeotrope		*240*
A =	**CH_4O**	**Methanol**	**64.72**			
1372	C_2Cl_4	Tetrachloroethylene	121.1	63.75	63.5	*254*
1373	C_2HCl_3	Trichloroethylene	87	59.3	38 V-l.	*117**, *126*
1374	C_2H_2BrCl	1-Bromo-2-chloroethylene	106.7	Nonazeotrope		*255*
1375	C_2H_2Br	*cis*-1,2-Dibromoethylene	112.5	Nonazeotrope		*243*
1376	$C_2H_2Br_2$	*trans*-1,2-Dibromoethylene	108	Nonazeotrope		*255*
1377	$C_2H_2Br_2$	*trans*-1,2-Dibromoethylene	108	~64.1	~72	*243*
1378	$C_2H_2Cl_2$	1,1-Dichloroethylene	31	27.5–28	6 vol.	*392*
1379	$C_2H_2Cl_2$	*cis*-1,2-Dichloroethylene	60.25	51.5	~13	*243*
1380	C_2H_3Br	Bromoethylene	15.8	<15.7	....	*255*
1381	$C_2H_3Cl_3$	1,1,1-Trichloroethane	....	56	21.7	*93*
1382	$C_2H_3Cl_3$	1,1,2-Trichloroethane	113.65	Nonazeotrope		*255*
1383	$C_2H_3Cl_3$	1,1,2-Trichloroethane	114	~64.5	97	*243*
1384	C_2H_3N	Acetonitrile	81.6	63.45	19	*243*
1385	C_2H_4BrCl	1-Bromo-2-chloroethane	106.7	64.5?	....	*243*
1386	$C_2H_4Br_2$	1,1-Dibromoethane	109.5	Nonazeotrope		*255*
1387	$C_2H_4Br_2$	1,1-Dibromoethane	~110	64.2	~82	*243*
1388	$C_2H_4Br_2$	1,2-Dibromoethane	131.65	Nonazeotrope		*254*
1389	$C_2H_4Cl_2$	1,1-Dichloroethane	57.3	59.05	11.5	*243*
1390	$C_2H_4Cl_2$	1,2-Dichloroethane	83.7	60.95	32	*252*
			....	....	40, V-l.	*119*
1391	C_2H_4O	Acetaldehyde	20.65	Nonazeotrope		*255*
1392	C_2H_4O	Ethylene oxide	10.75	Nonazeotrope		*255*
1393	$C_2H_4O_2$	Methyl formate	31.9	Nonazeotrope		*243*
1394	C_2H_4S	Ethylene sulfide	55.7	<47.0	<21	*255*
1395	C_2H_5Br	Bromoethane	38	35	5	*243**, *334*
1396	C_2H_5Cl	Chloroethane	13.5	Nonazeotrope		*243*
1397	C_2H_5ClO	Chloromethyl methyl ether	59.5	56	~35	*243*
1398	C_2H_5I	Iodoethane	72.3	55	17	*243**, *334*
1399	C_2H_5NO	Acetamide	220.9	Nonazeotrope		*207*
1400	$C_2H_5NO_2$	Nitroethane	114.2	Nonazeotrope		*256*
1401	$C_2H_5NO_3$	Ethyl nitrate	87.68	61.77	57	*240*
1402	C_2H_6	Ethane	−93	Nonazeotrope		*243*
1403	C_2H_6O	Ethyl alcohol	78.3	Nonazeotrope		*243*
1404	C_2H_6S	Ethanethiol	36.2	Nonazeotrope		*243*
1405	C_2H_6S	Methyl sulfide	37.3	<34.5	<13	*246*
1406	C_3H_3N	Acrylonitrile	77.3	61.4	61.3	*93*
1407	$C_3H_4Cl_2$	1,2-Dichloro-1-propene	76.8	56.5	25	*172*
1408	C_3H_4O	Acrolein	52.45	Nonazeotrope		*255*
1409	C_3H_5Br	*trans*-1-Bromopropene	63.25	50.8	15	*243*

No.	B-Component Formula	Name	B.P., ° C.	Azeotropic Data B.P., ° C.	Wt. % A	Ref.
A =	CH_4O	**Methanol** (*continued*)	**64.72**			
1410	C_3H_5Br	*cis*-1-Bromopropene	57.8	48	12	*243*
1411	C_3H_5Br	2-Bromopropene	48.35	42.7	11	*243*
1412	C_3H_5Br	3-Bromopropene	70.5	54.0	20.5	*247*
1413	C_3H_5Cl	2-Chloropropene	22.65	22.0	3	*253*
1414	C_3H_5Cl	3-Chloropropene	45.15	39.85	10	*247*
1415	C_3H_5ClO	Epichlorohydrin	116.4	Nonazeotrope		*236*
1416	$C_3H_5ClO_2$	Methyl chloroacetate	131.4	Nonazeotrope		*58*
1417	C_3H_5I	3-Iodopropene	102.0	63.5	~62	*243*
1418	C_3H_5N	Propionitrile	97.1	Nonazeotrope		*243*
1419	$C_3H_6Cl_2$	1,2-Dichloropropane	96.8	62.9	53	*117*
1420	$C_3H_6Cl_2$	2,2-Dichloropropane	69.8	55.5	21	*253*
1421	C_3H_6O	Acetone	56.15	55.5	12	*110*, 155*, 207, 334**
		100 mm.	....	Nonazeotrope, V-l.		*119*
			Effect of pressure, V-l.			*42*
1422	C_3H_6O	Propionaldehyde	48.7	Nonazeotrope		*255*
1423	C_3H_6OS	Methyl thioacetate	95.5	Nonazeotrope		*255*
1424	$C_3H_6O_2$	Ethyl formate	54.15	50.95	16	*243*
1425	$C_6H_6O_2$	Methyl acetate	57	54	19.5	*150, 334**
1426	$C_3H_6O_3$	Methyl carbonate	90.35	62.7	~70	*216*
1427	C_3H_7Br	1-Bromopropane	71.0	54.5	21	*163*, 215*
1428	C_3H_7Br	2-Bromopropane	59.4	49.0	14.5	*207*
1429	C_3H_7Cl	1-Chloropropane	46.6	40.6	10	*235*
1430	C_3H_7Cl	2-Chloropropane	36.25	33.4	6	*253*
1431	C_3H_7I	1-Iodopropane	102.4	63.1	50	*207*
1432	C_3H_7I	2-Iodopropane	89.35	61.0	38	*253*
1433	C_3H_7NO	Propionamide	222.1	Nonazeotrope		*211*
1434	C_3H_8	Propane	−40	Min. b.p.		*243*
1435	$C_3H_8O_2$	2-Methoxyethanol	124	Nonazeotrope, V-l.		*363*
1436	$C_3H_8O_2$	Methylal	42.3	41.82	7.85	*69, 131*, 225**
1437	C_3H_8S	Propanethiol	67.3	<58.0	<35	*246*
1438	$C_3H_9BO_3$	Methyl borate	68.7	54.6	32	*254*
1439	$C_4H_4Cl_2$	2,3-Dichloro-1,3-butadiene	98	61.5	50.0	*421*
		275 mm.	....	36.0	53.5	*421*
		475 mm.	....	50.0	52.0	*421*
		1000 mm.	....	70	....	*421*
1440	$C_4H_4N_2$	Pyrazine	114	Nonazeotrope		*299*
1441	C_4H_4O	Furan	31.7	<30.5	<7	*255*
1442	C_4H_4S	Thiophene	84	<59.55	<55	*207*
1443	C_4H_5NS	Allyl isothiocyanate	152.05	Nonazeotrope		*255*
1444	C_4H_6O	Crotonaldehyde	102	Nonazeotrope		*255*
1445	$C_4H_6O_2$	Biacetyl	87 5	Nonazeotrope		*97*
1446	$C_4H_6O_2$	Methyl acrylate	80	<62.0	<75	*232*
1447	C_4H_7N	Pyrroline	90.9	62.5	54	*319*, 320*
1448	C_4H_8O	2-Butanone	79.6	Nonazeotrope		*255*
				63.5	70	*42*
				Effect of pressure, V-l.		*42*
1449	C_4H_8O	Isobutyraldehyde	63.5	62.7	40	*255*
1450	$C_4H_8O_2$	1,2-Dimethoxyethylene	102	63–64	90	*143*
1451	$C_4H_8O_2$	Dioxane	101.05	Nonazeotrope, V-l.		*97*, 294*
1452	$C_4H_8O_2$	Ethyl acetate	77.1	62.25	44	*252, 334**
1453	$C_4H_8O_2$	Isopropyl formate	68.8	57.2	33	*247*
1454	$C_4H_8O_2$	Methyl propionate	79.8	62.45	47.5	*252*
1455	$C_4H_8O_2$	Propyl formate	80.8	61.9	50.2	*252*
1456	C_4H_8S	Tetrahydrothiophene	118.8	Nonazeotrope		*246*
1457	C_4H_9Br	1-Bromobutane	101.5	63.5	59	*207*
1458	C_4H_9Br	2-Bromobutane	91.2	61.5	41.5	*247*
1459	C_4H_9Br	1-Bromo-2-methylpropane	91.0	61.55	42	*163*, 235*
1460	C_4H_9Br	2-Bromo-2-methylpropane	73.3	55.6	~24	*243*
1461	C_4H_9Cl	1-Chlorobutane	78.05	57.2	28.5	*235*
1462	C_4H_9Cl	2-Chlorobutane	68.25	52.7	20	*247*
1463	C_4H_9Cl	1-Chloro-2-methylpropane	68.9	53.05	23	*243*
1464	C_4H_9Cl	2-Chloro-2-methylpropane	51.6	43.75	10	*212*
1465	C_4H_9I	1-Iodobutane	130.4	Nonazeotrope		*255*
1466	C_4H_9I	2-Iodobutane	120.0	<64.60	>65	*255*

	B-Component			Azeotropic Data		
No.	Formula	Name	B.P., ° C.	B.P., ° C.	Wt. % A	Ref.
A =	CH_4O	**Methanol** (*continued*)	**64.72**			
1467	C_4H_9I	1-Iodo-2-methylpropane	120.4	Nonazeotrope		212
			119	64	<70	334
1468	$C_4H_{10}O$	Ethyl ether	34.6	Nonazeotrope		334
1469	$C_4H_{10}O$	Methyl propyl ether	39	38	11.94	34
1470	$C_4H_{10}O$	Methyl propyl ether	38.95	38.85	10	225
1471	$C_4H_{10}O_2$	Acetaldehyde dimethyl acetal	64.3	57.5	24.2	20
1472	$C_4H_{10}O_2$	Ethoxymethoxymethane	65.90	57.1	25.3	429
1473	$C_4H_{10}S$	Ethyl sulfide	92.2	61.2	62	235
1474	$C_4H_{11}N$	Diethylamine	55.9	Nonazeotrope		225
1475	$C_4H_{11}N$	Isobutylamine	68.0	Reacts		225
1476	$C_4H_{12}SiO$	Methoxytrimethylsilane	57.0	....	14–16	338
1477	C_5H_5N	Pyridine	115.4	Nonazeotrope		233
1478	C_5H_6O	2-Methylfuran	63.7	51.5	22.3	310
1479	C_5H_8	Cyclopentene	43	37	20 vol.	360*, 417
1480	C_5H_8	Isoprene	34.8	~29.5	....	243
1481	C_5H_8	3-Methyl-1,2-butadiene	40.8	~35	~10	243
1482	C_5H_8	*cis*-Piperylene	42	37.5	16.7 vol.	417
1483	$C_5H_8O_2$	Ethyl acrylate, 103 mm.	43	64.5	84.4	319*, 320
1484	$C_5H_8O_2$	Methyl methacrylate	99.5	64.2	82, V-l.	426
		200 mm.	61.5	34.5	82, V-l.	426
1485	C_5H_{10}	Cyclopentane	49.4	38.8	14	247
1486	C_5H_{10}	2-Methyl-2-butene	37.15	31.75	7	243
1487	C_5H_{10}	3-Methyl-1-butene	22.5	19.8	3	217
1488	C_5H_{10}	2-Pentene	35.8	31.5	12 vol.	417
1489	$C_5H_{10}O$	3-Methyl-2-butanone	95.4	Nonazeotrope		232
1490	$C_5H_{10}O_2$	Butyl formate	106.8	Nonazeotrope		255
1491	$C_5H_{10}O_2$	Ethyl propionate	99.15	Nonazeotrope		217
1492	$C_5H_{10}O_2$	Isobutyl formate	97.9	64.6	~95	216
1493	$C_5H_{10}O_2$	Isopropyl acetate	91.0	64.5	80	216
1494	$C_5H_{10}O_2$	Methyl butyrate	102.65	Nonazeotrope		216
1495	$C_5H_{10}O_2$	Methyl isobutyrate	92.3	64.0	75	216
1496	$C_5H_{10}O_2$	Methyl isobutyrate	92.3	Nonazeotrope		243
1497	$C_5H_{10}O_2$	Propyl acetate	101.6	Nonazeotrope		216
1498	$C_5H_{11}Br$	1-Bromo-3-methylbutane	118.2	Nonazeotrope		
				B.p. curve		163
1499	$C_5H_{11}Cl$	1-Chloropentane	108.35	Nonazeotrope		171
1500	$C_5H_{11}Cl$	1-Chloro-3-methylbutane	99.4	62.0	57	207
1501	$C_5H_{11}N$	Piperidine	106.4	Nonazeotrope		255
1502	C_5H_{12}	2-Methylbutane	27.95	24.5	~4	243
1503	C_5H_{12}	*n*-Pentane	36.1	30.6	15 vol.	417
			37.15	30.8	9	218
1504	$C_5H_{12}O$	Butyl methyl ether	71	56.3	35.35	34
1505	$C_5H_{12}O$	Ethyl propyl ether	63.6	55.5	24	236
1506	$C_5H_{12}O$	Methyl *tert*-butyl ether	55	51.6	15	105
1507	$C_5H_{12}O_2$	Diethoxymethane	87.95	63.2	65	207
1508	$C_5H_{14}SiO$	Methoxymethyltrimethylsilane	83	60	36 vol.	374
1509	C_6H_5Cl	Chlorobenzene	132.0	Nonazeotrope		254
1510	C_6H_5F	Fluorobenzene	85.15	59.7	32	225
1511	$C_6H_5NO_2$	Nitrobenzene	210.75	Nonazeotrope		234
1512	C_6H_6	Benzene	80.1	57.50	39.1, V-l.	424
		770 mm.	....	58	38.4	126*, 329*
		400 mm.	....	40	36.8	334, 372*,
		223 mm.	....	25	33.1	431*
1513	C_6H_8	1,3-Cyclohexadiene	80.8	56.38	38.8	243
1514	C_6H_8	1,4-Cyclohexadiene	85.6	58	42.5	243
1515	C_6H_{10}	Biallyl	60.2	47.05	22.5	243
1516	C_6H_{10}	Cyclohexene	82.75	55.9	40	243
1517	C_6H_{10}	2,3-Dimethyl-1,3-butadiene	68.9	52	25	38
1518	C_6H_{10}	Methylcyclopentene	75.85	53.0	35	247
1519	$C_6H_{10}O_2$	Isopropyl acrylate	....	Min b.p.		319
1520	$C_6H_{10}O_2$	Propyl acrylate	....	Min. b.p.		319
1521	C_6H_{12}	Cyclohexane	80	54	38	117, 243*
1522	C_6H_{12}	Hexenes	68	49.5	27 vol	417
1523	C_6H_{12}	Methylcyclopentane	72.0	51.3	32	247
1524	C_6H_{14}	2,3-Dimethylbutane	58.0	45.0	20	247
1525	C_6H_{14}	Hexanes	68	50	26 vol.	221*, 417

No.	B-Component Formula	Name	B.P., ° C.	Azeotropic Data B.P., ° C.	Wt. % A	Ref.
A =	**CH_4O**	**Methanol (*continued*)**	**64.72**			
1526	$C_6H_{14}O$	*tert*-Amyl methyl ether	86–7	62.3	50	*105*
1527	$C_6H_{14}O$	Propyl ether	90.4	63.8	72	*225*
1528	$C_6H_{14}O_2$	Acetal	103.55	Nonazeotrope		*236*
1529	$C_6H_{14}S$	Isopropyl sulfide	120.5	Nonazeotrope		*246*
1530	$C_6H_{15}N$	Triethylamine	89.35	Nonazeotrope		*255*
1531	C_7H_8	Toluene	110.7	63.8	69	*23*
			....	0.5	71.6	*217*, 329, 334**
			....	25	73.0	
			....	50	74.0	
			....	62.5	75.0	
1532	C_7H_{14}	*trans*-1,3-Dimethylcyclopentane	90.7	....	~45	*383*
1533	C_7H_{14}	Methylcyclohexane	100.8	59.2	54	*23, 252**
1534	C_7H_{16}	*n*-Heptane	98.45	59.1	51.5	*252*
1535	C_7H_{16}	2-Methylhexane	90.0	....	~40	*383*
1536	C_7H_{16}	3-Methylhexane	91.8	....	~40	*383*
1537	C_8H_8	Styrene	145.8	64.2	....	*225*
1538	C_8H_{10}	Ethylbenzene	136.15	Nonazeotrope		*217*
1539	C_8H_{10}	*m*-Xylene	139.0	Nonazeotrope		*217*
1540	C_8H_{10}	*o*-Xylene	143.6	Nonazeotrope		*221*
1541	C_8H_{10}	*p*-Xylene	138.3	Nonazeotrope		*220*
1542	C_8H_{16}	1,3-Dimethylcyclohexane	120.7	<62.5	....	*255*
1543	C_8H_{18}	2,5-Dimethylhexane	109.2	61.0	60	*225*
1544	C_8H_{18}	Octane	125.6	63.0	72	*217*
1545	C_8H_{18}	2,2,4-Trimethylpentane	99.3	59.4	53	*255*
1546	C_9H_{12}	Cumene	152.8	Nonazeotrope		*255*
1547	C_9H_{12}	Mesitylene	164.6	Nonazeotrope		*217*
1548	C_9H_{12}	Propylbenzene	159.3	Nonazeotrope		*255*
1549	$C_{10}H_{14}$	Cymene	176.7	Nonazeotrope		*217*
1550	$C_{10}H_{16}$	Camphene	159.6	64.67?	98.8?	*254*
1551	$C_{10}H_{16}$	*d*-Limonene	177.8	64.63	99.2	*252*
1552	$C_{10}H_{16}$	α-Pinene	155.8	64.55	90.7	*208*
1553	$C_{10}H_{16}$	Thymene	179.7	Nonazeotrope		*217*
1554	$C_{10}H_{22}$	2,7-Dimethyloctane	160.1	<64.6	>3	*255*
A =	**CH_4S**	**Methanethiol**	**6.8**			
1555	$C_2H_4O_2$	Methyl formate	31.7	Nonazeotrope		*255*
1556	C_2H_5Cl	Chloroethane	12.4	Nonazeotrope		*255*
1557	$C_2H_5NO_2$	Ethyl nitrite	17.4	<6.4	>82	*255*
1558	C_4H_{10}	Butane	0.6	−0.5	25	*255*
1559	C_5H_{12}	2-Methylbutane	27.95	Nonazeotrope		*255*
A =	**CH_5N**	**Methylamine**	**−6.32**			
1560	C_2H_7N	Dimethylamine	+6.88	Nonazeotrope		*331*
1561	C_3H_9N	Trimethylamine, 60 lb./sq. inch gage	....	36	85	*331*
		210 lb./sq. inch gage	....	75	90–92	*331*
		370 lb./sq. inch gage	....	Nonazeotrope		*331*
			3.5	−5	70	*6, 7**
1562	C_4H_4	1-Butene-3-yne	+5.0	−6.8	97.5, V-l.	*43*
1563	C_4H_6	1,3-Butadiene	−4.5	−9.5	41.4, V-l.	*43*
1564	C_4H_6	1,3-Butadiene	−4.5	−10.4	....	*93*
1565	C_4H_8	1-Butene	−5.6	−13	22.2, V-l.	*43*
1566	C_4H_8	1-Butene	−6.0	−13.8	....	*93*
1567	C_4H_8	*trans*-2-Butene	6.9	−10.4	48.5, V-l.	*43*
1568	C_4H_8	*cis*-2-Butene	3.5	−9.6	47.5, V-l.	*43*
1569	C_4H_8	2-Methylpropene	−6.0	−14.3	32, V-l.	*43*
1570	C_4H_{10}	Butane	−0.6	Min. b.p.		*88*
1571	C_4H_{10}	Butane	+1.0	−14.0	37.6, V-l.	*43*
1572	C_4H_{10}	2-Methylpropane	−10.0	−19.9	25.5, V-l.	*43*
1573	C_5H_8	Isoprene	34	Min. b.p.		*331*
1574	C_5H_{10}	Amylenes	....	Min. b.p.		*101*
A =	**$C_2Br_2Cl_2$**	**1,2-Dibromo-1,2-dichloroethylene**	**172**			
1575	C_2H_6O	Ethyl alcohol	78.3	Nonazeotrope		*213*
1576	$C_4H_{10}O$	Butyl alcohol	117.75	Nonazeotrope		*213*

No.	Formula	B-Component Name	B.P., ° C.	Azeotropic Data B.P., ° C.	Wt. % A	Ref.
A =	**C_2Cl_3N**	**Trichloroacetonitrile**	....			
1577	C_2H_3N	Acetonitrile	82	75.6	71	*182*
A =	**C_2Cl_4**	**Tetrachloroethylene**	**121.1**			
1578	C_2HCl_3O	Chloral	97.5	Nonazeotrope		*255*
1579	$C_2H_3Cl_3$	1,1,2-Trichloroethane	112.4	112	57	*93*
1580	$C_2H_4Cl_2O$	2,2-Dichloroethanol	146.2	<119.5	<96	*255*
1581	$C_2H_4O_2$	Acetic acid	118.5	107.35	61.5	*243*
1582	C_2H_5BrO	2-Bromoethanol	150.2	116.5	85	*255*
1583	C_2H_5ClO	2-Chloroethanol	128.6	110.0	75.7	*248*
1584	C_2H_5NO	Acetamide	221.2	120.45	97.4	*254*
1585	C_2H_6O	Ethyl alcohol	78.3	76.75	~37	*254*
1586	$C_2H_6O_2$	Glycol	197.4	119.1	94	*254*
1587	C_3H_5BrO	Epibromohydrin	138.5	<119.5	<92	*255*
1588	C_3H_5ClO	1-Chloro-2-propanone	119	118	....	*243*
1589	C_3H_5ClO	Epichlorohydrin	116.45	110.12	48.5	*243*
1590	$C_3H_5ClO_2$	Methyl chloroacetate	129.95	120.8	94	*255*
1591	C_3H_6O	Allyl alcohol	96.95	93.15	55	*207, 357**
1592	$C_3H_6O_2$	Propionic acid	140.9	119.1	91.5	*207*
1593	C_3H_7ClO	1-Chloro-2-propanol	127.0	113.0	72	*247*
1594	C_3H_7ClO	2-Chloro-1-propanol	133.7	115.0	87	*247*
1595	C_3H_7NO	Propionamide	222.1	Nonazeotrope		*207*
1596	$C_3H_7NO_2$	Ethyl carbamate	185.25	<120.8	<96	*244*
1597	$C_3H_7NO_3$	Propyl nitrate	110.5	109.6	18	*240*
1598	C_3H_8O	Isopropyl alcohol	82.4	81.7	30	*215*
1599	C_3H_8O	Propyl alcohol	97.25	94.05	52	*215*
1600	$C_3H_8O_2$	2-Methoxyethanol	124.5	109.7	75.5	*250*
1601	C_4H_5N	Pyrrol	130.0	113.35	80.5	*233*
1602	$C_4H_8O_2$	Butyric acid	164.0	121.0	98.8	*207*
1603	$C_4H_8O_2$	Butyric acid	162.45	Nonazeotrope		*221*
1604	$C_4H_8O_2$	Dioxane	101.35	Nonazeotrope		*207*
1605	$C_4H_8O_2$	Isobutyric acid	154.35	120.5	~97	*221*
1606	$C_4H_8O_3$	Methyl lactate	143.8	120.0	90	*255*
1607	C_4H_9I	1-Iodo-2-methylpropane	120.8	119.2	40	*229*
1608	$C_4H_9NO_3$	Isobutyl nitrate	122.9	117.45	70	*240*
1609	$C_4H_{10}O$	Butyl alcohol	117.75	108.95	71	*254*
1610	$C_4H_{10}O$	*sec*-Butyl alcohol	99.5	97.0	43	*247*
1611	$C_4H_{10}O$	*tert*-Butyl alcohol	82.45	Nonazeotrope		*255*
1612	$C_4H_{10}O$	Isobutyl alcohol	108	103.05	60	*243*
1613	$C_4H_{10}O_2$	2-Ethoxyethanol	135.3	116.25	83.5	*207*
1614	$C_5H_4O_2$	2-Furaldehyde	161.45	Nonazeotrope		*207*
1615	C_5H_5N	Pyridine	115.4	112.85	51.5	*233*
1616	$C_5H_6O_2$	Furfuryl alcohol	169.35	Nonazeotrope		*255*
1617	C_5H_8O	Cyclopentanone	130.65	120.1	86	*232*
1618	C_5H_9N	Isovaleronitrile	130.5	113.5	72	*242*
1619	$C_5H_{10}O$	Cyclopentanol	140.85	118.8	92	*247*
1620	$C_5H_{10}O_2$	Isovaleric acid	176.5	Nonazeotrope		*207*
1621	$C_5H_{10}O_3$	Ethyl carbonate	126.0	118.55	74	*227*
1622	$C_5H_{10}O_3$	2-Methoxyethyl acetate	144.6	120.9	96	*236*
1623	$C_5H_{11}Br$	1-Bromo-3-methylbutane	120.65	119.25	48	*229*
1624	$C_5H_{12}O$	Amyl alcohol	138.2	117.0	85	*247*
1625	$C_5H_{12}O$	*tert*-Amyl alcohol	102.35	101.4	27	*247*
1626	$C_5H_{12}O$	Isoamyl alcohol	131.3	116.2	81	*207*
1627	$C_5H_{12}O$	2-Pentanol	119.8	113.2	66	*247*
1628	$C_5H_{12}O_2$	2-Propoxyethanol	151.35	120.6	95	*207*
1629	$C_6H_{10}O$	Mesityl oxide	129.45	119.8	83.5	*207*
1630	$C_6H_{10}S$	Allyl sulfide	139.35	Nonazeotrope		*246*
1631	$C_6H_{12}O$	3-Hexanone	123.3	118.15	55	*232*
1632	$C_6H_{12}O$	4-Methyl-2-pentanone	116.05	113.85	48	*250*
1633	$C_6H_{12}O_2$	Butyl acetate	126.0	120.1	79	*207*
1634	$C_6H_{12}O_2$	Butyl acetate	125.0	120.5	....	*227*
1635	$C_6H_{12}O_2$	Ethyl butyrate	119.9	119.5	57	*227*
1636	$C_6H_{12}O_2$	Ethyl isobutyrate	110.1	Nonazeotrope		*243*
1637	$C_6H_{12}O_2$	Isoamyl formate	123.6	117.9	65	*227*
1638	$C_6H_{12}O_2$	Isobutyl acetate	117.2	115.5	47	*253*
1639	$C_6H_{12}O_2$	Methyl isovalerate	116.5	Nonazeotrope		*255*
1640	$C_6H_{12}O_2$	Propyl propionate	122.5	120.0	....	*227*

No.	Formula	B-Component Name	B.P., ° C.	Azeotropic Data B.P., ° C.	Azeotropic Data Wt. % A	Ref.
A =	**C_2Cl_4**	**Tetrachloroethylene** (*continued*)	**121.1**			
1641	$C_6H_{12}O_3$	Paraldehyde	124	118.75	68	*243*
1642	$C_6H_{14}O_2$	2-Butoxyethanol	171.25	Nonazeotrope		*206*
1643	$C_6H_{15}BO_3$	Ethyl borate	118.6	117.5	48	*218*
1644	C_7H_8	Toluene	110.75	Nonazeotrope		*218*
1645	$C_7H_{14}O_2$	Ethyl isovalerate	134.7	Nonazeotrope		*255*
1646	$C_7H_{14}O_2$	Isobutyl propionate	136.9	Nonazeotrope		*227*
1647	$C_7H_{14}O_2$	Isopropyl isobutyrate	120.8	119.0	45	*227*
1648	$C_7H_{14}O_2$	Propyl isobutyrate	134.0	Nonazeotrope		*227*
1649	C_8H_{10}	Ethylbenzene	136.15	Nonazeotrope		*255*
1650	C_8H_{16}	1,3-Dimethylcyclohexane	~120.5	118	....	*243*
1651	C_8H_{18}	Octane	125.75	<120.5	<92	*255*
1652	$C_8H_{18}O$	Isobutyl ether	122.2	~119.5	~65	*228*
A =	**C_2Cl_6**	**Hexachloroethane**	**185**			
1653	$C_2HCl_3O_2$	Trichloroacetic acid	196	181	85	*243*
1654	$C_2H_3ClO_2$	Chloroacetic acid	189.35	171.2	75	*209*
1655	C_2H_5NO	Acetamide	221.2	Nonazeotrope		*215*
1656	$C_2H_6O_2$	Glycol	197.4	Nonazeotrope		*210*
1657	$C_2H_6SO_4$	Methyl sulfate	189.1	<181.5	<72	*255*
1658	C_3H_7NO	Propionamide	222.1	Nonazeotrope		*215*
1659	$C_4H_6O_4$	Methyl oxalate	164.2	Nonazeotrope		*227*
1660	$C_4H_8O_2$	Butyric acid	162.45	162.0	....	*222*
1661	$C_5H_4O_2$	2-Furaldehyde	161.45	Nonazeotrope		*236*
1662	$C_5H_8O_4$	Methyl malonate	181.4	176.0	45	*218*
1663	$C_5H_{10}O_2$	Isovaleric acid	176.5	172.6	63	*207*
1664	$C_5H_{10}O_2$	Valeric acid	186.35	179.0	70	*242*
1665	C_6H_6O	Phenol	182.2	173.7	~70	*254*
1666	C_6H_7N	Aniline	184.35	176.75	66	*231*
1667	$C_6H_{10}O_3$	Ethyl acetoacetate	180.4	172.5	51	*232*
1668	$C_6H_{10}O_4$	Ethylidene diacetate	168.5	Nonazeotrope		*255*
1669	$C_6H_{10}O_4$	Ethyl oxalate	185.65	178.6	57	*254*
1670	$C_6H_{10}O_4$	Methyl succinate	195.5	<184.0	....	*227*
1671	$C_6H_{12}O$	Cyclohexanol	160.65	Nonazeotrope		*211*
1672	C_7H_6O	Benzaldehyde	179.2	Nonazeotrope		*243*
1673	C_7H_7Br	*p*-Bromotoluene	185	~183.5	~70	*210*
1674	C_7H_8O	Benzyl alcohol	205.15	182.0	88	*209*
1675	C_7H_8O	*m*-Cresol	202.2	183.2	92	*255*
1676	C_7H_8O	*m*-Cresol	202.2	Nonazeotrope		*222*
1677	C_7H_8O	*o*-Cresol	191.1	181.3	72	*218*
1678	C_7H_8O	*p*-Cresol	201.7	183.0	90	*242*
1679	$C_7H_{12}O_4$	Ethyl malonate	199.2	Nonazeotrope		*227*
1680	$C_8H_8O_2$	Phenyl acetate	195.7	Nonazeotrope		*227*
1681	$C_9H_{18}O_2$	Butyl isovalerate	177.6	Nonazeotrope		*227*
1682	$C_9H_{18}O_2$	Isoamyl butyrate	178.5	Nonazeotrope		*218*
1683	$C_9H_{18}O_2$	Isobutyl isovalerate	171.2	Nonazeotrope		*255*
1684	$C_9H_{18}O_3$	Isobutyl carbonate	190.3	184.0	<80	*227*
1685	$C_{10}H_{14}$	Butylbenzene	183.1	Nonazeotrope		*255*
1686	$C_{10}H_{14}$	Cymene	176.7	Nonazeotrope		*255*
1687	$C_{10}H_{16}$	*d*-Limonene	177.8	Nonazeotrope		*210*
1688	$C_{10}H_{16}$	α-Terpinene	173.4	Nonazeotrope		*255*
1689	$C_{10}H_{16}$	Terpinolene	~185	~182.5	....	*243*
1690	$C_{10}H_{16}$	Thymene	179.7	Nonazeotrope		*210*
1691	$C_{10}H_{16}O$	Fenchone	193	Nonazeotrope		*243*
1692	$C_{10}H_{18}O$	Cineol	176.35	Nonazeotrope		*228*
1693	$C_{10}H_{18}O$	Linalool	198.6	Nonazeotrope		*212*
1694	$C_{10}H_{20}O_2$	Isoamyl isovalerate	192.7	Nonazeotrope		*227*
A =	**C_2HBrCl_2**	***cis*-1-Bromo-1,2-dichloroethylene**	**113.8**			
1695	C_2H_6O	Ethyl alcohol	78.3	77.4	30.9	*407*
A =	**C_2HBrCl_2**	***trans*-1-Bromo-1,2-dichloroethylene**	**....**			
1696	C_2H_6O	Ethyl alcohol	78.3	74.9	65.5	*407*
A =	**C_2HBrCl_2**	***trans*-1-Bromo-2,2-dichloroethylene**	**107–108**			
1697	C_2H_6O	Ethyl alcohol	78.3	77.25	39.5	*407*

No.	Formula	B-Component Name	B.P., ° C.	Azeotropic Data B.P., ° C.	Wt. % A	Ref.
A =	**C_2HBr_2Cl**	**1,2-Dibromochloroethylene**	**140**			
1698	C_2H_6O	Ethyl alcohol	78.3	74.9	65.5	*213*
1699	$C_4H_{10}O$	Butyl alcohol	117.75	117.0	....	*213*
A =	**C_2HBr_3O**	**Bromal**	**174**			
1700	$C_5H_{10}O_2$	Isovaleric acid	176.5	~170.3	....	*243*
A =	**C_2HClF_4**	**Tetrafluorochloroethane**	**−10**			
1701	C_4F_8	Octafluorocyclobutane	−4	−12	80 vol.	*22*
A =	**C_2HCl_3**	**Trichloroethylene**	**86.9**			
1702	C_2H_3N	Acetonitrile, 778 mm.	81.6	74.6	71	*309*
					V-l.	*309*
1703	$C_2H_4Cl_2$	1,2-Dichloroethane	83.7	82.1	43.5	*321*
1704	$C_2H_4Cl_2$	1,2-Dichloroethane	83.45	82.6	18	*229*
1705	$C_2H_4O_2$	Acetic acid	118.5	86.5	96.2	*225*
1706	C_2H_5BrO	2-Bromoethanol	150.2	Nonazeotrope		*255*
1707	C_2H_5ClO	2-Chloroethanol	128.6	Nonazeotrope		*244*
1708	C_2H_5ClO	2-Chloroethanol	128.6	86.55	97.5	*207*
1709	$C_2H_5NO_3$	Ethyl nitrate	87	83.5	62	*207*
1710	C_2H_6O	Ethyl alcohol	78.3	70.9	72.5	*126, 323*,*
					V-l.	*337**
1711	$C_2H_6O_2$	Glycol	197.4	Nonazeotrope		*255*
1712	C_3H_6O	Acetone	56.15	Nonazeotrope		*232*
1713	C_3H_6O	Allyl alcohol	96.9	80.9	84.4	*149, 243**
1714	$C_3H_6O_3$	Methyl carbonate	90.35	85.95	90	*207*
1715	C_3H_7ClO	1-Chloro-2-propanol	127.0	Nonazeotrope		*255*
1716	C_3H_7ClO	2-Chloro-1-propanol	133.7	Nonazeotrope		*255*
1717	C_3H_7I	2-Iodopropane	89.45	<86.5	<88	*255*
1718	C_3H_8O	Isopropyl alcohol	82.45	75.5	70	*253*
1719	C_3H_8O	Propyl alcohol	97.2	81.75	83	*243*
1720	$C_3H_9BO_3$	Methyl borate	68.7	Nonazeotrope		*255*
1721	C_4H_4S	Thiophene	84	Nonazeotrope		*243*
1722	C_4H_8O	2-Butanone	79.6	Nonazeotrope		*232*
1723	$C_4H_8O_2$	Butyric acid	162.5	Nonazeotrope		*277*
1724	$C_4H_8O_2$	Dioxane	101.35	Nonazeotrope		*207*
1725	$C_4H_8O_2$	Ethyl acetate	77.05	Nonazeotrope		*243*
1726	$C_4H_8O_2$	Methyl propionate	79.85	Nonazeotrope		*227*
1727	$C_4H_8O_2$	Propyl formate	80.85	79.5	20	*227*
1728	$C_4H_9NO_2$	Butyl nitrite	78.2	Nonazeotrope		*230*
1729	$C_4H_{10}O$	Butyl alcohol	117.75	86.65	97	*207*
1730	$C_4H_{10}O$	*sec*-Butyl alcohol	99.5	84.2	85	*247*
1731	$C_4H_{10}O$	*tert*-Butyl alcohol	82.55	75.8	~67	*212*
1732	$C_4H_{10}O$	Isobutyl alcohol	108	85.4	91	*243*
1733	$C_4H_{10}S$	2-Methyl-1-propanethiol	88	Nonazeotrope		*243*
1734	$C_5H_{10}O$	Isovaleraldehyde	92.1	Nonazeotrope		*255*
1735	$C_5H_{10}O$	3-Methyl-2-butanone	95.4	Nonazeotrope		*232*
1736	$C_5H_{10}O$	3-Pentanone	102.05	Nonazeotrope		*232*
1737	$C_5H_{10}O_2$	Ethyl propionate	99.1	Nonazeotrope		*255*
1738	$C_5H_{10}O_2$	Isobutyl formate	98.2	Nonazeotrope		*227*
1739	$C_5H_{10}O_2$	Isopropyl acetate	89.5	Nonazeotrope		*255*
1740	$C_5H_{10}O_2$	Methyl isobutyrate	92.5	Nonazeotrope		*227*
1741	$C_5H_{11}NO_2$	Isoamyl nitrite	97.15	Nonazeotrope		*230*
1742	$C_5H_{12}O$	*tert*-Amyl alcohol	102.25	86.67	92.5	*225*
1743	$C_5H_{12}O$	Isoamyl alcohol	131.3	Nonazeotrope		*207*
1744	$C_5H_{12}O$	3-Methyl-2-butanol	112.6	Nonazeotrope		*255*
1745	$C_5H_{12}O$	2-Pentanol	119.8	Nonazeotrope		*255*
1746	$C_5H_{12}O$	3-Pentanol	116.0	Nonazeotrope		*255*
1747	$C_5H_{12}O_2$	Diethoxymethane	87.9	89.2	53.5	*248*
1748	C_6H_6	Benzene	80.2	Nonazeotrope		*243*
1749	C_6H_{10}	Cyclohexene	82.75	Azeotrope doubtful		*243*
1750	C_6H_{12}	Cyclohexane	80.75	Nonazeotrope		*243*
1751	C_6H_{12}	Methylcyclopentane	72.0	Nonazeotrope		*255*
1752	C_6H_{14}	Hexane	68.8	Nonazeotrope		*255*
1753	$C_6H_{14}O$	Isopropyl ether	68.3	Nonazeotrope		*239*
1754	$C_6H_{14}O_2$	Acetal	103.55	Nonazeotrope		*239*
1755	C_7H_{14}	Methylcyclohexane	101.15	Nonazeotrope		*255*
1756	C_7H_{16}	Heptane	98.45	Nonazeotrope		*243*

No.	B-Component Formula	Name	B.P., ° C.	Azeotropic Data B.P., ° C.	Wt. % A	Ref.
A =	**C_2HCl_3O**	**Chloral**	**97.75**			
1757	$C_2H_4Cl_2$	1,2-Dichloroethane	83.75	Nonazeotrope		212
1758	$C_2H_5NO_2$	Nitroethane	114.2	Nonazeotrope		255
1759	C_2H_6O	Ethyl alcohol	78.3	116.2	....	243
1760	C_3H_5I	3-Iodopropene	101.8	~97.0	~80	228
1761	$C_3H_6O_3$	Methyl carbonate	90.35	~98.0	~85	228
1762	C_3H_7I	1-Iodopropane	102.4	~97.3	....	243
1763	C_3H_7I	2-Iodopropane	89.45	Nonazeotrope		228
1764	C_4H_8O	2-Butanone	79.6	Nonazeotrope		243
1765	$C_4H_8O_2$	Propyl formate	80.85	Nonazeotrope		228
1766	C_4H_9Br	1-Bromobutane	101.5	96.5	....	255
1767	C_4H_9Br	1-Bromo-2-methylpropane	96.6	Azeotrope doubtful		243
1768	C_4H_9Cl	1-Chlorobutane	78.5	Nonazeotrope		255
1769	C_4H_9I	1-Iodo-2-methylpropane	120.8	Nonazeotrope		255
1770	$C_4H_{10}O$	Isobutyl alcohol	108	~138	....	243
1771	$C_5H_{10}O$	3-Pentanone	102.2	102.9	~23	243
1772	$C_5H_{10}O_2$	Butyl formate	106.8	Nonazeotrope		225
1773	$C_5H_{10}O_2$	Ethyl propionate	99.15	100.8	....	225
1774	$C_5H_{10}O_2$	Isobutyl formate	97.9	100.1	~60	208
1775	$C_5H_{10}O_2$	Isopropyl acetate	90.8	98.2	~85	228
1776	$C_5H_{10}O$	Methyl butyrate	102.65	103.3	45	225
1777	$C_5H_{10}O$	Methyl isobutyrate	92.3	98.2	~90	225
1778	$C_5H_{10}O_2$	Propyl acetate	101.6	102.55	50.5	208
1779	$C_5H_{11}Br$	1-Bromo-3-methylbutane	120.65	Nonazeotrope		255
1780	$C_5H_{11}Cl$	1-Chloro-3-methylbutane	99.8	<97.0	<85	228
1781	C_6H_6	Benzene	80.2	Nonazeotrope		208
1782	C_6H_{12}	Cyclohexane	80.75	Nonazeotrope		225
1783	C_6H_{12}	Methylcyclopentane	72.0	Nonazeotrope		255
1784	$C_6H_{12}O_2$	Ethyl isobutyrate	110.1	Nonazeotrope		228
1785	C_6H_{14}	Hexane	68.8	Nonazeotrope		255
1786	C_7H_8	Toluene	110.75	Nonazeotrope		228
1787	C_7H_{14}	Methylcyclohexane	100.95	94.45	57	252
1788	C_7H_{16}	Heptane	98.45	93	53	225
1789	C_8H_{16}	1,3-Dimethylcyclohexane	120.7	Nonazeotrope		255
1790	C_8H_{18}	2,5-Dimethylhexane	109.3	<97.0	<90	225
1791	C_8H_{18}	Octane	125.75	Nonazeotrope		258
A =	**$C_2HCl_3O_2$**	**Trichloroacetic Acid**	**197.55**			
1792	C_2HCl_5	Pentachloroethane	161.95	161.8	3.5	254
1793	$C_2H_3ClO_2$	Chloroacetic acid	189.35	Nonazeotrope		210
1794	$C_2H_4O_2$	Methyl formate	31.9	Nonazeotrope		243
1795	$C_4H_{10}O$	Ethyl ether	34.6	Nonazeotrope		243
1796	C_6H_4BrCl	*p*-Bromochlorobenzene	196.4	<191.5	<47	255
1797	$C_6H_4Cl_2$	*p*-Dichlorobenzene	174.35	174.0	~12	210
1798	C_6H_5Br	Bromobenzene	156.1	Nonazeotrope		215
1799	C_6H_5I	Iodobenzene	188.55	~181	~25	243
1800	$C_6H_5NO_2$	Nitrobenzene	210.75	Nonazeotrope		234
1801	$C_6H_{12}O_2$	Caproic acid	205.15	210.4?	45?	255
1802	$C_6H_{12}O_2$	Caproic acid	204.5	Nonazeotrope		243
1803	C_7H_7Br	*o*-Bromotoluene	181.45	180.0	~18	215
1804	C_7H_7Cl	*α*-Chlorotoluene	179.3	~178.2	~14	210
1805	C_7H_7Cl	*o*-Chlorotoluene	159.2	Nonazeotrope		255
1806	C_7H_7I	*p*-Iodotoluene	214.5	<196.8	....	255
1807	C_7H_8O	*m*-Cresol	202.8	Nonazeotrope		243
1808	C_7H_8O	*o*-Cresol	190.8	Nonazeotrope		243
1809	C_7H_8O	*p*-Cresol	201.7	Reacts		215
1810	$C_7H_8O_2$	Guaiacol	205.05	Reacts		215
1811	C_8H_8O	Acetophenone	202.05	Nonazeotrope		210
1812	$C_{10}H_8$	Naphthalene	218.05	Nonazeotrope		210
1813	$C_{10}H_{14}$	Butylbenzene	183.1	181.3	20	242
1814	$C_{10}H_{14}$	Cymene	176.7	176.0?	....	255
1815	$C_{10}H_{16}$	*d*-Limonene	177.8	171	....	243
1816	$C_{11}H_{20}O$	Terpineol methyl ether	216.2	Nonazeotrope		217
A =	**C_2HCl_5**	**Pentachloroethane**	**162.0**			
1817	$C_2H_3BrO_2$	Bromoacetic acid	205.1	Nonazeotrope		207
1818	$C_2H_3ClO_2$	Chloroacetic acid	189.35	158.65	90.1	210

No.	B-Component Formula	Name	B.P., ° C.	Azeotropic Data B.P., ° C.	Wt. % A	Ref.
A =	C_2HCl_5	**Pentachloroethane** (*continued*)	**162.0**			
1819	$C_2H_4O_2$	Acetic acid	118.5	Nonazeotrope		*222*
1820	C_2H_5ClO	2-Chloroethanol	128.6	Nonazeotrope		*206*
1821	C_2H_5NO	Acetamide	221.2	160.5	97	*254*
1822	$C_2H_6O_2$	Glycol	197.4	154.5	~85	*208*
1823	$C_2H_6SO_4$	Methyl sulfate	189.1	Nonazeotrope		*227*
1824	$C_3H_5BrO_2$	α-Bromopropionic acid	205.8	Nonazeotrope		*255*
1825	$C_3H_6Cl_2O$	1,3-Dichloro-2-propanol	175.1	159.7	77.5	*209*
1826	$C_3H_6O_2$	Propionic acid	140.7	Nonazeotrope		*243*
1827	C_3H_7NO	Propionamide	222.1	Nonazeotrope		*207*
1828	$C_3H_7NO_2$	Ethyl carbamate	185.25	159.8	91	*207*
1829	$C_4H_6O_4$	Methyl oxalate	163.3	157.55	68	*243*
1830	$C_4H_7BrO_2$	Ethyl bromoacetate	158.8	158.5	30	*203*
1831	$C_4H_7ClO_2$	Ethyl chloroacetate	143.55	Nonazeotrope		*257*
1832	$C_4H_8O_2$	Butyric acid	163.5	156.75	74	*245*
1833	$C_4H_8O_2$	Isobutyric acid	154.35	152.9	57	*243*
1834	$C_4H_8O_3$	Methyl lactate	143.8	Nonazeotrope		*253*
1835	$C_4H_{10}O_2$	2-Ethoxyethanol	135.3	Nonazeotrope		*206*
1836	$C_5H_4O_2$	2-Furaldehyde	161.4	156.75	60	*236*
1837	...	.....	161.4	155.15	50	*208*
1838	$C_5H_8O_3$	Methyl acetoacetate	169.5	<159.4	>40	*243*
1839	$C_5H_8O_4$	Methyl malonate	181.5	Nonazeotrope		*227*
1840	$C_5H_9ClO_2$	Propyl chloroacetate	162.5	160.5	60	*255*
1841	$C_5H_{10}O_2$	Isovaleric acid	176.5	160.25	91	*207*
1842	$C_5H_{10}O_2$	Valeric acid	186.35	161.5	97.2	*207*
1843	$C_5H_{10}O_3$	Ethyl lactate	153.9	153.45	35	*209*
1844	$C_5H_{10}O_3$	2-Methoxyethyl acetate	144.6	Nonazeotrope		*255*
1845	$C_5H_{11}NO_3$	Isoamyl nitrate	~149.6	Nonazeotrope		*221*
1846	$C_5H_{12}O$	Isoamyl alcohol	131.3	Nonazeotrope		*207*
1847	$C_5H_{12}O_2$	2-Propoxyethanol	151.35	Nonazeotrope		*206*
1848	C_6H_5Br	Bromobenzene	156.1	Nonazeotrope		*255*
1849	C_6H_5ClO	o-Chlorophenol	176.8	Nonazeotrope		*255*
1850	C_6H_5ClO	o-Chlorophenol	175.5	160	....	*243*
1851	$C_6H_5NO_2$	Nitrobenzene	210.75	Nonazeotrope		*234*
1852	C_6H_6O	Phenol	181.5	160.85	90.5	*243*
1853	C_6H_7N	Aniline	184.35	Nonazeotrope		*231*
1854	$C_6H_{10}O$	Cyclohexanone	155.7	165.0	73	*232*
1855	$C_6H_{10}O_3$	Ethyl acetoacetate	180.4	Nonazeotrope		*232*
1856	$C_6H_{10}O_4$	Ethyl oxalate	185.65	Nonazeotrope		*207*
1857	$C_6H_{11}BrO_2$	Ethyl α-bromoisobutyrate	178	Nonazeotrope		*212*
1858	$C_6H_{11}ClO_2$	Isobutyl chloroacetate	174.5	Nonazeotrope		*255*
1859	$C_6H_{12}O$	Cyclohexanol	160.65	157.9	64	*243*
1860	$C_6H_{12}O_2$	Isocaproic acid	199.5	Nonazeotrope		*255*
1861	$C_6H_{12}O_3$	2-Ethoxyethyl acetate	156.8	Nonazeotrope		*236*
1862	$C_6H_{12}O_3$	Propyl lactate	171.7	Nonazeotrope		*243*
1863	$C_6H_{14}O$	Hexyl alcohol	157.95	155.75	54	*218*
1864	$C_6H_{14}O_2$	2-Butoxyethanol	171.15	Nonazeotrope		*255*
1865	$C_6H_{14}O_2$	Pinacol	174.35	158.8	~84	*209*
1866	C_7H_6O	Benzaldehyde	179.2	Nonazeotrope		*216*
1867	C_7H_7Cl	o-Chlorotoluene	159.2	Nonazeotrope		*255*
1868	C_7H_7Cl	p-Chlorotoluene	161.3	Nonazeotrope		*243*
1869	C_7H_8O	Anisole	153.85	Nonazeotrope		*209*
1870	C_7H_8O	o-Cresol	190.8	Nonazeotrope		*243*
1871	$C_7H_{14}O$	Heptaldehyde	155	Max. b.p.		*111*
1872	$C_7H_{14}O_2$	Amyl acetate	148.8	Nonazeotrope		*255*
1873	$C_7H_{14}O_2$	Ethyl valerate	145.45	Nonazeotrope		*255*
1874	$C_7H_{14}O_2$	Isoamyl acetate	142.1	Nonazeotrope		*255*
1875	$C_7H_{14}O_2$	Methyl caproate	149.8	Nonazeotrope		*255*
1876	$C_7H_{14}O_2$	Propyl butyrate	143.7	Nonazeotrope		*255*
1877	$C_7H_{14}O_3$	1,3-Butanediol methyl ether acetate	171.75	Nonazeotrope		*255*
1878	$C_7H_{16}O$	Heptyl alcohol	176.15	Nonazeotrope		*255*
1879	$C_7H_{16}O_3$	Ethyl orthoformate	145.75	Nonazeotrope		*239*
1880	C_8H_8	Styrene	145.8	Nonazeotrope		*255*
1881	C_8H_{10}	o-Xylene	144.3	Nonazeotrope		*255*
1882	$C_8H_{10}O$	Benzyl methyl ether	167.8	Nonazeotrope		*239*
1883	$C_8H_{10}O$	p-Methylanisole	177.05	Nonazeotrope		*239*
1884	$C_8H_{10}O$	Phenetole	170.35	Nonazeotrope		*210*

	B-Component			Azeotropic Data		
No.	Formula	Name	B.P., ° C.	B.P., ° C.	Wt. % A	Ref.
A =	**C_2HCl_5**	**Pentachloroethane (*continued*)**	**162.0**			
1885	$C_8H_{14}O$	Methyl heptenone	173.2	Nonazeotrope		*232*
1886	$C_8H_{16}O$	2-Octanone	174.1	Nonazeotrope		*253*
1887	$C_8H_{16}O_2$	Ethyl caproate	167.8	Nonazeotrope		*227*
1888	$C_8H_{16}O_2$	Hexyl acetate	171.5	Nonazeotrope		*255*
1889	$C_8H_{16}O_2$	Isoamyl propionate	160.3	158.7	50	*243*
1890	$C_8H_{16}O_2$	Isobutyl butyrate	157	<156.5	....	*227*
1891	$C_8H_{16}O_2$	Propyl isovalerate	155.7	Nonazeotrope		*227*
1892	$C_8H_{18}O$	*sec*-Octanol	179.0	Nonazeotrope		*209*
1893	$C_8H_{20}SiO_4$	Ethyl silicate	168.8	Nonazeotrope		*255*
1894	C_9H_{12}	Cumene	152.8	Nonazeotrope		*255*
1895	C_9H_{12}	Mesitylene	164.6	166.0	40	*209*
1896	C_9H_{12}	Pseudocumene	168.2	>168.35	<22	*255*
1897	C_9H_{12}	Pseudocumene	169	Nonazeotrope		*243*
1898	$C_9H_{13}N$	*N,N*-Dimethyl-*o*-toluidene	185.3	Nonazeotrope		*231*
1899	$C_9H_{18}O$	2,6-Dimethyl-4-heptanone	168.0	169.0	35	*232*
1900	$C_9H_{18}O_2$	Isoamyl isobutyrate	169.8	Nonazeotrope		*255*
1901	$C_9H_{18}O_2$	Isobutyl isovalerate	171.35	Nonazeotrope		*218*
1902	$C_{10}H_{14}$	Cymene	176.7	Nonazeotrope		*255*
1903	$C_{10}H_{16}$	Camphene	159.6	159.5	3	*209*
1904	$C_{10}H_{16}$	Dipentene	177.7	Nonazeotrope		*255*
1905	$C_{10}H_{16}$	α-Pinene	155.8	155.6	11	*209*
1906	$C_{10}H_{16}$	Nopinene	163.8	160.7	>62	*242*
1907	$C_{10}H_{16}$	Nopinene	163.8	~166	~42	*243*
1908	$C_{10}H_{16}$	α-Terpinene	173.4	Nonazeotrope		*255*
1909	$C_{10}H_{18}$	*m*-Menthene-8	170.8	Nonazeotrope		*255*
1910	$C_{10}H_{18}O$	Cineol	176.4	Nonazeotrope		*208*
1911	$C_{10}H_{22}$	Decane	173.3	Nonazeotrope		*255*
1912	$C_{10}H_{22}O$	Isoamyl ether	173.5	Nonazeotrope		*228*
A =	**C_2H_2**	**Acetylene**	**−84**			
1913	C_2H_4	Ethylene	−103.9	Min. b.p.		*72*
1914	C_2H_6	Ethane	−88.3	−94.5	40.75	*195*, 267*
A =	**C_2H_2BrCl**	***cis*-1-Bromo-2-chloroethylene**	**106.7**			
1915	C_2H_6O	Ethyl alcohol	78.3	72.4	73.3	*213*
1916	$C_5H_{10}O_2$	Ethyl propionate	99.1	Nonazeotrope		*255*
1917	$C_5H_{10}O_2$	Propyl acetate	101.6	Nonazeotrope		*255*
1918	$C_6H_{12}O_2$	Ethyl isobutyrate	110.1	Nonazeotrope		*255*
A =	**C_2H_2BrCl**	***trans*-1-Bromo-2-chloroethylene**	**75.3**			
1920	C_2H_6O	Ethyl alcohol	78.3	66.3	82	*213*
A =	**C_2H_2BrI**	***cis*-1-Bromo-2-iodoethylene**	**149.05**			
1921	$C_2H_4O_2$	Acetic acid	118.1	115.6	40.5	*255*
1922	$C_3H_6O_2$	Propionic acid	141.3	135.3	65.2	*255*
1923	$C_4H_{10}O$	Butyl alcohol	117.8	117.3	32.4	*255*
1924	$C_8H_{16}O_2$	Butyl butyrate	165.8	141.5	55	*255*
A =	**$C_2H_2Br_2$**	***cis*-1,2-Dibromoethylene**	**112.5**			
1925	C_2H_6O	Ethyl alcohol	78.3	77.7	32.5	*243*
A =	**$C_2H_2Br_2$**	***trans*-1,2-Dibromoethylene**	**108**			
1926	C_2H_6O	Ethyl alcohol	78.3	75.6	64	*243*
A =	**C_2H_2ClI**	***cis*-1-Chloro-2-iodoethylene**	**116–117**			
1927	C_3H_8O	Propyl alcohol	97.20	93.6	55.6	*407*
1928	$C_4H_{10}O$	Butyl alcohol	117.8	108.5	75	*255*
A =	**C_2H_2ClI**	***trans*-1-Chloro-2-iodoethylene**	**113–114**			
1929	C_3H_8O	Propyl alcohol	97.20	87.5	96	*407*
A =	**$C_2H_2Cl_2$**	***cis*-1,2-Dichloroethylene**	**60.25**			
1930	C_2H_6O	Ethyl alcohol	78.3	57.7	90.20	*71*
1931	C_6H_6	Benzene	80.15	Nonazeotrope		*255*
A =	**$C_2H_2Cl_2$**	***trans*-1,2-Dichloroethylene**	**48.35**			
1932	C_2H_6O	Ethyl alcohol	78.3	46.5	94.0	*71*

No.	B-Component Formula	Name	B.P., ° C.	Azeotropic Data B.P., ° C.	Wt. % A	Ref.
A =	**$C_2H_2Cl_2O_2$**	**Dichloroacetic Acid**	**190**			
1933	$C_2H_4O_2$	Methyl formate	31.9	Nonazeotrope		*243*
1934	$C_4H_{10}O$	Ethyl ether	34.6	Nonazeotrope		*243*
1935	$C_6H_5NO_2$	Nitrobenzene	210.75	Nonazeotrope		*234*
1936	C_6H_6O	Phenol	181.5	Nonazeotrope		*243*
1937	C_7H_7Br	*o*-Bromotoluene	181.75	175.5	25	*243*
1938	C_7H_8O	*m*-Cresol	202.2	Nonazeotrope		*224*
1939	C_7H_8O	*o*-Cresol	190.8	~189	....	*243*
1940	$C_7H_8O_2$	Guaiacol	205.05	Reacts		*255*
A =	**$C_2H_2Cl_4$**	**1,1,2,2-Tetrachloroethane**	**146.25**			
1941	$C_2H_3ClO_2$	Chloroacetic acid	189.35	Nonazeotrope		*255*
1942	$C_2H_3ClO_2$	Chloroacetic acid	189.35	146.25	98.2	*210*
1943	$C_2H_4Cl_2O$	2,2-Dichloroethanol	146.2	<144.0	52	*255*
1944	$C_2H_4O_2$	Acetic acid	118.5	Nonazeotrope		*243*
1945	C_2H_5BrO	2-Bromoethanol	150.2	141.5	....	*255*
1946	C_2H_5ClO	2-Chloroethanol	128.6	128.2	31	*244*
1947	C_2H_5IO	2-Iodoethanol	176.5	Nonazeotrope		*255*
1948	C_2H_5NO	Acetamide	221.2	Nonazeotrope		*207*
1949	$C_2H_6O_2$	Glycol	197.4	144.9	93	*206*
1950	$C_3H_5ClO_2$	Methyl chloroacetate	130.0	Nonazeotrope		*212*
1951	$C_3H_6Cl_2O$	1,3-Dichloro-2-propanol	174.5	Nonazeotrope		*243*
1952	$C_3H_6O_2$	Propionic acid	140.7	140.4	40	*159, 207**
1953	C_3H_7ClO	1-Chloro-2-propanol	127.0	Nonazeotrope		*255*
1954	C_3H_7NO	Propionamide	222.1	Nonazeotrope		*207*
1955	$C_3H_7NO_2$	Ethyl carbamate	185.25	Nonazeotrope		*244*
1956	C_3H_8O	Propyl alcohol	97.25	Nonazeotrope		*254*
1957	$C_3H_8O_2$	2-Methoxyethanol	124.5	Nonazeotrope		*206*
1958	$C_4H_6O_4$	Methyl oxalate	164.2	Nonazeotrope		*227*
1959	$C_4H_7BrO_2$	Ethyl bromoacetate	158.2	Nonazeotrope		*212*
1960	$C_4H_7ClO_2$	Ethyl chloroacetate	143.6	147.45	73	*208*
1961	$C_4H_8O_2$	Butyric acid	162.45	145.65	96.2	*207*
1962	$C_4H_8O_2$	Isobutyric acid	154.35	144.8	93	*243*
1963	$C_4H_8O_3$	Methyl lactate	143.8	Nonazeotrope		*252*
1964	$C_4H_{10}O$	Butyl alcohol	117.75	Nonazeotrope		*207*
1965	$C_4H_{10}O$	Isobutyl alcohol	107	Nonazeotrope, V-l.		*125*
1966	$C_4H_{10}O_2$	2-Ethoxyethanol	135.3	Nonazeotrope		*236*
1967	$C_5H_4O_2$	2-Furaldehyde	161.45	161.55	3	*236*
1968	$C_5H_6O_2$	Furfuryl alcohol	169.35	Nonazeotrope		*255*
1969	$C_5H_8O_3$	Methyl acetoacetate	169.5	Nonazeotrope		*243*
1970	$C_5H_9ClO_2$	Propyl chloroacetate	162.5	Nonazeotrope		*255*
1971	$C_5H_{10}O_2$	Isovaleric acid	176.5	Nonazeotrope		*207*
1972	$C_5H_{10}O_2$	Valeric acid	186.35	Nonazeotrope		*207*
1973	$C_5H_{10}O_3$	Ethyl carbonate	126.0	Nonazeotrope		*227*
1974	$C_5H_{10}O_3$	Ethyl lactate	153.9	Nonazeotrope		*253*
1975	$C_5H_{10}O_3$	2-Methoxyethyl acetate	144.6	150.9	63	*207*
1976	$C_5H_{11}I$	1-Iodo-3-methylbutane	147.65	Nonazeotrope		*252*
1977	$C_5H_{11}NO_3$	Isoamyl nitrate	149.75	Nonazeotrope		*240*
1978	$C_5H_{12}O$	Isoamyl alcohol	131.3	Nonazeotrope		*207*
1979	$C_5H_{12}O$	Isoamyl alcohol	131.3	131.25	2	*209*
1980	$C_5H_{12}O_2$	2-Propoxyethanol	151.35	Nonazeotrope		*236*
1981	C_6H_5Br	Bromobenzene	156.1	Nonazeotrope		*255*
1982	C_6H_5ClO	*o*-Chlorophenol	175.5	Nonazeotrope		*243*
1983	$C_6H_5NO_2$	Nitrobenzene	210.75	Nonazeotrope		*234*
1984	C_6H_6O	Phenol	181.5	Nonazeotrope		*243*
1985	C_6H_7N	Aniline	184.35	Nonazeotrope		*231*
1986	$C_6H_{10}O$	Cyclohexanone	155.7	159.0	45	*232*
1987	$C_6H_{10}O$	Mesityl oxide	129.4	147.5	85	*253*
1988	$C_6H_{10}S$	Allyl sulfide	139.35	>148.5	....	*246*
1989	$C_6H_{12}O$	Cyclohexanol	160.7	Nonazeotrope		*212*
1990	$C_6H_{12}O_2$	Isobutyl acetate	117.4	Nonazeotrope		*255*
1991	$C_6H_{12}O_3$	2-Ethoxyethyl acetate	156.8	158.25	26	*236*
1992	$C_6H_{14}O$	Hexyl alcohol	157.85	Nonazeotrope		*255*
1993	$C_6H_{14}O_2$	2-Butoxyethanol	171.25	Nonazeotrope		*206*
1994	$C_6H_{14}S$	Propyl sulfide	141.5	>150.0	82	*242*
1995	C_7H_8	Toluene	110.75	Nonazeotrope		*255*
1996	C_7H_8O	Anisole	153.85	Nonazeotrope		*252*

	B-Component			Azeotropic Data		
No.	Formula	Name	B.P., ° C.	B.P., ° C.	Wt. % A	Ref
A =	**$C_2H_2Cl_4$**	**1,1,2,2-Tetrachloroethane** *(continued)*	**146.25**			
1997	$C_7H_{14}O$	Heptaldehyde	155	Max. b.p.		*111*
1998	$C_7H_{14}O$	4-Heptanone	143.55	148.5	....	*232*
1999	$C_7H_{14}O_2$	Amyl acetate	148.8	153.1	40	*242*
2000	$C_7H_{14}O_2$	Butyl propionate	146.5	152.5	55	*227*
2001	$C_7H_{14}O_2$	Ethyl isovalerate	134.7	147.0	....	*218*
2002	$C_7H_{14}O_2$	Isoamyl acetate	142.1	150.1	68	*210*
			138.8	Nonazeotrope		*243*
2003	$C_7H_{14}O_2$	Isobutyl propionate	136.9	>148.5	90	*252*
			136.9	Nonazeotrope		*243*
2004	$C_7H_{14}O_2$	Methyl caproate	149.7	153	50	*253*
2005	$C_7H_{14}O_2$	Propyl butyrate	142.8	150.2	66	*218*
2006	$C_7H_{14}O_3$	1,3-Butanediol methyl ether acetate	171.75	Nonazeotrope		*255*
2007	$C_7H_{16}O_3$	Ethyl orthoformate	145.75	151.5	61	*248*
2008	C_8H_8	Styrene	145.7	~143.5	~55	*243*
2009	C_8H_{10}	Ethylbenzene	136.15	Nonazeotrope		*255*
2010	C_8H_{10}	*m*-Xylene	139.2	Nonazeotrope		*207*
2011	C_8H_{10}	*o*-Xylene	144.3	Nonazeotrope		*255*
2012	C_8H_{16}	1,3-Dimethylcyclohexane	120.7	Nonazeotrope		*255*
2013	$C_8H_{16}O_2$	Butyl butyrate	166.4	Nonazeotrope		*226*
2014	$C_8H_{16}O_2$	Isoamyl propionate	160.7	Nonazeotrope		*255*
2015	$C_8H_{16}O_2$	Isobutyl butyrate	156.8	158.0	~88	*218*
2016	$C_8H_{16}O_2$	Isobutyl isobutyrate	147.3	151.5	65	*253*
2017	$C_8H_{18}O$	Butyl ether	142.2	148.0	70	*239*
2018	C_9H_{12}	Cumene	152.8	Nonazeotrope		*255*
A =	**C_2H_3Br**	**Bromoethylene**	**15.8**			
2019	$C_2H_4O_2$	Methyl formate	31.9	Nonazeotrope		*243*
2020	C_2H_5Cl	Chloroethane	13.3	Nonazeotrope		*243*
2021	$C_2H_5NO_2$	Ethyl nitrite	17.4	<14.8	>64	*230*
2022	C_2H_6O	Ethyl alcohol	78.3	Nonazeotrope		*212*
2023	$C_3H_7NO_2$	Isopropyl nitrite	40.1	Nonazeotrope		*230*
2024	C_5H_8	Isoprene	34.3	Nonazeotrope		*255*
2025	C_5H_{10}	3-Methyl-1-butene	20.6	<15.0	<78	*255*
2026	C_5H_{12}	2-Methylbutane	27.95	<13.0	75	*255*
2027	C_5H_{12}	Pentane	36.15	Nonazeotrope		*255*
A =	**$C_2H_3BrO_2$**	**Bromoacetic Acid**	**205.1**			
2028	$C_6H_4Br_2$	*p*-Dibromobenzene	220.25	<201.5	>55	*207*
2029	$C_6H_4Cl_2$	*o*-Dichlorobenzene	179.5	177.0	16	*255*
2030	$C_6H_4Cl_2$	*p*-Dichlorobenzene	174.4	172.8	13	*207*
2031	C_6H_5Br	Bromobenzene	156.1	Nonazeotrope		*207*
2032	C_6H_5I	Iodobenzene	188.45	<184.3	20	*255*
2033	$C_6H_5NO_2$	Nitrobenzene	210.75	202.25	63	*234*
2034	$C_6H_{12}O_2$	Caproic acid	205.15	204.4	....	*255*
2035	C_7H_7Br	*m*-Bromotoluene	184.3	181.2	....	*204*
2036	C_7H_7Br	*o*-Bromotoluene	181.5	179.0	18	*207*
2037	C_7H_7I	*p*-Iodotoluene	214.5	<198.0	54	*255*
2038	C_7H_8O	*p*-Cresol	201.8	Nonazeotrope		*243*
2039	$C_7H_8O_2$	Guaiacol	205.05	203.7	40	*207*
			205.1	Nonazeotrope		*243*
2040	$C_7H_{14}O_2$	Enanthic acid	222.0	Nonazeotrope		*255*
2041	C_8H_8O	Acetophenone	202.0	206.5	70	*207*
2042	$C_8H_8O_2$	Methyl benzoate	199.4	Nonazeotrope		*207*
2043	$C_8H_{10}O_2$	*o*-Ethoxyphenol	216.5	Nonazeotrope		*207*
2044	$C_9H_{10}O_2$	Ethyl benzoate	212.5	Nonazeotropic		*255*
2045	C_9H_{12}	Mesitylene	164.6	Nonazeotrope		*255*
2046	C_9H_{12}	Propylbenzene	159.3	Nonazeotrope		*255*
2047	$C_{10}H_8$	Naphthalene	218.0	<201.3	>72	*242*
2048	$C_{10}H_{14}$	Butylbenzene	183.1	179.5	25	*242*
2049	$C_{10}H_{14}$	Cymene	176.7	174.7	15	*242*
2050	$C_{11}H_{10}$	2-Methylnaphthalene	241.15	Nonazeotrope		*255*
2051	$C_{11}H_{20}O$	Terpineol methyl ether	216	Reacts		*243*
2052	$C_{12}H_{18}$	1,3,5-Triethylbenzene	215.5	<199.0	<76	*242*

No.	B-Component Formula	Name	B.P., ° C.	Azeotropic Data B.P., ° C.	Wt. % A	Ref.
A =	**C_2H_3Cl**	**Chloroethylene**	**−13.6**			*93*
2053	C_4H_6	1,3-Butadiene	−4.5	Nonazeotrope		
2054	C_4H_8	1-Butene	−6	Nonazeotrope		*93*
A =	**$C_2H_3ClO_2$**	**Chloroacetic Acid**	**189.35**			
2055	$C_2H_4Br_2$	1,2-Dibromoethane	131.65	Nonazeotrope		*215*
2056	$C_2H_4O_2$	Methyl formate	31.9	Nonazeotrope		*243*
2057	$C_2H_6SO_4$	Methyl sulfate	189.1	194.5?	....	*255*
2058	$C_3H_5Cl_3$	1,2,3-Trichloropropane	156.85	154.5	10	*254*
2059	C_3H_8O	Propyl alcohol	97.2	Nonazeotrope		*255*
2060	$C_4H_6O_4$	Methyl oxalate	164.45	Nonazeotrope		*255*
2061	$C_4H_{10}O$	Ethyl ether	34.6	Nonazeotrope		*243*
2062	$C_5H_{10}O_2$	Isovaleric acid	176.5	Nonazeotrope		*243*
2063	$C_5H_{10}O_2$	Valeric acid	186.35	186.33	3	*207*
2064	$C_5H_{11}I$	1-Iodo-3-methylbutane	147.65	147.4	....	*225*
2065	$C_6H_3Cl_3$	1,3,5-Trichlorobenzene	208.4	<185.0	<72	*255*
2066	C_6H_4BrCl	*p*-Bromochlorobenzene	196.4	<181.5	<58	*255*
2067	$C_6H_4Br_2$	*p*-Dibromobenzene	220.25	186.3	74	*215*
2068	$C_6H_4Cl_2$	*o*-Dichlorobenzene	179.5	170.8	28	*225*
2069	$C_6H_4Cl_2$	*p*-Dichlorobenzene	174.1	167.55	24.5	*209*
2070	C_6H_5Br	Bromobenzene	156.1	154.3	11	*253*
2071	C_6H_5Cl	Chlorobenzene	132.0	Nonazeotrope		*253*
2072	C_6H_5I	Iodobenzene	188.55	175.3	~35	*243*
2073	$C_6H_5NO_2$	Nitrobenzene	210.75	Nonazeotrope		*234*
2074	C_6H_6O	Phenol	181.5	Nonazeotrope		*243*
2075	$C_6H_8O_4$	Methyl fumarate	193.25	195.7	42	*250*
2076	$C_6H_8O_4$	Methyl maleate	204.05	Nonazeotrope		*255*
2077	$C_6H_{10}O_4$	Methyl succinate	195.5	197.0	28	*242*
2078	$C_6H_{10}O_4$	Ethyl oxalate	185.65	190.25	70	*248*
2079	$C_6H_{12}O_2$	Caproic acid	205.15	Nonazeotrope		*255*
2080	$C_7H_6Cl_2$	*α,α*-Dichlorotoluene	205.2	189.1	97	*218*
			205.1	Nonazeotrope		*243*
2081	C_7H O	Benzaldehyde	179.2	Azeotrope doubtful		*243*
2082	C_7H_7Br	*α*-Bromotoluene	198.5	~183	~82	*243*
2083	C_7H_7Br	*m*-Bromotoluene	183.8	174	30	*207*
2084	C_7H_7Br	*o*-Bromotoluene	181.75	172.95	32	*243*
2085	C_7H_7Br	*p*-Bromotoluene	185.0	174.1	34	*254*
2086	C_7H_7Cl	*α*-Chlorotoluene	179.3	173.8	25	*210*
2087	C_7H_7Cl	*o*-Chlorotoluene	159.3	156.8	12	*225*
2088	C_7H_7Cl	*p*-Chlorotoluene	162.4	159.3	14	*225*
2089	C_7H_7I	*p*-Iodotoluene	214.5	<184.8	<78	*255*
2090	C_7H_8O	*m*-Cresol	202.2	Nonazeotrope		*255*
2091	C_7H_8O	*o*-Cresol	191.1	187.5	~54	*215*
			191.8	Nonazeotrope		*243*
2092	C_7H_8O	*p*-Cresol	201.7	Nonazeotrope		*224*
2093	$C_7H_8O_2$	Guaiacol	205.05	Nonazeotrope		*255*
2094	$C_7H_{13}ClO_2$	Isoamyl chloroacetate	190.5	Nonazeotrope		*243*
2095	C_8H_8	Styrene	145.8	144.8	14	*242*
2096	$C_8H_8O_2$	Methyl benzoate	199.4	Nonazeotrope		*255*
2097	$C_8H_8O_2$	Phenyl acetate	195.7	Nonazeotrope		*255*
2098	C_8H_{10}	Ethylbenzene	136.15	Nonazeotrope		*255*
2099	C_8H_{10}	*o*-Xylene	144.3	143.5	12	*242*
2100	C_8H_{10}	*m*-Xylene	139.2	139.05	7	*207*
2101	C_8H_{10}	*p*-Xylene	138.45	138.35	4?	*255*
2102	$C_8H_{10}O$	Phenetole	171.5	Nonazeotrope		*243*
2103	$C_8H_{12}O_4$	Ethyl maleate	223.3	195.7	42	*206*
2104	$C_8H_{16}O_2$	Butyl butyrate	166.4	Nonazeotrope		*255*
2105	$C_8H_{16}O_2$	Ethyl caproate	167.7	Nonazeotrope		*255*
2106	$C_8H_{16}O_2$	Hexyl acetate	171.5	Nonazeotrope		*255*
2107	C_8H_{18}	Octane	125.75	Nonazeotrope		*255*
2108	C_9H_8	Indene	182.5	174.5	....	*255*
2109	C_9H_{12}	Cumene	152.8	150.8	21	*242*
2110	C_9H_{12}	Mesitylene	164.6	162	17	*253*
2111	C_9H_{12}	Propylbenzene	158.9	156.0	....	*225*
2112	C_9H_{12}	Pseudocumene	168.2	162.8	34	*242*
2113	$C_9H_{18}O_2$	Butyl isovalerate	177.6	Nonazeotrope		*255*
2114	$C_9H_{18}O_2$	Ethyl enanthate	188.7	185.5	48	*242*

No.	Formula	Name (B-Component)	B.P., ° C. (B-Component)	B.P., ° C. (Azeotropic Data)	Wt. % A (Azeotropic Data)	Ref.
A =	**$C_2H_3ClO_2$**	**Chloroacetic Acid** (*continued*)	**189.35**			
2115	$C_9H_{18}O_2$	Isoamyl butyrate	181.05	Nonazeotrope		*255*
2116	$C_9H_{18}O_2$	Isobutyl isovalerate	171.2	Nonazeotrope		*255*
2117	$C_9H_{18}O_2$	Methyl caprylate	192.9	187.5	67	*242*
2118	$C_9H_{18}O_3$	Isobutyl carbonate	190.3	192.5	40	*242*
2119	$C_{10}H_8$	Naphthalene	218.05	187.1	78	*210*
			218.05	Nonazeotrope		*208*
2120	$C_{10}H_{14}$	Butylbenzene	183.1	172.8	52	*242*
2121	$C_{10}H_{14}$	Cymene	175.3	166	~35	*243*
2122	$C_{10}H_{14}$	Cymene	176.7	169.0	42	*242*
2123	$C_{10}H_{16}$	Camphene	159.6	~154.7	~15	*210*
2124	$C_{10}H_{16}$	*d*-Limonene	177.8	167.8	34	*243*
2125	$C_{10}H_{16}$	Nopinene	163.8	157.6	30	*242*
2126	$C_{10}H_{16}$	α-Phellandrene	171.5	~163.5	~20	*243*
2127	$C_{10}H_{16}$	α-Pinene	155.8	152.0	....	*225*
2128	$C_{10}H_{16}$	α-Terpinene	173.4	166.0	....	*255*
2129	$C_{10}H_{16}$	Terpinolene	185	~173	~47	*243*
2130	$C_{10}H_{16}$	Terpinene	180.5	170	~38	*243*
2131	$C_{10}H_{16}$	Terpinene	181.5	170	....	*225*
2132	$C_{10}H_{18}O$	Cineol	176.4	Nonazeotrope		*236*
2133	$C_{10}H_{20}O_2$	Isoamyl isovalerate	192.7	187.7	65	*244*
2134	$C_{10}H_{22}$	Decane	173.3	165.2	42	
2135	$C_{10}H_{22}$	2,7-Dimethyloctane	160.1	155.7	28	*255*
2136	$C_{10}H_{22}O$	Amyl ether	187.5	<184.3	<50	*255*
2137	$C_{10}H_{22}O$	Isoamyl ether	173.2	171.95	16	*236*
2138	$C_{10}H_{22}O$	Isoamyl ether	172.6	Nonazeotrope		*217*
2139	$C_{11}H_{10}$	2-Methylnaphthalene	241.15	Nonazeotrope		*255*
2140	$C_{11}H_{20}O$	Isobornyl methyl ether	192.2	Reacts		*243*
2141	$C_{12}H_{18}$	1,3,5-Triethylbenzene	215.5	185.5	75	*242*
A =	**$C_2H_3Cl_3$**	**1,1,2-Trichloroethane**	**113.65**			
2142	$C_2H_4O_2$	Acetic acid	118.1	106.0	70	*242*
2143	C_2H_5NO	Acetamide	221.2	Nonazeotrope		*215*
2144	C_2H_6O	Ethyl alcohol	78.3	77.8	30	*212*
2145	$C_2H_6O_2$	Glycol	197.4	Nonazeotrope		*255*
2146	C_3H_6O	Acetone	56.1	Nonazeotrope, V-l.		*400*
2147	$C_3H_6O_2$	Propionic acid	141.3	Nonazeotrope		*255*
2148	$C_4H_8O_2$	Butyric acid	164.0	Nonazeotrope		*255*
2149	$C_4H_8O_2$	Dioxane	101	Max. b.p.		*111*
2150	$C_4H_{10}O$	Isobutyl alcohol	108.0	<103.8	>62	*255*
2151	C_5H_5N	Pyridine	115	Max. b.p.		*111*
2152	$C_5H_{10}O_2$	Propyl acetate	101.6	Nonazeotrope		*255*
2153	$C_6H_{12}O_2$	Ethyl butyrate	121	Max. b.p.		*111*
2154	$C_6H_{12}O_2$	Ethyl isobutyrate	110.1	Nonazeotrope		*227*
2155	C_7H_{14}	Methylcyclohexane	101.15	Nonazeotrope		*255*
A =	**$C_2H_3Cl_3O$**	**Methyl Trichloromethyl Ether**	**131.2**			
2156	$C_3H_8O_2$	2-Methoxyethanol	124.5	123.0	75?	*255*
2157	C_4H_5N	Pyrrol	130.0	<127.5	....	*255*
2158	C_5H_8O	Cyclopentanone	130.65	<130.2	....	*255*
2159	$C_6H_{12}O$	2-Hexanone	127.2	Nonazeotrope		*255*
2160	$C_6H_{14}S$	Isopropyl sulfide	120.5	Nonazeotrope		*255*
2161	C_8H_{10}	Ethylbenzene	136.15	Nonazeotrope		*255*
A =	**$C_2H_3Cl_3O_2$**	**Chloral Hydrate**	**97.5**			
2162	$C_4H_8O_2$	Ethyl acetate	77.05	Nonazeotrope		*243*
2163	$C_5H_{10}O_2$	Propyl acetate	101.55	~96.5	....	*243*
2164	C_6H_5Cl	Chlorobenzene	131.8	Nonazeotrope		*243*
2165	C_6H_{12}	Cyclohexane	80.75	76	~22	*243*
A =	**C_2H_3N**	**Acetonitrile**	**81.6**			
2166	C_2H_5I	Iodoethane	72.3	<64.2	....	*245*
2167	C_2H_6O	Ethyl alcohol	78.3	72.5	44	*243*
2168	C_3H_6O	Acetone	56.4	Nonazeotrope, V-l.		*309*
2169	$C_3H_6O_2$	Methyl acetate	56.95	Nonazeotrope		*245*
2170	C_3H_7Br	1-Bromopropane	71.0	63.0	22	*245*

No.	B-Component Formula	B-Component Name	B.P., ° C.	Azeotropic Data B.P., ° C.	Wt. % A	Ref.
A =	**C_2H_3N**	**Acetonitrile (*continued*)**	**81.6**			
2171	C_3H_8	Propane, 280 lb./sq. inch abs.	....	55	2.2	*182*
2172	C_3H_8O	Isopropyl alcohol	82.5	74.5	52	*207*
2173	C_3H_8O	Propyl alcohol	97.2	81.2	~72	*243*
2174	C_3H_9SiCl	Chlorotrimethylsilane	57.5	56	7.4	*340, 342**
2175	$C_4H_8O_2$	Ethyl acetate	77.1	74.8	23	*207*
2176	$C_4H_8O_2$	Methyl propionate	79.85	76.2	30	*245*
2177	$C_4H_8O_2$	Propyl formate	80.85	76.5	33	*245*
2178	C_4H_9Br	1-Bromobutane	101.5	<79.0	....	*245*
2179	C_4H_9Br	1-Bromo-2-methylpropane	91.4	<74.5	....	*245*
2180	C_4H_9Cl	1-Chlorobutane	78.5	67.2	33	*245*
2181	C_4H_9Cl	1-Chloro-2-methylpropane	68.85	62.0	20	*245*
2182	$C_4H_9NO_2$	Butyl nitrite	78.2	<77.0	....	*255*
2183	$C_4H_{10}O$	Ethyl ether	34.6	Nonazeotrope		*255*
2184	$C_4H_{10}O$	Isobutyl alcohol	108.0	Nonazeotrope		*245*
2185	C_5H_{10}	Cyclopentane	49.3	<44.5	<14	*245*
2186	$C_5H_{10}O_2$	Ethyl propionate	99.1	Nonazeotrope		*245*
2187	$C_5H_{10}O_2$	Isopropyl acetate	89.5	79.5	60	*245*
2188	$C_5H_{10}O_2$	Propyl acetate	101.55	Nonazeotrope		*245*
2189	$C_5H_{11}Br$	1-Bromo-3-methylbutane	120.65	Nonazeotrope		*207*
2190	C_5H_{12}	Pentane	36	....	10	*182*
2191	$C_5H_{12}O$	*tert*-Amyl alcohol	102.35	Nonazeotrope		*245*
2192	$C_5H_{12}O$	3-Pentanol	116.0	Nonazeotrope		*245*
2193	C_6H_6	Benzene	80.1	73	34	*29*, 250*, 309*
2194	C_6H_{12}	Cyclohexane	80.8	62.2	33 vol.	*29, 245**
2195	C_6H_{12}	Methylcyclopentane	72.0	<60.5	....	*245*
2196	C_6H_{14}	2,3-Dimethylbutane	58.0	48	13	*207*
2197	C_6H_{14}	Hexane	68.8	56.8	25 vol.	*29, 182*, 245**
2198	C_7H_8	Toluene	110.7	81.1	78 vol.	*29, 245**
2199	C_7H_{14}	Methylcyclohexane	100.8	71.1	51 vol.	*29*
2200	C_7H_{16}	Heptane	98.4	69.4	44 vol.	*29, 182*, 245**
2201	C_8H_{10}	Ethylbenzene	136.2	Nonazeotrope		*29*
2202	C_8H_{10}	Mixed xylenes	138–144	Nonazeotrope		*29*
2203	C_8H_{16}	1-Octene	121.6	78.0	60 vol.	*29*
2204	C_8H_{16}	2-Octene	125.2	78.0	62 vol.	*29*
2205	C_8H_{18}	2,5-Dimethylhexane	209.4	<75.5	....	*245*
2206	C_8H_{18}	2-Methyl-3-ethylpentane	114	65	55	*182*
2207	C_8H_{18}	Octane	125.6	77.2	64 vol.	*29*
2208	C_8H_{18}	2,2,4-Trimethylpentane	99.2	68.9	38 vol.	*29*
2209	C_9H_{20}	2,2,5-Trimethylhexane	120.1	76.1	58 vol.	*29*
2210	$C_{10}H_{20}$	1-Decene	172.0	81.6	95 vol.	*29*
A =	**C_2H_3NS**	**Methyl Thiocyanate**	**132.5**			
2212	$C_4H_8Cl_2O$	1,2-Dichloroethyl ethyl ether	145.5	Nonazeotrope		*255*
A =	**C_2H_4**	**Ethylene**	**−103.9**			
2213	C_2H_6	Ethane	−88.3	Nonazeotrope		*72*
A =	**C_2H_4BrCl**	**1-Bromo-2-chloroethane**	**106.7**			
2214	$C_2H_4O_2$	Acetic acid	118.5	~102	~87	*243*
2215	C_2H_6O	Ethyl alcohol	78.3	~76.5	~50	*243*
2216	$C_2H_6O_2$	Glycol	197.4	Nonazeotrope		*255*
2217	C_3H_5ClO	Epichlorohydrin	116.45	103.5	83	*243*
2218	$C_3H_6O_2$	Propionic acid	141.3	Nonazeotrope		*255*
2219	$C_4H_{10}O$	Isobutyl alcohol	108	100	....	*243*
2220	$C_5H_{10}O$	2-Pentanone	102.25	Nonazeotrope		*243*
2221	$C_5H_{10}O$	3-Pentanone	102.2	Nonazeotrope		*243*
2222	$C_6H_{12}O_2$	Ethyl isobutyrate	110.1	Nonazeotrope		*243*
2223	$C_6H_{12}O_2$	Methyl isovalerate	116.3	Nonazeotrope		*243*
2224	$C_6H_{14}O_2$	Acetal	103.55	108.5	65	*239*
2225	C_7H_{14}	Methylcyclohexane	101.15	<100.8	>8	*255*

	B-Component			Azeotropic Data		
No.	Formula	Name	B.P., ° C.	B.P., ° C.	Wt. % A	Ref.
A =	**$C_2H_4Br_2$**	**1,1-Dibromoethane**	**109.5**			
2226	$C_2H_4O_2$	Acetic acid	118.1	103.7	75	*242*
2227	C_2H_5ClO	2-Chloroethanol	128.6	108.5	?	*255*
2228	C_2H_5NO	Acetamide	221.15	Nonazeotrope		*255*
2229	C_2H_6O	Ethyl alcohol	78.3	77	46	*243*
2230	$C_2H_6O_2$	Glycol	197.4	Nonazeotrope		*255*
2231	$C_3H_6O_2$	Propionic acid	141.3	Nonazeotrope		*255*
2232	$C_3H_7NO_3$	Propyl nitrate	110.5	<109.2	>58	*240*
2233	C_3H_8O	Isopropyl alcohol	82.4	<82.0	....	*255*
2234	C_3H_8O	Propyl alcohol	97.2	<94.0	>57	*247*
2235	C_4H_5N	Pyrrol	130.0	Nonazeotrope		*233*
2236	$C_4H_8O_2$	Butyric acid	164.0	Nonazeotrope		*255*
2237	$C_4H_{10}O$	Butyl alcohol	117.8	104.5	80	*247*
2238	$C_4H_{10}O$	Isobutyl alcohol	108	101	....	*243*
2239	$C_5H_{10}O$	3-Pentanone	102.05	Nonazeotrope		*232*
2240	$C_5H_{10}O_2$	Methyl butyrate	102.75	Nonazeotrope		*243*
2241	$C_5H_{10}O_2$	Propyl acetate	101.6	Nonazeotrope		*227*
2242	$C_5H_{11}NO_2$	Isoamyl nitrite	97.15	Nonazeotrope		*230*
2243	$C_5H_{12}O$	*tert*-Amyl alcohol	102.35	<101.3	>45	*255*
2244	$C_5H_{12}O$	Isoamyl alcohol	131.9	Nonazeotrope		*255*
2245	$C_6H_{12}O$	4-Methyl-2-pentanone	116.05	Nonazeotrope		*232*
2246	$C_6H_{12}O_2$	Methyl isovalerate	116.3	Nonazeotrope		*243*
2247	$C_6H_{14}O_2$	Acetal	103.55	Nonazeotrope		*239*
2248	C_7H_8	Toluene	110.75	Nonazeotrope		*255*
2249	C_7H_{16}	Heptane	98.4	Nonazeotrope		*255*
2250	$C_8H_{18}O$	Isobutyl ether	122.3	Nonazeotrope		*239*
A =	**$C_2H_4Br_2$**	**1,2-Dibromoethane**	**131.5**			
2251	$C_2H_4Cl_2$	1,2-Dichloroethane	83.7	Nonazeotrope		*243*
2252	$C_2H_4O_2$	Acetic acid	118.5	114.35	45	*243*
2253	C_2H_5BrO	2-Bromoethanol	150.2	130.5	90	*255*
2254	C_2H_5ClO	2-Chloroethanol	128.6	122.3	66.5	*206*
2255	C_2H_5NO	Acetamide	221.2	Nonazeotrope		*207*
2256	C_2H_6O	Ethyl alcohol	78.3	Nonazeotrope		*254*
2257	$C_2H_6O_2$	Glycol	197.4	130.85	96.5	*254*
2258	C_3H_5BrO	Epibromohydrin	138.5	<128.8	<80	*255*
2259	$C_3H_5ClO_2$	Methylchloroacetate	129.95	127.7	56	*252*
2260	$C_3H_6Br_2$	1,2-Dibromopropane	141	134	50	*243*
2261	C_3H_6O	Allyl alcohol	96.85	<96.7	....	*255*
2262	C_3H_6O	Allyl alcohol	96.95	Nonazeotrope		*212*
2263	$C_3H_6O_2$	Propionic acid	140.7	127.75	82.5	*243*
2264	C_3H_7ClO	1-Chloro-2-propanol	127.0	<124.8	>38	*255*
2265	C_3H_7ClO	2-Chloro-1-propanol	133.7	128.0	67	*246*
2266	C_3H_7NO	Propionamide	222.1	Nonazeotrope		*215*
2267	$C_3H_7NO_2$	Ethyl carbomate	185.25	Nonazeotrope		*207*
2268	$C_3H_7NO_2$	1-Nitropropane, 75° C	75/115	75/133.0	73	*198*
		120° C.	120/550.2	120/612.7	72	*198*
2269	C_3H_8O	Isopropyl alcohol	82.4	Nonazeotrope		*212*
2270	C_3H_8O	Propyl alcohol	97.2	Nonazeotrope		*253*
2271	$C_3H_8O_2$	2-Methoxyethanol	124.5	120.55	63.5	*207*
2272	C_4H_5N	Pyrrol	130.0	126.5	67	*233*
2273	$C_4H_7ClO_2$	Ethyl chloroacetate	143.6	Nonazeotrope		*212*
2274	$C_4H_8O_2$	Butyric acid	162.45	131.1	96.5	*207*
2275	$C_4H_8O_2$	Isobutyric acid	154.35	130.5	93.5	*221*
2276	$C_4H_8O_3$	Methyl lactate	143.8	130.0	82	*247*
2277	C_4H_9I	1-Iodobutane	130.4	129.0	65	*242*
2278	C_4H_9I	1-Iodo-2-methylpropane	120.4	Nonazeotrope		
				B.p. curve		*163*
2279	$C_4H_{10}O$	Butyl alcohol	117.75	114.75	56	*254*
2280	$C_4H_{10}O$	*sec*-Butyl alcohol	99.5	Nonazeotrope		*255*
2281	$C_4H_{10}O$	Isobutyl alcohol	108	105	38	*253**, *334*
2282	$C_4H_{10}O_2$	2-Ethoxyethanol	135.3	127.75	77	*236*
2283	$C_5H_4O_2$	2-Furaldehyde	161.45	Nonazeotrope		*207*
2284	C_5H_5N	Pyridine	115.5	Nonazeotrope		*228*
2285	C_5H_9N	Valeronitrile	141.3	<129.5	<83	*255*
2286	$C_5H_{10}O_2$	Isovaleric acid	176.5	Nonazeotrope		*207*
2287	$C_5H_{10}O_3$	Ethyl carbonate	125.9	Nonazeotrope		*252*

	B-Component			Azeotropic Data		
No.	Formula	Name	B.P., ° C.	B.P., ° C.	Wt. % A	Ref.
A =	**$C_2H_4Br_2$**	**1,2-Dibromoethane** *(continued)*	**131.5**			
2288	$C_5H_{10}O_3$	2-Methoxyethyl acetate	144.6	Nonazeotrope		*236*
2289	$C_5H_{12}O$	Amyl alcohol	138.2	<127.3	<78	*247*
2290	$C_5H_{12}O$	*tert*-Amyl alcohol	102.35	Nonazeotrope		*255*
2291	$C_5H_{12}O$	Isoamyl alcohol	131.8	124.15	69.5	*207, 334**
2292	$C_5H_{12}O$	2-Pentanol	119.8	<119.0	<47	*247*
2293	$C_5H_{12}O_2$	2-Propoxyethanol	151.35	Nonazeotrope		*236*
2294	C_6H_5Br	Bromobenzene	152	Nonazeotrope		*163*
2295	C_6H_5Cl	Chlorobenzene, 75° C.	75/121.9	75/128.4	61.6 V-l.	*198*
		100° C.	100/296.1	100/311.2	63.3, V-l	*198*
			131.75	130.05	59	*207*
2296	$C_6H_5NO_2$	Nitrobenzene	210.75	Nonazeotrope		*234*
2297	C_6H_6	Benzene	80.2	Nonazeotrope		*243*
2298	C_6H_6O	Phenol	182.2	Nonazeotrope		*255*
2299	C_6H_7N	Aniline	184.35	Nonazeotrope		*255*
2300	C_6H_{10}	Cyclohexene	82.75	Nonazeotrope		*243*
2301	$C_6H_{10}O$	Mesityl oxide	129.45	Nonazeotrope		*207*
2302	C_6H_{12}	Cyclohexane	80.75	Nonazeotrope		*243*
2303	$C_6H_{12}O_2$	Butyl acetate	124.8	Nonazeotrope		*207*
2304	$C_6H_{12}O_2$	Ethyl butyrate	121.5	Nonazeotrope		*227*
2305	$C_6H_{12}O_2$	Isoamyl formate	123.8	123.7	~12	*211*
2306	$C_6H_{12}O_2$	Propyl propionate	122.5	Nonazeotrope		*227*
2307	$C_6H_{12}O_3$	Paraldehyde	124	Nonazeotrope		*243*
2308	C_6H_{14}	Hexane	68.95	Nonazeotrope		*243*
2309	$C_6H_{14}O$	Hexyl alcohol	157.85	Nonazeotrope		*255*
2310	$C_6H_{14}O_2$	2-Butoxyethanol	171.25	Nonazeotrope		*206*
2311	C_7H_8	Toluene	110.7	Nonazeotrope		*243*
2312	$C_7H_{14}O$	4-Heptanone	143.55	Nonazeotrope		*232*
2313	$C_7H_{14}O_2$	Ethyl isovalerate	134.7	Nonazeotrope		*253*
2314	$C_7H_{14}O_2$	Isoamyl acetate	137.5	Nonazeotrope		*162*
2315	$C_7H_{14}O_2$	Isobutyl propionate	136.9	Nonazeotrope		*243*
2316	$C_7H_{14}O_2$	Propyl isobutyrate	134.0	Nonazeotrope		*255*
2317	C_7H_{16}	Heptane	98.4	Nonazeotrope		*207*
2318	C_8H_8	Styrene	68/60	Nonazeotrope		*26*
2319	C_8H_{10}	Ethylbenzene	136.15	131.1	90	*243*
		60 mm.	60.5	57	87	*26*
2320	C_8H_{10}	*m*-Xylene	139.0	Nonazeotrope		*207*
2321	C_8H_{10}	*p*-Xylene	138.45	Nonazeotrope		*255*
2322	C_8H_{10}	*p*-Xylene	138.25	131.3	~97	*243*
2323	C_8H_{16}	1,3-Dimethylcyclohexane	120.7	Nonazeotrope		*255*
2324	C_8H_{18}	2,5-Dimethylhexane	109.4	Nonazeotrope		*255*
2325	$C_8H_{18}O$	Butyl ether	142.4	Nonazeotrope		*239*
2326	C_9H_{12}	Mesitylene	164	Nonazeotrope		*243*
2327	$C_{10}H_{14}$	Cymene	175.3	Nonazeotrope		*243*
A =	**$C_2H_4Cl_2$**	**1,1-Dichloroethane**	**57.3**			
2328	$C_2H_4Cl_2$	1,2-Dichloroethane	83.7	V-l.		*180*
2329	C_2H_5ClO	Chloromethyl methyl ether	59.5	<54?	<80	*243*
2330	C_2H_6O	Ethyl alcohol	78.3	54.6	88.5	*253*
2331	C_3H_6O	Acetone	56.15	57.55	70	*232*
2332	C_3H_6O	Allyl alcohol	96.85	Nonazeotrope		*207*
2333	C_3H_6O	Propionaldehyde	50	Nonazeotrope		*111*
2334	$C_3H_6O_2$	Ethyl formate	54.15	Nonazeotrope		*243*
2335	$C_3H_6O_2$	Methyl acetate	57	~56	....	*111*, 243*
2336	C_3H_7Br	2-Bromopropane	59.4	Nonazeotrope		*255*
2337	$C_3H_7NO_2$	Propyl nitrite	47.75	Nonazeotrope		*230*
2338	C_3H_8O	Isopropyl alcohol	82.45	56.6	~92	*253*
2339	C_3H_8O	Propyl alcohol	97.2	Nonazeotrope		*253*
2340	$C_3H_8O_2$	Methylal	42.3	Nonazeotrope		*239*
2341	$C_3H_9BO_3$	Methyl borate	65	Nonazeotrope		*243*
2342	C_3H_9SiCl	Chlorotrimethylsilane	57.7	56.4	....	*343*
2343	C_4H_8O	2-Butanone	79.6	Nonazeotrope		*232*
2344	C_4H_8O	Isobutylene oxide	50	Max. b.p.		*111*
2345	C_4H_8O	Isobutyraldehyde	63	Nonazeotrope		*111*
2356	$C_4H_9NO_2$	Isobutyl nitrite	67.1	Nonazeotrope		*230*
2357	$C_4H_{10}O$	*tert*-Butyl alcohol	82.55	57.1	~94	*212*

No.	B-Component Formula	Name	B.P., ° C.	Azeotropic Data B.P., ° C.	Wt. % A	Ref.
A =	**$C_2H_4Cl_2$**	**1,1-Dichloroethane** (*continued*)	**57.3**			
2358	$C_4H_{11}N$	Diethylamine	56	52	~45	*243*
2359	C_5H_{10}	Cyclopentane	49.3	Nonazeotrope		*255*
2360	$C_5H_{12}O$	Ethyl propyl ether	63.6	Nonazeotrope		*228*
2361	C_6H_{10}	Biallyl	60.2	56.5	~77	*243*
2362	C_6H_{12}	Methylcyclopentane	72.0	Nonazeotrope		*255*
2363	C_6H_{14}	2,3-Dimethylbutane	58.0	<56.0	<58	*242*
2364	C_6H_{14}	Hexane	68.85	Nonazeotrope		*218*
2365	$C_6H_{14}O$	Isopropyl ether	68	Nonazeotrope		*111*
A =	**$C_2H_4Cl_2$**	**1,2-Dichloroethane**	**83.45**			
2366	C_2H_4O	Ethylene oxide	10.75	Nonazeotrope		*239*
2367	$C_2H_4O_2$	Acetic acid	118.1	Nonazeotrope, V-l.		*285*
2368	C_2H_5ClO	2-Chloroethanol	128.6	Nonazeotrope		*244*
2369	$C_2H_5NO_3$	Ethyl nitrate	87.68	Nonazeotrope		*207*
2370	C_2H_6O	Ethyl alcohol	78.3	70.5	63	*252*
2371	C_3H_6O	Acetone	56.25	Nonazeotrope, V-l.		*119, 232*, 295**
2372	C_3H_6O	Allyl alcohol	96.9	80.9	85.5	*149, 212*, 357**
2373	$C_3H_6O_3$	Methyl carbonate	90.35	Nonazeotrope		*252*
2374	C_3H_7ClO	1-Chloro-2-propanol	127.0	Nonazeotrope		*255*
2375	C_3H_8O	Isopropyl alcohol	82.45	74.7	56.5	*252*
2376	C_3H_8O	*n*-Propyl alcohol	97.2	80.65	~81	*252*
2377	$C_3H_9BO_3$	Methyl borate	68.7	Nonazeotrope		*227*
2378	C_4H_4S	Thiophene	84	83.5	....	*243*
2379	$C_4H_6O_2$	Allyl formate	80.0	83.55	....	*255*
2380	C_4H_8O	2-Butanone	80	Max. b.p.		*111*
			79.6	Nonazeotrope		*207*
2381	$C_4H_8O_2$	Butyric acid	162	Nonazeotrope		*277*
2382	$C_4H_8O_2$	Dioxane	101.35	Nonazeotrope		*207*
2383	$C_4H_8O_2$	Ethyl acetate	77	Nonazeotrope		*252*
2384	$C_4H_8O_2$	Propyl formate	80.8	84.05	~90	*252*
2385	C_4H_9ClO	1-Chloroethyl ethyl ether	98.5	Nonazeotrope		*255*
2386	$C_4H_9NO_2$	Butyl nitrite	77.8	Nonazeotrope		*227*
2387	$C_4H_{10}O$	Butyl alcohol	117.75	Nonazeotrope		*207, 254*
2388	$C_4H_{10}O$	*sec*-Butyl alcohol	99.5	<82.2	88	*255*
2389	$C_4H_{10}O$	*tert*-Butyl alcohol	82.45	<76.5	<78	*255*
2390	$C_4H_{10}O$	Ethyl ether	34.6	Nonazeotrope		*239*
2391	$C_4H_{10}O$	Isobutyl alcohol	107.85	83.45	93.5	*254*
2392	$C_4H_{10}S$	2-Methyl-1-propanethiol	88	Nonazeotrope		*248*
2393	$C_5H_{10}O$	Isovaleraldehyde	92.1	Nonazeotrope		*255*
2394	$C_5H_{10}O$	3-Methyl-2-butanone	95.4	Nonazeotrope		*232*
2395	$C_5H_{10}O_2$	Isopropyl acetate	90.8	Nonazeotrope		*227*
2396	$C_5H_{11}NO_2$	Isoamyl nitrite	97.15	Nonazeotrope		*230*
2397	$C_5H_{12}O$	*tert*-Amyl alcohol	102.35	Nonazeotrope		*255*
2398	$C_5H_{12}O$	Isoamyl alcohol	131.9	Nonazeotrope		*255*
2399	$C_5H_{12}O$	3-Methyl-2-butanol	112.6	Nonazeotrope		*255*
2400	$C_5H_{12}O$	3-Pentanol	116.0	Nonazeotrope		*255*
2401	$C_5H_{12}O_2$	Diethoxymethane	87.95	88.95	22	*207*
2402	C_6H_6	Benzene	80.2	Nonazeotrope		*188*, 295*
2403	C_6H_{10}	Cyclohexene	82.75	Azeotrope doubtful		*243*
2404	C_6H_{12}	Cyclohexane	....	74.4	49.6 V-l.	*117*, 119*, 243*, 295*
2405	C_6H_{12}	Methylcyclopentane	72.0	Nonazeotrope		*255*
2406	C_6H_{14}	Hexane	68.95	Nonazeotrope		*243*
2407	$C_6H_{14}O$	Isopropyl ether	68.3	Nonazeotrope		*239*
2408	$C_6H_{14}O$	Propyl ether	90.55	Nonazeotrope		*253*
2409	C_7H_8	Toluene, 25° C.	....	Nonazeotrope, V-l.		*119, 179*, 243**
			110.7	Nonazeotrope, V-l.		*3*
2410	C_7H_{14}	Methylcyclohexane	101.15	Nonazeotrope		*255*
2411	C_7H_{16}	*n*-Heptane	98.4	81	75.8	*114*
2412	C_7H_{16}	Heptane	98.45	Nonazeotrope		*207*
2413	C_8H_{18}	2,5-Dimethylhexane	109.4	Nonazeotrope		*255*

No.	B-Component Formula	Name	B.P., ° C.	Azeotropic Data B.P., ° C.	Wt. % A	Ref.
A =	**$C_2H_4Cl_2O$**	**Bis(chloromethyl) Ether**	**105.5**			
2414	$C_3H_6Cl_2$	2,2-Dichloropropane	70.4	Nonazeotrope		*255*
2415	C_3H_7Cl	1-Chloropropane	46.4	Nonazeotrope		*235*
2416	$C_3H_8O_2$	2-Methoxyethanol	124.5	Nonazeotrope		*255*
2417	C_4H_5N	Pyrrol	130.0	Nonazeotrope		*252*
2418	$C_4H_{10}S$	Ethyl sulfide	92.1	Nonazeotrope		*246*
2419	C_5H_7N	1-Methylpyrrol	112.8	<104.8	....	*255*
2420	$C_6H_{14}O$	Propyl ether	90.1	89.0	10	*255*
2421	$C_6H_{14}S$	Isopropyl sulfide	120.5	Nonazeotrope		*246*
2422	C_7H_8	Toluene	110.75	Nonazeotrope		*255*
2423	C_7H_{16}	Heptane	98.4	Nonazeotrope		*255*
A =	**$C_2H_4Cl_2O$**	**2,2-Dichloroethanol**	**146.2**			
2424	$C_3H_6Br_2$	1,3-Dibromopropane	166.9	Nonazeotrope		*255*
2425	C_3H_7I	1-Iodopropane	102.4	Nonazeotrope		*255*
2426	C_4H_9Br	1-Bromobutane	101.5	Nonazeotrope		*255*
2427	C_4H_9I	1-Iodobutane	130.4	128.0	15	*245*
2428	C_4H_9I	1-Iodo-2-methylpropane	120.8	<120.5	....	*255*
2429	$C_5H_{11}Cl$	1-Chloro-3-methylbutane	99.4	Nonazeotrope		*255*
2430	$C_5H_{11}I$	1-Iodo-3-methylbutane	147.65	138.5	50	*247*
2431	$C_6H_4Cl_2$	*p*-Dichlorobenzene	174.4	Nonazeotrope		*255*
2432	C_6H_5Br	Bromobenzene	156.1	142.5	70	*247*
2433	C_6H_5Cl	Chlorobenzene	131.75	130.0	20	*247*
2434	C_7H_8	Toluene	110.75	Nonazeotrope		*255*
2435	C_7H_8O	Anisole	153.85	145.5	....	*255*
2436	C_8H_8	Styrene	145.8	<140.0	....	*255*
2437	C_8H_{10}	*m*-Xylene	139.2	<136.0	>32	*255*
2438	C_8H_{10}	*o*-Xylene	144.3	139.0	50	*247*
2439	$C_8H_{10}O$	Phenetole	170.45	Nonazeotrope		*255*
2440	$C_8H_{18}O$	Butyl ether	142.4	136.0	45	*247*
2441	C_9H_8	Indene	182.6	Nonazeotrope		*255*
2442	C_9H_{12}	Cumene	152.8	142.0	65	*247*
2443	C_9H_{12}	Mesitylene	164.6	<145.0	....	*255*
2444	C_9H_{12}	Propylbenzene	159.3	143.5	75	*255*
2445	$C_{10}H_{14}$	Butylbenzene	183.1	Nonazeotrope		*255*
2446	$C_{10}H_{16}$	Camphene	159.6	139.0	75	*247*
2447	$C_{10}H_{16}$	Dipentene	177.7	143.0	80	*247*
2448	$C_{10}H_{22}O$	Isoamyl ether	173.2	<145.5	>85	*255*
A =	**C_2H_4O**	**Acetaldehyde**	**20.4**			
2449	C_2H_4O	Ethylene oxide	10.4	Nonazeotrope, V-l.		*77*
2450	$C_2H_4O_2$	Methyl formate	31.9	Nonazeotrope		*237*
2451	C_2H_5Br	Bromoethane	38.4	Nonazeotrope		*243*
2452	C_2H_5Cl	Chloroethane	14.0	<9	<32	*243*
2453	C_2H_6O	Ethyl alcohol	78.3	Nonazeotrope		*243*
2454	C_3H_6O	Acetone	56.15	Nonazeotrope		*232*
2455	C_3H_7Cl	2-Chloropropane	34.9	Nonazeotrope		*255*
2456	$C_3H_7NO_2$	Isopropyl nitrite	40.0	Nonazeotrope		*228*
2457	C_4H_6	1,3-Butadiene	−4.5	5.0	5.2, V-l.	*53*
2458	$C_5H_4O_2$	Furfuraldehyde	161.7	Nonazeotrope, V-l.		*285*
2459	C_5H_{12}	2-Methylbutane	27.95	~17	....	*243*
2460	C_5H_{12}	Pentane	36.15	Azeotrope doubtful		*243*
2461	C_6H_6	Benzene	80.1	Nonazeotrope, V-l.		*285*
2462	$C_6H_{12}O_3$	Paraldehyde	124	Nonazeotrope		*243*
2463	C_7H_8	Toluene	110.8	Nonazeotrope, V-l.		*285*
A =	**C_2H_4O**	**Ethylene Oxide**	**10.75**			
2464	$C_2H_4O_2$	Methyl formate	31.7	Nonazeotrope		*255*
2465	C_3H_6O	Propylene oxide	34.1	Nonazeotrope		*255*
2466	C_4H_6	1,3-Butadiene	−5.3	Nonazeotrope		*93*
2467	C_4H_8	1-Butene	−6.5	−7	....	*93, 123**
2468	C_4H_8	*cis*-2-Butene	3.6	Min. b.p.		*123*
2469	C_4H_8	*trans*-2-Butene	0.9	Min. b.p.		*123*
2470	C_4H_8	2-Methylpropene	−7.5	Min. b.p.		*123*
2471	C_4H_{10}	*n*-Butane	0.6	<0.0	>5	*123*, 238*
2472	C_4H_{10}	2-Methylpropane	−12.2	Min. b.p.		*123*
2473	C_5H_{10}	2-Methyl-1-butene	32.0	Min. b.p.		*123*
2474	C_5H_{10}	3-Methyl-1-butene	21.2	Min. b.p.		*123*

No.	B-Component Formula	Name	B.P., ° C.	Azeotropic Data B.P., ° C.	Wt. % A	Ref.
A =	C_2H_4O	**Ethylene Oxide** (*continued*)	**10.75**			
2475	C_5H_{10}	2-Methyl-2-butene	37.7	Min. b.p.		*123*
2476	C_5H_{19}	1-Pentene	30.2	Min. b.p.		*123*
2477	C_5H_{10}	2-Pentene	35.8	Min. b.p.		*3*
2478	C_5H_{12}	2-Methylbutane	27.9	Min. b.p.		*123*
			27.95	Nonazeotrope		*238*
2479	C_5H_{12}	Pentane	36.2	Min. b.p.		*123*
A =	C_2H_4OS	**Thioacetic Acid**	**89.5**			
2480	C_6H_6	Benzene	80.15	Nonazeotrope		*255*
2481	C_6H_{12}	Cyclohexane	80.75	Nonazeotrope		*255*
2482	C_6H_{12}	Methylcyclopentane	72.0	Nonazeotrope		*255*
A =	$C_2H_4O_2$	**Acetic Acid**	**118.5**			
2483	C_2H_5I	Iodoethane	72.3	Nonazeotrope		*222*
2484	C_2H_5NO	Acetamide	222.0	Nonazeotrope, V-l.		*285*
2485	$C_2H_5NO_2$	Nitroethane	114.2	112.4	30	*234*
2486	$C_2H_5NO_3$	Ethyl nitrate	87.7	Nonazeotrope		*207*
2487	C_2H_6S	Methyl sulfide	37.4	Nonazeotrope		*246*
2488	C_3H_5Br	3-Bromopropene	70.5	Nonazeotrope		*255*
2489	C_3H_5BrO	Epibromohydrin	138.5	Nonazeotrope		*236*
2490	C_3H_5ClO	Epichlorohydrin	116.4	115.05	34.5	*236*
2491	$C_3H_5ClO_2$	Methyl chloroacetate	129.95	Nonazeotrope		*255*
2492	$C_3H_5Cl_3$	1,2,3-Trichloropropane	156.85	Nonazeotrope		*221*
2493	C_3H_5I	3-Iodopropene	101.8	97.2	15	*242*
2494	$C_3H_6Br_2$	1,2-Dibromopropane	140.5	116.0	70	*235*
2495	$C_3H_6Br_2$	1,3-Dibromopropane	166.9	Nonazeotrope		*255*
2496	$C_3H_6Cl_2$	2,2-Dichloropropane	70.4	Nonazeotrope		*255*
2497	C_3H_6O	Acetone	56.1	Nonazeotrope, V-l.		*285*
2498	$C_3H_6O_3$	Methyl carbonate	90.35	Nonazeotrope		*255*
2499	C_3H_7Br	1-Bromopropane	71.0	Nonazeotrope		*255*
2500	C_3H_7Br	2-Bromopropane	59.4	Nonazeotrope		*207*
2501	C_3H_7I	1-Iodopropane	102.4	99.2	20	*221*
2502	C_3H_7I	2-Iodopropane	89.2	88.3	9	*225*
2403	$C_3H_7NO_3$	Propyl nitrate	110.5	107.5	23	*240*
2504	C_3H_9N	Trimethylamine, 37 mm.	....	80–81	20	*243*
			9	148–150	80	*151*
2505	C_4H_6O	Crotonaldehyde	102.2	Nonazeotrope		*255*
2506	$C_4H_6O_2$	Biacetyl	88.0	Nonazeotrope, V-l.		*285*
2507	$C_4H_6O_3$	Methyl pyruvate	137.5	Nonazeotrope		*232*
2508	$C_4H_8Cl_2O$	1,2-Dichloroethyl ethyl ether	145.5	Nonazeotrope		*255*
2509	C_4H_8O	2-Butanone	79.6	Nonazeotrope		*232*
2510	$C_4H_8O_2$	Butyric acid	163.5	Vapor pressure data		*243*
2511	$C_4H_8O_2$	Dioxane	101.35	119.5	77	*236*
2512	$C_4H_8O_2$	Propyl formate	80.85	Nonazeotrope		*255*
2513	C_4H_8S	Tetrahydrothiophene	118.8	<113.5	<4.7	*248*
2514	C_4H_9Br	1-Bromobutane	100.35	97.6	18	*221*
2515	C_4H_9Br	2-Bromobutane	91.2	89.0	13	*242*
2516	C_4H_9Br	1-Bromo-2-methylpropane	91.3	90.2	12	*221*
			91.6	Nonazeotrope		*243*
2517	C_4H_9Br	2-Bromo-2-methylpropane	73.25	73.2?	2?	*255*
2518	C_4H_9Cl	1-Chlorobutane	78.05	Nonazeotrope		*221*
2519	C_4H_9Cl	2-Chlorobutane	68.25	Nonazeotrope		*255*
2520	C_4H_9Cl	1-Chloro-2-methylpropane	68.85	Nonazeotrope		*255*
2521	C_4H_9I	1-Iodobutane	130.4	112.4	47	*242*
2522	C_4H_9I	2-Iodobutane	120.0	110.7	30	*242*
2523	C_4H_9I	1-Iodo-2-methylpropane	120.4	109.5	37	*221*
2524	$C_4H_9NO_3$	Isobutyl nitrate	123.5	114.2	50	*240*
2525	$C_4H_{10}O$	Ethyl ether	34.6	Nonazeotrope		*243*
2526	$C_4H_{10}S$	Ethyl sulfide	92.1	91.5	10	*246*
2527	$C_5H_4O_2$	Furfuraldehyde	161.45	Nonazeotrope, V-l.		*285*
2528	C_5H_5N	Pyridine	115.5	139–141	53	*151*
2529	C_5H_8O	Cyclopentanone	130.65	Nonazeotrope		*232*
2530	C_5H_{10}	Cyclopentane	49.3	Nonazeotrope		*255*
2531	$C_5H_{10}O$	Isovaleraldehyde	92.1	Nonazeotrope		*255*
2532	$C_5H_{10}O$	3-Pentanone	102.05	Nonazeotrope		*232*
2533	$C_5H_{10}O_2$	Butyl formate	106.8	Nonazeotrope		*255*
2534	$C_5H_{10}O_2$	Ethyl propionate	99.1	Nonazeotrope		*255*

No.	Formula	B-Component Name	B.P., ° C.	Azeotropic Data B.P., ° C.	Wt. % A	Ref.
A =	$C_2H_4O_2$	**Acetic Acid** (*continued*)	**118.5**			
2535	$C_5H_{10}O_2$	Isobutyl formate	78.3	Nonazeotrope		243
2536	$C_5H_{10}O_2$	Methyl butyrate	102.65	Nonazeotrope		255
2537	$C_5H_{10}O_2$	Methyl isobutyrate	92.5	Nonazeotrope		255
2538	$C_5H_{10}O_2$	Propyl acetate	101.6	Nonazeotrope, V-l.		285
2539	$C_5H_{10}O_3$	2-Methoxyethyl acetate	144.6	Nonazeotrope		206
2540	$C_5H_{11}Br$	1-Bromo-3-methylbutane	120.65	108.65	38	248
2541	$C_5H_{11}Cl$	1-Chloro-3-methylbutane	99.8	97.2	18.5	221
2542	$C_5H_{11}I$	1-Iodo-3-methylbutane	147.65	117.65	80	221
2543	$C_5H_{12}O_2$	Diethoxymethane	87.95	Nonazeotrope		255
2544	$C_6H_4Cl_2$	*p*-Dichlorobenzene	174.4	Nonazeotrope		255
2545	C_6H_5Br	Bromobenzene	156.1	118.35	95	221
			156.15	Nonazeotrope		243
2546	C_6H_5Cl	Chlorobenzene	131.8	114.65	58.5	243
2547	C_6H_5F	Fluorobenzene	84.9	Nonazeotrope		255
2548	$C_6H_5NO_2$	Nitrobenzene	210.85	Nonazeotrope		243
2549	C_6H_6	Benzene	80.2	80.05	2	255
			80.2	Nonazeotrope		334
2550	C_6H_7N	Aniline	184.35	Nonazeotrope		243
2551	C_6H_7N	2-Picoline	134	145	49	151
2552	C_6H_7N	3-Picoline	144	152.5	30.4	
		212 mm.	....	114.5	35.0	81*, 82,
2553	C_6H_7N	4-Picoline	145.3	154.3	30.3	327*
		212 mm.	....	116.5	36.1	
2554	C_6H_8	1,3-Cyclohexadiene	80.4	80.0	2	255
2555	C_6H_8	1,4-Cyclohexadiene	85.6	84.0	6	242
2556	C_6H_{10}	Cyclohexene	82.75	81.8	6.5	221
2557	$C_6H_{10}O$	Mesityl oxide	129.45	Nonazeotrope		232
2558	$C_6H_{10}S$	Allyl sulfide	139	116.55	78.5.	207
2559	C_6H_{12}	Cyclohexane	80.75	79.7	2	243
2560	C_6H_{12}	Methylcyclopentane	72.0	Nonazeotrope		255
2561	$C_6H_{12}O$	4-Methyl-2-pentanone	115.80	Nonazeotrope, V-l		285
2562	$C_6H_{12}O$	Pinacolone	106.2	Nonazeotrope		232
2563	$C_6H_{12}O_2$	Butyl acetate	125	Nonazeotrope, V-l.		285
2564	$C_6H_{12}O_2$	Ethyl butyrate	121.5	Nonazeotrope		255
2565	$C_6H_{12}O_2$	Ethyl isobutyrate	110.1	Nonazeotrope		221
2566	$C_6H_{12}O_2$	Isoamyl formate	123.8	Nonazeotrope		255
2567	$C_6H_{12}O_2$	Propyl propionate	123.0	Nonazeotrope		255
2568	$C_6H_{13}Br$	1-Bromohexane	156.5	117.5	92	255
2569	C_6H_{14}	2,3-Dimethylbutane	58.0	Nonazeotrope		255
2570	C_6H_{14}	Hexane	68.8	67.5?	5	255
2571	$C_6H_{14}O$	Propyl ether	90.55	Nonazeotrope		217
2572	$C_6H_{14}O_2$	Acetal	104.5	Azeotrope doubtful		243
2573	$C_6H_{14}S$	Isopropyl sulfide	120	111.5	48	235
2574	$C_6H_{14}S$	Propyl sulfide	141.5	116.9	83	246
2575	$C_6H_{15}N$	Triethylamine	89	163	67, V-l.	408
			....	162	81.3	151
		40 mm.	....	91–92	....	151
2576	C_7H_7Cl	*α*-Chlorotoluene	179.3	Nonazeotrope		255
2577	C_7H_7Cl	*o*-Chlorotoluene	159.3	Nonazeotrope		221
2578	C_7H_7Cl	*p*-Chlorotoluene	162.4	Nonazeotrope		255
2579	C_7H_8	Toluene	110.8	100.6	28.1 V-l.	285, 288*, 334*
2580	C_7H_8O	Anisole	153.85	Nonazeotrope		236
2581	C_7H_9N	2,6-Lutidine, 212 mm.	....	110–111	34.4	81*, 82,
			144	148	27.8	327*
2582	$C_7H_{12}O$	Methylcyclohexanone	165.0	Nonazeotrope, V-l.		285
2583	C_7H_{14}	Methylcyclohexane	101.1	963	31	221, 251*
2584	$C_7H_{14}O$	2-Heptanone	149	Nonazeotrope, V-l.		285
2585	$C_7H_{14}O_2$	Amyl acetate	149	Nonazeotrope		288
2586	$C_7H_{14}O_2$	Ethyl isovalerate	134.7	Nonazeotrope		255
2587	$C_7H_{14}O_2$	Isoamyl acetate	142.1	Nonazeotrope, V-l.		285
2588	$C_7H_{14}O_2$	Propyl isobutyrate	133.9	Nonazeotrope		223
2589	C_7H_{16}	*n*-Heptane	98.4	95	17	251*, 288
2590	C_8H_8	Styrene	145.8	116.0	17	225
2591	C_8H_{10}	Ethylbenzene, 60 mm.	60.5	48	75	26
			136.15	114.65	66	243

No.	Formula	B-Component Name	B.P., ° C.	Azeotropic Data B.P., ° C.	Wt. % A	Ref.
A =	$C_2H_4O_2$	**Acetic Acid** *(continued)*	**118.5**			
2592	C_8H_{10}	*m*-Xylene	139.0	115.35	72.5	207, 334*
2593	C_8H_{10}	*o*-Xylene	143.6	116.0	76	221
2594	C_8H_{10}	*p*-Xylene	138.4	115.25	72	222
2595	C_8H_{10}	Xylene	138.8	115.2	70.9	
					V-l.	285
2596	$C_8H_{10}O$	Benzyl methyl ether	167.8	Nonazeotrope		255
2597	$C_8H_{11}N$	Dimethylaniline	194.05	Nonazeotrope		243
2598	$C_8H_{14}O_2$	Cyclohexyl acetate	177.0	Nonazeotrope, V-l.		285
2599	$C_8H_{14}O_4$	*meso*-2,3-butanediol diacetate, 150–760 mm.	190–193	Nonazeotrope, V-l.		293
2600	C_8H_{16}	1,3-Dimethylcyclohexane	120.7	109.0	45	255
2601	C_8H_{16}	Ethylcyclohexane	131.8	107.9	....	419
2602	$C_8H_{16}O_2$	Methyl isoamyl acetate	....	Nonazeotrope, V-l.		285
2603	C_8H_{18}	2,5-Dimethylhexane	109.2	100.0	35	225, 251*
2604	C_8H_{18}	*n*-Octane	125.5	105.1	52.5 V-l.	221*, 288*, 349
2605	$C_8H_{18}O$	Butyl ether	141	Nonazeotrope		217
2606	$C_8H_{18}O$	Isobutyl ether	122.3	113.5?	48?	255
2607	$C_8H_{19}NO$	α-Diethylaminobutane-γ-ol, 7 mm.	....	83.5	43.6	402
2608	C_9H_7N	Quinoline	237.3	Nonazeotrope		233
2609	C_9H_{12}	Cumene	152.3	116.8	....	11*, 420
2610	C_9H_{12}	Mesitylene	164.6	Nonazeotrope		255
2611	C_9H_{12}	Propylbenzene	158.9	Nonazeotrope		222
2612	C_9H_{18}	Nonanaphthene	136.7	109.6	....	419
2613	$C_9H_{18}O$	2,6-Dimethyl-4-heptanone	164	Nonazeotrope, V-l.		285
2614	C_9H_{20}	2-Methyloctane	135.2	108.8	....	419
2615	C_9H_{20}	Nonane	150.7	112.6	....	420
2616	$C_{10}H_{14}$	Cymene	176.7	Nonazeotrope		255
2617	$C_{10}H_{16}$	Camphene	159.6	118.2	97	221
2618	$C_{10}H_{16}$	α-Pinene	155.8	117.2	83	221
2619	$C_{10}H_{16}$	α-Terpinene	173.4	Nonazeotrope		255
2620	$C_{10}H_{16}O$	Fenchone	193.0	Nonazeotrope, V-l.		285
2621	$C_{10}H_{22}$	2,7-Dimethyloctane	160.1	117.0	94	242
2622	$C_{10}H_{22}$	2,7-Dimethyloctane	160.25	Nonazeotrope		243
A =	$C_2H_4O_2$	**Methyl Formate**	**31.7**			
2623	C_2H_4S	Ethylene sulfide	55.7	Nonazeotrope		246
2624	C_2H_5Br	Bromoethane	38.4	29.85	>66	235
2625	C_2H_5Cl	Chloroethane	13.3	Nonazeotrope		243
2626	C_2H_5ClO	Chloromethyl methyl ether	59.5	Nonazeotrope		243
2627	$C_2H_5NO_2$	Ethyl nitrite	17.4	Nonazeotrope		229
2628	C_2H_6O	Ethyl alcohol	78.3	Nonazeotrope		216
2629	C_2H_6S	Ethanethiol	36.2	27	~30	243
2630	C_2H_6S	Methyl sulfide	37.2	29.0	62	235
2631	C_3H_5Cl	2-Chloropropene	22.65	<22.0	<13	255
2632	C_2H_5Cl	3-Chloropropene	46.15	Nonazeotrope		227
2633	C_3H_6O	Acetone	56.15	Nonazeotrope		232
2634	C_3H_7Cl	1-Chloropropane	46.65	Nonazeotrope		235
2635	C_3H_7Cl	2-Chloropropane	35.0	Nonazeotrope		235
2636	$C_3H_7NO_2$	Isopropyl nitrite	40.1	Nonazeotrope		229
2637	$C_3H_7NO_2$	Propyl nitrite	47.75	Nonazeotrope		229
2638	$C_3H_8O_2$	Methylal	42.25	Nonazeotrope		237
2639	C_4H_4O	Furan	31.7	<28.6	....	237
2640	C_4H_8	1-Butene	−6.5	Min. b.p.		123
2641	C_4H_8	*cis*-2-Butene	3.6	Min. b.p.		123
2642	C_4H_8	*trans*-2-Butene	0.9	Min. b.p.		123
2643	C_4H_8	2-Methylpropene	−7.5	Min. b.p.		123
2644	$C_4H_8O_2$	Butyric acid	163.5	Nonazeotrope		243
2645	C_4H_9Cl	2-Chloro-2-methylpropane	51.6	Nonazeotrope		243
2646	C_4H_{10}	*n*-Butane	−0.6	Min. b.p.		123
2647	C_4H_{10}	2-Methylpropane	−12.2	Min. b.p.		123
2648	$C_4H_{10}O$	Ethyl ether	34.6	28.2	56	237
2649	$C_4H_{10}O$	Methyl propyl ether	38.9	<31.2	<88	237
2650	C_5H_6	Cyclopentadiene	41.0	Min. b.p.		108
2651	C_5H_8	Cyclopentene	43	Min. b.p.		415

No.	B-Component Formula	Name	B.P., ° C.	Azeotropic Data B.P., ° C.	Wt. % A	Ref.
A =	**$C_2H_4O_2$**	**Methyl Formate** (*continued*)	**31.7**			
2652	C_5H_8	Isoprene	34.1	22.5	50	108*, 243, 415*
2653	C_5H_8	3-Methyl-1,2-butadiene	40.8	26.5	~68	243
2654	C_5H_8	Piperylene	42.5	Min. b.p.		108
2655	C_5H_{10}	Cyclopentane	49.3	26.0	60 Vol.	242*, 315
2656	C_5H_{10}	2-Methyl-1-butene	31.05	Min. b.p.		108, 123*, 415*
2657	C_5H_{10}	3-Methyl-1-butene	20.1	Min. b.p.		108, 123*
2658	C_5H_{10}	2-Methyl-2-butene	37.15	24.3	54	108*, 123*, 243
2659	C_5H_{10}	1-Pentene	30.1	Min. b.p.		108, 123*
2660	C_5H_{10}	2-Pentene	36.4	Min. b.p.		108, 123*, 415*
2661	C_5H_{12}	2-Methylbutane	27.95	17.05	47	123*, 243
2662	C_5H_{12}	Pentane	36.15	21.8	53	120*, 243
2663	C_6H_{10}	Biallyl	60.2	Nonazeotrope		243
2664	C_6H_{12}	Methylcyclopentane	72.0	Nonazeotrope		255
2665	C_6H_{14}	2,2-Dimethylbutane	49.7	25.4	55 vol.	315
2666	C_6H_{14}	2,3-Dimethylbutane	58.0	30.5	85	242
2667	C_6H_{14}	*n*-Hexane	69.0	Nonazeotrope		226
A =	**C_2H_4S**	**Ethylene Sulfide**	**55.7**			
2668	C_2H_5Br	Bromoethane	38.4	Nonazeotrope		246
2669	C_2H_5ClO	Chloromethyl methyl ether	59.15	Nonazeotrope		255
2670	C_3H_6O	Acetone	56.15	51.5	57	246
2671	$C_3H_6O_2$	Ethyl formate	54.15	50.5	53	246
2672	$C_3H_7NO_2$	Isopropyl nitrite	40.1	Nonazeotrope		246
2673	C_4H_8O	2-Butanone	79.6	Nonazeotrope		246
2674	$C_4H_{10}O$	Ethyl ether	34.6	Nonazeotrope		246
2675	C_5H_{12}	Pentane	36.15	Nonazeotrope		255
2676	C_6H_{14}	2,3-Dimethylbutane	58.0	54.0	65	255
2677	C_6H_{14}	Hexane	68.8	Nonazeotrope		255
A =	**C_2H_5Br**	**Bromoethane**	**38.4**			
2678	C_2H_5ClO	Chloromethyl methyl ether	59.15	Nonazeotrope		236
2679	C_2H_5I	Iodoethane	72.3	Nonazeotrope		243, 369*
2680	$C_2H_5NO_2$	Ethyl nitrite	17.4	Nonazeotrope		230
2681	C_2H_6O	Ethyl alcohol	78.3	37	97	243*, 334
2682	C_2H_6S	Ethanethiol	36.2	Nonazeotrope		243
2683	C_2H_6S	Methyl sulfide	37.4	<37.0	<46	246
2684	C_3H_6O	Acetone	56.1	Nonazeotrope		232*, 334
2685	C_3H_6O	Propionaldehyde	48.7	Nonazeotrope		255
2686	C_3H_6O	Propylene oxide	34.1	Nonazeotrope		239
2687	$C_3H_6O_2$	Ethyl formate	54.1	Nonazeotrope		211
2688	$C_3H_6O_2$	Methyl acetate	57.0	Nonazeotrope		243
2689	C_3H_7Cl	2-Chloropropane	34.9	Nonazeotrope		255
2690	$C_3H_7NO_2$	Isopropyl nitrite	40.1	37.7	68	230
2691	$C_3H_7NO_2$	Propyl nitrite	47.75	Nonazeotrope		230
2692	C_3H_8O	Isopropyl alcohol	82.4	Nonazeotrope		255
2693	C_3H_8O	Isopropyl alcohol	82.45	38.35?	99?	243
2694	C_3H_8O	Propyl alcohol	97.2	Nonazeotrope		255
2695	$C_3H_8O_2$	Methylal	42.2	Nonazeotrope		235
2696	$C_4H_8O_2$	Butyric acid	163.5	Nonazeotrope, vapor pressure data		243
2697	$C_4H_8O_2$	Ethyl acetate	77.1	Nonazeotrope		255
2698	$C_4H_{10}O$	*sec*-Butyl alcohol	99.5	Nonazeotrope		255
2699	$C_4H_{10}O$	Ethyl ether	34.6	Nonazeotrope		243
2700	$C_4H_{10}O$	Methyl propyl ether	38.8	Nonazeotrope		243
2701	$C_4H_{11}N$	Diethylamine	55.9	Nonazeotrope		211
2702	C_5H_8	Isoprene	34.1	32	<35	243
2703	C_5H_8	3-Methyl-1,2-butadiene	40.8	~36	....	243
2704	C_5H_{10}	Cyclopentane	49.3	<37.5	<80	255
2705	C_5H_{10}	2-Methyl-2-butene	37.15	35.0	<59	235
2706	C_5H_{12}	2-Methylbutane	27.95	23.7	70	235
2707	C_5H_{12}	Pentane	36.15	~33	~50	243
2708	C_6H_6	Benzene	80.2	Nonazeotrope, V-l.		243*, 405
2709	C_6H_{10}	Biallyl	60.2	Nonazeotrope		243

No.	Formula	B-Component Name	B.P., ° C.	Azeotropic Data B.P., ° C.	Wt. % A	Ref
A =	**C_2H_5Br**	**Bromoethane** (*continued*)	**38.4**			
2710	C_6H_{12}	Methylcyclopentane	72.0	Nonazeotrope		*255*
2711	C_6H_{14}	2,3-Dimethylbutane	58.0	Nonazeotrope		*255*
2712	C_6H_{14}	Hexane	68.85	Nonazeotrope		*218*
2713	C_7H_{16}	Heptane, 30° C.	98.4	Vapor pressure data		*369*
A =	**C_2H_5BrO**	**2-Bromoethanol**	**150.2**			
2714	$C_3H_6Br_2$	1,2-Dibromopropane	140.5	137.0	....	*255*
2715	$C_3H_8O_2$	2-Methoxyethanol	124.5	Nonazeotrope		*206*
2716	$C_4H_7ClO_2$	Ethyl chloroacetate	143.55	Nonazeotrope		*255*
2717	C_4H_9Br	1-Bromobutane	101.5	Nonazeotrope		*255*
2718	C_4H_9Br	1-Bromo-2-methylpropane	91.4	Nonazeotrope		*255*
2719	$C_4H_{10}O_2$	2-Ethoxyethanol	135.3	Nonazeotrope		*206*
2720	$C_5H_6O_2$	Furfuryl alcohol	169.35	Nonazeotrope		*255*
2721	$C_5H_{10}O$	Cyclopentanol	140.85	Nonazeotrope		*255*
2722	$C_5H_{10}O_3$	Ethyl carbonate	126.5	Nonazeotrope		*255*
2723	$C_5H_{10}O_3$	2-Methoxyethyl acetate	144.6	Nonazeotrope		*255*
2724	$C_5H_{11}Br$	1-Bromo-3-methylbutane	120.65	<119.5	>7	*255*
2725	$C_5H_{12}O$	Amyl alcohol	138.2	Nonazeotrope		*255*
2726	$C_5H_{12}O$	Isoamyl alcohol	131.9	Nonazeotrope		*207*
2727	C_6H_5Cl	Chlorobenzene	131.75	128.7	20	*255*
2728	$C_6H_{10}O$	Cyclohexanone	155.7	Nonazeotrope		*232*
2729	$C_6H_{10}O$	Mesityl oxide	129.45	Nonazeotrope		*255*
2730	$C_6H_{10}S$	Allyl sulfide	139.35	135.5	20	*246*
2731	$C_6H_{12}O_2$	Butyl acetate	126.0	Nonazeotrope		*255*
2732	$C_6H_{14}O_2$	2-Butoxyethanol	171.15	Nonazeotrope		*255*
2733	$C_6H_{14}S$	Isopropyl sulfide	120.5	Nonazeotrope		*246*
2734	$C_7H_{14}O$	4-Heptanone	143.55	Nonazeotrope		*255*
2735	$C_7H_{14}O_2$	Butyl propionate	146.8	146.6	50	*255*
2736	$C_7H_{14}O_2$	Isoamyl acetate	142.1	Nonazeotrope		*255*
2737	C_7H_{16}	Heptane	98.4	<97.5	....	*255*
2738	C_8H_{10}	Ethylbenzene	136.15	131.5	40	*255*
2739	C_8H_{10}	*m*-Xylene	139.2	133.5	43	*255*
2740	C_8H_{10}	*p*-Xylene	138.45	133.0	42	*255*
2741	C_8H_{16}	1,3-Dimethylcyclohexane	120.7	<117.0	....	*255*
2742	$C_8H_{18}O$	Butyl ether	142.4	<138.0	....	*255*
2743	$C_8H_{18}S$	Butyl sulfide	185.0	Nonazeotrope		*246*
2744	$C_9H_{18}O$	2,6-Dimethyl-4-heptanone	168.0	Nonazeotrope		*232*
A =	**C_2H_5BrO**	**Bromomethyl Methyl Ether**	**87.5**			
2745	C_6H_6	Benzene	80.15	Nonazeotrope		*255*
2746	C_6H_{14}	Hexane	68.8	Nonazeotrope		*255*
A =	**C_2H_5Cl**	**Chloroethane**	**12.4**			
2747	$C_2H_5NO_2$	Ethyl nitrite	17.4	<12.2	>85	*230*
2748	C_2H_6O	Ethyl alcohol	78.3	Nonazeotrope		*253*
2749	$C_3H_7NO_2$	Isopropyl nitrite	40.1	Nonazeotrope		*230*
2750	C_4H_4O	Furan	31.7	Nonazeotrope		*239*
2751	C_4H_{10}	*n*-Butane	0	....	20	*184*
2752	C_5H_{10}	3-Methyl-1-butene	20.6	<11.5	<73	*255*
2753	C_5H_{12}	2-Methylbutane	27.95	~12	95	*243*
2754	C_5H_{12}	Pentane	36.15	Nonazeotrope		*243*
A =	**C_2H_5ClO**	**2-Chloroethanol**	**128.6**			
2755	C_2H_5NO	Acetamide	221.15	Nonazeotrope		*207*
2756	$C_2H_5NO_2$	Nitroethane	114.2	Nonazeotrope		*234*
2757	$C_2H_6O_2$	Glycol	197.4	Nonazeotrope		*206*
2758	$C_3H_5ClO_2$	Methyl chloroacetate	129.95	<128.0	<85	*255*
2759	C_3H_5I	3-Iodopropene	101.8	100.2	8	*244*
2760	$C_3H_6Br_2$	1,2-Dibromopropane	140.5	126.0	....	*235*
2761	$C_3H_6Br_2$	1,3-Dibromopropane	166.9	Nonazeotrope		*244*
2762	C_3H_7I	1-Iodopropane	102.4	99.7	15	*247*
2763	C_3H_7I	2-Iodopropane	89.45	<88.5	>8	*255*
2764	C_3H_7N	Propionamide	222.2	Nonazeotrope		*206*
2765	$C_3H_8O_2$	2-Methoxyethanol	124.5	130.0	69	*248*
2766	$C_4H_7ClO_2$	Ethyl chloroacetate	143.55	Nonazeotrope		*255*
2767	$C_4H_8Cl_2O$	Bis(chloroethyl) ether	177.4	128.2	86.3, V-l.	*370*
2768	$C_4H_8O_2$	Dioxane	101.35	Nonazeotrope		*207*
2768a	C_4H_8S	Tetrahydrothiophene	118.8	115.0	~28	*255*

No.	B-Component Formula	Name	B.P., ° C.	Azeotropic Data B.P., ° C.	Wt. % A	Ref.
A =	**C_2H_5ClO**	**2-Chloroethanol** (*continued*)	**128.6**			
2769	C_4H_9Br	1-Bromobutane	101.5	100.1	10	*244*
2770	C_4H_9Br	1-Bromo-2-methylpropane	91.4	90.2	....	*206*
2771	C_4H_9I	Iodobutane	130.4	119.0	38	*244*
2772	C_4H_9I	1-Iodo-2-methylpropane	120.8	112.5	30	*247*
2773	$C_4H_{10}O$	Butyl alcohol	117.2	Nonazeotrope, V-l.		*370*
2774	$C_4H_{10}O$	Isobutyl alcohol	107.5	Nonazeotrope, V-l.		*370*
2775	$C_4H_{10}O_2$	2-Ethoxyethanol	135.3	135.65	15	*248*
2776	$C_4H_{10}S$	Butanethiol	97.5	Nonazeotrope		*255*
2777	$C_4H_{10}S$	Ethyl sulfide	92.1	Nonazeotrope		*246*
2778	$C_5H_4O_2$	2-Furaldehyde	161.45	Nonazeotrope		*255*
2779	C_5H_5N	Pyridine	115.4	Nonazeotrope (reacts)		*255*
2780	$C_5H_6O_2$	Furfuryl alcohol	169.35	Nonazeotrope		*255*
2781	$C_5H_{10}O$	Cyclopentanol	140.85	Nonazeotrope		*206*
2782	$C_5H_{10}O_2$	Isobutyl formate	97.9	Nonazeotrope		*255*
2783	$C_5H_{10}O_2$	Methyl butyrate	102.65	Nonazeotrope		*255*
2784	$C_5H_{10}O_2$	Propyl acetate	101.6	Nonazeotrope		*255*
2785	$C_5H_{10}O_3$	Ethyl carbonate	126.5	<125.7	>28	*255*
2786	$C_5H_{10}O_3$	2-Methoxyethyl acetate	144.6	Nonazeotrope		*206*
2788	$C_5H_{11}Br$	1-Bromo-3-methylbutane	120.3	113.5	30	*244*
2789	$C_5H_{11}Cl$	1-Chloro-3-methylbutane	99.4	98.5	8	*244*
2790	$C_5H_{11}I$	1-Iodo-3-methylbutane	147.65	125.0	55	*244*
2791	$C_5H_{12}O$	Amyl alcohol	138.2	Nonazeotrope		*206*
2792	$C_5H_{12}O$	Isoamyl alcohol	131.9	127.8	75	*207*
2793	$C_5H_{12}O$	2-Pentanol	119.8	Nonazeotrope		*206*
2794	$C_5H_{12}O$	3-Pentanol	116.0	Nonazeotrope		*255*
2795	$C_5H_{12}O_2$	2-Propoxyethanol	151.35	Nonazeotrope		*206*
2796	$C_5H_{13}ClSiO$	2-Chloroethoxytrimethylsilane	134.3	120–122	....	*341*
2797	$C_6H_4Cl_2$	*o*-Dichlorobenzene	179.5	Nonazeotrope		*244*
2798	$C_6H_4Cl_2$	*p*-Dichlorobenzene	174.6	Nonazeotrope		*244*
2799	C_6H_5Br	Bromobenzene	156.1	127.45	68	*244*
2800	C_6H_5Cl	Chlorobenzene	131.75	119.95	42	*244*
2801	C_6H_5F	Fluorobenzene	84.9	Nonazeotrope		*255*
2802	C_6H_6	Benzene	80.0	Nonazeotrope, V-l		*370*
2803	C_6H_6O	Phenol	182.2	Nonazeotrope		*255*
2804	C_6H_6S	Benzenethiol	169.5	Nonazeotrope		*246*
2805	C_6H_{10}	Cyclohexene	82.75	81.0	11	*255*
2806	$C_6H_{10}O$	Mesityl oxide	129.45	130.2	33	*207*
2807	$C_6H_{10}O_4$	Ethylidene diacetate	168.5	Nonazeotrope		*207*
2808	$C_6H_{10}S$	Allyl sulfide	139.35	124.5	61	*235*
2809	C_6H_{12}	Cyclohexane	80.75	78.5	10	*255*
2810	C_6H_{12}	Methylcyclopentane	72	<71.4	....	*255*
2811	$C_6H_{12}O$	2-Hexanone	127.2	129.0	75	*232*
2812	$C_6H_{12}O$	3-Hexanone	123.3	Nonazeotrope		*232*
2813	$C_6H_{12}O$	4-Methyl-2-pentanone	116.05	Nonazeotrope		*207*
2814	$C_6H_{12}O$	Pinacolone	106.2	Nonazeotrope		*232*
2815	$C_6H_{12}O_2$	Butyl acetate	126.0	125.6	31	*207*
2816	$C_6H_{12}O_2$	Isoamyl formate	123.8	123.15	21	*206*
2817	$C_6H_{12}O_2$	Isobutyl acetate	117.2	Nonazeotrope		*206*
2818	$C_6H_{12}O_2$	Methyl isovalerate	116.3	Nonazeotrope		*206*
2819	$C_6H_{12}O_2$	Propyl propionate	123.0	122.7	....	*255*
2820	$C_6H_{12}O_3$	Paraldehyde	124.35	Reacts		*206*
2821	$C_6H_{13}Br$	1-Bromohexane	156.5	126.5	....	*251*
2822	C_6H_{14}	Hexane	68.8	<68.0	<13	*255*
2823	$C_6H_{14}O$	Isopropyl ether	68.4	Nonazeotrope, V-l.		*370*
2824	$C_6H_{14}O$	Propyl ether	90.1	Nonazeotrope		*255*
2825	$C_6H_{14}O_2$	2-Butoxyethanol	171.25	Nonazeotrope		*206*
2826	$C_6H_{14}S$	Isopropyl sulfide	120	115.5	30	*235*
2827	$C_6H_{14}S$	Propyl sulfide	141.5	125.5	67	*246*
2828	C_7H_7Br	*m*-Bromotoluene	184.3	Nonazeotrope		*244*
2829	C_7H_7Br	*o*-Bromotoluene	181.5	Nonazeotrope		*244*
2830	C_7H_7Br	*p*-Bromotoluene	185.0	Nonazeotrope		*244*
2831	C_7H_7Cl	*o*-Chlorotoluene	159.2	128.0	75	*244*
2832	C_7H_7Cl	*p*-Chlorotoluene	162.4	Nonazeotrope		*255*
2833	C_7H_8	Toluene	110.6	106.9	24.4, V-l.	*251**, *370*
2834	C_7H_8O	Anisole	153.85	128.55	97.5	*236*
2835	C_7H_{14}	Methylcyclohexane	101.15	96.5	30	*244*

No.	Formula	B-Component Name	B.P., ° C.	Azeotropic Data B.P., ° C.	Wt. % A	Ref.
A =	C_2H_5ClO	**2-Chloroethanol** (*continued*)	**128.6**			
2836	$C_7H_{14}O$	4-Heptanone	143.55	Nonazeotrope		*232*
2837	$C_7H_{14}O$	5-Methyl-2-hexanone	144.2	Nonazeotrope		*232*
2838	$C_7H_{14}O_2$	Amyl acetate	148.8	Nonazeotrope		*255*
2839	$C_7H_{14}O_2$	Isoamyl acetate	142.1	Nonazeotrope		*206*
2840	$C_7H_{14}O_2$	Isobutyl propionate	137.5	Nonazeotrope		*206*
2841	$C_7H_{14}O_2$	Propyl butyrate	143.7	Nonazeotrope		*255*
2842	$C_7H_{14}O_2$	Propyl isobutyrate	134.0	<128.3	<94	*255*
2843	C_7H_{16}	Heptane	98.4	92.0	25	*244*
2844	$C_7H_{16}O_3$	Ethyl orthoformate	145.75	Reacts		*206*
2845	C_8H_8	Styrene	145.8	123.0	....	*244*
2846	C_8H_{10}	Ethylbenzene	136.15	121.0	62	*244*
2847	C_8H_{10}	*m*-Xylene	139.2	121.9	55.5	*206*
2848	C_8H_{10}	*o*-Xylene	144.3	123.2	68	*244*
2849	C_8H_{10}	*p*-Xylene	138.45	121.5	54	*247*
2850	$C_8H_{10}O$	Benzyl methyl ether	167.8	Nonazeotrope		*255*
2851	$C_8H_{10}O$	Phenetole	170.45	Nonazeotrope		*236*
2852	C_8H_{16}	1,3-Dimethylcyclohexane	120.7	109.5	42	*247*
2853	$C_8H_{16}O_2$	Isobutyl butyrate	156.9	Nonazeotrope		*255*
2854	C_8H_{18}	2,5-Dimethylhexane	109.2	100.5	33	*206*
2855	C_8H_{18}	Octane	125.75	115.0	....	*244*
2856	$C_8H_{18}O$	Butyl ether	141.7	123.0	56.8, V-l.	*370*
2857	$C_8H_{18}O$	Isobutyl ether	122.3	<117.0	<42	*247*
2858	$C_8H_{18}S$	Isobutyl sulfide	172.0	Nonazeotrope		*246*
2859	C_9H_8	Indene	182.6	Nonazeotrope		*244*
2860	C_9H_{12}	Cumene	152.8	125.35	70	*206*
2861	C_9H_{12}	Mesitylene	164.6	<128.0	....	*255*
2862	$C_{10}H_8$	Naphthalene	218.0	Nonazeotrope		*244*
2863	$C_{10}H_{14}$	Butylbenzene	183.1	Nonazeotrope		*244*
2864	$C_{10}H_{14}$	Cymene	176.7	Nonazeotrope		*255*
2865	$C_{10}H_{16}$	Camphene	159.6	125.5	80	*244*
2866	$C_{10}H_{16}$	α-Terpinene	173.4	<127.0	<85	*255*
2867	$C_{10}H_{22}$	2,7-Dimethyloctane	160.1	123.5	68	*206*
2868	$C_{10}H_{22}O$	Isoamyl ether	173.2	Nonazeotrope		*236*
A =	C_2H_5ClO	**Chloromethyl Methyl Ether**	**59.5**			
2869	C_2H_6O	Ethyl alcohol	78.3	58.4	~84	*245*
2870	C_2H_6S	Ethanethiol	35.8	Nonazeotrope (reacts)		*253*
2871	C_2H_6S	Methyl sulfide	37.4	Nonazeotrope		*246*
2872	C_3H_5Br	3-Bromopropene	70.0	Nonazeotrope		*228*
2873	C_3H_5Cl	3-Chloropropene	45.15	Nonazeotrope		*228*
2874	C_3H_6O	Acetone	56.15	55.9	13	*232*
2875	$C_3H_6O_2$	Ethyl formate	54.1	Nonazeotrope		*211*
2876	$C_3H_6O_2$	Methyl acetate	56.25	Nonazeotrope		*236*
2877	C_3H_7Br	1-Bromopropane	71.0	Nonazeotrope		*236*
2878	C_3H_7Br	2-Bromopropane	59.4	<57.1	>45	*255*
2879	C_3H_7Cl	1-Chloropropane	46.65	Nonazeotrope		*236*
2880	$C_3H_7NO_2$	Propyl nitrite	47.75	Nonazeotrope		*255*
2881	C_3H_8O	Propyl alcohol	97.2	Nonazeotrope		*243*
2882	$C_3H_8O_2$	Methylal	42.3	Nonazeotrope		*228*
2883	$C_3H_9BO_3$	Methyl borate	68.75	Nonazeotrope		*211*
2884	C_4H_8O	2-Butanone	79.6	Nonazeotrope		*232*
2885	$C_4H_8O_2$	Ethyl acetate	77.05	Nonazeotrope		*243*
2886	$C_4H_8O_2$	Isopropyl formate	68.8	Nonazeotrope		*228*
2887	C_4H_9Cl	1-Chlorobutane	78.5	Nonazeotrope		*236*
2888	C_4H_9Cl	1-Chloro-2-methylpropane	68.85	Nonazeotrope		*236*
2889	C_4H_9Cl	2-Chloro-2-methylpropane	50.8	Nonazeotrope		*228*
2890	$C_4H_{10}O$	Ethyl ether	34.6	Nonazeotrope		*228*
2891	C_5H_{10}	Cyclopentane	49.4	Nonazeotrope		*255*
2892	C_5H_{10}	2-Methyl-2-butene	37.15	Nonazeotrope		*243*
2893	$C_5H_{12}O$	Ethyl propyl ether	63.6	Nonazeotrope		*228*
2894	C_6H_6	Benzene	80.15	Nonazeotrope		*255*
2895	C_6H_{10}	Biallyl	60.1	~55.5	55	*228*
2896	C_6H_{14}	2,3-Dimethylbutane	58.0	56.0	42	*242*
2897	C_6H_{14}	Hexane	68.85	~58.5	~90	*228*
A =	C_2H_5I	**Iodoethane**	**72.3**			
2898	C_2H_6O	Ethyl alcohol	78.3	63	86	*243**, *334*

No.	B-Component Formula	Name	B.P., ° C.	Azeotropic Data B.P., ° C.	Wt. % A	Ref.
A =	**C_2H_5I**	**Iodoethane** (*continued*)	**72.3**			
2899	C_3H_5Br	3-Bromopropene	70.5	Nonazeotrope		*227*
2900	C_3H_6O	Acetone	56.2	55–56	40	*232*, 334*
2901	C_3H_6O	Allyl alcohol	46.85	69.4	88	*247*
2902	$C_3H_6O_2$	Ethyl formate	54.1	Nonazeotrope		*218*
2903	$C_3H_6O_2$	Methyl acetate	56.95	Nonazeotrope		*218*
2904	$C_3H_6O_3$	Methyl carbonate	90.35	Nonazeotrope		*227*
2905	C_3H_7Br	1-Bromopropane	71.0	Nonazeotrope		*229*
2906	C_3H_8O	Isopropyl alcohol	82.45	66	87	*253*, 334*
2907	C_3H_8O	Propyl alcohol	97.2	70	93	*243*, 334*
2908	$C_3H_9BO_3$	Methyl borate	68.7	67.8	48	*218*
2909	C_4H_4S	Thiophene	84.7	Nonazeotrope		*207*
2910	$C_4H_6O_2$	Allyl formate	80.0	<71.5	....	*255*
2911	C_4H_8O	2-Butanone	79.6	<71.5	>75	*232*
2912	$C_4H_8O_2$	Ethyl acetate	77.1	70	78	*253*, 334*
2913	$C_4H_8O_2$	Isopropyl formate	68.8	<66.5	>38	*255*
2914	$C_4H_8O_2$	Methyl propionate	79.85	Nonazeotrope		*227*
2915	$C_4H_8O_2$	Propyl formate	80.85	72.0	90	*227*
2916	C_4H_9Br	2-Bromo-2-methylpropane	73.25	Nonazeotrope		*229*
2917	$C_4H_{10}O$	Butyl alcohol	117.8	Nonazeotrope		*207*
2918	$C_4H_{10}O$	Isobutyl alcohol	108	Nonazeotrope		*334*
2919	$C_4H_{10}O_2$	Acetaldehyde dimethyl acetal	64.3	Nonazeotrope		*239*
2920	$C_5H_{10}O_2$	Methyl isobutyrate	92.3	Nonazeotrope		*243*
2921	$C_5H_{12}O$	*tert*-Amyl alcohol	102.35	Nonazeotrope		*255*
2922	$C_5H_{12}O$	Isoamyl alcohol	131.8	Nonazeotrope		*207*
2923	C_6H_6	Benzene	80.2	Nonazeotrope		*243*
			80.2	74–75	80	*334*
2924	C_6H_{12}	Cyclohexane	80.75	Nonazeotrope		*255*
2925	C_6H_{14}	Hexane	68.95	68	76	*243*
2926	$C_6H_{14}O$	Isopropyl ether	68.3	Nonazeotrope		*239*
2927	C_7H_{16}	Heptane	98.4	V.p. data		
				Nonazeotrope		*369*
A =	**C_2H_5IO**	**2-Iodoethanol**	**176.5**			
2928	$C_3H_6Br_2$	1,2-Dibromopropane	140.5	Nonazeotrope		*255*
2929	$C_5H_{11}I$	1-Iodo-3-methylbutane	147.65	145.8	23	*255*
2930	C_6H_5Br	Bromobenzene	156.1	153.5	25	*247*
2931	C_6H_6O	Phenol	182.2	Nonazeotrope		*255*
2932	C_7H_7Cl	*o*-Chlorotoluene	159.2	155.5	29	*247*
2933	C_7H_8	Toluene	110.75	Nonazeotrope		*255*
2934	C_8H_{10}	*o*-Xylene	144.3	<143.5	>10	*255*
2935	$C_8H_{10}O$	Benzyl methyl ether	167.8	164.0	40	*255*
2936	$C_8H_{10}O$	Phenetole	170.45	166.0	38	*247*
2937	$C_8H_{18}O$	Butyl ether	142.4	Nonazeotrope		*255*
2938	C_9H_{12}	Mesitylene	164.6	158.5	35	*247*
2939	C_9H_{12}	Propyl benzene	159.3	155.0	30	*247*
2940	$C_9H_{18}O_2$	Isoamyl isobutyrate	169.8	Nonazeotrope		*255*
2941	$C_{10}H_{22}O$	Isoamyl ether	173.2	166.5	50	*247*
A =	**C_2H_5NO**	**Acetamide**	**221.2**			
2942	$C_2H_6O_2$	Glycol	197.4	Nonazeotrope		*209*
2943	C_2H_7NO	2-Aminoethanol	170.8	Nonazeotrope		*231*
2944	$C_3H_5Br_3$	1,2,3-Tribromopropane	220	200	~17	*215*
2945	$C_3H_5Cl_3$	1,2,3-Trichloropropane	156.85	154.5	7.5	*215*
2946	$C_3H_6Br_2$	1,2-Dibromopropane	140.5	Nonazeotrope		*207*
2947	$C_3H_6Br_2$	1,3-Dibromopropane	166.9	<165.5	<11	*~255*
2948	$C_3H_6Cl_2O$	1,3-Dichloro-2-propanol	175.8	<175.5	....	*255*
2949	C_3H_7I	1-Iodopropane	102.4	Nonazeotrope		*207*
2950	C_3H_7NO	Propionamide	222.2	220.9	72	*218*
2951	$C_3H_7NO_2$	Ethyl carbamate	185.25	Nonazeotrope		*207*
2952	$C_3H_8O_2$	1,2-Propanediol	187.8	Nonazeotrope		*255*
2953	$C_3H_8O_3$	Glycerol	290	Nonazeotrope		*244*
2954	C_4H_5NS	Allyl isothiocyanate	152.0	Nonazeotrope		*255*
2955	$C_4H_6O_4$	Methyl oxalate	164.2	Nonazeotrope		*215*
2956	$C_4H_7BrO_2$	Ethyl bromoacetate	158.8	Nonazeotrope		*207*
2957	$C_4H_7ClO_2$	Ethyl chloroacetate	143.55	Nonazeotrope		*255*
2958	$C_4H_8Cl_2O$	1,2-Dichloroethyl ethyl ether	145.5	Nonazeotrope		*236*
2959	$C_4H_8Cl_2O$	Bis(2-chloroethyl) ether	178.65	178.25	3	*207*

No.	Formula	B-Component Name	B.P., ° C.	Azeotropic Data B.P., ° C.	Wt. % A	Ref.
A =	C_2H_5NO	**Acetamide** *(continued)*	**221.2**			
2960	$C_4H_8O_3$	Glycol monoacetate	190.9	190.7	5	*207*
2961	C_4H_9I	1-Iodobutane	130.4	130.1	~3	*255*
2962	C_4H_9I	1-Iodo-2-methylpropane	120.8	120.5	1.5	*255*
2963	$C_4H_{10}O$	Butyl alcohol	117.75	Nonazeotrope		*207*
2964	$C_4H_{10}O_3$	Diethylene glycol	245.5	Nonazeotrope		*207*
2965	$C_4H_{11}NO_2$	2,2′-Iminodiethanol	268.0	Nonazeotrope		*231*
2966	$C_5H_4O_2$	2-Furaldehyde	161.45	Reacts		*215*
2967	$C_5H_6O_2$	Furfuryl alcohol	169.35	Nonazeotrope		*255*
2968	$C_5H_8O_3$	Levulinic acid	252	Nonazeotrope		*207*
2969	$C_5H_9ClO_2$	Propyl chloroacetate	163.5	Nonazeotrope		*255*
2970	$C_5H_{10}O_2$	Isovaleric acid	176.5	Nonazeotrope		*255*
2971	$C_5H_{10}O_3$	Ethyl carbonate	126.5	Nonazeotrope		*255*
2972	$C_5H_{11}Br$	1-Bromo-3-methylbutane	120.65	Nonazeotrope		*207*
2973	$C_5H_{11}Br$	1-Bromo-3-methylbutane	120.3	120.0	~1	*215*
2974	$C_5H_{11}I$	1-Iodo-3-methylbutane	147.65	146	5	*215*
2975	$C_5H_{12}O$	Amyl alcohol	138.2	Nonazeotrope		*255*
2976	$C_5H_{12}O$	Isoamyl alcohol	131.3	Nonazeotrope		*207*
2977	$C_5H_{12}O$	2-Pentanol	119.8	Nonazeotrope		*255*
2978	$C_5H_{12}O_2$	2-Propoxyethanol	151.35	Nonazeotrope		*206*
2979	$C_5H_{12}O_3$	2-(2-Methoxyethoxy)ethanol	192.95	Nonazeotrope		*207*
2980	$C_6H_4Br_2$	*p*-Dibromobenzene	220.25	199.35	18	*254*
2981	C_6H_4BrCl	*p*-Bromochlorobenzene	196.4	<187.0	....	*242*
2982	$C_6H_4ClNO_2$	*m*-Chloronitrobenzene	235.5	212.5	50	*234*
2983	$C_6H_4ClNO_2$	*o*-Chloronitrobenzene	246.0	216.0	60	*234*
2984	$C_6H_4ClNO_2$	*p*-Chloronitrobenzene	239.1	213.6	55	*207*
2985	$C_6H_4Cl_2$	*o*-Dichlorobenzene	179.2	174.0	10	*244*
2986	$C_6H_4Cl_2$	*p*-Dichlorobenzene	174.35	169.9	10	*254*
2987	C_6H_5Br	Bromobenzene	156.1	154.85	4.2	*207*
2988	C_6H_5BrO	*o*-Bromophenol	194.8	223.0	50	*242*
2989	C_6H_5Cl	Chlorobenzene	132.0	~131.85	~3	*254*
2990	C_6H_5ClO	*o*-Chlorophenol	175.8	Nonazeotrope		*255*
2991	C_6H_5ClO	*p*-Chlorophenol	219.75	231.7	33	*254*
2992	C_6H_5I	Iodobenzene	188.5	180	13	*207*
2993	$C_6H_5NO_2$	Nitrobenzene	210.75	201.95	24	*234*
2994	$C_6H_5NO_3$	*o*-Nitrophenol	217.25	207.7	24.2	*207*
2995	C_6H_6O	Phenol	182.2	Nonazeotrope		*207*
2996	C_6H_6O	Phenol	182.2	221.3	~98	*209*
2997	$C_6H_6O_2$	Pyrocatechol	245.9	Nonazeotrope		*207*
2998	$C_6H_6O_2$	Resorcinol	281.4	Nonazeotrope		*221*
2999	C_6H_7N	Aniline	184.35	Nonazeotrope		*231*
3000	$C_6H_8N_2$	*o*-Phenylenediamine	258.6	Nonazeotrope		*207*
3001	$C_6H_8O_4$	Methyl maleate	204.05	201.9	11	*250*
3002	$C_6H_{10}O$	Cyclohexanone	155.7	Nonazeotrope		*232*
3003	$C_6H_{10}O_4$	Ethylidene diacetate	168.5	Nonazeotrope		*207*
3004	$C_6H_{10}O_4$	Ethyl oxalate	185.65	185.3	4.2	*254*
3005	$C_6H_{10}O_4$	Glycol diacetate	186.3	Nonazeotrope		*255*
3006	$C_6H_{10}S$	Allyl sulfide	139.35	Nonazeotrope		*246*
3007	$C_6H_{11}NO_2$	Nitrocyclohexane	205.3	<200	<22	*255*
3008	$C_6H_{12}O$	Cyclohexanol	160.7	Nonazeotrope		*207*
3009	$C_6H_{12}O_2$	Butyl acetate	126.0	Nonazeotrope		*207*
3010	$C_6H_{12}O_2$	Caproic acid	205.15	<202.8	....	*255*
3011	$C_6H_{12}O_2$	Isoamyl formate	123.8	Nonazeotrope		*255*
3012	$C_6H_{12}O_2$	Propyl propionate	123.0	Nonazeotrope		*255*
3013	$C_6H_{12}O_3$	2-Ethoxy ethyl acetate	156.8	Nonazeotrope		*206*
3014	$C_6H_{12}O_3$	Propyl lactate	171.7	Nonazeotrope		*255*
3015	$C_6H_{13}Br$	1-Bromohexane	156.5	154.5	7.5	*242*
3016	$C_6H_{14}O$	Hexyl alcohol	157.8	Nonazeotrope		*207*
3017	$C_6H_{14}O_2$	2-Butoxyethanol	171.15	Nonazeotrope		*207*
3018	$C_6H_{14}O_2$	Pinacol	174.3	Nonazeotrope		*215*
3019	$C_6H_{15}NO$	2-Diethylaminoethanol	162.2	Nonazeotrope		*231*
3020	$C_7H_5Cl_3$	α,α,α-Trichlorotoluene	220.9	Reacts		*215*
3021	$C_7H_6Cl_2$	α,α-Dichlorotoluene	205.15	190.8	15.5	*214*
3022	C_7H_6O	Benzaldehyde	179.2	178.6	6.5	*207*
3023	$C_7H_6O_2$	Benzoic acid	250.5	Nonazeotrope		*207*
3024	C_7H_7Br	*m*-Bromotoluene	184.3	177.05	11.0	*207*
3025	C_7H_7Br	*o*-Bromotoluene	181.45	175	11.0	*207*

No.	Formula	B-Component Name	B.P., ° C.	Azeotropic Data B.P., ° C.	Wt. % A	Ref.
A =	C_2H_5NO	**Acetamide** (*continued*)	**221.2**			
3026	C_7H_7Br	*p*-Bromotoluene	185.0	178.0	12	*215*
3027	C_7H_7BrO	*o*-Bromoanisole	217.7	<207.7	....	*255*
3028	C_7H_7Cl	α-Chlorotoluene	179.3	173.7	11	*214*
3029	C_7H_7Cl	*o*-Chlorotoluene	159.3	157.8	8	*215*
3030	C_7H_7Cl	*p*-Chlorotoluene	162.4	160.0	8.5	*207*
3031	C_7H_7ClO	*o*-Chloroanisole	195.7	191.0	20	*242*
3032	C_7H_7ClO	*p*-Chloroanisole	197.8	<193.0	<26	*255*
3033	C_7H_7I	*p*-Iodotoluene	212	195	17	*215*
3034	$C_7H_7NO_2$	*m*-Nitrotoluene	230.8	210.8	42	*234*
3035	$C_7H_7NO_2$	*o*-Nitrotoluene	221.75	206.45	32.5	*234*
3036	$C_7H_7NO_2$	*p*-Nitrotoluene	238.9	213.4	48	*207*
3037	C_7H_8	Toluene	110.75	Nonazeotrope		*207, 209*
3038	C_7H_8O	Anisole	153.85	Nonazeotrope		*207*
3039	C_7H_8O	Benzyl alcohol	205.1	Nonazeotrope		*207*
3040	C_7H_8O	*m*-Cresol	202.1	Nonazeotrope		*207*
3041	C_7H_8O	*o*-Cresol	191.1	Nonazeotrope		*207*
3042	C_7H_8O	*p*-Cresol	201.7	Nonazeotrope		*207*
3043	$C_7H_8O_2$	Guaiacol	205.05	204.55	7.5	*254*
3044	$C_7H_8O_2$	*m*-Methoxyphenol	244	220.8	~80	*215*
3045	C_7H_9N	Methylaniline	196.25	193.8	14	*231*
3046	C_7H_9N	*m*-Toluidine	203.1	200.95	14	*231*
3047	C_7H_9N	*o*-Toluidine	200.35	198.55	12	*207*
3048	C_7H_9N	*p*-Toluidine	200.55	198.7	12	*231*
3049	$C_7H_{13}ClO_2$	Isoamyl chloroacetate	195.0	<194.1	....	*255*
3050	C_7H_{14}	Methylcyclohexane	101.15	Nonazeotrope		*207*
3051	$C_7H_{14}O$	4-Heptanone	143.55	Nonazeotrope		*232*
3052	$C_7H_{14}O$	2-Methylcyclohexanol	168.5	Nonazeotrope		*255*
3053	$C_7H_{14}O$	5-Methyl-2-hexanone	144.2	Nonazeotrope		*232*
3054	$C_7H_{14}O_2$	Amyl acetate	148.8	Nonazeotrope		*255*
3055	$C_7H_{14}O_2$	Butyl propionate	146.8	Nonazeotrope		*207*
3056	$C_7H_{14}O_2$	Enanthic acid	222.0	<216.5	....	*255*
3057	$C_7H_{14}O_2$	Ethyl isovalerate	134.7	Nonazeotrope		*207*
3058	$C_7H_{14}O_2$	Ethyl valerate	145.45	Nonazeotrope		*207*
3059	$C_7H_{14}O_2$	Isoamyl acetate	142.1	Nonazeotrope		*207*
3060	$C_7H_{14}O_2$	Isobutyl propionate	137.5	Nonazeotrope		*255*
3061	$C_7H_{14}O_2$	Propyl butyrate	143.7	Nonazeotrope		*255*
3062	$C_7H_{14}O_3$	1,3-Butanediol methyl ether acetate	171.75	Nonazeotrope		*255*
3063	$C_7H_{14}O_3$	Isobutyl lactate	182.15	<181.5	<12	*255*
3064	C_7H_{16}	Heptane	98.4	Nonazeotrope		*207*
3065	$C_7H_{16}O$	Heptyl alcohol	176.35	Nonazeotrope		*207*
3066	$C_7H_{16}O_3$	Ethyl orthoformate	145.75	Nonazeotrope		*207*
3067	$C_7H_{16}O_4$	2-[2-(2-Methoxyethoxy)ethoxy]-ethanol	245.25	Nonazeotrope		*207*
3068	C_8H_7N	Indole	253.5	Nonazeotrope		*207*
3069	C_8H_8	Styrene	145.8	144	12	*254*
3070	C_8H_8O	Acetophenone	202.0	197.45	16.3	*207*
3071	$C_8H_8O_2$	Benzyl formate	203.0	193.0	22	*244*
3072	$C_8H_8O_2$	Methyl benzoate	199.45	193.8	15	*254*
3073	$C_8H_8O_2$	Phenyl acetate	195.7	~194.5	~7	*254*
3074	$C_8H_8O_2$	α-Toluic acid	266.5	Nonazeotrope		*207*
3075	$C_8H_8O_3$	Methyl salicylate	222.3	205.8	29	*208*
3076	C_8H_9BrO	*p*-Bromophenetole	234.2	212.0	35	*242*
3077	C_8H_{10}	Ethylbenzene	136.15	135.6	~8	*215*
3078	C_8H_{10}	*o*-Xylene	144.3	142.6	11	*242*
3079	C_8H_{10}	*m*-Xylene	139.0	138.4	10	*207*
3080	C_8H_{10}	*p*-Xylene	138.2	137.75	8	*207*
3081	$C_8H_{10}O$	Benzyl methyl ether	167.8	166.0	10	*255*
3082	$C_8H_{10}O$	*p*-Methyl anisole	177.05	174.2	11	*236*
3083	$C_8H_{10}O$	Phenethyl alcohol	219.5	214.05	35	*208*
3084	$C_8H_{10}O$	Phenetole	170.5	168.3	10.8	*254*
3085	$C_8H_{10}O$	2,4-Xylenol	210.5	Nonazeotrope		*255*
3086	$C_8H_{10}O$	3,4-Xylenol	226.8	221.1	96	*207*
3087	$C_8H_{10}O_2$	*m*-Dimethoxybenzene	214.7	199.0	25	*215*
3088	$C_8H_{10}O_2$	*o*-Ethoxyphenol	216.5	<215.0	....	*255*
3089	$C_8H_{10}O_2$	Veratrol	205.5	193.5	23	*215*
3090	$C_8H_{11}N$	Dimethylaniline	194.15	186.95	17.5	*231*

No.	B-Component Formula	Name	B.P., ° C.	Azeotropic Data B.P., ° C.	Wt. % A	Ref.
A =	C_2H_5NO	**Acetamide** *(continued)*	**221.2**			
3091	$C_8H_{11}N$	2,4-Xylidine	214.0	<209.5	21	*231*
3092	$C_8H_{11}N$	3,4-Xylidine	225.5	<213.5	<29	*231*
3093	$C_8H_{11}N$	Ethylaniline	205.5	199.0	18	*231*
3094	$C_8H_{11}NO$	*o*-Phenetidine	232.5	216.0	55	*207*
3095	$C_8H_{11}NO$	*p*-Phenetidine	249.9	Nonazeotrope		*231*
3096	$C_8H_{12}O_4$	Ethyl fumarate	217.85	205.5	26.7	*207*
3097	$C_8H_{12}O_4$	Ethyl maleate	223.3	210.15	32	*207*
3098	$C_8H_{14}O$	Methyl heptenone	173.2	Nonazeotrope		*232*
3099	$C_8H_{16}O$	2-Octanone	172.85	Nonazeotrope		*232*
3100	$C_8H_{16}O_2$	Butyl butyrate	166.4	164.5	7	*244*
3102	$C_8H_{16}O_2$	Caprylic acid	238.5	<219.5	....	*255*
3103	$C_8H_{16}O_2$	Hexyl acetate	171.5	169.5	10	*242*
3104	$C_8H_{16}O_2$	Isoamyl propionate	160.7	159.8	4	*244*
3105	$C_8H_{16}O_2$	Isobutyl butyrate	156.8	Nonazeotrope		*215*
3106	$C_8H_{16}O_2$	Isobutyl isobutyrate	148.6	Nonazeotrope		*255*
3107	$C_8H_{16}O_2$	Propyl isovalerate	155.7	<155.3	>3	*255*
3108	$C_8H_{16}O_3$	Isoamyl lactate	202.4	<196.0	<28	*255*
3109	C_8H_{18}	2,5-Dimethylhexane	109.4	Nonazeotrope		*207*
3110	C_8H_{18}	Octane	125.7	125.6	~1	*215*
3111	$C_8H_{18}O$	Butyl ether	142.4	<142.0	<10	*255*
3112	$C_8H_{18}O$	Octyl alcohol	195.2	194.45	9.5	*244*
3113	$C_8H_{18}O$	*sec*-Octyl alcohol	179.0	Nonazeotrope		*207*
3114	$C_8H_{18}S$	Butyl sulfide	185.0	180.0	8	*246*
3115	$C_8H_{18}S$	Isobutyl sulfide	172.0	<170.5	<7	*246*
3116	C_9H_7N	Quinoline	237.3	Nonazeotrope		*207*
3117	C_9H_8	Indene	183.0	177.2	17.5	*207*
3118	C_9H_8O	Cinnamaldehyde	253.5	Nonazeotrope		*207*
3119	$C_9H_{10}O$	Cinnamyl alcohol	257	Nonazeotrope		*244*
3120	$C_9H_{10}O$	*p*-Methyl acetophenone	226.35	209.8	38.3	*232*
3121	$C_9H_{10}O$	Propiophenone	217.7	204.0	31	*207*
3122	$C_9H_{10}O_2$	Benzyl acetate	~214.9	204.8	27.5	*254*
3123	$C_9H_{10}O_2$	Ethyl benzoate	212.6	200.85	24	*254*
3124	$C_9H_{10}O_2$	Methyl *α*-toluate	215.3	203.0	30	*242*
3125	$C_9H_{10}O_3$	Ethyl salicylate	233.7	209.2	40.2	*216*
3126	C_9H_{12}	Cumene	152.8	<150.8	>8	*255*
3127	C_9H_{12}	Mesitylene	164.6	~160.0	~15	*253*
3128	C_9H_{12}	Pseudocumene	168.2	<164.8	....	*255*
3129	$C_9H_{12}O$	Benzyl ethyl ether	185.0	179.0	17	*242*
3130	$C_9H_{12}O$	3-Phenyl propanol	235.6	Nonazeotrope		*207*
3131	$C_9H_{12}O$	Phenyl propyl ether	190.2	183.5	20	*215*
3132	$C_9H_{12}O_2$	2-Benzyloxyethanol	265.2	Nonazeotrope		*255*
3133	$C_9H_{13}N$	*N,N*-Dimethyl-*o*-toluidine	185.3	177.95	16.5	*231*
3134	$C_9H_{13}N$	*N,N*-Dimethyl-*p*-toluidine	210.2	194.0	22	*231*
3135	$C_9H_{14}O$	Phorone	197.8	194.8	12	*232*
3136	$C_9H_{18}O$	2,6-Dimethyl-4-heptanone	168.0	Nonazeotrope		*232*
3137	$C_9H_{18}O_2$	Ethyl enanthate	188.7	183.0	16	*242*
3138	$C_9H_{18}O_2$	Isoamyl butyrate	178.5	174.75	11.8	*216*
3139	$C_9H_{18}O_2$	Isoamyl isobutyrate	169.8	167.5	9	*244*
3140	$C_9H_{18}O_2$	Isobutyl isovalerate	171.35	169.3	10.5	*221*
3141	$C_9H_{18}O_2$	Methyl caprylate	192.9	186.0	15	*244*
3142	$C_{10}H_7Br$	1-Bromonaphthalene	281.8	217.35	56.5	*207*
3143	$C_{10}H_7Cl$	1-Chloronaphthalene	~262.7	213.9	52.2	*207*
3144	$C_{10}H_8$	Naphthalene	218.05	199.55	27	*207*
3145	$C_{10}H_8O$	1-Naphthol	288	Nonazeotrope		*207*
3146	$C_{10}H_8O$	2-Naphthol	290	Nonazeotrope		*224*
3147	$C_{10}H_9N$	1-Naphthylamine	300.8	Nonazeotrope		*231*
3148	$C_{10}H_9N$	Quinaldine	246.5	Nonazeotrope		*255*
3149	$C_{10}H_{10}O_2$	Isosafrol	252.1	214.0	47	*254*
3150	$C_{10}H_{10}O_2$	Methyl cinnamate	261.95	219.1	62	*207*
3151	$C_{10}H_{10}O_2$	Safrol	235.9	208.8	32	*207*
3152	$C_{10}H_{10}O_4$	Methyl phthalate	283.7	Nonazeotrope		*222*
3153	$C_{10}H_{12}O$	Anethole	235.7	208.0	38	*207*
3154	$C_{10}H_{12}O$	Estragole	215.8	~199.8	~24	*254*
3155	$C_{10}H_{12}O_2$	Ethyl *α*-toluate	228.75	209.6	35.5	*216*
3156	$C_{10}H_{12}O_2$	Eugenol	255	220.8	88	*207*
3157	$C_{10}H_{12}O_2$	Isoeugenol	268.8	Nonazeotrope		*207*

	B-Component			Azeotropic Data		
No.	Formula	Name	B.P., ° C.	B.P., ° C.	Wt. % A	Ref.
A =	C_2H_5NO	**Acetamide** (*continued*)	**221.2**			
3158	$C_{10}H_{12}O_2$	Propyl benzoate	230.85	209.0	38	*207*
3159	$C_{10}H_{14}$	Butylbenzene	183.1	<176.0	....	*255*
3160	$C_{10}H_{14}$	Cymene	176.7	170.5	19	*207*
3161	$C_{10}H_{14}O$	Carvacrol	237.85	<220.8	....	*255*
3162	$C_{10}H_{14}O$	Carvone	231	210.65	42.5	*207*
3163	$C_{10}H_{14}O$	Thymol	232.8	219.9	70.5	*207*
3164	$C_{10}H_{14}O_2$	*m*-Diethoxybenzene	235.0	208.5	34	*215*
3165	$C_{10}H_{15}N$	Diethylaniline	217.05	198.05	24	*231*
3166	$C_{10}H_{16}$	Camphene	159.6	155.5	12	*207*
3167	$C_{10}H_{16}$	Dipentene	177.7	169.15	18	*207*
3168	$C_{10}H_{16}$	*d*-Limonene	177.8	169.2	16	*209*
3169	$C_{10}H_{16}$	Nopinene	163.8	159.5	18	*207*
3170	$C_{10}H_{16}$	α-Pinene	155.8	152.5	13	*216*
3171	$C_{10}H_{16}$	α-Terpinene	173.4	167.5	18	*242*
3172	$C_{10}H_{16}$	γ-Terpinene	183	175.0	~20	*255*
3173	$C_{10}H_{16}$	Terpinolene	184.6	176.5	20	*242*
3174	$C_{10}H_{16}$	Thymene	179.7	169.8	18	*215*
3175	$C_{10}H_{16}O$	Camphor	209.1	199.8	23	*232*
3176	$C_{10}H_{16}O$	Carvenone	234.5	233.0	44	*232*
3177	$C_{10}H_{16}O$	Fenchone	193.6	<192.8	>5	*232*
3178	$C_{10}H_{16}O$	Pulegone	223.8	205.9	36	*207*
3179	$C_{10}H_{17}Cl$	Bornyl chloride	207.5	<195.0	....	*255*
3180	$C_{10}H_{18}O$	Borneol	213.4	205.4	26	*207*
3181	$C_{10}H_{18}O$	Cineol	176.35	170.9	17	*254*
3182	$C_{10}H_{18}O$	Citronellal	208.0	199	Reacts	*255*
3183	$C_{10}H_{18}O$	Geraniol	229.6	213.5	45	*207*
3184	$C_{10}H_{18}O$	Linaloöl	198.6	<198.0	<12	*255*
3185	$C_{10}H_{18}O$	α-Terpineol	217.8	205.2	28	*209*
3186	$C_{10}H_{18}O$	β-Terpineol	210.5	203.0	22	*247*
3187	$C_{10}H_{20}O$	Citronellol	224.4	209.5	40	*247*
3188	$C_{10}H_{20}O$	Menthol	216.4	204.45	27	*244*
3189	$C_{10}H_{20}O_2$	Ethyl caprylate	208.35	196.0	24	*242*
3190	$C_{10}H_{20}O_2$	Isoamyl isovalerate	192.7	184.85	16	*244*
3191	$C_{10}H_{20}O_2$	Isoamyl valerate	192.7	184.85	16	*221*
3192	$C_{10}H_{20}O_2$	Methyl pelargonate	213.7	268.5	28	*244*
3193	$C_{10}H_{22}$	2,7-Dimethyloctane	160.1	155.5	15	*242*
3194	$C_{10}H_{22}O$	*n*-Decyl alcohol	232.9	211.1	49	*209*
3195	$C_{10}H_{22}O$	Amyl ether	187.5	178.0	20	*236*
3196	$C_{10}H_{22}O$	Isoamyl ether	173.4	166.95	14.5	*236*
3197	$C_{10}H_{22}S$	Isoamyl sulfide	214.8	199.5	17	*246*
3198	$C_{11}H_{10}$	1-Methylnaphthalene	245.1	209.8	43.8	*254*
3199	$C_{11}H_{10}$	2-Methylnaphthalene	241.15	208.25	40	*207*
3200	$C_{11}H_{12}O_2$	Ethyl cinnamate	272.5	271.5	70	*244*
3201	$C_{11}H_{14}O_2$	1-Allyl-3,4-dimethoxybenzene	255.2	216.85	50	*207*
3202	$C_{11}H_{14}O_2$	Butyl benzoate	251.2	214.0	49	*215*
3203	$C_{11}H_{14}O_2$	1,2-Dimethoxy-4-propenylbenzene	270.5	219.55	69	*254*
3204	$C_{11}H_{14}O_2$	Ethyl β-phenyl propionate	248.1	215.5	48	*242*
3205	$C_{11}H_{14}O_2$	Isobutyl benzoate	241.9	211.2	42	*250*
3206	$C_{11}H_{20}O$	Isobornyl methyl ether	192.4	<185.5	<23	*242*
3207	$C_{11}H_{20}O$	Methyl α-terpineol ether	216.2	<200.5	<28	*242*
3208	$C_{11}H_{22}O_3$	Isoamyl carbonate	232.2	205.65	32	*244*
3209	$C_{12}H_{10}$	Acenaphthene	277.9	217.1	64.2	*207*
3210	$C_{12}H_{10}$	Biphenyl	255.9	212.95	50.5	*207*
3211	$C_{12}H_{10}O$	Phenyl ether	259.3	214.55	52	*254*
3212	$C_{12}H_{14}O_4$	Ethyl phthalate	295	Nonazeotrope		*207*
3213	$C_{12}H_{16}O_2$	Isoamyl benzoate	262.05	215.4	55	*254*
3214	$C_{12}H_{16}O_3$	Isoamyl salicylate	277.5	220.0	70	*255*
3215	$C_{12}H_{18}$	1,3,5-Triethylbenzene	215.5	198.0	27	*254*
3216	$C_{12}H_{20}O_2$	Bornyl acetate	227.6	205.0	32	*207*
3217	$C_{12}H_{22}O$	Ethyl isobornyl ether	203.8	<193.0	<25	*255*
3218	$C_{12}H_{22}O_4$	Isoamyl oxalate	268.0	~217	~60	*222*
3219	$C_{13}H_{10}$	Fluorene	295	<219.7	>72	*255*
3220	$C_{13}H_{10}O_2$	Phenyl benzoate	315	Nonazeotrope		*207*
3221	$C_{13}H_{12}$	Diphenyl methane	265.6	215.15	56.5	*254*
3222	$C_{13}H_{12}O$	Benzyl phenyl ether	286.5	<220.8	>92	*255*
3223	$C_{14}H_{12}$	Stilbene	306.5	220.5	~88	*255*

	B-Component			Azeotropic Data		
No.	Formula	Name	B.P., ° C.	B.P., ° C.	Wt. % A	Ref.
A =	**C_2H_5NO**	**Acetamide (*continued*)**	**221.2**			
3224	$C_{14}H_{14}$	1,2-Diphenylethane	284	218.2	68	*217*
3225	$C_{14}H_{14}O$	Benzyl ether	297	Nonazeotrope		*255*
A =	**$C_2H_5NO_2$**	**Ethyl Nitrite**	**17.4**			
3226	C_2H_6S	Methyl sulfide	37.4	Nonazeotrope		*230*
3227	C_3H_5Cl	2-Chloropropene	22.65	Nonazeotrope		*230*
3228	C_3H_7Cl	2-Chloropropane	34.9	Nonazeotrope		*230*
3229	C_3H_8O	Isopropyl alcohol	82.35	Min. b.p.		*256*
3230	$C_3H_8O_2$	Methylal	42.3	Nonazeotrope		*230*
3231	C_4H_4O	Furan	31.7	Nonazeotrope		*230*
3232	C_4H_{10}	Butane	0.6	Nonazeotrope		*230*
3233	$C_4H_{10}O$	Ethyl ether	34.6	Nonazeotrope		*230*
3234	C_5H_{10}	Cyclopentane	49.3	Nonazeotrope		*230*
3235	C_5H_{10}	3-Methyl-1-butene	20.6	15.5	60	*230*
3236	C_5H_{10}	2-Methyl-2-butene	37.15	Nonazeotrope		*230*
3237	C_5H_{12}	2-Methylbutane	27.95	16.7	90	*230*
3238	C_5H_{12}	Pentane	36.15	Nonazeotrope		*230*
3239	C_5H_{12}	Ethyl propyl ether	38.85	Nonazeotrope		*230*
A =	**$C_2H_5NO_2$**	**Nitroethane**	**114.2**			
3240	$C_2H_5NO_3$	Ethyl nitrate	87.7	Nonazeotrope		*234*
3241	C_2H_6O	Ethyl alcohol	78.3	Nonazeotrope		*234*
3242	$C_3H_6O_2$	Propionic acid	141.3	Nonazeotrope		*255*
3243	C_3H_7ClO	1-Chloro-2-propanol	127.0	Nonazeotrope		*234*
3244	$C_3H_7NO_3$	Propyl nitrate	110.5	<109.6	>21	*234*
3245	C_3H_8O	Propyl alcohol	97.2	<95.0	>23	*234*
3246	$C_4H_8O_2$	Dioxane	101.35	Nonazeotrope		*234*
3247	C_4H_9Br	1-Bromobutane	101.5	96.0	25	*234*
3248	C_4H_9Br	1-Bromo-2-methylpropane	91.4	89.5	10	*234*
3249	C_4H_9Cl	1-Chlorobutane	78.5	Nonazeotrope		*234*
3250	$C_4H_{10}O$	Butyl alcohol	117.8	107.7	55	*234*
3251	$C_4H_{10}O$	Isobutyl alcohol	108.0	102.5	40	*234*
3252	$C_5H_{10}O$	3-Pentanone	102.05	Nonazeotrope		*255*
3253	$C_5H_{10}O_2$	Propyl acetate	101.6	Nonazeotrope		*234*
3254	$C_5H_{11}Br$	1-Bromo-3-methylbutane	120.65	<108.5	>55	*234*
3255	$C_5H_{12}O$	Amyl alcohol	138.2	<137.8	>83	*234*
3256	$C_5H_{12}O$	*tert*-Amyl alcohol	102.35	<98.6	>30	*234*
3257	$C_5H_{12}O$	Isoamyl alcohol	131.9	112.0	78	*234*
3258	$C_5H_{12}O_2$	2-Propoxyethanol	151.35	Nonazeotrope		*234*
3259	C_6H_6	Benzene	80.15	Nonazeotrope		*234*
3260	C_6H_{12}	Methylcyclopentane	72.0	<71.2	>4	*234*
3261	$C_6H_{12}O$	4-Methyl-2-pentanone	116.05	<113.0	....	*255*
3262	$C_6H_{12}O_2$	Butyl acetate	126.0	Nonazeotrope		*234*
3263	$C_6H_{12}O_2$	Ethyl butyrate	121.5	<113.7	>73	*234*
3264	$C_6H_{12}O_2$	Ethyl isobutyrate	110.1	108.5	27	*234*
3265	$C_6H_{12}O_2$	Isobutyl acetate	117.4	112.5	60	*234*
3266	$C_6H_{14}S$	Isopropyl sulfide	120.5	<110.9	>60	*234*
3267	C_7H_8	Toluene	110.75	106.2	25	*74*, 234*
3268	C_7H_{14}	Methylcyclohexane	101.15	90.8	30	*234*
3269	C_nH_{2n+2}	Paraffins	07–110	82–104	....	*74*
3270	C_7H_{16}	*n*-Heptane	98.4	89.2	28	*234*
3271	C_8H_{10}	*m*-Xylene	139.2	Nonazeotrope		*234*
3272	C_8H_{18}	2,5-Dimethylhexane	109.4	<96.9	>62	*234*
A =	**$C_2H_5NO_3$**	**Ethyl Nitrate**	**87.68**			
3273	C_2H_6O	Ethyl alcohol	78.3	71.85	56	*216*
3274	C_3H_5Br	3-Bromopropene	70.5	Nonazeotrope		*240*
3275	C_3H_5I	3-Iodopropene	101.8	<87.0	....	*240*
3276	$C_3H_6Cl_2$	2,2-Dichloropropane	70.4	Nonazeotrope		*255*
3277	C_3H_6O	Allyl alcohol	96.95	83.15	77.5	*207*
3278	$C_3H_6O_3$	Methyl carbonate	90.25	Nonazeotrope		*207*
3279	C_3H_7Br	1-Bromopropane	71.0	Nonazeotrope		*207*
3280	C_3H_7I	1-Iodopropane	102.4	87.4	....	*240*
3281	C_3H_7I	2-Iodopropane	89.45	83.2	52	*207*
3282	C_3H_8O	Isopropyl alcohol	82.35	77.0	53	*240*
3283	C_3H_8O	Propyl alcohol	97.25	82.55	70	*216*
3284	C_4H_4S	Thiophene	84.7	Nonazeotrope		*207*

	B-Component			Azeotropic Data		
No.	Formula	Name	B.P., ° C.	B.P., ° C.	Wt. % A	Ref.
A =	$C_2H_5NO_3$	**Ethyl Nitrate** (*continued*)	**87.68**			
3285	C_4H_8O	2-Butanone	79.6	Nonazeotrope		*207*
3286	$C_4H_8O_2$	Dioxane	101.35	Nonazeotrope		*207*
3287	C_4H_9Br	1-Bromobutane	101.6	Nonazeotrope		*207*
3288	C_4H_9Br	2-Bromobutane	91.2	<85.5	<68	*240*
3289	C_4H_9Br	1-Bromo-2-methylpropane	91.4	85.0	65	*250*
3290	C_4H_9Br	2-Bromo-2-methylpropane	73.25	Nonazeotrope		*207*
3291	C_4H_9Cl	1-Chlorobutane	78.5	<78	<20	*207*
3292	C_4H_9Cl	1-Chloro-2-methylpropane	68.85	Nonazeotrope		*207*
3293	$C_4H_{10}O$	Butyl alcohol	117.75	87.45	96	*207*
3294	$C_4H_{10}O$	*sec*-Butyl alcohol	99.5	84.8	78	*207*
3295	$C_4H_{10}O$	*tert*-Butyl alcohol	82.55	78.1	45	*207*
3296	$C_4H_{10}O$	Isobutyl alcohol	107.85	86.4	86	*217*
3297	$C_4H_{10}S$	Ethyl sulfide	92.1	85.0	58	*240*
3298	C_5H_{10}	Cyclopentane	49.3	Nonazeotrope		*207*
3299	$C_5H_{10}O$	Isovaleraldehyde	92.1	Nonazeotrope		*207*
3300	$C_5H_{11}Cl$	1-Chloro-3-methylbutane	99.4	87.55	92	*207*
3301	$C_5H_{12}O$	*tert*-Amyl alcohol	102.35	<87.0	<95	*207*
3302	$C_5H_{12}O$	2-Pentanol	119.8	Nonazeotrope		*207*
3303	$C_5H_{12}O_2$	Diethoxymethane	87.95	85.85	49	*250*
3304	C_6H_5F	Fluorobenzene	84.9	<82.5	<42	*240*
3305	C_6H_6	Benzene	80.15	80.03	12	*240*
3306	C_6H_8	1.3-Cyclohexadiene	80.4	76	<38	*240*
3307	C_6H_{12}	Cyclohexane	80.75	74.5	36	*240*
3308	C_6H_{12}	Methylcyclopentane	72.0	68.7	20	*240*
3309	C_6H_{14}	Hexane	68.8	66.25	24	*250*
3310	$C_6H_{14}O$	Propyl ether	90.1	<87.0	>65	*207*
3311	$C_6H_{14}O_2$	Acetal	103.55	Nonazeotrope		*237*
3312	C_7H_8	Toluene	110.7	Nonazeotrope		*207*
3313	C_7H_{14}	Methylcyclohexane	101.15	83.85	....	*251*
3314	C_7H_{16}	Heptane	98.4	82.8	63	*207*
3315	C_8H_{16}	1,3-Dimethylcyclohexane	120.7	Nonazeotrope		*240*
3316	C_8H_{18}	2,5-Dimethylhexane	109.2	86	84	*240*
A =	C_2H_6	**Ethane**	**−93**			
3317	C_2H_6O	Ethyl alcohol	78.3	Nonazeotrope		*243*
3318	C_3H_8O	Isopropyl alcohol	82.45	Nonazeotrope		*243*
3319	C_3H_8O	Propyl alcohol	97.2	Nonazeotrope		*334*
3320	C_4H_{10}	Butane	0.6	Nonazeotrope		*243*
3321	$C_4H_{10}O$	Isobutyl alcohol	108	Nonazeotrope		*243*
A =	$C_2H_6Cl_2Si$	**Dichlorodimethylsilane**	**....**			
3322	C_7H_{16}	2-Methylhexane	90.1	Nonazeotrope		*343*
3323	C_7H_{16}	3-Methylhexane	91.96	Nonazeotrope		*343*
A =	C_2H_6O	**Ethyl Alcohol**	**78.3**			
3324	C_2H_6S	Methyl sulfide	37.4	Nonazeotrope		*246*
3325	C_3H_5Br	*trans*-1-Bromopropene	63.25	58.7	11	*243*
3326	C_3H_5Br	*cis*-1-Bromopropene	57.8	56.4	9	*243*
3327	C_3H_5Br	2-Bromopropene	48.35	46.2	6	*243*
3328	C_3H_5Br	3-Bromopropene	70.8	62.9	....	*257*
3329	C_3H_5Cl	*cis*-1-Chloropropene	32.8	32.1	....	*213*
3330	C_3H_5Cl	*trans*-1-Chloropropene	37.4	36.7	4	*255*
3331	C_3H_5Cl	2-Chloropropene	22.65	Nonazeotrope		*253*
3332	C_3H_5Cl	3-Chloropropene	45.7	44	5	*253*
3333	C_3H_5ClO	Epichlorohydrin	116.4	Nonazeotrope		*236*
3334	C_3H_5I	3-Iodoprene	102	75.4	42	*212*
3335	C_3H_5N	Propionitrile	97.1	77.5	....	*243*
		760 mm.	....	81	25.0	*129**, *165*
		760 mm.	97.1	....	27.5	*129**, *165*
		200 mm.	....	....	28.0	*129**, *165*
		100 mm.	....	....	35.5	*129**, *165*
		25 mm.	....	....	38.0	*129**, *165*
3336	$C_3H_6Cl_2$	1,1-Dichloropropane	96.2	74.7	52.74	*213*
3337	$C_3H_6Cl_2$	2,2-Dichloropropane	69.8	63.2	14.5	*253*
3338	C_3H_6O	Acetone	56.1	Nonazeotrope B.p. curve		*155*, *395**
3339	C_3H_6O	Propionaldehyde	48.7	Nonazeotrope		*255*

No.	B-Component Formula	Name	B.P., ° C.	Azeotropic Data B.P., ° C.	Wt. % A	Ref.
A =	**C_2H_6O**	**Ethyl Alcohol** (*continued*)	**78.3**			
3340	C_3H_6OS	Methyl thioacetate	95.5	77.8	....	*255*
3341	$C_3H_6O_2$	Ethyl formate	54.1	54.05	....	*216*
3342	$C_3H_6O_2$	Methyl acetate	56.95	56.9	~3	*216*
3343	$C_3H_6O_3$	Methyl carbonate	90.35	73.5	~45	*216*
3344	C_3H_7Br	1-Bromopropane	71	63.6	16.24	
				B.p. curve		*163*
3345	C_3H_7Br	2-Bromopropane	59.8	55.5	11.5	*207*
3346	C_3H_7Cl	1-Chloropropane	46.65	44.95	6	*235*
3347	C_3H_7Cl	2-Chloropropane	36.25	35.6	2.8	*253*
3348	C_3H_7I	1-Iodopropane	102.4	75.4	44	*253*
3349	C_3H_7I	2-Iodopropane	89.35	70.2	25	*235*
3350	$C_3H_7NO_3$	Propyl nitrate	110.5	75.0	....	*240*
3351	C_3H_8O	Isopropyl alcohol	82.45	Nonazeotrope		*243*
3352	C_3H_8O	Propyl alcohol	97.2	Nonazeotrope		*328*
3353	$C_3H_8O_2$	2-Methoxyethanol	124.5	Nonazeotrope		*255*
3354	$C_3H_8O_2$	Methylal	42.1	Nonazeotrope		*236*
3355	C_3H_8S	Propanethiol	67.3	<63.5	<19	*246*
3356	$C_3H_9BO_3$	Methyl borate	68.7	63.0	~25	*216*
3357	$C_4H_4N_2$	Pyrazine	114–115	Nonazeotrope		*299*
3358	C_4H_4S	Thiophene	84	70.0	45	*235*
3359	C_4H_6	1,3-Butadiene	−4.5	Nonazeotrope, V-l.		*63*
3360	C_4H_6O	Crotonaldehyde	102.2	Nonazeotrope		*97*
3361	$C_4H\ O_2$	Allyl formate	80.0	71.5	....	*247*
3362	$C_4H_6O_2$	Biacetyl	87.5	73.9	47?	*232*
3363	$C_4H_6O_2$	Methyl acrylate	80	73.5	42.4	*320*
3364	C_4H_7Br	*trans*-1-Bromo-1-butene	94.70	72.8	35.71	*257*
3365	C_4H_7Br	*cis*-1-Bromo-1-butene	86.15	69.6	77.48	*257*
3366	C_4H_7Br	2-Bromo-1-butene	81.0	67.4	22.18	*257*
3367	C_4H_7Br	*cis*-2-Bromo-2-butene	93.9	72.3	33.7	*257*
3368	C_4H_7Br	*trans*-2-Bromo-2-butene	85.55	69.1	26.7	*257*
3369	$C\ H_7Cl$	*trans*-1-Chloro-1-butene	68	61.2	20.2	*280*
3370	C_4H_7Cl	*cis*-1-Chloro-1-butene	63.4	57	14.8	*280*
3371	C_4H_7Cl	2-Chloro-1-butene	58.4	53.6	11.5	*280*
3372	C_4H_7Cl	*trans*-2-Chloro-2-butene	66.6	60	18.4	*280*
3373	C_4H_7Cl	*cis*-2-Chloro-2-butene	62.4	56.8	15.4	*280*
3374	$C_4H_7ClO_2$	Ethyl chloroacetate	143.5	Nonazeotrope		*58*
3375	C_4H_7N	Isobutyronitrile	103.85	Nonazeotrope		*255*
3376	C_4H_8O	2-Butanone	79.6	75.7	>46	*207, 271**
3377	C_4H_8O	Ethyl vinyl ether	35.5	Nonazeotrope		*362*
3378	C_4H_8O	Isobutyraldehyde	63.5	Nonazeotrope		*255*
3379	C_4H_8OS	Ethyl thioacetate	116.6	Nonazeotrope		*255*
3380	$C_4H_8O_2$	Dioxane	101.4	Nonazeotrope		*90*
			101.07	78.13	90.7	
				V-l.		*166*
3381	$C_4H_8O_2$	Ethyl acetate, 25 mm.	....	−1.39	12.81	*273, 334*, 428**
		300 mm.	....	47.83	23.22	
		760 mm.	77.05	71.81	30.98	
		1500 mm.	....	91.86	39.07	
3382	$C_4H_8O_2$	Methyl propionate	79.7	72.0	33	*216*
3383	$C_4H_8O_2$	Propyl formate	80.8	71.75	~41	*252*
3384	C_4H_9Br	1-Bromobutane	100.3	75.0	43	*253*
3385	C_4H_9Br	2-Bromobutane	91.2	72.5	33	*247*
3386	C_4H_9Br	1-Bromo-2-methylpropane	89.2	71.4	41.0	*163, 235**
				B.p. curve		
3387	C_4H_9Br	2-Bromo-2-methylpropane	73.3	63.8	15	*243*
3388	C_4H_9Cl	1-Chlorobutane	78.05	65.7	20.3	*253*
3389	C_4H_9Cl	2-Chlorobutane	68.25	61.2	15.8	*247*
3390	C_4H_9Cl	1-Chloro-2-methylpropane	68.9	61.45	16.3	*243*
3391	C_4H_9Cl	2-Chloro-2-methylpropane	51	~49	~6.5	*243*
3392	C_4H_9I	1-Iodobutane	130.4	<78.15	....	*247*
3393	C_4H_9I	2-Iodobutane	120.0	77.2	70	*247*
3394	C_4H_9I	1-Iodo-2-methylpropane	120	77	70	*334*
3395	C_4H_9I	1-Iodo-2-methylpropane	120.4	77.65	73	*253*
3396	$C_4H_{10}O$	*tert*-Butyl alcohol	82.55	Nonazeotrope		*243*
3397	$C_4H_{10}O$	Ethyl ether	34.5	Nonazeotrope		*155, 427**
				B.p. curve		

No.	B-Component Formula	Name	B.P., ° C.	Azeotropic Data B.P., ° C.	Wt. % A	Ref.
A =	C_2H_6O	**Ethyl Alcohol** (*continued*)	**78.3**			
3398	$C_4H_{10}O$	Methyl propyl ether	38.95	Nonazeotrope		*256*
3399	$C_4H_{10}O_2$	Acetaldehyde dimethyl acetal	64.3	61.6	12	*256*
3400	$C_4H_{10}O_2$	2-Ethoxyethanol	133	Nonazeotrope, V-l.		*14*
3401	$C_4H_{10}O_2$	Ethoxymethoxymethane	65.90	63.95	13.3	*429*
3402	$C_4H_{10}S$	Ethyl sulfide	92.2	72.6	56	*235*
3403	$C_4H_{11}ClSi$	Chloromethyltrimethylsilane	97	72	....	*374*
3404	C_5H_5N	Pyridine	115.4	Nonazeotrope		*233*
3405	C_5H_6O	2-Methylfuran	63.8	<60.5	<15	*255*
3406	C_5H_8	Isoprene	34.3	32.65	3	*217*
3407	C_5H_8	3-Methyl-1,2-butadiene	40.8	~39	....	*243*
3408	$C_5H_8O_2$	Ethyl acrylate	43/103	77.5	72.7	*320*
3409	C_5H_{10}	Cyclopentane	49.4	44.7	7.5	*247*
3410	C_5H_{10}	3-Methyl-1-butene	22.5	21.9	~2	*217*
3411	C_5H_{10}	2-Methyl-2-butene	37.15	Nonazeotrope		*243*
3412	C_5H_{10}	2-Methyl-2-butene	37.15	37.3	~4	*105*, 217*
3413	$C_5H_{10}O$	Allyl ethyl ether	63–65	60.5	....	*257*
3414	$C_5H_{10}O$	3-Methyl-2-butanone	95.4	Nonazeotrope		*232*
3415	$C_5H_{10}O$	2-Pentanone	102	77.7	91.17	*93*
			102	Effect of pressure		*42*
3416	$C_5H_{10}O_2$	Ethyl propionate	99.15	78.0	75	*217*
3417	$C_5H_{10}O_2$	Isobutyl formate	97.9	77.0	67	*216*
3418	$C_5H_{10}O_2$	Isopropyl acetate	91.0	76.8	53	*216*
3419	$C_5H_{10}O_2$	Methyl butyrate	102.65	78.0	~83	*216*
3420	$C_5H_{10}O_2$	Methyl isobutyrate	92.3	77.0	....	*216*
3421	$C_5H_{10}O_2$	Propyl acetate	101.6	78.18	~85	*216*
3422	$C_5H_{11}Br$	1-Bromo-3-methylbutane	118.2	77.3	72.0	*162, 253**
				B.p. curve		
3423	$C_5H_{11}Cl$	1-Chloro-3-methylbutane	99.8	74.8	41	*253*
3424	$C_5H_{11}Cl$	1-Chloropentane	108.35	72.5	....	*171*
3425	C_5H_{12}	2-Methylbutane	27.95	26.75	3.5	*217*
3426	C_5H_{12}	Pentane	36.15	34.3	5	*217*
3427	$C_5H_{12}O$	Ethyl propyl ether	63.6	61.2	25	*253*
3428	$C_5H_{12}O$	Isoamyl alcohol	131.8	Nonazeotrope		*243*
3429	$C_5H_{12}O_2$	Diethoxymethane	87.5	74.2	42	*131*
3430	$C_5H_{14}OSi$	Ethoxytrimethylsilane	75–76	....	30	*86*
			75	66.4	....	*338*
3431	C_6H_5Cl	Chlorobenzene	132.0	Nonazeotrope		*254*
3432	C_6H_5F	Fluorobenzene	85.15	70.0	25	*225*
3433	$C_6H_5NO_2$	Nitrobenzene	210.75	Nonazeotrope		*234*
3434	C_6H_6	Benzene	80.1	68.24	32.4	*431*
		198 mm.	....	34.8	25	*126*, 334*, 352*, 387*, 388*, 395*, 397*, 405*, 413*, 430*, 437**
		382 mm.	....	50	25	
		570 mm.	....	60	25	
		711 mm.	....	66	>25	
3435	$C_6H_6O_2$	Resorcinol	281.4	Nonazeotrope		*328*
3436	C_6H_8	1,3-Cyclohexadiene	80.8	60.7	34	*243*
3437	C_6H_8	1,4-Cyclohexadiene	85.6	68.5	....	*243*
3438	C_6H_{10}	Biallyl	60.2	53.5	13	*243*
3439	C_6H_{10}	Cyclohexene	82.7	66.7	34	*217*
3440	C_6H_{10}	1-Hexyne	70.2	62.8	23.2	*157*
3441	C_6H_{10}	3-Hexyne	80.5	67.5	34.4	*157*
3442	C_6H_{10}	Methylcyclopentene	75.85	63.3	28	*247*
3443	C_6H_{12}	Cyclohexane	80.75	64.9	30.5	*243*
3444	C_6H_{12}	Methylcyclopentane	72.0	60.3	25	*247*
3445	$C_6H_{12}O$	(1-Methylallyl) ethyl ether	76.65	69	....	*257*
3446	$C_6H_{12}O$	*trans*-2-Butenyl ethyl ether	100.45	77.5	....	*257*
3447	$C_6H_{12}O$	*cis*-2-Butenyl ethyl ether	100.3	76.2	....	*257*
3448	$C_6H_{12}O_2$	Ethyl isobutyrate	110.1	Nonazeotrope		*216*
3449	$C_6H_{12}O_2$	Methyl isovalerate	116.3	Nonazeotrope		*216*
3450	C_6H_{14}	2,3-Dimethylbutane	58.0	51.5	12	*247*
3451	C_6H_{14}	*n*-Hexane	68.95	58.68	21.0	*431*
3452	$C_6H_{14}O$	*tert*-Butyl ethyl ether	73	66.6	21	*105*
3453	$C_6H_{14}O$	Propyl ether	90.4	74.4	44	*236*
3454	$C_6H_{14}O_2$	Acetal	103.6	78.2	65.5	*20, 252**

No.	Formula	B-Component Name	B.P., ° C.	Azeotropic Data B.P., ° C.	Wt. % A	Ref.
A =	C_2H_6O	**Ethyl Alcohol** (*continued*)	**78.3**			
3455	$C_6H_{14}O_2$	Ethoxypropoxymethane	113.7	Nonazeotrope		*429*
3456	$C_6H_{14}S$	Isopropyl sulfide	120.5	Nonazeotrope		*246*
3457	$C_6H_{15}N$	Triethylamine	89.4	~75	....	*243*
3458	$C_6H_{16}SiO$	Ethoxymethyltrimethylsilane	102	74	....	*374*
3459	$C_6H_{16}O_2Si$	Diethoxydimethylsilane	114	77	83	*93*
3460	C_7H_8	Toluene	110.7	76.7	68	*23, 334*, 387**
			....	0.5	45.5	*329*
			....	25	62.5	*329*
			....	50	64.5	*329*
			....	75.5	65.5	*329*
			V-l. at 35° C., 55° C.			*193*
3461	C_7H_{12}	1-Heptyne	99.5	74.2	54.6	*157*
3462	C_7H_{12}	5-Methyl-1-hexyne	90.8	71.0	39.8	*157*
3463	C_7H_{14}	1,1-Dimethylcyclopentane	87.84	....	36	*383*
3464	C_7H_{14}	*cis*-1,2-Dimethylcyclopentane	99.53	....	~47	*383*
3465	C_7H_{14}	*trans*-1,2-Dimethylcyclopentane	....	....	~39	*383*
3466	C_7H_{14}	*trans*-1,3-Dimethylcyclopentane	90.77	....	~37	*383*
3467	C_7H_{14}	Ethylcyclopentane	103.45	....	~48	*383*
3468	C_7H_{14}	Methylcyclohexane	100.8	72.1	47	*23*
3469	C_7H_{14}		100.95	71.95	....	*252*
				V-l. at 35.55° C.		*194*
3470	C_7H_{16}	2,2-Dimethylpentane	79.1	....	~26	*383*
3471	C_7H_{16}	2,3-Dimethylpentane	89.79	....	~36	*383*
3472	C_7H_{16}	2,4-Dimethylpentane	80.8	....	29	*383*
3473	C_7H_{16}	3,3-Dimethylpentane	86.0	....	32	*383*
3474	C_7H_{16}	3-Ethylpentane	93.5	....	35	*383*
3475	C_7H_{16}	Heptane	98.45	70.9	49	*217*
3476	C_7H_{16}	2-Methylhexane	90.0	....	~36	*383*
3477	C_7H_{16}	3-Methylhexane	91.8	....	~36	*383*
3478	$C_7H_{16}O$	*tert*-Amyl ethyl ether	101–2	66.6	21	*105*
3479	C_8H_8	Styrene	145.8	Nonazeotrope		*225*
3480	C_8H_{10}	Ethylbenzene	136.15	Nonazeotrope		*217*
3481	C_8H_{10}	*m*-Xylene	139.0	Nonazeotrope		*217*
3482	C_8H_{10}	*o*-Xylene	143.6	Nonazeotrope		*225*
3483	C_8H_{10}	*p*-Xylene	138.3	Nonazeotrope		*220*
3484	C_8H_{16}	1,1-Dimethylcyclohexane	....	....	~36	*383*
3485	C_8H_{16}	1,3-Dimethylcyclohexane	120.7	175.8	70	*255*
3486	C_8H_{16}	*cis*-1,4-Dimethylcyclohexane	....	....	~70	*383*
3487	C_8H_{16}	*trans*-1,4-Dimethylcyclohexane	....	....	~64	*383*
3488	C_8H_{16}	*cis-trans-cis*-1,2,4-Trimethylcyclopentane	....	....	~52	*383*
3489	C_8H_{18}	2,2-Dimethylhexane	106.84	....	36	*383*
3490	C_8H_{18}	2,3-Dimethylhexane	115.8	....	55	*383*
3491	C_8H_{18}	2,5-Dimethylhexane	109.2	73.6	59	*225*
3492	C_8H_{18}	3,4-Dimethylhexane	117.9	....	60	*383*
3493	C_8H_{18}	2-Methylheptane	117.2	....	59	*383*
3494	C_8H_{18}	3-Methylheptane	119.0	....	61	*383*
3495	C_8H_{18}	4-Methylheptane	118	....	61	*383*
3496	C_8H_{18}	Octane	125.6	77	78	*217*
3497	C_8H_{18}	2,2,3-Trimethylpentane	109.8	....	53	*383*
3498	C_8H_{18}	2,2,4-Trimethylpentane, 96.1 mm.	....	25	30.4 V-l.	*192*
		318.8 mm.	....	50	36.7 V-l.	*192*
			....	0	24.8	*192*
			99.3	<72.4	<53	*255*
3499	C_8H_{18}	2,3,3-Trimethylpentane	113.6	....	57	*383*
3500	C_8H_{18}	2,3,4-Trimethylpentane	113.4	....	57	*383*
3501	$C_8H_{18}O$	Isobutyl ether	122.1	Nonazeotrope		*236*
3502	C_9H_{12}	Cumene	152.8	Nonazeotrope		*255*
3503	C_9H_{12}	Mesitylene	164.6	Nonazeotrope		*217*
3504	C_9H_{12}	Propylbenzene	159.3	Nonazeotrope		*255*
3505	$C_{10}H_{14}$	Cymene	176.7	Nonazeotrope		*217*
3506	$C_{10}H_{16}$	Camphene	159.6	Nonazeotrope		*217*
3507	$C_{10}H_{16}$	*d*-Limonene	177.8	Nonazeotrope		*217*

No.	B-Component Formula	B-Component Name	B-Component B.P., ° C.	Azeotropic Data B.P., ° C.	Azeotropic Data Wt. % A	Ref.
A =	**C_2H_6O**	**Ethyl Alcohol** (*continued*)	**78.3**			
3508	$C_{10}H_{16}$	α-Pinene	155.8	Nonazeotrope		*208*
3509	$C_{10}H_{16}$	α-Pinene	155.8	Min. b.p.		*243*
3510	$C_{10}H_{16}$	α-Terpinene	173.4	Nonazeotrope		*255*
3511	$C_{10}H_{16}$	Thymene	179.7	Nonazeotrope		*217*
3512	$C_{10}H_{22}$	2,7-Dimethyloctane	160.2	Nonazeotrope		*217*
A =	**C_2H_6O**	**Methyl Ether**	**−23.65**			
3513	C_3H_9N	Trimethylamine	3.5	Nonazeotrope		*158*
A =	**$C_2H_6O_2$**	**Glycol**	**197.4**			
3514	C_2H_7NO	2-Aminoethanol	170.8	Nonazeotrope		*207*
3515	$C_3H_5Cl_3$	1,2,3-Trichloropropane	156.85	150.8	13	*253*
3516	C_3H_5I	3-Iodopropene	101.8	<101.5	<1.5	*255*
3517	$C_3H_6Br_2$	1,2-Dibromobutane	140.5	139.0	6	*247*
3518	$C_3H_6Br_2$	1,3-Dibromopropane	166.9	160.2	10.2	*207*
3519	$C_3H_6Cl_2O$	1,3-Dichloro-2-propanol	175.8	Nonazeotrope		*221*
3520	$C_3H_6Cl_2O$	2,3-Dichloro-1-propanol	182.5	Nonazeotrope		*255*
3521	C_3H_7ClO	1-Chloro-2-propanol	127.5	Nonazeotrope		*255*
3522	C_3H_7NO	Propionamide	222.1	Nonazeotrope		*207*
3523	$C_3H_7NO_2$	Ethyl carbamate	185.25	Nonazeotrope		*207*
3524	$C_3H_8O_3$	Glycerol	290.5	Nonazeotrope		*255*
3525	C_4H_5N	Pyrrol	130.0	Nonazeotrope		*207*
3526	C_4H_5NS	Allyl isothiocyanate	152.05	<151.8	....	*255*
3527	$C_4H_6O_4$	Methyl oxalate	164.2	~163.5	~15	*210*
3528	$C_4H_7BrO_2$	Ethyl bromoacetate	158.8	157.3	12	*207*
3529	$C_4H_7ClO_2$	Ethyl chloroacetate	143.55	Nonazeotrope		*255*
3530	$C_4H_8Br_2O$	Bis(2-bromoethyl) ether, 760 mm.	....	180–185	~50	*93*
		50 mm.	....	105–115	~50	*93*
3531	$C_4H_8Cl_2O$	Bis(2-chloroethyl) ether	178	170.5	12.5	*58*
3532	$C_4H_8Cl_2O$	Bis(2-chloroethyl) ether	178.65	171.05	21	*236*
3533	$C_4H_8Cl_2S$	Bis(2-chloroethyl) sulfide	216.8	186.0?	....	*255*
3534	C_4H_8OS	Ethyl thioacetate	116.6	Nonazeotrope		*255*
3535	$C_4H_8O_2$	Dioxane	101.4	Nonazeotrope		*90*
3536	$C_4H_8O_3$	Glycol monoacetate	190.9	184.75	25	*250*
3537	C_4H_9Br	1-Bromobutane	101.5	101.3	1.7	*255*
3538	C_4H_9Br	1-Bromo-2-methylpropane	91.4	<91.35	<0.8	*255*
3539	C_4H_9I	1-Iodobutane	130.4	128.5	5	*247*
3540	C_4H_9I	1-Iodo-2-methylpropane	120.8	119.5	3.5	*255*
3541	$C_4H_{10}O$	Butyl alcohol	117.75	Nonazeotrope		*215*
3542	$C_5H_4O_2$	2-Furaldehyde	161.45	Nonazeotrope		*207*
3543	$C_5H_9ClO_2$	Propyl chloroacetate	163.5	162	20	*255*
3544	$C_5H_{10}O_3$	Ethyl carbonate	125.9	Nonazeotrope		*217*
3545	$C_5H_{10}O_3$	2-Methoxyethyl acetate	144.6	Nonazeotrope		*255*
3546	$C_5H_{11}Br$	1-Bromo-3-methylbutane	120.65	119.45	5.5	*207*
3547	$C_5H_{11}I$	1-Iodo-3-methylbutane	147.65	143.0	7	*247*
3548	$C_5H_{12}O$	Isoamyl alcohol	131.35	Nonazeotrope		*207*
3549	$C_5H_{12}O_2$	2-Propoxyethanol	151.35	Nonazeotrope		*206*
3550	$C_5H_{12}O_3$	2-(2-Methoxyethoxy)ethanol	194.2	192	30	*62, 207**
		50 mm.	....	114	4.0	*62, 207**
		200 mm.	....	149	12.0	*62, 207**
3551	$C_6H_3Cl_3$	1,3,5-Trichlorobenzene	208.4	181.0	....	*247*
3552	C_6H_4BrCl	*p*-Bromochlorobenzene	196.4	173.8	28	*247*
3553	$C_6H_4Br_2$	*p*-Dibromobenzene	220.25	183.9	32.5	*254*
3554	$C_6H_4ClNO_2$	*m*-Chloronitrobenzene	235.5	192.5	53	*234*
3555	$C_6H_4ClNO_2$	*o*-Chloronitrobenzene	246.0	193.5	68	*234*
3556	$C_6H_4ClNO_2$	*p*-Chloronitrobenzene	239.1	192.85	57.8	*234*
3557	$C_6H_4Cl_2$	*o*-Dichlorobenzene	179.5	165.8	20	*247*
3558	$C_6H_4Cl_2$	*p*-Dichlorobenzene	174.35	163	~23	*253*
3559	$C_6H_4Cl_2$	*p*-Dichlorobenzene	174.35	162.7	18	*254*
3560	C_6H_5Br	Bromobenzene	156.15	150.2	12.5	*210*
3561	C_6H_5Cl	Chlorobenzene	132	130.05	5.6	*206*
3562	C_6H_5ClO	*o*-Chlorophenol	175.8	Nonazeotrope		*255*
3563	C_6H_5ClO	*p*-Chlorophenol	219.75	Nonazeotrope		*215*
3564	C_6H_5I	Iodobenzene	188.55	171.5	....	*253*
3565	$C_6H_5NO_2$	Nitrobenzene	210.75	185.9	59	*234*
3566	$C_6H_5NO_3$	*o*-Nitrophenol	217.2	189.35	49	*207*
3567	C_6H_6	Benzene	80.2	Nonazeotrope		*217*

No.	B-Component Formula	Name	B.P., ° C.	Azeotropic Data B.P., ° C.	Wt. % A	Ref.
A =	$C_2H_6O_2$	**Glycol** *(continued)*	**197.4**			
3568	C_6H_6O	Phenol	182.2	Nonazeotrope		*222*
3569	C_6H_6O	Phenol	181.5	199	78	*243*
3570	$C_6H_6O_2$	Pyrocatechol	245.9	Nonazeotrope		*244*
3571	C_6H_7N	Aniline	184.35	180.55	24	*231*
3572	$C_6H_8N_2$	*o*-Phenylenediamine	258.6	Nonazeotrope		*207*
3573	$C_6H_8O_4$	Methyl maleate	204.05	189.6	42	*250*
3574	C_6H_9N	*N*-Ethylpyrrol	130.4	Nonazeotrope		*255*
3575	C_6H_{10}	Cyclohexene	82.7	Nonazeotrope		*220*
3576	$C_6H_{10}O_2$	2,5-Hexadiene	191.3	<180.5	<45	*232*
3577	$C_6H_{10}O_4$	Ethylidene diacetate	168.5	167.45	8.2	*207*
3578	$C_6H_{10}O_4$	Ethyl oxalate	185.65	176.5	25	*255*
3579	$C_6H_{10}O_4$	Ethyl oxalate	185.0	Reacts		*243*
3580	$C_6H_{10}O_4$	Glycol diacetate	186.3	<179.5	<24	*255*
3581	$C_6H_{10}O_4$	Methyl succinate	195	Reacts		*243*
3582	$C_6H_{11}ClO_2$	Butyl chloroacetate	181.9	176.0	30	*206*
3583	C_6H_{12}	Cyclohexane	80.75	Nonazeotrope		*217*
3584	C_6H_{12}	Methylcyclohexane	72.0	Nonazeotrope		*255*
3585	$C_6H_{12}O$	Cyclohexanol	160.65	Nonazeotrope		*210*
3586	$C_6H_{12}O_2$	Butyl acetate	126.0	Nonazeotrope		*255*
3587	$C_6H_{12}O_2$	Ethyl butyrate	121.5	Nonazeotrope		*255*
3588	$C_6H_{12}O_2$	Isoamyl formate	123.8	Nonazeotrope		*216*
3589	$C_6H_{12}O_3$	2-Ethoxyethyl acetate	156.8	Nonazeotrope		*206*
3590	$C_6H_{12}O_3$	Paraldehyde	124.35	Nonazeotrope		*236*
3591	$C_6H_{13}Br$	1-Bromohexane	156.5	150.5	14	*247*
3592	C_6H_{14}	2,3-Dimethylbutane	58.0	Nonazeotrope		*255*
3593	C_6H_{14}	Hexane	68.8	Nonazeotrope		*255*
3594	$C_6H_{14}O$	Hexyl alcohol	157.8	Nonazeotrope		*253*
3595	$C_6H_{14}O_2$	Acetal	103.55	Nonazeotrope		*215*
3596	$C_6H_{14}O_2$	2-Butoxyethanol	171.25	Nonazeotrope		*206*
3597	$C_6H_{14}O_2$	Pinacol	174.35	Nonazeotrope		*210*
3598	$C_7H_5Cl_3$	α,α,α-Trichlorotoluene	220.9	Reacts		*215*
3599	C_7H_5N	Benzonitrile	191.3	186.5	....	*243*
3600	$C_7H_6Cl_2$	α,α-Dichlorotoluene	205.1	Nonazeotrope		*222*
3601	C_7H_6O	Benzaldehyde	179.2	<173.5	>15	*255*
3602	C_7H_7Br	*m*-Bromotoluene	184.3	168.3	23	*207*
3603	C_7H_7Br	*o*-Bromotoluene	181.75	166.8	25	*208*
3604	C_7H_7Br	*p*-Bromotoluene	~184.5	169.2	30	*253*
3605	C_7H_7Cl	α-Chlorotoluene	179.3	~167.0	~30	*210*
3606	C_7H_7Cl	*o*-Chlorotoluene	159.2	152.5	13	*247*
3607	C_7H_7Cl	*p*-Chlorotoluene	162.4	155.0	....	*253*
3608	C_7H_7I	*p*-Iodotoluene	214.5	181.5	30	*247*
3609	$C_7H_7NO_2$	*m*-Nitrotoluene	230.8	192.5	57?	*234*
3610	$C_7H_7NO_2$	*o*-Nitrotoluene	221.75	188.55	48.5	*234*
3611	$C_7H_7NO_2$	*p*-Nitrotoluene	238.9	192.4	63.5	*234*
3612	C_7H_8	Toluene	110.75	110.20	6.5	*253*
3613	C_7H_8O	Anisole	153.85	150.45	10.5	*210*
3614	C_7H_8O	Benzyl alcohol	205.25	193.35	53.5	*229*
3615	C_7H_8O	*m*-Cresol	202.1	195.2	60	*221*
3616	C_7H_8O	*m*-Cresol	202.4	....	61, V-l.	*292*
3617	C_7H_8O	*o*-Cresol	191.1	189.6	27	*254*
3618	C_7H_8O	*p*-Cresol	202.0	....	59.5, V-l.	*292*
3619	C_7H_8O	*p*-Cresol	201.6	195.2	53.5	*208*
3620	$C_7H_8O_2$	Guaiacol	205.1	190.4	46	*236*
3621	$C_7H_8O_2$	*m*-Methoxyphenol	243.8	195.5	~80	*255*
3622	C_7H_9N	Methylaniline	196.25	181.6	40.2	*231*
3623	C_7H_9N	*m*-Toluidine	200.3	188.55	42	*231*
3624	C_7H_9N	*o*-Toluidine	200.35	186.45	42.5	*231*
3625	C_7H_9N	*p*-Toluidine	200.55	187.0	27	*231*
3626	C_7H_9NO	*o*-Anisidine	219.0	<193.5	<59	*231*
3627	$C_7H_{12}O_4$	Ethyl malonate	198.9	Reacts		*243*
3628	$C_7H_{13}ClO_2$	Isoamyl chloroacetate	195.0	<187.5	>38	*255*
3629	C_7H_{14}	Methylcyclohexane	101.1	100.8	~4	*217*
3630	$C_7H_{14}O_2$	Amyl acetate	148.7	147.6	6	*244*
3631	$C_7H_{14}O_2$	Butyl propionate	146.8	<146.0	<7	*255*
3632	$C_7H_{14}O_2$	Ethyl isovalerate	134.7	Nonazeotrope		*255*
3633	$C_7H_{14}O_2$	Ethyl valerate	145.45	144.7	3	*244*

No.	B-Component Formula	Name	B.P., ° C.	Azeotropic Data B.P., ° C.	Wt. % A	Ref.
A =	$C_2H_6O_2$	**Glycol** (*continued*)	**197.4**			
3634	$C_7H_{14}O_2$	Isoamyl acetate	142.1	141.95	~3	*216*
3635	$C_7H_{14}O_2$	Isobutyl propionate	137.5	Nonazeotrope		*255*
3636	$C_7H_{14}O_2$	Methyl caproate	149.8	148.0	7	*255*
3637	$C_7H_{14}O_2$	Propyl butyrate	142.8	142.7	~3	*216*
3638	$C_7H_{14}O_2$	Propyl isobutyrate	134.0	Nonazeotrope		*255*
3639	$C_7H_{14}O_3$	1,3-Butanediol methyl ether acetate	171.75	<171.0	<12	*255*
3640	C_7H_{16}	Heptane	98.45	97.9	3	*243*
3641	$C_7H_{16}O$	Heptyl alcohol	176.15	174.1	20	*244*
3642	C_8H_7N	Indole	253.5	Nonazeotrope		*255*
3643	C_8H_8	Styrene	145.8	139.5	16.5	*217*
3644	C_8H_8O	Acetophenone	202.0	185.65	52	*232*
3645	$C_8H_8O_2$	Benzyl formate	202.3	Reacts		*215*
3646	$C_8H_8O_2$	Methyl benzoate	199.45	182.2	36.5	*210*
3647	$C_8H_8O_2$	Phenyl acetate	195.7	182.9	34	*210*
3648	$C_8H_8O_3$	Methyl salicylate	222.35	188.8	48	*254*
3649	C_8H_{10}	Ethylbenzene	136.15	133.0	13.5	*217*
3650	C_8H_{10}	*m*-Xylene	139.0	135.6	~15	*254*
3651	C_8H_{10}	*o*-Xylene	143.6	139.6	16	*217*
3652	C_8H_{10}	*p*-Xylene	138.3	136.95	14.5	*217*
3653	$C_8H_{10}O$	Benzyl methyl ether	167.8	159.8	18	*247*
3654	$C_8H_{10}O$	*p*-Methylanisole	177.05	166.6	22.8	*221*
3655	$C_8H_{10}O$	*p*-Ethylphenol	218.8	Nonazeotrope		*236*
3656	$C_8H_{10}O$	Phenethyl alcohol	219.4	194.4	69	*229*
3657	$C_8H_{10}O$	Phenetole	170.45	161.45	19	*225*
3658	$C_8H_{10}O$	3,4-Xylenol	226.8	197.2	89	*244*
3659	$C_8H_{10}O_2$	*o*-Ethoxyphenol	216.5	192.6	....	*225*
3660	$C_8H_{10}O_2$	Veratrol	205.5	178.5	35	*254*
3661	$C_8H_{11}N$	Dimethylaniline	194.05	178.55	33.5	*231*
3662	$C_8H_{11}N$	2,4-Xylidine	214.0	188.6	47	*231*
3663	$C_8H_{11}N$	3,4-Xylidine	225.5	<189.0	<91.6	*231*
3664	$C_8H_{11}N$	Ethylaniline	205.5	183.7	43	*231*
3665	$C_8H_{11}NO$	*o*-Phenetidine	232.5	194.8	67.8	*231*
3666	$C_8H_{11}NO$	*p*-Phenetidine	249.9	197.35	97	*231*
3667	$C_8H_{12}O_4$	Ethyl fumarate	217.85	189.35	48.5	*250*
3668	$C_8H_{12}O_4$	Ethyl maleate	223.3	193.1	55	*250*
3669	$C_8H_{14}O$	Methyl heptenone	173.2	168.1	23	*232*
3670	$C_8H_{14}O_4$	Ethyl succinate	217.25	Reacts		*215*
3671	C_8H_{16}	1,3-Dimethylcyclohexane	120.7	119.2	9	*255*
3672	$C_8H_{16}O$	2-Octanone	172.85	168.0	20	*232*
3673	$C_8H_{16}O_2$	Butyl butyrate	166.4	160.6	16	*244*
3674	$C_8H_{16}O_2$	Isoamyl propionate	160.3	155.5	12	*216*
3675	$C_8H_{16}O_2$	Isobutyl butyrate	155.7	153.7	10	*244*
3676	$C_8H_{16}O_2$	Isobutyl isobutyrate	148.6	147.5	6	*244*
3677	$C_8H_{16}O_2$	Propyl isovalerate	155.7	~152	10	*216*
3678	$C_8H_{16}O_4$	2-(2-Ethoxyethoxy)ethyl acetate	218.5	195.0	....	*255*
3679	C_8H_{18}	2,5-Dimethylhexane	109.4	108.65	7.5	*255*
3680	C_8H_{18}	Octane	125.75	123.5	11.5	*247*
3681	$C_8H_{18}O$	Butyl ether	142.1	140.0	10	*225*
3682	$C_8H_{18}O$	Isobutyl ether	122.1	121.9	7	*256*
3683	$C_8H_{18}O$	*n*-Octyl alcohol	195.2	184.35	36.5	*229*
3684	$C_8H_{18}O$	*sec*-Octyl alcohol	180.4	175.55	21	*229*
3685	$C_8H_{18}O_3$	2-(2-Butoxyethoxy)ethanol	230.4	196.2	72.5	*62*
3686	$C_8H_{18}O_3$	Bis(2-ethoxyethyl) ether	186	178.0	26.1	*62*
3687	C_9H_7N	Isoquinoline	240.3	Nonazeotrope		*255*
3688	C_9H_7N	Quinoline	237.3	196.35	79.5	*233*
3689	C_9H_8	Indene	183.0	168.4	26	*221*
3690	C_9H_8O	Cinnamaldehyde	253.5	Nonazeotrope		*255*
3691	C_9H_9N	*β*-Methylindole	266.5	Nonazeotrope		*255*
3692	$C_9H_{10}O$	*p*-Methylacetophenone	226.35	192.2	60	*232*
3693	$C_9H_{10}O$	Propiophenone	217.7	190.2	57	*232*
3694	$C_9H_{10}O_2$	Benzyl acetate	214.9	186.5	45	*216*
3695	$C_9H_{10}O_2$	Ethyl benzoate	212.5	186.1	46	*250*
3696	$C_9H_{10}O_3$	Ethyl salicylate	234.0	190.7	51.5	*223*
3697	C_9H_{12}	Cumene	152.8	147.0	18	*247*
3698	C_9H_{12}	Mesitylene	164.6	156	13	*253*

No.	B-Component Formula	Name	B.P., ° C.	Azeotropic Data B.P., ° C.	Wt. % A	Ref.
A =	$C_2H_6O_2$	**Glycol** (*continued*)	**197.4**			
3699	C_9H_{12}	Propylbenzene	158.8	152	19	206
3700	C_9H_{12}	Pseudocumene	168.2	<157.7	83.2	221
3701	$C_9H_{12}O$	Benzyl ethyl ether	185.0	169.0	22	225
3702	$C_9H_{12}O$	3-Phenylpropanol	235.6	195.5	75	230
3703	$C_9H_{12}O$	Phenyl propyl ether	190.2	171.0	26	218
3704	$C_9H_{13}N$	*N,N*-Dimethyl-*o*-toluidine	185.3	169.3	23	231
3705	$C_9H_{13}N$	*N,N*-Dimethyl-*p*-toluidine	210.2	182.0	47	231
3706	$C_9H_{14}O$	Phorone	197.8	184.5	50	232
3707	$C_9H_{18}O$	2,6-Dimethyl-4-heptanone	168.0	164.2	35	232
3708	$C_9H_{18}O_2$	Butyl isovalerate	177.6	169.0	23	244
3709	$C_9H_{18}O_2$	Ethyl enanthate	188.7	174.0	30	255
3710	$C_9H_{18}O_2$	Isoamyl butyrate	178.5	167.9	24.5	216
3711	$C_9H_{18}O_2$	Isoamyl isobutyrate	168.5	161.5	20	216
3712	$C_9H_{18}O_2$	Isobutyl isovalerate	171.4	163.7	21.7	221
3713	$C_9H_{18}O_2$	Methyl caprylate	192.9	175.5	31	243
3714	$C_9H_{18}O_3$	Isobutyl carbonate	190.3	<180.5	28	247
3715	$C_{10}H_7Br$	1-Bromonaphthalene	281.8	194.95	71.2	221
3716	$C_{10}H_7Cl$	1-Chloronaphthalene	262.7	192.9	65.2	221
3717	$C_{10}H_8$	Naphthalene	218.05	183.9	51	208
3718	$C_{10}H_{10}O_2$	Isosafrol	252.1	192.8	64	254
3719	$C_{10}H_{10}O_2$	Methyl cinnamate	261.9	196.2	85	254
3720	$C_{10}H_{10}O_2$	Safrol	235.9	190.05	55	254
3721	$C_{10}H_{10}O_4$	Methyl phthalate	283.7	Nonazeotrope		244
3722	$C_{10}H_{12}O$	Anethole	235.7	189.35	56	207
3723	$C_{10}H_{12}O$	Estragol	215.6	182.3	40	225
3724	$C_{10}H_{12}O_2$	Ethyl α-toluate	228.7	190.0	54	216
3725	$C_{10}H_{12}O_2$	Eugenol	255.0	196.8	90	236
3726	$C_{10}H_{12}O_2$	Isoeugenol	268.8	Nonazeotrope		255
3727	$C_{10}H_{12}O_2$	Propyl benzoate	230.85	190.35	55	250
3728	$C_{10}H_{14}$	Butylbenzene	183.1	166.2	27	247
3729	$C_{10}H_{14}$	Cymene	176.7	163.2	25.5	217
3730	$C_{10}H_{14}O$	Carvone	231.0	192.5	60.8	232
3731	$C_{10}H_{14}O$	Thymol	232.9	195.5	62	244
3732	$C_{10}H_{14}O_2$	*m*-Diethoxybenzene	235	192.5	53	218
3733	$C_{10}H_{15}N$	Diethylaniline	217.05	183.4	33	231
3734	$C_{10}H_{16}$	Camphene	159.5	152.5	20	208
3735	$C_{10}H_{16}$	*d*-Limonene	177.8	163.5	26	217
3736	$C_{10}H_{16}$	Nopinene	163.8	155.0	19	206
3737	$C_{10}H_{16}$	α-Pinene	155.8	149.5	18.5	220
3738	$C_{10}H_{16}$	α-Terpinene	173.4	161.0	23.5	247
3739	$C_{10}H_{16}$	γ-Terpinene	183	166.5	26	255
3740	$C_{10}H_{16}$	Terpinolene	184.6	167.4	28.5	247
3741	$C_{10}H_{16}$	Thymene	179.7	164.5	27.5	253
3742	$C_{10}H_{16}O$	Camphor	209.1	186.15	40	232
3743	$C_{10}H_{16}O$	Pulegone	223.8	191.2	58	232
3744	$C_{10}H_{18}$	*m*-Menthene-8	170.8	159.5	~21	255
3745	$C_{10}H_{18}O$	Borneol	215.0	189.25	54.2	229
3746	$C_{10}H_{18}O$	Cineol	176.4	164.75	~15	208
3747	$C_{10}H_{18}O$	Citronellal	207.8	~188.5	~53	254
3748	$C_{10}H_{18}O$	Geraniol	229.6	194.65	67.5	229
3749	$C_{10}H_{18}O$	Linaloöl	198.6	182.2	40	229
3750	$C_{10}H_{18}O$	Menthone	209.5	<190.0	<62	232
3751	$C_{10}H_{18}O$	α-Terpineol	218.85	189.55	56	229
3752	$C_{10}H_{18}O$	β-Terpineol	210.5	188.4	50	207
3753	$C_{10}H_{18}O_4$	Propyl succinate	250.5	Nonazeotrope		255
3754	$C_{10}H_{20}O$	Citronellol	224.4	193.5	63	229
3755	$C_{10}H_{20}O$	Menthol	216.3	188.55	51.5	229
3756	$C_{10}H_{20}O_2$	Ethyl caprylate	208.35	182.5	41	255
3757	$C_{10}H_{20}O_2$	Isoamyl isovalerate	192.7	114.85	27.2	221
3758	$C_{10}H_{20}O_2$	Methyl pelargonate	213.8	186.0	45	247
3759	$C_{10}H_{22}$	Decane	173.3	161.0	23	247
3760	$C_{10}H_{22}$	2,7-Dimethyloctane	160.1	<153.0	<21	255
3761	$C_{10}H_{22}O$	*n*-Decyl alcohol	232.8	193.0	67	225
3762	$C_{10}H_{22}O$	Amyl ether	187.5	168.8	26	236
3763	$C_{10}H_{22}O$	Isoamyl ether	172.6	162.8	19	253
3764	$C_{10}H_{22}O_3$	Isoamyl carbonate	232.2	188.45	49	246

No.	B-Component Formula	Name	B.P., ° C.	Azeotropic Data B.P., ° C.	Wt. % A	Ref.
A =	$C_2H_6O_2$	**Glycol** (*continued*)	**197.4**			
3765	$C_{11}H_{10}$	1-Methylnaphthalene	245.1	190.25	60	254
3766	$C_{11}H_{10}$	2-Methylnaphthalene	241.15	189.1	57.2	207
3767	$C_{11}H_{12}O_2$	Ethyl cinnamate	272.0	197.0	72	247
3768	$C_{11}H_{14}O_2$	1-Allyl 3,4-dimethoxybenzene	255.2	195.1	68.5	254
3769	$C_{11}H_{14}O_2$	Butyl benzoate	251.2	193.2	68	215
3770	$C_{11}H_{14}O_2$	1,2-Dimethoxy-4-propenylbenzene	270.5	196.5	80	225
3771	$C_{11}H_{14}O_2$	Isobutyl benzoate	242.15	192.0	63	254
3772	$C_{11}H_{16}O$	Methyl thymyl ether	216.5	183.0	40	255
3773	$C_{11}H_{20}O$	Methyl isobornyl ether	192.2	191	<25	243
3774	$C_{11}H_{20}O$	Methyl terpineol ether	216.2	184.5	40	218
3775	$C_{11}H_{22}O_2$	Ethyl pelargonate	227	190.8	....	255
3776	$C_{11}H_{22}O_3$	Isoamyl carbonate	232.2	188.45	46	248
3777	$C_{12}H_{10}$	Acenaphthene	277.9	194.65	74.2	221
3778	$C_{12}H_{10}$	Biphenyl	256.1	192.25	66.5	248
3779	$C_{12}H_{10}O$	Phenyl ether	259.3	193.05	60	222
3780	$C_{12}H_{16}O_2$	Isoamyl benzoate	262.05	193.95	66.2	254
3781	$C_{12}H_{18}$	1,3,5-Triethylbenzene	215.4	183	49	253
3782	$C_{12}H_{20}O_2$	Bornyl acetate	227.6	190.0	53	216
3783	$C_{12}H_{22}O$	Bornyl ethyl ether	204.9	177.0	34	247
3784	$C_{12}H_{22}O$	Ethyl isobornyl ether	203.8	176.5	33	236
3785	$C_{12}H_{26}$	Dodecane, 748 mm.	216	179	....	177
		200 mm.	....	142	....	177
		150 mm.	....	135	....	177
		100 mm.	....	125	....	177
		50 mm.	....	110	....	177
3786	$C_{13}H_{10}$	Fluorene	296.4	196.0	82	244
3787	$C_{13}H_{10}O_2$	Phenyl benzoate	315	Nonazeotrope		255
3788	$C_{13}H_{12}$	Diphenylmethane	265.6	193.3	68.5	254
3789	$C_{13}H_{12}O$	Benzyl phenyl ether	286.5	195.5	87	247
3790	$C_{13}H_{28}$	Tridecane	234.0	188.0	55	206
3791	$C_{14}H_{12}$	Stilbene	306.4	196.8	87	244
3792	$C_{14}H_{12}O_2$	Benzyl benzoate	324	Nonazeotrope		255
3793	$C_{14}H_{14}$	1,2-Diphenylethane	284	195.2	77	217
3794	$C_{14}H_{14}O$	Benzyl ether	297	<196.5	<96	255
3795	$C_{14}H_{30}$	Tetradecane, 748 mm.	252.5	187.5	....	177
		200 mm.	....	150.5	....	177
		133 mm.	....	142.5	....	177
		118 mm.	....	118	....	177
A =	C_2H_6S	**Ethanethiol**	**35.8**			
3796	C_2H_6S	Methyl sulfide	37.4	<34.8	<62	255
3797	C_3H_6O	Acetone	56.25	Nonazeotrope		243
3798	C_3H_7Cl	2-Chloropropane	36.25	36.15	~45	243
3799	$C_3H_7NO_2$	Propyl nitrite	47.75	Nonazeotrope		246
3800	$C_3H_8O_2$	Methylal	42.3	34.5	>80	246
3801	$C_4H_{10}O$	Ethyl ether	34.6	34.0	35	246
3802	C_5H_8	Isoprene	34.1	Reacts		243
3803	C_5H_{10}	Cyclopentane	49.263	34.95	89	91
3804	C_5H_{10}	2-Methyl-2-butene	37.15	32.95	~60	243
3805	C_5H_{10}	3-Methyl-1-butene	20.6	Nonazeotrope		255
3806	C_5H_{12}	2-Methylbutane	27.854	25.72	29	91
3807	C_5H_{12}	2-Methylbutane	27.95	Nonazeotrope		243
3808	C_5H_{12}	Pentane	36.074	30.46	51	91, 243*
3809	C_6H_{14}	2,2-Dimethylbutane	49.743	34.41	83	91
A =	C_2H_6S	**Methyl Sulfide**	**37.3**			
3810	C_3H_6O	Acetone	56.25	Nonazeotrope		243
3811	C_3H_7Cl	1-Chloropropane	46.6	Nonazeotrope		243
3812	C_3H_7Cl	2-Chloropropane	36.25	36	....	243
3813	$C_3H_7NO_2$	Isopropyl nitrite	40.1	<36.6	>19	246
3814	$C_3H_7NO_2$	Propyl nitrite	47.75	Nonazeotrope		230
3815	C_3H_8O	Isopropyl alcohol	82.4	Nonazeotrope		246
3816	$C_3H_8O_2$	Methylal	42.25	35.7	....	235
3817	C_4H_8O	2-Butanone	79.6	Nonazeotrope		255
3818	C_4H_9ClO	Chloroethyl ethyl ether	98.5	Nonazeotrope		246
3819	$C_4H_{10}O$	*tert*-Butyl alcohol	82.45	Nonazeotrope		246
3820	$C_4H_{10}O$	Ethyl ether	34.6	34.0	20	246

No.	Formula	B-Component Name	B.P., ° C.	Azeotropic Data B.P., ° C.	Wt. % A	Ref.
A =	**C_2H_6S**	**Methyl Sulfide** (*continued*)	**37.3**			
3821	$C_4H_{10}O$	Methyl propyl ether	38.95	<37.0	>65	*255*
3822	C_5H_8	Isoprene	34.3	32.5	35	*246*
3823	C_5H_{10}	3-Methyl-1-butene	20.6	Nonazeotrope		*246*
3824	C_5H_{10}	2-Methyl-2-butene	37.15	34.5	52	*235*
3825	C_5H_{12}	2-Methylbutane	27	27.3	15	*211*
3826	C_5H_{12}	Pentane	36.15	~33.5	~45	*211*
3827	C_6H_{14}	2,3-Dimethylbutane	58.0	Nonazeotrope		*246*
A =	**$C_2H_6SO_4$**	**Methyl Sulfate**	**189.1**			
3828	$C_5H_{10}O_2$	Isovaleric acid	176.5	<175.0	<40	*255*
3829	$C_5H_{10}O_2$	Valeric acid	186.35	<182	<60	*255*
3830	$C_6H_4Cl_2$	*p*-Dichlorobenzene	174.6	Nonazeotrope		*227*
3831	C_6H_5Br	Bromobenzene	156.1	Nonazeotrope		*227*
3832	C_6H_5I	Iodobenzene	188.45	<184	>50	*227*
3833	C_6H_6O	Phenol	181.5	Reacts		*243*
3834	$C_6H_{10}O_4$	Ethyl oxalate	185	Nonazeotrope		*243*
3835	$C_6H_{13}Br$	1-Bromohexane	156.5	Nonazeotrope		*255*
3836	C_7H_7Br	*m*-Bromotoluene	184.3	<181.5	<27	*255*
3837	C_7H_7Br	*o*-Bromotoluene	181.5	<179.5	<28	*255*
3838	C_7H_7Br	*p*-Bromotoluene	185	181.5	....	*243*
3839	C_7H_7Cl	α-Chlorotoluene	179.35	Nonazeotrope		*243*
3840	C_7H_7Cl	*p*-Chlorotoluene	162.4	Nonazeotrope		*227*
3841	C_7H_8O	*m*-Cresol	202.2	Reacts		*222*
3842	$C_8H_{10}O$	Phenetole	170.45	Nonazeotrope		*237*
3843	$C_9H_{12}O$	Benzyl ethyl ether	185.0	<182.8	<47	*237*
3844	$C_9H_{18}O_2$	Ethyl enanthate	188.7	185.5	38	*255*
3845	$C_9H_{18}O_2$	Isoamyl butyrate	181.05	179.5	18	*255*
3846	$C_{10}H_{16}$	*d*-Limonene	177.8	~173	....	*243*
3847	$C_{10}H_{20}O_2$	Isoamyl isovalerate	192.7	185.8	63	*229*
3848	$C_{11}H_{20}O$	Isobornyl methyl ether	192.2	<185.5	<70	*237*
A =	**C_2H_7N**	**Dimethylamine**	**6.8**			
3849	C_3H_9N	Trimethylamine	3.5	3	26	*331*
		107 lb./sq. inch gage	....	73	72	*331*
		370 lb./sq. inch gage	....	Nonazeotrope		*11**, *12**, *331*
3850	C_4H_{10}	Butane	0.6	<0.2	<12	*255*
3851	C_5H_{10}	3-Methyl-1-butene	20.6	Nonazeotrope		*255*
A =	**C_2H_7N**	**Ethylamine**	**16.55**			
3852	C_3H_6O	Acetone	56.15	Nonazeotrope		*255*
3853	C_3H_6O	Propylene oxide	34.1	Nonazeotrope		*255*
3854	C_4H_4O	Furan	31.7	Nonazeotrope		*231*
3855	$C_4H_{10}O$	Ethyl ether	34.6	Nonazeotrope		*231*
3856	$C_4H_{10}O$	Methyl propyl ether	38.95	Nonazeotrope		*231*
3857	C_5H_{10}	3-Methyl-1-butene	20.6	<15.4	>54	*231*
3858	C_5H_{12}	2-Methylbutane	27.95	Nonazeotrope		*231*
A =	**C_2H_7NO**	**2-Aminoethanol**	**170.8**			
3859	C_3H_7NO	Propionamide	222.2	Nonazeotrope		*207*
3860	$C_3H_7NO_2$	Ethyl carbamate	185.25	Reacts		*207*
3861	$C_4H_8Cl_2O$	Bis(2-chloroethyl) ether	178.65	Reacts		*207*
3862	$C_4H_{10}O_2$	2-Ethoxyethanol	135.3	Nonazeotrope		*231*
3863	C_5H_8O	Cyclopentanone	130.65	Nonazeotrope		*231*
3864	$C_5H_{12}O_2$	2-Propoxyethanol	151.35	Nonazeotrope		*231*
3865	$C_5H_{12}O_3$	2-(2-Methoxyethoxy)ethanol	192.95	Nonazeotrope		*231*
3866	$C_6H_4Cl_2$	*o*-Dichlorobenzene	179.5	157.3	40	*231*
3867	$C_6H_4Cl_2$	*p*-Dichlorobenzene	174.4	154.6	35	*250*
3868	C_6H_5Br	Bromobenzene	156.1	145.0	22	*231*
3869	C_6H_5Cl	Chlorobenzene	131.75	128.55	13.5	*231*
			132	124	....	*373*
3870	C_6H_5I	Iodotoluene	188.45	161.0	45	*231*
3871	$C_6H_5NO_2$	Nitrobenzene	210.75	Nonazeotrope		*255*
3872	C_6H_6	Benzene	80.15	Nonazeotrope		*231*
3873	C_6H_6O	Phenol	182.2	Nonazeotrope		*231*
3874	C_6H_7N	Aniline	184.35	170.3	90	*231*
3875	$C_6H_{10}O$	Cyclohexanone	155.7	Nonazeotrope		*231*
3876	$C_6H_{10}S$	Allyl sulfide	139	137.2	8	*235*

No.	Formula	B-Component Name	B.P., ° C.	Azeotropic Data B.P., ° C.	Wt. % A	Ref.
A =	C_2H_7NO	**2-Aminoethanol** (*continued*)	**170.8**			
3877	$C_6H_{11}NO_2$	Nitrocyclobexane	205.3	Nonazeotrope		*255*
3878	C_6H_{12}	Cyclohexane	80.75	Nonazeotrope		*231*
3879	C_6H_{12}	Methylcyclopentane	72.0	Nonazeotrope		*255*
3880	C_6H_{14}	Hexane	68.8	Nonazeotrope		*231*
3881	$C_6H_{14}O_2$	2-Butoxyethanol	171.15	166.95	43	*231*
3882	$C_6H_{14}S$	Propyl sulfide	141.5	<139.7	<13	*246*
3883	C_7H_7Br	*m*-Bromotoluene	184.3	159.3	44	*231*
3884	C_7H_7Br	*o*-Bromotoluene	181.5	157.8	42	*231*
3885	C_7H_7Cl	*o*-Chlorotoluene	159.2	146.5	26	*231*
3886	C_7H_7Cl	*p*-Chlorotoluene	162.4	148.2	28	*231*
3887	$C_7H_7NO_2$	*o*-Nitrotoluene	221.75	Nonazeotrope		*255*
3888	C_7H_8O	Anisole	153.85	145.75	25.5	*231*
3889	C_7H_8O	*o*-Cresol	191.1	Nonazeotrope		*231*
3890	C_7H_8O	*p*-Cresol	201.7	Nonazeotrope		*231*
3891	C_7H_9N	Methylaniline	196.25	167.5	70	*231*
3892	C_7H_9N	*o*-Toluidine	200.35	Nonazeotrope		*231*
3893	C_7H_{14}	Methylcyclohexane	101.15	<100.5	<10	*231*
3894	$C_7H_{14}O$	4-Heptanone	143.55	Nonazeotrope		*231*
3895	C_7H_{16}	Heptane	98.4	<98.0	....	*255*
3896	C_8H_8O	Acetophenone	202.0	Nonazeotrope		*231*
3897	C_8H_{10}	Ethylbenzene	136.15	131.0	15	*231*
3898	C_8H_{10}	*m*-Xylene	139.2	133.0	18	*231*
3899	C_8H_{10}	*o*-Xylene	144.3	<138.0	20	*231*
3900	$C_8H_{10}O$	Benzyl methyl ether	167.8	150.5	28	*231*
3901	$C_8H_{10}O$	*p*-Methylanisole	177.05	154.5	37	*231*
3902	$C_8H_{10}O$	Phenetole	170.45	151.0	30	*231*
3903	$C_8H_{11}N$	Dimethylaniline	194.15	163.5	55	*231*
3904	$C_8H_{11}N$	2,4-Xylidine	214.0	Nonazeotrope		*231*
3905	$C_8H_{11}N$	Ethylaniline	206.05	<170.0	....	*255*
3606	C_8H_{18}	*n*-Octane	125.75	<123.0	<16	*231*
3907	$C_8H_{18}O$	Butyl ether	142.4	136.5	16	*231*
3908	$C_8H_{18}O$	Isobutyl ether	122.3	Nonazeotrope		*231*
3909	$C_8H_{18}S$	Butyl sulfide	185.0	<164.5	<53	*246*
3910	$C_8H_{18}S$	Isobutyl sulfide	172	156.0	33	*235*
3911	C_9H_8	Indene	187.4	Min. b.p.		*117*
3912	C_9H_{12}	Cumene	152.8	142.5	....	*255*
3913	C_9H_{12}	Mesitylene	164.6	148.5	30	*231*
3914	C_9H_{12}	Propylbenzene	159.3	<147.0	<30	*231*
3915	$C_9H_{12}O$	Benzyl ethyl ether	185.0	159.8	45	*231*
3916	$C_9H_{12}O$	Phenyl propyl ether	190.5	162.5	55	*231*
3917	$C_9H_{13}N$	*N,N*-Dimethyl-*o*-toluidine	185.3	161.0	50	*231*
3918	$C_9H_{13}N$	*N,N*-Dimethyl-*p*-toluidine	210.2	<169.0	>75	*231*
3919	$C_{10}H_8$	Naphthalene	218.0	Nonazeotrope		*231*
3920	$C_{10}H_{14}$	Butylbenzene	183.1	<158.5	<48	*231*
3921	$C_{10}H_{14}$	Cymene	176.7	154.7	37	*231*
3922	$C_{10}H_{15}N$	Diethylaniline	217.05	<169.0	>82	*231*
3923	$C_{10}H_{16}$	Camphene	159.6	144.0	28	*231*
3924	$C_{10}H_{16}$	α-Pinene	155.8	142.0	25	*231*
3925	$C_{10}H_{16}$	α-Terpinene	173.4	<154.0	<36	*231*
3926	$C_{10}H_{16}$	Dipentene	177.7	153.0	37	*231*
3927	$C_{10}H_{18}O$	Cineol	176.35	153.4	36	*231*
3928	$C_{10}H_{22}O$	Amyl ether	187.5	<160.0	<50	*231*
3929	$C_{10}H_{22}$	Isoamyl ether	173.2	149.5	30.5	*231*
3930	$C_{11}H_{10}$	1-Methylnaphthalene	244.6	Nonazeotrope		*231*
3931	$C_{11}H_{10}O$	2-Methylnaphthalene	241.15	Nonazeotrope		*207*
3932	$C_{11}H_{20}O$	Isobornyl methyl ether	192.4	<165.0	<62	*231*
3933	$C_{12}H_{10}$	Acenaphthene	277.9	Nonazeotrope		*255*
3934	$C_{13}H_{12}$	Diphenylmethane	265.4	Nonazeotrope		*231*
A =	$C_2H_8N_2$	**Ethylenediamine**	**116.5**			
3935	$C_3H_8O_2$	2-Methoxyethanol	124.5	130.0	31–32	*62*
3936	C_8H_{10}	Ethylbenzene	136	Min. b.p.		*140*
3937	C_8H_{10}	*m*-Xylene	139	Min. b.p.		*140*
3938	C_8H_{10}	*o*-Xylene	143.6	Min. b.p.		*140*
3939	C_8H_{10}	*p*-Xylene	138.4	Min. b.p.		*140*
3940	C_nH_{2n+2}	Paraffins	....	Min. b.p.		*140*

No.	Formula	B-Component Name	B.P., ° C.	Azeotropic Data B.P., ° C.	Wt. % A	Ref.
A =	**$C_3H_3Cl_3O$**	**Methyl Trichloroacetate**	**152.8**			
3942	C_3H_8O	Propyl alcohol	97.2	Nonazeotrope		*255*
3943	$C_4H_8O_2$	Butyric acid	164.0	Nonazeotrope		*255*
3944	$C_4H_8O_2$	Isobutyric acid	154.6	151.0	....	*242*
3945	$C_5H_{10}O_3$	Ethyl lactate	155	Azeotrope doubtful		*243*
3946	$C_6H_{12}O$	Cyclohexanol	160.8	<151.0	>72	*255*
3947	C_7H_8O	Anisole	153.85	149	>60	*243*
3948	$C_7H_{14}O_2$	Propyl butyrate	143	Azeotrope doubtful		*243*
A =	**C_3H_3N**	**Acrylonitrile**	**77.3**			
3949	C_3H_8O	Isopropyl alcohol	82.55	71.7	56	*93*
3950	C_3H_9ClSi	Chlorotrimethylsilane	57.5	57	7	*340, 342**
3951	C_6H_6	Benzene	80.2	73.3	47	*93*
A =	**C_3H_4**	**Propyne**	**79.4/322.5 lb./sq. inch abs.**			
3952	C_3H_8	Propane, 322.5 lb./sq. inch abs.	62.1	60.1	14.3	*414*
A =	**$C_3H_4Br_2$**	***cis*-1,2-Dibromopropene**	**135.2**			
3953	C_3H_8O	Propyl alcohol	97.2	97.05	3.45	*243*
A =	**$C_3H_4Br_2$**	***trans*-1,2-Dibromopropene**	**125.95**			
3954	C_3H_8O	Propyl alcohol	97.2	95.75	41.95	*243*
A =	**$C_3H_4Cl_2$**	**1,3-Dichloropropene**				
3955	C_3H_5Cl	3-Chloropropene	45.7	Nonazeotrope, V-l.		*422*
A =	**$C_3H_4Cl_4$**	**1,1,2,2-Tetrachloropropane**	**153**			
3956	$C_6H_{10}O$	Cyclohexanone	156	Max. b.p.		*111*
3957	C_7H_8O	Anisole	155	Max. b.p.		*111*
3958	$C_7H_{14}O$	Heptaldehyde	155	Max. b.p.		*111*
3959	$C_7H_{14}O$	2-Heptanone	150	Max. b.p.		*111*
A =	**$C_3H_4Cl_4$**	**1,1,2,3-Tetrachloropropane**	**180**			
3960	C_7H_6O	Benzaldehyde	179	Max. b.p.		*111*
3961	$C_9H_{18}O$	2,6-Dimethyl-4-heptanone	165	Max. b.p.		*111*
A =	**C_3H_4O**	**Acrolein**	**52.45**			
3962	C_3H_6O	Propionaldehyde	48.7	Nonazeotrope		*255*
3963	C_4H_8O	Isobutyraldehyde	63.5	Nonazeotrope		*255*
3964	C_5H_{12}	Pentane	36.15	Nonazeotrope		*255*
3965	C_6H_{14}	Hexane	68.8	Nonazeotrope		*255*
A =	**C_3H_4O**	**2-Propyn-1-ol**				
3966	C_6H_6	Benzene	80.1	V-l.		*364*
A =	**$C_3H_4O_2$**	**Acrylic Acid**	**140.5**			
3967	$C_3H_6O_2$	Propionic acid	140.7	140.3?	....	*243*
3968	C_nH_m	Hydrocarbon	138–140	133	68.2	*324*
A =	**$C_3H_4O_3$**	**Pyruvic Acid**	**166.8**			
3969	$C_3H_6O_2$	Propionic acid	141.3	Nonazeotrope		*232*
3970	$C_4H_8O_2$	Butyric acid	164.0	162.4	34	*250*
3971	$C_5H_{10}O_3$	2-Methoxy ethyl acetate	144.6	Nonazeotrope		*232*
3972	C_6H_5Br	Bromobenzene	156.1	147.0	34	*207*
3973	C_6H_5Cl	Chlorobenzene	131.75	128.6	15	*232*
3974	C_6H_6	Benzene	80.15	Nonazeotrope		*232*
3975	$C_6H_{12}O_3$	2-Ethoxyethyl acetate	156.8	Nonazeotrope		*232*
3976	C_7H_7Cl	*o*-Chlorotoluene	159.2	149.5	37	*232*
3977	C_7H_7Cl	*p*-Chlorotoluene	162.4	151.5	40	*232*
3978	C_7H_8	Toluene	110.75	110.05	7.5	*232*
3979	C_7H_8O	Anisole	153.85	148.5	28	*232*
3980	C_8H_{10}	Ethylbenzene	136.15	130.5	22	*232*
3981	C_8H_{10}	*m*-Xylene	139.2	132.85	24	*232*
3982	C_8H_{10}	*o*-Xylene	144.3	137.0	28	*232*
3983	$C_8H_{18}O$	Butyl ether	142.4	138.0	15	*232*
3984	C_9H_{12}	Cumene	152.8	143.0	33	*232*
3985	C_9H_{12}	Mesitylene	164.6	151.2	40	*232*
3986	C_9H_{12}	Propylbenzene	159.3	147.6	37	*232*
A =	**$C_3H_4N_2$**	**Pyrazole**	**187.5**			
3987	$C_4H_8Cl_2O$	Bis(2-chloroethyl) ether	178.65	Nonazeotrope		*255*
3988	C_6H_6O	Phenol	182.2	Nonazeotrope		*255*

	B-Component			Azeotropic Data		
No.	Formula	Name	B.P., ° C.	B.P., ° C.	Wt. % A	Ref.
A =	**$C_3H_4N_2$**	**Pyrazole (*continued*)**	**187.5**			
3989	C_7H_8O	*o*-Cresol	191.1	>194.8	>26	*255*
3990	$C_8H_{10}O$	*p*-Methylanisole	177.05	Nonazeotrope		*255*
3991	$C_8H_{18}S$	Butyl sulfide	185.0	<181.2	>28	*255*
3992	$C_9H_{12}O$	Benzyl ethyl ether	185.0	<184.2	>20	*255*
3993	$C_{10}H_{22}O$	Isoamyl ether	173.2	Nonazeotrope		*255*
A =	**C_3H_5Br**	**3-Bromopropene**	**70.5**			
3994	C_3H_6O	Acetone	56.15	56.05	8	*232*
3995	C_3H_6O	Allyl alcohol	96.85	<69.2	92	*255*
3996	$C_3H_6O_2$	Ethyl formate	54.15	Nonazeotrope		*227*
3997	$C_3H_6O_2$	Methyl acetate	57.0	Nonazeotrope		*227*
3998	C_3H_7Br	1-Bromopropane	71.0	Nonazeotrope		*255*
3999	C_3H_8O	Isopropyl alcohol	82.45	66.5	80	*253*
4000	C_3H_8O	Propyl alcohol	97.2	69.0	90	*253*
4001	$C_3H_9BO_3$	Methyl borate	68.7	67.5	....	*222*
4002	C_4H_8O	2-Butanone	79.6	Nonazeotrope		*237*
4003	$C_4H_8O_2$	Ethyl acetate	77.15	Nonazeotrope		*227*
4004	$C_4H_8O_2$	Propyl formate	80.85	Nonazeotrope		*255*
4005	C_4H_9Cl	1-Chloro-2-methylpropane	68.85	68.75	15	*229*
4006	$C_4H_9NO_2$	Isobutyl nitrite	67.1	66.9	12	*230*
4007	$C_4H_{10}O$	Butyl alcohol	117.8	Nonazeotrope		*255*
4008	$C_4H_{10}O$	*tert*-Butyl alcohol	82.45	<68.5	<90	*255*
4009	$C_4H_{10}O$	Isobutyl alcohol	108.0	Nonazeotrope		*255*
4010	$C_4H_{10}O_2$	Acetaldehyde dimethyl acetal	64.3	Nonazeotrope		*239*
4011	$C_4H_{10}O_2$	Ethoxymethoxymethane	65.9	Nonazeotrope		*239*
4012	C_6H_6	Benzene	80.15	Nonazeotrope		*255*
4013	C_6H_{14}	Hexane	68.8	66.9	45	*242*
A =	**C_3H_5BrO**	**Epibromohydrin**	**138.5**			
4014	$C_3H_6O_2$	Propionic acid	141.3	<138.0	<88	*255*
4015	$C_3H_6O_2$	Propionic acid	141.3	Nonazeotrope		*236*
4016	C_3H_8O	Propyl alcohol	97.2	Nonazeotrope		*255*
4017	$C_4H_8O_2$	Isobutyric acid	154.6	Nonazeotrope		*236*
4018	C_4H_9Br	1-Bromobutane	101.5	Nonazeotrope		*255*
4019	$C_4H_{10}O$	Butyl alcohol	117.8	117.0	20	*236*
4020	$C_4H_{10}O$	Isobutyl alcohol	108.0	Nonazeotrope		*255*
4021	$C_5H_{10}O_3$	2-Methoxyethyl acetate	144.6	<137.5	....	*255*
4022	$C_5H_{11}I$	1-Iodo-3-methylbutane	147.65	<136.0	>75	*255*
4023	$C_5H_{12}O$	Isoamyl alcohol	131.9	129.5	40	*255*
4024	$C_6H_{10}O$	Mesityl oxide	129.45	Nonazeotrope		*232*
A =	**C_3H_5BrO**	**Epibromohydrin**	**138.5**			
4025	$C_6H_{10}S$	Allyl sulfide	139.35	133.3	60	*246*
4026	$C_7H_{14}O$	4-Heptanone	143.55	Nonazeotrope		*255*
4027	C_8H_{10}	Ethylbenzene	136.15	133.3	40	*255*
4028	C_8H_{10}	*m*-Xylene	139.2	134.5	55	*255*
4029	C_9H_{12}	Cumene	152.8	Nonazeotrope		*255*
A =	**$C_3H_5BrO_2$**	**α-Bromopropionic Acid**	**205.8**			
4030	$C_6H_4Br_2$	*o*-Dibromobenzene	181.5	179.0	12	*255*
4031	$C_6H_4Cl_2$	*p*-Dichlorobenzene	174.4	<173.5	>7	*255*
4032	C_6H_5I	Iodobenzene	188.45	<184.8	....	*255*
4033	$C_6H_5NO_2$	Nitrobenzene	210.75	203.3	60	*234*
4034	C_7H_7Br	α-Bromotoluene	198.5	~195	....	*243*
4035	$C_7H_8O_2$	Guaiacol	205.05	<204.2	>45	*255*
4036	$C_8H_8O_2$	Methyl benzoate	199.4	Nonazeotrope		*255*
4037	C_9H_{12}	Mesitylene	164.6	Nonazeotrope		*255*
4038	$C_{10}H_8$	Naphthalene	218.0	<202.5	>73	*242*
4039	$C_{10}H_{14}$	Cymene	176.7	<176.4	>4	*255*
4040	$C_{11}H_{10}$	2-Methylnaphthalene	241.15	Nonazeotrope		*255*
A =	**$C_3H_5Br_3$**	**1,2,3-Tribromopropane**	**220**			
4041	$C_6H_5NO_2$	Nitrobenzene	210.85	Nonazeotrope		*243*
4042	C_6H_6O	Phenol	182.2	Nonazeotrope		*255*
4043	$C_7H_6O_2$	Benzoic acid	250.8	<220.5	>94	*255*
4044	$C_7H_7NO_2$	*o*-Nitrotoluene	~222.3	Nonazeotrope		*243*
4045	C_7H_8O	*p*-Cresol	201.8	Nonazeotrope		*243*
4046	$C_7H_{14}O_2$	Enanthic acid	222	<218	>62	*255*

No.	Formula	B-Component Name	B.P., ° C.	Azeotropic Data B.P., ° C.	Wt. % A	Ref.
A =	$C_3H_5Br_3$	**1,2,3-Tribromopropane** (*continued*)	**220**			
4047	$C_8H_{14}O_4$	Ethyl succinate	216.5	Azeotrope doubtful		*243*
4048	$C_9H_{10}O$	Propiophenone	217.7	223	~70	*253*
4049	$C_9H_{10}O_2$	Benzyl acetate	215.0	Nonazeotrope		*255*
4050	$C_9H_{10}O_2$	Ethyl benzoate	213	Nonazeotrope		*243*
4051	$C_9H_{10}O_3$	Ethyl salicylate	234.0	Nonazeotrope		*228*
4052	$C_9H_{18}O_2$	Pelargonic acid	254.0	Nonazeotrope		*255*
4053	$C_{10}H_8$	Naphthalene	218.05	Nonazeotrope		*216*
4054	$C_{10}H_{12}O_2$	Propyl benzoate	230.85	Nonazeotrope		*227*
4055	$C_{10}H_{14}O$	Thymol	232.9	Nonazeotrope		*218*
4056	$C_{10}H_{15}N$	Diethylaniline	216.5	<215	>15	*243*
4057	$C_{10}H_{16}O$	Pulegone	~224	226.5	~55	*253*
4058	$C_{10}H_{18}O$	Borneol	211.8	Nonazeotrope		*243*
4059	$C_{11}H_{20}O$	Terpineol methyl ether	216	Nonazeotrope		*243*
4060	$C_{11}H_{22}O_3$	Isoamyl carbonate	232.2	Nonazeotrope		*227*
A =	C_3H_5Cl	**2-Chloropropene**	**22.65**			
4061	C_3H_5Cl	3-Chloropropene	45.7	Nonazeotrope, V-l.		*422*
4062	$C_3H_7NO_2$	Isopropyl nitrite	40.1	Nonazeotrope		*230*
4063	C_4H_4O	Furan	31.7	Nonazeotrope		*239*
4064	$C_4H_{10}O$	Ethyl ether	34.6	Nonazeotrope		*239*
4065	C_5H_{10}	3-Methyl-1-butene	20.6	<18.5	>45	*242*
4066	C_5H_{12}	2-Methylbutane	27.95	19.0	64	*242*
4067	C_5H_{12}	Pentane	36.15	<22.4	>72	*255*
A =	C_3H_5Cl	**3-Chloropropene**	**45.15**			
4068	C_3H_6O	Acetone	56.15	44.6	90	*232*
4069	$C_3H_6O_2$	Ethyl formate	54.15	45.0	90.0	*227*
4070	$C_3H_6O_2$	Methyl acetate	56.95	Nonazeotrope		*255*
4071	C_3H_7Cl	1-Chloropropane	46.6	Nonazeotrope		*229*
4072	$C_3H_7NO_2$	Isopropyl nitrite	40.1	Nonazeotrope		*230*
4073	$C_3H_7NO_2$	Propyl nitrite	47.75	44.8	80	*230*
4074	C_3H_8O	Isopropyl alcohol	82.4	45.1	98	*255*
4075	$C_3H_8O_2$	Methylal	42.3	41.4	20	*239*
4076	$C_4H_{10}O$	*tert*-Butyl alcohol	82.45	Nonazeotrope		*255*
4077	$C_4H_{10}O$	Ethyl ether	34.6	Nonazeotrope		*239*
4078	C_5H_{10}	Cyclopentane	49.3	44.3	63	*255*
4079	C_5H_{12}	Pentane	36.15	<35.5	>28	*255*
4080	C_6H_{14}	2,3-Dimethylbutane	58.0	Nonazeotrope		*255*
A =	C_3H_5ClO	**1-Chloro-2-propanone**	**119.7**			
4081	C_3H_8O	Isopropyl alcohol	82.4	Nonazeotrope		*232*
4082	$C_4H_{10}O$	Butyl alcohol	117.8	112.5	57	*232*
4083	$C_4H_{10}O$	*sec*-Butyl alcohol	99.5	Nonazeotrope		*232*
4084	$C_4H_{10}O$	Isobutyl alcohol	108.0	106.0	37	*232*
4085	$C_5H_{10}O$	Cyclopentanol	140.85	Nonazeotrope		*232*
4086	$C_5H_{10}O_2$	Butyl formate	106.7	Nonazeotrope		*228*
4087	$C_5H_{10}O_2$	Methyl butyrate	102.65	Nonazeotrope		*232*
4088	$C_5H_{10}O_2$	Propyl acetate	101.6	Nonazeotrope		*232*
4089	$C_5H_{12}O$	Amyl alcohol	138.2	Nonazeotrope		*232*
4090	$C_5H_{12}O$	*tert*-Amyl alcohol	102.35	Nonazeotrope		*232*
4091	$C_5H_{12}O$	Isoamyl alcohol	131.9	<119.0	>83	*232*
4092	$C_5H_{12}O$	2-Pentanol	119.8	<116.0	<68	*232*
4093	$C_6H_{10}S$	Allyl sulfide	139.35	Nonazeotrope		*246*
4094	$C_6H_{12}O_2$	Ethyl butyrate	121.5	117.5	53	*232*
4095	$C_6H_{12}O_2$	Ethyl isobutyrate	110.1	Nonazeotrope		*232*
4096	$C_6H_{12}O_2$	Isobutyl acetate	117.4	116.9	30	*232*
4097	$C_6H_{14}S$	Propyl sulfide	141.5	Nonazeotrope		*246*
4098	$C_6H_{14}S$	Isopropyl sulfide	120.5	<116.0	....	*246*
4099	$C_6H_{15}BO_3$	Ethyl borate	118.6	109.4	36	*232*
4100	C_7H_8	Toluene	110.75	109.2	28.5	*232*
4102	C_7H_{14}	Methylcyclohexane	101.15	<100.5	....	*232*
4103	$C_7H_{14}O_2$	Ethyl isovalerate	134.7	Nonazeotrope		*232*
4104	$C_7H_{14}O_2$	Isoamyl acetate	142.1	Nonazeotrope		*232*
4105	$C_7H_{14}O_2$	Isopropyl isobutyrate	120.8	117.2	50	*232*
4106	$C_7H_{14}O_2$	Propyl butyrate	143.7	Nonazeotrope		*232*
4107	$C_7H_{14}O_2$	Propyl isobutyrate	134.0	Nonazeotrope		*232*
4108	C_8H_{10}	Ethylbenzene	136.15	Nonazeotrope		*232*

	B-Component			Azeotropic Data		
No.	Formula	Name	B.P., ° C.	B.P., ° C.	Wt. % A	Ref.
A =	**C_3H_5ClO**	**1-Chloro-2-propanone** (*continued*)	**119.7**			
4109	C_8H_{16}	*m*-Dimethylcyclohexane	120.7	<114.0	....	*232*
4110	C_8H_{18}	2,5-Dimethylhexane	109.3	<107.5	<35	*232*
4111	C_8H_{18}	Octane	125.75	<115.5	65	*232*
A =	**C_3H_5ClO**	**Epichlorohydrin**	**116.4**			
4112	$C_3H_6Br_2$	1,2-Dibromopropane	140.5	Nonazeotrope		*236*
4113	C_3H_6O	Allyl alcohol	96.95	95.8	22	*236**, *357*
4114	$C_3H_6O_2$	Propionic acid	141.3	Nonazeotrope		*255*
4115	C_3H_7I	1-Iodopropane	102.4	<100.5	<28	*255*
4116	C_3H_8O	Isopropyl alcohol	82.45	Nonazeotrope		*236*
4117	C_3H_8O	Propyl alcohol	97.2	96.0	23	*243*
4118	C_4H_5N	Pyrrole	130.5	Reacts		*243*
4119	C_4H_8S	Tetrahydrothiophene	118.8	<112.5	<70	*246*
4120	C_4H_9Br	1-Bromobutane	101.6	100.0	....	*228*
4121	C_4H_9Cl	1-Chlorobutane	78.5	Nonazeotrope		*255*
4122	C_4H_9I	1-Iodobutane	130.4	<115	<92	*228*
4123	C_4H_9I	1-Iodo-2-methylpropane	120.8	111.0	~47	*228*
4124	$C_4H_{10}O$	Butyl alcohol	116.9	112.0	57	*236*
4125	$C_4H_{10}O$	*sec*-Butyl alcohol	99.5	98.0	25	*236*
4126	$C_4H_{10}O$	*tert*-Butyl alcohol	82.45	Nonazeotrope		*236*
4127	$C_4H_{10}O$	Isobutyl alcohol	108.0	105.0	39.5	*243*
4128	C_5H_5N	Pyridine	115.5	Reacts		*243*
4129	C_5H_8O	Cyclopentanone	130.65	Nonazeotrope		*255*
4130	$C_5H_{10}O$	3-Pentanone	102.05	Nonazeotrope		*232*
4131	$C_5H_{10}O_2$	Methyl butyrate	102.65	Nonazeotrope		*255*
4132	$C_5H_{10}O_2$	Propyl acetate	101.6	Nonazeotrope		*255*
4133	$C_5H_{10}O_3$	Ethyl carbonate	126.0	Azeotrope doubtful		*243*
4134	$C_5H_{10}O_3$	2-Methoxyethyl acetate	144.6	Nonazeotrope		*255*
4135	$C_5H_{11}Br$	1-Bromo-3-methylbutane	120.65	111.2	63	*236*
4136	$C_5H_{12}O$	Amyl alcohol	138.2	<116.2	<95	*255*
4137	$C_5H_{12}O$	*tert*-Amyl alcohol	102.0	100.7	30	*236*
4138	$C_5H_{12}O$	Isoamyl alcohol	131.8	115.35	81	*243*
4139	$C_5H_{12}O$	3-Methyl-2-butanol	112.9	109.5	48	*236*
4140	$C_5H_{12}O$	2-Pentanol	119.8	113.0	60	*236*
4141	$C_5H_{12}O$	3-Pentanol	116.0	111.5	54	*236*
4142	C_6H_5Cl	Chlorobenzene	131.75	<116.2	....	*255*
4143	C_6H_5Cl	Chlorobenzene	131.8	Azeotrope doubtful		*243*
4144	C_6H_6	Benzene	80.15	Nonazeotrope		*255*
4145	$C_6H_{10}O$	Mesityl oxide	129.45	Nonazeotrope		*232*
4146	C_6H_{12}	Cyclohexane	80.75	Nonazeotrope		*255*
4147	$C_6H_{12}O$	Cyclohexanol	160.65	Nonazeotrope		*236*
4148	$C_6H_{12}O$	3-Hexanone	123.3	Nonazeotrope		*255*
4149	$C_6H_{12}O$	4-Methyl-2-pentanone	116.05	<115.5	>32	*255*
4150	$C_6H_{12}O$	Pinacolone	106.2	Nonazeotrope		*255*
4151	$C_6H_{12}O_2$	Butyl acetate	125.0	Nonazeotrope		*228*
4152	$C_6H_{12}O_2$	Ethyl butyrate	121.5	115.75	75	*236*
4153	$C_6H_{12}O_2$	Ethyl isobutyrate	110.1	109.8	~10	*255*
4154	$C_6H_{12}O_2$	Ethyl isobutyrate	110.1	Azeotrope doubtful		*243*
4155	$C_6H_{12}O_2$	Isoamyl formate	123.6	~116.2	....	*243*
4156	$C_6H_{12}O_2$	Isobutyl acetate	117.2	<115.3	>50	*228*
4157	$C_6H_{12}O_2$	Methyl isovalerate	116.3	115	45	*243*
4158	$C_6H_{12}O_2$	Propyl propionate	123.0	<116.3	>88	*255*
4159	$C_6H_{14}O$	Hexyl alcohol	157.85	Nonazeotrope		*236*
4160	$C_6H_{14}S$	Isopropyl sulfide	120.5	111.5	67	*246*
4161	C_7H_8	Toluene	110.75	108.4	29	*228*
4162	C_7H_{14}	Methylcyclohexane	101.15	<100.8	>5	*255*
4163	$C_7H_{14}O$	2-Methylcyclohexanol	168.5	Nonazeotrope		*255*
4164	C_7H_{16}	Heptane	98.4	<98.1	>4	*255*
4165	C_8H_{10}	Ethylbenzene	136.15	Nonazeotrope		*228*
4166	C_8H_{16}	1,3-Dimethylcyclohexane	120.7	113.6	65	*255*
4167	C_8H_{18}	2,5-Dimethylhexane	109.3	~107.0	25	*228*
4168	C_8H_{18}	Octane	125.8	114.5	~80	*228*
			125.8	<116	>90	*243*
4169	$C_8H_{18}O$	Isobutyl ether	122.2	Nonazeotrope		*228*

No.	Formula	B-Component Name	B.P., ° C.	Azeotropic Data B.P., ° C.	Wt. % A	Ref.
A =	**$C_3H_6ClO_2$**	**Methyl Chloroacetate**	**129.95**			
4170	$C_3H_6Br_2$	1,2-Dibromopropane	140.5	Nonazeotrope		*255*
4171	C_3H_6O	Allyl alcohol	96.85	Nonazeotrope		*255*
4172	$C_3H_6O_2$	Propionic acid	141.3	Nonazeotrope		*207*
4173	C_3H_8O	Isopropyl alcohol	82.45	Nonazeotrope		*253*
4174	C_3H_8O	Propyl alcohol	97.2	Nonazeotrope		*253*
4175	$C_3H_8O_2$	2-Methoxyethanol	124.5	122.5	65	*255*
4176	$C_4H_8O_3$	Methyl lactate	143.8	Nonazeotrope		*255*
4177	C_4H_9I	1-Iodobutane	130.4	125.5	42	*242*
4178	C_4H_9I	1-Iodo-2-methylpropane	120.8	<119.5	<22	*242*
4179	$C_4H_{10}O$	Butyl alcohol	117.5	116.3	26	*253*
4180	$C_4H_{10}O$	*sec*-Butanol	99.5	Nonazeotrope		*255*
4181	$C_4H_{10}O$	Isobutyl alcohol	107.85	107.55	12	*210*
4182	$C_4H_{10}O_2$	2-Ethoxyethanol	135.3	128.6	77	*206*
4183	C_5H_8O	Cyclopentanone	130.65	<129.6	....	*232*
4184	$C_5H_{10}O$	Cyclopentanol	140.85	127.5	77	*247*
4185	$C_5H_{10}O_3$	Ethyl carbonate	125.9	Nonazeotrope		*252*
4186	$C_5H_{10}O_3$	2-Methoxyethyl acetate	144.6	Nonazeotrope		*236*
4187	$C_5H_{11}Br$	1-Bromo-3-methylbutane	120.65	Nonazeotrope		*207*
4188	$C_5H_{11}I$	1-Iodo-3-methylbutane	147.65	Nonazeotrope		*255*
4189	$C_5H_{12}O$	Amyl alcohol	138.2	126.8	70	*247*
4190	$C_5H_{12}O$	*tert*-Amyl alcohol	102.35	Nonazeotrope		*255*
4191	$C_5H_{12}O$	Isoamyl alcohol	131.3	124.9	60.5	*207*
4192	$C_5H_{12}O$	2-Pentanol	119.8	117.0	40	*247*
4193	$C_5H_{12}O$	3-Pentanol	116.0	114.0	32	*247*
4194	C_6H_5Cl	Chlorobenzene	132.0	126	~60	*212*
4195	$C_6H_{10}O$	Mesityl oxide	129.45	128.8	42	*232*
4196	$C_6H_{10}S$	Allyl sulfide	139.35	Nonazeotrope		*246*
4197	$C_6H_{12}O$	Cyclohexanol	160.8	Nonazeotrope		*255*
4198	$C_6H_{12}O$	3-Hexanone	123.3	Nonazeotrope		*232*
4199	$C_6H_{12}O$	4-Methyl-2-pentanone	116.05	Nonazeotrope		*232*
4200	$C_6H_{12}O_2$	Butyl acetate	125.0	Nonazeotrope		*228*
4201	$C_6H_{12}O_2$	Ethyl butyrate	121.5	Nonazeotrope		*255*
4202	$C_6H_{12}O_2$	Isoamyl formate	123.8	Nonazeotrope		*212*
4203	$C_6H_{12}O_2$	Propyl propionate	122.1	Nonazeotrope		*212*
4204	$C_6H_{12}O_3$	Paraldehyde	124	Azeotrope doubtful		*243*
4205	$C_6H_{14}O$	Hexyl alcohol	157.85	Nonazeotrope		*255*
4206	$C_6H_{14}S$	Propyl sulfide	141.5	Nonazeotrope		*255*
4207	C_7H_8	Toluene	110.7	Nonazeotrope		*243*
4208	C_7H_{14}	Methylcyclohexane	101.15	Nonazeotrope		*255*
4209	$C_7H_{14}O$	4-Heptanone	143.55	Nonazeotrope		*232*
4210	$C_7H_{14}O_2$	Ethyl isovalerate	134.7	Nonazeotrope		*212*
4211	$C_7H_{14}O_2$	Isobutyl propionate	136.9	Nonazeotrope		*212*
4212	$C_7H_{14}O$	Propyl isobutyrate	134.0	Nonazeotrope		*228*
4213	C_8H_8	Styrene	145.8	Nonazeotrope		*218*
4214	C_8H_{10}	Ethylbenzene	136.15	127.2	62.5	*252*
4215	C_8H_{10}	*m*-Xylene	139.2	128.25	90	*255*
4216	C_8H_{10}	*m*-Xylene	139.0	Nonazeotrope		*243*
4217	C_8H_{10}	*p*-Xylene	138.45	128.3	85	*242*
4218	C_8H_{16}	1,3-Dimethylcyclohexane	120.7	118.5	15	*242*
4219	C_8H_{18}	Octane	125.8	123.5	~40	*243*
4220	$C_8H_{18}O$	Butyl ether	142.4	Nonazeotrope		*255*
4221	$C_8H_{18}O$	Isobutyl ether	122.3	<121.9	<18	*255*
4222	$C_{10}H_{16}$	α-Pinene	155.8	Nonazeotrope		*255*
A =	**$C_3H_5Cl_3$**	**1,1,3-Trichloropropane**	**148**			
4223	$C_7H_{14}O$	2-Heptanone	150	Max. b.p.		*111*
4224	$C_7H_{14}O_2$	Amyl acetate	148	Max. b.p.		*111*
A =	**$C_3H_5Cl_3$**	**1,2,2-Trichloropropane**	**122**			
4225	C_5H_5N	Pyridine	115	Nonazeotrope		*111*
4226	C_5H_8O	Cyclopentanone	129	Nonazeotrope		*111*
4227	$C_5H_{10}O_3$	Ethyl carbonate	126	Max. b.p.		*111*
4228	$C_6H_{12}O_2$	Butyl acetate	125	126.4	38	
					V-l.	*111*
4229	$C_7H_{14}O$	2,4-Dimethyl-3-pentanone	124	Max. b.p.		*123*
4230	$C_7H_{14}O_2$	Isopropyl butyrate	128	Nonazeotrope		*111*

No.	B-Component Formula	Name	B.P., ° C.	Azeotropic Data B.P., ° C.	Wt. % A	Ref.
A =	$C_3H_5Cl_3$	**1,2,3-Trichloropropane**	**158**			
4231	$C_3H_6O_2$	Propionic acid	140.7	~140.5	30?	*243*
4232	$C_3H_7NO_2$	Ethyl carbamate	185.25	155.0	90	*244*
4233	$C_4H_5Cl_3O$	α,α,β-Trichlorobutyraldehyde	164	Nonazeotrope		*243*
4234	$C_4H_6O_4$	Methyl oxalate	164.2	154.0	72	*218*
4235	$C_4H_7ClO_2$	Ethyl chloroacetate	156.85	Nonazeotrope		*218*
4236	$C_4H_8O_2$	Butyric acid	162.45	153.0	75	*221*
4237	$C_4H_8O_2$	Isobutyric acid	154.35	149.2	62	*222*
4238	$C_4H_8O_3$	Methyl lactate	143.8	Nonazeotrope		*253*
4239	$C_5H_4O_2$	2-Furaldehyde	161.45	Nonazeotrope		*252*
4240	$C_5H_{10}O_2$	Isovaleric acid	176.5	155.0	93?	*255*
4241	$C_5H_{10}O_3$	Ethyl lactate	153.9	~153.5	~15	*252*
4242	$C_5H_{11}NO_3$	Isoamyl nitrate	149.75	<149.5	>12	*240*
4243	$C_5H_{12}O$	Isoamyl alcohol	131.3	Nonazeotrope		*207*
4244	C_6H_5Br	Bromobenzene	156.1	155.6	30	*229*
4245	C_6H_6O	Phenol	182.2	Nonazeotrope		*210*
4246	$C_6H_{10}O$	Cyclohexanone	155.7	160.0	61	*232*
4247	$C_6H_{10}O_3$	Ethyl acetoacetate	180.4	Nonazeotrope		*215*
4248	$C_6H_{12}O$	Cyclohexanol	160.7	154.9	67	*252*
4249	$C_6H_{14}O$	Hexyl alcohol	157.85	152.8	60	*247*
4250	C_7H_7Cl	*o*-Chlorotoluene	159.2	Nonazeotrope		*255*
4251	C_7H_8O	Anisole	153.85	Nonazeotrope		*210*
			155	Max. b.p.		*111*
4252	C_7H_8O	*o*-Cresol	191.1	Nonazeotrope		*255*
4253	$C_7H_{14}O$	Heptaldehyde	155	Max. b.p.		*111*
4254	$C_8H_{10}O$	Benzyl methyl ether	167.8	Nonazeotrope		*239*
4255	$C_8H_{10}O$	Phenetole	170.45	Nonazeotrope		*228*
4256	$C_8H_{16}O_2$	Isobutyl isobutyrate	147.3	Nonazeotrope		*227*
4257	$C_8H_{18}O$	Butyl ether	142.4	Nonazeotrope		*239*
4258	$C_8H_{18}O$	*sec*-Octyl alcohol	179.0	Nonazeotrope		*253*
4259	$C_8H_{20}SiO_4$	Ethyl silicate	165	Nonazeotrope ?		*243*
4260	C_9H_{12}	Pseudocumene	168.2	Nonazeotrope		*255*
4261	$C_9H_{18}O_2$	Isoamyl isobutyrate	170.0	Nonazeotrope		*227*
4262	$C_9H_{18}O_2$	Isobutyl isovalerate	171.35	Nonazeotrope		*227*
4263	$C_{10}H_{14}$	Cymene	176.7	Nonazeotrope		*255*
4264	$C_{10}H_{16}$	Camphene	159.6	~152.9	~65	*209*
4265	$C_{10}H_{16}$	*d*-Limonene	177.8	Nonazeotrope		*215*
4266	$C_{10}H_{16}$	α-Pinene	155.8	150.0	~85	*252*
4267	$C_{10}H_{22}$	2,7-Dimethyloctane	160.25	~155.5	~70	*253*
A =	C_3H_5I	**3-Iodopropene**	**102**			
4268	C_3H_6O	Allyl alcohol	96.95	89.4	72	*212*
4269	$C_3H_6O_2$	Propionic acid	141.3	Nonazeotrope		*255*
4270	$C_3H_6O_3$	Methyl carbonate	90.25	<90.0	....	*255*
4271	C_3H_7I	1-Iodopropane	102.4	Nonazeotrope		*255*
4272	C_3H_8O	Isopropyl alcohol	82.45	~79	~58	*243*
4273	C_3H_8O	Propyl alcohol	97.2	90.0	71	*243*
4274	$C_3H_8O_2$	2-Methoxyethanol	124.5	100.5	~95	*255*
4275	C_4H_7N	Isobutyronitrile	103.85	<93.2	<68	*242*
4276	$C_4H_8O_2$	Dioxane	101.35	98.5	56	*207*
4277	$C_4H_{10}O$	Butyl alcohol	117.8	98.7	87	*247*
4278	$C_4H_{10}O$	Isobutyl alcohol	108	96	~83	*243*
4279	$C_5H_{10}O$	2-Pentanone	102.35	100.7	66	*232*
4280	$C_5H_{10}O$	3-Pentanone	102.05	100.5	65	*232*
4281	$C_5H_{10}O_2$	Butyl formate	106.7	100.0	>75	*227*
4282	$C_5H_{10}O_2$	Ethyl propionate	99.1	98.0	35	*227*
4283	$C_5H_{10}O_2$	Isobutyl formate	98.3	95.8	38	*243*
4284	$C_5H_{10}O_2$	Isopropyl acetate	89.5	Nonazeotrope		*255*
4285	$C_5H_{10}O_2$	Methyl butyrate	102.75	101.0	65	*253*
4286	$C_5H_{10}O_2$	Methyl isobutyrate	92.5	Nonazeotrope		*227*
4287	$C_5H_{10}O_2$	Propyl acetate	101.6	99.5	56	*218*
4288	$C_5H_{11}Cl$	1-Chloro-3-methylbutane	99.4	Nonazeotrope		*229*
4289	$C_5H_{11}NO_2$	Isoamyl nitrite	97.15	96.0	....	*230*
4290	$C_5H_{12}O$	*tert*-Amyl alcohol	102.35	<97.2	<75	*247*
4291	$C_5H_{12}O$	Isoamyl alcohol	131.9	Nonazeotrope		*207*
4292	$C_6H_{12}O_2$	Ethyl isobutyrate	110.1	Nonazeotrope ?		*243*
4293	$C_6H_{14}O_2$	Acetal	103.55	100.0	67	*239*

No.	B-Component Formula	Name	B.P., ° C.	Azeotropic Data B.P., ° C.	Wt. % A	Ref.
A =	C_3H_5I	**3-Iodopropene** (*countined*)	**102**			
4294	C_7H_8	Toluene	110.7	Nonazeotrope		243
4295	C_7H_{14}	Methylcyclohexane	101.8	99	~70	243
4296	C_7H_{16}	Heptane	98.45	97.0	48	218
A =	C_3H_5N	**Propionitrile**	**97.2**			
4297	C_3H_7I	2-Iodopropane	89.45	81.2	30	242
4298	C_3H_8O	Isopropyl alcohol	82.4	81.5	12	245
4299	C_3H_8O	Propyl alcohol	97.2	90.5	50	245
4300	C_3H_9ClSi	Chlorotrimethylsilane	57.7	Nonazeotrope		340
4301	$C_4H_8O_2$	Ethyl acetate	77.1	Nonazeotrope		245
4302	$C_4H_8O_2$	Methyl propionate	79.85	Nonazeotrope		245
4303	$C_4H_8O_2$	Propyl formate	80.85	Nonazeotrope		245
4304	C_4H_9Br	1-Bromo-2-methylpropane	91.4	85.0	35	242
4305	$C_4H_{10}O$	Butyl alcohol	117.75	Nonazeotrope		245
4306	$C_4H_{10}O$	Isobutyl alcohol	108.0	95.5	76	245
4307	$C_5H_{10}O_2$	Ethyl propionate	99.1	<94.5	>40	245
4308	$C_5H_{10}O_2$	Methyl butyrate	102.65	<96.0	>54	245
4309	$C_5H_{10}O_2$	Propyl acetate	101.55	95.4	55	255
4310	$C_5H_{12}O$	*tert*-Amyl alcohol	102.35	<94.5	>57	245
4311	$C_6H_{12}O_2$	Ethyl isobutyrate	110.1	Nonazeotrope		245
4312	$C_6H_{12}O_2$	Methyl isovalerate	116.5	Nonazeotrope		245
4313	C_6H_{14}	Hexane	68.8	63.5	9	245
4314	$C_6H_{14}O$	Isopropyl ether	68.3	<67.5	>4	255
4315	$C_6H_{14}O$	Propyl ether	90.1	<83.5	>18	242
4316	C_7H_8	Toluene	110.75	Min. b.p.		202
4317	C_7H_{14}	Methylcyclohexane	101.15	<85.0	>45	242
4318	C_7H_{16}	Heptane	98.4	<80.5	....	245
4319	C_8H_{10}	Ethylbenzene	136.15	Nonazeotrope		255
A =	$C_3H_5N_3O_9$	**Nitroglycerin**	....			
4320	C_3H_6O	Acetone	56.15	Nonazeotrope, V-l.		271
A =	$C_3H_6Br_2$	**1,2-Dibromopropane**	**140.5**			
4321	$C_3H_6O_2$	Propionic acid	141.3	134.5	67	207
4322	C_3H_7NO	Propionamide	222.2	Nonazeotrope		255
4323	C_3H_8O	Propyl alcohol	97.2	Nonazeotrope		255
4324	$C_3H_8O_2$	2-Methoxyethanol	124.5	124.0	....	206
4325	C_4H_5N	Pyrrole	130	Nonazeotrope		235
4326	$C_4H_7BrO_2$	Ethyl bromoacetate	158.8	Nonazeotrope		255
4327	$C_4H_8O_2$	Butyric acid	164.0	138.5	92	242
4328	$C_4H_8O_2$	Isobutyric acid	154.6	137.0	85	242
4329	$C_4H_{10}O$	Butyl alcohol	117.8	<117.1	39	255
4330	$C_4H_{10}O$	Isobutyl alcohol	108.0	Nonazeotrope		255
4331	$C_4H_{10}O_2$	2-Ethoxyethanol	135.3	132.5	50	235
4332	$C_5H_4O_2$	2-Furaldehyde	161.45	Nonazeotrope		236
4333	$C_5H_{10}O_2$	Isovaleric acid	176.5	Nonazeotrope		255
4334	$C_5H_{10}O_2$	Valeric acid	186.35	Nonazeotrope		255
4335	$C_5H_{11}NO_3$	Isoamyl nitrate	149.5	Nonazeotrope		227
4336	$C_5H_{12}O$	Isoamyl alcohol	131.9	<128.5	>52	207
4337	C_6H_6O	Phenol	182.2	Nonazeotrope		255
4338	$C_6H_{10}O$	Mesityl oxide	129.45	Nonazeotrope		232
4339	$C_6H_{10}S$	Allyl sulfide	~138.7	Nonazeotrope		243
4340	$C_6H_{12}O$	Cyclohexanol	160.65	Nonazeotrope		243
4341	$C_6H_{12}O_3$	2-Ethoxyethyl acetate	156.8	Nonazeotrope		255
4342	$C_6H_{14}O$	Hexyl alcohol	157.85	Nonazeotrope		255
4343	C_7H_8O	Anisole	153.85	Nonazeotrope		239
4344	$C_7H_{14}O$	4-Heptanone	143.55	Nonazeotrope		232
4345	$C_7H_{14}O$	5-Methyl-2-hexanone	144.2	Nonazeotrope		232
4346	$C_7H_{14}O_2$	Amyl acetate	148.8	Nonazeotrope		255
4347	$C_7H_{14}O_2$	Butyl propionate	146.5	Nonazeotrope		227
4348	$C_7H_{14}O_2$	Ethyl isovalerate	134.7	Nonazeotrope		255
4349	$C_7H_{14}O_2$	Ethyl valerate	145.45	Nonazeotrope		255
4350	$C_7H_{14}O_2$	Isoamyl acetate	142.1	<140.2	>91	255
4351	$C_7H_{14}O_2$	Isobutyl propionate	136.9	Nonazeotrope		227
4352	$C_7H_{14}O_2$	Propyl butyrate	134.7	Nonazeotrope		227
4353	$C_7H_{14}O_2$	Propyl isobutyrate	134.0	Nonazeotrope		227
4354	C_8H_{10}	Ethylbenzene	136.15	135.95	5	243

No.	Formula	Name	B.P., ° C.	Azeotropic Data B.P., ° C.	Wt. % A	Ref.
A =	$C_3H_6Br_2$	**1,2-Dibromopropane** (*continued*)	**140.5**			
4355	C_8H_{10}	*m*-Xylene	139.0	138	30	*243*
4356	C_8H_{10}	*o*-Xylene	142.6	139.2	~70	*243*
4357	C_8H_{10}	*p*-Xylene	138.2	137.5	~22	*243*
4358	$C_8H_{18}O$	Butyl ether	142.4	146.0	40	*239*
4359	C_9H_{12}	Cumene	152.8	Nonazeotrope		*255*
4360	$C_{10}H_{16}$	α-Pinene	155.8	Nonazeotrope		*255*
A =	$C_3H_6Br_2$	**1,3-Dibromopropane**	**166.9**			
4361	$C_3H_6O_2$	Propionic acid	141.3	Nonazeotrope		*207*
4362	C_3H_7NO	Propionamide	222.2	Nonazeotrope		*207*
4363	$C_3H_7NO_2$	Ethyl carbamate	185.25	164.05	87.8	*207*
4364	$C_4H_7BrO_2$	Ethyl bromoacetate	158.8	Nonazeotrope		*207*
4365	$C_4H_7Cl_3O$	Ethyl 1,1,2-trichloroethyl ether	172.5	Nonazeotrope		*255*
4366	$C_4H_8Cl_2O$	Bis(2-chloroethyl) ether	178.65	Nonazeotrope		*207*
4367	$C_4H_8O_2$	Butyric acid	163.5	158.4	70	*207*
4368	$C_4H_8O_2$	Isobutyric acid	154.6	151.5	40	*242*
4369	$C_5H_4O_2$	2-Furaldehyde	161.45	159.45	54	*207*
4370	$C_5H_6O_2$	Furfuryl alcohol	169.35	164.0	74	*255*
4371	$C_5H_8O_4$	Methyl malonate	181.5	Nonazeotrope		*227*
4372	$C_5H_{10}O_2$	Isovaleric acid	176.5	163.35	84.5	*207*
4373	$C_5H_{10}O_2$	Valeric acid	186.35	166.0	92	*207*
4374	$C_5H_{11}NO_3$	Isoamyl nitrate	149.5	Nonazeotrope		*227*
4375	$C_5H_{12}O_2$	2-Propoxyethanol	151.35	Nonazeotrope		*236*
4376	C_6H_6O	Phenol	182.2	Nonazeotrope		*255*
4377	C_6H_7N	Aniline	184.35	Nonazeotrope		*255*
4378	$C_6H_{10}O$	Cyclohexanone	155.7	Nonazeotrope		*232*
4379	$C_6H_{10}O_4$	Ethyl oxalate	185.65	Nonazeotrope		*207*
4380	$C_6H_{12}O$	Cyclohexanol	160.65	158.5	....	*243*
4381	$C_6H_{12}O_2$	Caproic acid	205.15	Nonazeotrope		*255*
4382	$C_6H_{12}O_2$	Isocaproic acid	199.5	Nonazeotrope		*255*
4383	$C_6H_{12}O_3$	2-Ethoxyethyl acetate	156.8	Nonazeotrope		*236*
4384	$C_6H_{14}O_2$	2-Butoxyethanol	171.15	164.55	77	*207*
4385	C_7H_5N	Benzonitrile	191.1	Nonazeotrope		*245*
4386	C_7H_6O	Benzaldehyde	179.2	Nonazeotrope		*255*
4387	C_7H_7Cl	*p*-Chlorotoluene	162.4	Nonazeotrope		*255*
4388	C_7H_8O	Benzyl alcohol	105.25	Nonazeotrope		*255*
4389	C_7H_8O	*o*-Cresol	191.1	Nonazeotrope		*255*
4390	$C_7H_{14}O_3$	1,3-Butanediol methyl ether acetate	171.75	Nonazeotrope		*255*
4391	$C_8H_{10}O$	Benzyl methyl ether	167.8	>170	>45	*239*
4392	$C_8H_{10}O$	*p*-Methylanisole	177.05	Nonazeotrope		*239*
4393	$C_8H_{10}O$	Phenetole	170.45	Nonazeotrope		*239*
4394	$C_8H_{16}O$	2-Octanone	172.85	Nonazeotrope		*232*
4395	$C_8H_{16}O_2$	Hexyl acetate	171.5	Nonazeotrope		*227*
4396	$C_8H_{16}O_2$	Isoamyl propionate	160.4	Nonazeotrope		*227*
4397	$C_8H_{18}O$	Octyl alcohol	195.2	Nonazeotrope		*255*
4398	$C_8H_{18}O$	*sec*-Octyl alcohol	180.4	Nonazeotrope		*255*
4399	C_9H_8	Indene	182.6	Nonazeotrope		*255*
4400	C_9H_{12}	Mesitylene	164.6	Nonazeotrope		*255*
4401	$C_9H_{18}O_2$	Isobutyl isovalerate	171.35	Nonazeotrope		*227*
4402	$C_{10}H_{14}$	Cymene	176.7	Nonazeotrope		*255*
4403	$C_{10}H_{16}$	Dipentene	177.7	Nonazeotrope		*255*
4404	$C_{10}H_{16}$	α-Pinene	155.8	Nonazeotrope		*255*
A =	$C_3H_6Br_2O$	**2,3-Dibromo-1-propanol**	**219.5**			
4405	$C_4H_{10}O_3$	Diethylene glycol	245.5	Nonazeotrope		*255*
4406	$C_6H_4Cl_2$	*o*-Dichlorobenzene	179.5	Nonazeotrope		*255*
4407	C_6H_5I	Iodobenzene	188.45	Nonazeotrope		*255*
4408	$C_6H_{14}O_3$	Dipropylene glycol	229.2	Nonazeotrope		*255*
4409	C_7H_7Br	*o*-Bromotoluene	181.5	Nonazeotrope		*255*
4410	C_7H_7I	*p*-Iodotoluene	214.5	<209.0	<40	*255*
4411	$C_8H_{10}O_2$	2-Phenoxyethanol	245.2	Nonazeotrope		*255*
4412	$C_8H_{10}O_2$	Veratrole	206.8	Nonazeotrope		*255*
4413	$C_8H_{18}O$	Octyl alcohol	195.2	Nonazeotrope		*255*
4414	$C_8H_{18}O_3$	2-(2-Butoxyethoxy)ethanol	231.2	Nonazeotrope		*255*
4415	C_9H_8	Indene	182.6	Nonazeotrope		*255*
4416	$C_9H_{10}O$	*p*-Methylacetophenone	226.35	228.2	....	*255*
4417	$C_9H_{10}O$	Propiophenone	217.7	<222.0	....	*255*

No.	B-Component Formula	B-Component Name	B.P., ° C.	Azeotropic Data B.P., ° C.	Azeotropic Data Wt. % A	Ref.
A =	$C_3H_6Br_2O$	**2,3-Dibromo-1-propanol** (*continued*)	**219.5**			
4418	$C_{10}H_{14}$	Butylbenzene	183.1	Nonazeotrope		*255*
4419	$C_{10}H_{14}$	Cymene	176.7	Nonazeotrope		*255*
4420	$C_{10}H_{16}$	Dipentene	177.7	<176.5	>12	*255*
4421	$C_{10}H_{20}O$	Menthol	216.3	<216.2	<22	*255*
4422	$C_{11}H_{20}O$	Methyl α-terpineol ether	216.2	Nonazeotrope		*255*
4423	$C_{11}H_{20}O$	Isobornyl methyl ether	192.4	Nonazeotrope		*255*
4424	$C_{12}H_{22}O$	Bornyl ethyl ether	204.9	Nonazeotrope		*255*
A =	$C_3H_6Cl_2$	**1,1-Dichloropropane**	**90**			
4425	$C_5H_{10}O_2$	Isopropyl acetate	90	Max. b.p.		*111*
4426	$C_6H_{15}N$	Triethylamine	89	Max. b.p.		*111*
A =	$C_3H_6Cl_2$	**1,2-Dichloropropane**	**97**			
4427	C_3H_8O	Isopropyl alcohol	82.4	....	50, V-l.	*119*
		At 30° C.	....	....	75, V-l.	*119*
4428	$C_4H_8O_2$	Butyric acid	162.4	Nonazeotrope		*277*
4429	$C_4H_8O_2$	Dioxane	101	Max. b.p.		*111*
4430	$C_5H_{10}O$	2-Pentanone	102	Max. b.p.		*111*
4431	$C_5H_{10}O_2$	Ethyl propionate	99	Max. b.p.		*111*
4432	C_6H_{12}	Cyclohexane	80	80.4	16	*117*
A =	$C_3H_6Cl_2$	**1,3-Dichloropropane**	**129.8**			
4433	$C_5H_{10}O_3$	2-Methoxy ethyl acetate	144.6	Nonazeotrope		*255*
4434	C_6H_6O	Phenol	182.2	Nonazeotrope		*255*
4435	$C_6H_{12}O_3$	2-Ethoxyethyl acetate	156.8	Nonazeotrope		*255*
A =	$C_3H_6Cl_2$	**2,2-Dichloropropane**	**70.4**			
4436	C_3H_6O	Allyl alcohol	96.85	<70.0	....	*255*
4437	$C_3H_6O_2$	Ethyl formate	54.15	Nonazeotrope		*227*
4438	$C_3H_6O_2$	Methyl acetate	57.0	Nonazeotrope		*227*
4439	C_3H_8O	Isopropyl alcohol	82.4	66.8	83	*247*
4440	C_3H_8O	Propyl alcohol	97.2	<70.1	>89	*255*
4441	$C_4H_8O_2$	Ethyl acetate	77.15	Nonazeotrope		*227*
4442	$C_4H_8O_2$	Methyl propionate	79.85	Nonazeotrope		*227*
4443	$C_4H_8O_2$	Propyl formate	80.85	Nonazeotrope		*227*
4444	$C_4H_9NO_2$	Butyl nitrite	78.2	Nonazeotrope		*230*
4445	$C_4H_9NO_2$	Isobutyl nitrite	67.1	Nonazeotrope		*230*
4446	$C_4H_{10}O$	Butyl alcohol	117.8	Nonazeotrope		*255*
4447	$C_4H_{10}O$	Isobutyl alcohol	108.8	Nonazeotrope		*255*
4448	C_6H_6	Benzene	80.15	Nonazeotrope		*255*
4449	C_6H_{12}	Cyclohexane	80.75	Nonazeotrope		*255*
4450	C_6H_{12}	Methylcyclopentane	72.0	<69.5	<70	*255*
4451	C_6H_{14}	Hexane	68.8	<68.0	>40	*255*
4452	$C_6H_{14}O$	Isopropyl ether	68.3	74.0	60	*239*
A =	$C_3H_6Cl_2O$	**1,3-Dichloro-2-propanol**	**175.8**			
4453	$C_3H_7NO_2$	Ethyl carbamate	185.25	Nonazeotrope		*255*
4454	$C_4H_6O_4$	Methyl oxalate	164.45	Nonazeotrope		*255*
4455	$C_5H_4O_2$	2-Furaldehyde	161.45	Nonazeotrope		*207*
4456	$C_5H_{11}I$	1-Iodo-3-methylbutane	147.65	<147.4	>4	*255*
4457	$C_5H_{12}O_2$	2-Propoxyethanol	151.35	Nonazeotrope		*206*
4458	$C_6H_3Cl_3$	1,3,5-Trichlorobenzene	208.4	Nonazeotrope		*255*
4459	C_6H_4BrCl	*p*-Bromochlorobenzene	196.4	Nonazeotrope		*255*
4460	$C_6H_4Cl_2$	*o*-Dichlorobenzene	179.5	170.5	60	*247*
4461	$C_6H_4Cl_2$	*p*-Dichlorobenzene	174.35	168.2	45	*210*
4462	C_6H_5Br	Bromobenzene	156.1	155.5	~9	*252*
4463	C_6H_5I	Iodobenzene	188.55	173	~70	*253*
4464	C_6H_6O	Phenol	181.5	Nonazeotrope		*243*
4465	$C_6H_{10}O$	Cyclohexanone	155.7	Nonazeotrope		*232*
4466	$C_6H_{10}O_4$	Ethyl oxalate	185.65	Nonazeotrope		*255*
4467	$C_6H_{12}O$	Cyclohexanol	160.7	Nonazeotrope		*210*
4468	$C_6H_{12}O_3$	Propyl lactate	171.7	~170	....	*243*
4469	$C_6H_{13}Br$	1-Bromohexane	156.5	154.5	15	*247*
4470	$C_6H_{14}O$	Hexyl alcohol	157.85	Nonazeotrope		*255*
4471	$C_6H_{14}O_2$	2-Butoxyethanol	171.25	Nonazeotrope		*206*
4472	$C_6H_{14}O_2$	Pinacol	174.35	<173.6	<45	*255*

No.	B-Component Formula	Name	B.P., ° C.	Azeotropic Data B.P., ° C.	Wt. % A	Ref.
A =	**$C_3H_6Cl_2O$**	**1,3-Dichloro-2-propanol** (*continued*)	**175.8**			
4473	C_7H_6O	Benzaldehyde	179.2	<174	>85	*243*
4474	C_7H_7Br	*m*-Bromotoluene	184.3	171.8	36	*244*
4475	C_7H_7Br	*o*-Bromotoluene	181.45	170.45	61	*253*
4476	C_7H_7Br	*p*-Bromotoluene	185.0	172.8	~68	*214*
4477	C_7H_7Cl	*α*-Chlorotoluene	179.3	168.9	57	*253*
4478	C_7H_7Cl	*o*-Chlorotoluene	159.3	158.0	15	*218*
4479	C_7H_7Cl	*p*-Chlorotoluene	162.4	160.0	22	*218*
4480	C_7H_8O	Anisole	153.85	Nonazeotrope		*236*
4481	C_7H_8	Toluene	110.75	Nonazeotrope		*255*
4482	C_7H_8O	*o*-Cresol	191.1	Nonazeotrope		*255*
4483	C_7H_{14}	Methylcyclohexane	101.15	Nonazeotrope		*255*
4484	C_7H_{16}	Heptane	98.4	Nonazeotrope		*207*
4485	$C_7H_{16}O$	Heptyl alcohol	176.15	174.2	47	*255*
4486	C_8H_8O	Acetophenone	202.0	Nonazeotrope		*232*
4487	C_8H_8	Styrene	145.8	~143.5	~15	*212*
4488	C_8H_{10}	Ethylbenzene	136.15	Nonazeotrope		*255*
4489	C_8H_{10}	*m*-Xylene	139.0	Nonazeotrope		*243*
4490	C_8H_{10}	*p*-Xylene	138.45	Nonazeotrope		*255*
4491	$C_8H_{10}O$	Benzyl methyl ether	167.8	<167.0	....	*255*
4492	$C_8H_{10}O$	*p*-Methylanisole	177.05	173.1	59	*236*
4493	$C_8H_{10}O$	Phenetole	170.45	168.8	37	*236*
4494	$C_8H_{14}O$	Methyl heptenone	173.2	179.0	65?	*232*
4495	$C_8H_{16}O$	2-Octanone	172.85	179.0	67?	*232*
4496	$C_8H_{16}O_2$	Isoamyl propionate	160.7	Nonazeotrope		*255*
4497	$C_8H_{18}O$	Octyl alcohol	195.2	Nonazeotrope		*255*
4498	$C_8H_{18}O$	*sec*-Octyl alcohol	180.4	175.35	85	*244*
4499	C_9H_8	Indene	183.0	173.5	66.5	*221*
4500	C_9H_{12}	Cumene	152.8	<152.5	....	*255*
4501	C_9H_{12}	Mesitylene	164.6	161.5	32	*247*
4502	C_9H_{12}	Propylbenzene	159.3	157.5	20	*255*
4503	C_9H_{12}	Pseudocumene	168.2	164.4	37	*221*
4504	$C_9H_{18}O$	2,6-Dimethyl-4-heptanone	168.0	177.5	>85	*232*
4505	$C_9H_{18}O_2$	Isoamyl butyrate	181.05	Nonazeotrope		*255*
4506	$C_9H_{18}O_2$	Isoamyl isobutyrate	169.8	Nonazeotrope		*255*
4507	$C_9H_{18}O_2$	Isobutyl isovalerate	171.35	Nonazeotrope		*221*
4508	$C_9H_{18}O_3$	Isobutyl carbonate	190.3	Nonazeotrope		*255*
4509	$C_{10}H_8$	Naphthalene	218.0	Nonazeotrope		*255*
4510	$C_{10}H_{14}$	Butylbenzene	183.1	172.0	65	*247*
4511	$C_{10}H_{14}$	Cymene	~176.7	165.5	55	*212*
4512	$C_{10}H_{16}$	Camphene	159.5	152.8	~38	*252*
4513	$C_{10}H_{16}$	*d*-Limonene	177.8	165.75	57	*243*
4514	$C_{10}H_{16}$	Nopinene	163.8	156.5	43	*247*
4515	$C_{10}H_{16}$	*α*-Terpinene	173.4	<165.0	<56	*255*
4516	$C_{10}H_{16}$	*α*-Phellandrene	171.5	163	43	*243*
4517	$C_{10}H_{16}$	*α*-Pinene	155.8	150.4	36.5	*208*
4518	$C_{10}H_{16}$	*γ*-Terpinene	181.5	166.8	62	*218*
4519	$C_{10}H_{16}$	Terpinolene	185	168	70	*243*
4520	$C_{10}H_{16}$	Thymene	179.7	166.5	60	*212*
4521	$C_{10}H_{18}O$	Linaloöl	198.6	Nonazeotrope		*255*
4522	$C_{10}H_{20}O_2$	Isoamyl isovalerate	192.7	Nonazeotrope		*255*
4523	$C_{10}H_{22}$	2,7-Dimethyloctane	160.2	155	~38	*212*
4524	$C_{10}H_{22}O$	Isoamyl ether	173.4	165.9	48	*221*
4525	$C_{11}H_{20}O$	Isoboronyl methyl ether	192.4	Nonazeotrope		*255*
4526	$C_{12}H_{18}$	1,3,5-Triethylbenzene	215.5	Nonazeotrope		*255*
A =	**$C_3H_6Cl_2O$**	**2,3-Dichloro-1-propanol**	**182.5**			
4527	$C_3H_7NO_2$	Ethyl carbamate	185.25	>186.5	>20	*255*
4528	$C_4H_6O_4$	Methyl oxalate	164.45	Nonazeotrope		*255*
4529	$C_5H_{12}O_3$	2-(2-Methoxyethoxy)ethanol	192.95	Nonazeotrope		*255*
4530	$C_6H_4Cl_2$	*o*-Dichlorobenzene	179.5	174.2	40	*247*
4531	$C_6H_4Cl_2$	*p*-Dichlorobenzene	174.4	170.8	30	*255*
4532	C_6H_5Br	Bromobenzene	156.1	Nonazeotrope		*255*
4533	C_6H_5I	Iodobenzene	188.45	177.2	57	*247*
4534	C_6H_6O	Phenol	181.5	Azeotrope doubtful		*243*
4535	C_6H_7N	Aniline	184.35	~181	....	*243*

	B-Component			Azeotropic Data		
No.	Formula	Name	B.P., ° C.	B.P., ° C.	Wt. % A	Ref.
A =	$C_3H_6Cl_2O$	**2,3-Dichloro-1-propanol** *(continued)*	**182.5**			
4536	$C_6H_{10}O$	Cyclohexanone	155.7	Nonazeotrope		*232*
4537	$C_6H_{10}O_4$	Ethyl oxalate	185.65	Nonazeotrope		*255*
4538	$C_6H_{12}O$	Cyclohexanol	160.8	Nonazeotrope		*255*
4539	$C_6H_{14}O$	Hexyl alcohol	157.85	Nonazeotrope		*255*
4540	$C_6H_{14}O_2$	2-Butoxyethanol	171.15	Nonazeotrope		*255*
4541	C_7H_7Br	*m*-Bromotoluene	184.3	175.8	50	*247*
4542	C_7H_7Br	*o*-Bromotoluene	181.75	171.6	45	*243*
4543	C_7H_7Br	*p*-Bromotoluene	185	176.2	52	*255*
4544	C_7H_7Cl	*α*-Chlorotoluene	179.35	171	40	*243*
4545	C_7H_7Cl	*o*-Chlorotoluene	159.2	Nonazeotrope		*255*
4546	C_7H_8	Toluene	110.75	Nonazeotrope		*255*
4547	C_7H_8O	Benzyl alcohol	205.25	Nonazeotrope		*255*
4548	C_7H_8O	*o*-Cresol	191.1	Nonazeotrope		*222*
4549	C_7H_{14}	Methylcyclohexane	101.15	Nonazeotrope		*255*
4550	$C_7H_{14}O$	2-Methylcyclohexanol	168.5	Nonazeotrope		*255*
4551	C_7H_{16}	Heptane	98.4	Nonazeotrope		*255*
4552	C_8H_8O	Acetophenone	202.0	Nonazeotrope		*232*
4553	C_8H_{10}	*m*-Xylene	139.0	Nonazeotrope		*212*
4554	C_8H_{10}	*o*-Xylene	144.3	Nonazeotrope		*255*
4555	$C_8H_{10}O$	Benzyl methyl ether	167.8	Nonazeotrope		*255*
4556	$C_8H_{10}O$	*p*-Methylanisole	177.05	175.5	32	*255*
4557	$C_8H_{16}O$	2-Octanone	172.85	184.0	....	*232*
4558	$C_8H_{18}O$	Octyl alcohol	195.2	Nonazeotrope		*255*
4559	$C_8H_{18}O$	*sec*-Octyl alcohol	178.7	~175	....	*243*
4560	C_9H_8	Indene	182.4	172.5	~57	*212*
4561	C_9H_{12}	Mesitylene	164.6	163	18	*255*
4562	$C_9H_{18}O_2$	Isoamyl butyrate	181.05	180.9?	....	*255*
4563	$C_9H_{12}O_2$	Isobutyl isovalerate	171.2	Nonazeotrope		*255*
4564	$C_{10}H_8$	Naphthalene	218.1	Nonazeotrope		*243*
4565	$C_{10}H_{14}$	Cymene	176.7	172.5	42	*247*
4566	$C_{10}H_{16}$	Camphene	159.6	156.0	25	*212*
4567	$C_{10}H_{16}$	*d*-Limonene	177.8	169.3	40	*243*
4568	$C_{10}H_{16}$	Nopinene	163.8	158.0	37	*247*
4569	$C_{10}H_{16}$	*α*-Pinene	155.8	153	20	*212*
4570	$C_{10}H_{16}$	*α*-Terpinene	173.4	<167.5	>40	*255*
4571	$C_{10}H_{16}$	*γ*-Terpinene	183	<173.5	<60	*255*
4572	$C_{10}H_{16}$	Terpinolene	~185	~174	....	*243*
4573	$C_{10}H_{16}$	Thymene	179.7	170.8	50	*212*
4574	$C_{10}H_{18}O$	Cineole	176.35	Nonazeotrope (reacts)		*255*
4575	$C_{10}H_{20}O_2$	Isoamyl isovalerate	192.7	Nonazeotrope		*255*
4576	$C_{12}H_{18}$	1,3,5-Triethylbenzene	215.5	Nonazeotrope		*255*
A =	C_3H_6O	**Acetone**	**56.15**			
4577	C_3H_6O	Allyl alcohol	96.85	Nonazeotrope		*232*
4578	C_3H_6O	Propionaldehyde	48.7	Nonazeotrope		*232*
4579	$C_3H_6O_2$	Ethyl formate	54.15	Nonazeotrope		*232*
4580	$C_3H_6O_2$	Methyl acetate	57	55	50	*232*, 334*
4581	C_3H_7Br	1-Bromopropane	71.0	56.13	98	*232*
		1-Bromopropane	71.0	Nonazeotrope		*163*
4582	C_3H_7Br	2-Bromopropane	59.4	54.12	42	*232*
4583	C_3H_7Cl	1-Chloropropane	46.65	45.8	15	*235*
4584	C_3H_7Cl	2-Chloropropane	34.9	Nonazeotrope		*232*
4585	C_3H_7I	2-Iodopropane	89.45	Nonazeotrope		*232*
4586	$C_3H_7NO_2$	Isopropyl nitrite	40.1	Nonazeotrope		*232*
4587	$C_3H_7NO_2$	Propyl nitrite	47.75	Nonazeotrope		*232*
4588	C_3H_8O	Isopropyl alcohol	82.4	Nonazeotrope		*232*
4589	C_3H_8O	*n*-Propyl alcohol	97.2	Nonazeotrope		*232*
4590	$C_3H_8O_2$	Methylal	42.3	Nonazeotrope		*232*
4591	C_3H_8S	Propanethiol	67.5	54.5	~67	*243*
4592	$C_3H_9BO_3$	Methyl borate	68.7	55.45	82.5	*232*
4593	C_3H_9N	Propylamine	49.7	<48.0	>20	*231*
4594	C_4H_4S	Thiophene	84.7	Nonazeotrope		*232*
4595	C_4H_8O	2-Butanone	79.6	Nonazeotrope		*328*
4596	C_4H_8O	Butyraldehyde	75.2	Nonazeotrope		*232*
4597	C_4H_8O	Isobutyraldehyde	63.5	Nonazeotrope		*232*

No.	Formula	B-Component Name	B.P., ° C.	Azeotropic Data B.P., ° C.	Wt. % A	Ref.
A =	C_3H_6O	**Acetone** (*continued*)	**56.15**			
4598	$C_4H_8O_2$	Dioxane	101.4	Nonazeotrope		*90*
4599	$C_4H_8O_2$	Ethyl acetate	77.1	Nonazeotrope		*334*
4600	$C_4H_8O_2$	Isopropyl formate	68.8	Nonazeotrope		*232*
4601	C_4H_9Br	2-Bromo-2-methylpropane	73.25	Nonazeotrope		*232*
4602	C_4H_9Cl	1-Chlorobutane	78.5	Nonazeotrope		*232*
4603	C_4H_9Cl	2-Chlorobutane	68.25	55.75	80	*232*
4604	C_4H_9Cl	1-Chloro-2-methylpropane	68.85	55.75	75	*232*
4605	C_4H_9Cl	2-Chloro-2-methylpropane	50.8	49.2	25	*232*
4606	$C_4H_9NO_2$	Butyl nitrite	78.2	Nonazeotrope		*232*
4607	$C_4H_9NO_2$	Isobutyl nitrite	67.1	Nonazeotrope		*232*
4608	$C_4H_{10}O$	Butyl alcohol	117.7	Nonazeotrope, V-l.		*48*
		At 25° C.	....	Nonazeotrope, V-l.		*119*
4609	$C_4H_{10}O$	*tert*-Butyl alcohol	82.45	Nonazeotrope		*232*
4610	$C_4H_{10}O$	Ethyl ether	34.6	Nonazeotrope		*155**, *243**, *334*
4611	$C_4H_{10}O$	Isobutyl alcohol	108.0	Nonazeotrope		*232*
4612	$C_4H_{10}O$	Methyl propyl ether	38.9	Nonazeotrope		*243*
4613	$C_4H_{10}S$	Ethyl sulfide	92.1	Nonazeotrope		*246*
4614	$C_4H_{11}N$	Butylamine	77.8	Nonazeotrope		*231*
4615	$C_4H_{11}N$	Diethylamine	55.5	51.39	38.21	*231**, *271*
4616	$C_4H_{11}N$	Isobutylamine	68.0	<56.0	<96	*231*
4617	C_5H_6	Cyclopentadiene	41.0	Min. b.p.		*107*
4618	C_5H_8	Isoprene	34.3	30.5	20	*107**, *232*
4619	C_5H_8	3-Methyl-1,2-butadiene	40.8	35.3	27	*232*
4620	C_5H_8	Piperylene	42.5	Min. b.p.		*107*
4621	C_5H_{10}	Cyclopentane	49.3	41.0	36	*232*
4622	C_5H_{10}	2-Methyl-1-butene	31.05	Min. b.p.		*107*
4623	C_5H_{10}	2-Methyl-2-butene	37.1	32.5	22	*107**, *232*
4624	C_5H_{10}	3-Methyl-1-butene	20.6	19.7	7	*107**, *232*
4625	C_5H_{10}	1-Pentene	30.1	Min. b.p.		*107*
4626	C_5H_{10}	2-Pentene	36.4	Min. b.p.		*107*
4627	C_5H_{12}	2-Methylbutane	27.95	25.7	12	*232*
4628	C_5H_{12}	Pentane	36.15	31.9	21	*232*
4629	$C_5H_{12}O$	*tert*-Amyl alcohol	102.35	Nonazeotrope		*232*
4630	$C_5H_{12}O$	Ethyl propyl ether	63.6	<56.1	<95	*232*
4631	$C_5H_{12}O_2$	Diethoxymethane	87.95	Nonazeotrope		*232*
4632	C_6H_5Cl	Chlorobenzene	131.6	Nonazeotrope, V-l.		*285*
4633	C_6H_5F	Fluorobenzene	84.9	Nonazeotrope		*232*
4634	C_6H_6	Benzene	80.1	Nonazeotrope, V-l.		*110**, *285*, *322**, *372**
4635	C_6H_6O	Phenol	181.5	Nonazeotrope		*243*
4636	C_6H_8	1,3-Cyclohexadiene	80.4	<55	<85	*232*
4637	C_6H_{10}	Biallyl	60.1	47.1	45	*232*
4638	C_6H_{12}	Cyclohexane	80.75	53.0	67	*115**, *232*
4639	C_6H_{12}	Methylcyclopentane	72.0	50.3	57	*203**, *232*
4640	C_6H_{14}	2,3-Dimethylbutane	58.0	46.3	42	*232*
4641	C_6H_{14}	*n*-Hexane	68.8	49.7	53.5	*232*
4642	$C_6H_{14}O$	Isopropyl ether	69.0	54.2	61	*110*
4643	$C_6H_{14}O$	Propyl ether	90.1	Nonazeotrope		*232*
4644	$C_6H_{14}O_2$	Acetal	104.5	Nonazeotrope		*243*
4645	$C_6H_{15}N$	Triethylamine	89.35	Nonazeotrope		*231*
4646	$C_7H_6O_2$	Benzoic acid	249.5	Nonazeotrope		*255*
4647	C_7H_8	Toluene	110.75	Nonazeotrope		*232*
4648	C_7H_{14}	Methylcyclohexane	101.15	Nonazeotrope		*232*
4649	C_7H_{16}	Heptane	98.4	55.85	89.5	*232*
			98.45	Nonazeotrope		*150*
4650	C_8H_{18}	2,5-Dimethylhexane	109.4	Nonazeotrope		*232*
A =	C_3H_6O	**Allyl Alcohol**	**96.95**			
4651	$C_3H_6O_3$	Methyl carbonate	90.5	86.4	23	*207*
4652	C_3H_7Br	1-Bromopropane	71.0	69.5	9	*212*
4653	C_3H_7Br	2-Bromopropane	59.4	Nonazeotrope		*207*
4654	C_3H_8O	Propyl alcohol	97.2	96.73	74	*250*
4655	$C_4H_7ClO_2$	Ethyl chloroacetate	143.55	Nonazeotrope		*255*
4656	C_4H_8O	2-Butanone	79.6	Nonazeotrope		*232*
4657	C_4H_8OS	Ethyl thioacetate	116.5	<96.5	....	*255*
4658	$C_4H_8O_2$	Dioxane	101.35	Nonazeotrope		*207*

	B-Component			Azeotropic Data		
No.	Formula	Name	B.P., ° C.	B.P., ° C.	Wt. % A	Ref.
A =	**C_3H_6O**	**Allyl Alcohol** (*continued*)	**96.95**			
4659	$C_4H_8O_2$	Ethyl acetate	77.05	Nonazeotrope		*243*
4660	$C_4H_8O_2$	Methyl propionate	79.7	Nonazeotrope		*207*
4661	$C_4H_8O_2$	Propyl formate	80.8	80.5	....	*216*
4662	C_4H_9Br	1-Bromobutane	101.5	89.5	30	*207*
4663	C_4H_9Br	1-Bromo-2-methylpropane	91.6	83.9	18	*357*
4664	C_4H_9Cl	1-Chlorobutane	78.5	74.5	15	*247*
4665	C_4H_9Cl	1-Chloro-2-methylpropane	68.85	67	~7	*357*
4666	C_4H_9I	1-Iodobutane	130.4	<96.4	<74	*255*
4667	$C_4H_{10}O$	*sec*-Butyl alcohol	99.6	Nonazeotrope		*243*
4668	$C_4H_{10}S$	Ethyl sulfide	92.1	85.1	45	*207*
4669	C_5H_5N	Pyridine	115.4	Nonazeotrope		*233*
4670	$C_5H_8O_2$	Allyl acetate	104	Min. b.p.		*1*
4671	$C_5H_{10}O$	3-Methyl-2-butanone	95.4	93.5	36	*232*
4672	$C_5H_{10}O$	2-Pentanone	102.35	96.0	70	*232*
4673	$C_5H_{10}O$	3-Pentanone	102.05	95.95	72	*232*
4674	$C_5H_{10}O_2$	Ethyl propionate	99.1	~93.2	~54	*357*
4675	$C_5H_{10}O_2$	Isobutyl formate	98.3	93	~52	*357*
4676	$C_5H_{10}O_2$	Methyl butyrate	102.75	<94.7	<51	*207*
4677	$C_5H_{10}O_2$	Methyl isobutyrate	92.5	89.8	28	*207*
4678	$C_5H_{10}O_2$	Propyl acetate	101.6	94.6	52	*207*
4679	$C_5H_{11}Cl$	1-Chloro-3-methylbutane	99.4	88.3	29	*207*
4680	$C_5H_{12}O_2$	Diethoxymethane	87.95	<87.0	>11	*207*
4681	C_6H_5Cl	Chlorobenzene	131.8	96.5	82.5	*207*
4682	C_6H_6	Benzene	80.2	76.75	17.36	*334**, *357**, *413*
4683	C_6H_8	1,3-Cyclohexadiene	80.8	75.9	~21	*357*
4684	C_6H_{10}	Cyclohexene	82.75	76.3	~21.7	*357*
4685	$C_6H_{10}O$	Allyl ether	94.84	89.8	30.0	*357*
4686	C_6H_{12}	Cyclohexane	80.75	74	~20	*357*
4687	C_6H_{12}	Methylcyclopentane	72.0	67.8	<10	*247*
4688	$C_6H_{12}O_2$	Ethyl isobutyrate	110.1	~96.2	....	*216*
4689	$C_6H_{12}O_2$	Isobutyl acetate	117.4	Nonazeotrope		*207*
4690	C_6H_{14}	2,3-Dimethylbutane	58.0	<56.7	....	*255*
4691	C_6H_{14}	Hexane	68.95	65.5	4.5	*357*
4692	$C_6H_{14}O$	Propyl ether	90.1	85.7	30	*207*
4693	C_7H_8	Toluene	110.6	91-92	50	*334*, *357**
4694	C_7H_{14}	Methylcyclohexane	101.1	85.0	42	*217*
4695	C_7H_{16}	Heptane	98.45	84.5	~37	*217*
4696	C_8H_{10}	*m*-Xylene	139.0	Nonazeotrope		*217*
4697	C_8H_{18}	2,5-Dimethylhexane	109.4	89.3	50	*247*
4698	C_8H_{18}	Octane	125.75	93.4	68	*247*
4699	C_9H_{12}	Cumene	152.8	Nonazeotrope		*255*
4700	$C_{10}H_{16}$	Camphene	159.6	Nonazeotrope		*255*
4701	$C_{10}H_{16}$	*d*-Limonene	177.8	Nonazeotrope		*217*
4702	$C_{10}H_{16}$	α-Pinene	155.8	Nonazeotrope		*217*
A =	**C_3HO**	**Propionaldehyde**	**48.7**			
4703	$C_3H_6O_2$	Methyl acetate	56.95	Nonazeotrope		*255*
4704	C_3H_7Cl	1-Chloropropane	46.65	<46.4	....	*255*
4705	$C_3H_7NO_2$	Isopropyl nitrite	40.0	Nonazeotrope		*228*
4706	$C_3H_7NO_2$	Propyl nitrite	57.75	<47.3	>18	*228*
4707	C_4H_8O	Cyclopropyl methyl ether	44.73	43	....	*360*
4708	C_5H_6O	2-Methylfuran	63.7	Nonazeotrope		*310*
A =	**C_3H_6O**	**Propylene Oxide**	**43.6**			
4709	C_5H_8	Cyclopentene	43.6	Min. b.p		*416*
4710	C_5H_8	Isoprene	34.5	31.6	60	*416*
4711	C_5H_{10}	Cyclopentane	49.4	Min. b.p.		*416*
4712	C_5H_{10}	2-Methyl-1-butene	32	27	47	*416*
4713	C_5H_{10}	Pentenes	....	Min. b.p.		*416*
4714	C_5H_{10}	2-Pentene	35.8	30	54	*416*
4715	C_5H_{12}	2-Methylbutane	27.95	Nonazeotrope		*238*
4716	C_5H_{12}	Pentanes	....	Min. b.p., azeotrope		*416*
4717	C_5H_{12}	Pentane	36	27.5	57	*416*
4718	C_6H_{12}	Cyclohexane	80.75	Min. b.p.		*416*
4719	C_6H_{12}	Hexenes	....	Min. b.p.		*416*
4720	C_6H_{14}	Hexanes	....	Min. b.p., azeotrope		*416*

No.	B-Component Formula	Name	B.P., ° C.	Azeotropic Data B.P., ° C.	Wt. % A	Ref.
A =	**C_3H_6OS**	**Methyl Thioacetate**	**95.5**			
4721	C_3H_8O	Isopropyl alcohol	82.4	<81.5	....	*255*
4722	C_3H_8O	Propyl alcohol	97.2	<91.5	....	*255*
4722a	C_4H_9ClO	Chloroethyl ethyl ether	98.5	<95.2	>85	*255*
4722b	$C_4H_{10}S$	Ethyl sulfide	92.1	<91.0	>28	*255*
4722c	$C_4H_{10}S$	2-Methyl-1-propanethiol	87.8	<87.2	<12	*255*
A =	**$C_3H_6O_2$**	**1,3-Dioxolane**	**75**			
4723	C_6H_6	Benzene	80.2	74	85	*202*
A =	**$C_3H_6O_2$**	**Ethyl Formate**	**54.1**			
4724	$C_3H_6O_2$	Methyl acetate	56.25	Nonazeotrope		*212*
4725	C_3H_7Br	1-Bromopropane	71.0	Nonazeotrope		*218*
4726	C_3H_7Br	2-Bromopropane	59.35	53	69	*207*
4727	C_3H_7Cl	1-Chloropropane	46.65	46.25	15	*235*
4728	C_3H_7Cl	2-Chloropropane	54.15	Nonazeotrope		*227*
4729	$C_3H_7NO_2$	Isopropyl nitrite	40.1	Nonazeotrope		*229*
4730	$C_3H_7NO_2$	Propyl nitrite	47.75	47.4	12	*207*
4731	C_3H_8O	Isopropyl alcohol	82.35	Nonazeotrope		*216*
4732	$C_3H_8O_2$	Methylal	42.25	Nonazeotrope		*237*
4733	C_3H_8S	1-Propanethiol	67.5	~52	....	*241*
4734	C_4H_8O	Isobutyraldehyde	63.5	Nonazeotrope		*255*
4735	C_4H_9Cl	1-Chloro-2-methylpropane	68.9	Nonazeotrope		*243*
4736	C_4H_9Cl	2-Chloro-2-methylpropane	51.6	48.5	35	*227*
4737	$C_4H_{10}O$	Ethyl ether	34.6	Nonazeotrope		*237*
4738	$C_4H_{10}O_2$	Acetaldehyde dimethyl acetal	64.3	Nonazeotrope		*237*
4739	C_5H_8	Isoprene	34.2	<32.5	<24	*242*
4740	C_5H_{10}	Cyclopentane	49.4	<42.0	<45.0	*242*
4741	C_5H_{10}	2-Methyl-2-butene	37.15	Nonazeotrope		*243*
4742	C_5H_{12}	2-Methylbutane	27.95	26.5	18	*211*
4743	C_5H_{12}	Pentane	36.2	32.5	30	*226*
4744	$C_5H_{12}O$	Ethyl propyl ether	63.6	Nonazeotrope		*237*
4745	C_6H_6	Benzene	80.2	Nonazeotrope		*243*
4746	C_6H_{10}	Biallyl	60.2	~45.2	~58	*253*
4747	C_6H_{12}	Methylcyclopentane	72.0	51.2	75	*242*
4748	C_6H_{14}	2,3-Dimethylbutane	58.0	45.0	52	*242*
4749	C_6H_{14}	*n*-Hexane	68.95	49.0	~67	*253*
4750	$C_9H_{10}O_2$	Ethyl benzoate	213	Vapor pressure curve		*243*
4751	C_9H_{12}	Pseudocumene	169	Vapor pressure data		*243*
A =	**$C_3H_6O_2$**	**Methyl Acetate**	**56.95**			
4752	C_3H_7Br	1-Bromopropane	71.0	Nonazeotrope		*218*
4753	C_3H_7Br	2-Bromopropane	59.35	56	68	*207*
4754	C_3H_7Cl	1-Chloropropane	46.65	Nonazeotrope		*235*
4755	$C_3H_7NO_2$	Isopropyl nitrite	40.1	Nonazeotrope		*230*
4756	$C_3H_7NO_2$	Propyl nitrite	47.75	Nonazeotrope		*229*
4757	C_3H_8O	Isopropyl alcohol	82.35	Nonazeotrope		*216*
4758	$C_3H_8O_2$	Methylal	42.25	Nonazeotrope		*237*
4759	$C_3H_9BO_3$	Methyl borate	68.7	Nonazeotrope		*255*
4760	C_4H_8O	2-Butanone	79.6	Nonazeotrope		*207*
4761	C_4H_8O	Butyraldehyde	75.5	Nonazeotrope		*228*
4762	C_4H_8O	Isobutyraldehyde	63.5	Nonazeotrope		*255*
4763	$C_4H_8O_2$	Isopropyl formate	68.8	Nonazeotrope		*255*
4764	C_4H_9Cl	2-Chlorobutane	68.25	Nonazeotrope		*255*
4765	C_4H_9Cl	1-Chloro-2-methylpropane	68.9	Nonazeotrope		*243*
4766	C_4H_9Cl	2-Chloro-2-methylpropane	51.6	Nonazeotrope		*218*
4767	$C_4H_9NO_2$	Isobutyl nitrite	67.1	Nonazeotrope		*230*
4768	$C_4H_{10}O$	Ethyl ether	34.6	Nonazeotrope		*237*
4769	$C_4H_{10}O_2$	Ethoxymethoxymethane	65.9	Nonazeotrope		*237*
4770	$C_4H_{10}O_2$	Acetaldehyde dimethyl acetal	64.3	Nonazeotrope		*237*
4771	$C_4H_{11}N$	Diethylamine	56	~53	....	*243*
4772	C_5H_6O	2-Methylfuran	63.7	Nonazeotrope		*237, 310**
4773	C_5H_{10}	2-Methyl-2-butene	37.2	<36.9	<12	*255*
4774	C_5H_{12}	Pentane	36.15	Nonazeotrope		*217*
4775	C_6H_6	Benzene	80.2	Nonazeotrope		*243*
4776	C_6H_{10}	Biallyl	60.0	51	60	*217*
4777	C_6H_{10}	Cyclohexene	83	Nonazeotrope		*226*
4778	C_6H_{12}	Cyclohexane	80.8	Nonazeotrope		*226*

No.	B-Component Formula	Name	B.P., ° C.	Azeotropic Data B.P., ° C.	Wt. % A	Ref.
A =	$C_3H_6O_2$	**Methyl Acetate** (*continued*)	**56.95**			
4779	C_6H_{14}	2,3-Dimethylbutane	58.0	51.2	50	*255*
4780	C_6H_{14}	*n*-Hexane	68.95	<56.65	<90	*255*
A =	$C_3H_6O_2$	**Propionic Acid**	**140.9**			
4781	C_3H_7I	1-Iodopropane	102.4	Nonazeotrope		*222*
4782	$C_4H_6Cl_2O_2$	Ethyl dichloroacetate	158.1	Nonazeotrope		*255*
4783	$C_4H_6O_3$	Methyl pyruvate	137.5	<137.2	>75	*232*
4784	$C_4H_7BrO_2$	Ethyl bromoacetate	158.8	Nonazeotrope		*207*
4785	$C_4H_7ClO_2$	Ethyl chloroacetate	143.55	<140.35	<61	*207*
4786	C_4H_8O	2-Butanone	79.6	Nonazeotrope, V-l.		*285*
4787	$C_4H_8O_2$	Dioxane	101.35	Nonazeotrope		*207*
4788	C_4H_9Br	1-Bromobutane	101.5	Nonazeotrope		*207*
4789	C_4H_9I	1-Iodobutane	130.4	126.8	15	*207*
4790	C_4H_9I	1-Iodo-2-methylpropane	120.4	119.3	7	*207*
4791	$C_4H_9NO_3$	Isobutyl nitrate	123.5	122.0	9	*239*
4792	$C_4H_{10}S$	Ethyl sulfide	92.1	Nonazeotrope		*246*
4793	$C_5H_4O_2$	2-Furaldehyde	161.5	Nonazeotrope		*243*
4794	C_5H_5N	Pyridine	115.5	148–150	74	*151*
4795	C_5H_8O	Cyclopentanone	130.65	Nonazeotrope		*232*
4796	$C_5H_8O_2$	2,4-Pentanedione	138	144	~70	*243*
4797	$C_5H_8O_3$	Ethyl pyruvate	155.5	Nonazeotrope		*232*
4798	$C_5H_9ClO_2$	Propyl chloroacetate	163.5	Nonazeotrope		*255*
4799	$C_5H_{10}O_3$	Ethyl carbonate	126.5	Nonazeotrope		*255*
4800	$C_5H_{10}O_3$	2-Methoxy ethyl acetate	144.6	146.85	36	*248*
4801	$C_5H_{11}Br$	1-Bromo-3-methylbutane	120.65	119.45	7.5	*207*
4802	$C_5H_{11}Cl$	1-Chloro-3-methylbutane	99.4	Nonazeotrope		*207*
4803	$C_5H_{11}I$	1-Iodo-3-methylbutane	147.65	136.5	42	*207*
4804	$C_5H_{11}NO_3$	Isoamyl nitrate	~149.6	138.8	59	*207*
4805	$C_6H_4Cl_2$	*o*-Dichlorobenzene	179.5	Nonazeotrope		*207*
4806	$C_6H_4Cl_2$	*p*-Dichlorobenzene	174.6	Nonazeotrope		*207*
4807	C_6H_5Br	Bromobenzene	156.1	140.15	....	*251*
4808	C_6H_5Cl	Chlorobenzene	132.0	128.9	18	*222*
4809	C_3H_6	Benzene	80.15	Nonazeotrope		*207*
4810	C_6H_7N	2-Picoline	131	~164	....	*243*
4811	C_6H_7N	3-Picoline	144	155–163	....	*426*
		At 212 mm.	....	122	48.5	*81*, 82*
4812	C_6H_7N	4-Picoline	145.3	155–163	....	*327*
		At 212 mm.	....	124	48.1	*81*, 82*
4813	$C_6H_{10}O$	Cyclohexanone	155.7	Nonazeotrope		*232*
4814	$C_6H_{10}O$	Mesityl oxide	129.45	Nonazeotrope		*232*
4815	$C_6H_{10}S$	Allyl sulfide	139.35	134.6	40	*235*
4816	C_6H_{12}	Cyclohexane	80.75	Nonazeotrope		*207*
4817	$C_6H_{12}O$	2-Hexanone	127.2	Nonazeotrope		*232*
4818	$C_6H_{12}O$	3-Hexanone	123.3	Nonazeotrope		*232*
4819	$C_6H_{12}O$	4-Methyl-2-pentanone	116.05	Nonazeotrope		*207*
4820	$C_6H_{12}O_2$	Butyl acetate	126.0	Nonazeotrope		*207*
4821	$C_6H_{12}O_2$	Isoamyl formate	123.6	Nonazeotrope		*243*
4822	$C_6H_{12}O_2$	Propyl propionate	123.0	Nonazeotrope		*207*
4823	$C_6H_{12}O_3$	2-Ethoxyethyl acetate	156.8	Nonazeotrope		*206*
4824	$C_6H_{13}Br$	1-Bromohexane	156.5	139.0	60	*255*
4825	$C_6H_{14}O$	Propyl ether	90.1	Nonazeotrope		*207*
4826	$C_6H_{14}S$	Propyl sulfide	141.5	136.5	45	*246*
4827	C_7H_6O	Benzaldehyde	179.2	Nonazeotrope		*255*
4828	C_7H_7Br	*m*-Bromotoluene	184.3	Nonazeotrope		*207*
4829	C_7H_7Br	*o*-Bromotoluene	181.5	Nonazeotrope		*207*
4830	C_7H_7Cl	*α*-Chlorotoluene	179.3	Nonazeotrope		*207*
4831	C_7H_7Cl	*o*-Chlorotoluene	159.3	139.4	67	*218*
4832	C_7H_7Cl	*p*-Chlorotoluene	162.4	139.8	~75	*218*
4833	C_7H_8	Toluene	110.75	110.45	3	*207*
4834	C_7H_8O	Anisole	153.85	141.17	87	*207*
4835	C_7H_9N	2,6-Lutidine	144	155–163	....	*327*
		At 212 mm.	....	119	48.8	*81*, 82*
4836	C_7H_{14}	Methylcyclohexane	101.15	Nonazeotrope		*255*
4837	$C_7H_{14}O_2$	Ethyl isovalerate	134.7	Nonazeotrope		*255*
4838	$C_7H_{14}O_2$	Ethyl valerate	145.45	Nonazeotrope		*255*
4839	$C_7H_{14}O_2$	Isoamyl acetate	142.1	Nonazeotrope		*207*

No.	B-Component Formula	Name	B.P., ° C.	Azeotropic Data B.P., ° C.	Wt. % A	Ref.
A =	$C_3H_6O_2$	**Propionic Acid** (*continued*)	**140.9**			
4840	$C_7H_{14}O_2$	Methyl caproate	149.7	Nonazeotrope		255
4841	$C_7H_{14}O_2$	Propyl butyrate	142.8	Nonazeotrope		221
4842	C_nH_x	Hydrocarbons	138–140	134	67	324
4843	C_8H_8	Styrene	145.8	135.0	~47	225
4844	C_8H_{10}	Ethylbenzene	136.15	131.1	28	243
		At 60 mm.	60.5	58.5	10	26
4845	C_8H_{10}	*m*-Xylene	139.0	132.65	35.5?	243
4846	C_8H_{10}	*o*-Xylene	143.6	135.4	43	207
4847	C_8H_{10}	*p*-Xylene	138.2	132.5	34	207
4848	$C_8H_{10}O$	Benzyl methyl ether	167.8	Nonazeotrope		207
4849	$C_8H_{10}O$	*p*-Methylanisole	177.05	Nonazeotrope		255
4850	$C_8H_{10}O$	Phenetole	170.45	Nonazeotrope		207
4851	C_8H_{16}	1,3-Dimethylcyclohexane	120.7	118.2	18	242
4852	$C_8H_{16}O_2$	Amyl propionate	....	Nonazeotrope		324
4853	$C_8H_{16}O_2$	Isobutyl isobutyrate	148.6	Nonazeotrope		255
4854	$C_8H_{16}O_2$	Propyl isovalerate	155.7	Nonazeotrope		207
4855	C_8H_{18}	2,5-Dimethylhexane	109.4	108.0	8	243
4856	C_8H_{18}	Octane	125.75	121.5	<30	243
4857	$C_8H_{18}O$	Butyl ether	142.4	136.0	45	207
4858	$C_8H_{18}O$	Isobutyl ether	122.3	<121.5	<6	255
4859	C_9H_7N	Quinoline	237.3	Nonazeotrope		233
4860	C_9H_8	Indene	182.6	Nonazeotrope		207
4861	C_9H_{12}	Cumene	152.8	139.0	65	207
4862	C_9H_{12}	Mesitylene	164.0	139.3	77	243
4863	C_9H_{12}	Propylbenzene	158	139.5	75	207
4864	C_9H_{12}	Pseudocumene	168.2	Nonazeotrope		221
4865	$C_{10}H_{14}$	Butylbenzene	183.1	Nonazeotrope		207
4866	$C_{10}H_{14}$	Cymene	175.5	Nonazeotrope		207
4867	$C_{10}H_{16}$	Camphene	159.6	138	65	207
4868	$C_{10}H_{16}$	*d*-Limonene	177	Nonazeotrope		243
4869	$C_{10}H_{16}$	Nopinene	164	~139.0	~24	243
4870	$C_{10}H_{16}$	α-Phellandrene	171.5	Nonazeotrope		243
4871	$C_{10}H_{16}$	α-Pinene	155.8	136.4	58.5	222
4872	$C_{10}H_{16}$	α-Terpinene	173.4	141.2	97	255
4873	$C_{10}H_{16}$	Terpinolene	184.6	Nonazeotrope		255
4874	$C_{10}H_{16}$	Thymene	165	139	~88	243
4875	$C_{10}H_{18}O$	Cineol	176.35	Nonazeotrope		207
4876	$C_{10}H_{20}O_2$	Isoamyl isovalerate	134.7	Nonazeotrope		222
4877	$C_{10}H_{22}$	Decane	173.3	<140.5	<95	242
4878	$C_{10}H_{22}$	2,7-Dimethyloctane	160.25	138.3	70	243
4879	$C_{10}H_{22}O$	Isoamyl ether	173.2	Nonazeotrope		207
A =	$C_3H_6O_3$	**Methyl Carbonate**	**90.35**			
4880	C_3H_7Br	1-Bromopropane	71.0	Nonazeotrope		227
4881	C_3H_7I	1-Iodopropane	102.4	89.5	90	243
4882	C_3H_7I	2-Iodopropane	89.35	86.0	<45	227
4883	C_3H_8O	Isopropyl alcohol	82.45	78.75	44	252
4884	C_3H_8O	Propyl alcohol	97.2	87	75	212
4885	C_4H_8O	2-Butanone	79.6	Nonazeotrope		207
4886	$C_4H_8O_2$	Dioxane	101.35	Nonazeotrope		237
4887	$C_4H_8O_2$	Ethyl acetate	77.1	Nonazeotrope		255
4888	C_4H_9Br	1-Bromobutane	101.6	Nonazeotrope		227
4889	C_4H_9Br	2-Bromobutane	91.2	<88.5	<54	255
4890	C_4H_9Br	1-Bromo-2-methylpropane	91.6	87.5	<50	227
4891	C_4H_9Br	2-Bromo-2-methylpropane	73.25	Nonazeotrope		255
4892	C_4H_9Cl	1-Chlorobutane	78.5	Nonazeotrope		227
4893	$C_4H_{10}O$	Butyl alcohol	117.75	Nonazeotrope		207
4894	$C_4H_{10}O$	*sec*-Butyl alcohol	99.5	89.0	85	243
4895	$C_4H_{10}O$	*tert*-Butyl alcohol	82.45	80.65	33	250
4896	$C_4H_{10}O$	Isobutyl alcohol	108.0	90.05	92	207
4897	$C_4H_{10}S$	Butanethiol	97.5	88.2	70	248
4898	$C_4H_{10}S$	Ethyl sulfide	92.1	86.8	53	248
4899	$C_5H_{10}O$	3-Methyl-2-butanone	95.4	Nonazeotrope		232
4900	$C_5H_{10}O_2$	Isobutyl formate	98.2	Nonazeotrope		255
4901	$C_5H_{10}O_2$	Isopropyl acetate	91.0	Nonazeotrope		211
4902	$C_5H_{10}O_2$	Methyl isobutyrate	92.5	Nonazeotrope		229

No.	Formula	B-Component Name	B.P., ° C	Azeotropic Data B.P., ° C.	Wt. % A	Ref.
A =	$C_3H_6O_3$	**Methyl Carbonate** (*continued*)	**90.35**			
4903	$C_5H_{11}Cl$	1-Chloro-3-methylbutane	99.4	<90	....	*255*
4904	$C_5H_{12}O$	2-Pentanol	119.8	Nonazeotrope		*255*
4905	$C_5H_{12}O_2$	Diethoxymethane	87.95	86.0	40	*207*
4906	C_6H_6	Benzene	80.2	80.17	1	*252*
4907	$C_6H_{10}O$	Mesityl oxide	129.45	126.45	94	*232*
4908	C_6H_{12}	Cyclohexane	80.75	~75	....	*243*
4909	C_6H_{12}	Methylcyclopentane	72.0	<69.5	>12	*255*
4910	C_6H_{14}	*n*-Hexane	68.95	<67.0	<20	*255*
4911	$C_6H_{14}O$	Propyl ether	90.55	<87.5	<58	*237*
4912	$C_6H_{14}O_2$	Acetal	103.55	Nonazeotrope		*237*
4913	C_7H_8	Toluene	110.75	Nonazeotrope		*255*
4914	C_7H_{14}	Methylcyclohexane	101.15	<85.0	<75	*243*
4915	C_7H_{16}	*n*-Heptane	98.4	82.35	61	*250*
4916	C_7H_{16}	*n*-Heptane	98.45	~85.5	~70	*243*
4917	C_8H_8	Styrene	145	Min. b.p.		*141*
4918	C_8H_{10}	Ethylbenzene	136	Min. b.p.		*141*
4919	C_8H_{10}	Xylenes	140	Min. b.p.		*141*
4920	C_8H_{16}	1,3-Dimethylcyclohexane	120.7	Nonazeotrope		*255*
4921	C_8H_{18}	2,5-Dimethylhexane	109.4	87.0	80	*242*
4922	C_8H_{18}	Octane	125.75	Nonazeotrope		*255*
A =	$C_3H_6O_3$	**Trioxane**	**114.5**			
4923	C_6H_{12}	Naphthenes	~80	Min. b.p.		*200*
4924	C_6H_{14}	Hexanes	~70	Min. b.p.		*200*
4925	C_7H_{14}	Naphthenes	~100	Min. b.p.		*200*
4926	C_7H_{16}	Heptanes	~100	Min. b.p.		*200*
4927	C_8H_{10}	Xylene	140	Min. b.p.		*202*
4928	C_8H_{16}	Naphthenes	~120	Min. b.p.		*200*
4929	C_8H_{18}	Octanes	~120	Min. b.p.		*200*
4930	C_9H_{20}	Nonanes	~130	Min. b.p.		*200*
A =	C_3H_7Br	**1-Bromopropane**	**71.0**			
4931	C_3H_8O	Isopropyl alcohol	82.45	66.75	79.5	*253*
4932	C_3H_8O	Isopropyl alcohol	82.45	65.2	84	*243*
4933	C_3H_8O	Propyl alcohol	95.6	69.75	90	*163*
4934	C_3H_8S	1-Propanethiol	87.5	Nonazeotrope		*243*
4935	$C_3H_9BO_3$	Methyl borate	68.75	~67.8	~55	*211*
4936	C_4H_4S	Thiophene	84.7	Nonazeotrope		*207*
4937	C_4H_8O	Butyraldehyde	75.2	Nonazeotrope		*255*
4938	C_4H_8O	Isobutyraldehyde	63.5	Nonazeotrope		*255*
4939	C_4H_8O	2-Butanone	79.6	Nonazeotrope		*207*
4940	$C_4H_8O_2$	Ethyl acetate	77.05	70	~80	*243*
4941	$C_4H_8O_2$	Ethyl acetate	77.05	Nonazeotrope		*212*
4942	$C_4H_8O_2$	Isopropyl formate	68.8	66.0	<45	*227*
4943	$C_4H_8O_2$	Methyl propionate	79.7	Azeotrope doubtful		*243*
4944	$C_4H_8O_2$	Propyl formate	80.85	Nonazeotrope		*218*
4945	C_4H_9Cl	1-Chloro-2-methylpropane	68.85	Nonazeotrope		*229*
4946	C_4H_9Cl	1-Chloro-2-methylpropane	68.85	68.8	5	*212*
4947	$C_4H_9NO_2$	Butyl nitrite	78.2	Nonazeotrope		*230*
4948	$C_4H_9NO_2$	Isobutyl nitrite	67.1	67.05	5	*230*
4949	$C_4H_{10}O$	Butyl alcohol	117.75	Nonazeotrope		*207*
4950	$C_4H_{10}O$	*tert*-Butyl alcohol	82.45	68.0	88	*247*
4951	$C_4H_{10}O$	Isobutyl alcohol	105.5	Nonazeotrope, b.p. curve		*163*
4952	$C_4H_{10}O_2$	Acetaldehyde dimethyl acetal	64.3	Nonazeotrope		*239*
4953	$C_4H_{10}O_2$	Ethoxymethoxymethane	65.9	Nonazeotrope		*239*
4954	$C_5H_{10}O_2$	Isopropyl acetate	89.5	Nonazeotrope		*255*
4955	$C_5H_{12}O$	*tert*-Amyl alcohol	102.0	Nonazeotrope		*215*
4956	$C_5H_{12}O$	Ethyl propyl ether	63.85	Nonazeotrope		*239*
4957	$C_5H_{12}O$	Isoamyl alcohol	129.3	Nonazeotrope, b.p. curve		*163*
4958	C_6H_6	Benzene	80.2	Nonazeotrope		*243*
4959	C_6H_{12}	Cyclohexane	80.75	Nonazeotrope		*243*
4960	C_6H_{12}	Methylcyclopentane	72.0	68.8	58	*242*
4961	C_6H_{14}	2,3-Dimethylbutane	58.0	Nonazeotrope		*255*
4962	C_6H_{14}	Hexane	68.85	67.2	50	*218*

No.	B-Component Formula	B-Component Name	B.P., ° C.	Azeotropic Data B.P., ° C.	Azeotropic Data Wt. % A	Ref.
A =	**C_3H_7Br**	**2-Bromopropane**	**59.4**			
4963	$C_3H_7NO_2$	Propyl nitrite	47.75	Nonazeotrope		230
4964	C_3H_8O	Isopropyl alcohol	82.45	57.7	93	207
4965	C_3H_8O	Propyl alcohol	97.2	Nonazeotrope		207
4966	C_3H_8O	Propyl alcohol	97.2	58.4	96	253
4967	C_3H_8S	Propanethiol	67.3	Nonazeotrope		255
4968	$C_3H_9BO_3$	Methyl borate	68.7	Nonazeotrope		227
4969	C_4H_8O	2-Butanone	79.6	Nonazeotrope		207
4970	C_4H_8O	Butyraldehyde	75.2	Nonazeotrope		255
4971	C_4H_8O	Isobutyraldehyde	63.5	Nonazeotrope		255
4972	$C_4H_8O_2$	Ethyl acetate	77.1	Nonazeotrope		207
4973	$C_4H_9NO_2$	Isobutyl nitrite	67.1	Nonazeotrope		230
4974	$C_4H_{10}O$	*sec*-Butyl alcohol	99.5	Nonazeotrope		207
4975	$C_4H_{10}O$	*tert*-Butyl alcohol	82.45	59.0	94.8	207
4976	$C_4H_{10}O_2$	Acetaldehyde dimethyl acetal	64.3	Nonazeotrope		239
4977	$C_5H_{12}O$	Ethyl propyl ether	63.6	Nonazeotrope		228
4978	C_6H_6	Benzene	80.15	Nonazeotrope		207
4979	C_6H_{12}	Cyclohexane	80.75	Nonazeotrope		255
4980	C_6H_{12}	Methylcyclopentane	72.0	Nonazeotrope		207
4981	C_6H_{14}	2,3-Dimethylbutane	58.0	55.8	50	207
4982	C_6H_{14}	Hexane	68.8	59.3	98.5	207
4893	C_6H_{14}	Hexane	68.85	Nonazeotrope		218
4984	$C_6H_{14}O$	Isopropyl ether	68.3	Nonazeotrope		207
A =	**C_3H_7Cl**	**1-Chloropropane**	**46.65**			
4985	$C_3H_7NO_2$	Isopropyl nitrite	40.1	Nonazeotrope		230
4986	$C_3H_7NO_2$	Propyl nitrite	47.75	45.6	62	235
4987	C_3H_8O	Isopropyl alcohol	82.4	46.4	97.2	235
4988	C_3H_8O	Propyl alcohol	97.2	Nonazeotrope		235
4989	$C_3H_8O_2$	Methylal	42.15	Nonazeotrope		235
4990	C_3H_8S	Propanethiol	67.3	Nonazeotrope		255
4991	$C_3H_9BO_3$	Methyl borate	68.7	Nonazeotrope		255
4992	$C_4H_8O_2$	Ethyl acetate	77.05	Nonazeotrope		235
4993	$C_4H_9NO_2$	Isobutyl nitrite	67.1	Nonazeotrope		235
4994	$C_4H_{10}O$	*tert*-Butyl alcohol	82.55	Nonazeotrope		235
4995	$C_4H_{10}O$	Ethyl ether	34.5	Nonazeotrope		235
4996	$C_4H_{10}O$	Methyl propyl ether	38.9	Nonazeotrope		239
4997	C_5H_8	Isoprene	34.3	Nonazeotrope		255
4998	C_5H_{10}	Cyclopentane	49.3	<44.5	<64	255
4999	C_5H_{12}	Pentane	36	<34.8	<32	235
5000	C_6H_{14}	Hexane	68.8	Nonazeotrope		255
A =	**C_3H_7Cl**	**2-Chloropropane**	**34.9**			
5001	$C_3H_7NO_2$	Isopropyl nitrite	40.1	Nonazeotrope		230
5002	$C_3H_7NO_2$	Propyl nitrite	47.75	Nonazeotrope		230
5003	C_3H_8O	Isopropyl alcohol	82.5	Nonazeotrope		93
5004	$C_3H_8O_2$	Methylal	42.3	Nonazeotrope		228
5005	C_5H_{10}	Cyclopentane	49.3	<44.5	<64	242
			49.3	Nonazeotrope		255
5006	C_5H_{10}	2-Methyl-2-butene	37.1	32.8	58	255
5007	C_5H_{10}	2-Methyl-2-butene	37.15	34	61	243
5008	C_5H_{10}	3-Methyl-1-butene	37.1	32.8	58	242
5009	C_5H_{12}	2-Methylbutane	27.95	~24	....	243
5010	C_5H_{12}	Pentane	36.15	~32	~52	243
A =	**C_3H_7ClO**	**1-Chloro-2-propanol**	**127.0**			
5011	C_4H_9I	1-Iodobutane	130.4	120.0	45	247
5012	C_4H_9I	1-Iodo-2-methylpropane	120.8	115.0	25	247
5013	$C_4H_{10}O$	Butyl alcohol	117.8	Nonazeotrope		255
5014	$C_4H_{10}O$	Isobutyl alcohol	108.0	Nonazeotrope		255
5015	$C_4H_{10}O_2$	2-Ethoxyethanol	135.3	Nonazeotrope		255
5016	$C_5H_{11}Br$	1-Bromo-3-methylbutane	120.65	115.5	~30	255
5017	$C_5H_{12}O$	Isoamyl alcohol	131.9	<127.3	>81	255
5018	$C_5H_{12}O_2$	2-Propoxyethanol	151.35	Nonazeotrope		255
5019	C_6H_5Br	Bromobenzene	156.1	Nonazeotrope		255
5020	C_6H_5Cl	Chlorobenzene	131.75	122.2	55	247
5021	C_6H_6	Benzene	80.15	Nonazeotrope		255
5022	C_6H_{12}	Cyclohexane	80.75	Nonazeotrope		255
5023	$C_6H_{12}O$	3-Hexanone	123.3	Nonazeotrope		232

No.	Formula	Name	B.P., ° C.	B.P., ° C.	Wt. % A	Ref.
	B-Component			Azeotropic Data		
A =	C_3H_7ClO	**1-Chloro-2-propanol** (*continued*)	**127.0**			
5024	$C_6H_{12}O$	4-Methyl-2-pentanone	116.05	Nonazeotrope		*207*
5025	$C_6H_{12}O_2$	Butyl acetate	126.0	125.5	~25	*255*
5026	$C_6H_{12}O_2$	Ethyl isobutyrate	110.1	Nonazeotrope		*255*
5027	$C_6H_{12}O_2$	Isoamyl formate	123.8	123.0	~30	*255*
5028	$C_6H_{14}O_2$	Isobutyl acetate	117.4	Nonazeotrope		*255*
5029	C_7H_8	Toluene	110.75	109.0	15	*247*
5030	C_7H_8O	Anisole	153.85	Nonazeotrope		*255*
5031	C_7H_{16}	Heptane	98.4	96.5	17	*255*
5032	C_8H_{10}	*m*-Xylene	139.2	124.5	75	*247*
5033	C_8H_{10}	*o*-Xylene	144.3	125.5	85	*255*
5034	C_8H_{18}	2,5-Dimethylhexane	109.4	105.0	30	*247*
5035	$C_8H_{18}O$	Isobutyl ether	122.3	<118.0	>35	*255*
A =	C_3H_7ClO	**2-Chloro-1-propanol**	**133.7**			
5036	C_4H_9I	1-Iodobutane	130.4	123.5	30	*247*
5037	$C_5H_{11}Br$	1-Bromo-3-methylbutane	120.65	118.0	15	*255*
5038	C_6H_5Br	Bromobenzene	156.1	Nonazeotrope		*255*
5039	C_6H_5Cl	Chlorobenzene	13.75	126.0	36	*247*
5040	C_6H_6O	Phenol	182.2	Nonazeotrope		*255*
5041	C_6H_{12}	Cyclohexane	80.75	Nonazeotrope		*255*
5042	$C_6H_{12}O_2$	Isoamyl formate	123.8	<123.7	>5	*255*
5043	$C_6H_{12}O_2$	Isobutyl acetate	126.0	Nonazeotrope		*255*
5044	$C_7H_{14}O_2$	Ethyl isovalerate	134.7	133.5?	60?	*255*
4045	$C_7H_{14}O_2$	Isoamyl acetate	142.1	Nonazeotrope		*255*
5046	C_8H_{10}	*m*-Xylene	139.2	129.0	53	*247*
5047	C_8H_{10}	*o*-Xylene	144.3	130.5	70	*247*
5048	C_8H_{16}	1,3-Dimethylcyclohexane	120.7	115.0	35	*247*
5049	$C_8H_{18}O$	Butyl ether	142.4	130.5	70	*255*
5050	$C_8H_{18}O$	Isobutyl ether	122.3	120.0	25	*255*
A =	$C_3H_7ClO_2$	**Chloromethylal**	**95**			
5051	C_4H_8O	2-Butanone	79.6	Nonazeotrope		*255*
5052	$C_5H_{10}O$	3-Pentanone	95.0	Nonazeotrope		*255*
5053	C_6H_6	Benzene	80.15	Nonazeotrope		*255*
5054	C_6H_{12}	Cyclohexane	80.75	Nonazeotrope		*255*
5055	C_7H_{16}	Heptane	98.4	93.0	62	*242*
A =	$C_3H_7ClO_2$	**1-Chloro-2,3-propanediol**	**213**			
5056	$C_6H_5NO_2$	Nitrobenzene	210.85	~208	....	*243*
5057	C_7H_7Cl	α-Chlorotoluene	179.35	179.2?	....	*243*
5058	C_7H_8O	Benzyl alcohol	205.5	204.5	....	*243*
5059	C_7H_8O	*p*-Cresol	201.8	Nonazeotrope		*243*
5060	$C_{10}H_{16}O$	Camphor	208.9	Nonazeotrope		*243*
A =	C_3H_7I	**1-Iodopropane**	**102.4**			
5061	C_3H_8O	Isopropyl alcohol	82.45	79.8	58	*253*
5062	C_3H_8O	Propyl alcohol	97.2	90.2	70	*243*
5063	$C_3H_8O_2$	2-Methoxyethanol	124.5	101.0	....	*255*
5064	C_4H_6O	Crotonaldehyde	102.15	<99.7	....	*243*
5065	$C_4H_8O_2$	Dioxane	101.35	98.75	60	*239*
5066	$C_4H_{10}O$	Butyl alcohol	117.75	99.5	86.5	*215*
5067	$C_4H_{10}O$	Isobutyl alcohol	108	96	~82	*243*
5068	$C_4H_{10}O_2$	2-Ethoxyethanol	135.3	Nonazeotrope		*236*
5069	$C_5H_{10}O$	3-Methyl-2-butanone	95.4	Nonazeotrope		*232*
5070	$C_5H_{10}O$	2-Pentanone	102.35	100.8	65	*232*
5071	$C_5H_{10}O$	3-Pentanone	102.05	100.8	62	*232*
5072	$C_5H_{10}O_2$	Isopropyl acetate	89.5	Nonazeotrope		*255*
5073	$C_5H_{10}O_2$	Methyl butyrate	102.65	101.0	56	*227*
5074	$C_5H_{10}O_2$	Methyl isobutyrate	92.5	Nonazeotrope		*227*
5075	$C_5H_{10}O_2$	Propyl acetate	101.6	99.0	>46	*207*
5076	$C_5H_{11}NO_2$	Isoamyl nitrite	97.15	<96.7	....	*230*
5077	$C_5H_{12}O$	*tert*-Amyl alcohol	102.35	97.2	70	*247*
5078	$C_5H_{12}O$	3-Pentanol	116.0	100.5	89	*247*
5079	$C_6H_{12}O_2$	Ethyl isobutyrate	110.1	Nonazeotrope		*227*
5080	$C_6H_{14}O_2$	Acetal	103.55	101.0	60	*239*
5081	C_7H_8	Toluene	110.7	Nonazeotrope		*243*
5082	C_7H_{14}	Methylcyclohexane	101.1	99.4	~60	*253*
5083	C_7H_{16}	Heptane	98.4	<97.5	>40	*242*

No.	Formula	B-Component Name	B.P., ° C.	Azeotropic Data B.P., ° C.	Wt. % A	Ref.
A =	C_3H_7I	**2-Iodopropane**	**89.35**			
5084	C_3H_8O	Isopropyl alcohol	82.45	76.0	68	253
5085	C_3H_8O	Propyl alcohol	97.2	82.95	83	207
5086	C_4H_8O	2-Butanone	79.6	Nonazeotrope		207
5087	$C_4H_8O_2$	Dioxane	101.35	Nonazeotrope		239
5088	$C_4H_8O_2$	Methyl propionate	79.84	Nonazeotrope		227
5089	$C_4H_8O_2$	Propyl formate	80.85	Nonazeotrope		227
			80.85	<80.2	>16	255
5090	$C_4H_{10}O$	Butyl alcohol	117.8	88.6	94	247
5091	$C_4H_{10}O$	*sec*-Butyl alcohol	99.5	85.4	83	247
5092	$C_4H_{10}O$	*tert*-Butyl alcohol	82.45	<77.75	<69	247
5093	$C_4H_{10}O$	Isobutyl alcohol	107.85	86.8	88	207
5094	$C_5H_{10}O_2$	Isobutyl formate	98.2	Nonazeotrope		227
			98.2	<88.5	>82	255
5095	$C_5H_{10}O_2$	Isopropyl acetate	90.8	87.0	60	227
5096	$C_5H_{10}O_2$	Methyl isobutyrate	92.5	<88.8	>80	255
5097	$C_5H_{11}NO_2$	Isoamyl nitrite	97.15	Nonazeotrope		230
5098	$C_5H_{12}O$	*tert*-Amyl alcohol	102.35	88.6	92	247
5099	$C_5H_{12}O$	3-Methyl-2-butanol	112.6	Nonazeotrope		255
5100	$C_5H_{12}O_2$	Diethoxymethane	87.95	86.15	37	207
5101	C_6H_6	Benzene	80.2	Nonazeotrope		218
5102	C_6H_{12}	Cyclohexane	80.75	Nonazeotrope		255
5103	$C_6H_{14}O$	Propyl ether	90.55	~89.0	~65	228
5104	C_7H_{14}	Methylcyclohexane	100.8	88	65	384
A =	C_3H_7NO	**Acetoxime**	**135.8**			
5105	$C_6H_{10}S$	Allyl sulfide	138.7	134	....	243
A =	C_3H_7NO	**Propionamide**	**222.2**			
5106	$C_3H_7NO_2$	Ethyl carbamate	185.25	Nonazeotrope		255
5107	C_4H_5NS	Allyl isothiocyanate	152.0	Nonazeotrope		255
5108	$C_4H_6O_4$	Methyl oxalate	164.45	Nonazeotrope		255
5109	$C_4H_7BrO_2$	Ethyl bromoacetate	158.8	Nonazeotrope		207
5110	$C_4H_8Cl_2O$	Bis(2-chloroethyl) ether	178.65	Nonazeotrope		207
5111	$C_4H_8O_3$	Glycol monoacetate	190.9	Nonazeotrope		255
5112	C_4H_9I	1-Iodobutane	130.4	Nonazeotrope		207
5113	$C_4H_{10}O_3$	Diethylene glycol	245.5	Nonazeotrope		206
5114	$C_5H_6O_2$	Furfuryl alcohol	169.35	Nonazeotrope		255
5115	$C_5H_8O_3$	Levulinic acid	252	Nonazeotrope		207
5116	$C_5H_9ClO_2$	Propyl chloroacetate	163.5	Nonazeotrope		255
5117	$C_5H_{11}Br$	1-Bromo-3-methylbutane	120.65	Nonazeotrope		207
5118	$C_5H_{11}I$	1-Iodo-3-methylbutane	147.65	Nonazeotrope		207
5119	$C_5H_{12}O$	Isoamyl alcohol	131.3	Nonazeotrope		207
5120	$C_5H_{12}O_2$	2-Propoxyethanol	151.35	Nonazeotrope		206
5121	$C_5H_{12}O_3$	2-(2-Methoxyethoxy)ethano	192.95	Nonazeotrope		206
5122	C_6H_4BrCl	*p*-Bromochlorobenzene	196.4	189.5	16	255
5123	$C_6H_4Br_2$	*p*-Dibromobenzene	220.25	204.9	22	207
5124	$C_6H_4ClNO_2$	*m*-Chloronitrobenzene	235.5	216.5	>48	234
5125	$C_6H_4ClNO_2$	*o*-Chloronitrobenzene	246.0	<220.6	>54	234
5126	$C_6H_4ClNO_2$	*p*-Chloronitrobenzene	239.1	217.5	49.8	207
5127	$C_6H_4Cl_2$	*o*-Dichlorobenzene	179.5	177.0	9	244
5128	$C_6H_4Cl_2$	*p*-Dichlorobenzene	174.4	172.55	8	207
5129	C_6H_5Br	Bromobenzene	156.1	Nonazeotrope		207
5130	C_6H_5BrO	*o*-Bromophenol	194.8	Nonazeotrope		255
5131	C_6H_5Cl	Chlorobenzene	132.0	Nonazeotrope		207
5132	C_6H_5ClO	*p*-Chlorophenol	219.75	228.0	33	242
5133	C_6H_5I	Iodobenzene	188.45	183.5	10	250
5134	$C_6H_5NO_2$	Nitrobenzene	210.75	205.4	24	207
5135	$C_6H_5NO_3$	*o*-Nitrophenol	217.25	211.15	24.8	222
5136	C_6H_6O	Phenol	182.2	Nonazeotrope		222
5137	$C_6H_6O_2$	Pyrocatechol	245.9	Nonazeotrope		222
5138	$C_6H_6O_2$	Resorcinol	281.4	Nonazeotrope		224
5139	C_6H_7N	Aniline	184.35	Nonazeotrope		207
5140	$C_6H_8N_2$	*o*-Phenylenediamine	258.6	Nonazeotrope		231
5141	$C_6H_8O_4$	Methyl fumarate	193.25	Nonazeotrope		207
5142	$C_6H_8O_4$	Methyl maleate	204.05	Nonazeotrope		207
5143	$C_6H_{10}O_4$	Ethylidene diacetate	168.5	Nonazeotrope		207
5144	$C_6H_{10}O_4$	Ethyl oxalate	185.65	Nonazeotrope		207

No.	B-Component Formula	Name	B.P., ° C.	Azeotropic Data B.P., ° C.	Wt. % A	Ref.
A =	**C_3H_7NO**	**Propionamide (*continued*)**	**222.2**			
5145	$C_6H_{10}O_4$	Glycol diacetate	186.3	Nonazeotrope		*255*
5146	$C_6H_{11}ClO_2$	Butyl chloroacetate	181.9	Nonazeotrope		*255*
5147	$C_6H_{11}NO_2$	Nitrocyclohexane	205.3	<203.0	>11	*255*
5148	$C_6H_{12}O$	Cyclohexanol	160.7	Nonazeotrope		*207*
5149	$C_6H_{12}O_2$	Caproic acid	205.15	Nonazeotrope		*255*
5150	$C_6H_{12}O_3$	2-Ethoxyethyl acetate	156.8	Nonazeotrope		*206*
5151	$C_6H_{12}O_3$	Propyl lactate	171.7	Nonazeotrope		*255*
5152	$C_6H_{13}Br$	1-Bromohexane	156.5	Nonazeotrope		*255*
5153	$C_6H_{14}O$	Hexyl alcohol	157.85	Nonazeotrope		*207*
5154	$C_6H_{14}O_2$	2-Butoxyethanol	171.15	Nonazeotrope		*207*
5155	$C_6H_{14}O_2$	Pinacol	174.35	Nonazeotrope		*255*
5156	$C_6H_{14}S$	Propyl sulfide	141.5	Nonazeotrope		*246*
5157	$C_7H_5Cl_3$	α,α,α-Trichlorotoluene	220.9	Reacts		*215*
5158	C_7H_6O	Benzaldehyde	179.2	Nonazeotrope		*255*
5159	$C_7H_6O_2$	Benzoic acid	250.5	Nonazeotrope		*222*
5160	C_7H_7Br	*o*-Bromotoluene	181.5	178.2	....	*207*
5161	C_7H_7Br	*m*-Bromotoluene	184.3	180.4	....	*207*
5162	C_7H_7Br	*p*-Bromotoluene	185.0	181.0	10	*242*
5163	C_7H_7BrO	*o*-Bromoanisole	217.7	208.0	27	*242*
5164	C_7H_7Cl	*o*-Chlorotoluene	159.2	Nonazeotrope		*207*
5165	C_7H_7ClO	*o*-Chloroanisole	195.7	194.0	10	*255*
5166	C_7H_7ClO	*p*-Chloroanisole	197.8	<196.5	~12	*255*
5167	C_7H_7I	*p*-Iodotoluene	214.5	201.5	20	*242*
5168	$C_7H_7NO_2$	*m*-Nitrotoluene	230.8	214.5	44	*234*
5169	$C_7H_7NO_2$	*o*-Nitrotoluene	221.75	210.2	30	*207*
5170	$C_7H_7NO_2$	*p*-Nitrotoluene	238.9	217.5	50	*207*
5171	C_7H_8	Toluene	110.75	Nonazeotrope		*207*
5172	C_7H_8O	Benzyl alcohol	205.1	Nonazeotrope		*207*
5173	C_7H_8O	*m*-Cresol	202.2	Nonazeotrope		*222*
5174	C_7H_8O	*o*-Cresol	191.1	Nonazeotrope		*224*
5175	C_7H_8O	*p*-Cresol	201.7	Nonazeotrope		*224*
5176	$C_7H_8O_2$	Guaiacol	205.05	Nonazeotrope		*207*
5177	$C_7H_8O_2$	*m*-Methoxyphenol	244	Nonazeotrope		*215*
5178	C_7H_9N	Methylaniline	196.25	Nonazeotrope		*231*
5179	C_7H_9N	*m*-Toluidine	203.1	Nonazeotrope		*207*
5180	C_7H_9N	*o*-Toluidine	200.35	200.25	2.5	*207*
5181	C_7H_9N	*p*-Toluidine	200.55	Nonazeotrope		*231*
5182	$C_7H_{14}O_3$	1,3-Butanediol methyl ether acetate	171.75	Nonazeotrope		*255*
5183	$C_7H_{14}O_3$	Isobutyl lactate	182.15	Nonazeotrope		*255*
5184	$C_7H_{16}O_4$	2-[2-(2-Methoxyethoxy)ethoxy]-ethanol	245.25	Nonazeotrope		*255*
5185	C_8H_8O	Acetophenone	202.0	200.35	15	*232*
5186	$C_8H_8O_2$	Methyl benzoate	199.4	196.95	....	*251*
5187	$C_8H_8O_2$	Phenyl acetate	195.7	Nonazeotrope		*215*
5188	$C_8H_8O_3$	Methyl salicylate	222.35	210.55	34	*210*
5189	C_8H_{10}	*m*-Xylene	139.2	Nonazeotrope		*207*
5190	C_8H_{10}	*m*-Xylene	139.0	138.5	....	*211*
5191	C_8H_{10}	*o*-Xylene	144.3	144.0	2	*255*
5192	$C_8H_{10}O$	Phenethyl alcohol	219.4	217.8	31	*209*
5193	$C_8H_{10}O$	Phenetole	170.5	Nonazeotrope		*215*
5194	$C_8H_{10}O$	3,4-Xylenol	226.8	221.1	96	*244*
			226.8	Nonazeotrope		*255*
5195	$C_8H_{10}O_2$	*o*-Ethoxyphenol	216.5	Nonazeotrope		*255*
5196	$C_8H_{11}N$	Dimethylaniline	194.15	190.5	15.5	*231*
5197	$C_8H_{11}N$	2,4-Xylidine	214.0	<212.0	<27	*231*
5198	$C_8H_{11}N$	3,4-Xylidine	225.5	217.2	28	*255*
5199	$C_8H_{11}N$	Ethylaniline	205.5	<204.0	>12	*231*
5200	$C_8H_{11}NO$	*o*-Phenetidine	232.5	<222.0	....	*231*
5201	$C_8H_{12}O_4$	Ethyl fumarate	217.85	<211.0	....	*242*
5202	$C_8H_{12}O_4$	Ethyl maleate	223.3	214.0	38	*250*
5203	$C_8H_{14}O$	Methyl heptenone	173.2	Nonazeotrope		*232*
5204	$C_8H_{16}O$	2-Octanone	172.85	Nonazeotrope		*232*
5205	$C_8H_{16}O_2$	Butyl butyrate	166.4	Nonazeotrope		*207*
5206	$C_8H_{16}O_2$	Isoamyl propionate	160.7	Nonazeotrope		*207*
5207	$C_8H_{16}O_2$	Isobutyl butyrate	156.9	Nonazeotrope		*207*
5208	$C_8H_{16}O_2$	Propyl isovalerate	155.7	Nonazeotrope		*207*

	B-Component			Azeotropic Data		
No.	Formula	Name	B.P., ° C.	B.P., ° C.	Wt. % A	Ref.
A =	C_3H_7NO	**Propionamide** (*continued*)	222.2			
5209	$C_8H_{18}O$	Octyl alcohol	195.2	Nonazeotrope		*207*
5210	$C_8H_{18}O$	*sec*-Octyl alcohol	179.0	Nonazeotrope		*207*
5211	C_9H_7N	Quinoline	237.3	Nonazeotrope		*233*
5212	C_9H_8	Indene	182.6	179.5	12	*242*
5213	C_9H_8O	Cinnamaldehyde	253.5	Nonazeotrope		*255*
5214	$C_9H_{10}O$	Cinnamyl alcohol	257.0	Nonazeotrope		*255*
5215	$C_9H_{10}O$	*p*-Methylacetophenone	226.35	214.0	40	*232*
5216	$C_9H_{10}O$	Propiophenone	217.7	207.0	28	*232*
5217	$C_9H_{10}O_2$	Benzyl acetate	~214.9	208.8	29	*254*
5218	$C_9H_{10}O_2$	Ethyl benzoate	212.6	205.0	25	*254*
5219	$C_9H_{10}O_2$	Methyl α-toluate	215.3	206.5	28	*242*
5220	$C_9H_{10}O_3$	Ethyl salicylate	233.7	214.0	~50	*216*
5221	C_9H_{12}	Cumene	152.8	151.8	4	*255*
5222	C_9H_{12}	Mesitylene	164.6	162.3	10	*242*
5223	C_9H_{12}	Propyl benzene	159.3	157.7	....	*207*
5224	$C_9H_{12}O$	Benzyl ethyl ether	185.0	182.5	8	*255*
5225	$C_9H_{12}O$	3-Phenylpropanol	235.6	Nonazeotrope		*207*
5226	$C_9H_{13}N$	*N,N*-Dimethyl-*m*-toluidine	203.1	Nonazeotrope		*244*
5227	$C_9H_{13}N$	*N,N*-Dimethyl-*o*-toluidine	185.3	182.5	....	*231*
5228	$C_9H_{13}N$	*N,N*-Dimethyl-*p*-toluidine	200.5	Nonazeotrope		*244*
5229	$C_9H_{13}N$	*N,N*-Dimethyl-*p*-toluidine	210.2	199.0	20	*231*
5230	$C_9H_{14}O$	Phorone	197.8	Nonazeotrope		*232*
5231	$C_9H_{18}O$	2,6-Dimethyl-4-heptanone	168.0	Nonazeotrope		*232*
5232	$C_9H_{18}O_2$	Isoamyl butyrate	181.05	180.6	3?	*255*
5233	$C_9H_{18}O_2$	Isoamyl butyrate	178.5	Nonazeotrope		*216*
5234	$C_9H_{18}O_2$	Isoamyl isobutyrate	169.8	Nonazeotrope		*244*
5235	$C_9H_{18}O_2$	Isobutyl isovalerate	171.2	Nonazeotrope		*207*
5236	$C_9H_{18}O_3$	Isobutyl carbonate	190.3	<186.5	>8	*255*
5237	$C_{10}H_7Br$	1-Bromonaphthalene	281.2	222.0?	95?	*255*
5238	$C_{10}H_7Br$	1-Bromonaphthalene	281.8	Nonazeotrope		*244*
5239	$C_{10}H_7Cl$	1-Chloronaphthalene	262.7	218.6	39	*207*
5240	$C_{10}H_8$	Naphthalene	218.05	204.65	31.5	*207*
5241	$C_{10}H_9N$	1-Naphthylamine	300.8	Nonazeotrope		*231*
5242	$C_{10}H_9N$	Quinaldine	246.5	Nonazeotrope		*255*
5243	$C_{10}H_{10}O_2$	Isosafrol	252.1	~218.5	....	*215*
5244	$C_{10}H_{10}O_2$	Methyl cinnamate	261.95	Nonazeotrope		*207*
5245	$C_{10}H_{10}O_2$	Safrol	235.9	~213.2	35	*215*
5246	$C_{10}H_{10}O_4$	Methyl phthalate	283.2	Nonazeotrope		*207*
5247	$C_{10}H_{12}O$	Anethole	235.7	212.0	39	*242*
5248	$C_{10}H_{12}O_2$	Ethyl α-toluate	248.1	220.0	60	*242*
5249	$C_{10}H_{12}O_2$	Eugenol	255.0	Nonazeotrope		*207*
5250	$C_{10}H_{12}O_2$	Propyl benzoate	230.85	213.0	45	*244*
5251	$C_{10}H_{14}$	Cymene	176.7	172.8	15	*242*
5252	$C_{10}H_{14}O$	Carvacrol	237.85	Nonazeotrope		*255*
5253	$C_{10}H_{14}O$	Carvone	231.0	214.5	48	*232*
5254	$C_{10}H_{14}O$	Thymol	232.8	Nonazeotrope		*215*
5255	$C_{10}H_{14}O_2$	*m*-Diethoxybenzene	235.4	<213.5	....	*255*
5256	$C_{10}H_{15}N$	Diethylaniline	217.05	203.15	23	*231*
5257	$C_{10}H_{16}$	Camphene	159.6	156.5	13	*207*
5258	$C_{10}H_{16}$	Dipentene	177.7	171.8	15	*207*
5259	$C_{10}H_{16}$	*d*-Limonene	177.8	172	20	*253*
5260	$C_{10}H_{16}$	Nopinene	163.8	161.0	10	*242*
5261	$C_{10}H_{16}$	α-Pinene	155.8	154.0	5	*255*
5262	$C_{10}H_{16}$	α-Terpinene	173.4	169.8	13	*242*
5263	$C_{10}H_{16}O$	Camphor	209.1	203.5	17	*232*
5264	$C_{10}H_{16}O$	Pulegone	223.8	212.0	38	*232*
5265	$C_{10}H_{18}O$	Borneol	213.4	209.2	22	*207*
5266	$C_{10}H_{18}O$	Cineol	176.35	173.8	8	*207*
5267	$C_{10}H_{18}O$	Citronellal	208.0	203? (reacts)		*255*
5268	$C_{10}H_{18}O$	Geraniol	229.6	217.0	54	*207*
5269	$C_{10}H_{18}O$	Linaloöl	198.6	Nonazeotrope		*207*
5270	$C_{10}H_{18}O$	α-Terpineol	217.8	209.6	25	*207*
5271	$C_{10}H_{20}O$	Citronellol	224.5	~211.5	~40	*215*
5272	$C_{10}H_{20}O$	Menthol	216.4	208.5	25	*244*
5273	$C_{10}H_{20}O_2$	Ethyl caprylate	208.35	200.2	22	*242*
5274	$C_{10}H_{20}O_2$	Methyl pelargonate	213.8	204.0	18	*207*

No.	B-Component Formula	Name	B.P., ° C.	Azeotropic Data B.P., ° C.	Wt. % A	Ref.
A =	**C_3H_7NO**	**Propionamide** (*continued*)	**222.2**			
5275	$C_{10}H_{20}O_2$	Isoamyl isovalerate	192.7	188.45	12.2	*221*
5276	$C_{10}H_{22}O$	Amyl ether	187.5	181.0	12	*242*
5277	$C_{10}H_{22}O$	Decyl alcohol	~232.9	215.9	70	*211*
5278	$C_{10}H_{22}O$	Isoamyl ether	173.2	170.5	7	*255*
5279	$C_{10}H_{22}S$	Isoamyl sulfide	214.8	204.0	20	*246*
5280	$C_{11}H_{10}$	1-Methylnaphthalene	245.1	213.8	52	*207*
5281	$C_{11}H_{10}$	2-Methylnaphthalene	241.15	213.0	50	*207*
5282	$C_{11}H_{12}O_2$	Ethyl cinnamate	272.0	Nonazeotrope		*207*
5283	$C_{11}H_{14}O_2$	1-Allyl-3,4-dimethoxybenzene	255.2	220.0	60	*254*
5284	$C_{11}H_{14}O_2$	Butyl benzoate	249.0	218.0	64	*242*
5285	$C_{11}H_{14}O_2$	1,2-Dimethoxy-4-propenylbenzene	270.5	Nonazeotrope		*215*
5286	$C_{11}H_{14}O_2$	Isobutyl benzoate	242.15	215.5	60	*207*
5287	$C_{11}H_{20}O$	Methyl isobornyl ether	192.4	187.5	13	*242*
5288	$C_{11}H_{20}O$	Methyl α-terpineol ether	216.2	203.5	27	*242*
5289	$C_{11}H_{22}O_2$	Ethyl pelargonate	227	211.0	40	*255*
5290	$C_{11}H_{22}O_3$	Isoamyl carbonate	232.2	208.5	35	*244*
5291	$C_{12}H_{10}$	Acenaphthene	277.9	220.8	75	*207*
5292	$C_{12}H_{10}$	Biphenyl	256.1	216.0	55	*255*
5293	$C_{12}H_{10}O$	Phenyl ether	259.3	219.0	~62	*254*
5294	$C_{12}H_{16}O_2$	Isoamyl benzoate	262.05	219	67	*207*
5295	$C_{12}H_{16}O_3$	Isoamyl salicylate	227.5	Nonazeotrope		*255*
5296	$C_{12}H_{20}O_2$	Bornyl acetate	227.6	209.5	38	*250*
5297	$C_{12}H_{22}O$	Ethyl isobornyl ether	203.8	196.0	20	*242*
5298	$C_{13}H_{10}$	Fluorene	295	221.5	90	*255*
5299	$C_{13}H_{12}$	Diphenylmethane	265.6	218.2	60	*207*
5300	$C_{14}H_{12}$	Stilbene	306.5	Nonazeotrope		*255*
5301	$C_{14}H_{14}$	1,2-Diphenylethane	284.5	221.0	80	*255*
5302	$C_{14}H_{14}O$	Benzyl ether	297	Nonazeotrope		*255*
A =	**$C_3H_7NO_2$**	**Ethyl Carbamate**	**185.25**			
5303	$C_3H_8O_2$	1,2-Propanediol	187.8	<183.5	....	*255*
5304	$C_4H_6O_4$	Methyl oxalate	164.45	Nonazeotrope		*207*
5305	$C_4H_7Cl_3O$	Ethyl 1,1,2-trichloroethyl ether	173	169.5	....	*255*
5306	$C_4H_8Cl_2O$	Bis(2-chloroethyl) ether	178.65	171.5	25	*242*
5307	C_4H_9I	1-Iodobutane	130.4	Nonazeotrope		*244*
5308	C_4H_9I	1-Iodo-2-methylpropane	120.8	Nonazeotrope		*244*
5309	$C_5H_4O_2$	2-Furaldehyde	161.45	Nonazeotrope		*207*
5310	$C_5H_6O_2$	Furfuryl alcohol	169.35	Nonazeotrope		*255*
5311	$C_5H_8O_4$	Methyl malonate	181.4	<178.65	<35	*255*
5312	$C_5H_{10}O_3$	2-Methoxyethyl acetate	144.6	Nonazeotrope		*236*
5313	$C_5H_{11}Br$	1-Bromo-3-methylbutane	120.3	Nonazeotrope		*244*
5314	$C_5H_{11}I$	1-Iodo-3-methylbutane	147.65	146.5	2	*244*
5315	$C_5H_{11}NO_3$	Isoamyl nitrate	149.75	149.1	7	*240*
5316	$C_5H_{12}O$	Isoamyl alcohol	131.9	Nonazeotrope		*207*
5317	$C_5H_{12}O_2$	2-Propoxyethanol	151.35	Nonazeotrope		*207*
5318	$C_5H_{12}O_3$	2-(2-Methoxyethoxy)ethanol	192.95	Nonazeotrope		*207*
5319	$C_6H_4Br_2$	*p*-Dibromobenzene	220.25	183.6	64	*243*
5320	$C_6H_4Cl_2$	*o*-Dichlorobenzene	179.5	170.0	27	*244*
5321	$C_6H_4Cl_2$	*p*-Dichlorobenzene	174.35	167.0	24.2	*235*
5322	C_6H_5Br	Bromobenzene	156.1	153.95	9.8	*244*
5323	C_6H_5Cl	Chlorobenzene	131.75	Nonazeotrope		*207*
5324	C_6H_5I	Iodobenzene	188.45	174.5	33	*244*
5325	$C_6H_5NO_2$	Nitrobenzene	210.75	184.95	88	*234*
5326	$C_6H_5NO_3$	*o*-Nitrophenol	217.2	Nonazeotrope		*255*
5327	C_6H_6O	Phenol	182.2	190.75	53.5	*244*
5328	$C_6H_8O_4$	Methyl fumarate	193.25	184.2	79	*207*
5329	$C_6H_8O_4$	Methyl maleate	204.05	Nonazeotrope		*207*
5330	$C_6H_{10}O$	Cyclohexanone	155.75	Nonazeotrope		*244*
5331	$C_6H_{10}O_4$	Ethylidene diacetate	168.5	Nonazeotrope		*207*
5332	$C_6H_{10}O_4$	Ethyl oxalate	185.65	181.0	38	*244*
5333	$C_6H_{10}O_4$	Methyl succinate	195.5	184.3	80	*207*
5334	$C_6H_{10}S$	Allyl sulfide	139.35	Nonazeotrope		*246*
5335	$C_6H_{12}O$	Cyclohexanol	160.8	Nonazeotrope		*207*
5336	$C_6H_{12}O_3$	2-Ethoxyethyl acetate	156.8	Nonazeotrope		*236*
5337	$C_6H_{13}Br$	1-Bromohexane	156.5	154.0	10	*244*
5338	$C_6H_{13}ClO_2$	Chloroacetal	157.4	156.8	10	*255*

No.	B-Component Formula	Name	B.P., ° C.	Azeotropic Data B.P., ° C.	Wt. % A	Ref.
A =	**$C_3H_7NO_2$**	**Ethyl Carbamate** (*continued*)	**185.25**			
5339	$C_6H_{14}O$	*n*-Hexanol	157.85	Nonazeotrope		207
5340	$C_6H_{14}O_2$	2-Butoxyethanol	171.15	Nonazeotrope		207
5341	$C_6H_{14}O_2$	Pinacol	174.35	173.5	....	255
5342	$C_6H_{14}O_3$	2-(2-Ethoxyethoxy)ethanol	201.9	Nonazeotrope		255
5343	$C_6H_{14}S$	Isopropyl sulfide	120.5	Nonazeotrope		246
5344	C_7H_5N	Benzonitrile	191.1	182.1	57	250
5345	C_7H_7Br	*m*-Bromotoluene	184.3	171.9	30.5	207
5346	C_7H_7Br	*o*-Bromotoluene	181.5	170.5	28	207
5347	C_7H_7Br	*p*-Bromotoluene	185.0	172.3	32	207
5348	C_7H_7Cl	*o*-Chlorotoluene	159.2	156.4	13	244
5349	C_7H_7Cl	*p*-Chlorotoluene	162.4	158.7	15	244
5350	C_7H_7ClO	*m*-Chloroanisole	193.3	179.5	20	242
5351	C_7H_7ClO	*o*-Chloroanisole	195.7	180.0	18	242
5352	C_7H_7I	*p*-Iodotoluene	214.5	183.2	58	244
5353	$C_7H_7NO_2$	*m*-Nitrotoluene	230.8	Nonazeotrope		234
5354	$C_7H_7NO_2$	*o*-Nitrotoluene	221.75	Nonazeotrope		234
5355	$C_7H_7NO_2$	*p*-Nitrotoluene	238.9	Nonazeotrope		234
5356	C_7H_8	Toluene	110.75	Nonazeotrope		207
5357	C_7H_8O	Anisole	153.85	153.5	5	244
5358	C_7H_8O	Benzyl alcohol	205.25	Nonazeotrope		207
5359	C_7H_8O	*m*-Cresol	202.2	202.6	8	244
5360	C_7H_8O	*o*-Cresol	191.1	193.45	30	244
5361	C_7H_8O	*p*-Cresol	201.7	202.2	10	244
5362	$C_7H_{12}O_4$	Ethyl malonate	199.2	185.15	95	244
5363	$C_7H_{14}O$	2-Methylcyclohexanol	168.5	Nonazeotrope		207
5364	$C_7H_{14}O_2$	Amyl acetate	148.8	Nonazeotrope		207
5365	$C_7H_{14}O_3$	1,3-Butanediol methyl ether acetate	171.75	Nonazeotrope		255
5366	$C_7H_{16}O$	*n*-Heptyl alcohol	176.15	175.1	28.5	244
5367	C_8H_8	Styrene	145.8	Nonazeotrope		207
5368	C_8H_8O	Acetophenone	202.0	184.85	86	232
5369	$C_8H_8O_2$	Benzyl formate	203.0	182.5	62	244
5370	$C_8H_8O_2$	Methyl benzoate	199.4	183.8	67	244
5371	$C_8H_8O_2$	Phenyl acetate	195.7	180.0	52	244
5372	C_8H_{10}	Ethylbenzene	136.15	Nonazeotrope		207
5373	C_8H_{10}	*m*-Xylene	139.2	Nonazeotrope		207
5374	$C_8H_{10}O$	Benzyl methyl ether	167.8	163.5	18	207
5375	$C_8H_{10}O$	*p*-Ethylphenol	218.8	Nonazeotrope		255
5376	$C_8H_{10}O$	*m*-Methylanisole	177.2	171.5	26	244
5377	$C_8H_{10}O$	*p*-Methylanisole	177.05	171.3	25	244
5378	$C_8H_{10}O$	Phenethyl alcohol	219.4	Nonazeotrope		255
5379	$C_8H_{10}O$	Phenetole	170.45	166.2	22	244
5380	$C_8H_{10}O$	2,4-Xylenol	210.5	Nonazeotrope		255
5381	$C_8H_{10}O$	3,4-Xylenol	226.8	Nonazeotrope		244
5382	$C_8H_{10}O_2$	Veratrole	206.8	182.0	67	244
5383	$C_8H_{12}O_4$	Ethyl fumarate	217.85	Nonazeotrope		207
5384	$C_8H_{12}O_4$	Ethyl maleate	223.3	Nonazeotrope		207
5385	$C_8H_{14}O$	Methylheptenone	173.2	171.5	30	232
5386	$C_8H_{14}O_4$	Ethyl succinate	217.25	Nonazeotrope		207
5387	$C_8H_{16}O$	2-Octanone	172.85	171.5	28	232
5388	$C_8H_{16}O_2$	Butyl butyrate	166.4	164.8	15	244
5389	$C_8H_{16}O_2$	Ethyl caproate	167.7	165.0	16	244
5390	$C_8H_{16}O_2$	Isoamyl propionate	160.7	<159.5	>7	207
5391	$C_8H_{16}O_2$	Isobutyl butyrate	156.9	<156.3	>6.5	255
5392	$C_8H_{16}O_2$	Isobutyl isobutyrate	148.6	Nonazeotrope		207
5393	$C_8H_{18}O$	Butyl ether	142.4	<141.5	<5	242
5394	$C_8H_{18}O$	Octyl alcohol	195.2	183.5	72.5	244
5395	$C_8H_{18}O$	*sec*-Octyl alcohol	180.4	177.0	37	244
5396	$C_8H_{18}S$	Butyl sulfide	185.0	<175.5	<44	246
5397	$C_8H_{18}S$	Isobutyl sulfide	172	166.5	23	235
5398	C_9H_8	Indene	182.6	172.65	35	207
5399	$C_9H_{10}O$	*p*-Methylacetophenone	226.35	Nonazeotrope		232
5400	$C_9H_{10}O$	Propiophenone	217.7	Nonazeotrope		232
5401	$C_9H_{10}O_2$	Ethyl benzoate	212.5	Nonazeotrope		207
5402	C_9H_{12}	Cumene	152.8	151.5	6	255
5403	C_9H_{12}	Mesitylene	164.6	159.0	22	244
5404	C_9H_{12}	Propylbenzene	159.3	157.0	15	207

No.	B-Component Formula	Name	B.P., ° C.	Azeotropic Data B.P., ° C.	Wt. % A	Ref.
A =	**$C_3H_7NO_2$**	**Ethyl Carbamate (*continued*)**	**185.25**			
5405	C_9H_{12}	Pseudocumene	168.2	161.4	25	*244*
5406	$C_9H_{12}O$	Benzyl ethyl ether	185.2	175.0	34	*244*
5407	$C_9H_{12}O$	Phenyl propyl ether	190.5	176.2	45	*242*
5408	$C_9H_{14}O$	Phorone	197.8	<184.5	<82	*232*
5409	$C_9H_{18}O_2$	Butyl isovalerate	177.6	171.3	28	*207*
5410	$C_9H_{18}O_2$	Ethyl enanthate	188.7	<178.0	<48	*242*
5411	$C_9H_{18}O_2$	Isoamyl butyrate	181.05	173.7	33	*244*
5412	$C_9H_{18}O_2$	Isoamyl isobutyrate	169.8	166.5	21	*242*
5413	$C_9H_{18}O_2$	Isobutyl isovalerate	171.2	167.65	20	*250*
5414	$C_9H_{18}O_2$	Methyl capraylate	192.9	178.5	48	*244*
5415	$C_9H_{18}O_3$	Isobutyl carbonate	190.3	176.5	42	*244*
5416	$C_{10}H_8$	Naphthalene	218.0	184.05	77	*244*
5417	$C_{10}H_{12}O_2$	Ethyl α-toluate	228.75	Nonazeotrope		*207*
5418	$C_{10}H_{12}O_2$	Propyl benzoate	230.85	Nonazeotrope		*207*
5419	$C_{10}H_{14}$	Butylbenzene	183.1	172.0	37	*207*
5420	$C_{10}H_{14}$	Cymene	176.7	169.0	31	*244*
5421	$C_{10}H_{16}$	Camphene	159.6	157.0	15	*244*
5422	$C_{10}H_{16}$	Limonene	177.6	168.0	32	*244*
5423	$C_{10}H_{16}$	α-Terpinene	173.5	166.0	28	*244*
5424	$C_{10}H_{16}$	γ-Terpinene	183.0	171.5	38	*244*
5425	$C_{10}H_{16}O$	Camphor	209.1	184.85	84	*232*
5426	$C_{10}H_{16}O$	Fenchone	193.6	<182.0	<75	*232*
5427	$C_{10}H_{18}O$	Borneol	215.0	Nonazeotrope		*207*
5428	$C_{10}H_{18}O$	Cineol	176.35	168.4	28	*244*
5429	$C_{10}H_{18}O$	Linaloöl	198.6	<185.0	....	*255*
5430	$C_{10}H_{18}O$	α-Terpineol	218.85	Nonazeotrope		*207*
5431	$C_{10}H_{18}O$	β-Terpineol	210.5	Nonazeotrope		*255*
5432	$C_{10}H_{20}O$	Menthol	216.3	Nonazeotrope		*207*
5433	$C_{10}H_{20}O_2$	Ethyl caprylate	208.35	<184.0	72	*207*
5434	$C_{10}H_{20}O_2$	Isoamyl isovalerate	192.7	177.75	46	*244*
5435	$C_{10}H_{20}O_2$	Methyl pelargonate	213.8	184.3	85	*255*
5436	$C_{10}H_{22}$	2,7-Dimethyloctane	160.1	<157.5	<19	*207*
5437	$C_{10}H_{22}O$	Amyl ether	187.4	171.0	37	*244*
5438	$C_{10}H_{22}O$	Isoamyl ether	173.35	163.15	27	*244*
5439	$C_{11}H_{10}$	1-Methylnaphthalene	244.6	Nonazeotrope		*207*
5440	$C_{11}H_{10}$	2-Methylnaphthalene	241.15	Nonazeotrope		*207*
5441	$C_{11}H_{20}O$	Isobornyl methyl ether	192.4	177.0	45	*244*
5442	$C_{11}H_{20}O$	Methyl α-terpineol ether	216.2	184.9	96	*255*
5443	$C_{11}H_{22}O_3$	Isoamyl carbonate	232.2	Nonazeotrope		*207*
5444	$C_{12}H_{20}O_2$	Bornyl acetate	227.6	Nonazeotrope		*207*
5445	$C_{12}H_{22}O$	Ethyl isobornyl ether	203.8	181.2	82	*242*
A =	**$C_3H_7NO_2$**	**Isopropyl Nitrite**	**40.1**			
5446	$C_3H_7NO_2$	Propyl nitrite	47.75	Nonazeotrope		*230*
5447	$C_3H_7NO_3$	Propyl nitrate	47.75	Nonazeotrope		*240*
5448	$C_3H_8O_2$	Methylal	42.3	39.75	80	*230*
5449	C_4H_4O	Furan	31.7	Nonazeotrope		*230*
5450	C_4H_9Cl	2-Chloro-2-methylpropane	50.8	Nonazeotrope		*230*
5451	$C_4H_{10}O$	Ethyl ether	34.6	Nonazeotrope		*217*
5452	$C_4H_{10}O$	Methyl propyl ether	38.85	<37.5	33	*230*
5453	C_5H_8	Isoprene	34.3	33.5	28	*230*
5454	C_5H_{10}	Cyclopentane	49.3	<39.9	<92	*230*
5455	C_5H_{10}	2-Methyl-2-butene	37.1	35.5	38	*230*
5456	C_5H_{10}	3-Methyl-1-butene	20.6	Nonazeotrope		*230*
5457	C_5H_{12}	2-Methylbutane	27.95	27.65	7.5	*207*
5457	C_5H_{12}	Pentane	36.15	34.5	35	*230*
5458	C_6H_{10}	Biallyl	60.1	Nonazeotrope		*230*
5460	C_6H_{14}	2,3-Dimethylbutane	58.0	Nonazeotrope		*230*
5461	C_6H_{14}	Hexane	68.8	Nonazeotrope		*230*
A =	**$C_3H_7NO_2$**	**1-Nitropropane**	**131**			
5462	C_6H_5Cl	Chlorobenzene, 75° C.	120.8	129.8	44.0, V-l.	*197*
		120° C.	545.2	597.6	44.0, V-l.	*197*
5463	C_8H_6	Phenylacetylene	....	Azeotropic		*100*
5464	C_8H_8	Styrene	145	Azeotropic		*100*
5465	C_8H_8	Styrene	68/60 mm.	Nonazeotrope		*26*

No.	B-Component Formula	Name	B.P., ° C.	Azeotropic Data B.P., ° C.	Wt. % A	Ref.
A =	**$C_3H_7NO_2$**	**1-Nitropropane (*continued*)**	**131**			
5466	C_8H_{10}	Ethylbenzene, 60 mm.	60.5	56.4	61	*26*
			136	127.5	59	*25*
A =	**$C_3H_7NO_2$**	**2-Nitropropane**	**120**			
5467	C_7H_8	Toluene	110.8	110	....	*74*
5468	C_nH_{2n+2}	Paraffins	107–110	96–108	....	*74*
A =	**$C_3H_7NO_2$**	**Propyl Nitrite**	**47.75**			
5469	C_3H_8O	Propyl alcohol	97.25	Nonazeotrope		*219*
5470	$C_3H_8O_2$	Methylal	42.3	Nonazeotrope		*230*
5471	C_4H_9Cl	2-Chloro-2-methylpropane	50.8	47.5	>79	*230*
5472	$C_4H_{10}O$	Ethyl ether	34.6	Nonazeotrope		*230*
5473	C_5H_{10}	Cyclopentane	49.3	45.5	54	*230*
5474	C_5H_{12}	2-Methylbutane	27.95	Nonazeotrope		*230*
5475	C_5H_{12}	Pentane	36.15	35.8	9	*230*
5476	$C_5H_{12}O$	Ethyl propyl ether	63.85	Nonazeotrope		*230*
5477	C_6H_{14}	2,3-Dimethylbutane	58.0	Nonazeotrope		*230*
5478	C_6H_{14}	Hexane	68.8	Nonazeotrope		*230*
A =	**$C_3H_7NO_3$**	**Propyl Nitrate**	**110.5**			
5479	C_3H_8O	Isopropyl alcohol	82.42	<81.5	....	*240*
5480	C_3H_8O	Propyl alcohol	97.2	93.7	30	*240*
5481	$C_3H_8O_2$	2-Methoxyethanol	124.5	108.0	80	*240*
5482	$C_4H_8O_2$	Dioxane	101.35	Nonazeotrope		*237*
5483	C_4H_8S	Tetrahydrothiophene	118.8	109.0	73	*240*
5484	C_4H_9Br	1-Bromobutane	101.5	<101.0	....	*240*
5485	C_4H_9Br	1-Bromo-2-methylpropane	91.4	Nonazeotrope		*227*
5486	C_4H_9I	2-Iodobutane	120.0	<109.5	<85	*240*
5487	C_4H_9I	1-Iodo-2-methylpropane	120.8	<109.5	<89	*240*
5488	$C_4H_{10}O$	Butyl alcohol	117.8	106.5	68	*240*
5489	$C_4H_{10}O$	Isobutyl alcohol	108.0	<103.5	>47	*240*
5490	$C_4H_{10}O_2$	2-Ethoxyethanol	135.3	Nonazeotrope		*236*
5491	$C_5H_{12}O$	*tert*-Amyl alcohol	102.35	<100.1	<23	*240*
5492	$C_5H_{12}O$	Isoamyl alcohol	131.9	<110.0	....	*240*
5493	$C_5H_{12}O$	2-Pentanol	119.8	<108.0	<90	*240*
5494	C_6H_6	Benzene	80.15	Nonazeotrope		*240*
5495	$C_6H_{12}O_2$	Ethyl isobutyrate	110.1	109.7	....	*243*
5496	$C_6H_{14}O_2$	Acetal	103.55	Nonazeotrope		*240*
5497	$C_6H_{14}O_2$	Ethoxypropoxymethane	113.7	<110.0	....	*237*
5498	C_7H_8	Toluene	110.75	<109.0	>47	*240*
5499	C_7H_{14}	Methylcyclohexane	101.15	97.0	25	*240*
5500	C_7H_{16}	Heptane	98.4	95.0	25	*240*
5501	C_8H_{18}	2,5-Dimethylhexane	109.4	101.2	45	*240*
A =	**C_3H_8O**	**Isopropyl Alcohol**	**82.45**			
5502	$C_3H_8O_2$	Methylal	42.3	Nonazeotrope		*236*
5503	C_4H_4S	Thiophene	84.7	<76.0	<43	*246*
5504	$C_4H_6O_2$	Biacetyl	88	77.3	~60	*264*
5505	$C_4H_6O_2$	Biacetyl	87.5	<79	<60	*232*
5506	$C_4H_6O_2$	Methyl acrylate	80	76.0	46.5	*319**, *320*
5507	C_4H_7N	Isobutyronitrile	103.85	Nonazeotrope		*255*
5508	C_4H_8O	2-Butanone	79.6	77.9	32	*10**, *207*
5509	C_4H_8OS	Ethyl thioacetate	116.6	Nonazeotrope		*255*
5510	$C_4H_8O_2$	Dioxane	101.35	Nonazeotrope		*207*
5511	$C_4H_8O_2$	Ethyl acetate	77.1	74	26	*252**, *334*
5512	$C_4H_8O_2$	Methyl propionate	79.8	76.35	38	*252*
5513	$C_4H_8O_2$	Propyl formate	80.8	75.85	~36	*252*
5514	C_4H_8S	Tetrahydrothiophene	118.8	Nonazeotrope		*246*
5515	C_4H_9Br	2-Bromobutane	91.2	77.5	34	*247*
5516	C_4H_9Br	1-Bromo-2-methylpropane	90.95	77.5	33	*235*
5517	C_4H_9Br	2-Bromo-2-methylpropane	73.3	67	<20	*243*
5518	C_4H_9Cl	1-Chlorobutane	78.05	70.8	23	*253*
5519	C_4H_9Cl	2-Chlorobutane	68.25	64.0	18	*247*
5520	C_4H_9Cl	1-Chloro-2-methylpropane	68.85	64.8	17	*253*
5521	C_4H_9I	1-Iodobutane	130.4	Nonazeotrope		*255*
5522	C_4H_9I	1-Iodo-2-methylpropane	120	81–82	70	*212**, *334*
5523	$C_4H_{10}O$	*tert*-Butyl alcohol	82.45	Nonazeotrope		*229*
5524	$C_4H_{10}S$	Ethyl sulfide	92.2	78.0	~52	*211*

No.	Formula	B-Component Name	B.P., ° C.	Azeotropic Data B.P., ° C.	Wt. % A	Ref.
A =	C_3H_8O	**Isopropyl Alcohol** (*continued*)	**82.45**			
5525	C_5H_{10}	Cyclopentane	49.4	<47.3	....	*247*
5526	C_5H_{10}	2-Methyl-2-butene	37.15	Nonazeotrope		*243*
5527	C_5H_{10}	3-Methyl-1-butene	22.5	Nonazeotrope		*220*
5528	$C_5H_{10}O$	3-Methyl-2-butanone	95.4	Nonazeotrope		*232*
5529	$C_5H_{10}O$	3-Pentanone	102.05	Nonazeotrope		*232*
5530	$C_5H_{10}O_2$	Butyl formate	106.8	Nonazeotrope		*255*
5531	$C_5H_{10}O_2$	Isobutyl formate	97.9	Nonazeotrope		*212*
5532	$C_5H_{10}O_2$	Isopropyl acetate	91	80.1	52.3	*75, 216**
5533	$C_5H_{10}O_2$	Methyl butyrate	102.65	Nonazeotrope		*216*
5534	$C_5H_{10}O_2$	Methyl isobutyrate	92.5	81.4	65	*255*
5535	$C_5H_{10}O_2$	Propyl acetate	101.6	Nonazeotrope		*217*
5536	$C_5H_{11}Br$	1-Bromo-3-methylbutane	120.65	Nonazeotrope		*207*
5537	$C_5H_{11}Br$	1-Bromo-3-methylbutane	120.3	82.2	~82	*215*
5538	$C_5H_{11}Cl$	1-Chloro-3-methylbutane	99.8	79.2	43	*253*
5539	C_5H_{12}	2-Methylbutane	27.95	Nonazeotrope		*217*
			27.95	27.8	5	*218*
5540	C_5H_{12}	Pentane	36.15	35.5	6	*218*
5541	$C_5H_{12}O$	Ethyl propyl ether	63.6	62.0	10	*225*
5542	$C_5H_{12}O_2$	Diethoxymethane	87.95	79.6	52	*236*
5543	C_6H_5Cl	Chlorobenzene	132.0	Nonazeotrope		*212*
5544	C_6H_5F	Fluorobenzene	85.15	74.5	30	*225*
5545	C_6H_6	Benzene	80.2	71.92	33.3	*334*, 431*
5546	C_6H_8	1,3-Cyclohexadiene	80.8	70.4	36	*243*
5547	C_6H_8	1,4-Cyclohexadiene	85.6	72.3	....	*243*
5548	C_6H_{10}	Biallyl	60.0	55.8	11	*217*
5549	C_6H_{10}	Cyclohexene	82.7	70.5	27	*217*
5550	C_6H_{12}	Cyclohexane	80.75	68.6	33	*243*
5551	C_6H_{12}	Methylcyclopentane	72.0	63.3	25	*248*
5552	$C_6H_{12}O$	Pinacolone	106.2	Nonazeotrope		*232*
5553	$C_6H_{12}O_2$	Methyl isovalerate	116.5	Nonazeotrope		*255*
5554	C_6H_{14}	2,3-Dimethylbutane	58.0	53.8	9	*247*
5555	C_6H_{14}	Hexane	68.85	62.7	23	*218*
5556	$C_6H_{14}O$	Isopropyl ether	69.0	66.2	16.3	*93*
5557	$C_6H_{14}O$	Propyl ether	90.55	78.2	52	*253*
5558	$C_6H_{14}O_2$	Acetal	103.55	Nonazeotrope		*236*
5559	$C_6H_{14}O_2$	Acetal	103.55	81.3	~63	*253*
5560	$C_6H_{14}S$	Isopropyl sulfide	120.5	Nonazeotrope		*246*
5561	C_7H_8	Toluene	110.7	80.6	58	*23*
			....	20	47.7	*329*
			....	40	58.8	*329*
			....	60	67.4	*329*
			....	78	73.1	*329*
5562	C_7H_{14}	Methylcyclohexane	100.8	77.6	53	*23, 217**
5563	C_7H_{16}	*n*-Heptane	78.45	76.4	50.5	*207*
5564	$C_7H_{16}O$	Butyl isopropyl ether	103	79	71.91	*34*
5565	C_8H_8	Styrene	145.8	Nonazeotrope		*225*
5566	C_8H_{10}	Ethylbenzene	136.15	Nonazeotrope		*217*
5567	C_8H_{10}	*o*-Xylene	144.3	Nonazeotrope		*255*
5568	C_8H_{10}	*m*-Xylene	139.0	Nonazeotrope		*217*
5569	C_8H_{10}	*p*-Xylene	138.2	Nonazeotrope		*221*
5570	C_8H_{16}	1,3-Dimethylcyclohexane	120.7	81.0	78	*255*
5571	C_8H_{16}	*trans*-1,2-Dimethylcyclohexane	....	....	~79	*383*
5572	C_8H_{16}	1,1,2-Trimethylcyclopentane	....	....	~67	*383*
5573	C_8H_{16}	1,1,3-Trimethylcyclopentane	104.9	....	~54	*383*
5574	C_8H_{16}	*cis-cis-trans*-1,2,4-Trimethylcyclopentane	....	....	~70	*383*
5575	C_8H_{18}	2,5-Dimethylhexane	109.2	79.0	62	*215*
5576	C_8H_{18}	Octane	124.75	81.6	84	*255*
5577	C_8H_{18}	2,2,4-Trimethylpentane	99.3	76.8	54	*255*
5578	$C_8H_{18}O$	Isobutyl ether	122.1	Nonazeotrope		*236*
5579	C_9H_8	Indene	182.6	Nonazeotrope		*255*
5580	C_9H_{12}	Cumene	152.8	Nonazeotrope		*255*
5581	C_9H_{12}	Mesitylene	164.6	Nonazeotrope		*220*
5582	C_9H_{12}	Propylbenzene	159.3	Nonazeotrope		*255*
5583	$C_{10}H_{14}$	Butylbenzene	183.1	Nonazeotrope		*255*
5584	$C_{10}H_{14}$	Cymene	176.7	Nonazeotrope		*255*

No.	Formula	B-Component Name	B.P., ° C.	Azeotropic Data B.P., ° C.	Wt. % A	Ref.
A =	C_3H_8O	**Isopropyl Alcohol** (*continued*)	**82.45**			
5585	$C_{10}H_{16}$	Camphene	159.6	Nonazeotrope		*220*
5586	$C_{10}H_{16}$	*d*-Limonene	177.8	Nonazeotrope		*217*
5587	$C_{10}H_{16}$	α-Pinene	155.8	Nonazeotrope		*217*
5588	$C_{10}H_{16}$	α-Terpinene	173.4	Nonazeotrope		*255*
5589	$C_{10}H_{16}$	Thymene	179.7	Nonazeotrope		*217*
5590	$C_{10}H_{22}$	2,7-Dimethyloctane	160.2	Nonazeotrope		*217*
A =	C_3H_8O	**Propyl Alcohol**	**97.2**			
5591	$C_3H_8O_2$	Methylal	42.3	Nonazeotrope		*255*
5592	C_4H_6O	Crotonaldehyde	102.15	<97?	....	*243*
5593	$C_4H_6O_2$	Biacetyl	87.5	85.0	25	*232*
5594	$C_4H_6O_2$	Methyl acrylate	80	70.9	5.4	*320*
5595	$C_4H_7ClO_2$	Ethyl chloroacetate	143.55	Nonazeotrope		*255*
5596	C_4H_7N	Butyronitrile	118.5	Azeotrope doubtful		*243*
5597	C_4H_7N	Isobutyronitrile	103.85	95	70	*247*
5598	C_4H_7N	Pyrroline	90.9	<89.0	....	*255*
5599	$C_4H_8Cl_2O$	1,2-Dichloroethyl ethyl ether	145.5	Nonazeotrope		*255*
5600	C_4H_8O	2-Butanone	79.6	Nonazeotrope		*10*
5601	C_4H_8OS	Ethyl thioacetate	116.6	Nonazeotrope		*255*
5602	$C_4H_8O_2$	Dioxane	101.35	95.3	55	*207*
5603	$C_4H_8O_2$	Ethyl acetate	77.05	Nonazeotrope		*334*
5604	$C_4H_8O_2$	Methyl propionate	79.85	Nonazeotrope		*212*
5605	$C_4H_8O_2$	Propyl formate	80.9	80.6	9.8	*150*
5606	$C_4H_8O_2$	Propyl formate	80.8	80.65	<3	*252*
5607	C_4H_8S	Tetrahydrothiophene	118.8	96.5	90	*235*
5608	C_4H_9Br	1-Bromobutane	100.3	89.5	29	*253*
5609	C_4H_9Br	2-Bromobutane	91.2	85.3	20.5	*247*
5610	C_4H_9Br	1-Bromo-2-methylpropane	89.2	86.1	19.25	*163, 235**
				B.p. curve		
5611	C_4H_9Br	2-Bromo-2-methylpropane	73.3	72.2	....	*243*
5612	C_4H_9Cl	1-Chlorobutane	78.05	74.8	~18	*253*
5613	C_4H_9Cl	2-Chlorobutane	68.25	67.2	>9	*247*
5614	C_4H_9Cl	1-Chloro-2-methylpropane	68.85	67.7	22	*252*
5615	C_4H_9Cl	2-Chloro-2-methylpropane	68.25	67.2	>9	*255*
5616	C_4H_9I	1-Iodobutane	130.4	96.2	66	*247*
5617	C_4H_9I	1-Iodo-2-methylpropane	120	93	45	*253*, 334*
5618	C_4H_9I	2-Iodobutane	120.0	94.5	53	*255*
5619	$C_4H_{10}O$	*sec*-Butyl alcohol	99.5	Nonazeotrope		*229*
5620	$C_4H_{10}O$	Ethyl ether	34.6	Nonazeotrope		*236*
5621	$C_4H_{10}O$	Isobutyl alcohol	108.0	Nonazeotrope		*334*
5622	$C_4H_{10}O_2$	Acetaldehyde dimethyl acetal	64.3	Nonazeotrope		*255*
5623	$C_4H_{10}S$	Butanethiol	97.5	<92.0	<41	*255*
5624	$C_4H_{10}S$	Ethyl sulfide	92.2	85.5	28	*235*
5625	C_5H_5N	Pyridine	115.4	Nonazeotrope		*233*
5626	C_5H_7N	*N*-Methylpyrrol	112.8	Nonazeotrope		*255*
5627	$C_5H_9ClO_2$	Propyl chloroacetate	162.3	Nonazeotrope		*58*
5628	$C_5H_{10}O$	3-Methyl-2-butanone	95.4	93.5	35	*232*
5629	$C_5H_{10}O$	2-Pentanone	102.35	96.0	68	*232*
5630	$C_5H_{10}O$	3-Pentanone	102.05	96.0	63	*232*
5631	$C_5H_{10}O_2$	Butyl formate	106.8	95.5	64	*247*
5632	$C_5H_{10}O_2$	Ethyl propionate	99.1	93.4	51	*243*
5633	$C_5H_{10}O_2$	Isobutyl formate	97.9	93.2	40	*212*
5634	$C_5H_{10}O_2$	Methyl butyrate	102.65	94.4	47	*252*
5635	$C_5H_{10}O_2$	Methyl isobutyrate	92.3	89.5	~26	*212*
5636	$C_5H_{10}O_2$	Propyl acetate	101.6	94.2	40	*150, 252**
5637	$C_5H_{11}Br$	1-Bromo-3-methylbutane	118.2	94.0	70.7	*162, 235**
				B.p. curve		
5638	$C_5H_{11}Cl$	1-Chloro-3-methylbutane	99.8	89.4	31	*253*
5639	$C_5H_{11}I$	1-Iodo-3-methylbutane	146.5	Nonazeotrope		*162*
5640	C_5H_{12}	Pentane	36.15	Nonazeotrope		*217*
5641	$C_5H_{12}O$	Ethyl propyl ether	63.85	Nonazeotrope		*255*
5642	$C_5H_{12}O$	Isoamyl alcohol	131.9	Nonazeotrope		*255*
5643	$C_5H_{12}O_2$	Diethoxymethane	88.0	86.15	11	*429*
5644	C_6H_5Br	Bromobenzene	156.1	Nonazeotrope		*255*
5645	C_6H_5Cl	Chlorobenzene	132.0	96.9	83	*253*
5646	C_6H_5F	Fluorobenzene	85.15	80.2	18	*235*

No.	Formula	B-Component Name	B.P., ° C.	Azeotropic Data B.P., ° C.	Wt. % A	Ref.
A =	C_3H_8O	**Propyl Alcohol** (*continued*)	**97.2**			
5647	C_6H_6	Benzene	80.2	77.12	16.9	*431, 436**
			....	76–77	16.5	*334*
			....	0	4.5	*312*
			....	35.5	12	*312*
			....	76.5	21	*312*
		10.5 atm.	....	160	45	*312*
5648	C_6H_8	1,3-Cyclohexadiene	80.4	75.8	20	*217*
5649	C_6H_{10}	Cyclohexene	82.75	76.6	21.6	*243*
5650	C_6H_{10}	Methylcyclopentene	75.85	<71.7	<13	*247*
5651	C_6H_{12}	Cyclohexane	80.75	74.3	20	*243*
5652	C_6H_{12}	Methylcyclopentane	72.0	68.5	7	*247*
5653	$C_6H_{12}O$	Pinacolone	106.2	Nonazeotrope		*228*
5654	$C_6H_{12}O_2$	Ethyl butyrate	120.0	Nonazeotrope		*216*
5655	$C_6H_{12}O_2$	Ethyl isobutyrate	110.1	96.8	....	*216*
5656	$C_6H_{12}O_2$	Isobutyl acetate	117.2	Nonazeotrope		*212*
5657	$C_6H_{12}O_2$	Methyl isovalerate	116.3	Nonazeotrope		*216*
5658	$C_6H_{12}O_2$	Propyl propionate	123.0	Nonazeotrope		*255*
5659	$C_6H_{12}O_3$	Paraldehyde	123.9	Nonazeotrope		*256*
5660	C_6H_{14}	2,3-Dimethylbutane	58.0	<56.8	<6	*247*
5661	C_6H_{14}	Hexane	68.95	65.65	4	*243*
5662	$C_6H_{14}O$	Propyl ether	90.7	85.8	32.2	*225*, 307*
5663	$C_6H_{14}O_2$	Acetal	103.55	92.4	37	*252*
5664	$C_6H_{14}O_2$	Ethoxypropoxymethane	113.7	Nonazeotrope		*429*
5665	C_7H_8	Toluene	110.7	92.6	43	*24, 217*, 334*, 436**
			....	0.5	19.5	*329*
			....	25	29.2	*329*
			....	50	38.9	*329*
			....	71.1	45.5	*329*
			....	91.1	50.5	*329*
5666	C_7H_{14}	Methylcyclohexane	100.8	86.3	35	*23*
5667	C_7H_{16}	*n*-Heptane	98.45	87.5	36	*253*
5668	$C_7H_{16}O_2$	Dipropoxymethane	137.2	Nonazeotrope		*131*
5669	C_8H_8	Styrene	145.8	97.0	8	*225*
5670	C_8H_{10}	Ethylbenzene, 60 mm.	60.5	41	68	*26*
			136	Nonazeotrope		*221*
5671	C_8H_{10}	*m*-Xylene	139.2	97.08	94	*207*
5672	C_8H_{10}	*o*-Xylene	143.6	Nonazeotrope		*225*
5673	C_8H_{10}	*p*-Xylene	138.45	97.0	....	*255*
5674	C_8H_{16}	1,3-Dimethylcyclohexane	120.5	<94	<70	*243*
5675	C_8H_{18}	2,5-Dimethylhexane	109.2	89.5	47	*225*
5676	C_8H_{18}	Octane	125.6	93.9	70	*217*
5677	C_8H_{18}	2,2,4-Trimethylpentane	99.3	<85.3	<41	*255*
5678	$C_8H_{18}O$	Isobutyl ether	122.3	Nonazeotrope		*236*
5679	$C_8H_{18}O$	Isobutyl ether	122.1	96.8	....	*256*
5680	$C_8H_{18}O_2$	1,1-Dipropoxyethane	147.7	Nonazeotrope		*20*
5681	C_9H_8	Indene	182.6	Nonazeotrope		*255*
5682	C_9H_{12}	Cumene	152.8	Nonazeotrope		*255*
5683	C_9H_{12}	Mesitylene	164.6	Nonazeotrope		*217*
5684	C_9H_{12}	Propylbenzene	158.9	Nonazeotrope		*221*
5685	$C_{10}H_{14}$	Cymene	176.7	Nonazeotrope		*220*
5686	$C_{10}H_{14}$	Butylbenzene	183.1	Nonazeotrope		*255*
5687	$C_{10}H_{16}$	Camphene	159.6	Nonazeotrope		*220*
5688	$C_{10}H_{16}$	*d*-Limonene	177.8	Nonazeotrope		*217*
5689	$C_{10}H_{16}$	*α*-Pinene	155.8	97.1	98–99?	*243*
5690	$C_{10}H_{16}$	*α*-Terpinene	173.4	Nonazeotrope		*255*
A =	$C_3H_8O_2$	**2-Methoxyethanol**	**124.5**			
5691	$C_4H_4N_2$	Pyrazine	117.2	Nonazeotrope		*255*
5692	C_4H_5N	Pyrrol	130.0	Nonazeotrope		*207*
5693	$C_4H_7ClO_2$	Ethyl chloroacetate	143.45	Nonazeotrope		*255*
5694	$C_4H_8O_2$	Dioxane	101.35	Nonazeotrope		*207*
5695	$C_4H_8O_3$	Methyl lactate	143.8	Nonazeotrope		*255*
5696	C_4H_9I	1-Iodobutane	130.4	115.5	....	*206*
5697	C_4H_9I	1-Iodo-2-methylpropane	120.8	110.5	25	*206*
5698	$C_4H_9NO_3$	Isobutyl nitrate	123.5	<115.0	<44	*240*

No.	Formula	B-Component Name	B.P., ° C.	Azeotropic Data B.P., ° C.	Wt. % A	Ref.
A =	$C_3H_8O_2$	**2-Methoxyethanol** (*continued*)	**124.5**			
5699	$C_4H_{10}O$	Butyl alcohol	117.8	Nonazeotrope		*206*
5700	$C_4H_{10}O$	*sec*-Butyl alcohol	99.5	Nonazeotrope		*255*
5701	$C_4H_{10}O$	Isobutyl alcohol	108.0	Nonazeotrope		*255*
5702	$C_5H_4O_2$	2-Furaldehyde	161.45	Nonazeotrope		*255*
5703	C_5H_5N	Pyridine	115.4	Nonazeotrope		*233*
5704	C_5H_7N	1-Methylpyrrol	112.8	Nonazeotrope		*255*
5705	C_5H_9N	Isovaleronitrile	130.5	<130.0	....	*255*
5706	C_5H_9N	Valeronitrile	141.3	Nonazeotrope		*236*
5707	$C_5H_{10}O$	Cyclopentanol	140.85	Nonazeotrope		*255*
5708	$C_5H_{10}O_3$	2-Methoxyethyl acetate	144.6	Nonazeotrope		*236*
5709	$C_5H_{11}Br$	1-Bromo-3-methylbutane	120.65	111.5	20	*206*
5710	$C_5H_{11}Cl$	1-Chloro-3-methylbutane	99.4	Nonazeotrope		*206*
5711	$C_5H_{11}I$	1-Iodo-3-methylbutane	147.65	Nonazeotrope		*206*
5712	$C_5H_{11}NO_3$	Isoamyl nitrate	149.75	Nonazeotrope		*236*
5713	$C_5H_{12}O$	Amyl alcohol	138.2	Nonazeotrope		*255*
5714	$C_5H_{12}O$	*tert*-Amyl alcohol	102.15	Nonazeotrope		*255*
5715	$C_5H_{12}O$	Isoamyl alcohol	131.9	Nonazeotrope		*207*
5716	$C_5H_{12}O$	2-Pentanol	119.8	119.7	4	*206*
5717	$C_5H_{12}O$	3-Pentanol	116.0	Nonazeotrope		*255*
5718	$C_5H_{12}O_3$	2-(2-Methoxyethoxy)ethanol	192.95	Nonazeotrope		*363*
5719	C_6H_5Cl	Chlorobenzene	131	119.45	47.5	*207*
5720	C_6H_6	Benzene	....	Nonazeotrope		*236*
5721	C_6H_6O	Phenol	181.2	Nonazeotrope		*255*
5722	C_6H_7N	2-Picoline	130.7	Nonazeotrope		*255*
5723	$C_6H_{10}O$	Mesityl oxide	129.45	122.5	59	*232*
5724	$C_6H_{10}S$	Allyl sulfide	139	122.5	75	*235*
5725	C_6H_{12}	Cyclohexane	80.75	<79.8	8	*255*
5726	$C_6H_{12}O$	2-Hexanone	127.2	<121.5	<56	*232*
5727	$C_6H_{12}O$	3-Hexanone	123.3	<119.5	<43	*232*
5728	$C_6H_{12}O$	4-Methyl-2-pentanone	116.05	114.2	25	*207*
5729	$C_6H_{12}O_2$	Butyl acetate	126.0	119.45	48	*236*
5730	$C_6H_{12}O_2$	Ethyl butyrate	121.5	117.8	32	*236*
5731	$C_6H_{12}O_2$	Ethyl isobutyrate	110.1	Nonazeotrope		*206*
5732	$C_6H_{12}O_2$	Isoamyl formate	123.8	119.25	40	*236*
5733	$C_6H_{12}O_2$	Isobutyl acetate	117.2	115.5	16	*236*
5734	$C_6H_{12}O_2$	Methyl isovalerate	116.5	115.0	15	*206*
5735	$C_6H_{12}O_2$	Propyl propionate	123.0	118.5	38	*206*
5736	$C_6H_{12}O_3$	2-Ethoxy ethyl acetate	156.8	Nonazeotrope		*236*
5737	$C_6H_{12}O_3$	Paraldehyde	124.35	118.6	35	*236*
5738	$C_6H_{14}O$	Propyl ether	90.1	Nonazeotrope		*236*
5739	C_7H_8	Toluene	110.75	106.1	25.5	*207*
5740	C_7H_8O	Anisole	153.85	Nonazeotrope		*236*
5741	C_7H_{14}	Methylcyclohexane	101.15	94.2	25	*236*
5742	$C_7H_{14}O_2$	Isoamyl acetate	142.1	Nonazeotrope		*206*
5743	$C_7H_{14}O_2$	Isobutyl propionate	137.5	Nonazeotrope		*206*
5744	C_7H_{16}	Heptane	98.4	92.5	23	*207*
5745	$C_7H_{16}O_4$	2-[2-(2-Methoxyethoxy)ethoxy]-ethanol	245.25	Nonazeotrope		*255*
5746	C_8H_8	Styrene	145.8	121.0	62	*247*
5747	C_8H_{10}	Ethylbenzene	136	117	51.2	*30*
		62 mm.	....	51	39	*30*
		60 mm.	60.5	51	43	*26, 236**
5748	C_8H_{10}	*m*-Xylene	139.2	119.5	58	*207*
5849	C_8H_{10}	*o*-Xylene	144.3	121.0	63	*206*
5750	C_8H_{10}	*m,p*-Xylene	139	120	....	*201*
5751	C_8H_{10}	Xylenes	140	Min. b.p.		*30*
5752	C_8H_{16}	1,1,3-Trimethylcyclopentane	104.9	....	~20	*383*
5753	$C_8H_{16}O_2$	Propyl isovalerate	155.7	Nonazeotrope		*206*
5754	C_8H_{18}	2,5-Dimethylhexane	109.4	100.0	33	*236*
5755	C_8H_{18}	2,4-Dimethylhexane	109.4	....	~25	*383*
5756	C_8H_{18}	2,2,3-Trimethylpentane	109.8	....	~24	*383*
5757	C_8H_{18}	Octane	125.75	110.0	48	*236*
5758	$C_8H_{18}O$	Butyl ether	142.4	122.0	68	*206*
5759	$C_8H_{18}O$	Isobutyl ether	122.3	115.0	48	*236*
5760	C_9H_{12}	Cumene	152.8	122.4	73.5	*207*
5761	C_9H_{12}	Mesitylene	164.6	<124.3	....	*255*

No.	Formula	B-Component Name	B.P., ° C.	Azeotropic Data B.P., ° C.	Wt. % A	Ref.
A =	**$C_3H_8O_2$**	**2-Methoxyethanol** (*continued*)	**124.5**			
5762	C_9H_{12}	Mesitylene	164.6	Nonazeotrope		*206*
5763	C_9H_{12}	Propylbenzene	159.3	<124.0	>82	*255*
5764	C_9H_{12}	Propylbenzene	159.3	Nonazeotrope		*236*
5765	C_9H_{20}	2,2,3,4-Tetramethylpentane	....	....	~42	*383*
5766	$C_{10}H_{14}$	Cymene	176.7	Nonazeotrope		*255*
5767	$C_{10}H_{16}$	Camphene	159.6	121.0	70	*206*
5768	$C_{10}H_{16}$	Nopinene	163.8	121.8	5	*247*
5769	$C_{10}H_{16}$	α-Pinene	155.8	120.2	66	*206*
5770	$C_{10}H_{22}$	Decane	173.3	<123.5	<92	*255*
5771	$C_{10}H_{22}$	2,7-Dimethyloctane	160.1	121.0	70	*206*
A =	**$C_3H_8O_2$**	**Methylal**	**42.3**			
5772	C_3H_8S	Propanethiol	67.3	Nonazeotrope		*255*
5773	C_3H_9N	Propylamine	49.7	Nonazeotrope		*231*
5774	C_4H_9Cl	2-Chloro-2-methylpropane	50.8	Nonazeotrope		*239*
5775	$C_4H_{10}O$	Methyl propyl ether	38.9	Nonazeotrope		*241*
5776	$C_4H_{11}N$	Diethylamine	55.9	Nonazeotrope		*231*
5777	C_5H_8	3-Methyl-1,2-pentadiene	40.8	38.0	45	*238*
5778	C_5H_8	Isoprene	34.3	32.8	30	*238*
5779	C_5H_{10}	Cyclopentane	49.3	40.0	62	*238*
5780	C_5H_{10}	3-Methyl-1-butene	21.5	Nonazeotrope		*238*
5781	C_5H_{10}	2-Methyl-2-butene	37.15	35.2	32	*238*
5782	C_5H_{10}	1-Pentene	30.1	29.8	26 vol.	*336*
5783	C_5H_{10}	2-Pentene	36.5	34.9	29 vol.	*336*
5784	C_5H_{12}	2-Methylbutane	27.9	24.1	30 vol.	*336*
			27.95	27.0	23	*238*
5785	C_5H_{12}	Pentane	36.08	31.5	28 vol.	*336*
			36.15	33.6	35	*238*
5786	C_6H_6	Benzene	80.15	Nonazeotrope		*255*
5787	C_6H_{10}	Biallyl	60.1	41.8	85	*238*
5788	C_6H_{14}	2,3-Dimethylbutane	58.0	41.5	80	*238*
5789	C_6H_{14}	Hexane	68.85	Nonazeotrope		*238*
A =	**$C_3H_8O_2$**	**1,2-Propanediol**	**187.8**			
5790	C_4H_5N	Pyrrol	130.0	Nonazeotrope		*255*
5791	C_4H_5NS	Allyl isothiocyanate	152.05	<151.5	....	*255*
5792	$C_4H_8Br_2O$	Bis(2-bromoethyl) ether	....	176–180	....	*93*
5793	C_6H_5ClO	*p*-Chlorophenol	219.75	Nonazeotrope		*255*
5794	$C_6H_5NO_3$	*o*-Nitrophenol	217.2	<186.0	>62	*255*
5795	C_6H_7N	Aniline	184.35	179.5	43	*231*
5796	$C_6H_{12}O_3$	2-Ethoxyethyl acetate	156.8	Nonazeotrope		*255*
5797	C_7H_8O	*p*-Cresol	201.8	Azeotrope doubtful		*243*
5798	$C_7H_8O_2$	*m*-Methoxyphenol	243.8	242.2	~7	*255*
5799	C_7H_9N	Methylaniline	196.25	<181.0	>46	*231*
5800	$C_7H_{14}O_3$	1,3-Butanediol methyl ether actate	171.75	<170	....	*255*
5801	C_8H_8O	Acetophenone	202.0	<183.5	....	*232*
5802	$C_8H_{11}N$	Dimethylaniline	194.05	<177.0	>45	*231*
5803	$C_8H_{16}O$	2-Octanone	172.85	<169.5	....	*232*
5804	C_9H_8	Indene	182.4	Min. b.p.		*117*
5805	$C_9H_{13}N$	*N,N*-Dimethyl-*o*-toluidine	185.3	<174.0	37	*231*
5806	$C_9H_{13}N$	*N,N*-Dimethyl-*p*-toluidine	210.2	178.0	60	*255*
5807	$C_{10}H_{16}O$	Camphor	209.1	<185.0	....	*232*
5808	$C_{10}H_{18}O$	Menthone	209.5	<185.0	<85	*232*
5809	$C_{12}H_{26}$	Dodecane, 743 mm.	216	175	....	*177*
		200 mm.	....	137	....	*177*
		150 mm.	....	130	....	*177*
		100 mm.	145	120.5	60	*177*
		50 mm.	....	105.7	....	*177*
5810	$C_{14}H_{30}$	Tetradecane, 748 mm.	252.5	179	70	*177*
		200 mm.	....	142.5	....	*177*
		150 mm.	....	135	....	*177*
		100 mm.	....	126	....	*177*
		50 mm.	....	111	....	*177*

No.	B-Component Formula	Name	B.P., ° C.	Azeotropic Data B.P., ° C.	Wt. % A	Ref.
A =	$C_3H_8O_3$	**Glycerol**	**290.5**			
5811	$C_4H_{10}O_3$	Diethylene glycol	245.5	Nonazeotrope		206
5812	$C_6H_4Br_2$	*p*-Dibromobenzene	220.25	217.1	10	254
5813	$C_6H_4ClNO_2$	*m*-Chloronitrobenzene	235.5	232.2	10	234
5814	$C_6H_4ClNO_2$	*o*-Chloronitrobenzene	246.0	242.1	15?	234
5815	$C_6H_4ClNO_2$	*p*-Chloronitrobenzene	239.1	235.6	13	234
5816	$C_6H_5NO_2$	Nitrobenzene	210.75	Nonazeotrope		210
5817	$C_6H_6O_2$	Pyrocatechol	232.9	Nonazeotrope		222
5818	$C_6H_6O_2$	Resorcinol	281.4	Nonazeotrope		222
5819	$C_6H_8O_4$	Methyl maleate	204.05	Nonazeotrope		255
5820	$C_6H_{10}O_4$	Ethyl oxalate	185.65	Nonazeotrope		255
5821	$C_6H_{10}O_4$	Glycol diacetate	186.3	Nonazeotrope		255
5822	$C_6H_{14}O_4$	Triethylene glycol	288.7	285.1	37	207
5823	$C_7H_7NO_2$	*m*-Nitrotoluene	230.8	228.8	13	234
5224	$C_7H_7NO_2$	*o*-Nitrotoluene	221.75	220.7	8	234
5825	$C_7H_7NO_2$	*p*-Nitrotoluene	238.9	235.6	17	234
5826	C_7H_8	Toluene	110.75	Nonazeotrope		217
5827	C_7H_8O	*o*-Cresol	191.1	Nonazeotrope		222
5828	C_7H_8O	*p*-Cresol	201.7	Nonazeotrope		224
5829	$C_7H_8O_2$	Guaiacol	205.05	Nonazeotrope		236
5830	C_8H_8	Styrene	145.8	Nonazeotrope		220
5831	$C_8H_8O_2$	Benzyl formate	202.3	Nonazeotrope		217
5832	$C_8H_8O_2$	Methyl benzoate	199.45	Nonazeotrope		217
5833	$C_8H_8O_2$	Phenyl acetate	195.7	Nonazeotrope		255
5834	$C_8H_8O_3$	Methyl salicylate	222.35	221.4	7.5	217
5835	C_8H_{10}	*m*-Xylene	139.0	Nonazeotrope		207
5836	C_8H_{10}	*o*-Xylene	143.6	Nonazeotrope		217
5837	$C_8H_{10}O$	Phenethyl alcohol	219.4	Nonazeotrope		229
5838	$C_8H_{10}O$	3,4-Xylenol	226.8	Nonazeotrope		255
5839	$C_8H_{10}O_2$	*m*-Dimethoxybenzene	214.7	212.5	7	256
5840	$C_8H_{10}O_2$	*o*-Ethoxyphenol	216.5	Nonazeotrope		255
5841	$C_8H_{12}O_4$	Ethyl fumarate	217.85	Nonazeotrope		255
5842	$C_8H_{12}O_4$	Ethyl maleate	223.3	Nonazeotrope		255
5843	C_8H_{18}	2,5-Dimethylhexane	109.4	Nonazeotrope		255
5844	$C_8H_{18}O_3$	2-(2-Butoxyethoxy)ethanol	231.2	Nonazeotrope		255
5845	C_9H_7N	Quinoline	237.3	Nonazeotrope		233
5846	C_9H_8	Indene	182.6	182.4	2	255
5847	$C_9H_{10}O$	*p*-Methylacetophenone	226.35	Nonazeotrope		232
5848	$C_9H_{10}O_2$	Benzyl acetate	214.9	Nonazeotrope		216
5849	$C_9H_{10}O_2$	Ethyl benzoate	212.6	Nonazeotrope		216
5850	$C_9H_{10}O_3$	Ethyl salicylate	233.7	230.5	10.3	217
5851	C_9H_{12}	Mesitylene	164.6	Nonazeotrope		217
5852	C_9H_{12}	Propylbenzene	158.8	Nonazeotrope		220
5853	$C_9H_{12}O$	3-Phenylpropanol	235.6	Nonazeotrope		229
5854	$C_9H_{12}O$	Phenyl propyl ether	190.5	190.0	<8	255
5855	$C_9H_{18}O_3$	Isobutyl carbonate	190.3	Nonazeotrope		255
5856	$C_{10}H_7Br$	1-Bromonaphthalene	281.0	272.5	....	255
5857	$C_{10}H_7Cl$	1-Chloronaphthalene	262.7	256.0	17	255
5858	$C_{10}H_8$	Naphthalene	218.05	215.2	10	210
5859	$C_{10}H_{10}O_2$	Isosafrole	252.0	243.8	~16	218
5860	$C_{10}H_{10}O_2$	Methyl cinnamate	261.9	Reacts		215
5861	$C_{10}H_{10}O_2$	Safrol	235.9	231.3	14.5	210
5862	$C_{10}H_{10}O_4$	Methyl phthalate	283.2	271.5	31	247
5863	$C_{10}H_{12}O$	Anethol	235.7	230.8	14	236
5864	$C_{10}H_{12}O$	Estragol	215.6	213.5	7.5	225
5865	$C_{10}H_{12}O_2$	Ethyl α-toluate	228.75	228.6	7	210
5866	$C_{10}H_{12}O_2$	Eugenol	254.5	251.3	14	236
5867	$C_{10}H_{12}O_2$	Isoeugenol	268.8	263.5	25	255
5868	$C_{10}H_{12}O_2$	Propyl benzoate	230.85	228.8	8	216
5869	$C_{10}H_{14}$	Butylbenzene	183.1	<182.9	....	255
5870	$C_{10}H_{14}$	Cymene	176.7	Nonazeotrope		255
5871	$C_{10}H_{14}O$	Carvacrol	237.85	Nonazeotrope		255
5872	$C_{10}H_{14}O$	Carvone	231.0	230.85	3	232
5873	$C_{10}H_{14}O$	Thymol	232.8	Nonazeotrope		210
5874	$C_{10}H_{14}O_2$	*m*-Diethoxybenzene	235.4	231.0	13	256
5875	$C_{10}H_{16}$	Camphene	159.6	Nonazeotrope		217
5876	$C_{10}H_{16}$	*d*-Limonene	177.8	177.7	~1	217

No.	B-Component Formula	B-Component Name	B.P., ° C.	Azeotropic Data B.P., ° C.	Azeotropic Data Wt. % A	Ref.
A =	**$C_3H_8O_3$**	**Glycerol (*continued*)**	**290.5**			
5877	$C_{10}H_{16}$	α-Pinene	159.6	Nonazeotrope		*217*
5878	$C_{10}H_{16}$	Nopinene	163.8	Nonazeotrope		*255*
5879	$C_{10}H_{16}$	α-Terpinene	173.4	Nonazeotrope		*255*
5880	$C_{10}H_{16}$	Terpinolene	184.6	184.2	....	*255*
5881	$C_{10}H_{16}$	Thymene	179.7	179.6	1	*221*
5882	$C_{10}H_{18}O$	α-Terpineol	218.85	Nonazeotrope		*255*
5883	$C_{10}H_{20}O$	Menthol	216.3	Nonazeotrope		*255*
5884	$C_{10}H_{20}O_2$	Ethyl caprylate	208.35	Nonazeotrope		*255*
5885	$C_{10}H_{20}O_2$	Isoamyl isovalerate	192.7	Nonazeotrope		*255*
5886	$C_{10}H_{20}O_2$	Methyl pelargonate	213.8	Nonazeotrope		*255*
5887	$C_{10}H_{22}$	Decane	173.3	Nonazeotrope		*255*
5888	$C_{10}H_{22}$	2,7-Dimethyloctane	160.1	Nonazeotrope		*255*
5889	$C_{11}H_{10}$	1-Methylnaphthalene	244.9	237.25	~18	*217*
5890	$C_{11}H_{10}$	2-Methylnaphthalene	241.15	233.7	16.5	*250*
5891	$C_{11}H_{12}O_2$	Ethyl cinnamate	271.5	Reacts		*216*
5892	$C_{11}H_{14}O_2$	1-Allyl-3,4-dimethoxybenzene	255.0	248.3	18	*218*
5893	$C_{11}H_{14}O_2$	Butyl benzoate	249.8	243	17	*216*
5894	$C_{11}H_{14}O_2$	1,2-Dimethoxy-4-propenylbenzene	270.5	258.4	25	*254*
5895	$C_{11}H_{14}O_2$	Ethyl β-phenyl propionate	248.1	242.0	15	*247*
5896	$C_{11}H_{14}O_2$	Isobutyl benzoate	241.9	~237.4	14	*216*
5897	$C_{11}H_{20}O$	Isobornyl methyl ether	192.4	<192.0	7.5	*255*
5898	$C_{11}H_{20}O$	Terpineol methyl ether	216.2	214.0	8	*225*
5899	$C_{12}H_{10}$	Acenaphthene	277.9	259.1	29	*223*
5900	$C_{12}H_{10}$	Biphenyl	254.9	246.1	25	*244*
5901	$C_{12}H_{10}O$	Phenyl ether	259.3	247.9	22	*210*
5902	$C_{12}H_{16}O_2$	Isoamyl benzoate	262.05	251.6	22	*216*
5903	$C_{12}H_{16}O_3$	Isoamyl salicylate	279	267	....	*225*
5904	$C_{12}H_{18}$	1,3,5-Triethylbenzene	215.5	212.9	8	*218*
5905	$C_{12}H_{20}O_2$	Bornyl acetate	227.7	226.0	10	*210*
5906	$C_{12}H_{22}O$	Bornyl ethyl ether	204.9	203.5	~5	*255*
5907	$C_{13}H_{10}O_2$	Phenyl benzoate	315	279	~55	*216*
5908	$C_{13}H_{12}$	Diphenylmethane	265.6	250.8	27	*210*
5909	$C_{13}H_{12}O$	Benzyl phenyl ether	286.5	264.5	30	*247*
5910	$C_{14}H_{12}O_2$	Benzyl benzoate	324	282.5	....	*216*
5911	$C_{14}H_{14}$	1,2-Diphenylethane	284	261.3	32	*217*
5912	$C_{14}H_{14}O$	Benzyl ether	297.0	269.5	36	*247*
A =	**C_3H_8S**	**1-Propanethiol**	**67.3**			
5913	C_4H_4S	Thiophene	84.7	Nonazeotrope		*255*
5914	C_4H_8O	2-Butanone	79.6	~55.5	~75	*243*
5915	C_5H_8	3-Methyl-1,2-butadiene	40.8	Reacts		*243*
5916	C_5H_{10}	Cyclopentane	49.4	Nonazeotrope		*246*
5917	C_5H_{10}	2-Methyl-2-butene	37.15	Nonazeotrope		*243*
5918	C_5H_{12}	Pentane	36.07	Nonazeotrope		*91*
5919	$C_5H_{12}O$	Ethyl propyl ether	63.85	<63.5	>9	*255*
5920	C_6H_6	Benzene	80.103	Nonazeotrope		*91*
5921	C_6H_{10}	Biallyl	60.2	Reacts		*255*
5922	C_6H_{12}	Cyclohexane	80.738	67.77	97.6	*91*
5923	C_6H_{12}	Methylcyclopentane	71.812	66.45	64.2, V-l.	*91*
5924	C_6H_{14}	2,2-Dimethylbutane	49.743	Nonazeotrope		*91*
5925	C_6H_{14}	2,3-Dimethylbutane	57.990	57.54	16.3	*91*
5926	C_6H_{14}	Hexane	68.742	64.35	52.6, V-l.	*91, 246**
5927	C_6H_{14}	2-Methylpentane	60.274	59.20	23.9, V-l.	*91*
5928	C_6H_{14}	3-Methylpentane	63.284	61.26	34.2	*91*
5929	$C_6H_{14}O$	Isopropyl ether	68.3	66.0	65	*242*
5930	C_7H_{16}	2,2-Dimethylpentane	79.205	67.20	81.3	*91*
5931	C_7H_{16}	2,4-Dimethylpentane	80.51	67.48	85.1	*91*
5932	C_7H_{16}	2,2,3-Trimethylbutane	80.871	67.57	87.4	*91*
A =	**C_3H_8S**	**2-Propanethiol**	**52.60**			
5933	C_5H_{10}	Cyclopentane	49.263	47.75	35.3	*91*
5934	C_5H_{12}	Pentane	34.074	Nonazeotrope		*91*
5935	C_6H_{14}	2,2-Dimethylbutane	49.743	47.41	37.7	*91*
5936	C_6H_{14}	2,3-Dimethylbutane	57.990	51.24	67.5	*91*
5937	C_6H_{14}	Hexane	68.742	Nonazeotrope		*91*
5938	C_6H_{14}	2-Methylpentane	60.274	51.70	75.9	*91*
5939	C_6H_{14}	3-Methylpentane	63.284	52.40	87.0	*91*

No.	Formula	Name	B.P., ° C.	Azeotropic Data B.P., ° C.	Wt. % A	Ref.
A =	**$C_3H_9BO_3$**	**Methyl Borate**	**68.7**			
5940	C_4H_8O	2-Butanone	79.6	68.0	85	*232*
5941	C_4H_8O	Butyraldehyde	75.5	Nonazeotrope		*228*
5942	$C_4H_8O_2$	Ethyl acetate	77.1	Nonazeotrope		*229*
5943	$C_4H_8O_2$	Isopropyl formate	68.8	<67.0	<58	*229*
5944	C_4H_9Br	2-Bromo-2-methylpropane	73.3	Nonazeotrope		*218*
5945	C_4H_9Cl	1-Chlorobutane	78.5	Nonazeotrope		*255*
5946	C_4H_9Cl	2-Chlorobutane	68.25	66.9	45	*242*
5947	C_4H_9Cl	1-Chloro-2-methylpropane	68.85	67.3	54	*211*
5948	C_4H_9Cl	2-Chloro-2-methylpropane	50.8	Nonazeotrope		*255*
5949	$C_4H_9NO_2$	Butyl nitrite	78.2	Nonazeotrope		*229*
5950	$C_4H_9NO_2$	Isobutyl nitrite	67.1	<66.9	....	*229*
5951	$C_4H_{10}O$	*tert*-Butyl alcohol	82.45	<66.0	>75	*255*
5952	C_5H_{12}	Pentane	36.2	Nonazeotrope		*226*
5953	C_6H_5F	Fluorobenzene	84.9	Nonazeotrope		*255*
5954	C_6H_6	Benzene	80.2	Nonazeotrope		*218*
5955	C_6H_8	1,3-Cyclohexadiene	80.4	Nonazeotrope		*226*
5956	C_6H_{12}	Cyclohexane	80.8	Nonazeotrope		*226*
5957	C_6H_{12}	Methylcyclopentane	72.0	67.5	58	*242, 384**
5958	C_6H_{14}	2,3-Dimethylbutane	58.0	Nonazeotrope		*255*
5959	C_6H_{14}	*n*-Hexane	68.95	~66.3	50	*211*
A =	**C_3H_9ClSi**	**Chlorotrimethylsilane**	**57.7**			
5960	C_6H_{14}	2-Methylpentane	60.4	56.4	65	*343*
5961	C_6H_{14}	3-Methylpentane	63.3	57.3	70	*343*
A =	**C_3H_9N**	**Propylamine**	**49.7**			
5962	C_4H_8O	2-Butanone	79.6	Nonazeotrope		*207*
5963	$C_4H_{10}O$	Ethyl ether	34.6	Nonazeotrope		*231*
5964	C_5H_{10}	Cyclopentane	49.3	47.0	52	*231*
5965	C_5H_{10}	2-Methyl-2-butene	37.15	~32	~32	*243*
5966	C_5H_{12}	2-Methylbutane	27.95	Nonazeotrope		*231*
5967	C_6H_{14}	2,3-Dimethylbutane	58.0	Nonazeotrope		*231*
A =	**C_3H_9N**	**Trimethylamine**	**3.5**			
5968	C_4H_4	1-Buten-3-yne	5.0	Nonazeotrope		*43*
5969	C_4H_6	1,3-Butadiene	−4.6	Nonazeotrope		*43*
5970	C_4H_8	1-Butene	−6	Nonazeotrope		*43, 158**
5971	C_4H_8	*cis*-2-Butene	1.0	Nonazeotrope		*43*
5972	C_4H_8	*trans*-2-Butene	3.5	Nonazeotrope		*43*
5973	C_4H_8	2-Methylpropene	−6	Nonazeotrope		*43, 158**
5974	C_4H_{10}	Butane	0	Nonazeotrope		*43, 158**
5975	C_4H_{10}	2-Methylpropane	−10	Nonazeotrope		*43, 158**
A =	**$C_3H_{10}OSi$**	**Trimethylsilanol**	**99**			
5976	$C_6H_{18}OSi_2$	Hexamethyldisiloxane	100	90	33–35	*338*
A =	**C_4H_4**	**1-Buten-3-yne**	**5.0**			
5977	C_4H_8	2-Butene	3.5	Min. b.p.		*50*
A =	**C_4H_4O**	**Furan**	**31.7**			
5978	C_5H_{10}	3-Methyl-1-butene	20.6	Nonazeotrope		*238*
5979	C_5H_{12}	2-Methylbutane	27.95	<27.0	>8	*238*
A =	**$C_4H_4N_2$**	**Pyrazine**	**117.2**			
5980	$C_6H_{14}S$	Isopropyl sulfide	120.5	116.0	>5	*255*
A =	**$C_4H_4N_2$**	**Pyridazine**	**207.2**			
5981	$C_6H_5NO_3$	*o*-Nitrophenol	217.2	Nonazeotrope		*255*
5982	C_6H_6O	Phenol	182.2	209.0	88	*255*
5983	C_7H_7ClO	*m*-Chloroanisole	193.3	Nonazeotrope		*255*
5984	C_7H_7ClO	*p*-Chloroanisole	197.8	Nonazeotrope		*255*
5985	C_7H_8O	*m*-Cresol	202.2	211.8	68	*255*
5986	C_7H_8O	*p*-Cresol	201.7	211.5	70	*255*
5987	$C_7H_8O_2$	Guaiacol	205.05	203.5	....	*255*
5988	$C_8H_{10}O$	*p*-Ethylphenol	218.8	220.5	15	*255*
5989	$C_8H_{10}O$	2,4-Xylenol	210.5	215.5	25	*255*
5990	$C_{12}H_{22}O$	Ethyl isobornyl ether	203.8	<203.5	>13	*255*

No.	B-Component Formula	B-Component Name	B.P., ° C.	Azeotropic Data B.P., ° C.	Azeotropic Data Wt. % A	Ref.
A =	**C_4H_4S**	**Thiophene**	**84.7**			
5991	C_4H_7N	Pyrroline	90.9	Nonazeotrope		255
5992	C_4H_8O	2-Butanone	79.6	Nonazeotrope		207
5993	C_4H_8O	Butyraldehyde	75.2	Nonazeotrope		246
5994	$C_4H_8O_2$	Ethyl acetate	77.1	Nonazeotrope		207
			....	<73	>20	243
5995	$C_4H_8O_2$	Methyl propionate	79.85	Nonazeotrope		207
5996	$C_4H_8O_2$	Propyl formate	80.85	Nonazeotrope		207
5997	C_4H_9Cl	1-Chlorobutane	78.5	Nonazeotrope		207
5998	C_4H_9ClO	1-Chloroethyl ethyl ether	98.5	Nonazeotrope		246
5999	$C_4H_9NO_2$	Butyl nitrite	78.2	Nonazeotrope		207
6000	$C_4H_9NO_2$	Isobutyl nitrite	67.1	Nonazeotrope		230
6001	$C_5H_{10}O$	3-Methyl-2-butanone	95.4	Nonazeotrope		255
6002	$C_5H_{11}NO_2$	Isoamyl nitrile	97.15	Nonazeotrope		207
6003	$C_5H_{12}O_2$	Diethoxymethane	87.95	<83.9	....	246
6004	C_6H_6	Benzene	80.2	Nonazeotrope		207
6005	C_6H_{10}	Cyclohexene	82.75	<82.5	>15	241
6006	C_6H_{12}	Methylcyclopentane	72.0	Nonazeotrope		246
6007	C_6H_{14}	Hexane	86.95	Nonazeotrope		207
6008	$C_6H_{14}O$	Isopropyl ether	68.3	Nonazeotrope		246
A =	**$C_4H_5ClO_2$**	**α-Chlorocrotonic Acid**	**212.5**			
6009	$C_6H_5NO_2$	Nitrobenzene	210.75	<208.0	>30	234
6010	$C_7H_7NO_2$	*o*-Nitrotoluene	221.75	<211.2	>72	234
A =	**$C_4H_5Cl_3O_2$**	**Ethyl Trichloroacetate**	**167.2**			
6011	$C_4H_8O_2$	Butyric acid	164.0	<163.5	....	255
6012	$C_4H_8O_2$	Isobutyric acid	154.6	Nonazeotrope		255
6013	$C_5H_{10}O_2$	Valeric acid	186.35	Nonazeotrope		255
6014	C_7H_6O	Benzaldehyde	179.2	Nonazeotrope		243
6015	$C_7H_{14}O$	2-Methylcyclohexanol	168.5	<165.5	>62	255
6016	$C_8H_{18}O$	Octyl alcohol	195.2	Nonazeotrope		255
A =	**C_4H_5N**	**Pyrrol**	**129.2**			
6017	C_4H_9I	1-Iodobutane	130.4	<123.2	32	233
6018	$C_4H_{10}O$	Butyl alcohol	117.8	Nonazeotrope		207
6019	$C_4H_{10}O$	Isobutyl alcohol	108.0	Nonazeotrope		255
6020	$C_4H_{10}O_2$	2-Ethoxyethanol	135.3	Nonazeotrope		255
6021	$C_4H_{10}S$	Butanethiol	97.8	Nonazeotrope		255
6022	$C_4H_{10}S$	Ethyl sulfide	92.1	Nonazeotrope		233
6023	$C_5H_{10}O$	Cyclopentanol	140.85	Nonazeotrope		233
6024	$C_5H_{10}O_3$	Ethyl carbonate	126.5	131.6	49	233
6025	$C_5H_{11}Br$	1-Bromo-3-methylbutane	120.65	<116.4	>10	233
6026	$C_5H_{12}O$	Amyl alcohol	138.2	Nonazeotrope		207
6027	$C_5H_{12}O$	*tert*-Amyl alcohol	102.35	Nonazeotrope		255
6028	$C_5H_{12}O$	Isoamyl alcohol	131.9	<129.4	>21	233
6029	$C_5H_{12}O$	2-Pentanol	119.8	Nonazeotrope		207
6030	$C_5H_{12}O_2$	2-Propoxyethanol	151.35	Nonazeotrope		207
6031	C_6H_5Br	Bromobenzene	156.1	Nonazeotrope		233
6032	C_6H_5Cl	Chlorobenzene	131.75	124.5	43	207
6033	C_6H_7N	3-Picoline	143.8	145–148	....	98
6034	C_6H_7N	4-Picoline	144.8	145–148	....	98
6035	$C_6H_{10}O$	Mesityl oxide	130.5	~128	....	241
6036	$C_6H_{10}S$	Allyl sulfide	139.35	127.0	70	255
6037	$C_6H_{12}O_2$	Isoamyl formate	123.8	~130.0	~60	228
6038	$C_6H_{12}O_2$	Isobutyl acetate	117.4	Nonazeotrope		207
6039	$C_6H_{14}S$	Isopropyl sulfide	120.5	117.5	20	233
6040	$C_6H_{14}S$	Propyl sulfide	140.8	127.5	65	233
6041	C_7H_7Cl	*o*-Chlorotoluene	159.2	Nonazeotrope		233
6042	C_7H_8	Toluene	110.75	Nonazeotrope		233
6043	$C_7H_{14}O_2$	Isoamyl acetate	142.1	Nonazeotrope		207
6044	$C_7H_{14}O_2$	Propyl isobutyrate	134.0	>134.8	>25	228
6045	C_8H_{10}	Xylenes	140	Min. b.p.		202
6046	C_8H_{18}	*n*-Octane	125.75	<124.3	<36	233
6047	$C_8H_{18}O$	Isobutyl ether	122.3	<121.5	>12	242

No.	B-Component Formula	Name	B.P., ° C.	Azeotropic Data B.P., ° C.	Wt. % A	Ref.
A =	**C_4H_5NS**	**Allyl Isothiocyanate**	**152.0**			
6048	$C_4H_8Cl_2O$	1,2-Dichloroethyl ethyl ether	145.5	Nonazeotrope		*255*
6049	$C_5H_4O_2$	2-Furaldehyde	161.45	Nonazeotrope		*255*
6050	$C_5H_{10}O$	Cyclopentanol	140.85	Nonazeotrope		*255*
6051	$C_6H_{12}O$	Cyclohexanol	160.8	Nonazeotrope		*255*
6052	$C_6H_{13}ClO_2$	Chloroacetal	152.0	Nonazeotrope		*255*
6053	$C_6H_{14}O$	Hexyl alcohol	157.85	<151.8	....	*255*
6054	$C_6H_{14}O_2$	Pinacol	174.35	Nonazeotrope		*255*
6055	$C_6H_{14}S$	Propyl sulfide	141.5	<141.1	<19	*255*
6056	C_7H_8O	Anisole	153.85	151.5	68	*255*
6057	$C_8H_{10}O$	Benzyl methyl ether	167.8	Nonazeotrope		*255*
6058	$C_8H_{18}S$	Isobutyl sulfide	172.0	Nonazeotrope		*255*
A =	**C_4H_6**	**1,3-Butadiene**	**−4.5**			
6059	C_4H_8	1-Butene	−5	Nonazeotrope		*241*
6060	C_4H_8	2-Butene	1.5–3	5.53	76.5, V-l.	*53*
6061	C_4H_{10}	Butane	−0.5	Min. b.p.		*50*
6062	$C_4H_{10}O$	Ethyl ether	34.5	Nonazeotrope, V-l.		*53*
A =	**C_4H_6**	**1-Butyne**	**9**			
6063	C_4H_8	*cis*-2-Butene	1	Min. b.p.	9.5	*50*
6064	C_4H_8	*trans*-2-Butene	3.5	....	25.5	*50*
A =	**$C_4H_6Cl_2O_2$**	**Ethyl Dichloroacetate**	**158.1**			
6065	$C_4H_8O_2$	Butyric acid	164.0	157.0	....	*242*
6066	$C_4H_8O_2$	Isobutyric acid	154.6	<153.8	....	*242*
6067	$C_4H_{10}O$	Butyl alcohol	117.8	Nonazeotrope		*255*
6068	$C_5H_4O_2$	2-Furaldehyde	161.5	Nonazeotrope		*243*
6069	$C_5H_{10}O_3$	Ethyl lacetate	154.1	Nonazeotrope		*255*
6070	$C_5H_{11}NO_3$	Isoamyl nitrate	149.75	Nonazeotrope		*240*
6071	$C_5H_{12}O_2$	2-Propoxyethanol	151.35	Nonazeotrope		*255*
6072	$C_6H_{14}O$	Hexyl alcohol	157.85	<156.0	58	*255*
6073	$C_6H_{14}O_2$	2-Butoxyethanol	171.15	Nonazeotrope		*255*
6074	$C_7H_{16}O$	Heptyl alcohol	176.15	Nonazeotrope		*255*
6075	$C_8H_{16}O_2$	Butyl butyrate	166.4	Nonazeotrope		*255*
6076	$C_8H_{16}O_2$	Isoamyl propionate	160.7	Nonazeotrope		*255*
A =	**C_4H_6O**	**Crotonaldehyde**	**102.15**			
6077	C_4H_9Br	1-Bromo-2-methylpropane	91.6	Nonazeotrope		*243*
6078	$C_5H_{10}O$	3-Methyl-2-butanone	95.4	Nonazeotrope		*232*
6079	$C_5H_{10}O$	2-Pentanone	102.35	101.2	....	*232*
6080	$C_5H_{10}O$	3-Pentanone	102.05	<101.4	....	*232*
6081	$C_5H_{10}O_2$	Ethyl propionate	99.1	98.0	25	*255*
6082	$C_5H_{10}O_2$	Methyl butyrate	102.75	<101	....	*243*
6083	C_6H_6	Benzene	80.2	Nonazeotrope		*243*
6084	C_6H_{12}	Cyclohexane	80.75	Nonazeotrope		*255*
6085	C_7H_8	Toluene	110.65	Min. b.p.		*385*
			110.65	Nonazeotrope		*255*
6086	C_7H_{14}	Methylcyclohexane	101.15	<99.5	....	*255*
6087	C_nH_{2n+2}	Paraffins	109.5–110.5	102.8	....	*97, 385**
A =	**$C_4H_6O_2$**	**Allyl Formate**	**80.0**			
6088	C_4H_9Cl	1-Chlorobutane	78.5	<76.0	>40	*255*
6089	$C_4H_9NO_2$	Butyl nitrite	78.2	<77.0	>30	*229*
6090	C_6H_6	Benzene	80.15	79.2	>45	*255*
6091	C_6H_{14}	Hexane	68.8	<64.5	>26	*255*
A =	**$C_4H_6O_2$**	**Biacetyl**	**87.5**			
6092	$C_5H_{12}O$	Isoamyl alcohol	131.9	Nonazeotrope		*232*
6093	C_6H_6	Benzene	80	79.3	~55	*264*
6094	$C_6H_{15}N$	Dipropylamine	109.2	Nonazeotrope		*255*
A =	**$C_4H_6O_2$**	**Methyl Acrylate**	**80**			
6095	$C_4H_{10}O$	Butyl alcohol	117	Nonazeotrope		*320*
6096	$C_4H_{10}O$	Isobutyl alcohol	108	Nonazeotrope		*320*
6097	$C_5H_8O_2$	Ethyl acrylate, 103 mm.	43	Nonazeotrope		*320*

No.	B-Component Formula	Name	B.P., ° C.	Azeotropic Data B.P., ° C.	Wt. % A	Ref.
A =	**$C_4H_6O_2$**	**Methacrylic Acid**				
6098	$C_5H_8O_2$	Methyl methacrylate	....	Nonazeotrope		426
A =	**$C_4H_6O_3$**	**Acetic Anhydride**	**138**			
6099	C_5H_5N	Pyridine	115	Nonazeotrope, V-l.		281
6100	C_7H_{14}	Methylcyclohexane	101	99	~18	118
6102	C_7H_{16}	*n*-Heptane	98.4	Azeotropic		118
6103	C_8H_{16}	Ethylcyclohexane	131	118	~37	118
6104	C_8H_{18}	*n*-Octane	125.8	Azeotropic		118
6105	C_9H_{20}	*n*-Nonane	150	Azeotropic		118
6106	$C_{10}H_{22}$	*n*-Decane	173	Azeotropic		118
6107	$C_{11}H_{24}$	*n*-Undecane	194.5	Azeotropic		118
A =	**$C_4H_6O_3$**	**Methyl Pyruvate**	**137.5**			
6108	$C_4H_8O_2$	Isobutyric acid	154.6	Nonazeotrope		232
6109	C_4H_9I	1-Iodobutane	130.4	<127.0	....	232
6110	$C_5H_8O_2$	2,4-Pentanedione	137.7	<136.2	....	232
6111	$C_5H_{10}O_2$	Methyl butyrate	102.65	Nonazeotrope		255
6112	$C_5H_{10}O_2$	Propyl acetate	101.6	Nonazeotrope		232
6113	$C_5H_{11}I$	1-Iodo-3-methylbutane	147.65	<136.0	....	232
6114	C_6H_5Br	Bromobenzene	156.1	Nonazeotrope		232
6115	C_6H_5Cl	Chlorobenzene	131.75	129.0	30	232
6116	$C_6H_{10}O$	Mesityl oxide	129.45	Nonazeotrope		232
6117	$C_6H_{10}S$	Allyl sulfide	139.35	<134.4	>53	246
6118	$C_6H_{12}O$	2-Hexanone	127.2	Nonazeotrope		232
6119	$C_6H_{12}O_2$	Isobutyl acetate	117.4	Nonazeotrope		232
6120	$C_6H_{12}O_2$	Methyl isovalerate	116.5	Nonazeotrope		255
6121	$C_6H_{14}O$	Propyl ether	90.1	Nonazeotrope		232
6122	$C_6H_{14}S$	Isopropyl sulfide	120.5	Nonazeotrope		246
6123	C_7H_8O	Anisole	153.85	Nonazeotrope		232
6124	$C_7H_{14}O_2$	Ethyl isovalerate	134.7	<132.0	....	232
6125	$C_7H_{14}O_2$	Isoamyl acetate	142.1	135.0	65	232
6126	C_8H_{10}	*m*-Xylene	139.2	130.0	50	232
6127	C_8H_{16}	1,3-Dimethylcyclohexane	120.7	<117.0	....	232
6128	$C_8H_{16}O_2$	Isoamyl propionate	160.7	Nonazeotrope		255
6129	$C_8H_{18}O$	Butyl ether	142.4	130.2	....	232
6130	$C_8H_{18}O$	Isobutyl ether	122.3	<121.5	....	232
6131	$C_{10}H_{16}$	Camphene	159.6	<135.2	....	232
6132	$C_{10}H_{16}$	*α*-Pinene	155.8	<134.5	....	232
A =	**$C_4H_6O_4$**	**Methyl Oxalate**	**163.3**			
6133	$C_4H_7ClO_2$	Ethyl chloroacetate	143.5	Nonazeotrope		243
6134	$C_4H_8O_2$	Butyric acid	164.0	<160.8	>54	242
6135	$C_4H_8O_2$	Isobutyric acid	154.6	<154.2	<18	242
6136	$C_4H_8O_3$	Glycol monoacetate	190.9	Nonazeotrope		255
6137	$C_5H_4O_2$	2-Furaldehyde	161.45	Nonazeotrope		252
6138	$C_5H_{10}O_3$	Ethyl lactate	154.1	Nonazeotrope		255
6139	$C_5H_{10}O_3$	2-Methoxyethyl acetate	144.6	Nonazeotrope		255
6140	$C_5H_{11}I$	1-Iodo-3-methylbutane	147.6	Nonazeotrope		227
6141	$C_6H_4Cl_2$	*o*-Dichlorobenzene	179.5	<163.8	<89	255
6142	$C_6H_4Cl_2$	*p*-Dichlorobenzene	174.35	162.05	65	210
6143	C_6H_5Br	Bromobenzene	156.1	153.05	28	243
6144	C_6H_6O	Phenol	182.2	182.35	~8	253
6145	$C_6H_{10}O$	Cyclohexanone	155.7	Nonazeotrope		232
6146	$C_6H_{12}O$	Cyclohexanol	160.65	155.6	41	243
6147	$C_6H_{13}Br$	1-Bromohexane	156.5	<154.0	<30	255
6148	$C_6H_{13}ClO_2$	Chloroacetal	157.4	Nonazeotrope		211
6149	$C_6H_{14}O$	Hexyl alcohol	157.85	<155.5	....	247
6150	$C_6H_{14}O_2$	2-Butoxyethanol	171.25	Nonazeotrope		255
6151	$C_6H_{14}O_2$	Pinacol	174.35	163.15	81	210
6152	C_7H_7Br	*m*-Bromotoluene	184.3	Nonazeotrope		207
6153	C_7H_7Br	*o*-Bromotoluene	181.5	164.1	98	218
6154	C_7H_7Br	*p*-Bromotoluene	185.0	Nonazeotrope		218
6155	C_7H_7Cl	*α*-Chlorotoluene	179.3	Nonazeotrope		210
6156	C_7H_7Cl	*o*-Chlorotoluene	159.2	154.8	35	250
6157	C_7H_7Cl	*p*-Chlorotoluene	162.4	156.6	30	218
6158	C_7H_8	Toluene	110.75	Nonazeotrope		255

No.	B-Component Formula	Name	B.P., ° C.	Azeotropic Data B.P., ° C.	Wt. % A	Ref.
A =	**$C_4H_6O_4$**	**Methyl Oxalate (*continued*)**	**163.3**			
6159	C_7H_8O	Anisole	153.85	153.65	~15	*237*
6160	$C_7H_{14}O$	2-Methylcyclohexanol	168.5	<161.2	....	*255*
6161	C_7H_{16}	Heptyl alcohol	176.15	<163.8	....	*255*
6162	C_8H_8	Styrene	145.7	<142.5	~12	*243*
6163	C_8H_{10}	Ethylbenzene	136.15	Nonazeotrope		*255*
6164	C_8H_{10}	*m*-Xylene	139.2	<138.8	....	*255*
6165	C_8H_{10}	*o*-Xylene	144.3	<143.0	....	*242*
6166	$C_8H_{10}O$	Benzyl methyl ether	167.8	<161.9	<60	*237*
6167	$C_8H_{10}O$	Phenetole	170.45	161.35	....	*251*
6168	C_8H_{16}	1,3-Dimethylcyclohexane	120.7	Nonazeotrope		*255*
6169	$C_8H_{16}O_2$	Butyl butyrate	166.4	160.5	58	*229*
6170	$C_8H_{16}O_2$	Ethyl caproate	167.7	161.0	60	*229*
6171	$C_8H_{16}O_2$	Hexyl acetate	171.5	<162.5	<76	*255*
6172	$C_8H_{16}O_2$	Isoamyl propionate	160.7	157.5	38	*229*
6173	$C_8H_{16}O_2$	Isobutyl butyrate	156.9	<155.5	>23	*229*
6174	$C_8H_{16}O_2$	Propyl isovalerate	155.7	<154.5	>20	*229*
6175	$C_8H_{18}O$	*sec*-Octyl alcohol	179.0	~163.8	86?	*210*
6176	$C_8H_{20}SiO_4$	Ethyl silicate	165	162.5	....	*243*
6177	C_9H_8	Indene	182.6	163.6	83	*244*
6178	C_9H_{12}	Cumene	152.8	148.5	....	*242*
6179	C_9H_{12}	Mesitylene	164.0	154.8	49.8	*243*
6180	C_9H_{12}	Propylbenzene	158	~152	~38	*243*
6181	C_9H_{12}	Pseudocumene	169	~157	~65	*243*
6182	$C_9H_{18}O_2$	Isoamyl isobutyrate	169.8	161.0	65	*229*
6183	$C_{10}H_8$	Naphthalene	218.0	Nonazeotrope		*255*
6184	$C_{10}H_{14}$	Butylbenzene	183.2	<163.5	....	*226*
6185	$C_{10}H_{14}$	Cymene	175.3	~161	~80	*243*
6186	$C_{10}H_{16}$	Camphene	159.6	146.65	42	*250*
6187	$C_{10}H_{16}$	*d*-Limonene	177.8	156.7	~75	*243*
6188	$C_{10}H_{16}$	Nopinene	163.8	147.1	51	*243*
6189	$C_{10}H_{16}$	*α*-Phellandrene	171.5	153	~68	*243*
6190	$C_{10}H_{16}$	*α*-Pinene	155.8	144.1	39	*243*
6191	$C_{10}H_{16}$	Terpinene	180.5	~159.5	~88	*243*
6192	$C_{10}H_{16}$	*α*-Terpinene	173.3	159.5	82	*242*
6193	$C_{10}H_{16}$	*γ*-Terpinene	183	159.5	82	*255*
6194	$C_{10}H_{16}$	Terpinolene	185.2	160.0	<90	*226*
6195	$C_{10}H_{16}$	Terpinolene	185	Azeotrope doubtful		*243*
6196	$C_{10}H_{16}$	Terpinylene	175	~155	<80	*243*
6197	$C_{10}H_{16}$	Thymene	165	150	54	*243*
6198	$C_{10}H_{18}$	*p*-Menthen	170.8	154.0	70	*226*
6199	$C_{10}H_{18}O$	Cineol	176.35	158.85	55	*237*
6200	$C_{10}H_{20}O_2$	Isoamyl isovalerate	171.2	162.2	70	*229*
6201	$C_{10}H_{22}$	2,7-Dimethyloctane	160.2	147.0	45	*226*
6202	$C_{10}H_{22}O$	Isoamyl ether	173.2	154.8	54	*237*
6203	$C_{10}H_{22}O$	Isoamyl ether	173.4	162.2	~80	*228*
6204	$C_{12}H_{18}$	1,3,5-Triethylbenzene	215.5	Nonazeotrope		*255*
6205	$C_{12}H_{22}O_4$	Isoamyl oxalate	172.7	Azeotrope doubtful		*243*
A =	**$C_4H_7BrO_2$**	**Ethyl Bromoacetate**	**158.8**			
6206	$C_4H_8O_2$	Butyric acid	164.0	157.4	84	*207*
6207	$C_4H_8O_2$	Isobutyric acid	154.6	153.0	40	*207*
6208	$C_4H_8O_3$	Methyl lactate	143.8	Nonazeotrope		*207*
6209	$C_4H_{10}O$	*n*-Butyl alcohol	117.8	Nonazeotrope		*207*
6210	$C_4H_{10}O$	Isobutyl alcohol	108.0	Nonazeotrope		*255*
6211	$C_4H_{10}O_2$	2-Ethoxyethanol	135.3	Nonazeotrope		*255*
6212	$C_5H_{10}O_2$	Isovaleric acid	176.5	Nonazeotrope		*207*
6213	$C_5H_{10}O_3$	Ethyl lactate	154.1	Nonazeotrope		*207*
6214	$C_5H_{10}O_3$	Ethyl lactate	155	152.5	....	*243*
6215	$C_5H_{10}O_3$	2-Methoxyethyl acetate	144.6	Nonazeotrope		*207*
6216	$C_5H_{11}I$	1-Iodo-3-methylbutane	147.65	<147.5	<10	*207*
6217	$C_5H_{11}NO_3$	Isoamyl nitrate	149.75	Nonazeotrope		*240*
6218	$C_5H_{12}O$	Isoamyl alcohol	131.9	Nonazeotrope		*207*
6219	$C_5H_{12}O_2$	2-Propoxyethanol	151.35	151.25	5	*207*
6220	$C_6H_4Cl_2$	*p*-Dichlorobenzene	174.4	Nonazeotrope		*207*
6221	C_6H_5Br	Bromobenzene	156.1	155.3	28	*207*
6222	$C_6H_{10}O_4$	Ethylidene diacetate	168.5	Nonazeotrope		*207*

No.	B-Component Formula	Name	B.P., ° C.	Azeotropic Data B.P., ° C.	Wt. % A	Ref.
A =	$C_4H_7BrO_2$	**Ethyl Bromoacetate** (*continued*)	**158.8**			
6223	$C_6H_{12}O$	Cyclohexanol	160.8	155.5	65	207
6224	$C_6H_{12}O$	Cyclohexanol	160.65	~156	....	243
6225	$C_6H_{12}O_3$	2-Ethoxy ethylacetate	156.8	Nonazeotrope		207
6226	$C_6H_{12}O_3$	Isopropyl lactate	166.8	Nonazeotrope		255
6227	$C_6H_{12}O_3$	Propyl lactate	171.7	Nonazeotrope		207
6228	$C_6H_{13}Br$	1-Bromohexane	156.5	<155.0	<39	243
6229	$C_6H_{14}O$	*n*-Hexanol	157.85	154.0	55	207
6230	$C_6H_{14}O_2$	2-Butoxyethanol	171.15	Nonazeotrope		207
6231	$C_6H_{14}S$	Propyl sulfide	141.5	Nonazeotrope		246
6232	C_7H_7Cl	*o*-Chlorotoluene	159.3	156.2	52	207
6233	C_7H_7Cl	*p*-Chlorotoluene	162.4	<158.5	<90	255
6234	C_7H_8O	Anisole	153.85	153.8	....	207
6235	$C_7H_{14}O$	2-Methylcyclohexanol	168.5	157.5	85	255
6236	$C_7H_{14}O_3$	Methyl-1,3-butanediol acetate	171.35	Nonazeotrope		207
6237	$C_7H_{16}O$	*n*-Heptyl alcohol	176.15	Nonazeotrope		207
6238	C_8H_8	Styrene	145.8	Nonazeotrope		255
6239	$C_8H_{10}O$	Benzyl methyl ether	167.8	Nonazeotrope		255
6240	$C_8H_{10}O$	*p*-Methylanisole	177.05	Nonazeotrope		255
6241	$C_8H_{10}O$	Phenetole	170.45	Nonazeotrope		255
6242	$C_8H_{16}O$	2-Octanone	172.85	Nonazeotrope		232
6243	$C_8H_{16}O_2$	Isobutyl isobutyrate	147.3	Nonazeotrope		212
6244	$C_8H_{18}O$	Butyl ether	142.4	Nonazeotrope		255
6245	$C_8H_{18}O$	*sec*-Octanol	180.4	Nonazeotrope		207
6246	$C_8H_{18}S$	Isobutyl sulfide	172.0	Nonazeotrope		246
6247	C_9H_{12}	Mesitylene	164.6	<158.4	<88	255
6248	C_9H_{12}	Propylbenzene	159.3	155.8	50	242
6249	$C_9H_{18}O_2$	Isoamyl butyrate	181.05	Nonazeotrope		255
6250	$C_9H_{18}O_2$	Isobutyl isovalerate	171.2	Nonazeotrope		207
6251	$C_{10}H_{14}$	Cymene	176.7	Nonazeotrope		255
6252	$C_{10}H_{16}$	Camphene	~158	~154	....	243
6253	$C_{10}H_{16}$	Dipentene	177.7	Nonazeotrope		255
6254	$C_{10}H_{16}$	Nopinene	163.8	156.5	78	242
6255	$C_{10}H_{16}$	α-Pinene	155.8	152.5	~46	243
6256	$C_{10}H_{16}$	α-Terpinene	173.4	Nonazeotrope		255
6257	$C_{10}H_{18}O$	Cineol	176.35	Nonazeotrope		255
6258	$C_{10}H_{22}O$	Isoamyl ether	173.2	Nonazeotrope		255
A =	C_4H_7ClO	**2-Chloroethyl Vinyl Ether**	**108**			
6259	$C_4H_8O_2$	Dioxane	101	Nonazeotrope		85*, 318
A =	$C_4H_7ClO_2$	**Ethyl Chloroacetate**	**143.55**			
6260	$C_4H_8O_2$	Butyric acid	164	Nonazeotrope		207
6261	$C_4H_8O_2$	Isobutyric acid	154.6	Nonazeotrope		255
6262	$C_4H_8O_3$	Methyl lactate	144.8	140.4	~52	243
6263	C_4H_9I	1-Iodobutane	130.4	<130.0	<10	255
6264	$C_4H_{10}O$	Butyl alcohol	117.75	Nonazeotrope		215
6265	$C_4H_{10}O$	Isobutyl alcohol	108.0	Nonazeotrope		255
6266	$C_4H_{10}O_2$	2-Ethoxyethanol	135.3	134.8	32	236
6267	C_5H_8O	Cyclopentanone	130.65	Nonazeotrope		232
6268	$C_5H_{10}O$	Cyclopentanol	140.85	137.6	50	247
6269	$C_5H_{10}O_3$	Ethyl lactate	154.1	Nonazeotrope		255
6270	$C_5H_{10}O_3$	2-Methoxyethyl acetate	144.6	144.95	38	236, 250
6271	$C_5H_{11}I$	1-Iodo-3-methylbutane	147.65	140.2	49	252
6272	$C_5H_{11}NO_3$	Isoamyl nitrate	149.75	Nonazeotrope		240
6273	$C_5H_{12}O$	Isoamyl alcohol	131.3	131	23	207
6274	$C_5H_{12}O$	2-Pentanol	119.8	Nonazeotrope		255
6875	$C_5H_{12}O_2$	2-Propoxyethanol	151.35	Nonazeotrope		206
6276	C_6H_5Br	Bromobenzene	156.1	Nonazeotrope		255
6277	C_6H_5Cl	Chlorobenzene	131.75	Nonazeotrope		255
6278	$C_6H_{10}O$	Cyclohexanone	155.7	Nonazeotrope		232
6279	$C_6H_{10}O$	Mesityl oxide	129.45	Nonazeotrope		207, 232
6280	$C_6H_{10}S$	Allyl sulfide	139.35	138.5	22	246
6281	$C_6H_{12}O$	Cyclohexanol	160.8	Nonazeotrope		255
6282	$C_6H_{12}O$	2-Hexanone	127.2	Nonazeotrope		232

No.	B-Component Formula	Name	B.P., ° C.	Azeotropic Data B.P., ° C.	Wt. % A	Ref.
A =	**$C_4H_7ClO_2$**	**Ethyl Chloroacetate** (*continued*)	**143.55**			
6283	$C_6H_{12}O_3$	2-Ethoxyethyl acetate	156.8	Nonazeotrope		*236*
6284	$C_6H_{13}Br$	1-Bromohexane	156.5	Nonazeotrope		*255*
6285	$C_6H_{14}O$	Hexyl alcohol	157.8	142	~75	*215*
6286	$C_6H_{14}S$	Propyl sulfide	141.5	<140.3	<44	*246*
6287	C_7H_7Cl	*o*-Chlorotoluene	159.3	Nonazeotrope		*212*
6288	C_7H_8O	Anisole	153.85	Nonazeotrope		*255*
6289	$C_7H_{14}O$	4-Heptanone	143.55	142.75	47	*232*
6290	$C_7H_{14}O$	2-Methylcyclohexanol	168.5	Nonazeotrope		*255*
6291	$C_7H_{14}O_2$	Butyl propionate	146.5	Nonazeotrope		*228*
6292	$C_7H_{14}O_2$	Ethyl isovalerate	134.7	Nonazeotrope		*255*
6293	$C_7H_{14}O_2$	Ethyl valerate	145.45	<143.4	....	*255*
6294	$C_7H_{14}O_2$	Isoamyl acetate	142.1	141.7	40	*252*
6295	$C_7H_{14}O_2$	Isobutyl propionate	136.9	Nonazeotrope		*212*
6296	$C_7H_{14}O_2$	Propyl butyrate	142.8	141.7	47	*210*
6297	C_8H_8	Styrene	145.7	140.2	~60	*243*
6298	C_8H_{10}	Ethylbenzene	136.15	135.3	18	*242*
6299	C_8H_{10}	*m*-Xylene	139.0	137.45	32	*207*
6300	C_8H_{10}	*o*-Xylene	144.3	140.2	58	*242*
6301	C_8H_{10}	*p*-Xylene	138.2	137.0	~28	*243*
6302	$C_8H_{16}O_2$	Isobutyl isobutyrate	147.3	Nonazeotrope		*212*
6303	C_8H_{18}	Octane	125.75	Nonazeotrope		*255*
6304	$C_8H_{18}O$	Butyl ether	142.4	139.8	45	*242*
6305	C_9H_{12}	Propylbenzene	159.3	Nonazeotrope		*255*
6306	$C_{10}H_{16}$	Camphene	159.6	Nonazeotrope		*255*
6307	$C_{10}H_{16}$	*α*-Pinene	155.8	<142.8	>88	*255*
A =	**$C_4H_7Cl_3O$**	**Ethyl 1,1,2-Trichloroethyl Ether**	**173.0**			
6308	$C_5H_4O_2$	2-Furaldehyde	161.45	Nonazeotrope		*255*
6309	$C_5H_8O_3$	Methyl acetoacetate	169.5	Nonazeotrope		*255*
6310	$C_6H_4Cl_2$	*o*-Dichlorobenzene	179.5	Nonazeotrope		*255*
6311	$C_6H_4Cl_2$	*p*-Dichlorobenzene	174.4	171.3	75	*236*
6312	C_6H_5Br	Bromobenzene	156.1	Nonazeotrope		*236*
6313	$C_6H_{10}O_3$	Ethyl acetoacetate	180.4	Nonazeotrope		*255*
6314	C_7H_7Br	*o*-Bromotoluene	181.5	Nonazeotrope		*236*
6315	C_7H_7Cl	*p*-Chlorotoluene	162.4	Nonazeotrope		*255*
6316	$C_8H_{18}S$	Butyl sulfide	185.0	Nonazeotrope		*255*
6317	$C_8H_{18}S$	Isobutyl sulfide	172.0	<171.3	<55	*255*
6318	C_9H_{12}	Mesitylene	164.6	Nonazeotrope		*255*
6319	$C_9H_{18}O$	2,6-Dimethyl-4-heptanone	168.0	Nonazeotrope		*255*
6320	$C_{10}H_{16}$	Nopinene	163.8	Nonazeotrope		*255*
6321	$C_{10}H_{16}$	*α*-Terpinene	173.4	172.0	58	*242*
A =	**C_4H_7N**	**Butyronitrile**	**117.9**			
6322	C_4H_9I	1-Iodo-2-methylpropane	120.8	108.5	46	*242*
6323	$C_4H_{10}O$	Butyl alcohol	117.8	113.0	50	*247*
6324	$C_4H_{10}O$	Isobutyl alcohol	108	<106.8	>10	*247*
6325	$C_4H_{10}O$	Isobutyl alcohol	108	<105	>25	*243*
6326	$C_5H_{11}Br$	1-Bromo-3-methylbutane	120.65	109.8	50	*242*
6327	C_6H_{12}	Cyclohexane	80.75	<79.0	>5	*255*
6328	C_7H_8	Toluene	110.75	107.0	27	*242*
6329	C_7H_{14}	Methylcyclohexane	101.15	90.5	20	*242*
A =	**C_4H_7N**	**Isobutyronitrile**	**103.85**			
6330	$C_5H_{11}Cl$	1-Chloro-3-methylbutane	99.4	91.0	35	*242*
6331	$C_5H_{12}O$	*tert*-Amyl alcohol	102.35	<99.5	>42	*247*
6332	C_6H_6	Benzene	80.15	Nonazeotrope		*255*
6333	C_6H_{12}	Cyclohexane	80.75	<74.5	>13	*242*
6334	C_7H_{14}	Methylcyclohexane	101.15	85.5	40	*242*
6335	C_7H_{16}	Heptane	98.4	80.5	38	*242*
A =	**C_4H_7N**	**Pyrroline**	**90.9**			
6336	$C_6H_{14}O$	Propyl ether	90.1	<88.5	<43	*255*
A =	**C_4H_8**	**1-Butene**	**−5**			
6337	C_4H_8	2-Methylpropene	−6	Nonazeotrope		*255*

No.	B-Component Formula	Name	B.P., ° C.	Azeotropic Data B.P., ° C.	Wt. % A	Ref.
A =	$C_4H_8Cl_2O$	**Bis(2-chloroethyl) Ether**	**178.65**			
6338	$C_4H_8O_2$	Butyric acid	164.0	Nonazeotrope		*255*
6339	$C_4H_8O_3$	Glycol monoacetate	190.9	Nonazeotrope		*207*
6340	$C_4H_{10}O$	Butyl alcohol	117.8	Nonazeotrope		*207*
6341	$C_5H_4O_2$	2-Furaldehyde	161.45	Nonazeotrope		*207*
6342	$C_5H_8O_3$	Methyl acetoacetate	169.5	Nonazeotrope		*232*
6343	$C_5H_{10}O$	Cyclopentanol	140.85	Nonazeotrope		*207*
6344	$C_5H_{12}O$	Isoamyl alcohol	131.9	Nonazeotrope		*207*
6345	$C_5H_{12}O_2$	2-Propoxyethanol	151.35	Nonazeotrope		*207*
6346	$C_6H_4Cl_2$	*o*-Dichlorobenzene	179.5	176.5	60	*207*
6347	$C_6H_4Cl_2$	*p*-Dichlorobenzene	174.4	173.45	28	*207*
6348	C_6H_5Br	Bromobenzene	156.1	Nonazeotrope		*207*
6349	C_6H_5BrO	*o*-Bromophenol	195.0	Nonazeotrope		*207*
6350	C_6H_5ClO	*o*-Chlorophenol	176.8	<176.5	>14	*255*
6351	C_6H_5I	Iodobenzene	188.45	Nonazeotrope		*207*
6352	C_6H_6O	Phenol	182.2	<176.2	>60	*242*
6353	$C_6H_{10}O_3$	Ethyl acetoacetate	180.4	Nonazeotrope		*207*
6354	$C_6H_{10}O_4$	Ethyl oxalate	185.65	Nonazeotrope		*207*
6355	$C_6H_{12}O_3$	2-Ethoxyethyl acetate	156.8	Nonazeotrope		*207*
6356	$C_6H_{12}O_3$	Propyl lactate	171.7	Nonazeotrope		*255*
6357	$C_6H_{13}Br$	Bromohexane	156.5	Nonazeotrope		*207*
6358	$C_6H_{14}O$	Hexanol	157.85	<157.5	<22	*207*
6359	$C_6H_{14}O_2$	2-Butoxyethanol	171.15	170.85	25	*207*
6360	C_7H_6O	Benzaldehyde	179.2	Nonazeotrope		*207*
6361	C_7H_7Br	*o*-Bromotoluene	181.45	<177.9	>63	*207*
6362	C_7H_7Cl	*p*-Chlorotoluene	162.4	Nonazeotrope		*207*
6363	$C_7H_{14}O$	2-Methylcyclohexanol	168.5	<167.5	<40	*255*
6364	$C_7H_{14}O_3$	1,3-Butanediol methyl ether acetate	171.75	Nonazeotrope		*255*
6365	$C_7H_{16}O$	*n*-Heptyl alcohol	176.15	173.5	50	*207*
6366	$C_8H_{16}O$	2-Octanone	172.85	Nonazeotrope		*232*
6367	$C_8H_{16}O_2$	Butyl butyrate	166.4	Nonazeotrope		*207*
6368	$C_8H_{18}O$	*n*-Octyl alcohol	195.2	Nonazeotrope		*207*
6369	$C_8H_{18}O$	*sec*-Octyl alcohol	180.4	<177.2	<62	*207*
6370	$C_8H_{18}S$	Butyl sulfide	185	178.4	88	*236*
6371	C_9H_{12}	Mesitylene	164.6	Nonazeotrope		*255*
6372	$C_9H_{18}O_2$	Butyl isovalerate	177.6	177.0	80	*255*
6373	$C_9H_{18}O_2$	Isoamyl isobutyrate	169.8	Nonazeotrope		*255*
6374	$C_9H_{18}O_2$	Isobutyl isovalerate	171.2	Nonazeotrope		*207*
6375	$C_{10}H_{16}$	Butylbenzene	183.1	<178.0	....	*207*
6376	$C_{10}H_{14}$	Cymene	176.7	<176.4	>11	*255*
6377	$C_{10}H_{16}$	Dipentene	177.7	<176.5	....	*207*
6378	$C_{10}H_{16}$	Terpinolene	184.6	Nonazeotrope		*255*
6379	$C_{10}H_{18}O$	Cineol	176.35	173.35	43	*207*
6380	$C_{10}H_{22}O$	Amyl ether	187.5	<176.5	....	*207*
6381	$C_{10}H_{22}O$	Isoamyl ether	173.2	169.35	39	*236*
A =	$C_4H_8Cl_2O$	**1,2-Dichloroethyl Ethyl Ether**	**145.5**			
6382	$C_4H_{10}O$	Butyl alcohol	117.8	<117.0	>0.6	*255*
6383	$C_4H_{10}O$	*sec*-Butyl alcohol	99.5	Nonazeotrope		*255*
6384	$C_5H_4O_2$	2-Furaldehyde	161.45	Nonazeotrope		*255*
6385	$C_5H_{10}O$	Cyclopentanol	140.85	<136.5	<50	*255*
6386	$C_5H_{10}O_3$	Ethyl lactate	154.1	Nonazeotrope		*255*
6387	$C_5H_{10}O_3$	2-Methoxyethyl acetate	144.6	<143.0	>38	*255*
6388	$C_5H_{12}O$	*tert*-Amyl alcohol	102.35	Nonazeotrope		*255*
6389	$C_5H_{12}O$	Isoamyl alcohol	131.9	129.2	30	*255*
6390	$C_5H_{12}O_2$	2-Propoxyethanol	151.35	144.3	70	*255*
6391	C_6H_5Br	Bromobenzene	156.1	Nonazeotrope		*236*
6392	C_6H_5Cl	Chlorobenzene	131.75	Nonazeotrope		*236*
6393	$C_6H_{10}O$	Cyclohexanone	155.7	Nonazeotrope		*255*
6394	$C_6H_{12}O_3$	2-Ethoxyethyl acetate	156.8	Nonazeotrope		*255*
6395	$C_6H_{13}Br$	1-Bromohexane	156.5	Nonazeotrope		*255*
6396	$C_6H_{14}S$	Isopropyl sulfide	120.5	Nonazeotrope		*246*
6397	$C_6H_{14}S$	Propyl sulfide	141.5	<141.0	>23	*246*
6398	C_7H_8O	Anisole	153.85	Nonazeotrope		*255*
6399	$C_7H_{14}O$	4-Heptanone	143.55	<143.4	Nonazeotrope	*255*
6400	$C_7H_{14}O_2$	Butyl propionate	146.8	145.3	70	*255*

No.	B-Component Formula	Name	B.P., ° C.	Azeotropic Data B.P., ° C.	Wt. % A	Ref.
A =	**$C_4H_8Cl_2O$**	**1,2-Dichloroethyl Ethyl Ether** (*continued*)	**145.5**			
6401	$C_7H_{14}O_2$	Ethyl isovalerate	134.7	Nonazeotrope		*255*
6402	$C_7H_{14}O_2$	Isobutyl propionate	137.5	Nonazeotrope		*255*
6403	$C_7H_{14}O_2$	Propyl butyrate	143.7	<143.55	>10	*255*
6404	$C_7H_{16}O$	Heptyl alcohol	176.15	Nonazeotrope		*255*
6405	C_8H_8	Styrene	145.8	144.0	53	*255*
6406	C_8H_{10}	Ethylbenzene	136.15	Nonazeotrope		*255*
6407	$C_8H_{16}O_2$	Propyl isovalerate	155.7	Nonazeotrope		*255*
6408	$C_8H_{18}O$	Butyl ether	142.4	138.0	72	*242*
6409	$C_8H_{18}O$	*sec*-Octyl alcohol	180.4	Nonazeotrope		*255*
6410	$C_{10}H_{16}$	α-Pinene	155.8	Nonazeotrope		*255*
A =	**$C_4H_8Cl_2S$**	**Bis(2-chloroethyl) Sulfide**	**216.8**			
6411	$C_6H_5NO_3$	*o*-Nitrophenol	217.2	<215.5	>48	*255*
6412	C_7H_7ClO	*o*-Chloroanisole	195.7	Nonazeotrope		*255*
6413	C_7H_8O	Benzyl alcohol	205.25	195.5	....	*255*
6414	$C_8H_{10}O$	*p*-Ethylphenol	218.8	220.8	42	*255*
6415	$C_8H_{10}O$	2,4-Xylenol	210.5	>218.5	>75	*255*
6416	$C_8H_{10}O$	3,4-Xylenol	226.8	227.5	10	*255*
6417	$C_8H_{10}O_2$	*o*-Ethoxyphenol	216.5	<215.2	>42	*255*
6418	$C_9H_{12}O$	Mesitol	220.5	223.0	28	*255*
6419	$C_{10}H_{18}O$	β-Terpineol	210.5	Nonazeotrope		*255*
A =	**C_4H_8O**	**2-Butanone**	**79.6**			
6420	C_4H_8O	Butyraldehyde	75.2	Nonazeotrope		*207*
6421	C_4H_8O	Isobutyraldehyde	63.5	Nonazeotrope		*207*
6422	$C_4H_8O_2$	Dioxane	101.35	Nonazeotrope		*232*
6423	$C_4H_8O_2$	Ethyl acetate	77.1	77.0	18	*207*
6424	$C_4H_8O_2$	Isopropyl formate	68.8	Nonazeotrope		*232*
6425	$C_4H_8O_2$	Methyl propionate	79.85	79.0	60	*232*
6426	$C_4H_8O_2$	Propyl formate	80.85	Nonazeotrope		*207*
6427	C_4H_9Br	2-Bromobutane	91.2	Nonazeotrope		*232*
6428	C_4H_9Br	1-Bromo-2-methylpropane	91.4	Nonazeotrope		*207*
6429	C_4H_9Br	2-Bromo-2-methylpropane	73.25	Nonazeotrope		*207*
6430	C_4H_9Cl	1-Chlorobutane	78.5	77.0	38	*207*
6431	C_4H_9Cl	2-Chlorobutane	68.25	Nonazeotrope		*232*
6432	C_4H_9Cl	1-Chloro-2-methylpropane	68.85	Nonazeotrope		*207*
6433	$C_4H_9NO_2$	Butyl nitrite	78.2	76.7	30	*207*
6434	$C_4H_9NO_2$	Isobutyl nitrite	67.1	Nonazeotrope		*207*
6435	$C_4H_{10}O$	*n*-Butyl alcohol	117.8	Nonazeotrope		*207*
6436	$C_4H_{10}O$	*tert*-Butyl alcohol	82.45	78.7	69	*10**, *207*
6437	$C_4H_{10}O$	Isobutyl alcohol	108.0	Nonazeotrope		*207*
6438	$C_4H_{10}S$	Ethyl sulfide	92.1	<79.4	....	*246*
6439	$C_4H_{11}N$	Butylamine	77.8	74.0	35	*231*
6440	$C_4H_{11}N$	Diethylamine	55.9	Nonazeotrope		*207*
6441	C_5H_6O	2-Methylfuran	63.7	Nonazeotrope		*310*
6442	$C_5H_{10}O$	Isovaleraldehyde	92.1	Nonazeotrope		*232*
6443	$C_5H_{10}O_2$	Isopropyl acetate	89.5	Nonazeotrope		*232*
6444	$C_5H_{12}O_2$	Diethoxymethane	87.95	Nonazeotrope		*232*
6445	C_6H_5F	Fluorobenzene	84.9	79.3	75	*232*
6446	C_6H_6	Benzene	80.1	78.33	44, V-l.	*379*, *436**
6447	C_6H_8	1,3-Cyclohexadiene	80.8	~73	~40	*243*
6448	C_6H_{10}	Cyclohexene	82.75	73.0	47	*232*
6449	C_6H_{12}	Cyclohexane	80.75	71.8	40	*207*
6450	C_6H_{14}	2,3-Dimethylbutane	58.0	56.0	15	*207*
6451	C_6H_{14}	Hexane	68.8	64.3	29.5	*207*
6452	$C_6H_{14}O$	Propyl ether	90.1	Nonazeotrope		*232*
6453	$C_6H_{14}O_2$	Acetal	104.5	Nonazeotrope		*243*
6454	$C_6H_{15}N$	Dipropylamine	109.2	Nonazeotrope		*207*
6455	$C_6H_{15}N$	Triethylamine	89.35	<79.0	>75	*231*
6456	C_7F_{16}	Perfluoroheptane	81.6	62–63	....	*106*
6457	C_7H_8	Toluene	110.75	Nonazeotrope, V-l.		*379*
6458	C_7H_{14}	Methylcyclohexane	101.15	77.7	80	*207*
6459	C_7H_{16}	Heptane	98.4	77	73, V-l.	*379*
6460	C_8H_{18}	2,5-Dimethylhexane	109.4	109.0	95	*232*

No.	Formula	B-Component Name	B.P., ° C.	Azeotropic Data B.P., ° C.	Wt. % A	Ref.
A =	C_4H_8O	**1-Butene-3-ol**				
6461	$C_4H_{10}O_2$	2,3-Butanediol	....	Nonazeotrope, V-l.		293
A =	C_4H_8O	**Butyraldehyde**	**75.2**			
6462	$C_4H_8O_2$	Propyl formate	80.85	Nonazeotrope		255
6463	C_4H_9Cl	1-Chloro-2-methylpropane	68.85	Nonazeotrope		255
6464	C_6H_6	Benzene	80.1	Nonazeotrope		139
6465	C_7H_{16}	Paraffins	75–80	~61	....	139
A =	C_4H_8O	**Isobutyraldehyde**	**63.5**			
6466	C_4H_9Cl	2-Chloro-2-methylpropane	50.8	Nonazeotrope		255
6467	C_6H_6	Benzene	81	Nonazeotrope ?		139
6468	C_7H_{16}	Paraffins	75–80	~50	....	139
A =	C_4H_8O	**2-Methyl-2-propen-1-ol**	**113.8**			
6469	$C_8H_{14}O$	2-Methyl allyl ether	134.6	114.1	81.3	369
A =	C_4H_8O	**Tetrahydrofuran**	**65**			
6470	C_6H_{14}	Hexane	68.9	63	53.5	87
A =	C_4H_8OS	**Ethyl Thioacetate**	**116.6**			
6471	$C_4H_{10}O$	Butyl alcohol	117.8	113.5	....	255
6472	$C_4H_{10}O$	*sec*-Butyl alcohol	99.5	Nonazeotrope		255
6473	$C_4H_{10}O$	Isobutyl alcohol	108.0	<107.2	....	255
6474	$C_5H_{12}O$	Amyl alcohol	138.2	Nonazeotrope		255
6475	$C_5H_{12}O$	*tert*-Amyl alcohol	102.35	Nonazeotrope		255
6476	$C_5H_{12}O$	3-Pentanol	116.0	<114.0	....	255
6476a	$C_6H_{10}S$	Allyl sulfide	139.35	Nonazeotrope		255
6476b	$C_8H_{18}O$	Isobutyl ether	122.3	Nonazeotrope		255
A =	$C_4H_8O_2$	**Butyric Acid**	**164.0**			
6477	C_4H_9I	Iodobutane	130.4	129.8	2.5	242
6478	C_4H_9I	1-Iodo-2-methylpropane	120.8	Nonazeotrope		207
6479	$C_4H_{10}O$	Ethyl ether	34.6	Nonazeotrope		207
6480	$C_5H_4O_2$	2-Furaldehyde	161.45	159.4	42.5	243
6481	$C_5H_8O_3$	Ethyl pyruvate	155.5	Nonazeotrope		254
6482	$C_5H_9ClO_2$	Propyl chloroacetate	162.5	160.5	40	232
6483	$C_5H_{10}O_3$	2-Methoxyethyl acetate	144.6	Nonazeotrope		242
6484	$C_5H_{11}Br$	1-Bromo-3-methylbutane	120.65	Nonazeotrope		206
6485	$C_5H_{11}I$	1-Iodo-3-methylbutane	147.6	144.4	13	207
6486	$C_5H_{11}NO_3$	Isoamyl nitrate	149.75	147.85	12	207
6487	C_5H_{12}	2-Methylbutane	27.95	Nonazeotrope		250
6488	C_6H_4BrCl	*p*-Bromochlorobenzene	196.4	Nonazeotrope		243
6489	$C_6H_4Cl_2$	*o*-Dichlorobenzene	179.5	163.0	65	207
6490	$C_6H_4Cl_2$	*p*-Chlorobenzene	174.4	162.0	57	207
6491	C_6H_5Br	Bromobenzene	156	147–148	19	207
6492	C_6H_5Cl	Chlorobenzene	132.0	131.75	2.8	243*, 334
6493	C_6H_5ClO	*o*-Chlorophenol	175.5	Nonazeotrope		207
6494	C_6H_5I	Iodobenzene	188.55	161.6	....	243
6495	C_6H_6O	Phenol	181.5	Nonazeotrope		218
6496	C_6H_{10}	Cyclohexene	82.75	Nonazeotrope		207
6497	$C_6H_{10}O$	Cyclohexanone	156.7	164.5	....	277
6498	$C_6H_{10}O_3$	Ethyl acetoacetate	180.4	Nonazeotrope		243
6499	$C_6H_{10}O_4$	Ethylidene diacetate	168.5	Nonazeotrope		207
6500	$C_6H_{10}S$	Allyl sulfide	139.35	Nonazeotrope		207
6501	$C_6H_{11}BrO_2$	Ethyl *α*-bromoisobutyrate	163.7	161.5	....	246
6502	C_6H_{12}	Cyclohexane	80.75	Nonazeotrope		255
6503	$C_6H_{12}O_2$	Isoamyl formate	123.3	Nonazeotrope		277
6504	$C_6H_{12}O_3$	2-Ethoxyethyl acetate	156.8	164.3?	18	255
6505	$C_6H_{13}Br$	1-Bromohexane	156.5	151.5	25	206
6506	$C_6H_{14}S$	Propyl sulfide	141.5	Nonazeotrope		207
6507	$C_7H_6Cl_2$	*α,α*-Dichlorotoluene	205.2	Nonazeotrope		246
6508	C_7H_6O	Benzaldehyde	179.2	Nonazeotrope		222
6509	C_7H_7Br	*α*-Bromotoluene	198.5	Nonazeotrope		222
6510	C_7H_7Br	*m*-Bromotoluene	184.3	163.62	79.5	255
6511	C_7H_7Br	*o*-Bromotoluene	181.5	163	72	207
6512	C_7H_7Br	*p*-Bromotoluene	185.0	161.5	75	207
6513	C_7H_7Cl	*α*-Chlorotoluene	179.3	160.8	65	221
6514	C_7H_7Cl	*α*-Chlorotoluene	179.35	161.5	93	222
6515	C_7H_7Cl	*o*-Chlorotoluene	159.3	154.5	27	243

No.	B-Component Formula	Name	B.P., ° C.	Azeotropic Data B.P., ° C.	Wt. % A	Ref.
A =	$C_4H_8O_2$	**Butyric Acid** (*continued*)	**164.0**			
6516	C_7H_7Cl	*p*-Chlorotoluene	162.4	156.8	32	207
6517	C_7H_8	Toluene	110.7	Nonazeotrope		207
6518	C_7H_8O	Anisole	153.85	152.85	12	207
6519	C_7H_{14}	Methylcyclohexane	101.8	Nonazeotrope		207, 277*
6520	$C_7H_{14}O$	5-Methyl-2-hexanone	144.2	Nonazeotrope		207
6521	$C_7H_{14}O_2$	Methyl-1,3-butanediol acetate	171.75	172.0?	5?	255
6522	C_7H_{16}	*n*-Heptane	98.4	Nonazeotrope		207
6523	C_8H_8	Styrene	145.8	143.5	15	255
6524	C_8H_9Cl	*o,m,p*-Chloroethylbenzene, 10 mm.	67.5	63.3	34	24
6525	C_8H_{10}	Ethylbenzene	136.15	135.8	4	255
6526	C_8H_{10}	*m*-Xylene	139.0	138.5	6	207
6527	C_8H_{10}	*o*-Xylene	144.3	143.0	10	207
6528	C_8H_{10}	*p*-Xylene	138.45	137.8	5.5	207
6529	$C_8H_{10}O$	Benzyl methyl ether	167.8	160.0	55	242
6530	$C_8H_{10}O$	Phenetole	170.5	162.35	65	236
6531	$C_8H_{14}O$	Methylheptenone	173.2	Nonazeotrope		207
6532	C_8H_{16}	1,3-Dimethylcyclohexane	120.7	Nonazeotrope		255
6533	$C_8H_{16}O$	2-Octanone	172.85	Nonazeotrope		207
6534	$C_8H_{16}O_2$	Butyl butyrate	166.4	Nonazeotrope		207
6535	$C_8H_{16}O$	Isoamyl propionate	160.7	Nonazeotrope		207
6536	$C_8H_{16}O_2$	Isobutyl butyrate	156.8	Nonazeotrope		207
6537	$C_8H_{16}O_2$	Isobutyl isobutyrate	148.6	Nonazeotrope		255
6538	C_8H_{18}	Octane	125.75	<124.5	<15	242
6539	$C_8H_{18}O$	Isobutyl ether	122.3	Nonazeotrope		207
6540	$C_8H_{18}O$	Butyl ether	141.0	Nonazeotrope		223
6541	$C_8H_{18}S$	Butyl sulfide	185.0	Nonazeotrope		246
6542	$C_8H_{18}S$	Isobutyl sulfide	172.0	<162.5	<78	246
6543	C_9H_8	Indene	182.6	163.65	84	207
6544	C_9H_{12}	Cumene	152.8	149.5	20	207
6545	C_9H_{12}	Mesitylene	164.6	158.0	38	207
6546	C_9H_{12}	Propylbenzene	158.9	11	28	207
6547	C_9H_{12}	Pseudocumene	169	159.5	45	207
6548	$C_9H_{12}O$	Benzyl ethyl ether	185.0	Nonazeotrope		207
6549	$C_9H_{12}O$	Phenyl propyl ether	190.5	Nonazeotrope		255
6550	$C_9H_{18}O$	2,6-Dimethyl-4-heptanone	168.0	Nonazeotrope		207
6551	$C_9H_{18}O_2$	Isoamyl butyrate	178.5	Nonazeotrope		207
6552	$C_9H_{18}O_2$	Isoamyl isobutyrate	170.0	Nonazeotrope		225
6553	$C_9H_{18}O_2$	Isobutyl isovalerate	172.2	Nonazeotrope		207
6554	$C_{10}H_8$	Naphthalene	218.1	Nonazeotrope		207
6555	$C_{10}H_{14}$	Butylbenzene	183.1	162.5	75	242
6556	$C_{10}H_{14}$	Cymene	176.7	161.0	60	207
6557	$C_{10}H_{16}$	Camphene	159.6	152.3	2.8	207
6558	$C_{10}H_{16}$	*d*-Limonene	177.8	160.75	55	243
6559	$C_{10}H_{16}$	Nopinene	164	156	38	207
6560	$C_{10}H_{16}$	α-Phellandrene	~171.5	160	~47	243
6561	$C_{10}H_{16}$	α-Pinene	155.8	150.2	28	207
6562	$C_{10}H_{16}$	α-Terpinene	173.4	160.65	46	255
6563	$C_{10}H_{16}$	γ-Terpinene	180.5	161.5	70	243
6564	$C_{10}H_{16}$	Terpinolene	184.6	162.5	72	255
6565	$C_{10}H_{16}$	Terpinylene	~175	160.5	40	243
6566	$C_{10}H_{16}$	Thymene	179.7	160.5	68	221
6567	$C_{10}H_{17}Cl$	Bornyl chloride	207.5	Nonazeotrope		255
6568	$C_{10}H_{18}O$	Cineol	176.35	Nonazeotrope		207
6569	$C_{10}H_{22}$	2,7-Dimethyloctane	160.2	152.5	33	207
6570	$C_{10}H_{22}O$	Amyl ether	187.5	Nonazeotrope		207
6571	$C_{10}H_{22}O$	Isoamyl ether	173.2	161.8	54	236
6572	$C_{12}H_{18}$	1,3,5-Triethylbenzene	215.5	Nonazeotrope		207
A =	$C_4H_8O_2$	**Dioxane**	**101.35**			
6573	$C_4H_8O_2$	Isobutyric acid	154.6	Nonazeotrope		207
6574	C_4H_9Br	1-Bromobutane	101.5	98.0	47	207
6575	C_4H_9Br	1-Bromo-2-methylpropane	91.4	Nonazeotrope		207
6576	C_4H_9Cl	1-Chloro-2-methylpropane	99.4	97.5	36	206
6577	$C_4H_{10}O$	Butyl alcohol	117.8	Nonazeotrope		207
6578	$C_4H_{10}O$	*sec*-Butyl alcohol	99.5	<98.8	<60	207
6579	$C_4H_{10}O$	*tert*-Butyl alcohol	82.45	Nonazeotrope		207

No.	B-Component Formula	Name	B.P., ° C.	Azeotropic Data B.P., ° C.	Wt. % A	Ref.
A =	$C_4H_8O_2$	**Dioxane** (*continued*)	**101.35**			
6580	$C_4H_{10}O$	Isobutyl alcohol	108.0	Nonazeotrope		*207*
6581	C_5H_5N	Pyridine	115.4	Nonazeotrope		*207*
6582	$C_5H_{10}O$	3-Methyl-2-butanone	95.4	Nonazeotrope		*255*
6583	$C_5H_{10}O_2$	Isobutyl formate	98.2	Nonazeotrope		*207*
6584	$C_5H_{10}O_2$	Isopropyl acetate	89.5	Nonazeotrope		*237*
6585	$C_5H_{10}O_2$	Methyl butyrate	102.65	<100.9	....	*237*
6586	$C_5H_{10}O_2$	Propyl acetate	101.6	<100.8	....	*237*
6587	$C_5H_{11}Br$	1-Bromo-3-methylbutane	120.65	Nonazeotrope		*237*
6588	$C_5H_{11}Cl$	1-Chloro-3-methylbutane	99.4	97.5	36	*207*
6589	$C_5H_{11}N$	Piperidine	106.4	Nonazeotrope		*255*
6590	$C_5H_{11}NO_2$	Isoamyl nitrite	97.15	Nonazeotrope		*207*
6591	$C_5H_{12}O$	*tert*-Amyl alcohol	102.35	100.65	80	*255*
6592	$C_5H_{12}O$	2-Pentanol	119.8	Nonazeotrope		*207*
6593	$C_5H_{12}O$	3-Pentanol	116.0	Nonazeotrope		*255*
6594	C_6H_6	Benzene	80.15	Nonazeotrope		*207*
6595	C_6H_6	Benzene	80.2	82.4	12	*90*
		25° C.	....	Nonazeotrope, V-l.		*393*
6596	C_6H_{10}	Cyclohexene	82.75	<81.8	>20	*238*
6597	$C_6H_{10}O$	Cyclohexanone	156.7	Nonazeotrope		*90*
6598	C_6H_{12}	Cyclohexane	80.75	79.5	24.6	*90*
6599	C_6H_{12}	Methylcyclopentane	72.0	<71.5	>5	*207*
6600	$C_6H_{12}O$	Cyclohexanol	160.65	Nonazeotrope		*90*
6601	$C_6H_{12}O$	Pinacolone	106.2	Nonazeotrope		*255*
6602	$C_6H_{12}O_2$	Ethyl isobutyrate	110.1	Nonazeotrope		*237*
6603	$C_6H_{12}O_2$	Isobutyl acetate	117.4	Nonazeotrope		*207*
6604	$C_6H_{15}BO_3$	Ethyl borate	118.6	100.7	92	*237*
6605	C_7H_8	Toluene	110.75	Nonazeotrope		*207*
6606	C_7H_8	Toluene	110.7	101.8	80	*90, 97**
6607	C_7H_{14}	Methylcyclohexane	101.15	93.7	>45	*207*
6608	C_7H_{16}	Heptane	98.4	91.85	44	*207*
6609	C_8H_{18}	2,5-Dimethylhexane	109.4	97.0	65	*207*
6610	C_8H_{18}	*n*-Octane	125.75	<100.5	....	*207*
6611	C_nH_{2n+2}	Paraffins	109.5–110.5	96.6–98.9	....	*97*
A =	$C_4H_8O_2$	***m*-Dioxane**	**105**			
6612	C_7H_8	Toluene	110.7	....	85	*208*
A =	$C_4H_8O_2$	**Ethyl Acetate**	**77.1**			
6613	$C_4H_8O_2$	Isopropyl formate	68.8	Nonazeotrope		*255*
6614	$C_4H_8O_2$	Methyl propionate	79.85	Nonazeotrope		*212*
6615	$C_4H_8O_2$	Propyl formate	80.85	Nonazeotrope		*255*
6616	C_4H_9Br	1-Bromo-2-methylpropane	91.4	Nonazeotrope		*227*
6617	C_4H_9Br	2-Bromo-2-methylpropane	73.5	71.5	30	*243*
6618	C_4H_9Cl	1-Chlorobutane	78.05	76.0	<35	*227*
6619	C_4H_9Cl	2-Chlorobutane	68.25	Nonazeotrope		*255*
6620	C_4H_9Cl	1-Chloro-2-methylpropane	68.9	Nonazeotrope		*243*
6621	$C_4H_9NO_2$	Butyl nitrite	78.2	76.3	71	*207*
6622	$C_4H_9NO_2$	Isobutyl nitrite	67.1	Nonazeotrope		*230*
6623	$C_4H_{10}O$	Butyl alcohol	117.7	Nonazeotrope		*261*
6624	$C_4H_{10}O$	*sec*-Butyl alcohol	99.5	Nonazeotrope		*255*
6625	$C_4H_{10}O$	Isobutyl alcohol	108.0	Nonazeotrope		*255*
6626	$C_4H_{10}O$	Isobutyl alcohol	108.0	B.p. curve		*243*
6627	$C_4H_{10}O$	*tert*-Butyl alcohol	82.45	76.0	73	*250*
6628	$C_4H_{10}S$	Ethyl sulfide	92.2	Nonazeotrope		*212*
6629	$C_5H_{10}O$	Isovaleraldehyde	92.3	Nonazeotrope		*228*
6630	$C_5H_{10}O_2$	Ethyl propionate	99.12	Nonazeotrope (b.p. curve)		*432*
6631	$C_5H_{12}O_2$	Diethoxymethane	87.95	Nonazeotrope		*207*
6632	C_6H_5F	Fluorobenzene	84.9	Nonazeotrope		*255*
6633	C_6H_5Cl	Chlorobenzene	131.8	Nonazeotrope		*243*
6634	C_6H_6	Benzene	80.2	Nonazeotrope		*334, 387**
6635	C_6H_8	1,3-Cyclohexadiene	80.8	73.5	....	*243*
6636	C_6H_{10}	Cyclohexene	82.75	75.5	<85	*243*
6637	C_6H_{12}	Cyclohexane	80.75	72.8	54	*243*
6638	C_6H_{12}	Methylcyclopentane	72.0	67.2	38	*255*
6639	$C_6H_{12}O_2$	Ethyl butyrate	119.9	Nonazeotrope		*243*

No.	B-Component Formula	Name	B.P., ° C.	Azeotropic Data B.P., ° C.	Wt. % A	Ref.
A =	**$C_4H_8O_2$**	**Ethyl Acetate (*continued*)**	**77.1**			
6640	C_6H_{14}	2,3-Dimethylbutane	58.0	<57.2	10	*255*
6641	C_6H_{14}	*n*-Hexane	68.8	65.1	....	*251*
6642	$C_6H_{14}O$	Propyl ether	90.55	Nonazeotrope		*237*
6643	C_7H_8	Toluene	110.7	Nonazeotrope		*261*
6644	C_7H_{14}	Methylcyclohexane	101.1	Nonazeotrope		*217*
6645	C_7H_{16}	Heptane	98.4	<76.9	<94	*255*
6646	C_7H_{16}	Heptane	98.45	Nonazeotrope		*217*
A =	**$C_4H_8O_2$**	**Isobutyric Acid**	**154.6**			
6647	C_4H_9I	Iodobutane	130.4	128.8	7	*242*
6648	$C_4H_{10}O$	Ethyl ether	34.6	Vapor pressure data		*243*
6649	$C_5H_4O_2$	2-Furaldehyde	161.45	153.8	....	*255*
6650	C_5H_8O	Cyclopentanone	130.65	Nonazeotrope		*255*
6651	$C_5H_8O_3$	Ethyl pyruvate	155.5	153.0	60	*232*
6652	$C_5H_8O_3$	Methyl acetoacetate	169.5	Nonazeotrope		*232*
6653	$C_5H_{10}O_3$	2-Methoxyethyl acetate	144.6	Nonazeotrope		*255*
6654	$C_5H_{10}O_3$	2-Methoxyethyl acetate	144.6	159.5	62	*206*
6655	$C_5H_{11}Br$	1-Bromo-3-methylbutane	120.65	120.2	3	*255*
6656	$C_5H_{11}I$	1-Iodo-3-methylbutane	147.65	143.8	22	*221*
6657	$C_5H_{11}NO_3$	Isoamyl nitrate	149.75	146.25	30	*250*
6658	$C_6H_4Cl_2$	*p*-Dichlorobenzene	174.5	153.0	~75	*218*
6659	C_6H_5Br	Bromobenzene	156.15	148.6	35	*243*
6660	C_6H_5Cl	Chlorobenzene	132.0	131.2	8	*221*
6661	C_6H_5I	Iodobenzene	188.55	154.2	....	*222*
6662	C_6H_6O	Phenol	182.2	Nonazeotrope		*255*
6663	$C_6H_{10}O$	Cyclohexanone	155.7	152.5	....	*255*
6664	$C_6H_{12}O_3$	2-Ethoxyethyl acetate	156.8	159.2	38	*255*
6665	$C_6H_{12}O_3$	Paraldehyde	123.2	Nonazeotrope		*221*
6666	$C_6H_{13}Br$	1-Bromohexane	156.5	148.0	35	*242*
6667	$C_6H_{13}ClO_2$	Chloroacetal	156.8	~153	....	*243*
6668	$C_7H_6Cl_2$	*α,α*-Dichlorotoluene	205.2	Nonazeotrope		*255*
6669	C_7H_6O	Benzaldehyde	179.2	Nonazeotrope		*243*
6670	C_7H_7Br	*α*-Bromotoluene	198.5	Nonazeotrope		*255*
6671	C_7H_7Br	*o*-Bromotoluene	181.5	153.9	85	*221*
6672	C_7H_7Cl	*α*-Chlorotoluene	179.3	153.5	80	*221*
6673	C_7H_7Cl	*o*-Chlorotoluene	159.3	<150.0	42	*218*
6674	C_7H_7Cl	*p*-Chlorotoluene	162.4	151.5	47	*218*
6675	C_7H_8	Toluene	110.75	Nonazeotrope		*222*
6676	C_7H_8O	Anisole	153.85	149	42	*236*
6677	$C_7H_{14}O$	4-Heptanone	143.55	Nonazeotrope		*232*
6678	$C_7H_{14}O$	5-Methyl-2-hexanone	144.2	Nonazeotrope		*232*
6679	$C_7H_{14}O_2$	Isoamyl acetate	142.1	Nonazeotrope		*255*
6680	$C_7H_{14}O_2$	Propyl butyrate	143.7	Nonazeotrope		*255*
6681	$C_7H_{14}O_3$	Methyl-1,3-butanediol acetate	171.75	Nonazeotrope		*255*
6682	C_8H_8	Styrene	145.8	142.0	27	*242*
6683	C_8H_{10}	Ethylbenzene	136.15	134.3	12	*221*
6684	C_8H_{10}	*m*-Xylene	139.0	136.9	15	*207*
6685	C_8H_{10}	*o*-Xylene	144.3	141.0	22	*242*
6686	C_8H_{10}	*p*-Xylene	138.4	136.4	13	*221*
6687	$C_8H_{10}O$	Benzyl methyl ether	170.5	Nonazeotrope		*243*
6688	$C_8H_{10}O$	*p*-Methylanisole	177.05	Nonazeotrope		*255*
6689	$C_8H_{10}O$	Phenetole	170.45	Nonazeotrope		*222*
6690	C_8H_{16}	1,3-Dimethylcyclohexane	120.7	<120.2	<10	*255*
6691	$C_8H_{16}O_2$	Isoamyl propionate	160.7	Nonazeotrope		*255*
6692	$C_8H_{16}O_2$	Ethyl caproate	167.7	Nonazeotrope		*255*
6693	$C_8H_{16}O_2$	Isobutyl butyrate	156.9	Nonazeotrope		*255*
6694	$C_8H_{16}O_2$	Isobutyl isobutyrate	148.6	Nonazeotrope		*255*
6695	$C_8H_{16}O_2$	Propyl isovalerate	155.7	Nonazeotrope		*255*
6696	C_8H_{18}	Octane	125.75	<124.0	<18	*255*
6697	$C_8H_{18}O$	Butyl ether	142.4	<140.5	<22	*242*
6698	$C_8H_{18}O$	Isobutyl ether	122	Nonazeotrope		*236*
6699	C_9H_8	Indene	182.4	Nonazeotrope		*223*
6700	C_9H_{12}	Cumene	152.8	146.8	35	*242*
6701	C_9H_{12}	Mesitylene	164.6	151.8	~57	*221*
6702	C_9H_{12}	Mesitylene	164.0	148.5	~48	*243*
6703	C_9H_{12}	Propylbenzene	158.9	149.3	49	*221*

No.	Formula	B-Component Name	B.P., ° C.	Azeotropic Data B.P., ° C.	Wt. % A	Ref.
A =	**$C_4H_8O_2$**	**Isobutyric Acid (*continued*)**	**154.6**			
6704	C_9H_{12}	Pseudocumene	168.2	152.3	63	*221*
6705	$C_9H_{12}O$	Benzyl ethyl ether	185.0	Nonazeotrope		*255*
6706	$C_9H_{18}O$	2,6-Dimethyl-4-heptanone	168.0	Nonazeotrope		*232*
6707	$C_{10}H_{14}$	Butylbenzene	183.1	Nonazeotrope		*255*
6708	$C_{10}H_{14}$	Cymene	176.7	153.4	80	*242*
6709	$C_{10}H_{16}$	Camphene	159.6	148.1	45	*221*
6710	$C_{10}H_{16}$	*d*-Limonene	177.8	152.5	78	*222*
6711	$C_{10}H_{16}$	Nopinene	163.8	149.2	52	*242*
6712	$C_{10}H_{16}$	α-Pinene	155.8	146.7	35	*243*
6713	$C_{10}H_{16}$	α-Phellandrene	171.5	150	~72	*243*
6714	$C_{10}H_{16}$	α-Terpinene	173.4	152.0	70	*242*
6715	$C_{10}H_{16}$	Thymene	179.7	~154.0	....	*221*
6716	$C_{10}H_{18}$	Cineol	176.35	Nonazeotrope		*255*
6717	$C_{10}H_{22}$	Decane	173.3	<151.2	<72	*242*
6718	$C_{10}H_{22}$	2,7-Dimethyloctane	160.2	148.55	48	*222*
6719	$C_{10}H_{22}O$	Isoamyl ether	173.2	154.2	93	*255*
A =	**$C_4H_8O_2$**	**Isopropyl Formate**	**68.8**			
6720	C_4H_9Cl	1-Chloro-2-methylpropane	68.85	65	48	*227*
6721	$C_4H_9NO_2$	Isobutyl nitrite	67.1	65.5	40	*229*
6722	C_5H_{10}	Cyclopentane	49.4	<47.0	18	*242*
6723	C_6H_6	Benzene	68.8	Nonazeotrope		*255*
6724	C_6H_{12}	Methylcyclopentane	72.0	<61.5	55	*242*
6725	C_6H_{14}	Hexane	68.8	57.0	48	*242*
A =	**$C_4H_8O_2$**	**Methyl Propionate**	**79.85**			
6726	$C_4H_8O_2$	Propyl formate	80.85	Nonazeotrope		*211*
6727	C_4H_9Br	2-Bromobutane	91.2	Nonazeotrope		*255*
6728	C_4H_9Br	1-Bromo-2-methylpropane	91.4	Nonazeotrope		*227*
6729	C_4H_9Br	2-Bromo-2-methylpropane	73.25	Nonazeotrope		*227*
6730	C_4H_9Cl	1-Chlorobutane	78.05	76.8	~38	*218*
6731	C_4H_9Cl	1-Chloro-2-methylpropane	68.9	Nonazeotrope		*243*
6732	$C_4H_9NO_2$	Butyl nitrite	78.2	77.7	12	*229*
6733	$C_4H_{10}O$	Butyl alcohol	117.8	Nonazeotrope		*207*
6734	$C_4H_{10}O$	*sec*-Butyl alcohol	99.5	Nonazeotrope		*255*
6735	$C_4H_{10}O$	*tert*-Butyl alcohol	82.55	77.6	~63	*216*
6736	$C_4H_{10}S$	Ethyl sulfide	92.2	Nonazeotrope		*212*
6737	$C_5H_{10}O$	Isovaleraldehyde	92.3	Nonazeotrope		*228*
6738	$C_5H_{12}O_2$	Diethoxymethane	87.95	Nonazeotrope		*237*
6739	C_6H_6	Benzene	80.2	79.45	52	*252*
6740	C_6H_{10}	Cyclohexene	82.75	~75.5	....	*243*
6741	C_6H_{12}	Cyclohexane	80.75	75	52	*253*
6742	C_6H_{12}	Methylcyclopentane	72.0	69.5	28	*242*
6743	C_6H_{14}	*n*-Hexane	68.95	67	~12	*253*
6744	$C_6H_{14}O$	Propyl ether	90.55	Nonazeotrope		*237*
6745	C_7H_{14}	Methylcyclohexane	101.1	Nonazeotrope		*226*
6746	C_7H_{16}	Heptane	98.4	<79.6	<92	*255*
6747	C_7H_{16}	Heptane	98.5	Nonazeotrope		*226*
A =	**$C_4H_8O_2$**	**Propyl Formate**	**80.85**			
6748	C_4H_9Br	2-Bromobutane	91.2	Nonazeotrope		*255*
6749	C_4H_9Br	1-Bromo-2-methylpropane	91.4	Nonazeotrope		*227*
6750	C_4H_9Br	2-Bromo-2-methylpropane	73.3	71.8	28	*253*
6751	C_4H_9Cl	1-Chlorobutane	78.5	76.1	38	*250*
6752	C_4H_9Cl	2-Chlorobutane	68.25	Nonazeotrope		*255*
6753	C_4H_9Cl	1-Chloro-2-methylpropane	68.85	Nonazeotrope		*250*
6754	$C_4H_9NO_2$	Butyl nitrite	78.2	76.8	35	*229*
6755	$C_4H_{10}O$	Butyl alcohol	117.75	Nonazeotrope		*207*
6756	$C_4H_{10}O$	*sec*-Butyl alcohol	99.5	Nonazeotrope		*255*
6757	$C_4H_{10}O$	*tert*-Butyl alcohol	82.6	78.0	60	*217*
6758	$C_4H_{10}O$	Isobutyl alcohol	107.85	Nonazeotrope		*216*
6759	$C_4H_{10}S$	Ethyl sulfide	92.1	<80.2	<87	*255*
6760	$C_4H_{10}S$	Ethyl sulfide	92.2	Nonazeotrope		*212*
6761	$C_4H_{10}S$	Butanethiol	97.5	Nonazeotrope		*246*
6762	C_5H_{10}	Cyclopentane	49.3	Nonazeotrope		*255*

No.	Formula	B-Component Name	B.P., ° C.	Azeotropic Data B.P., ° C.	Wt. % A	Ref.
A =	$C_4H_8O_2$	**Propyl Formate** (*continued*)	**80.85**			
6763	$C_5H_{11}Cl$	1-Chloro-3-methylbutane	99.8	Nonazeotrope		*227*
6764	$C_5H_{12}O_2$	Diethoxymethane	87.95	Nonazeotrope		*207*
6765	C_6H_5F	Fluorobenzene	84.9	<79.5	<78	*255*
6766	C_6H_6	Benzene	80.2	78.5	47	*252*
6767	C_6H_{10}	Cyclohexene	82.75	<75.0	<53	*255*
6768	C_6H_{12}	Cyclohexane	80.75	75	48	*253*
6769	C_6H_{12}	Methylcyclopentane	72.0	<67.5	<35	*255*
6770	C_6H_{14}	2,3-Dimethylbutane	58.0	56.0	15	*242*
6771	C_6H_{14}	*n*-Hexane	68.95	63	~20	*251*
6772	$C_6H_{14}O$	Propyl ether	90.55	Nonazeotrope		*237*
6773	$C_6H_{14}O_2$	Acetal	103.55	Nonazeotrope		*237*
6774	C_7H_8	Toluene	110.75	Nonazeotrope		*255*
6775	C_7H_{14}	Methylcyclohexane	101.15	<80.2	<88	*255*
6776	C_7H_{16}	Heptane	98.5	78.2	71	*207*
6777	C_8H_{18}	2,5-Dimethylhexane	109.4	Nonazeotrope		*255*
A =	$C_4H_8O_3$	**Glycol Monoacetate**	**190.9**			
6778	$C_5H_4O_2$	2-Furaldehyde	161.45	Nonazeotrope		*207*
6779	$C_5H_{12}O_3$	2-(2-Methoxyethoxy)ethanol	192.95	<188.0	>65	*255*
6780	$C_6H_4Cl_2$	*o*-Dichlorobenzene	179.5	<179.3	....	*255*
6781	$C_6H_4Cl_2$	*p*-Dichlorobenzene	174.4	Nonazeotrope		*207*
6782	C_6H_5I	Iodobenzene	188.45	184.0	....	*247*
6783	$C_6H_5NO_2$	Nitrobenzene	210.75	Nonazeotrope		*207*
6784	C_6H_6O	Phenol	182.2	197.5	65	*207*
6785	$C_6H_8O_4$	Methyl fumarate	193.25	<189.0	<65	*207*
6786	$C_6H_{10}O_4$	Ethyl oxalate	185.65	Nonazeotrope		*207*
6787	$C_6H_{11}NO_2$	Nitrocyclohexane	205.4	Nonazeotrope		*255*
6788	$C_6H_{14}O_2$	2-Butoxyethanol	171.15	Nonazeotrope		*207*
6789	C_7H_7Br	*m*-Bromotoluene	184.3	182.0	32	*247*
6790	C_7H_7Cl	*p*-Chlorotoluene	162.4	Nonazeotrope		*255*
6791	C_7H_8O	Benzyl alcohol	205.25	Nonazeotrope		*207*
6792	C_7H_8O	*m*-Cresol	202.2	206.5	31	*207*
6793	C_7H_8O	*o*-Cresol	191.1	199.45	51	*250*
6794	C_7H_8O	*p*-Cresol	201.7	206.0	33	*207*
6795	$C_7H_8O_2$	Guaiacol	205.05	Nonazeotrope		*207*
6796	$C_7H_{13}ClO_2$	Isoamyl chloroacetate	190.5	189.3	50	*255*
6797	$C_7H_{16}O_3$	1,3-Butanediol methyl ether acetal	171.75	Nonazeotrope		*255*
6798	$C_7H_{16}O$	Heptyl alcohol	176.15	Nonazeotrope		*255*
6799	C_8H_8O	Acetophenone	202.0	Nonazeotrope		*207*
6800	$C_8H_8O_2$	Methyl benzoate	199.4	Nonazeotrope		*207*
6801	$C_8H_8O_2$	Phenyl acetate	195.7	<190.0	....	*255*
6802	$C_8H_{10}O$	Benzyl methyl ether	167.8	<167.0	....	*255*
6803	$C_8H_{10}O$	Phenethyl alcohol	219.4	Nonazeotrope		*207*
6804	$C_8H_{10}O$	2,4-Xylenol	~210.5	<212.0	<18	*255*
6805	$C_8H_{12}O_4$	Ethyl fumarate	217.85	Nonazeotrope		*207*
6806	$C_8H_{18}O$	Octyl alcohol	195.2	189.5	71	*207*
6807	$C_8H_{18}O$	*sec*-Octyl alcohol	180.4	<180.3	....	*207*
6808	C_9H_8	Indene	182.6	180.0	20	*255*
6809	$C_9H_{10}O_2$	Ethyl benzoate	212.5	Nonazeotrope		*207*
6810	$C_9H_{12}O$	Benzyl ethyl ether	185.0	180.5	35	*255*
6811	$C_9H_{14}O$	Phorone	197.8	Nonazeotrope		*232*
6812	$C_9H_{18}O_2$	Isoamyl butyrate	181.05	180.2	21	*207*
6813	$C_9H_{18}O_2$	Isobutyl isovalerate	171.2	Nonazeotrope		*255*
6814	$C_{10}H_8$	Naphthalene	218.0	Nonazeotrope		*207*
6815	$C_{10}H_{14}$	Butylbenzene	183.1	<181.5	....	*207*
6816	$C_{10}H_{18}O$	Borneol	215.0	Nonazeotrope		*255*
6817	$C_{10}H_{18}O$	Cineol	176.35	174.1	22	*207*
6818	$C_{10}H_{18}O$	Citronellal	208.0	Nonazeotrope		*207*
6819	$C_{10}H_{20}O$	Menthol	216.3	Nonazeotrope		*207*
6820	$C_{10}H_{20}O_2$	Isoamyl isovalerate	192.7	187.0	57	*207*
6821	$C_{10}H_{20}O_2$	Ethyl caprylate	208.35	Nonazeotrope		*207*
6822	$C_{10}H_{22}O$	Amyl ether	187.5	180.8	42	*236*
6823	$C_{10}H_{22}O$	Isoamyl ether	173.2	170.2	28	*236*
6824	$C_{11}H_{20}O$	Isobornyl methyl ether	192.4	185.0	60	*255*
6825	$C_{12}H_{18}$	1,3,5-Triethylbenzene	215.5	Nonazeotrope		*255*

No.	B-Component Formula	Name	B.P., ° C.	Azeotropic Data B.P., ° C.	Wt. % A	Ref.
A =	**$C_4H_8O_3$**	**Methyl Lactate**	**143.8**			
6826	C_4H_9I	1-Iodobutane	130.4	<128.5	>20	247
6827	C_4H_9I	1-Iodo-2-methylpropane	120.8	<120.0	>6	255
6828	$C_4H_{10}O$	Butyl alcohol	117.8	Nonazeotrope		255
6829	$C_4H_{10}O_2$	2-Ethoxyethanol	135.3	Nonazeotrope		255
6830	C_5H_8O	Cyclopentanone	130.65	Nonazeotrope		232
6831	$C_5H_{10}O$	Cyclopentanol	140.85	<140.2	<81	255
6832	$C_5H_{10}O_3$	2-Methoxyethyl acetate	144.6	143.2	55	255
6833	$C_5H_{11}I$	1-Iodo-3-methylbutane	147.65	139.0	52	247
6834	$C_5H_{11}NO_3$	Isoamyl nitrate	149.75	141.4	168	207
6835	$C_5H_{12}O$	Amyl alcohol	138.2	<138.0	....	255
6836	$C_5H_{12}O$	Isoamyl alcohol	131.9	Nonazeotrope		207
6837	$C_5H_{12}O$	2-Pentanol	119.8	Nonazeotrope		255
6838	$C_5H_{12}O_2$	2-Propoxyethanol	151.35	Nonazeotrope		206
6839	C_6H_5Br	Bromobenzene	156.1	141.5	22	247
6840	C_6H_5Br	Bromobenzene	156.1	Nonazeotrope		.215
6841	C_6H_5Cl	Chlorobenzene	131.75	<130.8	....	255
6842	C_6H_6O	Phenol	182.2	Nonazeotrope		255
6843	$C_6H_{10}O$	Cyclohexanone	155.7	Nonazeotrope		232
6844	$C_6H_{10}O$	Mesityl oxide	129.45	Nonazeotrope		232
6845	$C_6H_{12}O$	Cyclohexanol	160.65	Nonazeotrope		243
6846	$C_6H_{12}O_3$	2-Ethoxyethyl acetate	156.8	Nonazeotrope		206
6847	$C_6H_{14}O$	Hexyl alcohol	157.85	Nonazeotrope		255
6848	$C_6H_{14}O_2$	2-Butoxyethanol	171.15	Nonazeotrope		255
6849	$C_6H_{14}S$	Propyl sulfide	141.5	<138.0	<40	246
6850	C_7H_8	Toluene	110.75	~110.4	~18	253
6851	C_7H_8O	Anisole	153.85	142.8	82	236
6852	C_7H_8O	*o*-Cresol	191.1	Nonazeotrope		255
6853	$C_7H_{14}O$	4-Heptanone	143.55	142.7	47	232
6854	$C_7H_{14}O_2$	Butyl propionate	146.5	~141.3	>55	228
6855	$C_7H_{14}O_2$	Isobutyl propionate	137.5	135.8	40	255
6856	$C_7H_{14}O_2$	Ethyl isovalerate	134.7	Nonazeotrope		212
6857	$C_7H_{14}O_2$	Ethyl valerate	145.45	140.0	58	207
6858	$C_7H_{14}O_2$	Isoamyl acetate	142.1	~138.5	44	209
6859	$C_7H_{14}O_2$	Methyl caproate	149.8	141.7	70	255
6860	$C_7H_{14}O_2$	Propyl butyrate	142.8	137.5	46	252
6861	$C_7H_{14}O_2$	Propyl isobutyrate	134.7	Nonazeotrope		212
6862	C_8H_8	Styrene	145.8	~134.5	~50	228
		26 mm.	....	....	~33 vol.	141
6863	C_8H_{10}	Ethylbenzene	136.15	129.4	35	253
		26 mm.	....	....	~26 vol.	141
6864	C_8H_{10}	*m*-Xylene	139.0	131.2	42.5	207
6865	C_8H_{10}	*p*-Xylene	138.2	130.8	40	253
6866	$C_8H_{10}O$	Benzyl methyl ether	167.8	Nonazeotrope		255
6867	$C_8H_{16}O_2$	Butyl butyrate	166.4	Nonazeotrope		255
6868	$C_8H_{16}O_2$	Isoamyl propionate	160.7	Nonazeotrope		255
6869	$C_8H_{16}O_2$	Isobutyl isobutyrate	147.3	141.5	70	207
6870	$C_8H_{16}O_2$	Propyl isovalerate	155.7	Nonazeotrope		228
6871	C_8H_{18}	2,5-Dimethylhexane	109.4	<108.5	<17	255
6872	C_8H_{18}	Octane	125.8	120.3	30	247
6873	$C_8H_{18}O$	Butyl ether	102.4	137.0	42	255
6874	C_9H_{12}	Cumene	152.8	137.8	62	247
6875	C_9H_{12}	Mesitylene	164.6	142.0	>85	228
6876	C_9H_{12}	Propylbenzene	158.9	140	~88	218
6877	C_9H_{12}	Pseudocumene	168.2	~143.0	<90	255
6878	$C_{10}H_{14}$	Cymene	176.7	Nonazeotrope		255
6879	$C_{10}H_{16}$	Camphene	159.6	140	85	253
6880	$C_{10}H_{16}$	*d*-Limonene	177.8	Nonazeotrope		215
6881	$C_{10}H_{16}$	Nopinene	163.8	138.5	70	247
6882	$C_{10}H_{16}$	α-Pinene	155.8	<144.2	>90	243
6883	$C_{10}H_{16}$	α-Terpinene	173.4	<142.5	<88	255
6884	$C_{10}H_{22}$	2,7-Dimethyloctane	160.1	137.8	68	247
A =	**C_4H_8S**	**Tetrahydrothiophene**	**118.8**			
6885	C_5H_5N	Pyridine	115.4	113.5	45	233
6886	C_5H_7N	1-Methylpyrrol	112.8	111.5	18	255
6887	$C_5H_{10}O$	3-Pentanone	102.05	Nonazeotrope		255

	B-Component			Azeotropic Data		
No.	Formula	Name	B.P., ° C.	B.P., ° C.	Wt. % A	Ref.
A =	C_4H_8S	**Tetrahydrothiophene** (*continued*)	**118.8**			
6888	$C_5H_{10}O_2$	Isobutyl formate	98.2	Nonazeotrope		*246*
6889	$C_5H_{10}O_2$	Propyl acetate	101.6	Nonazeotrope		*246*
6890	$C_5H_{11}Cl$	1-Chloro-3-methylbutane	99.4	Nonazeotrope		*246*
6890a	$C_5H_{12}O_2$	Diethoxymethane	87.95	Nonazeotrope		*255*
6891	$C_6H_{12}O$	Pinacolone	186.2	Nonazeotrope		*255*
6892	$C_6H_{14}O$	Propyl ether	90.1	Nonazeotrope		*255*
6892a	$C_6H_{14}O_2$	Acetal	103.55	Nonazeotrope		*255*
6893	$C_6H_{14}S$	Isopropyl sulfide	120.5	<117.5	>60	*255*
6894	C_7H_8	Toluene	110.75	Nonazeotrope		*246*
6895	C_7H_{16}	Heptane	98.4	Nonazeotrope		*246*
6896	C_8H_{18}	2,5-Dimethylhexane	109.4	<109.1	>6	*255*
A =	C_4H_9Br	**1-Bromobutane**	**101.5**			
6897	C_4H_9Cl	1-Chlorobutane	77.9	Nonazeotrope		
				Vapor pressure data		*369*
6898	$C_4H_{10}O$	Butyl alcohol	117.8	98.6	87	*207*
6899	$C_4H_{10}O$	*sec*-Butyl alcohol	99.5	93.0	70	*247*
6900	$C_4H_{10}O$	*tert*-Butyl alcohol	82.45	<81.8	<37	*255*
6901	$C_4H_{10}O$	Isobutyl alcohol	107.85	95	79	*253*
6902	$C_4H_{10}S$	Ethyl sulfide	92.1	Nonazeotrope		*246*
6903	$C_5H_{10}O$	2-Pentanone	102.35	100.1	63	*232*
6904	$C_5H_{10}O$	3-Pentanone	102.05	100.0	63	*232*
6905	$C_5H_{10}O_2$	Butyl formate	106.7	100.0	75	*227*
6906	$C_5H_{10}O_2$	Ethyl propionate	79.1	<98.8	....	*255*
6907	$C_5H_{10}O_2$	Isobutyl formate	98.2	95.5	>35	*227*
6908	$C_5H_{10}O_2$	Isopropyl acetate	89.5	Nonazeotrope		*255*
6909	$C_5H_{10}O_2$	Methyl butyrate	102.65	99.5	65	*227*
6910	$C_5H_{10}O_2$	Methyl isobutyrate	92.5	Nonazeotrope		*227*
6911	$C_5H_{10}O_2$	Propyl acetate	101.6	99.9	52	*206*
6912	$C_5H_{10}O_2$	Propyl acetate	101.6	100.0	55	*227*
6913	$C_5H_{11}NO_2$	Isoamyl nitrite	97.15	Nonazeotrope		*230*
6914	$C_5H_{12}O$	*tert*-Amyl alcohol	102.35	<97.8	<74	*255*
6915	$C_5H_{12}O$	Isoamyl alcohol	131.9	Nonazeotrope		*207*
6916	$C_5H_{12}O$	3-Methyl-2-butanol	112.9	99.7	86	*247*
6917	$C_5H_{12}O$	3-Pentanol	116.0	<100.7	>86	*255*
6918	$C_6H_5NO_2$	Nitrobenzene	210.75	Nonazeotrope		*234*
6919	$C_6H_{10}S$	Allyl sulfide	139.35	Nonazeotrope		*246*
6920	$C_6H_{12}O$	4-Methyl-2-pentanone	116.05	Nonazeotrope		*207*
6921	$C_6H_{12}O$	Pinacolone	106.2	101.1	86	*232*
6922	$C_6H_{12}O$	Pinacolone	106.2	Nonazeotrope		*228*
6923	$C_6H_{12}O_2$	Ethyl isobutyrate	110.1	Nonazeotrope		*227*
6924	$C_6H_{14}O$	Propyl ether	90.1	Nonazeotrope		*239*
6925	$C_6H_{14}S$	Isopropyl sulfide	120.5	Nonazeotrope		*246*
6926	C_7H_8	Toluene	110.75	Nonazeotrope		*255*
6927	C_7H_{14}	Methylcyclohexane	101.15	<99.5	55	*242*
6928	C_7H_{16}	Heptane	98.45	96.7	50	*218*
		50° C.		Vapor pressure data	42.5	*369*
A =	C_4H_9Br	**2-Bromobutane**	**91.2**			
6929	C_4H_9Br	1-Bromo-2-methylpropane	91.4	Nonazeotrope		*229*
6930	$C_4H_{10}O$	Butyl alcohol	117.8	90.6	94	*255*
6931	$C_4H_{10}O$	*sec*-Butyl alcohol	99.5	87.2	81.9	*169*
6932	$C_4H_{10}O$	Isobutyl alcohol	108.0	88.6	−86	*247*
6933	$C_5H_{10}O$	3-Pentanone	102.05	Nonazeotrope		*232*
6934	$C_5H_{10}O_2$	Methyl isobutyrate	92.5	90.5	70	*242*
6935	$C_5H_{11}NO_2$	Isoamyl nitrite	97.15	Nonazeotrope		*230*
6936	C_6H_{12}	Cyclohexane	80.75	Nonazeotrope		*255*
6937	C_7H_{16}	Heptane	98.4	<91.0	>80	*255*
A =	C_4H_9Br	**1-Bromo-2-methylpropane**	**91.4**			
6938	C_4H_9ClO	Chloroethyl ethyl ether	98.5	Nonazeotrope		*255*
6938a	$C_4H_9NO_2$	Butyl nitrite	78.2	Nonazeotrope		*230*
6939	$C_4H_{10}O$	Butyl alcohol	117.75	90.2	93	*215*
6940	$C_4H_{10}O$	*sec*-Butyl alcohol	99.5	87.0	80.5	*247*
6941	$C_4H_{10}O$	*tert*-Butyl alcohol	82.45	79.0	58	*255*

No.	B-Component Formula	Name	B.P., ° C	Azeotropic Data B.P., ° C.	Wt.% A	Ref.
A =	C_4H_9Br	**1-Bromo-2-methylpropane** (*continued*)	**91.4**			
6942	$C_4H_{10}O$	Isobutyl alcohol	107.85	89.2	<84	*207*
			108	Nonazeotrope		
				B.p. curve		*163*
6943	$C_4H_{10}S$	Ethyl sulfide	92.1	<90.2	<54	*246*
6944	$C_5H_{10}O$	3-Methyl-2-butanone	95.4	90.8	82	*232*
6945	$C_5H_{10}O$	2-Pentanone	102.35	Nonazeotrope		*232*
6946	$C_5H_{10}O$	3-Pentanone	102.05	Nonazeotrope		*232*
6947	$C_5H_{10}O_2$	Butyl formate	106.8	Nonazeotrope		*255*
6948	$C_5H_{10}O_2$	Ethyl propionate	99.15	Nonazeotrope		*227*
6949	$C_5H_{10}O_2$	Isobutyl formate	97.9	90.0	~70	*218*
6950	$C_5H_{10}O_2$	Isopropyl acetate	90.8	89.0	55	*218*
6951	$C_5H_{10}O_2$	Methyl butyrate	102.65	Nonazeotrope		*255*
6952	$C_5H_{10}O_2$	Methyl isobutyrate	92.3	90	61	*253*
6953	$C_5H_{10}O_2$	Propyl acetate	101.6	Nonazeotrope		*227*
6954	$C_5H_{11}NO_2$	Isoamyl nitrite	97.15	Nonazeotrope		*230*
6955	$C_5H_{12}O$	*tert*-Amyl alcohol	102.0	87.5	82	*212*
6956	$C_5H_{12}O$	Isoamyl alcohol	131.3	Nonazeotrope		*207*
6957	$C_5H_{12}O$	3-Methyl-2-butanol	112.6	Nonazeotrope		*255*
6958	$C_5H_{12}O$	2-Pentanol	119.8	Nonazeotrope		*255*
6959	$C_5H_{12}O$	3-Pentanol	116.0	Nonazeotrope		*255*
6960	C_6H_6	Benzene	80.2	Nonazeotrope		*243*
6961	C_6H_{12}	Cyclohexane	80.75	Nonazeotrope		*255*
6962	$C_6H_{14}O_2$	Acetal	103.55	Nonazeotrope		*239*
6963	C_7H_{14}	Methylcyclohexane	101.15	Nonazeotrope		*255*
6964	C_7H_{16}	Heptane	98.4	<91.0	>80	*207*
6965	C_8H_{18}	2,5-Dimethylhexane	109.4	Nonazeotrope		*255*
A =	C_4H_9Br	**2-Bromo-2-methylpropane**	**73.25**			
6966	$C_4H_9NO_2$	Butyl nitrite	78.2	Nonazeotrope		*230*
6967	$C_4H_9NO_2$	Isobutyl nitrite	67.1	Nonazeotrope		*230*
6968	$C_4H_{10}O$	*tert*-Butyl alcohol	82.5	Min. b.p.		*396*
6969	$C_4H_{10}O$	Isobutyl alcohol	108	Nonazeotrope		*243*
6970	$C_4H_{10}O_2$	Ethoxymethoxymethane	65.9	Nonazeotrope		*239*
6971	C_6H_6	Benzene	80.2	Nonazeotrope		*243*
6972	C_6H_{12}	Cyclohexane	80.75	Nonazeotrope		*255*
6973	C_6H_{12}	Methylcyclopentane	72.0	<70.5	>48	*242*
6974	C_6H_{14}	Hexane	68.85	68.0	~38	*218*
6975	$C_6H_{14}O$	Isopropyl ether	68.3	Nonazeotrope		*239*
A =	C_4H_9Cl	**1-Chlorobutane**	**78.5**			
6976	C_4H_9ClO	1-Chloroethyl ethyl ether	98.5	Nonazeotrope		*255*
6977	$C_4H_9NO_2$	Butyl nitrite	78.2	77.0	48	*230*
6978	$C_4H_9NO_2$	Isobutyl nitrite	67.1	Nonazeotrope		*230*
6979	$C_4H_{10}O$	Butyl alcohol	117.75	Nonazeotrope		*207*
			117	77.7	98.1	*93*
6980	$C_4H_{10}O$	*sec*-Butyl alcohol	99.5	77.7	92	*255*
6981	$C_4H_{10}O$	*tert*-Butyl alcohol	82.45	72.8	80	*247*
6982	$C_4H_{10}O$	Isobutyl alcohol	107.85	77.65	96	*253*
6983	$C_4H_{10}O_2$	Acetaldehyde dimethyl acetal	64.3	Nonazeotrope		*239*
6984	$C_4H_{10}S$	Butanethiol	97.5	Nonazeotrope		*255*
6985	$C_5H_{10}O$	Isovaleraldehyde	92.1	Nonazeotrope		*255*
6986	$C_5H_{10}O$	3-Methyl-2-butanone	95.4	Nonazeotrope		*232*
6987	$C_5H_{10}O_2$	Isopropyl acetate	89.5	Nonazeotrope		*255*
6988	$C_5H_{11}NO_2$	Isoamyl nitrite	97.15	Nonazeotrope		*230*
6989	$C_5H_{12}O$	*tert*-Amyl alcohol	102.35	Nonazeotrope		*255*
6990	$C_5H_{12}O$	3-Pentanol	116.0	Nonazeotrope		*255*
6991	$C_5H_{12}O_2$	Diethoxymethane	87.95	Nonazeotrope		*207*
6992	$C_6H_5NO_2$	Nitrobenzene	210.75	Nonazeotrope		*234*
6993	C_6H_{12}	Cyclohexane	80.75	<78.0	>64	*255*
6994	C_6H_{14}	Hexane	68.8	Nonazeotrope		*255*
6995	$C_6H_{14}O$	Isopropyl ether	68.3	Nonazeotrope		*239*
6996	$C_6H_{14}O$	Propyl ether	90.1	Nonazeotrope		*239*
6997	C_7H_{16}	Heptane	98.4	Nonazeotrope		
				Vapor pressure data		*369*

No.	Formula	B-Component Name	B.P., ° C.	Azeotropic Data B.P., ° C.	Wt. % A	Ref.
A =	C_4H_9Cl	**2-Chlorobutane**	**68.25**			
6998	C_4H_9Cl	1-Chloro-2-methylpropane	68.85	Nonazeotrope		*255*
6999	$C_4H_9NO_2$	Butyl nitrite	78.2	Nonazeotrope		*230*
7000	$C_4H_9NO_2$	Isobutyl nitrite	67.1	66.2	38	*230*
7001	$C_5H_{12}O$	Ethyl propyl ether	63.85	Nonazeotrope		*239*
7002	$C_6H_5NO_2$	Nitrobenzene	210.75	Nonazeotrope		*234*
7003	C_6H_6	Benzene	80.15	Nonazeotrope		*255*
7004	C_6H_{14}	Hexane	68.8	65.85	57	*242*
A =	C_4H_9Cl	**1-Chloro-2-methylpropane**	**68.85**			
7005	$C_4H_9NO_2$	Butyl nitrite	78.2	Nonazeotrope		*230*
7006	$C_4H_9NO_2$	Isobutyl nitrite	67.1	66.5	33	*230*
7007	$C_4H_{10}O$	Butyl alcohol	117.75	Nonazeotrope		*207*
7008	$C_4H_{10}O$	*sec*-Butyl alcohol	99.5	Nonazeotrope		*255*
7009	$C_4H_{10}O$	*tert*-Butyl alcohol	82.55	65.5	83	*215*
7010	$C_4H_{10}O$	Isobutyl alcohol	107.85	Nonazeotrope		*212*
7011	$C_4H_{10}O_2$	Acetaldehyde dimethyl acetal	64.3	Nonazeotrope		*239*
7012	C_5H_{10}	Cyclopentane	49.3	Nonazeotrope		*255*
7013	$C_5H_{12}O$	*tert*-Amyl alcohol	102.0	Nonazeotrope		*215*
7014	$C_5H_{12}O$	Ethyl propyl ether	63.6	Nonazeotrope		*228*
7015	C_6H_6	Benzene	80.2	Nonazeotrope		*209*
7016	C_6H_8	1,3-Cyclohexadiene	80.8	Nonazeotrope		*243*
7017	C_6H_{10}	Cyclohexene	82.75	Nonazeotrope		*255*
7018	C_6H_{12}	Cyclohexane	80.75	Nonazeotrope		*243*
7019	C_6H_{12}	Methylcyclopentane	72.0	67.8	63	*242*
7020	C_6H_{14}	2,3-Dimethylhexane	58.0	Nonazeotrope		*255*
7021	C_6H_{14}	Hexane	68.95	66.3	55	*243*
7022	$C_6H_{14}O$	Isopropyl ether	68.3	>69.0	....	*239*
A =	C_4H_9Cl	**2-Chloro-2-methylpropane**	**50.8**			
7023	$C_4H_9NO_2$	Isobutyl nitrite	67.1	Nonazeotrope		*230*
7024	$C_4H_{10}O$	*tert*-Butyl alcohol	82.5	Nonazeotrope		*396*
7025	C_5H_{10}	Cyclopentane	49.3	47.5	50	*242*
7026	C_5H_{12}	Pentane	36.15	<35.8	>16	*242*
7027	C_6H_{10}	Biallyl	60.2	Nonazeotrope		*243*
7028	C_6H_{12}	Methylcyclopentane	72.0	Nonazeotrope		*255*
7029	C_6H_{14}	2,3-Dimethylbutane	58.0	<50.5	<40	*255*
7030	C_6H_{14}	Hexane	68.9	Nonazeotrope		*243*
A =	C_4H_9ClO	**Chloroethyl Ethyl Ether**	**98.5**			
7032	$C_4H_{10}S$	Ethyl sulfide	92.1	91.8	6	*255*
7033	C_5H_7N	1-Methylpyrrol	112.8	Nonazeotrope		*255*
7034	$C_5H_{10}O$	3-Methyl-2-butanone	95.4	Nonazeotrope		*255*
7035	$C_5H_{10}O$	3-Pentanone	102.05	Nonazeotrope		*255*
7036	C_6H_6	Benzene	80.15	Nonazeotrope		*255*
7037	C_6H_{12}	Cyclohexane	80.75	Nonazeotrope		*255*
7038	$C_6H_{14}O$	Propyl ether	90.1	Nonazeotrope		*255*
7039	C_7H_{14}	Methylcyclohexane	101.15	<97.5	>65	*242*
7040	C_7H_{16}	Heptane	98.4	96.0	48	*242*
A =	C_4H_9I	**1-Iodobutane**	**130.4**			
7041	$C_4H_9NO_3$	Isobutyl nitrate	123.5	<121.7	>27	*240*
7042	$C_4H_{10}O$	Butyl alcohol	117.8	113.8	58.5	*255*
7043	$C_4H_{10}O$	*tert*-Butyl alcohol	82.45	Nonazeotrope		*255*
7044	$C_4H_{10}O$	Isobutyl alcohol	108.0	106.2	50	*247*
7045	$C_4H_{10}O_2$	2-Ethoxyethanol	135.3	123.0	70	*206*
7046	$C_5H_4O_2$	2-Furaldehyde	161.45	Nonazeotrope		*207*
7047	C_5H_5N	Pyridine	115.5	Nonazeotrope		*228*
7048	C_5H_8O	Cyclopentanone	130.65	129.0	60	*232*
7049	C_5H_9N	Isovaleronitrile	130.5	118.5	60	*243*
7050	$C_5H_{10}O$	Cyclopentanol	140.85	127.0	84	*247*
7051	$C_5H_{10}O_2$	Isovaleric acid	176.5	Nonazeotrope		*207*
7052	$C_5H_{10}O_3$	Ethyl carbonate	126.0	124.5	30	*227*
7053	$C_5H_{10}O_3$	2-Methoxyethyl acetate	144.6	<129.5	<13	*255*
7054	$C_5H_{12}O$	Amyl alcohol	138.2	125.0	78	*207*
7055	$C_5H_{12}O$	Isoamyl alcohol	131.9	123.2	72	*207*
7056	$C_5H_{12}O$	2-Pentanol	119.8	117.0	54	*247*

No.	Formula	B-Component Name	B.P., ° C.	Azeotropic Data B.P., ° C.	Wt. % A	Ref.
A =	**C_4H_9I**	**1-Iodobutane (*continued*)**	**130.4**			
7057	C_6H_6O	Phenol	182.2	Nonazeotrope		255
7058	$C_6H_{10}O$	Mesityl oxide	129.5	128.0	56	207
7059	$C_6H_{12}O$	3-Hexanone	123.3	Nonazeotrope		232
7060	$C_6H_{12}O_2$	Butyl acetate	126.0	124.8	25	242
7061	$C_6H_{12}O_2$	Ethyl butyrate	121.5	Nonazeotrope		255
7062	$C_6H_{12}O_2$	Isoamyl formate	123.8	122.0	26	242
7063	$C_6H_{12}O_2$	Isobutyl acetate	117.4	Nonazeotrope		255
7064	$C_6H_{12}O_2$	Propyl propionate	122.5	Nonazeotrope		227
7065	$C_6H_{12}O_3$	2-Ethoxyethyl acetate	156.8	Nonazeotrope		255
7066	$C_6H_{14}O$	Hexyl alcohol	157.85	Nonazeotrope		255
7067	C_7H_8	Toluene	110.75	Nonazeotrope		255
7068	$C_7H_{14}O_2$	Ethyl isovalerate	134.7	<130.3	....	255
7069	$C_7H_{14}O_2$	Isobutyl propionate	136.9	Nonazeotrope		227
7070	C_8H_{10}	Ethylbenzene	136.15	<130.0	>85	255
A =	**C_4H_9I**	**2-Iodobutane**	**120.0**			
7071	$C_6H_{12}O_2$	Ethyl isobutyrate	110.1	Nonazeotrope		255
7072	$C_6H_{12}O_2$	Isobutyl acetate	117.4	<116.0	>30	255
7073	$C_6H_{12}O_2$	Methyl isovalerate	116.5	<116.0	>28	255
7074	C_7H_8	Toluene	110.75	Nonazeotrope		255
A =	**C_4H_9I**	**1-Iodo-2-methylpropane**	**120.8**			
7075	$C_4H_9NO_3$	Isobutyl nitrate	123.5	<117.5	>60	240
7076	$C_4H_{10}O$	Butyl alcohol	117.75	110.5	70	215
7077	$C_4H_{10}O$	Isobutyl alcohol	108	101	>67	334
			107.85	104	64	253
7078	$C_4H_{10}O_2$	2-Ethoxyethanol	135.3	117.5	....	255
7079	C_5H_5N	Pyridine	115.5	~114.0	~35	228
7080	$C_5H_{10}N_2$	Butyl formate	106.8	Nonazeotrope		255
7081	$C_5H_{10}O_2$	Methyl butyrate	102.65	Nonazeotrope		255
7082	$C_5H_{10}O_2$	Propyl acetate	101.6	Nonazeotrope		255
7083	$C_5H_{10}O_3$	Ethyl carbonate	126.0	118.2	80	227
7084	$C_5H_{10}O_3$	2-Methoxyethyl acetate	144.6	Nonazeotrope		206
7085	$C_5H_{11}Br$	1-Bromo-3-methylbutane	120.2	~119.1	....	243
7086	$C_5H_{12}O$	Isoamyl alcohol	131.8	115	<80	334
			131.3	117.5	83	207
7087	$C_5H_{12}O_2$	2-Propoxyethanol	151.35	<130.0	....	255
7088	$C_6H_{12}O_2$	Butyl acetate	125.0	120.0	....	227
7089	$C_6H_{12}O_2$	Ethyl butyrate	120.0	119	64	253
7090	$C_6H_{12}O_2$	Ethyl isobutyrate	110.1	Nonazeotrope		243
A =	**C_4H_9I**	**1-Iodo-2-methylpropane**	**120.8**			
7091	$C_6H_{12}O_2$	Isoamyl formate	123.6	117.5	70	243
7092	$C_6H_{12}O_2$	Isobutyl acetate	117.2	116.0	50	251
7093	$C_6H_{12}O_2$	Methyl isovalerate	116.5	Nonazeotrope		227
7094	$C_6H_{15}BO_3$	Ethyl borate	118.6	117.2	35	227
7095	C_7H_8	Toluene	110.7	Nonazeotrope		334
7096	$C_7H_{14}O_2$	Ethyl isovalerate	134.7	Nonazeotrope		255
7097	$C_7H_{14}O_2$	Isoamyl acetate	137.5	Nonazeotrope		163
7098	$C_7H_{14}O_2$	Isopropyl isobutyrate	120.8	119.5	53	227
7099	$C_7H_{14}O_2$	Propyl isobutyrate	134.0	Nonazeotrope		227
7100	C_8H_{16}	1,3-Dimethylcyclohexane	120.7	<119.0	>60	242
A =	**C_4H_9N**	**Pyrrolidine**				
7101	C_6H_6	Benzene	80.1	Min. b.p.		202
A =	**C_4H_9NO**	**Morpholine**	**128**			
7102	C_8H_{10}	*o*-Xylene	143.6	Nonazeotrope		139
A =	**$C_4H_9NO_2$**	**Butyl Nitrite**	**78.2**			
7103	$C_4H_{10}S$	Ethyl sulfide	92.1	Nonazeotrope		230
7104	$C_5H_{10}O$	3-Methyl-2-butanone	95.4	Nonazeotrope		232
7105	$C_5H_{10}O_2$	Isopropyl acetate	89.5	Nonazeotrope		230
7106	$C_5H_{12}O_2$	Diethoxymethane	87.95	Nonazeotrope		207
7107	C_6H_5F	Fluorobenzene	84.9	Nonazeotrope		230

No.	Formula	B-Component Name	B.P., ° C.	Azeotropic Data B.P., ° C.	Wt. % A	Ref.
A =	$C_4H_9NO_2$	**Butyl Nitrite** (*continued*)	**78.2**			
7108	C_6H_6	Benzene	80.15	77.95	75	*230*
7109	C_6H_{12}	Cyclohexane	80.75	76.5	63	*250*
7110	C_6H_{12}	Methylcyclopentane	72.0	<71.5	<2.8	*255*
7111	C_6H_{14}	Hexane	68.8	68.5	18	*230*
7112	$C_6H_{14}O$	Propyl ether	90.1	Nonazeotrope		*230*
7113	C_7H_{14}	Methylcyclohexane	101.15	Nonazeotrope		*230*
7114	C_7H_{16}	Heptane	98.4	Nonazeotrope		*207*
A =	$C_4H_9NO_2$	**Isobutyl Nitrite**	**67.1**			
7115	$C_4H_{10}O_2$	Acetaldehyde dimethyl acetal	64.3	Nonazeotrope		*230*
7116	C_5H_{10}	Cyclopentane	49.3	Nonazeotrope		*230*
7117	C_5H_{12}	Pentane	36.15	Nonazeotrope		*230*
7118	$C_5H_{12}O$	Ethyl propyl ether	63.85	<63.7	5	*230*
7119	C_6H_6	Benzene	80.15	Nonazeotrope		*230*
7120	C_6H_{12}	Cyclohexane	80.75	Nonazeotrope		*230*
7121	C_6H_{12}	Methylcyclopentane	72.0	65.9	68	*250*
7122	C_6H_{14}	Hexane	68.8	65.0	54	*207*
A =	$C_4H_9NO_3$	**Isobutyl Nitrate**	**123.5**			
7123	$C_4H_{10}O$	Butyl alcohol	117.8	112.8	45	*207*
7124	$C_4H_{10}O$	Isobutyl alcohol	107.85	105.6	36	*240*
7125	$C_4H_{10}O_2$	2-Ethoxyethanol	135.3	121.0	82	*240*
7126	$C_5H_{10}O$	Cyclopentanol	140.85	<122.2	....	*240*
7127	$C_5H_{10}O_3$	Ethyl carbonate	126.5	Nonazeotrope		*229*
7128	$C_5H_{10}O_3$	2-Methoxyethyl acetate	144.6	Nonazeotrope		*240*
7129	$C_5H_{11}Br$	1-Bromo-3-methylbutane	120.65	118.0	32	*240*
7130	$C_5H_{12}O$	Amyl alcohol	138.2	122.0	....	*240*
7131	$C_5H_{12}O$	Isoamyl alcohol	131.3	~120.0	~74	*240*
7132	$C_5H_{12}O$	2-Pentanol	119.8	<115.3	<48	*240*
7133	$C_5H_{12}O_2$	2-Propoxyethanol	151.35	Nonazeotrope		*240*
7134	C_6H_5Cl	Chlorobenzene	131.75	Nonazeotrope		*240*
7135	$C_6H_{12}O_2$	Isoamyl formate	123.8	<122.0	>54	*229*
7136	$C_6H_{12}O_2$	Propyl propionate	123.0	<121.7	>41	*229*
7137	$C_6H_{12}O_3$	Paraldehyde	124.35	<122.8	....	*237*
7138	$C_6H_{14}S$	Propyl sulfide	141.5	Nonazeotrope		*240*
7139	C_7H_8	Toluene	110.75	Nonazeotrope		*240*
7140	C_8H_{10}	Ethylbenzene	136.15	Nonazeotrope		*240*
7141	C_8H_{16}	1,3-Dimethylcyclohexane	120.7	<114.5	<41	*240*
7142	$C_8H_{18}O$	Isobutyl ether	122.3	<121.0	....	*237*
A =	$C_4H_{10}O$	**Butyl Alcohol**	**117.8**			
7143	$C_4H_{10}O_2$	2-Ethoxyethanol	135.3	Nonazeotrope		*206*
7144	$C_4H_{10}S$	Ethyl sulfide	92.1	Nonazeotrope		*207*
7145	C_5H_5N	Pyridine	115.4	118.7	71	*233*
7146	C_5H_7N	*N*-Methylpyrrol	112.8	<112.2	....	*255*
7147	$C_5H_9ClO_2$	Propyl chloroacetate	163.5	Nonazeotrope		*255*
7148	C_5H_9N	Valeronitrile	141.3	Nonazeotrope		*245*
7149	C_5H_{10}	2-Methyl-2-butene	37.75	Nonazeotrope		*105*
7150	$C_5H_{10}O$	3-Methyl-2-butanone	95.4	Nonazeotrope		*232*
7151	$C_5H_{10}O$	2-Pentanone	102.35	Nonazeotrope		*207*
7152	$C_5H_{10}O$	3-Pentanone	102.05	Nonazeotrope		*207*
7153	$C_5H_{10}O_2$	Butyl formate	106.6	105.8	23.6	*150*
7154	$C_5H_{10}O_2$	Ethyl propionate	99.1	Nonazeotrope		*207*
7155	$C_5H_{10}O_2$	Isobutyl formate	97.9	Nonazeotrope		*207*
7156	$C_5H_{10}O_2$	Isopropyl acetate	89.5	Nonazeotrope		*255*
7157	$C_5H_{10}O_2$	Methyl butyrate	102.75	Nonazeotrope		*207*
7158	$C_5H_{10}O_2$	Methyl isobutyrate	92.3	Nonazeotrope		*207*
7159	$C_5H_{10}O_2$	Propyl acetate	101.6	Nonazeotrope		*207*
7160	$C_5H_{10}O_3$	Ethyl carbonate	125.9	116.5	63	*207*
7161	$C_5H_{10}O_3$	2-Methoxyethyl acetate	144.6	Nonazeotrope		*206*
7162	$C_5H_{11}Br$	1-Bromo-3-methylbutane	120.3	110.65	31.5	*235*
7163	$C_5H_{11}Cl$	1-Chloro-3-methylbutane	99.4	97.0	12	*247*
7164	$C_5H_{11}I$	1-Iodo-3-methylbutane	147.65	117.3	~78	*215*
7165	$C_5H_{12}O$	2-Pentanol	119.8	Nonazeotrope		*255*
7166	$C_5H_{12}O$	3-Pentanol	116.0	Nonazeotrope		*255*
7167	C_6H_5Br	Bromobenzene	156.1	Nonazeotrope		*207*
7168	C_6H_5Cl	Chlorobenzene	132.0	115.3	56	*254*

No.	B-Component Formula	Name	B.P., ° C	Azeotropic Data B.P., ° C.	Wt. % A	Ref.
A =	$C_4H_{10}O$	**Butyl Alcohol** (*continued*)	**117.8**			
7169	C_6H_5F	Fluorobenzene	84.9	Nonazeotrope		*255*
7170	$C_6H_5NO_2$	Nitrobenzene	210.75	Nonazeotrope		*234*
7171	C_6H_6	Benzene	80.2	Nonazeotrope		*243*
7172	C_6H_6O	Phenol	182.2	Nonazeotrope		*255*
7173	C_6H_7N	Aniline	184.35	Nonazeotrope		*231*
7174	C_6H_7N	2-Picoline	130.7	Nonazeotrope		*255*
7175	C_6H_8	1,3-Cyclohexadiene	80.8	Nonazeotrope		*243*
7176	C_6H_9N	*N*-Ethylpyrrol	130.4	Nonazeotrope		*255*
7177	C_6H_{10}	Cyclohexene	82.7	82.0	5	*217*
7178	$C_6H_{10}O$	Mesityl oxide	129.45	Nonazeotrope		*207, 232*
7179	$C_6H_{10}S$	Allyl sulfide	130.35	Nonazeotrope		*207*
7180	$C_6H_{11}ClO_2$	Butyl chloroacetate	181.9	Nonazeotrope		*58*
7181	C_6H_{12}	Cyclohexane	80.75	79.8	4	*217*
7182	C_6H_{12}	Methylcyclopentane	72.0	71.8	<8	*255*
7183	$C_6H_{12}O$	Butyl vinyl ether	93.8	93.3	7.75	*362*
			93.8	Nonazeotrope?		*103*, 362*
7184	$C_6H_{12}O$	2-Hexanone	127.2	116.5	81.8	*380*
7185	$C_6H_{12}O$	2-Hexanone	127.2	Nonazeotrope		*207*
7186	$C_6H_{12}O$	3-Hexanone	123.3	117.2	80	*207*
7187	$C_6H_{12}O$	4-Methyl-2-pentanone	116.05	114.35	30	*232*
7188	$C_6H_{12}O_2$	Butyl acetate	125.5	116.2	63.3, V-l.	*48, 150*, 207**
7189	$C_6H_{12}O_2$	Ethyl butyrate	120.0	115.7	~64	*216*
7190	$C_6H_{12}O_2$	Ethyl isobutyrate	110.1	109.2	17	*217*
7191	$C_6H_{12}O_2$	Isoamyl formate	123.8	115.9	69	*216*
7192	$C_6H_{12}O_2$	Isobutyl acetate	117.2	114.5	50	*216*
7193	$C_6H_{12}O_2$	Methyl isovalerate	116.3	113.5	40	*217*
7194	$C_6H_{12}O_2$	Propyl propionate	123.0	117.5	....	*255*
7195	$C_6H_{12}O_3$	2-Ethoxyethyl acetate	156.8	Nonazeotrope		*255*
7196	$C_6H_{12}O_3$	Paraldehyde	123.9	115.75	52	*207*
7197	$C_6H_{13}Br$	1-Bromohexane	156.5	Nonazeotrope		*255*
7198	C_6H_{14}	Hexane	68.85	Nonazeotrope		*221*
7199	$C_6H_{14}O$	Propyl ether	90.4	Nonazeotrope		*207*
7200	$C_6H_{14}O_2$	Acetal	103.55	101	13	*253*
7201	$C_6H_{14}S$	Isopropyl sulfide	100.5	112.0	45	*235*
7202	$C_6H_{14}S$	Propyl sulfide	141.5	Nonazeotrope		*246*
7203	$C_6H_{15}BO_3$	Ethyl borate	118.6	113	52	*216*
7204	C_7H_8	Toluene	110.7	105.5	32	*23, 207*, 261**
			....	0.5	5.6	*329*
			....	25	6.0	
			....	50	7.1	
			....	73	11.5	
			....	103.1	28.1	
7205	C_7H_8O	Anisole	153.85	Nonazeotrope		*207*
7206	C_7H_{14}	1-Heptene, 729 mm.	....	90	13	*306*
7207	C_7H_{14}	Methylcyclohexane	100.8	95.3	20	*23, 251**
7208	$C_7H_{14}O_2$	Butyl propionate	146.8	Nonazeotrope		*255*
7209	$C_7H_{14}O_2$	Ethyl isovalerate	134.7	Nonazeotrope		*207*
7210	$C_7H_{14}O_2$	Isoamyl acetate	142.1	Nonazeotrope		*207*
7211	$C_7H_{14}O_2$	Isobutyl propionate	137.5	Nonazeotrope		*255*
7212	$C_7H_{14}O_2$	Isopropyl isobutyrate	120.8	115.5	54	*247*
7213	$C_7H_{14}O_2$	Propyl butyrate	143.7	Nonazeotrope		*255*
7214	$C_7H_{14}O_2$	Propyl isobutyrate	133.9	Nonazeotrope		*207*
7215	C_7H_{16}	Heptane	98.45	93.95	18	*207*
7216	$C_7H_{18}SiO$	Butoxytrimethylsilane	124.5	111.0	40–44	*338, 374**
7217	C_8H_8	Styrene	145.8	~116.5	79	*217*
		60 mm.	68	57	59	*26*
7218	C_8H_{10}	Ethylbenzene	136.15	114.8	~67	*217*
		60 mm.	60.5	53	37	*26*
7219	C_8H_{10}	Xylene	....	20	29.6	*329*
			....	40	38.4	
			....	60	47.5	
			....	80	56.5	
			....	115	73.0	
7220	C_8H_{10}	*m*-Xylene	139	116.5	71.5	*207*

No.	B-Component Formula	Name	B.P., ° C.	Azeotropic Data B.P., ° C.	Wt. % A	Ref.
A =	$C_4H_{10}O$	**Butyl Alcohol** (*continued*)	**117.8**			
7221	C_8H_{10}	*o*-Xylene	143.6	116.8	75	*221*
7222	C_8H_{10}	*p*-Xylene	138.3	115.7	68	*217*
7223	C_8H_{16}	1,3-Dimethylcyclohexane	120.7	108.5	43	*247*
7224	$C_8H_{16}O_2$	Butyl butyrate	166	Nonazeotrope, V-l.		*285*
7225	C_8H_{18}	2,5-Dimethylhexane	109.4	101.9	28	*247*
7226	C_8H_{18}	Octane	125.75	110.2	50	*247*
7227	$C_8H_{18}O$	Butyl ether	141.9	117.25	88	*307*
7228	$C_8H_{18}O$	Butyl ether	142.4	Nonazeotrope		*207*
7229	$C_8H_{18}O$	Isobutyl ether	122.3	113.5	48	*207*
7230	C_9H_8	Indene	182.6	Nonazeotrope		*255*
7231	C_9H_{12}	Cumene	152.8	Nonazeotrope		*207*
7232	C_9H_{12}	Mesitylene	164.6	Nonazeotrope		*221*
7233	C_9H_{12}	Propylbenzene	158.8	Nonazeotrope		*217*
7234	C_9H_{12}	Pseudocumene	168.2	Nonazeotrope		*255*
7235	$C_9H_{20}O_2$	Diisobutoxymethane	163.8	Nonazeotrope		*255*
7236	$C_9H_{20}O_2$	Dibutoxymethane	181.8	Nonazeotrope		*131*
7237	$C_{10}H_{14}$	Butylbenzene	183.1	Nonazeotrope		*255*
7238	$C_{10}H_{14}$	Cymene	176.7	Nonazeotrope		*217*
7239	$C_{10}H_{16}$	Camphene	159.6	117.73?	98	*254*
7240	$C_{10}H_{16}$	*d*-Limonene	177.8	Nonazeotrope		*217*
7241	$C_{10}H_{16}$	Nopinene	163.8	Nonazeotrope		*207*
7242	$C_{10}H_{16}$	α-Pinene	155.8	117.4	~88	*217*
7243	$C_{10}H_{16}$	Thymene	179.7	Nonazeotrope		*221*
7244	$C_{10}H_{22}$	Decane	173.3	Nonazeotrope		*255*
7245	$C_{10}H_{22}$	2,7-Dimethyloctane	160.2	Nonazeotrope		*217*
7246	$C_{10}H_{22}O_2$	1,1-Dibutoxyethane	187.8	Nonazeotrope, V-l.		*20**, *79*
A =	$C_4H_{10}O$	***sec*-Butyl Alcohol**	**99.5**			
7247	$C_4H_{10}S$	Ethyl sulfide	92.1	<89.0	<32	*246*
7248	C_5H_5N	Pyridine	115.4	Nonazeotrope		*255*
7249	$C_5H_{10}O$	3-Pentanone	102.05	98.0	58	*214*
7250	$C_5H_{10}O_2$	Butyl formate	106.8	98.0	68	*247*
7251	$C_5H_{10}O_2$	Ethyl propionate	99.15	95.7	47	*216*
7252	$C_5H_{10}O_2$	Isobutyl formate	98.2	94.7	40	*255*
7253	$C_5H_{10}O_2$	Methyl butyrate	102.65	<97.7	<59	*255*
7254	$C_5H_{10}O_2$	Methyl isobutyrate	92.5	<92.0	<23	*255*
7255	$C_5H_{10}O_2$	Propyl acetate	101.55	~96.5	~52	*243*
7256	$C_5H_{11}Cl$	1-Chloro-3-methylbutane	99.4	91.5	29	*250*
7257	$C_5H_{11}I$	1-Iodo-3-methylbutane	147.65	Nonazeotrope		*255*
7258	C_5H_{12}	2-Methylbutane	27.95	Nonazeotrope		*255*
7259	C_5H_{12}	Pentane	36.15	Nonazeotrope		*217*
7260	$C_5H_{12}O$	*tert*-Amyl alcohol	102.35	Nonazeotrope		*255*
7261	C_6H_5Cl	Chlorobenzene	131.75	Nonazeotrope		*255*
7262	$C_6H_5NO_2$	Nitrobenzene	210.75	Nonazeotrope		*234*
7263	C_6H_6	Benzene	80.2	78.5	15.4, V-l.	*217**, *295*
7264	C_6H_{10}	Cyclohexene	82.7	78.7	21	*217*
7265	C_6H_{12}	Cyclohexane	80.75	76.0	18	*221*
7266	C_6H_{12}	Methylcyclopentane	72.0	69.7	11.5	*247*
7267	$C_6H_{12}O$	Pinacolone	106.2	99.1	84	*232*
7268	$C_6H_{12}O_2$	*sec*-Butyl acetate	112.2	99.6	86.3	*75*
7269	$C_6H_{12}O$	Isobutyl acetate	117.4	Nonazeotrope		*255*
7270	$C_6H_{12}O$	Methyl isovalerate	116.5	Nonazeotrope		*255*
7271	C_6H_{14}	2,3-Dimethylbutane	58.0	<57.75	<8	*255*
7272	C_6H_{14}	Hexane	68.9	67.2	8	*217*
7273	$C_6H_{14}O$	*tert*-Amyl methyl ether	86.7	86.0	7	*105*
7274	$C_6H_{14}O$	*tert*-Butyl ethyl ether	73	Nonazeotrope		*105*
7275	$C_6H_{14}O$	Propyl ether	90.4	87.0	22	*256*
7276	C_7H_8	Toluene	110.7	95.3	55	*23*, *217**
7277	C_7H_{14}	Methylcyclohexane	100.8	89.9	41	*23*
7278	C_7H_{16}	Heptane	98.45	89	38	*217*
7279	$C_7H_{16}O$	*tert*-Amyl ethyl ether	101–2	94.5	39	*105*
7280	C_8H_8	Styrene, 60 mm.	68	45	96	*26*
7281	C_8H_{10}	Ethylbenzene	136.15	Nonazeotrope		*255*
7282	C_8H_{10}	Ethylbenzene, 60 mm.	60.5	44	84	*26*
7283	C_8H_{10}	*m*-Xylene	139.2	Nonazeotrope		*255*
7284	C_8H_{18}	2,5-Dimethylhexane	109.4	93.0	54	*247*

No.	Formula	B-Component Name	B.P., ° C.	Azeotropic Data B.P., ° C.	Wt. % A	Ref.
A =	**$C_4H_{10}O$**	***tert*-Butyl Alcohol**	**82.9**			
7285	$C_4H_{10}O$	Isobutyl alcohol	108	Nonazeotrope		*93*
7286	$C_4H_{10}S$	Ethyl sulfide	92.1	79.8	70	*246*
7287	C_5H_{10}	Cyclopentane	49.4	48.2	~7	*255*
7288	C_5H_{10}	2-Methyl-2-butene	37.15	Nonazeotrope		*243*
7289	$C_5H_{10}O$	3-Pentanone	102.05	Nonazeotrope		*232*
7290	$C_5H_{10}O_2$	Isobutyl formate	97.9	Nonazeotrope		*216*
7291	$C_5H_{10}O_2$	Methyl isobutyrate	92.3	82.2	....	*216*
7292	$C_5H_{10}O_2$	Propyl acetate	101.6	Nonazeotrope		*255*
7293	$C_5H_{11}Br$	1-Bromo-3-methylbutane	120.65	Nonazeotrope		*255*
7294	$C_5H_{11}Cl$	1-Chloro-3-methylbutane	99.4	<81.15	>59	*247*
7295	C_5H_{12}	2-Methylbutane	27.95	Nonazeotrope		*217*
7296	C_5H_{12}	*n*-Pentane	36.15	35.9	3	*255*
			....	Nonazeotrope		*217*
7297	C_6H_5F	Fluorobenzene	85.15	76.0	31	*225*
7298	C_6H_6	Benzene	80.2	73.95	36.6	*431*
7299	C_6H_8	1,3-Cyclohexadiene	80.8	73.4	38.5	*243*
7300	C_6H_{10}	Cyclohexene	82.7	73.2	40	*217*
7301	C_6H_{10}	Methylcyclopentene	75.85	69.5	30	*247*
7302	C_6H_{12}	Cyclohexane	80.75	71.3	37	*221*
7303	C_6H_{12}	Methylcyclopentane	72.0	66.6	26	*247*
7304	C_6H_{14}	2,3-Dimethylbutane	58.0	55.3	13	*247*
7305	C_6H_{14}	Hexane	68.85	63.7	22	*221*
7306	$C_6H_{14}O$	Propyl ether	90.4	79.0	52	*256*
7307	C_7H_8	Toluene	110.7	Nonazeotrope		*23*
7308	C_7H_{14}	Methylcyclohexane	100.8	78.8	66	*23*
7309	C_7H_{16}	Heptane	98.45	78	62	*217*
7310	C_8H_8	Styrene, 60 mm.	68	Nonazeotrope		*26*
7311	C_8H_{10}	Ethylbenzene, 60 mm.	60.5	28	95	*26*
7312	C_8H_{10}	*p*-Xylene	138.45	Nonazeotrope		*255*
7313	C_8H_{16}	1,3-Dimethylcyclohexane	120.7	<82.2	>90	*255*
7314	C_8H_{18}	2,5-Dimethylhexane	109.2	81.5	77	*225*
7315	$C_{10}H_{16}$	α-Pinene	155.8	Nonazeotrope		*217*
A =	**$C_4H_{10}O$**	**Ethyl Ether**	**34.6**			
7316	$C_4H_{10}O$	Methyl propyl ether	38.9	Nonazeotrope		*243*
7317	$C_4H_{11}N$	Diethylamine	55.9	Nonazeotrope		*231*
7318	C_5H_8	Isoprene	34.3	33.2	48	*238*
7319	C_5H_8	3-Methyl-1,2-butadiene	40.8	Nonazeotrope		*243*
7320	C_5H_{10}	Cyclopentane	49.3	Nonazeotrope		*238*
7321	C_5H_{10}	2-Methyl-2-butene	37.1	34.2	85	*238*
7322	C_5H_{10}	3-Methyl-1-butene	20.6	Nonazeotrope		*238*
7323	C_5H_{12}	2-Methylbutane	27.95	Nonazeotrope		*243*
7324	C_5H_{12}	Pentane	36.15	33.4	68	*238*
7325	$C_6H_5NO_2$	Nitrobenzene	210.75	Nonazeotrope		*234*
7326	C_6H_6	Benzene	80.2	Nonazeotrope		*238*
7327	C_6H_{10}	Biallyl	60.1	Nonazeotrope		*238*
7328	C_6H_{14}	2,3-Dimethylbutane	58.0	Nonazeotrope		*238*
7329	C_6H_{14}	Hexane	68.85	Nonazeotrope		*238*
7330	$C_6H_{14}O$	Hexyl alcohol	155.8	Nonazeotrope		*93*
7331	$C_6H_{15}N$	Triethylamine	89.35	Nonazeotrope		*231*
7332	C_7H_8	Toluene	110.75	Nonazeotrope		*238*
A =	**$C_4H_{10}O$**	**Isobutyl Alcohol**	**108.0**			
7333	$C_4H_{10}O_2$	2-Ethoxyethanol	135.3	Nonazeotrope		*255*
7334	C_5H_5N	Pyridine	115.4	Nonazeotrope		*233*
7335	C_5H_7N	*N*-Methylpyrrol	112.8	<107.5	....	*255*
7336	$C_5H_9ClO_2$	Propyl chloroacetate	163.5	Nonazeotrope		*255*
7337	C_5H_{10}	Cyclopentane	49.4	Nonazeotrope		*255*
7338	$C_5H_{10}O$	3-Methyl-2-butanone	95.4	Nonazeotrope		*232*
7339	$C_5H_{10}O$	2-Pentanone	102.35	101.8	19	*232*
7340	$C_5H_{10}O$	3-Pentanone	102.05	101.7	20	*232*
7341	$C_5H_{10}O_2$	Butyl formate	106.8	103.0	40	*247*
7342	$C_5H_{10}O_2$	Ethyl propionate	99.1	<98.9	13	*255*
7343	$C_5H_{10}O_2$	Isobutyl formate	98.3	Nonazeotrope		*427*
			98.4	97.8	20.6	*150,216**

No.	Formula	B-Component Name	B.P., ° C.	Azeotropic Data B.P., ° C.	Wt. % A	Ref.
A =	$C_4H_{10}O$	**Isobutyl Alcohol** (*continued*)	**108.0**			
7344	$C_5H_{10}O_2$	Isopropyl acetate	89.5	Nonazeotrope		*255*
7345	$C_5H_{10}O_2$	Methyl butyrate	102.65	101.3	25	*216*
7346	$C_5H_{10}O_2$	Methyl isobutyrate	92.3	Nonazeotrope		*216*
7347	$C_5H_{10}O_2$	Propyl acetate	101.6	101.0	17	*252*
7348	$C_5H_{10}O_3$	Ethyl carbonate	125.9	Nonazeotrope		*216*
7349	$C_5H_{10}O_3$	2-Methoxyethyl acetate	144.6	Nonazeotrope		*255*
7350	$C_5H_{11}Br$	1-Bromo-3-methylbutane	118.1	103.4	63.6	*162*
				B.p. curve		*235**
7351	$C_5H_{11}Cl$	1-Chloro-3-methylbutane	99.8	94.5	22	*253*
7352	$C_5H_{11}I$	1-Iodo-3-methylbutane	146.5	Nonazeotrope, b.p. curve		*162*
7353	C_5H_{12}	*p*-Pentane	36.15	Nonazeotrope		*255*
7354	$C_5H_{12}O$	Isoamyl alcohol	131.9	Nonazeotrope		*255*
7355	$C_5H_{12}O_2$	Diethoxymethane	87.95	Nonazeotrope		*207*
7356	C_6H_5Br	Bromobenzene	156.1	Nonazeotrope		*212*
7357	C_6H_5Cl	Chlorobenzene	132.0	107.1	63	*212*
7358	C_6H_5F	Fluorobenzene	84.9	84.0	9	*255*
7359	C_6H_6	Benzene	80.2	79.84	9.3	*431*
			....	Nonazeotrope		*334*
7360	C_6H_8	1,3-Cyclohexadiene	80.8	79.35	12	*243*
7361	C_6H_{10}	Cyclohexene	82.7	80.5	14.2	*221*
7362	$C_6H_{10}S$	Allyl sulfide	139.35	Nonazeotrope		*246*
7363	$C_6H_{11}ClO_2$	Isobutylchloro acetate	97.8	Nonazeotrope		*58*
7364	C_6H_{12}	Cyclohexane	80.75	78.1	14	*221*
7365	C_6H_{12}	Methylcyclopentane	72.0	71.0	5	*255*
7366	$C_6H_{12}O$	2-Hexanone	127.2	Nonazeotrope		*232*
7367	$C_6H_{12}O$	3-Hexanone	123.3	Nonazeotrope		*232*
7368	$C_6H_{12}O$	Isobutyl vinyl ether	83.0	82.7	6.2	*362*
7369	$C_6H_{12}O$	4-Methyl-2-pentanone	116.05	107.85	91	*232*
7370	$C_6H_{12}O$	Pinacolone	106.2	<105.5	<42	*228*
7371	$C_6H_{12}O_2$	Butyl acetate	126.0	Nonazeotrope		*207*
7372	$C_6H_{12}O_2$	Ethyl butyrate	120.6	Nonazeotrope, b.p. curve		*163*
7373	$C_6H_{12}O_2$	Ethyl isobutyrate	110.1	105.5	52	*243*
7374	$C_6H_{12}O_2$	Isoamyl formate	123.8	Nonazeotrope		*216*
7375	$C_6H_{12}O_2$	Isobutyl acetate	117.2	107.4	55	*150*
			116.3	Nonazeotrope, b.p. curve		*163, 252**
7376	$C_6H_{12}O_2$	Methyl isovalerate	116.3	~107.5	~90	*243*
7377	$C_6H_{12}O_2$	Propyl propionate	123.0	Nonazeotrope		*255*
7378	$C_6H_{12}O_3$	2-Ethoxyethyl acetate	156.8	Nonazeotrope		*255*
7379	$C_6H_{13}Br$	1-Bromohexane	156.5	Nonazeotrope		*255*
7380	C_6H_{14}	Hexane	68.9	68.3	2.5	*217*
7381	$C_6H_{14}O$	Ethyl isobutyl ether	79	78/743	18.43	*34*
7382	$C_6H_{14}O$	Propyl ether	90.55	89.5	10	*236*
7383	$C_6H_{14}O_2$	Acetal	103.55	98.2	20	*253*
7384	$C_6H_{14}S$	Isopropyl sulfide	100.5	105.8	73	*235*
7385	$C_6H_{14}S$	Propyl sulfide	141.5	Nonazeotrope		*246*
7386	$C_6H_{15}BO_3$	Ethyl borate	118.6	Nonazeotrope		*210*
7387	C_7H_8	Toluene	110.7	101.2	45	*23, 334*, 436**
7388	C_7H_{14}	Methylcyclohexane	100.8	92.6	32	*23*
7389	$C_7H_{14}O_2$	Ethyl isovalerate	134.7	Nonazeotrope		*255*
7390	$C_7H_{14}O_2$	Isoamyl acetate	137.5	Nonazeotrope, b.p. curve		*163*
7391	$C_7H_{14}O_2$	Isobutyl propionate	137.5	Nonazeotrope		*255*
7392	$C_7H_{14}O_2$	Isopropyl isobutyrate	120.8	Nonazeotrope		*255*
7393	$C_7H_{14}O_2$	Propyl isobutyrate	134.0	Nonazeotrope		*255*
7394	C_7H_{16}	Heptane	98.45	90.8	27	*217*
7395	$C_7H_{16}O_2$	Dipropoxymethane	137.2	Nonazeotrope		*255*
7296	C_8H_8	Styrene	145.8	Nonazeotrope		*217*
		60 mm.	68	49	75	*26*
7397	C_8H_{10}	Ethylbenzene	136.15	107.2	80	*221*
		60 mm.	60.5	48	61	*26*
7398	C_8H_{10}	*m*-Xylene	139	107.78	85.5	*207*
			....	Nonazeotrope		*334*
			143.6	Nonazeotrope		*217*
7399	C_8H_{10}	*o*-Xylene	138.2	~107.5	~83	*221*
7400	C_8H_{10}	*p*-Xylene	120.7	102.2	56	*255*
7401	C_8H_{16}	1,3-Dimethylcyclohexane				

No.	B-Component Formula	Name	B.P., ° C.	Azeotropic Data B.P., ° C.	Wt. % A	Ref.
A =	$C_4H_{10}O$	**Isobutyl Alcohol** (*continued*)	**108.0**			
7402	C_8H_{18}	2,5-Dimethylhexane	109.2	98.7	42	*225*
7403	C_8H_{18}	Octane	125.8	104	....	*243*
7404	C_8H_{18}	2,2,4-Trimethylpentane	99.3	92.0	27	*255*
7405	$C_8H_{18}O$	Butyl ether	142.4	Nonazeotrope		*255*
7406	$C_8H_{18}O$	Isobutyl ether	122.3	107.8?	....	*243*
7407	C_9H_{12}	Cumene	152.8	Nonazeotrope		*255*
7408	C_9H_{12}	Mesitylene	164.6	Nonazeotrope		*255*
7409	C_9H_{12}	Propylbenzene	158.8	Nonazeotrope		*217*
7410	$C_9H_{20}O_2$	Diisobutoxymethane	163.8	Nonazeotrope		*131*
7411	$C_{10}H_{14}$	Cymene	176.7	Nonazeotrope		*255*
7412	$C_{10}H_{16}$	Camphene	159.6	Nonazeotrope		*217*
7413	$C_{10}H_{16}$	*d*-Limonene	177.8	Nonazeotrope		*221*
7414	$C_{10}H_{16}$	Nopinene	163.8	Nonazeotrope		*255*
7415	$C_{10}H_{16}$	α-Pinene	155.8	107.95	>99	*208*
7416	$C_{10}H_{16}$	Thymene	179.7	Nonazeotrope		*217*
7417	$C_{10}H_{22}$	2,7-Dimethyloctane	160.1	Nonazeotrope		*255*
7418	$C_{10}H_{22}O_2$	Acetaldehyde diisobutyl acetal	171.3	Nonazeotrope		*20*
A =	$C_4H_{10}O$	**Methyl Propyl Ether**	**38.95**			
7419	$C_4H_{11}N$	Diethylamine	55.9	Nonazeotrope		*231*
7420	C_5H_8	Isoprene	34.3	Nonazeotrope		*238*
7421	C_5H_{10}	2-Methyl-2-butene	37.15	36.3	25	*238*
7422	C_5H_{12}	Pentane	36.2	35.3	22	*238*
A =	$C_4H_{10}O_2$	**Acetaldehyde Dimethyl Acetal**	**64.3**			
7423	$C_4H_{11}N$	Diethylamine	55.9	Nonazeotrope		*231*
7424	C_6H_6	Benzene	80.15	Nonazeotrope		*238*
7425	C_6H_{12}	Methylcyclopentane	72.0	64.0	83	*238*
7426	C_6H_{14}	Hexane	68.8	64.0	70	*238*
A =	$C_4H_{10}O_2$	***l*-2,3-Butanediol**	**183–184**			
7427	$C_8H_{14}O_4$	*meso*-2,3-Butanediol diacetate	190–193	177.6	60.5, V-l.	*293*
		500 mm.	....	164.6	55.5, V-l.	*293*
		350 mm.	....	153.0	49.9, V-l.	*293*
		250 mm.	....	143.5	46.6, V-l.	*293*
A =	$C_4H_{10}O_2$	**2-Ethoxyethanol**	**135.3**			
7428	$C_5H_4O_2$	2-Furaldehyde	161.45	Nonazeotrope		*207*
7429	C_5H_5N	Pyridine	115.4	Nonazeotrope		*233*
7430	C_5H_7N	2-Methylpyrrol	147.5	Nonazeotrope		*255*
7431	C_5H_8O	Cyclopentanone	130.65	<130.2	<27	*232*
7432	C_5H_9N	Valeronitrile	141.3	<135.0	....	*255*
7433	$C_5H_{10}O$	Cyclopentanol	140.85	Nonazeotrope		*206*
7434	$C_5H_{10}O_3$	Ethyl lactate	154.1	Nonazeotrope		*255*
7435	$C_5H_{10}O_3$	2-Methoxyethyl acetate	144.6	Nonazeotrope		*236*
7436	$C_5H_{11}Br$	1-Bromo-3-methylbutane	120.65	118.0	~8	*255*
7437	$C_5H_{11}I$	1-Iodo-3-methylbutane	147.65	132.0	60?	*206*
7438	$C_5H_{11}NO_3$	Isoamyl nitrate	149.75	133.7	72	*207*
7439	$C_5H_{12}O$	Amyl alcohol	138.2	Nonazeotrope		*206*
7440	$C_5H_{12}O$	Isoamyl alcohol	131.9	Nonazeotrope		*207*
7441	$C_5H_{12}O$	2-Pentanol	119.8	Nonazeotrope		*255*
7442	C_6H_5Br	Bromobenzene	156.1	135.22	86	*236*
7443	C_6H_5Cl	Chlorobenzene	131.75	127.15	32	*207*
7444	C_6H_5I	Iodobenzene	188.45	Nonazeotrope		*255*
7445	C_6H_6	Benzene	80.15	Nonazeotrope		*255*
7446	C_6H_6O	Phenol	182.2	Nonazeotrope		*236*
7447	C_6H_{10}	Cyclohexene	82.75	Nonazeotrope		*206*
7448	$C_6H_{10}O$	Mesityl oxide	129.45	128.9	18	*207*
7449	$C_6H_{11}N$	Capronitrile	163.9	Nonazeotrope		*255*
7450	C_6H_{12}	Cyclohexane	80.75	Nonazeotrope		*255*
7451	$C_6H_{12}O$	3-Hexanone	123.3	Nonazeotrope		*232*
7452	$C_6H_{12}O$	4-Methyl-2-pentanone	116.05	Nonazeotrope		*232*
7453	$C_6H_{12}O_2$	Butyl acetate	124.8	125.8	35.7	*62*
7454	$C_6H_{12}O_2$	Ethyl butyrate	121.5	Nonazeotrope		*255*
7455	$C_6H_{12}O_2$	Isoamyl formate	123.8	Nonazeotrope		*236*

No	B-Component Formula	Name	B.P., ° C.	Azeotropic Data B.P., ° C.	Wt. % A	Ref.
A =	$C_4H_{10}O_2$	**2-Ethoxyethanol** (*continued*)	**135.3**			
7456	$C_6H_{12}O_2$	Isobutyl acetate	117.4	Nonazeotrope		*255*
7457	$C_6H_{12}O_2$	Methyl isovalerate	116.5	Nonazeotrope		*255*
7458	$C_6H_{12}O_2$	Propyl propionate	123.0	Nonazeotrope		*206*
7459	$C_6H_{12}O_3$	2-Ethoxyethyl acetate	156.8	Nonazeotrope		*236*
7460	$C_6H_{12}O_3$	Paraldehyde	124.35	123.8	14	*435*
7461	$C_6H_{14}O_2$	1,2-Diethoxyethane	123	121.0	3.1	*62*
7462	$C_6H_{14}S$	Propyl sulfide	140.8	130.2	52	*235*
7463	$C_6H_{15}NO$	2-Diethylaminoethanol	162.2	Nonazeotrope		*232*
7464	C_7H_7Cl	*o*-Chlorotoluene	159.2	Nonazeotrope		*206*
7465	C_7H_7Cl	*p*-Chlorotoluene	162.4	Nonazeotrope		*236*
7466	C_7H_8	Toluene	110.75	110.15	10.8	*236*
7467	C_7H_8O	Anisole	153.85	135.25	94	*236*
7468	C_7H_{14}	Methylcyclohexane	101.15	98.6	15	*206*
7469	$C_7H_{14}O$	5-Methyl-2-hexanone	144.2	Nonazeotrope		*232*
7470	$C_7H_{14}O_2$	Amyl acetate	148.8	Nonazeotrope		*255*
7471	$C_7H_{14}O_2$	Ethyl isovalerate	134.7	130.5	42	*206*
7472	$C_7H_{14}O_2$	Isoamyl acetate	142.1	133.8	70	*206*
7473	$C_7H_{14}O_2$	Isobutyl propionate	137.5	131.5	35	*247*
7474	$C_7H_{14}O_2$	Methyl caproate	149.8	Nonazeotrope		*255*
7475	$C_7H_{14}O_2$	Propyl butyrate	143.7	133.5	72	*236*
7476	$C_7H_{14}O_3$	1,3-Butanediol methyl ether acetate	171.75	Nonazeotrope		*255*
7477	C_7H_{16}	Heptane	98.4	96.5	14	*236*
7478	C_8H_8	Styrene	145.8	130.0	55	*255, 298**
7479	C_8H_{10}	Ethylbenzene	136.15	127.8	48	*206, 298**
7480	C_8H_{10}	*m*-Xylene	139.2	128.85	51	*207*
7481	C_8H_{10}	*o*-Xylene	144.3	130.8	55	*206*
7482	C_8H_{10}	*p*-Xylene	138.45	128.6	50	*236*
7483	$C_8H_{10}O$	Benzyl methyl ether	167.8	Nonazeotrope		*206*
7484	$C_8H_{10}O$	*p*-Methylanisole	177.05	Nonazeotrope		*255*
7485	$C_8H_{10}O$	Phenetole	170.45	Nonazeotrope		*255*
7486	C_8H_{16}	1,3-Dimethylcyclohexane	120.7	114.0	30	*255, 383**
7487	C_8H_{16}	Ethylcyclohexane	131.8	....	37	*383*
7488	$C_8H_{16}O_2$	Propyl isovalerate	155.7	Nonazeotrope		*255*
7489	C_8H_{18}	2,5-Dimethylhexane	109.4	....	~16	*383*
			109.4	105.0	22.5	*206*
7490	C_8H_{18}	3,3-Dimethylhexane	111.9	....	~17	*383*
7491	C_8H_{18}	3-Ethyl-3-methylpentane	....	....	~24	*383*
7492	C_8H_{18}	*n*-Octane	125.75	116.0	38	*250*
			125.75	....	~28	*383*
7493	$C_8H_{18}O$	Butyl ether	141	127.0	50	*62*
7494	$C_8H_{18}O$	Isobutyl ether	122.3	119.0	33	*206*
7495	C_9H_8	Indene	182.8	Nonazeotrope		*255*
7496	C_9H_{12}	Cumene	152.8	133.2	67	*207*
7497	C_9H_{12}	*o*-Ethyltoluene	....	....	~92	*383*
7498	C_9H_{12}	Mesitylene	164.6	Nonazeotrope		*255*
7499	C_9H_{12}	Propylbenzene	159.3	134.6	80	*206*
			....	....	~77	*383*
7500	C_9H_{12}	Pseudocumene	168.2	Nonazeotrope		*255*
7501	C_9H_{20}	3,3-Diethylpentane	....	....	~45	*383*
7502	C_9H_{20}	*n*-Nonane	150.7	....	~51	*383*
7503	C_9H_{20}	2,2,3,3-Tetramethylpentane	....	....	~39	*383*
7504	C_9H_{20}	2,2,4,4-Tetramethylpentane	....	....	~24	*383*
7505	C_9H_{20}	2,3,3,4-Tetramethylpentane	....	....	~42	*383*
7506	C_9H_{20}	2,4,4-Trimethylhexane	....	....	~30	*383*
7507	$C_{10}H_{14}$	Cymene	176.7	Nonazeotrope		*236*
7508	$C_{10}H_{16}$	Camphene	159.6	131.0	65	*206*
7509	$C_{10}H_{16}$	Nopinene	163.8	<133.0	....	*255*
7510	$C_{10}H_{16}$	α-Pinene	155.8	<131.0	57	*255*
7511	$C_{10}H_{16}$	α-Terpinene	173.4	<135.0	<87	*255*
7512	$C_{10}H_{18}O$	Cineol	176.35	Nonazeotrope		*255*
7513	$C_{10}H_{22}$	2,7-Dimethyloctane	160.2	130.8	63	*236*
7514	$C_{10}H_{22}O$	Isoamyl ether	173.2	Nonazeotrope		*255*
A =	$C_4H_{10}O_2$	**1-Methoxy-2-propanol**	**118**			
7515	C_7H_8	Toluene	110.7	106.5	30	*93*

No.	B-Component			Azeotropic Data		Ref.
	Formula	Name	B.P., ° C.	B.P., ° C.	Wt. % A	
A =	**$C_4H_{10}O_3$**	**Diethylene Glycol**	**245.5**			
7516	$C_6H_4Br_2$	*p*-Dibromobenzene	220.25	212.85	13	*207*
7517	$C_6H_4ClNO_2$	*m*-Chloronitrobenzene	235.5	228.2	32	*234*
7518	$C_6H_4ClNO_2$	*o*-Chloronitrobenzene	246.0	233.5	41	*234*
7519	$C_6H_4ClNO_2$	*p*-Chloronitrobenzene	239.1	229.5	34	*207*
7520	$C_6H_5NO_2$	Nitrobenzene	210.75	210.0	10	*207*
7521	$C_6H_5NO_3$	*o*-Nitrophenol	217.2	216.0	10.5	*207*
7522	$C_6H_6O_2$	Pyrocatechol	245.9	259.5	46	*250*
7523	$C_6H_8O_4$	Methyl fumarate	193.25	Nonazeotrope		*206*
7524	$C_6H_8O_4$	Methyl maleate	204.05	Nonazeotrope		*206*
7525	C_7H_7BrO	*o*-Bromoanisole	217.7	211.0	25	*255*
7526	$C_7H_7NO_2$	*m*-Nitrotoluene	230.8	224.2	25	*234*
7527	$C_7H_7NO_2$	*o*-Nitrotoluene	221.75	218.2	17.5	*207*
7528	$C_7H_7NO_2$	*p*-Nitrotoluene	238.9	228.75	35	*207*
7529	C_7H_8O	Benzyl alcohol	205.25	Nonazeotrope		*206*
7530	C_7H_8O	*m*-Cresol	202.4	Nonazeotrope, V-l.		*292*
7531	C_7H_8O	*p*-Cresol	202.0	Nonazeotrope, V-l.		*292*
7532	$C_7H_{12}O_4$	Ethyl malonate	199.35	Reacts		*206*
7533	$C_7H_{16}O_4$	2-[2-(2-Methoxyethoxy)ethoxy]-ethanol	245.25	245.0	22	*207*
7534	C_8H_8O	Acetophenone	202.0	Nonazeotrope		*232*
7535	$C_8H_8O_2$	Anisaldehyde	249.5	<244	....	*255*
7536	$C_8H_8O_2$	Benzyl formate	202.3	Nonazeotrope		*206*
7537	$C_8H_8O_2$	Methyl benzoate	199.4	Nonazeotrope		*206*
7538	$C_8H_8O_2$	Phenyl acetate	195.7	Nonazeotrope		*255*
7539	$C_8H_8O_3$	Methyl salicylate	222.95	220.55	16	*207*
7540	C_8H_9BrO	*p*-Bromophenetole	234.2	222.0	32	*255*
7541	$C_8H_{10}O$	Phenethyl alcohol	219.4	Nonazeotrope		*206*
7542	$C_8H_{10}O$	3,4-Xylenol	226.8	Nonazeotrope		*236*
7543	$C_8H_{10}O_2$	2-Phenoxyethanol	245.2	<244.5	....	*255*
7544	$C_8H_{11}NO$	*o*-Phenetidine	232.5	<225.0	<18	*255*
7545	$C_8H_{11}NO$	*p*-Phenetidine	249.9	<232.0	>52	*255*
7546	$C_8H_{12}O_4$	Ethyl fumarate	217.85	217.1	10	*207*
7547	$C_8H_{12}O_4$	Ethyl maleate	223.3	222.65	10.0	*207*
7548	$C_8H_{14}O_4$	Ethyl succinate	217.25	Reacts		*206*
7549	C_9H_7N	Quinoline	237.3	233.6	29	*207*
7550	$C_9H_{10}O_2$	Benzyl acetate	215.0	214.85	7	*207*
7551	$C_9H_{10}O_2$	Ethyl benzoate	212.5	211.65	10	*207*
7552	$C_9H_{10}O_3$	Ethyl salicylate	233.8	225.15	30	*250*
7553	$C_9H_{12}O$	3-Phenylpropanol	235.6	Nonazeotrope		*255*
7554	$C_9H_{12}O$	Phenyl propyl ether	190.5	Nonazeotrope		*206*
7555	$C_{10}H_7Br$	1-Bromonaphthalene	281.2	240.8	59.5	*207*
7556	$C_{10}H_7Cl$	1-Chloronaphthalene	262.7	234.1	47	*207*
7557	$C_{10}H_8$	Naphthalene	218.0	212.6	22.0	*207*
7558	$C_{10}H_8O$	1-Naphthol	288.5	Nonazeotrope		*236*
7559	$C_{10}H_9N$	Quinaldine	246.5	<241.0	....	*255*
7560	$C_{10}H_{10}O_2$	Isosafrol	252.0	233.5	46	*206*
7561	$C_{10}H_{10}O_2$	Methyl cinnamate	261.9	240.0	63	*207*
7562	$C_{10}H_{10}O_2$	Safrole	235.9	225.5	33	*236*
7563	$C_{10}H_{10}O_4$	Methyl phthalate	283.7	245.4	96.3	*236*
7564	$C_{10}H_{12}O$	Anethole	235.7	210.0	20	*247*
7565	$C_{10}H_{12}O_2$	Ethyl α-toluate	228.75	224.0	20	*247*
7566	$C_{10}H_{12}O_2$	Propyl benzoate	230.85	222.7	26	*236*
7567	$C_{10}H_{14}$	Butylbenzene	183.1	Nonazeotrope		*236*
7568	$C_{10}H_{14}$	Cymene	176.7	Nonazeotrope		*255*
7569	$C_{10}H_{14}O$	Carvacrol	237.85	236.0	27	*206*
7570	$C_{10}H_{14}O$	Thymol	232.9	232.25	13	*207*
7571	$C_{10}H_{16}O$	Camphor	209.1	Nonazeotrope		*232*
7572	$C_{10}H_{18}O$	α-Terpineol	218.85	217.45	13.5	*207*
7573	$C_{10}H_{20}O$	Citronellol	224.4	Nonazeotrope		*255*
7574	$C_{11}H_{10}$	1-Methylnaphthalene	244.6	227.0	45	*206*
7575	$C_{11}H_{10}$	2-Methylnaphthalene	241.15	225.45	39	*236*
7576	$C_{11}H_{12}O_2$	Ethyl cinnamate	272.0	244.5	85?	*206*
7577	$C_{11}H_{14}O_2$	1-Allyl-3,4-dimethoxybenzene	254.7	235.0	47	*206*
7578	$C_{11}H_{14}O_2$	Butyl benzoate	249.0	232.2	43	*236*
7579	$C_{11}H_{14}O_2$	1,2-Dimethoxy-4-propenylbenzene	270.5	238.8	60	*247*
7580	$C_{11}H_{14}O_2$	Isobutyl benzoate	241.9	228.65	37	*236*

No.	Formula	B-Component Name	B.P., ° C.	Azeotropic Data B.P., ° C.	Wt. % A	Ref.
A =	**$C_4H_{10}O_3$**	**Diethylene Glycol (*continued*)**	**245.5**			
7581	$C_{11}H_{16}O$	Methyl thymyl ether	216.5	210.5	~19	*255*
7582	$C_{11}H_{20}O$	Isobornyl methyl ether	192.4	<191.0	<9	*255*
7583	$C_{11}H_{20}O$	Methyl α-terpineol ether	216.2	210.5	20	*247*
7584	$C_{12}H_{10}$	Acenaphthene	277.9	239.6	62	*207*
7585	$C_{12}H_{10}$	Biphenyl	256.1	232.65	48	*207*
7586	$C_{12}H_{10}O$	Phenyl ether	259.0	234.4	49.5	*207*
7587	$C_{12}H_{14}O_4$	Ethyl phthalate	297.5	Nonazeotrope		*206*
7588	$C_{12}H_{16}O_2$	Isoamyl benzoate	262.0	236.55	52.5	*207*
7589	$C_{12}H_{16}O_3$	Isoamyl salicylate	277.5	Nonazeotrope		*206*
7590	$C_{12}H_{18}$	1,3,5-Triethylbenzene	215.5	210.0	22	*206*
7591	$C_{12}H_{20}O_2$	Bornyl acetate	227.6	223.0	18	*247*
7592	$C_{12}H_{22}O_4$	Isoamyl oxalate	268.0	Reacts		*206*
7593	$C_{13}H_{10}$	Fluorene	295.0	243.0	80	*206*
7594	$C_{13}H_{12}$	Diphenylmethane	265.4	236.0	52	*236*
7595	$C_{13}H_{12}O$	Benzyl phenyl ether	286.5	241.5	80	*255*
7596	$C_{14}H_{14}$	1,2-Diphenylethane	284.5	241.0	66	*206*
7597	$C_{14}H_{14}O$	Benzyl ether	297	<243.8	>87	*255*
A =	**$C_4H_{10}S$**	**1-Butanethiol**	**97.8**			
7598	$C_4H_{10}S$	Ethyl sulfide	92.1	Nonazeotrope		*255*
7599	C_5H_5N	Pyridine	115.4	Nonazeotrope		*255*
7600	C_6H_6	Benzene	80.15	Nonazeotrope		*246*
7601	C_6H_{12}	Cyclohexane	80.75	Nonazeotrope		*246*
7602	C_7H_8	Toluene	110.623	Nonazeotrope		*91*
7603	C_7H_{14}	*cis*-1,2-Dimethylcyclopentane	99.53	96.35	48.0	*91*
7604	C_7H_{14}	Ethylcyclopentane	103.45	97.76	72.15	*91*
7605	C_7H_{14}	*trans*-1,3-Dimethylcyclopentane	90.77	90.54	12.7	*91*
7606	C_7H_{14}	Methylcyclohexane	100.934	97.00	58.2	*91*
7607	C_7H_{16}	2,3-Dimethylpentane	89.79	59.53	15.1	*91*
7608	C_7H_{16}	Heptane	98.428	95.45	49.4	*91*
7609	C_7H_{16}	2-Methylhexane	90.05	89.74	15.4	*91*
7610	C_7H_{16}	3-Methylhexane	91.95	91.20	22.8	*91*
7611	C_8H_{18}	2,2-Dimethylhexane	106.843	98.01	78.8	*91*
7612	C_8H_{18}	2,5-Dimethylhexane	109.106	98.22	88.0	*91*
7613	C_8H_{18}	3,3-Dimethylhexane	111.927	98.56	97.6	*91*
7614	C_8H_{18}	2,2,4-Trimethylpentane	99.237	95.50	50.3	*91*
A =	**$C_4H_{10}S$**	**2-Butanethiol**	**85.15**			
7615	C_6H_6	Benzene	80.103	Nonazeotrope		*91*
7616	C_6H_{12}	Cyclohexane	80.738	79.97	25.5	*91*
7617	C_6H_{12}	Methylcyclopentane	71.812	Nonazeotrope		*91*
7618	C_7H_{14}	1,1-Dimethylcyclopentane	87.84	83.90	64.1	*91*
7619	C_7H_{14}	*trans*-1,3-Dimethylcyclopentane	90.77	84.75	78.1	*91*
7620	C_7H_{16}	2,2-Dimethylpentane	79.205	78.60	23.1	*91*
7621	C_7H_{16}	2,3-Dimethylpentane	69.79	84.16	68.6	*91*
7622	C_7H_{16}	2,4-Dimethylpentane	80.51	79.55	28.1	*91*
7623	C_7H_{16}	Heptane	98.428	Nonazeotrope		*91*
7624	C_7H_{16}	2-Methylhexane	90.05	84.30	72.1	*91*
7625	C_7H_{16}	3-Methylhexane	91.95	84.70	80.8	*91*
A =	**$C_4H_{10}S$**	**Ethyl Sulfide**	**92.1**			
7626	$C_4H_{10}S$	2-Methyl-1-propanethiol	87.8	87.0	85	*255*
7627	C_5H_5N	Pyridine	115.4	Nonazeotrope		*246*
7628	C_5H_7N	1-Methylpyrrol	112.8	Nonazeotrope		*255*
7629	$C_5H_{10}O$	Isovaleraldehyde	92.1	88.5	53	*246*
7630	$C_5H_{10}O$	3-Methyl-2-butanone	95.4	78.0	70	*246*
7631	$C_5H_{10}O$	3-Pentanone	102.05	Nonazeotrope		*246*
7632	$C_5H_{10}O_2$	Methyl butyrate	102.65	Nonazeotrope		*228*
7633	$C_5H_{10}O_2$	Methyl isobutyrate	92.5	<91.7	>56	*246*
7634	$C_5H_{10}O_2$	Propyl acetate	101.6	Nonazeotrope		*228*
7635	$C_5H_{12}O$	Isoamyl alcohol	131.9	Nonazeotrope		*207*
7636	$C_5H_{12}O_2$	Diethoxymethane	87.95	85.9	35	*246*
7637	C_6H_6	Benzene	80.2	Nonazeotrope		*211*
7638	C_6H_{12}	Cyclohexane	80.75	Nonazeotrope		*211*
7639	$C_6H_{14}O$	Isopropyl ether	68.3	Nonazeotrope		*246*
7640	$C_6H_{14}O$	Propyl ether	90.1	<89.5	>25	*246*

No.	Formula	B-Component Name	B.P., ° C.	Azeotropic Data B.P., ° C.	Wt. % A	Ref.
A =	**$C_4H_{10}S$**	**Ethyl Sulfide (*continued*)**	**92.1**			
7641	$C_6H_{14}O_2$	Acetal	104.5	Nonazeotrope		*243*
7642	C_7H_{14}	Methylcyclohexane	101.1	Nonazeotrope		*211*
7643	C_7H_{16}	Heptane	98.4	<91.8	>78	*246*
A =	**$C_4H_{10}S$**	**2-Methyl-1-propanethiol**	**88.72**			
7644	C_6H_6	Benzene	80.103	Nonazeotrope		*91*
7645	C_6H_8	1,3-Cyclohexadiene	80.8	Reacts		*243*
7646	C_6H_8	1,4-Cyclohexadiene	85.6	Reacts		*243*
7647	C_6H_{10}	Cyclohexene	82.75	Reacts		*243*
7648	C_6H_{12}	Cyclohexane	80.738	80.70	11.7	*91*
7649	C_6H_{14}	Hexane	68.8	Nonazeotrope		*255*
7650	C_7H_{14}	1,1-Dimethylcyclopentane	87.84	85.69	44.25	*91*
7651	C_7H_{14}	*cis*-1,2-Dimethylcyclopentane	99.53	88.52	98.6	*91*
7652	C_7H_{14}	*trans*-1,3-Dimethylcyclopentane	90.77	87.02	58.6	*91*
7653	C_7H_{14}	Ethylcyclopentane	103.46	Nonazeotrope		*91*
7654	C_7H_{14}	Methylcyclohexane	100.934	88.55	98.9	*91*
7655	C_7H_{16}	2,2-Dimethylpentane	79.205	79.12	10.3	*91*
7656	C_7H_{16}	2,3-Dimethylpentane	89.79	86.28	54.1	*91*
7657	C_7H_{16}	2,4-Dimethylpentane	80.51	80.28	14.1	*91*
7658	C_7H_{16}	Heptane	98.428	88.50	91.3	*91*
7659	C_7H_{16}	3-Methylhexane	91.95	87.16	62.8	*91*
7660	C_7H_{16}	2,2,3-Trimethylbutane	80.871	80.60	16.4	*91*
7661	C_8H_{18}	2,2,4-Trimethylpentane	99.237	88.41	90.0	*91*
A =	**$C_4H_{10}S$**	**2-Methyl-2-propanethiol**	**64.35**			
7662	C_6H_{12}	Methylcyclopentane	71.812	63.37	95.3	*91*
7663	C_6H_{14}	2,3-Dimethylbutane	57.990	57.82	21.1	*91*
7664	C_6H_{14}	Hexane	68.742	63.78	75.8	*91*
7665	C_6H_{14}	2-Methylpentane	60.274	59.55	30.4	*91*
7666	C_6H_{14}	3-Methylpentane	63.284	61.51	46.5	*91*
A =	**$C_4H_{10}SO_4$**	**Ethyl Sulfate**	**208.0**			
7667	C_7H_8O	*m*-Cresol	202.2	Reacts		*222*
A =	**$C_4H_{11}N$**	**Butylamine**	**77.8**			
7668	C_6H_{12}	Cyclohexane	80.75	76.5	60	*231*
7669	C_6H_{12}	Methylcyclopentane	72.0	<77.5	....	*231*
A =	**$C_4H_{11}N$**	**Diethylamine**	**55.9**			
7670	C_5H_{10}	2-Methyl-2-butene	37.1	Nonazeotrope		*231*
7671	$C_5H_{10}O$	3-Methyl-2-butanone	95.4	Nonazeotrope		*231*
7672	C_5H_{12}	Pentane	36.15	Nonazeotrope		*231*
7673	$C_5H_{12}O$	Ethyl propyl ether	63.85	Nonazeotrope		*231*
7674	C_6H_{10}	Biallyl	60.1	<55.5	....	*255*
7675	C_6H_{12}	Methylcyclopentane	72.0	Nonazeotrope		*231*
7676	C_6H_{14}	2,3-Dimethylbutene	58.0	<55.0	<62	*231*
7677	C_6H_{14}	*n*-Hexane	68.8	Nonazeotrope		*231*
A =	**$C_4H_{11}N$**	**Isobutylamine**	**68.0**			
7678	C_5H_{10}	Cyclopentane	49.3	Nonazeotrope		*231*
7679	$C_5H_{10}O$	3-Methyl-2-butanone	95.4	Nonazeotrope		*231*
7680	C_5H_{12}	*n*-Pentane	36.15	Nonazeotrope		*231*
7681	C_6H_6	Benzene	80.15	Nonazeotrope		*231*
7682	C_6H_{12}	Cyclohexane	80.75	Nonazeotrope		*231*
7683	C_6H_{12}	Methylcyclopentane	72.0	<67.6	>59	*255*
7684	C_6H_{14}	*n*-Hexane	68.8	<66.5	>52	*231*
A =	**$C_4H_{11}NO$**	**2-Amino-2-methyl-1-propanol**	**165.4**			
7685	C_8H_9Cl	*o,m,p*-Chloroethylbenzene, 10 mm.	67.5	59.0	46	*24*
A =	**$C_4H_{11}NO_2$**	**2,2′-Iminodiethanol**	**268.0**			
7686	$C_{10}H_{10}O_2$	Isosafrole	252.0	<246.0	....	*255*
7687	$C_{10}H_{15}N$	*N,N*-Diethylaniline	217.05	Nonazeotrope		*255*
7688	$C_{11}H_{14}O_2$	1-Allyl-3,4-dimethoxybenzene	254.7	<247.0	....	*255*
7689	$C_{12}H_{10}O$	Phenyl ether	259.0	<250.0	....	*255*
A =	**$C_4H_{12}SiO_4$**	**Methyl Silicate**	**121.8**			
7690	$C_6H_{12}O_3$	Paraldehyde	124.35	<121.3	....	*237*

No.	B-Component Formula	Name	B.P., ° C.	Azeotropic Data B.P., ° C.	Wt. % A	Ref.
A =	$C_5H_4O_2$	**2-Furaldehyde**	**161.45**			
7691	$C_5H_6O_2$	Furfuryl alcohol	169	Nonazeotrope, V-l.		*95*
7692	$C_5H_8O_3$	Methyl acetoacetate	~169.5	Reacts		*243*
7693	$C_5H_{10}O_2$	Isovaleric acid	176.5	Nonazeotrope		*222*
7694	$C_5H_{10}O_3$	Ethyl lactate	154.1	Nonazeotrope		*255*
7695	$C_5H_{10}O_3$	2-Methoxyethyl acetate	144.6	Nonazeotrope		*255*
7696	$C_5H_{11}Br$	1-Bromo-3-methylbutane	120.65	Nonazeotrope		*207*
7697	$C_5H_{11}I$	1-Iodo-3-methylbutane	147.6	146.5	~15	*228*
7698	$C_5H_{12}O_2$	2-Propoxyethanol	151.35	151.1	14	*207*
7699	$C_5H_{12}O_3$	2-(2-Methoxyethoxy)ethanol	192.95	Nonazeotrope		*255*
7700	$C_6H_4Cl_2$	*o*-Dichlorobenzene	179.5	161.0	78	*207*
7701	$C_6H_4Cl_2$	*p*-Dichlorobenzene	174.35	160.3	63.5	*207*
7702	C_6H_5Br	Bromobenzene	156.1	153.3	23	*236*
7703	C_6H_5Cl	Chlorobenzene	132.0	Nonazeotrope		*207*
7704	C_6H_5I	Iodobenzene	188.45	Nonazeotrope		*207*
7705	C_6H_6O	Phenol	181.5	Nonazeotrope		*243*
7706	$C_6H_{10}O$	Cyclohexanone	155.6	Nonazeotrope		*218*
7707	$C_6H_{12}O$	Cyclohexanol	160.7	156.5	5.5	*207*
7708	$C_6H_{12}O_2$	Methyl isovalerate	155.8	Nonazeotrope		*243*
7709	$C_6H_{12}O_3$	2-Ethoxyethyl acetate	156.8	Nonazeotrope		*207*
7710	$C_6H_{12}O_3$	Propyl lactate	171.7	Nonazeotrope		*255*
7711	$C_6H_{14}O$	Hexyl alcohol	157.85	154.1	44	*244*
7712	$C_6H_{14}O_2$	2-Butoxyethanol	171.15	161.2	88	*207*
7713	$C_6H_{14}S$	Propyl sulfide	141.5	Nonazeotrope		*236*
7714	C_7H_7Br	*o*-Bromotoluene	181.5	<161.3	>80	*207*
7715	C_7H_7Br	*o*-Bromotoluene	181.45	Nonazeotrope		*212*
7716	C_7H_7Cl	α-Chlorotoluene	179.3	Nonazeotrope		*212*
7717	C_7H_7Cl	*o*-Chlorotoluene	159.3	155.4	35	*207*
7718	C_7H_7Cl	*p*-Cylorotoluene	162.4	157.2	42	*207*
7719	C_7H_7ClO	*m*-Chloroanisole	193.3	Nonazeotrope		*255*
7720	C_7H_8	Toluene	110.75	Nonazeotrope		*208*
7721	C_7H_8O	Anisole	153.85	153.25	22	*236*
7722	$C_7H_{14}O$	2-Methylcyclohexanol	176.15	<160.9	<94	*207*
7723	$C_7H_{14}O_3$	1,3-Butanediol methyl ether acetate	171.75	Nonazeotrope		*207*
7724	C_8H_8	Styrene	145.8	<145	....	*207*
7725	C_8H_{10}	Ethylbenzene	136.15	Nonazeotrope		*207*
7726	C_8H_{10}	*m*-Xylene	139.0	138.4	12	*211*
7727	C_8H_{10}	*o*-Xylene	143.6	140.5	13	*225*
7728	C_8H_{10}	*p*-Xylene	138.4	138.0	5	*225*
7729	$C_8H_{10}O$	Benzyl methyl ether	167.8	<160.3	>85	*255*
7730	$C_8H_{10}O$	*p*-Methylanisole	177.05	161.35	89	*244*
7731	$C_8H_{10}O$	Phenetole	170.45	~161.0	~83	*228*
7732	$C_8H_{14}O$	Methylheptenone	173.2	Nonazeotrope		*225*
7733	C_8H_{16}	1,3-Dimethylcyclohexane	120.7	Nonazeotrope		*236*
7734	$C_8H_{16}O$	2-Octanone	172.9	Nonazeotrope		*225*
7735	$C_8H_{16}O_2$	Butyl butyrate	166.4	Nonazeotrope		*228*
7736	$C_8H_{16}O_2$	Isoamyl propionate	160.7	<159.5	>52	*255*
7737	$C_8H_{16}O_2$	Isobutyl butyrate	156.8	Nonazeotrope		*212*
7738	$C_8H_{16}O_2$	Propyl isovalerate	155.7	Nonazeotrope		*218*
7739	C_8H_{18}	Octane	125.8	Nonazeotrope		*207*
7740	$C_8H_{18}O$	Butyl ether	142.4	<138.5	>11	*207*
7741	$C_8H_{18}O$	Octyl alcohol	195.2	Nonazeotrope		*207*
7742	$C_8H_{18}S$	Butyl sulfide	185.0	Nonazeotrope		*236*
7743	$C_8H_{18}S$	Isobutyl sulfide	172.0	<161.3	....	*255*
7744	C_9H_8	Indene	182.6	Nonazeotrope		*207*
7745	C_9H_{12}	Cumene	152.8	148.5	27	*207*
7746	C_9H_{12}	Mesitylene	164.6	155.2	60	*236*
7747	C_9H_{12}	Pseudocumene	168.2	157.0	67	*207*
7748	C_9H_{12}	Propylbenzene	159.2	151.4	42	*207*
7749	$C_9H_{12}O$	Benzyl ethyl ether	185.0	Nonazeotrope		*207*
7750	$C_9H_{18}O_2$	Butyl isovalerate	177.6	Nonazeotrope		*255*
7751	$C_9H_{18}O_2$	Isoamyl isobutyrate	169.8	Nonazeotrope		*255*
7752	$C_9H_{18}O_2$	Isobutyl isovalerate	168.7	Nonazeotrope		*212*
7753	$C_{10}H_8$	Naphthalene	218.0	Nonazeotrope		*207*
7754	$C_{10}H_{14}$	Butylbenzene	183.1	Nonazeotrope		*255*
7755	$C_{10}H_{14}$	Butylbenzene	183.2	160.5	82	*228*
7756	$C_{10}H_{14}$	Cymene	176.7	157.8	68	*211*

No.	Formula	B-Component Name	B.P., ° C.	Azeotropic Data B.P., ° C	Wt % A	Ref.
A =	**$C_5H_4O_2$**	**2-Furaldehyde (*continued*)**	**161.45**			
7757	$C_{10}H_{16}$	Camphene	159.5	146.75	40	236
7758	$C_{10}H_{16}$	*d*-Limonene	177.8	155.95	35	209
7759	$C_{10}H_{16}$	α-Pinene	155.8	143.4	38	236
7760	$C_{10}H_{16}$	Nopinene	163.8	147.1	50	207
7761	$C_{10}H_{16}$	α-Terpinene	173.3	155.0	60	207
7762	$C_{10}H_{16}$	δ-Terpinene	183	<160.0	....	255
7763	$C_{10}H_{16}$	Terpinolene	185.2	159.5	80	207
7764	$C_{10}H_{16}$	Thymene	179.7	158.5	72	211
7765	$C_{10}H_{16}$	Dipentene	177.7	155.95	65	207
7766	$C_{10}H_{18}O$	Cineol	176.35	157.25	59	250
7767	$C_{10}H_{18}O$	Linaloöl	198.6	Nonazeotrope		255
7768	$C_{10}H_{22}$	2,7-Dimethyloctane	160.25	<147.0	<48	207
7769	$C_{10}H_{22}O$	Amyl ether	187.5	<158.5	>83	207
7770	$C_{10}H_{22}O$	Isoamyl ether	173.4	153.9	55	236
7771	$C_{11}H_{20}O$	Isobornyl methyl ether	192.4	Nonazeotrope		255
7772	$C_{12}H_{18}$	1,3,5-Triethylbenzene	215.5	Nonazeotrope		207
A =	**C_5H_5N**	**Pyridine**	**115.4**			
7773	$C_5H_{10}O$	2-Pentanone	102.35	Nonazeotrope		255
7774	$C_5H_{10}O$	3-Pentanone	102.05	Nonazeotrope		233
7775	$C_5H_{10}O_2$	Butyl formate	106.8	Nonazeotrope		233
7776	$C_5H_{10}O_3$	Ethyl carbonate	126.0	Nonazeotrope		242
7777	$C_5H_{11}Br$	1-Bromo-3-methylbutane	120.3	<114.5	>60	228
7778	$C_5H_{11}N$	Piperidine	105.8	106.1	8	376, 377*
7779	$C_5H_{12}O$	Amyl alcohol	138.2	Nonazeotrope		233
7780	$C_5H_{12}O$	*tert*-Amyl alcohol	102.35	Nonazeotrope		233
7781	$C_5H_{12}O$	Isoamyl alcohol	131.9	Nonazeotrope		207
7782	$C_5H_{12}O$	3-Pentanol	116.0	117.4	45	233
7783	C_6H_5Cl	Chlorobenzene	132.0	Nonazeotrope		228
7784	C_6H_6	Benzene	80.15	Nonazeotrope		233
7785	C_6H_7N	2-Picoline	130.7	Nonazeotrope		255
7786	$C_6H_{10}O$	Mesityl oxide	129.45	Nonazeotrope		207
7787	$C_6H_{10}S$	Allyl sulfide	139.35	Nonazeotrope		246
7788	C_6H_{12}	Cyclohexane	80.75	Nonazeotrope		233
7789	$C_6H_{12}O$	Pinacoline	106.2	Nonazeotrope		233
7790	$C_6H_{12}O$	3-Hexanone	123.3	Nonazeotrope		233
7791	$C_6H_{12}O$	4-Methyl-2-pentanone	116.05	114.9	60	207
7792	$C_6H_{12}O_2$	Butyl acetate	126.0	Nonazeotrope		233
7793	$C_6H_{12}O_2$	Ethyl butyrate	121.5	Nonazeotrope ?		228
7794	$C_6H_{12}O_2$	Isoamyl formate	123.8	Nonazeotrope		233
7795	$C_6H_{12}O_2$	Isobutyl acetate	117.4	114.5	....	233
7796	$C_6H_{12}O_2$	Methyl isovalerate	116.5	<115.0	>52	233
7797	$C_6H_{12}O_2$	Propyl propionate	123.0	Nonazeotrope		233
7798	$C_6H_{14}O$	Propyl ether	90.1	Nonazeotrope		233
7799	$C_6H_{14}S$	Isopropyl sulfide	120.5	<114.5	<72	233
7800	C_7H_8	Toluene	110.75	110.15	22	233
7801	C_7H_{14}	Methylcyclohexane	100	Min. b.p.		233
7802	C_7H_{16}	*n*-Heptane	98.4	<97.0	<14	233
7803	C_8H_{10}	Ethylbenzene	136.15	Nonazeotrope		233
7804	C_8H_{10}	*m*-Xylene	139.2	Nonazeotrope		233
7805	C_8H_{16}	1,3-Dimethylcyclohexane	120.7	<111.0	....	233
7806	C_8H_{18}	2,5-Dimethylhexane	109.4	<105.5	<40	233
7807	C_8H_{18}	*n*-Octane	125.75	<112.8	<90	233
7808	C_8H_{18}	2,2,4-Trimethylpentane	99.3	95.75	23.4	233
7809	$C_8H_{18}O$	Isobutyl ether	122.3	Nonazeotrope		233
A =	**$C_5H_6O_2$**	**Furfuryl Alcohol**	**169.35**			
7810	$C_5H_{11}NO_3$	Isoamyl nitrate	149.75	<149.6	....	240
7811	$C_6H_4Cl_2$	*p*-Dichlorobenzene	174.4	172.5	70	255
7812	C_6H_5Cl	Chlorobenzene	131.75	Nonazeotrope		255
7813	C_6H_6O	Phenol	182.2	187.0	30	247
7814	C_6H_7N	Aniline	184.35	Nonazeotrope		255
7815	$C_6H_{12}O$	Cyclohexanol	160.8	Nonazeotrope		255
7816	$C_6H_{12}O_3$	2-Ethoxyethyl acetate	156.8	Nonazeotrope		255
7817	$C_6H_{14}O$	Hexyl alcohol	157.85	Nonazeotrope		255
7818	$C_6H_{14}O_2$	2-Butoxyethanol	171.15	<167.5	>60	255
7819	C_7H_6O	Benzaldehyde	179.2	Nonazeotrope		255

No.	B-Component Formula	Name	B.P., ° C.	Azeotropic Data B.P., ° C.	Wt. % A	Ref.
A =	$C_5H_6O_2$	**Furfuryl Alcohol** (*continued*)	**169.35**			
7820	C_7H_8O	Anisole	153.85	153.3	10	225
7821	$C_7H_{14}O$	2-Methylcyclohexanol	168.5	<168.3	....	255
7822	$C_7H_{14}O_3$	1,3-Butanediol methyl ether acetate	171.75	168.5	82	255
7823	C_8H_9Cl	*o,m,p*-Chloroethylbenzene, 10 mm.	67.5	60.5	32	24
7824	$C_8H_{10}O$	Phenetole	170.45	165.0	46	225
7825	$C_8H_{11}N$	Dimethylaniline	194.15	Nonazeotrope		255
7826	$C_8H_{16}O_2$	Butyl butyrate	166.4	164.0	30	255
7827	$C_8H_{16}O_2$	Isoamyl propionate	160.7	Nonazeotrope		255
7828	$C_8H_{16}O_2$	Propyl isovalerate	155.7	Nonazeotrope		255
7829	C_9H_7N	Quinoline	237.3	Nonazeotrope		233
7830	$C_9H_{13}N$	Dimethyl-*o*-toluidine	185.3	Nonazeotrope		255
7831	$C_{10}H_{22}O$	Isoamyl ether	173.4	165.7	50	225
A =	C_5H_7N	**2-Methylpyrrol**	**147.5**			
7832	$C_5H_{12}O$	Isoamyl alcohol	131.9	Nonazeotrope		255
A =	C_5H_8	**Cyclopentene**	**43.6**			
7833	C_5H_8	*cis*-Piperylene	43.6	43.2	....	84
			....	....	50 vol.	415
A =	C_5H_8	**Isoprene**	**34.2**			
7834	C_5H_8	3-Methyl-1,2-butadiene	40.8	Nonazeotrope		243
7835	C_5H_8	*trans*-Piperylene	42	....	9	415
7836	C_5H_{10}	Cyclopentane	49.4	Nonazeotrope		241
7837	C_5H_{10}	2-Methyl-2-butene	37.1	34.0	86	241
7838	C_5H_{10}	3-Methyl-1-butene	20.6	Nonazeotrope		241
7839	C_5H_{12}	2-Methylbutane	27.95	<27.7	>8	241
7840	C_5H_{12}	*n*-Pentane	36.15	33.8	90	241
A =	C_5H_8	**3-Methyl-1,2-butadiene**	**40.8**			
7841	C_5H_{10}	2-Methyl-2-butene	37.15	Nonazeotrope		243
A =	C_5H_8O	**Cyclopentanone**	**130.65**			
7842	$C_5H_{10}O_3$	Ethyl carbonate	126.5	Nonazeotrope		232
7843	$C_5H_{11}Br$	1-Bromo-3-methylbutane	120.65	Nonazeotrope		232
7844	$C_5H_{12}O$	Isoamyl alcohol	131.9	<130.0	>58	207
7845	$C_5H_{12}O$	2-Pentanol	119.8	Nonazeotrope		232
7846	C_6H_5Cl	Chlorobenzene	131.75	Nonazeotrope		232
7847	$C_6H_{12}O_2$	Butyl acetate	126.0	Nonazeotrope		232
7848	$C_6H_{12}O_2$	Isoamyl formate	123.8	Nonazeotrope		232
7849	C_7H_8	Toluene	110.75	Nonazeotrope		232
7850	$C_7H_{14}O_2$	Ethyl isovalerate	134.7	Nonazeotrope		232
7851	C_8H_{10}	Ethylbenzene	136.15	Nonazeotrope		232
7852	C_8H_{16}	1,3-Dimethylcyclohexane	120.7	118.0	20	232
A =	$C_5H_8O_2$	**2,4-Pentanedione**	**137.7**			
7853	$C_5H_{10}O$	Cyclopentanol	140.85	<135.5	>68	232
7854	$C_5H_{12}O$	Isoamyl alcohol	131.9	<130.0	>35	232
7855	$C_5H_{12}O$	Isoamyl alcohol	131.8	Nonazeotrope		243
7856	C_6H_5Br	Bromobenzene	156.15	154.7	~10	243
7857	C_6H_5Cl	Chlorobenzene	131.8	Nonazeotrope		243
7858	C_6H_5I	Iodobenzene	188.55	~169	>90	243
7859	C_7H_7Cl	α-Chlorotoluene	179.35	~167.5	80	243
7860	C_7H_8	Toluene	110.75	Nonazeotrope		228
7861	$C_7H_{14}O_2$	Isobutyl propionate	137.5	136.4	45	232
7862	$C_7H_{14}O_2$	Propyl isobutyrate	134.0	Nonazeotrope		232
7863	C_8H_{10}	Ethylbenzene	136.15	~135	~35	228
7864	$C_8H_{18}O$	Isobutyl ether	122.2	Nonazeotrope		228
A =	$C_5H_8O_3$	**Ethyl Pyruvate**	**155.5**			
7865	C_6H_5Br	Bromobenzene	156.1	149.5	48	232
7866	C_6H_5Cl	Chlorobenzene	131.75	Nonazeotrope		232
7867	$C_6H_{10}O$	Cyclohexanone	155.7	153.5	....	232
7868	$C_6H_{12}O_2$	Butyl acetate	126.0	Nonazeotrope		232
7869	$C_6H_{12}O_2$	Isoamyl formate	123.8	Nonazeotrope		255
7870	$C_6H_{14}S$	Propyl sulfide	141.5	Nonazeotrope		246
7871	C_7H_7Br	*o*-Bromotoluene	181.5	Nonazeotrope		232

No.	B-Component Formula	Name	B.P., ° C.	Azeotropic Data B.P., ° C.	Wt. % A	Ref.
A =	$C_5H_8O_3$	**Ethyl Pyruvate** (*continued*)	**155.5**			
7872	C_7H_7Cl	*o*-Chlorotoluene	159.2	151.5	52	*232*
7873	C_7H_7Cl	*p*-Chlorotoluene	162.4	153.2	58	*232*
7874	C_7H_8O	Anisole	153.85	148.0	50	*232*
7875	$C_7H_{14}O$	5-Methyl-2-hexanone	144.2	Nonazeotrope		*232*
7876	$C_7H_{14}O_2$	Butyl propionate	146.8	<145.5	>23	*232*
7877	$C_7H_{14}O_2$	Ethyl isovalerate	134.7	Nonazeotrope		*232*
7878	$C_7H_{14}O_2$	Propyl isobutyrate	134.0	Nonazeotrope		*255*
7879	C_8H_{10}	*m*-Xylene	139.2	137.2	30	*232*
7880	$C_8H_{10}O$	Phenetole	170.45	Nonazeotrope		*232*
7881	$C_8H_{16}O$	2-Octanone	172.85	Nonazeotrope		*232*
7882	$C_8H_{16}O_2$	Isoamyl propionate	160.7	153.0	67	*232*
7883	$C_8H_{16}O_2$	Isobutyl isobutyrate	148.6	147.0	33	*232*
7884	$C_8H_{16}O_2$	Propyl isovalerate	155.7	<151.8	....	*232*
7885	$C_8H_{18}O$	Isobutyl ether	142.4	140.4	....	*232*
7886	$C_8H_{18}S$	Isobutyl sulfide	172.0	Nonazeotrope		*246*
7887	C_9H_{12}	Cumene	152.8	146.2	45	*232*
7888	C_9H_{12}	Mesitylene	164.6	<151.5	....	*232*
7889	$C_9H_{18}O$	2,6-Dimethyl-4-heptanone	168.0	Nonazeotrope		*232*
7890	$C_{10}H_{16}$	Camphene	159.6	<148.0	....	*232*
7891	$C_{10}H_{16}$	α-Pinene	155.8	<147.0	....	*232*
7892	$C_{10}H_{18}O$	Cineol	176.35	Nonazeotrope		*232*
A =	$C_5H_8O_3$	**Levulinic Acid**	**252**			
7893	$C_6H_4ClNO_2$	*p*-Chloronitrobenzene	239.1	Reacts		*245*
7894	$C_6H_5NO_2$	Nitrobenzene	210.75	Nonazeotrope		*232*
7895	$C_7H_7NO_2$	*m*-Nitrotoluene	230.8	229.5	15	*232*
7896	$C_7H_7NO_2$	*o*-Nitrotoluene	221.75	221.55	4	*232*
7897	$C_7H_7NO_2$	*p*-Nitrotoluene	238.9	236.4	22	*232*
7898	$C_7H_{14}O_2$	Enanthic acid	222.0	Nonazeotrope		*232*
7899	$C_8H_8O_3$	Methyl salicylate	222.95	222.75	6	*232*
7900	$C_8H_{10}O$	3,4-Xylenol	226.8	Nonazeotrope		*232*
7901	$C_8H_{12}O_4$	Ethyl maleate	223.3	Nonazeotrope		*232*
7902	$C_8H_{16}O_2$	Caprylic acid	238.5	Nonazeotrope		*232*
7903	$C_9H_{10}O_3$	Ethyl salicylate	233.8	230.5	18	*207*, *232*
7904	$C_{10}H_8$	Naphthalene	218.0	216.7	11	*232*
7905	$C_{10}H_{10}O_2$	Safrol	235.9	232.5	17	*207*
7906	$C_{10}H_{12}O$	Anethole	235.7	232.0	22	*232*
7907	$C_{10}H_{12}O_2$	Propyl benzoate	230.85	230.0	7	*232*
7908	$C_{10}H_{14}O$	Thymol	232.9	Nonazeotrope		*232*
7909	$C_{10}H_{14}O$	Carvacrol	237.85	Nonazeotrope		*232*
7910	$C_{11}H_{10}$	1-Methylnaphthalene	244.6	237.0	36	*232*
7911	$C_{11}H_{10}$	2-Methylnaphthalene	241.15	234.55	29	*207*
7912	$C_{11}H_{14}O_2$	Isobutyl benzoate	241.9	238.6	25	*232*
7913	$C_{11}H_{22}O_3$	Isoamyl carbonate	232.2	Nonazeotrope		*232*
7914	$C_{12}H_{18}$	1,3,5-Triethylbenzene	215.5	214.0	11	*232*
7915	$C_{12}H_{22}O$	Bornyl ethyl ether	204.9	Nonazeotrope		*232*
A =	$C_5H_8O_3$	**Methyl Acetoacetate**	**169.5**			
7916	$C_5H_{10}O_2$	Valeric acid	186.35	Nonazeotrope		*232*
7917	$C_6H_4Cl_2$	*o*-Dichlorobenzene	179.5	Nonazeotrope		*255*
7918	$C_6H_4Cl_2$	*p*-Dichlorobenzene	174.4	167.2	33	*232*
7919	C_6H_5Br	Bromobenzene	156.15	154.7	~10	*243*
7920	C_6H_5I	Iodobenzene	188.45	Nonazeotrope		*255*
7921	C_6H_6O	Phenol	181.5	Reacts		*243*
7922	$C_6H_{10}O$	Cyclohexanone	155.7	Nonazeotrope		*232*
7923	$C_6H_{10}O_4$	Ethyl oxalate	185.65	Nonazeotrope		*255*
7924	$C_6H_{12}O$	Cyclohexanol	160.65	Azeotrope doubtful		*243*
7925	C_7H_6O	Benzaldehyde	179.2	Reacts		*243*
7926	C_7H_7Cl	α-Chlorotoluene	179.35	~167.5	<80	*243*
7927	C_7H_7Cl	*o*-Chlorotoluene	159.2	<158.2	>16	*232*
7928	C_7H_7Cl	*p*-Chlorotoluene	162.4	160.0	26	*232*
7929	C_7H_8O	Anisole	153.85	Nonazeotrope		*232*
7930	C_8H_8	Styrene	145.8	<145.0	27	*232*
7931	C_8H_9Cl	*o,m,p*-Chloroethylbenzene, 10 mm.	67.5	60.0	52	*24*
7932	C_8H_{10}	*m*-Xylene	139.2	Nonazeotrope		*232*
7933	$C_8H_{10}O$	Benzyl methyl ether	167.8	<160.0	>47	*232*

No.	B-Component Formula	Name	B.P., ° C.	Azeotropic Data B.P., ° C.	Wt. % A	Ref.
A =	$C_5H_8O_3$	**Methyl Acetoacetate** (*continued*)	**169.5**			
7934	$C_8H_{10}O$	Phenetole	170.45	<163.5	>52	*232*
7935	$C_8H_{14}O$	Methylheptenone	173.2	167.7	....	*232*
7936	$C_8H_{16}O$	2-Octanone	172.85	168.5	....	*232*
7937	$C_8H_{16}O_2$	Ethyl caproate	167.7	164.0	55	*232*
7938	$C_8H_{16}O_2$	Isoamyl propionate	160.7	<159.5	>20	*232*
7939	$C_8H_{16}O_2$	Isobutyl butyrate	156.9	<156.5	>5	*255*
7940	$C_8H_{16}O_2$	Isobutyl isobutyrate	148.6	Nonazeotrope		*232*
7941	$C_8H_{18}O$	Butyl ether	142.4	Nonazeotrope		*232*
7942	$C_8H_{18}S$	Isobutyl sulfide	172.0	166.0	58	*246*
7943	C_9H_{12}	Mesitylene	164.6	159.5	43	*232*
7944	C_9H_{12}	Pseudocumene	169	~165	....	*243*
7945	$C_9H_{18}O$	2,6-Dimethyl-4-heptanone	168.0	<166.8	....	*232*
7946	$C_9H_{18}O_2$	Isoamyl butyrate	181.05	<168.5	>75	*232*
7947	$C_9H_{18}O_2$	Isobutyl isovalerate	171.2	165.0	60	*232*
7948	$C_{10}H_{14}$	Cymene	176.7	165.0	56	*232*
7949	$C_{10}H_{16}$	Camphene	159.6	152.8	40	*232*
7950	$C_{10}H_{16}$	Dipentene	177.7	162.3	61	*232*
7951	$C_{10}H_{16}$	*d*-Limonene	177.8	162.7	61	*243*
7952	$C_{10}H_{16}$	α-Phellandrene	171.5	~160	....	*243*
7953	$C_{10}H_{16}$	α-Pinene	155.8	150.0	36	*232*
7954	$C_{10}H_{16}$	Terpinene	180.5	<165	....	*243*
7955	$C_{10}H_{18}$	Menthene	170.8	160	52	*243*
7956	$C_{10}H_{18}O$	Cineol	176.35	<164.5	80	*232*
7957	$C_{10}H_{20}O_2$	Isoamyl isovalerate	192.7	Nonazeotrope		*232*
7958	$C_{10}H_{22}O$	Amyl ether	187.5	Nonazeotrope		*232*
7959	$C_{10}H_{22}O$	Isoamyl ether	173.2	160.5	60	*232*
A =	$C_5H_8O_4$	**Methyl Malonate**	**181.4**			
7960	$C_5H_{10}O_2$	Isovaleric acid	176.5	<180.5	<45	*207*
7961	$C_5H_{10}O_2$	Valeric acid	186.35	<180.5	<85	*207*
7962	$C_6H_4Cl_2$	*o*-Dichlorobenzene	179.5	173.0	46	*242*
7963	$C_6H_4Cl_2$	*p*-Dichlorobenzene	174.4	171.0	30	*250*
7964	C_6H_5Br	Bromobenzene	156.1	Min. b. p		*227*
7965	C_6H_5I	Iodobenzene	188.55	178.0	30	*227*
7966	C_6H_6O	Phenol	181.5	Reacts		*243*
7967	C_6H_7N	Aniline	184.35	Reacts		*243*
7968	$C_6H_{10}O_4$	Ethylidene diacetate	168.5	Nonazeotrope		*207*
7969	$C_6H_{10}O_4$	Ethyl oxalate	185.65	Nonazeotrope		*207*
7970	$C_6H_{10}O_4$	Glycol diacetate	186.3	Nonazeotrope		*229*
7971	$C_6H_{11}BrO_2$	Ethyl α-bromoisobutyrate	178	<176.5	<40	*243*
7972	$C_6H_{12}O_2$	Isocaproic acid	199.5	Nonazeotrope		*255*
7973	$C_6H_{12}O_3$	2-Ethoxyethyl acetate	156.8	Nonazeotrope		*255*
7974	$C_6H_{13}Br$	1-Bromohexane	156.5	Nonazeotrope		*255*
7975	C_7H_7Br	α-Bromotoluene	198.5	Nonazeotrope		*255*
7976	C_7H_7Br	*m*-Bromotoluene	184.3	176.0	62	*207*
7977	C_7H_7Br	*o*-Bromotoluene	181.4	174.45	44.5	*209*
7978	C_7H_7Br	*p*-Bromotoluene	185.0	176.5	55	*218*
7979	C_7H_7Cl	α-Chlorotoluene	179.35	~178	....	*243*
7980	C_7H_7Cl	*o*-Chlorotoluene	159.15	Nonazeotrope		*227*
7981	C_7H_7Cl	*p*-Chlorotoluene	162.4	Nonazeotrope		*227*
7982	C_7H_8O	Anisole	153.85	Nonazeotrope		*237*
7983	C_7H_8O	*o*-Cresol	190.8	Reacts		*243*
7984	C_7H_8O	*p*-Cresol	201.7	Nonazeotrope		*255*
7985	C_8H_8	Styrene	145.8	Nonazeotrope		*255*
7986	C_8H_8O	Acetophenone	202.0	201.0	39	*232*
7987	$C_8H_{10}O$	Benzyl methyl ether	167.8	Nonazeotrope		*237*
7988	$C_8H_{10}O$	*p*-Methylanisole	177.05	<174.8	40?	*237*
7989	$C_8H_{10}O$	Phenetole	171.5	169.9	23	*237*
7990	$C_8H_{10}O_2$	Veratrole	206.8	Nonazeotrope		*237*
7991	$C_8H_{14}O$	Methylheptenone	173.2	Nonazeotrope		*232*
7992	$C_8H_{16}O_2$	Hexyl acetate	171.5	<170.8	>12	*255*
7993	$C_8H_{18}O$	Octyl alcohol	195.15	Reacts		*216*
7994	$C_8H_{18}O$	*sec*-Octyl alcohol	178.5	Chem. action		*243*
7995	$C_8H_{18}S$	Butyl sulfide	185.0	176.2	50	*246*
7996	C_9H_8	Indene	182.6	<176.2	50?	*242*
7997	C_9H_{12}	Mesitylene	164.6	162	>10	*226*

No.	B-Component Formula	Name	B.P., ° C.	Azeotropic Data B.P., ° C.	Wt. % A	Ref.
A =	$C_5H_8O_4$	**Methyl Malonate** (*continued*)	**181.4**			
7998	C_9H_{12}	Propylbenzene	158.9	<159	....	226
7999	C_9H_{12}	Pseudocumene	168.2	<165.5	>20	226
8000	$C_9H_{12}O$	Benzyl ethyl ether	185.0	178.0	37	436
8001	$C_9H_{18}O_2$	Butyl isovalerate	177.6	175.0	30	229
8002	$C_9H_{18}O_2$	Isoamyl butyrate	181.05	<177.2	>39	229
8003	$C_9H_{18}O_2$	Isobutyl isovalerate	171.2	<170.5	>17	229
8004	$C_{10}H_8$	Naphthalene	218.0	Nonazeotrope		255
8005	$C_{10}H_{14}$	Butylbenzene	183.2	173	52	226
8006	$C_{10}H_{14}$	Cymene	176.7	169.0	40	226
8007	$C_{10}H_{16}$	Camphene	159.6	154.6	26	209
8008	$C_{10}H_{16}$	*d*-Limonene	177.8	167.3	48	209
8009	$C_{10}H_{16}$	Nopinene	164	158	28	226
8010	$C_{10}H_{16}$	*α*-Pinene	155.8	151.5	~22	209
8011	$C_{10}H_{16}$	*α*-Terpinene	173.3	167	<45	226
8012	$C_{10}H_{16}$	Terpinene	181.5	164.5	51	218
8013	$C_{10}H_{16}$	Terpinolene	185.2	171.0	<62	226
8014	$C_{10}H_{16}$	Thymene	179.7	~169.0	50	217
8015	$C_{10}H_{18}$	Menthene	170.8	164	37	226
8016	$C_{10}H_{18}O$	Cineol	176.35	169.1	40.5	237
8017	$C_{10}H_{18}O$	Linaloöl	198.6	Reacts		216
8018	$C_{10}H_{20}O_2$	Isoamyl isovalerate	192.7	<180.8	>75	229
8019	$C_{10}H_{22}$	2,7-Dimethyloctane	160.2	<157	<30	226
8020	$C_{10}H_{22}O$	Amyl ether	187.5	<175.0	<62	237
8021	$C_{10}H_{22}O$	Isoamyl ether	173.4	165.5	35	237
8022	$C_{11}H_{20}O$	Isobornyl methyl ether	192.4	<177.5	<90	237
8023	$C_{12}H_{18}$	1,3,5-Triethylbenzene	215.5	Nonazeotrope		255
A =	$C_5H_9ClO_2$	**Propyl Chloroacetate**	**163.5**			
8024	$C_5H_{10}O_2$	Isovaleric acid	176.5	Nonazeotrope		255
8025	$C_5H_{12}O$	Isoamyl alcohol	131.9	Nonazeotrope		255
8026	$C_6H_{12}O$	Cyclohexanol	160.8	159.0	47	255
8027	$C_6H_{12}O_3$	2-Ethoxyethyl acetate	156.8	Nonazeotrope		255
8028	$C_6H_{14}O$	Hexyl alcohol	157.85	156.4	40	255
8029	C_7H_7Cl	*o*-Chlorotoluene	159.2	<158.5	<35	255
8030	C_7H_7Cl	*p*-Chlorotoluene	162.4	160.2	49	242
8031	C_7H_8O	Anisole	153.85	Nonazeotrope		255
8032	$C_7H_{16}O$	Heptyl alcohol	176.15	Nonazeotrope		255
8033	$C_8H_{10}O$	Phenetole	170.45	Nonazeotrope		255
8034	$C_8H_{16}O$	2-Octanone	172.85	Nonazeotrope		255
8035	$C_8H_{16}O_2$	Butyl butyrate	166.4	Nonazeotrope		255
8036	$C_8H_{16}O_2$	Isoamyl propionate	160.7	<160.5	>20	255
8037	$C_8H_{16}O_2$	Isobutyl butyrate	156.9	Nonazeotrope		255
8038	$C_8H_{18}O$	*sec*-Octyl alcohol	180.4	Nonazeotrope		255
8039	C_9H_{12}	Mesitylene	164.6	<161.0	<72	255
8040	C_9H_{12}	Propylbenzene	159.3	157.0	40	242
8041	$C_9H_{18}O_2$	Isobutyl isovalerate	171.2	Nonazeotrope		255
8042	$C_{10}H_{14}$	Cymene	176.7	Nonazeotrope		255
8043	$C_{10}H_{16}$	Camphene	159.6	156.2	42	242
8044	$C_{10}H_{16}$	*α*-Pinene	155.8	154.0	25	242
8045	$C_{10}H_{22}O$	Isoamyl ether	173.2	Nonazeotrope		255
A =	C_5H_9N	**Isovaleronitrile**	**130.5**			
8046	$C_6H_{14}O$	Propyl ether	90.1	Nonazeotrope		255
8046a	C_8H_{10}	Ethylbenzene	136.15	126.3	60	242
8047	$C_8H_{18}O$	Isobutyl ether	122.3	115.5	24	242
A =	C_5H_9N	**Valeronitrile**	**141.3**			
8048	$C_5H_{12}O$	Amyl alcohol	138.2	<136.5	<42	245
8049	$C_5H_{12}O$	2-Pentanol	119.8	Nonazeotrope		245
8050	$C_6H_{12}O_2$	Butyl acetate	126.0	Nonazeotrope		245
8051	$C_6H_{12}O_2$	Ethyl butyrate	121.5	Nonazeotrope		245
8052	$C_6H_{12}O_2$	Isobutyl acetate	117.4	Nonazeotrope		245
8052a	$C_6H_{14}O$	Propyl ether	90.1	Nonazeotrope		255
8053	$C_6H_{14}S$	Propyl sulfide	141.5	<137.5	....	245
8054	C_7H_8	Toluene	110.75	Nonazeotrope		245
8055	$C_7H_{14}O_2$	Isobutyl propionate	137.5	136.0	27	245
8056	C_8H_{10}	*m*-Xylene	139.2	<136.5	....	245

No.	B-Component Formula	Name	B.P., ° C.	Azeotropic Data B.P., ° C.	Wt. % A	Ref.
A =	C_5H_9N	**Valeronitrile** (*continued*)	**141.3**			
8057	$C_8H_{18}O$	Butyl ether	142.4	<130.5	>42	*242*
8057a	$C_8H_{18}O$	Isobutyl ether	122.3	119.0	10	*255*
8058	C_9H_{12}	Propylbenzene	159.3	Nonazeotrope		*245*
A =	C_5H_{10}	**Amylene**	**37**			
8059	$C_6H_5NO_2$	Nitrobenzene	210.75	Nonazeotrope		*234*
8060	C_6H_7N	Aniline	184.35	Nonazeotrope		*243*
A =	C_5H_{10}	**Cyclopentane**	**49.4**			
8061	C_5H_{10}	2-Methyl-2-butene	37.1	Nonazeotrope		*241*
8062	C_5H_{12}	Pentane	36.15	Nonazeotrope		*241*
8063	$C_5H_{12}O$	Ethyl propyl ether	63.85	Nonazeotrope		*238*
8064	C_6H_{10}	Biallyl	60.1	Nonazeotrope		*241*
8065	C_6H_{14}	2,2-Dimethylbutane	49.7	Nonazeotrope		*315*
8066	C_6H_{14}	2,3-Dimethylbutane	58.0	Nonazeotrope		*241*
A =	C_5H_{10}	**2-Methyl-2-butene**	**37.15**			
8067	C_5H_{12}	2-Methylbutane	27.95	27.7?	....	*243*
8068	C_5H_{12}	Pentane	36.15	35.5	~43	*243*
A =	C_5H_{10}	**3-Methyl-1-butene**	**22.5**			
8069	C_5H_{12}	2-Methylbutane	27.95	<20.4	>86	*241*
A =	$C_5H_{10}O$	**Cyclopentanol**	**140.85**			
8070	$C_5H_{10}O_3$	2-Methoxyethyl acetate	144.6	139.0	25	*206*
8071	$C_5H_{10}O_3$	Ethyl carbonate	126.5	125	....	*247*
8072	$C_5H_{10}O_3$	Ethyl lactate	154.1	Nonazeotrope		*255*
8073	$C_5H_{10}O_3$	2-Methoxyethyl acetate	144.6	139.0	75	*255*
8074	$C_5H_{11}Br$	1-Bromo-3-methylbutane	120.65	<120.2	>5	*255*
8075	$C_5H_{12}O_2$	2-Propoxyethanol	151.35	Nonazeotrope		*206*
8076	C_6H_5Cl	Chlorobenzene	131.75	<128.5	>20	*247*
8077	C_6H_6	Benzene	80.15	Nonazeotrope		*255*
8078	C_6H_6O	Phenol	182.2	Nonazeotrope		*255*
8079	C_6H_7N	Aniline	184.35	Nonazeotrope		*231*
8080	C_6H_7N	2-Picoline	130.7	Nonazeotrope		*255*
8081	$C_6H_{10}O$	Mesityl oxide	129.45	Nonazeotrope		*232*
8082	$C_6H_{10}S$	Allyl sulfide	139.35	<135.5	>33	*246*
8083	$C_6H_{11}N$	Capronitrile	163.9	Nonazeotrope		*255*
8084	C_6H_{12}	Cyclohexane	80.75	Nonazeotrope		*255*
8085	$C_6H_{12}O_2$	Butyl acetate	126.0	Nonazeotrope		*255*
8086	$C_6H_{12}O_2$	Isoamyl formate	123.8	Nonazeotrope		*255*
8087	$C_6H_{12}O_3$	Paraldehyde	124.35	Nonazeotrope		*255*
8088	C_7H_8	Toluene	110.75	Nonazeotrope		*255*
8089	$C_7H_{14}O_2$	Ethyl isovalerate	134.7	<134.5	~15	*255*
8090	$C_7H_{14}O_2$	Isoamyl acetate	142.1	<139.4	>48	*247*
8091	$C_7H_{14}O_2$	Isobutyl propionate	137.5	136.5	28	*247*
8092	C_8H_{10}	*m*-Xylene	139.2	132.8	40	*247*
8093	C_8H_{10}	*p*-Xylene	138.45	132.2	38	*255*
8094	C_8H_{16}	1,3-Dimethylcyclohexane	120.7	119.0	15	*247*
8095	$C_8H_{18}O$	Butyl ether	142.4	<136.7	>39	*207*
8096	$C_8H_{18}O$	Isobutyl ether	122.3	<122.0	>3	*255*
A =	$C_5H_{10}O$	**Isovaleraldehyde**	**92.1**			
8097	$C_5H_{10}O$	3-Pentanone	102.05	Nonazeotrope		*232*
8098	$C_5H_{10}O_2$	Methyl isobutyrate	92.5	<92.2	>30	*228*
8099	C_6H_6	Benzene	80.15	Nonazeotrope		*255*
8100	C_6H_{14}	Hexane	68.8	Nonazeotrope		*255*
A =	$C_5H_{10}O$	**3-Methyl-2-butanone**	**95.4**			
8101	$C_5H_{10}O_2$	Ethyl propionate	99.1	Nonazeotrope		*232*
8102	$C_5H_{10}O_2$	Isopropyl acetate	90.8	Nonazeotrope		*228*
8103	$C_5H_{10}O_2$	Methyl isobutyrate	92.5	Nonazeotrope		*232*
8104	$C_5H_{11}Cl$	1-Chloro-3-methylbutane	99.4	95.0	65	*232*
8105	$C_5H_{11}NO_2$	Isoamyl nitrite	97.15	94.0	50	*232*
8106	$C_5H_{12}O_2$	Diethoxymethane	87.95	Nonazeotrope		*255*
8107	C_6H_6	Benzene	80.15	Nonazeotrope		*232*
8108	C_6H_{12}	Cyclohexane	80.75	78.5	15	*232*

No.	B-Component Formula	Name	B.P., ° C.	Azeotropic Data B.P., ° C.	Wt. % A	Ref.
A =	$C_5H_{10}O$	**3-Methyl-2-butanone** (*continued*)	**95.4**			
8109	$C_6H_{15}N$	Triethylamine	89.35	<88.0	....	*255*
8110	C_7H_{16}	Heptane	98.4	89.5	48	*232*
A =	$C_5H_{10}O$	**2-Pentanone**	**102.25**			
8111	$C_5H_{10}O$	3-Pentanone	102.2	Nonazeotrope		*243*
8112	$C_5H_{10}O_2$	Butyl formate	106.8	Nonazeotrope		*232*
8113	$C_5H_{10}O_2$	Ethyl propionate	99.1	Nonazeotrope		*232*
8114	$C_5H_{10}O_2$	Isobutyl formate	98.2	Nonazeotrope		*232*
8115	$C_5H_{10}O_2$	Methyl butyrate	102.65	101.9	50	*232*
8116	$C_5H_{10}O_2$	Methyl isobutyrate	92.5	Nonazeotrope		*232*
8117	$C_5H_{10}O_2$	Propyl acetate	101.6	100.8	35	*232*
8118	$C_5H_{11}NO_2$	Isoamyl nitrite	97.15	96.5	20	*232*
8119	$C_5H_{12}O$	*tert*-Amyl alcohol	102.35	100.9	58	*232*
8120	C_6H_6	Benzene	80.15	Nonazeotrope		*255*
8121	C_6H_{12}	Cyclohexane	80.75	79.8	5	*232*
8122	C_6H_{14}	Hexane	68.8	Nonazeotrope		*255*
8123	C_7H_8	Toluene	110.7	Nonazeotrope		*243*
8124	C_7H_{14}	Methylcyclohexane	101.15	95.2	40	*232*
8125	C_7H_{16}	Heptane	98.4	93.2	34	*232*
A =	$C_5H_{10}O$	**3-Pentanone**	**102.05**			
8126	$C_5H_{10}O_2$	Butyl formate	106.8	Nonazeotrope		*232*
8127	$C_5H_{10}O_2$	Ethyl propionate	99.1	Nonazeotrope		*232*
8128	$C_5H_{10}O_2$	Isobutyl formate	98.2	Nonazeotrope		*232*
8129	$C_5H_{10}O_2$	Methylbutyrate	102.65	101.45	55	*232*
8130	$C_5H_{10}O_2$	Methyl isobutyrate	92.5	Nonazeotrope		*232*
8131	$C_5H_{10}O_2$	Propyl acetate	101.6	100.75	40	*232*
8132	$C_5H_{11}Cl$	1-Chloro-3-methylbutane	99.4	98.5	25	*232*
8133	$C_5H_{11}N$	Piperidine	106.4	Nonazeotrope		*255*
8134	$C_5H_{11}NO_2$	Isoamyl nitrite	97.15	96.45	21	*232*
8135	$C_5H_{12}O$	*tert*-Amyl alcohol	102.35	100.7	60	*232*
8136	$C_5H_{12}O$	Isoamyl alcohol	131.9	Nonazeotrope		*207*
8137	$C_5H_{12}O$	2-Pentanol	119.8	Nonazeotrope		*232*
8138	$C_5H_{12}O$	3-Pentanol	116.0	Nonazeotrope		*232*
8139	C_6H_6	Benzene	80.15	Nonazeotrope		*232*
8140	C_6H_{12}	Cyclohexane	80.8	Nonazeotrope		*232*
8141	C_6H_{12}	Methylcyclopentane	72.0	Nonazeotrope		*228*
8142	$C_6H_{12}O_2$	Ethyl isobutyrate	110.1	Nonazeotrope		*232*
8143	C_6H_{14}	Hexane	68.8	Nonazeotrope		*232*
8144	$C_6H_{14}O$	Propyl ether	90.1	Nonazeotrope		*232*
8145	$C_6H_{14}O_2$	Acetal	103.55	<101.8	>75	*232*
8146	$C_6H_{14}S$	Isopropyl sulfide	120.5	Nonazeotrope		*246*
8147	$C_6H_{15}N$	Dipropylamine	109.2	<101.0	<82	*231*
8148	C_7H_8	Toluene	110.75	Nonazeotrope		*232*
8149	C_7H_{14}	Methylcyclohexane	101.15	95.0	40	*232*
8150	C_7H_{16}	Heptane	98.45	93.0	35	*207*
8151	C_8H_{16}	1,3-Dimethylcyclohexane	120.7	100.5	83	*232*
8152	C_8H_{18}	2,5-Dimethylhexane	109.4	97.5	60	*232*
A =	$C_5H_{10}O_2$	**Butyl Formate**	**106.8**			
8153	$C_5H_{10}O_2$	Methyl butyrate	102.65	Nonazeotrope		*255*
8154	$C_5H_{10}O_2$	Propyl acetate	101.6	Nonazeotrope		*255*
8155	$C_5H_{11}Br$	1-Bromo-3-methylbutane	120.65	Nonazeotrope		*255*
8156	$C_5H_{12}O$	*tert*-Amyl alcohol	102.35	101.0	35	*247*
8157	$C_5H_{12}O$	Isoamyl alcohol	131.9	Nonazeotrope		*207*
8158	$C_5H_{12}O$	2-Pentanol	119.8	Nonazeotrope		*255*
8159	$C_5H_{12}O$	3-Pentanol	116.0	<106.5	<98.5	*255*
8160	C_6H_6	Benzene	80.15	Nonazeotrope		*255*
8161	C_6H_{12}	Cyclohexane	80.75	Nonazeotrope		*255*
8162	$C_6H_{12}O$	Pinacolone	106.2	106.0	38	*232*
8163	$C_6H_{12}O_2$	Ethyl isobutyrate	110.1	Nonazeotrope		*255*
8164	$C_6H_{14}O$	Propyl ether	90.1	Nonazeotrope		*237*
8165	$C_6H_{14}O_2$	Acetal	103.55	Nonazeotrope		*237*
8166	C_7H_8	Toluene	110.75	<106.4	>70	*255*
8167	C_7H_{14}	Methylcyclohexane	101.15	96.0	35	*242*
8168	C_7H_{16}	Heptane	98.45	90.7	40	*218*
8169	$C_8H_{18}O$	Isobutyl ether	122.3	Nonazeotrope		*237*

	B-Component			Azeotropic Data		
No.	Formula	Name	B.P., ° C.	B.P., ° C.	Wt. % A	Ref.
A =	**$C_5H_{10}O_2$**	**Ethyl Propionate**	**99.15**			
8170	$C_5H_{10}O_2$	Isobutyl formate	97.9	Nonazeotrope		*211*
8171	$C_5H_{10}O_2$	Methyl butyrate	102.65	Nonazeotrope		*255*
8172	$C_5H_{10}O_2$	Propyl acetate	101.55	Nonazeotrope		*243*
8173	$C_5H_{11}Cl$	1-Chloro-3-methylbutane	99.8	98.4	55	*218*
8174	$C_5H_{12}O$	*tert*-Amyl alcohol	102.0	98	62	*216*
8175	$C_5H_{12}O$	3-Pentanol	116.0	Nonazeotrope		*255*
8176	C_6H_6	Benzene	80.15	Nonazeotrope		*255*
8177	C_6H_{12}	Cyclohexane	80.8	Nonazeotrope		*226*
8178	$C_6H_{12}O$	Pinacolone	106.2	Nonazeotrope		*232*
8179	C_6H_{14}	Hexane	69.0	Nonazeotrope		*226*
8180	$C_6H_{14}O$	Propyl ether	90.1	Nonazeotrope		*237*
8181	$C_6H_{14}O_2$	Acetal	103.55	Nonazeotrope		*237*
8182	$C_6H_{14}O_2$	Ethoxypropoxymethane	113.7	Nonazeotrope		*237*
8183	C_7H_8	Toluene	110.7	Nonazeotrope		*226*
8184	C_7H_{14}	Methylcyclohexane	101.1	94.5	~53	*253*
8185	C_7H_{16}	*n*-Heptane	98.45	93.0	47	*207*
8186	C_8H_{18}	2,5-Dimethylhexane	109.4	<97.5	<78	*242*
A =	**$C_5H_{10}O_2$**	**Isobutyl Formate**	**98.2**			
8187	$C_5H_{10}O_2$	Methyl isobutyrate	92.5	Nonazeotrope		*255*
8188	$C_5H_{10}O_2$	Propyl acetate	101.6	Nonazeotrope		*255*
8189	$C_5H_{11}Cl$	1-Chloro-3-methylbutane	99.8	94.5	50	*218*
8190	$C_5H_{11}NO_2$	Isoamyl nitrite	97.15	95.5	43	*229*
8191	$C_5H_{12}O$	*tert*-Amyl alcohol	102.35	<97.0	<81	*247*
8192	$C_5H_{12}O_2$	Diethoxymethane	87.95	Nonazeotrope		*237*
8193	C_6H_6	Benzene	80.2	Nonazeotrope		*253*
8194	C_6H_{12}	Cyclohexane	80.8	80	<20	*226*
8195	$C_6H_{12}O$	Pinacolone	106.2	Nonazeotrope		*232*
8196	C_6H_{14}	Hexane	69.0	68.5	12	*226*
8197	$C_6H_{14}O_2$	Acetal	103.55	Nonazeotrope		*237*
8198	C_7H_8	Toluene	110.7	Azeotrope doubtful		*243*
8199	C_7H_{14}	Methylcyclohexane	100.95	92.4	~57	*252*
8200	C_7H_{16}	*n*-Heptane	98.45	<90.5	<50	*207*
8201	C_8H_{18}	2,5-Dimethylhexane	109.4	93.5	63	*242*
A =	**$C_5H_{10}O_2$**	**Isopropyl Acetate**	**91.0**			
8202	$C_5H_{10}O_2$	Methyl isobutyrate	92.3	Nonazeotrope		*211*
8203	$C_5H_{11}Cl$	1-Chloro-3-methylbutane	99.8	Nonazeotrope		*227*
8204	$C_5H_{11}NO_2$	Isoamyl nitrite	97.15	Nonazeotrope		*229*
8205	$C_5H_{12}O_2$	Diethoxymethane	87.95	<87.6	<42	*255*
8206	C_6H_6	Benzene	80.2	Nonazeotrope		*218*
8207	C_6H_{12}	Cyclohexane	80.75	78.9	25	*218*
8208	C_6H_{14}	Hexane	68.8	<68.5	<9	*255*
8209	C_6H_{14}	Hexane	69.0	Nonazeotrope		*226*
8210	$C_6H_{14}O$	Propyl ether	90.55	88.5	50	*237*
8211	$C_6H_{14}O_2$	Acetal	103.55	Nonazeotrope		*228*
8212	C_7H_8	Toluene	110.75	Nonazeotrope		*255*
8213	C_7H_{14}	Methylcyclohexane	101.1	89	78	*226*
8214	C_7H_{16}	Heptane	98.45	87.5	67	*218*
8215	C_8H_{18}	2,5-Dimethylhexane	109.4	<89.0	<95	*255*
A =	**$C_5H_{10}O_2$**	**Isovaleric Acid**	**176.5**			
8216	$C_5H_{11}Br$	1-Bromo-3-methylbutane	120.65	Nonazeotrope		*207*
8217	$C_5H_{11}I$	1-Iodo-3-methylbutane	147.65	147.0	3	*242*
8218	$C_6H_3Cl_3$	1,3,5-Trichlorobenzene	208.4	Nonazeotrope		*222*
8219	C_6H_4BrCl	*p*-Bromochlorobenzene	196.4	175.5	75	*242*
8220	$C_6H_4Cl_2$	*o*-Dichlorobenzene	179.5	171.2	42	*207*
8221	$C_6H_4Cl_2$	*p*-Dichlorobenzene	174.5	168.85	28	*207*
8222	C_6H_5Br	Bromobenzene	156.15	154.75	8	*207*
8223	C_6H_5Cl	Chlorobenzene	131.75	Nonazeotrope		*207*
8224	C_6H_5ClO	*o*-Chlorophenol	175.5	172	....	*243*
8225	C_6H_5I	Iodobenzene	188.55	174.0	~55	*218*
8226	C_6H_6O	Phenol	181.5	Nonazeotrope		*207*
8227	$C_6H_8O_4$	Methyl fumarate	193.25	Nonazeotrope		*207*
8228	$C_6H_{10}O$	Cyclohexanone	155.7	Nonazeotrope		*207*
8229	$C_6H_{10}O_3$	Ethyl acetoacetate	180.4	176.1	77	*207*

No.	B-Component Formula	Name	B.P., ° C.	Azeotropic Data B.P., ° C.	Wt. % A	Ref.
A =	$C_5H_{10}O_2$	**Isovaleric Acid** (*continued*)	**176.5**			
8230	$C_6H_{10}O_4$	Ethylidene diacetate	168.5	Nonazeotrope		207
8231	$C_6H_{10}O_4$	Ethyl oxalate	185.65	176.3	84	250
8232	$C_6H_{10}O_4$	Glycol diacetate	186.3	Nonazeotrope		207
8233	$C_6H_{10}S$	Allyl sulfide	139.35	Nonazeotrope		246
8234	$C_6H_{12}O_3$	2-Ethoxyethyl acetate	156.8	Nonazeotrope		207
8235	$C_6H_{13}Br$	1-Bromohexane	156.5	155.0	10	242
8236	$C_6H_{14}S$	Propyl sulfide	141.5	Nonazeotrope		255
8237	$C_7H_6Cl_2$	α,α-Dichlorotoluene	205.2	Nonazeotrope		207
8238	C_7H_6O	Benzaldehyde	179.2	174.5	~68	221
8239	C_7H_7Br	α-Bromotoluene	198.5	175.2	72	242
8240	C_7H_7Br	α-Bromotoluene	198.5	Nonazeotrope		243
8241	C_7H_7Br	*m*-Bromotoluene	184.3	172.5	45	207
8242	C_7H_7Br	*o*-Bromotoluene	181.75	172.1	39.5	207
8243	C_7H_7Br	*p*-Bromotoluene	185.2	173.0	48	235
8244	C_7H_7Cl	α-Chlorotoluene	179.35	171.2	38	207
8245	C_7H_7Cl	*o*-Chlorotoluene	159	157.5	12	207
8246	C_7H_7Cl	*p*-Chlorotoluene	161.3	160.0	15	207
8247	C_7H_8	Toluene	110.95	Nonazeotrope		207
8248	C_7H_8O	Anisole	153.85	Nonazeotrope		207
8249	C_7H_8O	*o*-Cresol	191.1	Nonazeotrope		255
8250	$C_7H_{13}ClO$	Isoamyl chloroacetate	190.5	Nonazeotrope		255
8251	$C_7H_{14}O_3$	1,3-Butanediol methyl ether acetate	171.75	178.0	66	207
8252	C_8H_8	Styrene	145.8	145.2	8	255
8253	$C_8H_8O_2$	Phenyl acetate	195.5	Nonazeotrope		243
8254	C_8H_{10}	Ethylbenzene	136.15	Nonazeotrope		207
8255	C_8H_{10}	*m*-Xylene	139.0	Nonazeotrope		207
8256	C_8H_{10}	*o*-Xylene	144.3	143.8	5	207
8257	C_8H_{10}	*p*-Xylene	138	Nonazeotrope		207
8258	$C_8H_{10}O$	Benzyl methyl ether	167.8	<167.0	<22	255
8259	$C_8H_{10}O$	*p*-Methylanisole	177.05	172.0	45	242
8260	$C_8H_{10}O$	Phenetole	171.5	168.5	23	207
8261	$C_8H_{14}O$	Methylheptenone	173.2	Nonazeotrope		232
8262	$C_8H_{16}O$	2-Octanone	172.85	Nonazeotrope		207
8263	$C_8H_{16}O_2$	Isobutyl butyrate	157	Nonazeotrope		243
8264	$C_8H_{16}O_2$	Hexyl acetate	171.5	Nonazeotrope		255
8265	C_8H_{18}	Octane	125.75	Nonazeotrope		207
8266	$C_8H_{18}O$	Butyl ether	153.85	Nonazeotrope		207
8267	$C_8H_{18}S$	Butyl sulfide	185	175	73	235
8268	C_9H_8	Indene	183.0	173.0	60	207
8269	C_9H_{12}	Cumene	152.8	152.0	12	207
8270	C_9H_{12}	Mesitylene	164.6	162.5	19	207
8271	C_9H_{12}	Propylbenzene	159.3	157.5	14	242
8272	C_9H_{12}	Pseudocumene	168.2	165.7	23	221
8273	$C_9H_{12}O$	Phenyl propyl ether	190.2	Nonazeotrope		221
8274	$C_9H_{18}O$	2,6-Dimethyl-4-heptanone	168.0	Nonazeotrope		207
8275	$C_9H_{18}O_2$	Isoamyl butyrate	181.05	Nonazeotrope		255
8276	$C_9H_{18}O_2$	Isoamyl butyrate	178.5	176.1	70	218
8277	$C_9H_{18}O_2$	Isobutyl isovalerate	171.2	Nonazeotrope		207
8278	$C_{10}H_8$	Naphthalene	218.05	Nonazeotrope		207
8279	$C_{10}H_{14}$	Butylbenzene	183.1	173.0	50	207
8280	$C_{10}H_{14}$	Cymene	175.3	170.8	38	207
8281	$C_{10}H_{16}$	Camphene	159.6	156.5	17	207
8282	$C_{10}H_{16}$	*d*-Limonene	177.8	168.9	41	243
8283	$C_{10}H_{16}$	Nopinene	163.8	160.5	22	207
8284	$C_{10}H_{16}$	α-Phellandrene	171.5	165	~35	243
8285	$C_{10}H_{16}$	α-Pinene	155.8	154.2	11	207
8286	$C_{10}H_{16}$	α-Terpinene	173.4	168.0	32	242
8287	$C_{10}H_{16}$	γ-Terpinene	183	172.5	47	242
8288	$C_{10}H_{16}$	Terpinene	180.5	170	~43	243
8289	$C_{10}H_{16}$	Terpinolene	184.6	171.5	52	242
8290	$C_{10}H_{16}$	Thymene	179.7	170.5	44	221
8291	$C_{10}H_{18}O$	Cineol	176.3	175.0	42.5	207
8292	$C_{10}H_{20}O_2$	Isoamyl isovalerate	192.7	Nonazeotrope		207
8293	$C_{10}H_{22}$	Decane	173.3	167.0	33	242
8294	$C_{10}H_{22}$	2,7-Dimethyloctane	160.25	158.0	20	207

No.	B-Component Formula	Name	B.P., ° C.	Azeotropic Data B.P., ° C.	Wt. % A	Ref.
A =	$C_5H_{10}O_2$	**Isovaleric Acid** (*continued*)	**176.5**			
8295	$C_{10}H_{22}O$	Amyl ether	187.5	<175.0	<70	207
8296	$C_{10}H_{22}O$	Isoamyl ether	173.4	168.85	27	244
8297	$C_{11}H_{20}O_2$	Isobornyl methyl ether	192.4	Nonazeotrope		255
8298	$C_{12}H_{18}$	Triethylbenzene	215.5	Nonazeotrope		207
8299	$C_{13}H_{28}$	Tridecane	234.0	Nonazeotrope		255
A =	$C_5H_{10}O_2$	**Methyl Butyrate**	**102.65**			
8300	$C_5H_{10}O_2$	Propyl acetate	101.60	Nonazeotrope		229
8301	$C_5H_{11}Cl$	1-Chloro-3-methylbutane	99.4	Nonazeotrope		255
8302	$C_5H_{12}O$	*tert*-Amyl alcohol	102.0	~99	~57	243
8303	$C_5H_{12}O$	3-Pentanol	116.0	Nonazeotrope		255
8304	C_6H_6	Benzene	80.15	Nonazeotrope		255
8305	$C_6H_{12}O$	Pinacolone	106.2	Nonazeotrope		232
8306	$C_6H_{14}O$	Propyl ether	90.1	Nonazeotrope		237
8307	$C_6H_{14}O_2$	Acetal	103.55	102	~55	237
8308	C_7H_8	Toluene	110.7	Nonazeotrope		243
8309	C_7H_{14}	Methylcyclohexane	101.1	97.0	45	226
8310	C_7H_{16}	*n*-Heptane	98.45	95.1	35	207
8311	C_8H_{16}	1,3-Dimethylcyclohexane	120.7	Nonazeotrope		255
8312	C_8H_{18}	2,5-Dimethylhexane	109.2	100.0	<75	226
8313	C_8H_{18}	*n*-Octane	125.8	Nonazeotrope		226
A =	$C_5H_{10}O_2$	**Methyl Isobutyrate**	**92.5**			
8314	$C_5H_{11}Cl$	1-Chloro-3-methylbutane	99.8	Nonazeotrope		227
8315	$C_5H_{11}NO_2$	Isoamyl nitrite	97.15	Nonazeotrope		229
8316	$C_5H_{12}O$	*tert*-Amyl alcohol	102.35	Nonazeotrope		255
8317	$C_5H_{12}O_2$	Diethoxymethane	87.95	Nonazeotrope		207
8318	C_6H_6	Benzene	80.2	Nonazeotrope		253
8319	C_6H_{12}	Cyclohexane	80.75	~78.6	~12	253
8320	C_6H_{12}	Methylcyclopentane	72.0	Nonazeotrope		255
8321	C_6H_{14}	Hexane	69.0	Nonazeotrope		226
8322	$C_6H_{14}O$	Propyl ether	90.1	89.7	75	237
8323	$C_6H_{14}O_2$	Acetal	104.5	Nonazeotrope		237
8324	C_7H_8	Toluene	110.75	Nonazeotrope		255
8325	C_7H_{14}	Methylcyclohexane	101.1	91	75	226
8326	C_7H_{16}	*n*-Heptane	98.45	89.7	65	207
A =	$C_5H_{10}O_2$	**Propyl Acetate**	**101.6**			
8327	$C_5H_{11}Cl$	1-Chloro-3-methylpropane	99.8	98.5	40	227
8328	$C_5H_{11}NO_2$	Isoamyl nitrite	97.15	Nonazeotrope		230
8329	$C_5H_{12}O$	*tert*-Amyl alcohol	102.0	99.5	58	216
8330	$C_5H_{12}O$	3-Pentanol	116.0	Nonazeotrope		255
8331	C_6H_6	Benzene	80.2	Nonazeotrope		217
8332	C_6H_{12}	Cyclohexane	80.75	Nonazeotrope		217
8333	$C_6H_{12}O$	Pinacolone	106.2	Nonazeotrope		232
8334	C_6H_{14}	Hexane	69.0	Nonazeotrope		226
8335	$C_6H_{14}O$	Propyl ether	90.55	Nonazeotrope		237
8336	$C_6H_{14}O_2$	Acetal	103.55	101.25	68	237
8337	$C_6H_{14}O_2$	Ethoxypropoxymethane	113.7	Nonazeotrope		237
8338	$C_6H_{14}S$	Isopropyl sulfide	120.5	Nonazeotrope		246
8339	C_7H_8	Toluene	110.6	Nonazeotrope		252
8340	C_7H_{14}	Methylcyclohexane	101.15	95.45	....	251
8341	C_7H_{16}	*n*-Heptane	98.4	93.6	....	251
8342	C_8H_{18}	Octane	125.8	Nonazeotrope		226
A =	$C_5H_{10}O_2$	**Tetrahydrofurfuryl Alcohol**	**72.1/10 mm.**			
8343	C_8H_9Cl	*o,m,p*-Chloroethylbenzene, 10 mm.	67.5	63.0	29.5	24
A =	$C_5H_{10}O_2$	**Valeric Acid**	**186.35**			
8344	$C_5H_{11}I$	1-Iodo-3-methylbutane	147.65	Nonazeotrope		207
8345	$C_6H_4Cl_2$	*o*-Dichlorobenzene	179.5	175.8	22	207
8346	$C_6H_4Cl_2$	*p*-Dichlorobenzene	174.6	171.8	14.7	244
8347	C_6H_5Br	Bromobenzene	156.1	155.65	3.5	244
8348	C_6H_5I	Iodobenzene	188.45	180.15	35	207
8349	C_6H_6O	Phenol	182.2	Nonazeotrope		207

No.	B-Component Formula	Name	B.P., ° C.	Azeotropic Data B.P., ° C.	Wt. % A	Ref.
A =	**$C_5H_{10}O_2$**	**Valeric Acid (*continued*)**	**186.35**			
8350	$C_6H_{10}O_3$	Ethyl acetoacetate	180.4	Nonazeotrope		*232*
8351	$C_6H_{10}O_4$	Ethyl oxalate	185.65	182.5	37	*249, 250*
8352	$C_6H_{10}O_4$	Glycol diacetate	186.3	<185.6	>38	*207*
8353	$C_6H_{13}Br$	1-Bromohexane	156.5	155.5	4.5	*242*
8354	$C_6H_{14}S$	Propyl sulfide	141.5	Nonazeotrope		*246*
8355	C_7H_6O	Benzaldehyde	189.2	178.5	....	*207*
8356	$C_7H_6O_2$	Salicylaldehyde	196.7	Nonazeotrope		*255*
8357	C_7H_7Br	α-Bromotoluene	198.5	183.0	53	*242*
8358	C_7H_7Br	*m*-Bromotoluene	184.3	178.55	25.5	*207*
8359	C_7H_7Br	*o*-Bromotoluene	181.5	176.8	23	*207*
8360	C_7H_7Br	*p*-Bromotoluene	185.0	179.2	32	*242*
8361	C_7H_7Cl	α-Chlorotoluene	179.3	175.0	25	*207*
8362	C_7H_7Cl	*o*-Chlorotoluene	159.2	158.5	5	*207*
8363	C_7H_7Cl	*p*-Chlorotoluene	162.4	161.2	6	*207*
8364	C_7H_8O	Anisole	153.85	Nonazeotrope		*207*
8365	C_7H_7I	*p*-Iodotoluene	214.5	184.5	80	*255*
8366	C_7H_8O	*o*-Cresol	191.1	Nonazeotrope		*207*
8367	C_7H_8O	*p*-Cresol	201.7	Nonazeotrope		*207*
8368	$C_7H_{13}ClO_2$	Isoamyl chloroacetate	190.5	<185.8	....	*255*
8369	$C_7H_{14}O_3$	1,3-Butanediol methyl ether acetate	171.75	Nonazeotrope		*207*
8370	C_8H_8O	Acetophenone	202.0	Nonazeotrope		*232*
8371	C_8H_{10}	*m*-Xylene	139.2	Nonazeotrope		*207*
8372	C_8H_{10}	*o*-Xylene	144.3	Nonazeotrope		*255*
8373	$C_8H_{10}O$	Benzyl methyl ether	167.8	Nonazeotrope		*207*
8374	$C_8H_{10}O$	*p*-Methylanisole	177.05	<176.0	<22	*242*
8375	$C_8H_{10}O$	Phenetole	170.45	Nonazeotrope		*207*
8376	$C_8H_{16}O$	2-Octanone	172.85	Nonazeotrope		*232*
8377	C_9H_8	Indene	182.6	178.5	30	*242*
8378	C_9H_{12}	Mesitylene	164.6	164.0	10	*207*
8379	C_9H_{12}	Propylbenzene	159.3	158.4	7	*255*
8380	$C_9H_{12}O$	Benzyl ethyl ether	185.0	180.5	40	*242*
8381	$C_9H_{12}O$	Phenyl propyl ether	190.5	184.3	58	*242*
8382	$C_9H_{14}O$	Phorone	197.8	Nonazeotrope		*232*
8383	$C_9H_{18}O_2$	Butyl isovalerate	177.6	Nonazeotrope		*207*
8384	$C_9H_{18}O_2$	Isoamyl butyrate	181.05	Nonazeotrope		*207*
8385	$C_{10}H_8$	Naphthalene	218.0	186.0	96	*255*
8386	$C_{10}H_{14}$	Cymene	176.7	176.5	22	*207*
8387	$C_{10}H_{16}$	Camphene	159.6	158.5	8	*207*
8388	$C_{10}H_{16}$	Dipentene	177.7	173.4	27	*207*
8389	$C_{10}H_{16}$	Nopinene	163.8	162.2	10	*207*
8390	$C_{10}H_{16}$	α-Pinene	155.8	155.5	5?	*255*
8391	$C_{10}H_{16}$	α-Terpinene	173.4	171.0	20	*242*
8392	$C_{10}H_{16}$	γ-Terpinene	183	178.5	33	*242*
8393	$C_{10}H_{16}$	Terpinolene	184.6	178.0	35	*242*
8394	$C_{10}H_{18}O$	Cineol	176.35	176.3	3	*207*
8395	$C_{10}H_{18}O$	Citronellal	208.0	Nonazeotrope		*255*
8396	$C_{10}H_{20}O_2$	Isoamyl isovalerate	192.7	Nonazeotrope		*207*
8397	$C_{10}H_{22}O$	Amyl ether	187.5	181.5	45	*207*
8398	$C_{10}H_{22}O$	Isoamyl ether	173.2	171.8	12.5	*236*
A =	**$C_5H_{10}O_3$**	**Ethyl Carbonate**	**126.5**			
8400	$C_5H_{10}O_3$	2-Methoxyethyl acetate	144.6	Nonazeotrope		*206*
8401	$C_5H_{11}Br$	1-Bromo-3-methylbutane	120.65	<119.8	<28	*255*
8402	$C_5H_{11}I$	1-Iodo-3-methylbutane	147.65	Nonazeotrope		*255*
8403	$C_5H_{11}I$	2-Iodo-2-methylbutane	127.5	123.4	~50	*243*
8404	$C_5H_{12}O$	Amyl alcohol	138.2	<125.5	<96	*255*
8405	$C_5H_{12}O$	Isoamyl alcohol	131.8	125.3	73.5	*207*
8406	C_6H_5Cl	Chlorobenzene	131.75	Nonazeotrope		*255*
8407	$C_6H_{10}O$	Mesityl oxide	129.4	126.45	6	*207*
8408	$C_6H_{10}S$	Allyl sulfide	139.35	126.0	90	*246*
8409	$C_6H_{12}O$	2-Hexanone	127.2	125.7	65	*232*
8410	$C_6H_{12}O$	3-Hexanone	123.3	Nonazeotrope		*232*
8411	$C_6H_{12}O_2$	Isoamyl formate	123.8	Nonazeotrope		*229*
8412	$C_6H_{12}O_3$	2-Ethoxyethyl acetate	156.8	Nonazeotrope		*255*
8413	$C_6H_{12}O_3$	Paraldehyde	124	Nonazeotrope		*237*

No.	Formula	B-Component Name	B.P., ° C.	Azeotropic Data B.P., ° C.	Wt. % A	Ref.
A =	$C_5H_{10}O_3$	**Ethyl Carbonate** (*continued*)	**126.5**			
8414	C_7H_8	Toluene	110.7	Nonazeotrope		*243*
8415	$C_7H_{14}O_2$	Ethyl isovalerate	134.7	Nonazeotrope		*255*
8416	$C_7H_{14}O_2$	Propyl isobutyrate	134.0	Nonazeotrope		*255*
8417	$C_7H_{16}O_2$	Dipropoxymethane	137.2	Nonazeotrope		*237*
8418	C_8H_{10}	Ethylbenzene	136.15	Nonazeotrope		*253*
8419	C_8H_{10}	*m*-Xylene	139.0	Nonazeotrope		*207*
8420	C_8H_{10}	*p*-Xylene	138.45	Nonazeotrope		*255*
8421	C_8H_{16}	1,3-Dimethylcyclohexane	120.7	<115.0	<42	*255*
8422	$C_8H_{18}O$	Isobutyl ether	122.3	<120.8	<65	*237*
A =	$C_5H_{10}O_3$	**Ethyl Lactate**	**154.1**			
8423	$C_5H_{10}O_3$	2-Methoxyethyl acetate	144.6	Nonazeotrope		*206*
8424	$C_5H_{11}I$	1-Iodo-3-methylbutane	147.6	~146.0	<25	*228*
8425	$C_5H_{11}NO_3$	Isoamyl nitrate	149.75	146.7	33	*242*
8426	$C_5H_{12}O$	Isoamyl alcohol	131.9	Nonazeotrope		*207*
8427	$C_5H_{12}O_2$	2-Propoxyethanol	151.35	151.33	5	*206*
8428	$C_6H_4Cl_2$	*p*-Dichlorobenzene	174.5	Nonazeotrope		*218*
8429	C_6H_5Br	Bromobenzene	156.1	149.7	53	*252*
8430	C_6H_5Cl	Chlorobenzene	132.0	Nonazeotrope		*228*
8431	C_6H_6O	Phenol	182.2	Nonazeotrope		*222*
8432	$C_6H_{10}O$	Cyclohexanone	155.7	153.7	66	*232*
8433	$C_6H_{12}O$	Cyclohexanol	160.7	153.75	~95	*252*
8434	$C_6H_{12}O_3$	2-Ethoxyethyl acetate	156.8	Nonazeotrope		*255*
8435	$C_6H_{13}ClO_2$	Chloroacetal	157.4	~152.5	73	*252*
8436	$C_6H_{14}O$	Hexyl alcohol	157.95	153.6	82	*221*
8437	$C_6H_{14}O_2$	2-Butoxyethanol	171.15	Nonazeotrope		*255*
8438	C_7H_7Cl	*o*-Chlorotoluene	159.15	152.0	~65	*228*
8439	C_7H_7Cl	*p*-Chlorotoluene	162.4	~153.0	....	*228*
8440	C_7H_8	Toluene	110.75	Nonazeotrope		*255*
8441	C_7H_8O	Anisole	153.85	150.1	55.5	*236*
8442	C_7H_8O	*o*-Cresol	191.1	Nonazeotrope		*255*
8443	C_7H_{14}	Methylcyclohexane	101.45	Nonazeotrope		*255*
8444	$C_7H_{14}O$	2-Methylcyclohexanol	168.5	Nonazeotrope		*255*
8445	$C_7H_{14}O$	5-Methyl-2-hexanone	144.2	Nonazeotrope		*232*
8446	$C_7H_{14}O_2$	Methyl caproate	151.0	<150.0	<32	*228*
8447	C_7H_{16}	Heptane	98.4	Nonazeotrope		*207*
8448	C_8H_8	Styrene	145.8	140.5	25	*228*
		32 mm.	....	....	16 vol.	*141*
8449	C_8H_{10}	Ethylbenzene	....	~16 vol.		*141*
8450	C_8H_{10}	*m*-Xylene	139.0	137.4	19.5	*207*
8451	C_8H_{10}	*o*-Xylene	144.3	140.2	30	*247*
8452	C_8H_{10}	*p*-Xylene	138.45	136.6	17	*255*
8453	$C_8H_{10}O$	Phenetole	170.45	Nonazeotrope		*236*
8454	C_8H_{16}	1,3-Dimethylcyclohexane	120.7	Nonazeotrope		*255*
8455	$C_8H_{16}O_2$	Butyl butyrate	166.4	Nonazeotrope		*228*
8456	$C_8H_{16}O_2$	Isoamyl propionate	160.7	152.8	78	*255*
8457	$C_8H_{16}O_2$	Isobutyl butyrate	156.9	151.5	62	*207*
8458	$C_8H_{16}O_2$	Isobutyl isobutyrate	148.6	146.5	30	*207*
8459	$C_8H_{16}O_2$	Propyl isovalerate	155.7	150	~60	
8460	$C_8H_{18}O$	Butyl ether	142.4	<141.5	....	*255*
8461	C_9H_8	Indene	182.6	Nonazeotrope		*255*
8462	C_9H_{12}	Cumene	152.8	143.5	48	*250*
8463	C_9H_{12}	Mesitylene	164.9	150.05	73	*210*
8464	C_9H_{12}	Propylbenzene	159.2	147	58	*228*
8465	C_9H_{12}	Pseudocumene	168.2	152.4	73	*221*
8466	$C_9H_{18}O$	2,6-Dimethyl-4-heptanone	168.0	Nonazeotrope		*232*
8467	$C_{10}H_{14}$	Butylbenzene	183.1	Nonazeotrope		*255*
8468	$C_{10}H_{14}$	Cymene	176.7	Nonazeotrope		*218*
8469	$C_{10}H_{16}$	Camphene	159.5	144.95	55	*208*
8470	$C_{10}H_{16}$	*d*-Limonene	177.8	Nonazeotrope		*253*
8471	$C_{10}H_{16}$	Nopinene	163.8	147.3	62	*247*
8472	$C_{10}H_{16}$	α-Pinene	155.8	143.1	49.8	*208*
			155.8	<152.0	<82	*255*
8473	$C_{10}H_{16}$	Terpinolene	181.6	Nonazeotrope		*255*
8474	$C_{10}H_{16}$	Thymene	179.7	Nonazeotrope		*253*
8475	$C_{10}H_{22}$	2,7-Dimethyloctane	160.2	146.0	60	*253*

No.	B-Component Formula	B-Component Name	B.P., ° C.	Azeotropic Data B.P., ° C.	Wt. % A	Ref.
A =	**$C_5H_{10}O_3$**	**2-Methoxyethyl Acetate**	**144.6**			
8476	$C_5H_{11}Br$	1-Bromo-3-methylbutane	120.65	Nonazeotrope		*255*
8477	$C_5H_{11}I$	1-Iodo-3-methylbutane	147.65	<141.5	<65	*255*
8378	$C_5H_{11}NO_3$	Isoamyl nitrate	149.75	144.4	87	*239*
8479	$C_5H_{12}O$	Amyl alcohol	138.2	<137.0	....	*255*
8480	$C_5H_{12}O$	*tert*-Amyl alcohol	102.35	Nonazeotrope		*255*
8481	$C_5H_{12}O$	Isoamyl alcohol	131.9	Nonazeotrope		*207*
8482	$C_5H_{12}O$	2-Pentanol	119.8	Nonazeotrope		*255*
8483	$C_5H_{12}O_2$	2-Propoxyethanol	151.35	Nonazeotrope		*236*
8484	C_6H_5Br	Bromobenzene	156.1	Nonazeotrope		*236*
8485	C_6H_5Cl	Chlorobenzene	131.75	Nonazeotrope		*236*
8486	C_6H_6O	Phenol	182.2	183.6	18	*236*
8487	$C_6H_{10}O_4$	Ethylidene diacetate	168.5	Nonazeotrope		*207*
8488	$C_6H_{12}O_2$	Butyl acetate	126.0	Nonazeotrope		*206*
8489	$C_6H_{12}O_2$	Ethyl butyrate	121.5	Nonazeotrope		*255*
8490	$C_6H_{12}O_2$	Isoamyl formate	123.8	Nonazeotrope		*255*
8491	$C_6H_{12}O_2$	Isobutyl acetate	117.4	Nonazeotrope		*255*
8492	$C_6H_{13}Br$	1-Bromohexane	156.5	<144.2	<92	*255*
8493	$C_6H_{14}O$	Hexyl alcohol	157.85	Nonazeotrope		*206*
8494	C_7H_7Cl	*o*-Chlorotoluene	159.2	Nonazeotrope		*255*
8495	C_7H_8	Toluene	110.75	Nonazeotrope		*236*
8496	C_7H_8O	Anisole	153.85	Nonazeotrope		*236*
8497	C_7H_8O	*m*-Cresol	202.2	Nonazeotrope		*255*
8498	C_7H_8O	*o*-Cresol	191.1	Nonazeotrope		*236*
8499	C_7H_8O	*p*-Cresol	201.7	Nonazeotrope		*206*
8500	$C_7H_{14}O$	5-Methyl-2-hexanone	144.2	<144.0	>35	*255*
8501	$C_7H_{14}O_2$	Amyl acetate	148.8	<144.45	<92	*255*
8502	$C_7H_{14}O_2$	Ethyl isovalerate	134.7	Nonazeotrope		*255*
8503	$C_7H_{14}O_2$	Ethyl valerate	145.45	143.8	70	*206*
8504	$C_7H_{14}O_2$	Isoamyl acetate	142.1	141.5	20	*206*
8505	$C_7H_{14}O_2$	Propyl butyrate	143.7	<143.2	<68	*255*
8506	$C_7H_{16}O_3$	Ethyl orthoformate	145.75	143.45	51	*207*, *236*
8507	C_8H_8	Styrene	145.8	143.0	61	*242*
8508	C_8H_{10}	Ethylbenzene	136.15	135.5	15	*206*
8509	C_8H_{10}	*m*-Xylene	139.2	137.7	28	*201**, *207*
8510	C_8H_{10}	*o*-Xylene	144.3	141.5	50	*206*
8511	C_8H_{10}	*p*-Xylene	138.45	137.2	26	*201**, *206*
8512	C_8H_{16}	1,3-Dimethylcyclohexane	120.7	Nonazeotrope		*255*
8513	$C_8H_{16}O_2$	Ethyl caproate	167.7	Nonazeotrope		*255*
8514	$C_8H_{16}O_2$	Isoamyl propionate	160.7	Nonazeotrope		*255*
8515	$C_8H_{16}O_2$	Isobutyl butyrate	156.9	Nonazeotrope		*255*
8516	$C_8H_{16}O_2$	Isobutyl isobutyrate	171.2	Nonazeotrope		*255*
8517	$C_8H_{16}O_2$	Propyl isovalerate	155.7	Nonazeotrope		*255*
8518	C_8H_{18}	Octane	125.75	<125.2	<11	*255*
8519	$C_8H_{18}O$	Butyl ether	142.4	138.0	30	*206*
8520	$C_8H_{18}O$	Isobutyl ether	122.3	Nonazeotrope		*206*
8521	C_9H_{12}	Cumene	152.8	144.3	94	*207*
8522	C_9H_{12}	Mesitylene	164.6	Nonazeotrope		*255*
8523	C_9H_{12}	Propylbenzene	159.3	Nonazeotrope		*206*
8524	C_9H_{12}	Pseudocumene	168.2	Nonazeotrope		*255*
8525	$C_9H_{18}O_2$	Isoamyl isobutyrate	169.8	Nonazeotrope		*255*
8526	$C_{10}H_{16}$	Camphene	159.6	143.3	82	*206*
8527	$C_{10}H_{16}$	Nopinene	163.8	143.5	83	*255*
8528	$C_{10}H_{16}$	α-Terpinene	173.4	Nonazeotrope		*255*
8529	$C_{10}H_{16}$	α-Pinene	155.8	142.0	80	*206*
8530	$C_{10}H_{22}$	2,7-Dimethyloctane	160.1	142.5	80	*242*
A =	**$C_5H_{11}Br$**	**1-Bromo-3-methylbutane**	**120.65**			
8533	$C_5H_{12}O$	Amyl alcohol	138.2	118.2	85	*247*
8534	$C_5H_{12}O$	*tert*-Amyl alcohol	102.35	Nonazeotrope		*207*
8535	$C_5H_{12}O$	Isoamyl alcohol	129.0	116.15	87.3	*162*, *207**
8536	$C_5H_{12}O$	2-Pentanol	119.8	<115.0	<74	*207*
8537	$C_5H_{12}O_2$	2-Propoxyethanol	151.35	Nonazeotrope		*207*
8538	$C_6H_{10}O$	Mesityl oxide	129.45	Nonazeotrope		*207*
8539	$C_6H_{10}S$	Allyl sulfide	139.35	Nonazeotrope		*246*
8540	$C_6H_{12}O$	3-Hexanone	123.3	119.8	45	*232*
8541	$C_6H_{12}O$	4-Methyl-2-pentanone	116.05	115.6	30	*207*

No.	B-Component Formula	Name	B.P., ° C.	Azeotropic Data B.P., ° C.	Wt. % A	Ref.
A =	**$C_5H_{11}Br$**	**1-Bromo-3-methylbutane** (*continued*)	**120.65**			
8542	$C_6H_{12}O_2$	Butyl acetate	125.0	Nonazeotrope		*207*
8543	$C_6H_{12}O_2$	Ethyl butyrate	121.5	119.8	65	*162**, *207*
8544	$C_6H_{12}O_2$	Ethyl isobutyrate	110.1	Nonazeotrope		*227*
8545	$C_6H_{12}O_2$	Isoamyl formate	123.8	120.0	76	*207*
8546	$C_6H_{12}O_2$	Isobutyl acetate	117.4	117.2	<28	*207*
8547	$C_6H_{12}O_2$	Methyl isovalerate	116.5	Nonazeotrope		*227*
8548	$C_6H_{12}O_2$	Propyl propionate	123.0	120.2	75	*242*
8549	$C_6H_{12}O_3$	Paraldehyde	124	118.5	~24	*243*
8550	$C_6H_{14}S$	Isopropyl sulfide	120.5	<118.9	<48	*246*
8551	$C_6H_{15}BO_3$	Ethyl borate	118.6	117.7	38	*207*
8552	C_7H_8	Toluene	109.5	Nonazeotrope		*247*
8553	$C_7H_{14}O_2$	Ethyl isovalerate	134.7	Nonazeotrope		*207*
A =	**$C_5H_{11}Br$**	**1-Bromo-3-methylbutane**	**120.65**			
8554	$C_7H_{14}O_2$	Isoamyl acetate	137.5	Nonazeotrope		*162*
8555	$C_7H_{14}O_2$	Isopropyl isobutyrate	120.8	119.5	60	*227*
8556	C_8H_{16}	1,3-Dimethylcyclohexane	120.7	<118.9	<60	*207*
8557	C_8H_{18}	*n*-Octane	125.75	<120.2	<90	*207*
A =	**$C_5H_{11}Br$**	**1-Bromopentane**	**130.0**			
8558	C_7H_8	Toluene	110.7	Nonazeotrope		*328*
A =	**$C_5H_{11}Cl$**	**1-Chloro-3-methylbutane**	**99.4**			
8559	$C_5H_{11}NO_2$	Isoamyl nitrite	97.15	<96.9	<20	*230*
8560	$C_5H_{12}O$	*tert*-Amyl alcohol	102.25	95.85	73.5	*225*
8561	$C_5H_{12}O$	Isoamyl alcohol	131.9	Nonazeotrope		*207*
8562	$C_5H_{12}O_2$	Diethoxymethane	87.95	Nonazeotrope		*207*
8563	C_6H_6	Benzene	80.15	Nonazeotrope		*255*
8564	$C_6H_{10}S$	Allyl sulfide	139.35	Nonazeotrope		*255*
8565	$C_6H_{12}O$	Pinacolone	106.2	Nonazeotrope		*228*
8566	$C_6H_{12}O_2$	Ethyl isobutyrate	110.1	Nonazeotrope		*227*
8567	$C_6H_{14}O$	Propyl ether	90.1	Nonazeotrope		*239*
8568	$C_6H_{14}O_2$	Acetal	103.55	Nonazeotrope		*239*
8569	C_7H_{14}	Methylcyclohexane	101.15	98.0	64	*242*
8570	C_7H_{16}	Heptane	78.4	96.5	52	*207*
8571	C_8H_{18}	2,5-Dimethylhexane	109.4	Nonazeotrope		*255*
A =	**$C_5H_{11}I$**	**1-Iodo-3-methylbutane**	**147.65**			
8572	$C_5H_{11}NO_3$	Isoamyl nitrate	149.75	<144.5	>57	*240*
8573	$C_5H_{12}O$	Isoamyl alcohol	128.9	127.3	48	*162*, *207**
8574	$C_5H_{12}O_2$	2-Propoxyethanol	143.0	....	....	*206*
8575	C_6H_5ClO	*o*-Chlorophenol	176.8	Nonazeotrope		*255*
8576	C_6H_6O	Phenol	182.2	Nonazeotrope		*222*
8577	$C_6H_{10}O$	Cyclohexanone	155.7	Nonazeotrope		*232*
8578	$C_6H_{10}O$	Mesityl oxide	129.45	Nonazeotrope		*207*
8579	$C_6H_{12}O$	Cyclohexanol	160.65	147.0	~90	*253*
8580	$C_6H_{12}O_3$	2-Ethoxyethyl acetate	156.8	<147.4	....	*255*
8581	$C_6H_{14}O$	Hexyl alcohol	157.85	145.2	87	*247*
8582	$C_6H_{14}O_2$	2-Butoxyethanol	171.15	Nonazeotrope		*255*
8583	$C_6H_{14}O_2$	Pinacol	174.35	145.5	~90	*255*
8584	C_7H_8O	Anisole	153.85	Nonazeotrope		*253*
8585	$C_7H_{14}O$	4-Heptanone	143.55	143.0	35	*232*
8586	$C_7H_{14}O$	2-Methylcyclohexanol	168.5	Nonazeotrope		*255*
8587	$C_7H_{14}O_2$	Isoamyl acetate	142.1	141.7	~18	*208*
			137.5	Nonazeotrope		*162*
8588	$C_7H_{14}O_2$	Amyl acetate	148.8	145.9	60	*242*
8589	$C_7H_{14}O_2$	Ethyl isovalerate	134.7	Nonazeotrope		*255*
8590	$C_7H_{14}O_2$	Ethyl valerate	145.45	<145.1	<30	*255*
8591	$C_7H_{14}O_2$	Isobutyl propionate	136.9	Nonazeotrope		*226*
8592	$C_7H_{14}O_2$	Propyl butyrate	143.7	Nonazeotrope		*227*
8593	$C_7H_{14}O_2$	Methyl caproate	149.8	<147.5	<70	*255*
8594	$C_7H_{14}O_2$	Propyl isobutyrate	134.0	Nonazeotrope		*227*
8595	$C_7H_{14}O_3$	1,3-Butanediol methyl ether acetate	171.75	Nonazeotrope		*255*
8596	$C_7H_{16}O$	Heptyl alcohol	176.15	A Nonazeotrope		*255*
8597	C_8H_8	Styrene	145.8	<145.0	....	*255*

No.	Formula	B-Component Name	B.P., ° C.	Azeotropic Data B.P., ° C.	Wt. % A	Ref.
A =	**$C_5H_{11}I$**	**1-Iodo-3-methylbutane** *(continued)*	**147.65**			
8598	C_8H_{10}	*m*-Xylene	139.0	Nonazeotrope		*218*
8599	$C_8H_{16}O_2$	Isobutyl butyrate	156.8	Nonazeotrope		*227*
8600	$C_8H_{16}O_2$	Isobutyl isobutyrate	147.3	146.5	58	*218*
8601	$C_8H_{18}O$	Butyl ether	142.4	Nonazeotrope		*239*
8602	$C_{10}H_{16}$	Camphene	159.6	Nonazeotrope		*255*
8603	$C_{10}H_{16}$	Nopinene	163.8	Nonazeotrope		*255*
8604	$C_{10}H_{16}$	α-Pinene	155.8	<147.4	>80	*255*
A =	**$C_5H_{11}N$**	**Piperidine**	**106.4**			
8605	$C_6H_{14}O$	Propyl ether	90.1	Nonazeotrope		*255*
8606	C_7H_8	Toluene	110.7	Min. b.p.		*203*
8607	C_7H_{14}	Methylcyclohexane	100	Min. b.p.		*96*
8608	C_7H_{16}	Heptane	98.4	<97.5	>9	*255*
A =	**$C_5H_{11}NO_2$**	**Ethyl-*N*-ethylamino Formate**				
8609	$C_6H_4Cl_2$	*p*-Dichlorobenzene	174.4	167.0	24.2	*235*
8610	$C_8H_{18}S$	Isobutyl sulfide	172	166.5	23	*235*
A =	**$C_5H_{11}NO_2$**	**Isoamyl Nitrite**	**97.15**			
8611	$C_5H_{12}O_2$	Diethoxymethane	87.95	Nonazeotrope		*207*
8612	C_6H_6	Benzene	80.15	Nonazeotrope		*230*
8613	C_6H_{12}	Cyclohexane	80.75	Nonazeotrope		*230*
8614	C_6H_{12}	Methylcyclopentane	72.0	Nonazeotrope		*230*
8615	$C_6H_{12}O$	Pinacolone	106.2	Nonazeotrope		*232*
8616	C_6H_{14}	Hexane	68.8	Nonazeotrope		*230*
8617	$C_6H_{14}O$	Propyl ether	90.1	Nonazeotrope		*230*
8618	$C_6H_{14}O_2$	Acetal	103.55	Nonazeotrope		*230*
8619	C_7H_8	Toluene	110.75	Nonazeotrope		*230*
8620	C_7H_{14}	Methylcyclohexane	101.15	95.5	79	*230*
8621	C_7H_{16}	Heptane	98.4	94.8	52	*230*
8622	C_8H_{16}	1,3-Dimethylcyclohexane	120.7	Nonazeotrope		*230*
8623	C_8H_{18}	2,5-Dimethylhexane	109.4	Nonazeotrope		*230*
8624	C_8H_{18}	Octane	125.75	Nonazeotrope		*230*
A =	**$C_5H_{11}NO_3$**	**Isoamyl Nitrate**	**149.75**			
8625	$C_5H_{12}O_2$	2-Propoxyethanol	151.35	<143.5	>57	*240*
8626	$C_5H_{12}O_3$	2-(2-Methoxyethoxy)ethanol	192.95	Nonazeotrope		*240*
8627	C_6H_5Br	Bromobenzene	156.1	Nonazeotrope		*240*
8628	$C_6H_{12}O$	Cyclohexanol	160.8	<148	....	*240*
8629	$C_6H_{12}O_3$	2-Ethoxyethyl acetate	156.8	Nonazeotrope		*240*
8630	$C_6H_{13}Br$	1-Bromohexane	156.5	<148.5	<80	*240*
8631	$C_6H_{14}O$	Hexyl alcohol	157.85	<148.0	>11	*240*
8632	$C_6H_{14}O_2$	2-Butoxyethanol	171.15	Nonazeotrope		*236*
8633	C_7H_7Cl	*o*-Chlorotoluene	159.2	Nonazeotrope		*240*
8634	C_7H_7Cl	*p*-Chlorotoluene	162.4	Nonazeotrope		*227*
8635	C_7H_8O	Anisole	153.85	Nonazeotrope		*237*
8636	$C_7H_{14}O$	2-Methylcyclohexanol	168.5	Nonazeotrope		*240*
8637	$C_7H_{14}O_2$	Methyl caproate	149.8	148.5	55	*229*
8638	$C_7H_{14}O_3$	1,3-Butanediol methyl ether acetate	171.75	Nonazeotrope		*207*
8639	C_8H_8	Styrene	145.8	<145.6	<38	*240*
8640	C_8H_{10}	*m*-Xylene	139.0	Nonazeotrope		*207*
8641	$C_8H_{16}O_2$	Isoamyl propionate	160.7	Nonazeotrope		*240*
8642	$C_8H_{16}O_2$	Isobutyl butyrate	156.9	Nonazeotrope		*229*
8643	$C_8H_{16}O_2$	Isobutyl isobutyrate	148.6	<147.5	<40	*229*
8644	C_9H_{12}	Mesitylene	164.6	Nonazeotrope		*240*
8645	C_9H_{12}	Propylbenzene	158.9	Nonazeotrope		*226*
8646	$C_9H_{20}O_2$	Diisobutoxymethane	163.8	Nonazeotrope		*237*
8647	$C_{10}H_{16}$	Camphene	159.6	149.0	72	*240*
8648	$C_{10}H_{16}$	Nopinene	163.8	149.2	80	*240*
8649	$C_{10}H_{16}$	α-Pinene	155.8	147.75	65	*240*
8650	$C_{10}H_{22}$	2,7-Dimethyloctane	160.1	<148.6	<83	*240*
A =	**C_5H_{12}**	**2-Methylbutane**	**27.95**			
8651	C_5H_{12}	Pentane	36.15	Nonazeotrope		*244*
8652	$C_6H_5NO_2$	Nitrobenzene	210.75	Nonazeotrope		*233*

No.	B-Component Formula	Name	B.P., ° C.	Azeotropic Data B.P., ° C.	Wt. % A	Ref.
A =	C_5H_{12}	**Pentane**	**36.15**			
8653	$C_5H_{12}O$	*tert*-Amyl alcohol	102.35	Nonazeotrope		*255*
8654	$C_6H_5NO_2$	Nitrobenzene	210.75	Nonazeotrope		*234*
A =	$C_5H_{12}O$	**Amyl Alcohol**	**138.2**			
8655	C_6H_5Cl	Chlorobenzene	131.75	126.2	25	*247*
8656	C_6H_6	Benzene	80.15	Nonazeotrope		*255*
8657	C_6H_6O	Phenol	182.2	Nonazeotrope		*255*
8658	$C_6H_{10}S$	Allyl sulfide	139.35	<134.5	>42	*246*
8659	C_6H_{12}	Cyclohexane	80.75	Nonazeotrope		*255*
8660	$C_6H_{12}O_2$	Amyl formate	132	131.4	43	*150*
8661	$C_6H_{12}O_2$	Butyl acetate	126.0	Nonazeotrope		*207*
8662	$C_6H_{12}O_2$	Ethyl butyrate	121.5	Nonazeotrope		*255*
8663	$C_6H_{12}O_2$	Isoamyl formate	123.8	Nonazeotrope		*255*
8664	$C_6H_{12}O_3$	Paraldehyde	123.9	Nonazeotrope		*256*
8665	C_6H_{14}	Hexane	69.0	Nonazeotrope		*328*
8666	C_7H_8	Toluene	110.75	Nonazeotrope		*255*
8667	C_7H_{14}	Methylcyclohexane	101.15	<101.0	....	*255*
8668	$C_7H_{14}O$	4-Heptanone	143.55	Nonazeotrope		*228*
8669	$C_7H_{14}O_2$	Amyl acetate	148.8	Nonazeotrope		*150*
8670	$C_7H_{14}O_2$	Propyl isobutyrate	134.0	<133.5	>19	*255*
8671	C_8H_{10}	Ethylbenzene	136.15	129.8	40	*247*
8672	C_8H_{10}	Ethylbenzene, 60 mm.	60.5	57.5	20	*26*
8673	C_8H_{10}	*p*-Xylene	138.45	131.3	42	*247*
8674	C_8H_{16}	1,3-Dimethylcyclohexane	120.7	118.2	20	*247*
8675	$C_8H_{18}O$	Butyl ether	142.1	134.5	50	*236*
8676	$C_8H_{18}O$	Isobutyl ether	122.2	121.2	10	*256*
8677	$C_{10}H_{22}O$	Amyl ether	188	Nonazeotrope		*307*
8678	$C_{11}H_{24}O_2$	Diamyloxymethane	221.6	Nonazeotrope		*131*
8679	$C_{12}H_{26}O_2$	Acetaldehyde diamyl acetal	225.3	Nonazeotrope		*20*
A =	$C_5H_{12}O$	***tert*-Amyl Alcohol**	**102.35**			
8680	$C_5H_{12}O_2$	Diethoxymethane	87.95	Nonazeotrope		*207*
8681	C_6H_5Cl	Chlorobenzene	131.75	Nonazeotrope		*255*
8682	C_6H_6	Benzene	80.2	~80.0	~15	*217*
8683	C_6H_8	1,3-Cyclohexadiene	80.4	79.7	~15	*221*
8684	C_6H_{10}	Cyclohexene	82.7	80.8	17	*217*
8685	C_6H_{12}	Cyclohexane	80.75	78.5	16	*217*
8686	C_6H_{12}	Methylcyclopentane	72.0	71.5	5	*255*
8687	$C_6H_{12}O_2$	Methyl isovalerate	116.5	Nonazeotrope		*255*
8688	C_6H_{14}	2,3-Dimethylbutane	58.0	Nonazeotrope		*255*
8689	C_6H_{14}	Hexane	68.9	68.3	4	*217*
8690	$C_6H_{14}O$	Propyl ether	90.4	88.8	20	*225*
8691	C_7H_8	Toluene	110.7	100.5	56	*23, 217**
8692	C_7H_{14}	Methylcyclohexane	100.8	92.0	40	*23, 251**
8693	C_7H_{16}	Heptane	98.45	92.2	26.5	*225, 251**
8694	C_8H_{10}	Ethylbenzene	136.15	Nonazeotrope		*217*
		60 mm.	60.5	45	83	*26*
8695	C_8H_{10}	*m*-Xylene	139.0	Nonazeotrope		*220*
8696	C_8H_{10}	*o*-Xylene	144.3	Nonazeotrope		*255*
8697	C_8H_{16}	1,3-Dimethylcyclohexane	120.7	100.1	68	*247*
8698	C_8H_{18}	2,5-Dimethylhexane	109.4	97.0	50	*247*
8699	C_8H_{18}	Octane	125.75	101.1	75	*247*
8700	$C_8H_{18}O$	Isobutyl ether	122.1	Min. b.p.		*256*
8701	$C_{10}H_{16}$	α-Pinene	155.8	Nonazeotrope		*217*
A =	$C_5H_{12}O$	**Ethyl Propyl Ether**	**63.6**			
8702	C_6H_{10}	Biallyl	60.1	<60.0	>5	*238*
8703	C_6H_{12}	Methylcyclopentane	72.0	Nonazeotrope		*238*
8704	C_6H_{14}	2,3-Dimethylbutane	58.0	Nonazeotrope		*238*
8705	C_6H_{14}	Hexane	68.85	Nonazeotrope		*238*
8706	$C_6H_{15}N$	Triethylamine	89.35	Nonazeotrope		*231*
A =	$C_5H_{12}O$	**Isoamyl Alcohol**	**131.9**			
8707	$C_5H_{12}O_2$	2-Propoxyethanol	151.35	Nonazeotrope		*207*
8708	C_6H_5Br	Bromobenzene	156.15	131.65	85	*207*
8709	C_6H_5Cl	Chlorobenzene	131.8	124.35	34	*207*
8710	C_6H_6	Benzene	80.2	Nonazeotrope		*431*

No.	B-Component Formula	Name	B.P., ° C.	Azeotropic Data B.P., ° C.	Wt. % A	Ref.
A =	**$C_5H_{12}O$**	**Isoamyl Alcohol** (*continued*)	**131.9**			
8711	C_6H_6O	Phenol	181.5	Nonazeotrope		*207*
8712	C_6H_6S	Benzenethiol	169.5	Nonazeotrope		*255*
8713	C_6H_7N	Aniline	184.35	Nonazeotrope		*207*
8714	C_6H_7N	2-Picoline	130.7	>132.5	....	*255*
8715	C_6H_7N	3-Picoline	143.4	Nonazeotrope		*255*
8716	C_6H_8	1,3-Cyclohexadiene	80.4	Nonazeotrope		*255*
8716a	C_6H_9N	*N*-Ethylpyrrol	130.4	<129.0	....	*255*
8717	C_6H_{10}	Cyclohexene	82.7	Nonazeotrope		*217*
8718	$C_6H_{10}O$	Mesityl oxide	129.45	129.15	24	*232*
8719	$C_6H_{10}S$	Allyl sulfide	139.35	<131.5	....	*207*
8720	$C_6H_{11}ClO_2$	Butyl chloroacetate	181.9	Nonazeotrope		*255*
8721	$C_6H_{11}N$	Capronitrile	163.9	Nonazeotrope		*255*
8722	C_6H_{12}	Cyclohexane	80.75	Nonazeotrope		*217*
8723	C_6H_{12}	Methylcyclopentane	72.0	Nonazeotrope		*255*
8724	$C_6H_{12}O$	4-Methyl-2-pentanone	116.05	Nonazeotrope		*207*
8725	$C_6H_{12}O_2$	Butyl acetate	126.0	125.85	17.5	*207*
8726	$C_6H_{12}O_2$	Ethyl butyrate	120.6	Nonazeotrope		*162*
8727	$C_6H_{12}O_2$	Isoamyl formate	124.2	123.6	25.5	*150, 207**
8728	$C_6H_{12}O_2$	Isobutyl acetate	117.4	Nonazeotrope		*207*
8729	$C_6H_{12}O_2$	Propyl propionate	122.1	Nonazeotrope		*212*
8730	$C_6H_{12}O_3$	2-Ethoxyethyl acetate	156.8	Nonazeotrope		*207*
8731	$C_6H_{12}O_3$	Paraldehyde	124	123.5	22	*236*
8732	C_6H_{14}	2,3-Dimethylbutane	73.9	Nonazeotrope		*255*
8733	C_6H_{14}	Hexane	68.95	Nonazeotrope		*243*
8734	$C_6H_{14}S$	Propyl sulfide	141.5	<130.5	<79	*246*
8735	$C_6H_{15}BO_3$	Ethyl borate	118.6	Nonazeotrope		*212*
8736	C_7H_7Cl	*o*-Chlorotoluene	159.2	Nonazeotrope		*207*
8737	C_7H_7Cl	*p*-Chlorotoluene	162.4	Nonazeotrope		*207*
8738	C_7H_8	Toluene	110.7	Nonazeotrope		*23, 207*, 334**
8739	C_7H_8O	Anisole	153.85	Nonazeotrope		*435*
8740	$C_7H_{13}ClO_2$	Isoamyl chloroacetate	195.2	Nonazeotrope		*58*
8741	C_7H_{14}	Methylcyclohexane	100.8	98.2	13	*23, 207**
8742	$C_7H_{14}O$	4-Heptanone	143.55	Nonazeotrope		*207*
8743	$C_7H_{14}O$	Isoamyl vinyl ether	112.6	112.1	12	*362*
8744	$C_7H_{14}O$	5-Methyl-2-hexanone	144.2	Nonazeotrope		*207, 232*
8745	$C_7H_{14}O_2$	Ethyl isovalerate	134.7	130.5	58	*207*
8746	$C_7H_{14}O_2$	Ethyl valerate	145.45	Nonazeotrope		*207*
8747	$C_7H_{14}O_2$	Isoamyl acetate	137.5	129.1	97.4	*247*
			142	Nonazeotrope		*150*
8748	$C_7H_{14}O_2$	Isobutyl propionate	136.9	131.2	72	*207*
8749	$C_7H_{14}O_2$	Propyl butyrate	143	Nonazeotrope		*207*
8750	$C_7H_{14}O_2$	Propyl isobutyrate	134.0	130.2	53	*207*
8751	C_7H_{16}	Heptane	98.45	97.7	7	*207*
8752	C_8H_8	Styrene, 60 mm.	68	64.8	43	*26*
			145.8	128.5	63	*217*
8753	C_8H_{10}	Ethylbenzene, 60 mm.	136.15	125.9	49	*219*
			60.5	58.5	26	*26*
8754	C_8H_{10}	*m*-Xylene	139	125–126	52	*243*, 334*
8785	C_8H_{10}	*o*-Xylene	142.6	127	>52	*207*, 334*
8756	C_8H_{10}	*p*-Xylene	138.2	125–126	52	*221*, 334*
8757	$C_8H_{10}O$	Benzyl methyl ether	167.8	Nonazeotrope		*255*
8758	$C_8H_{10}O$	Phenetole	170.45	Nonazeotrope		*255*
8759	C_8H_{16}	1,3-Dimethylcyclohexane	120.7	116.6	27	*247*
8760	C_8H_{16}	6-Methyl-1-heptene, 751 mm.	....	109	18	*306*
8761	$C_8H_{16}O_2$	Isoamyl propionate	160.7	Nonazeotrope		*255*
8762	C_8H_{18}	2,5-Dimethylhexane	109.4	107.6	15	*247*
8763	C_8H_{18}	Octane	125.8	120.0	35	*225*
8764	C_8H_{18}	2,2,4-Trimethylpentane	99.3	99.0	5	*255*
8765	$C_8H_{18}O$	Butyl ether	142.1	129.8	65	*207*
8766	$C_8H_{18}O$	Isobutyl ether	122.1	119.8	22	*207*
8767	C_9H_8	Indene	181.7	Nonazeotrope		*217*
8768	C_9H_{12}	Cumene	152.8	131.6	94	*217*
8769	C_9H_{12}	Mesitylene	164.0	Nonazeotrope		*243*
8770	C_9H_{12}	Propylbenzene	159.3	Nonazeotrope		*207*
8771	C_9H_{12}	Pseudocumene	169	Nonazeotrope		*243*

No	Formula	B-Component Name	B.P., ° C.	Azeotropic Data B.P., ° C.	Wt. % A	Ref.
A =	$C_5H_{12}O$	**Isoamyl Alcohol** (*continued*)	**131.9**			
8772	$C_{10}H_{14}$	Butylbenzene	183.1	Nonazeotrope		*255*
8773	$C_{10}H_{14}$	Cymene	175.3	Nonazeotrope		*243*
8774	$C_{10}H_{16}$	Camphene	159.6	130.9	24	*207*
8775	$C_{10}H_{16}$	*d*-Limonene	177.8	Nonazeotrope		*243*
8776	$C_{10}H_{16}$	α-Phellandrene	171.5	Nonazeotrope		*243*
8777	$C_{10}H_{16}$	α-Pinene	155.8	130.7	74	*207*
8778	$C_{10}H_{16}$	Terpinolene	184.6	Nonazeotrope		*255*
8779	$C_{10}H_{16}$	Thymene	179.7	Nonazeotrope		*217*
8780	$C_{10}H_{22}$	2,7-Dimethyloctane	160.2	129.7	~85	*217*
8781	$C_{10}H_{22}O$	Isoamyl ether	171	Nonazeotrope		*427*
8782	$C_{12}H_{26}O_2$	Acetaldehyde diisoamyl acetal	213.6	Nonazeotrope		*20*
A =	$C_5H_{12}O$	**2-Methyl-1-butanol**	**70/60 mm.**			
8783	C_8H_8	Styrene, 60 mm.	68	60	52	*26*
8784	C_8H_{10}	Ethylbenzene, 60 mm.	60.5	56	33	*26*
A =	$C_5H_{12}O$	**3-Methyl-2-butanol**	**112.9**			
8785	C_6H_6	Benzene	80.15	Nonazeotrope		*255*
8786	C_6H_{10}	Cyclohexene	82.75	<82.5	>3.5	*255*
8787	C_6H_{14}	Hexane	68.8	Nonazeotrope		*255*
8788	C_7H_8	Toluene	110.75	<105.8	>38	*255*
8789	C_7H_{14}	Methylcyclohexane	101.15	97.0	25	*247*
8790	C_7H_{16}	Heptane	98.4	95.0	23	*247*
8791	C_8H_{10}	Ethylbenzene, 60 mm.	60.5	51	62	*26*
8792	C_8H_{18}	2,5-Dimethylhexane	109.4	<103.5	>32	*255*
A =	$C_5H_{12}O$	**2-Pentanol**	**119.8**			
8793	C_6H_5Cl	Chlorobenzene	131.75	<118.2	>55	*247*
8794	C_6H_6	Benzene	80.15	Nonazeotrope		*255*
8795	C_6H_7N	2-Picoline	130.7	Nonazeotrope		*255*
8796	C_6H_{10}	Cyclohexene	82.75	Nonazeotrope		*255*
8797	$C_6H_{10}O$	Mesityl oxide	129.45	Nonazeotrope		*207*
8798	C_6H_{12}	Cyclohexane	80.75	Nonazeotrope		*255*
8799	C_6H_{12}	Methylcyclopentane	72.0	Nonazeotrope		*255*
8800	$C_6H_{12}O$	2-Hexanone	127.2	Nonazeotrope		*232*
8801	$C_6H_{12}O_2$	Butyl acetate	126.0	Quasi-azeotrope		*207*
8802	$C_6H_{12}O_2$	Ethyl butyrate	121.5	<118.5	>47	*247*
8803	$C_6H_{12}O_2$	Ethyl isobutyrate	110.1	Nonazeotrope		*255*
8804	$C_6H_{12}O_2$	Isobutyl acetate	117.4	116.5	32	*247*
8805	$C_6H_{12}O_2$	Methyl isovalerate	116.5	<115.8	>20	*255*
8806	$C_6H_{12}O_3$	Paraldehyde	124.35	118.5	52	*255*
8807	C_6H_{14}	Hexane	68.8	Nonazeotrope		*255*
8808	$C_6H_{14}O$	*tert*-Amyl methyl ether	86–7	Nonazeotrope		*105*
8809	$C_6H_{14}O$	*tert*-Butyl ethyl ether	73	Nonazeotrope		*105*
8810	$C_6H_{14}S$	Propyl sulfide	141.5	Nonazeotrope		*246*
8811	C_7H_8	Toluene	110.75	107.0	28	*247*
8812	C_7H_{14}	Methylcyclohexane	101.15	98.6	18	*247*
8813	C_7H_{16}	Heptane	98.4	96.0	15	*247*
8814	C_8H_8	Styrene, 60 mm.	68	60	69	*26*
8815	C_8H_{10}	Ethylbenzene	136.15	118.0	67	*191*
8816	C_8H_{10}	Ethylbenzene, 60 mm.	60.5	54	50	*26*
8817	C_8H_{10}	*m*-Xylene	139.2	118.3	70	*255*
8818	C_8H_{16}	1,3-Dimethylcyclohexane	120.7	<113.0	>38	*247*
8819	C_8H_{18}	Octane	125.75	<114.8	<56	*247*
8820	$C_8H_{18}O$	Isobutyl ether	122.1	115.0	41	*256*
A =	$C_5H_{12}O$	**3-Pentanol**	**116.0**			
8821	C_6H_6	Benzene	80.2	Nonazeotrope		*217*
8822	C_6H_{12}	Cyclohexane	80.8	80.0	3	*220*
8823	$C_6H_{12}O$	4-Methyl-2-pentanone	116.05	<115.0	>35	*232*
8824	C_6H_{14}	Hexane	68.95	Nonazeotrope		*217*
8825	$C_6H_{14}O$	Propyl ether	90.4	Nonazeotrope		*256*
8826	C_7H_8	Toluene	110.75	~106	~35	*217*
8827	C_7H_{14}	Methylcyclohexane	101.1	97.4	23	*217*
8828	C_7H_{16}	Heptane	98.4	96.0	20	*247*
8829	C_8H_{10}	Ethylbenzene, 60 mm.	60.5	51	50	*26*
8830	$C_8H_{18}O$	Isobutyl ether	122.1	112	....	*256*

No.	Formula	B-Component Name	B.P., ° C.	Azeotropic Data B.P., ° C.	Wt. % A	Ref.
A =	$C_5H_{12}O_2$	**Diethoxymethane**	**87.95**			
8831	C_6H_6	Benzene	80.15	Nonazeotrope		*238*
8832	C_6H_{12}	Cyclohexane	80.75	80.1	17	*207*
8833	C_6H_{14}	*n*-Hexane	68.8	Nonazeotrope		*207*
8834	$C_6H_{14}O$	Isopropyl ether	68.3	Nonazeotrope		*255*
8835	$C_6H_{15}N$	Triethylamine	89.35	<86.8	....	*231*
8836	C_7H_{14}	Methylcyclohexane	101.15	Nonazeotrope		*207*
8837	C_7H_{16}	*n*-Heptane	98.4	87.8	96	*238*
A =	$C_5H_{12}O_2$	**2-Propoxyethanol**	**151.35**			
8838	$C_6H_4Cl_2$	*p*-Dichlorobenzene	174.4	Nonazeotrope		*236*
8839	C_6H_5Br	Bromobenzene	156.1	148.2	48	*236*
8840	C_6H_5Cl	Chlorobenzene	131.75	Nonazeotrope		*206*
8841	C_6H_5I	Iodobenzene	188.45	Nonazeotrope		*206*
8842	C_6H_6O	Phenol	182.2	182.65	14	*236*
8843	C_6H_7N	Aniline	184.35	Nonazeotrope		*231*
8844	$C_6H_{10}O_4$	Ethylidene diacetate	168.5	Nonazeotrope		*207*
8845	$C_6H_{10}S$	Allyl sulfide	139.35	<137.5	<20	*246*
8846	$C_6H_{11}N$	Capronitrile	163.9	Nonazeotrope		*255*
8847	$C_6H_{12}O$	Cyclohexanol	160.8	Nonazeotrope		*206*
8848	$C_6H_{12}O_2$	Butyl acetate	126.0	Nonazeotrope		*255*
8849	$C_6H_{12}O_3$	2-Ethoxyethyl acetate	156.8	151.25	87.5	*236*
8850	$C_6H_{12}O_3$	Paraldehyde	124.35	Nonazeotrope		*236*
8851	$C_6H_{12}O_3$	Propyl lactate	171.7	Nonazeotrope		*255*
8852	$C_6H_{14}O_2$	Hexyl alcohol	157.85	Nonazeotrope		*206*
8853	$C_6H_{14}O_2$	Pinacol	174.35	Nonazeotrope		*255*
8854	$C_6H_{15}NO$	2-Diethylaminoethanol	162.2	Nonazeotrope		*231*
8855	C_7H_6O	Benzaldehyde	179.2	Nonazeotrope		*206*
8856	C_7H_7Cl	*o*-Chlorotoluene	159.2	149.5	60	*206*
8857	C_7H_7Cl	*p*-Chlorotoluene	162.4	149.7	70	*236*
8858	C_7H_8	Toluene	110.75	Nonazeotrope		*206*
8859	C_7H_8O	Anisole	153.85	148.15	58	*207*
8860	C_7H_8O	*o*-Cresol	191.1	Nonazeotrope		*236*
8861	C_7H_9N	Benzylamine	185.0	Nonazeotrope		*231*
8862	C_7H_9N	*N*-Methylaniline	196.25	Nonazeotrope		*206*
8863	$C_7H_{14}O$	4-Heptanone	143.55	Nonazeotrope		*232*
8864	$C_7H_{14}O$	5-Methyl-2-hexanone	144.2	Nonazeotrope		*232*
8865	$C_7H_{14}O_2$	Butyl propionate	146.8	<145.0	~20	*255*
8866	$C_7H_{14}O_2$	Ethyl isovalerate	134.7	Nonazeotrope		*206*
8867	$C_7H_{14}O_2$	Ethyl valerate	145.75	144.0	22	*236*
8868	$C_7H_{14}O_2$	Isobutyl propionate	137.5	Nonazeotrope		*255*
8869	$C_7H_{14}O_2$	1,3-Butanediol methyl ether acetate	171.75	Nonazeotrope		*207*
8870	C_8H_8	Styrene	145.8	140.5	37	*247*
8871	C_8H_{10}	Ethylbenzene	136.15	134.5	20	*236*
8872	C_8H_{10}	*m*-Xylene	139.2	136.95	25.5	*207*
8873	C_8H_{10}	*o*-Xylene	144.3	140.5	35	*206*
8874	C_8H_{10}	*p*-Xylene	138.45	136.3	24	*206*
8875	$C_8H_{10}O$	*p*-Methylanisole	177.05	Nonazeotrope		*206*
8876	$C_8H_{10}O$	Phenetole	170.45	Nonazeotrope		*236*
8877	$C_8H_{11}N$	*N*-Dimethylaniline	194.15	Nonazeotrope		*255*
8878	C_8H_{16}	1,3-Dimethylcyclohexane	120.7	119.0	15	*255*
8879	$C_8H_{16}O_2$	Butyl butyrate	166.4	Nonazeotrope		*206*
8880	$C_8H_{16}O_2$	Isobutyl butyrate	156.9	149.0	62	*206*
8881	$C_8H_{16}O_2$	Propyl isovalerate	155.7	147.5	65	*247*
8882	C_8H_{18}	Octane	125.75	122.8	18	*206*
8883	$C_8H_{18}O$	Butyl ether	142.4	138.5	37	*206*
8884	$C_8H_{18}O$	Isobutyl ether	122.3	<122.0	....	*255*
8885	C_9H_8	Indene	182.6	Nonazeotrope		*255*
8886	C_9H_{12}	Cumene	152.8	147.0	50	*206*
8887	C_9H_{12}	Mesitylene	164.6	149.4	68	*206*
8888	C_9H_{12}	Propylbenzene	159.3	147.8	60	*236*
8889	C_9H_{12}	Pseudocumene	168.2	150.2	82	*255*
8890	$C_9H_{13}N$	*N*,*N*-Dimethyl-*o*-toluidine	185.3	Nonazeotrope		*231*
8891	$C_9H_{18}O$	2,6-Dimethyl-4-heptanone	168.0	Nonazeotrope		*232*
8892	$C_{10}H_{14}$	Butylbenzene	183.1	Nonazeotrope		*255*
8893	$C_{10}H_{14}$	Cymene	176.7	Nonazeotrope		*236*

No.	B-Component Formula	Name	B.P., ° C.	Azeotropic Data B.P., ° C.	Wt. % A	Ref.
A =	**$C_5H_{12}O_2$**	**2-Propoxyethanol** (*continued*)	**151.35**			
8894	$C_{10}H_{16}$	Camphene	159.6	144	52	*206*
8895	$C_{10}H_{16}$	Dipentene	177.7	148.5	68	*247*
8896	$C_{10}H_{16}$	α-Pinene	155.8	142.0	48	*247*
8897	$C_{10}H_{16}$	α-Terpinene	173.4	148.0	65	*247*
8898	$C_{10}H_{16}$	Terpinolene	184.6	<150.8	....	*255*
8899	$C_{10}H_{18}O$	Cineole	176.35	Nonazeotrope		*236*
8900	$C_{10}H_{22}$	2,7-Dimethylhexane	160.1	143.7	52	*207*
8901	$C_{10}H_{22}O$	Amyl ether	187.5	Nonazeotrope		*255*
8902	$C_{10}H_{22}O$	Isoamyl ether	173.2	150.1	77	*236*
A =	**$C_5H_{12}O_3$**	**2-(2-Methoxyethoxy)ethanol**	**192.95**			
8903	$C_6H_5NO_2$	Nitrobenzene	210.75	Nonazeotrope		*234*
8904	C_6H_6O	Phenol	182.2	199.65	61	*236*
8905	C_6H_7N	Aniline	184.35	Nonazeotrope		*231*
8906	$C_6H_8O_4$	Methyl fumarate	193.25	185.5	44	*206*
8907	$C_6H_{10}O_4$	Ethylidene diacetate	168.5	Nonazeotrope		*255*
8908	$C_6H_{10}O_4$	Glycol diacetate	186.0	181.5	30	*247*
8909	$C_6H_{11}NO_2$	Nitrocyclohexane	205.3	<192.7	....	*234*
8910	C_7H_5N	Benzonitrile	191.1	<190.5	....	*255*
8911	$C_7H_7NO_2$	o-Nitrotoluene	221.75	Nonazeotrope		*234*
8912	C_7H_8O	Benzyl alcohol	205.25	<192.5	....	*255*
8913	C_7H_8O	o-Cresol	191.1	201.5	52	*207*
8914	C_7H_8O	p-Cresol	201.7	208.0	30	*206*
8915	$C_7H_8O_2$	Guaiacol	205.05	Nonazeotrope		*206*
8916	C_7H_9N	Benzylamine	185.0	Nonazeotrope		*255*
8917	C_7H_9N	Methylaniline	196.25	190.0	60	*231*
8918	$C_7H_{13}ClO_2$	Isoamyl chloroacetate	190.5	187.0	55	*255*
8919	$C_7H_{14}O_3$	Isobutyl lactate	182.15	Nonazeotrope		*255*
8920	$C_7H_{16}O_4$	2-[2-(2-Methoxyethoxy)ethoxy]-ethanol	245.25	Nonazeotrope		*255*
8921	C_8H_8O	Acetophenone	202.0	191.9	80	*207*
8922	$C_8H_8O_2$	Methyl benzoate	199.4	188.8	50	*206*
8923	$C_8H_8O_2$	Phenyl acetate	195.7	188.6	45	*206*
8924	$C_8H_8O_3$	Methyl salicylate	222.95	Nonazeotrope		*255*
8925	$C_8H_{10}O$	Benzyl methyl ether	167.8	Nonazeotrope		*255*
8926	$C_8H_{10}O$	Phenethyl alcohol	219.4	Nonazeotrope		*255*
8927	$C_8H_{11}N$	Dimethylaniline	194.15	184.85	49	*231*
8928	$C_8H_{16}O_2$	Isoamyl propionate	160.7	Nonazeotrope		*255*
8929	$C_8H_{16}O_3$	Isoamyl lactate	202.4	Nonazeotrope		*255*
8930	C_9H_7N	Quinoline	237.3	Nonazeotrope		*233*
8931	C_9H_8	Indene	182.3	177.5	30	*117*, 247*
8932	$C_9H_{10}O_2$	Benzyl acetate	215.0	Nonazeotrope		*255*
8933	C_9H_{12}	m-Ethyltoluene	161.3	....	~8	*269*
8934	C_9H_{12}	o-Ethyltoluene	165.1	....	~16	*383*
8935	C_9H_{12}	p-Ethyltoluene	162.0	....	~9	*383*
8936	C_9H_{12}	Mesitylene	164.6	162.5	13	*255, 383**
8937	C_9H_{12}	Pseudocumene	168.2	....	~15	*383*
8938	C_9H_{12}	1,2,3-Trimethylbenzene	176.1	....	~26	*383*
8939	$C_9H_{12}O$	Benzyl ethyl ether	185.0	<183.2	....	*255*
8940	$C_9H_{13}N$	N,N-Dimethyl-o-toluidine	185.3	<183.0	....	*231*
8941	$C_9H_{13}N$	Dimethyl-p-toluidine	210.2	Nonazeotrope		*255*
8942	$C_9H_{14}O$	Phorone	197.8	190.5	<75	*232*
8943	$C_9H_{18}O_2$	Isoamyl butyrate	181.05	176.55	22	*207*
8944	$C_9H_{18}O_2$	Isobutyl isovalerate	171.2	<170.5	....	*255*
8945	$C_{10}H_8$	Naphthalene	218.0	192.2	89	*236*
8946	$C_{10}H_{14}$	Butylbenzene	183.1	178.5	33	*206*
8947	$C_{10}H_{14}$	sec-Butylbenzene	173.1	....	~17	*383*
8948	$C_{10}H_{14}$	tert-Butylbenzene	168.5	....	~14	*383*
8949	$C_{10}H_{14}$	Cymene	176.7	172.0	27	*255*
8950	$C_{10}H_{15}N$	Diethylaniline	217.05	Nonazeotrope		*231*
8951	$C_{10}H_{16}$	Dipentene	177.7	168.5	33	*255*
8952	$C_{10}H_{16}$	Nopinene	163.8	159.0	~22	*255*
8953	$C_{10}H_{16}$	α-Pinene				
8953	$C_{10}H_{16}$	α-Terpinene	173.4	166.0	30	*255*
8954	$C_{10}H_{16}O$	Camphor	209.1	Nonazeotrope		*232*
8955	$C_{10}H_{18}O$	Borneol	215.0	Nonazeotrope		*206*

No.	Formula	B-Component Name	B.P., ° C.	Azeotropic Data B.P., ° C.	Wt. % A	Ref.
A =	$C_5H_{12}O_3$	**2-(2-Methoxyethoxy)ethanol** *(continued)*	**192.95**			
8956	$C_{10}H_{18}O$	Cineole	176.35	173.0	22	*236*
8957	$C_{10}H_{18}O$	Citronellal	208.0	Nonazeotrope		*255*
8958	$C_{10}H_{18}O$	Geraniol	229.6	Nonazeotrope		*255*
8959	$C_{10}H_{18}O$	α-Terpineol	218.85	Nonazeotrope		*255*
8960	$C_{10}H_{20}O$	Menthol	216.3	Nonazeotrope		*255*
8961	$C_{10}H_{20}O_2$	Isoamyl isovalerate	192.7	<185.0	<45	*247*
8962	$C_{10}H_{22}O$	Amyl ether	187.5	179.5	46	*206*
8963	$C_{10}H_{22}O$	Decyl alcohol	232.8	Nonazeotrope		*255*
8964	$C_{10}H_{22}O$	Isoamyl ether	173.2	168.85	23	*207*
8965	$C_{11}H_{10}$	2-Methylnaphthalene	241.15	Nonazeotrope		*207*
8966	$C_{11}H_{20}O$	Isobornyl methyl ether	192.4	187.5	50	*247*
8967	$C_{12}H_{18}$	1,3,5-Triethylbenzene	215.5	190.0	65	*247*
A =	$C_5H_{12}S$	**3-Methyl-1-butanethiol**	**~120**			
8968	$C_6H_{10}O$	1-Hexene-5-one	129	Reacts		*243*
A =	$C_5H_{14}OSi$	**Ethoxytrimethylsilane**	**75–76**			
8969	C_6H_6	Benzene	80.2	Min. b.p.		*86*
A =	$C_6H_3Cl_3$	**1,3,5-Trichlorobenzene**	**208.4**			
8970	$C_6H_5NO_2$	Nitrobenzene	210.75	~207.0	....	*225*
8971	C_6H_6O	Phenol	181.5	181.3	5	*243*
8972	C_6H_6O	Phenol	182.2	Nonazeotrope		*224*
8973	$C_6H_6O_2$	Pyrocatechol	245.9	Nonazeotrope		*224*
8974	C_6H_7N	Aniline	184.35	Nonazeotrope		*255*
8975	$C_6H_{10}O_3$	Ethyl acetoacetate	180.4	Nonazeotrope		*225*
8976	$C_6H_{12}O_2$	Caproic acid	205.2	204.0	57	*223*
8977	$C_7H_6O_2$	Benzoic acid	250.8	Nonazeotrope		*255*
8978	$C_7H_7NO_2$	*o*-Nitrotoluene	221.75	Nonazeotrope		*234*
8979	C_7H_8O	Benzyl alcohol	202.25	202.5	....	*255*
8980	C_7H_8O	*m*-Cresol	202.2	200.5	40	*222*
8981	C_7H_8O	*o*-Cresol	190.8	Nonazeotrope		*243*
8982	C_7H_8O	*p*-Cresol	201.7	200.2	40	*222*
8983	C_7H_9N	Methylaniline	196.25	Nonazeotrope		*231*
8984	C_7H_9N	*m*-Toluidine	203.1	<202.5	>25	*255*
8985	C_7H_9N	*p*-Toluidine	200.3	~199	....	*243*
8986	$C_7H_{12}O_4$	Ethyl malonate	198.9	Nonazeotrope		*243*
8987	C_8H_8O	Acetophenone	202	Nonazeotrope		*243*
8988	$C_8H_8O_2$	Methyl benzoate	199.55	Nonazeotrope		*243*
8989	$C_8H_8O_3$	Methyl salicylate	222.95	Nonazeotrope		*228*
8990	$C_8H_{10}O$	Phenethyl alcohol	219.4	<207.5	....	*255*
8991	$C_8H_{11}N$	Dimethylaniline	194.15	Nonazeotrope		*231*
8992	$C_8H_{11}N$	Ethylaniline	206.5	203	65	*243*
8993	$C_8H_{18}O$	Octyl alcohol	195.2	Nonazeotrope		*255*
8994	$C_8H_{18}O_3$	2-(2-Butoxyethoxy)ethanol	231.2	Nonazeotrope		*255*
8995	$C_9H_{10}O_2$	Benzyl acetate	215.6	Nonazeotrope ?		*243*
8996	$C_9H_{10}O_2$	Ethyl benzoate	213	Nonazeotrope		*243*
8997	$C_9H_{13}N$	*N,N*-Dimethyl-*o*-toluidine	185.3	Nonazeotrope		*255*
8998	$C_{10}H_8$	Naphthalene	218.0	Nonazeotrope		*255*
8999	$C_{10}H_{14}O$	Thymol	232.9	Nonazeotrope		*224*
9000	$C_{10}H_{16}O$	Camphor	209.1	211.5	52	*231*
9001	$C_{10}H_{18}O$	Borneol	215.0	Nonazeotrope		*255*
9002	$C_{10}H_{18}O$	Menthone	~207	~209.5	....	*243*
9003	$C_{10}H_{20}O$	Menthol	216.3	Nonazeotrope		*255*
9004	$C_{11}H_{24}O_2$	Diisoamyloxymethane	210.8	213.0	35	*239*
A =	C_6H_4BrCl	***p*-Bromochlorobenzene**	**196.4**			
9005	C_6H_6O	Phenol	182.2	181.0	38	*242*
9006	C_6H_7N	Aniline	184.35	Nonazeotrope		*231*
9007	$C_6H_{10}O_3$	Ethyl acetoacetate	180.4	Nonazeotrope		*255*
9008	$C_6H_{10}O_4$	Methyl succinate	195.5	<191.3	>46	*255*
9009	$C_6H_{12}O_2$	Caproic acid	205.15	193.0	80	*242*
9010	$C_6H_{14}O_2$	2-Butoxyethanol	171.15	Nonazeotrope		*255*
9011	C_7H_5N	Benzonitrile	191.1	<190.5	<30	*255*
9012	C_7H_8O	Benzyl alcohol	205.25	194.0	....	*255*
9013	C_7H_8O	*o*-Cresol	191.1	189.0	47	*242*

No.	B-Component Formula	Name	B.P., ° C.	Azeotropic Data B.P., ° C.	Wt. % A	Ref.
A =	C_6H_4BrCl	**p-Bromochlorobenzene** *(continued)*	**196.4**			
9014	C_7H_8O	p-Cresol	201.7	194.5	75	242
9015	C_7H_9N	o-Toluidine	200.35	194.6	....	255
9016	C_7H_9N	p-Toluidine	200.55	<195.2	>68	255
9017	$C_7H_{12}O_4$	Ethyl malonate	199.35	<193.5	>40	255
9018	C_8H_8O	Acetophenone	202.0	Nonazeotrope		232
9019	$C_8H_8O_2$	Methyl benzoate	199.4	Nonazeotrope		255
9020	$C_8H_{11}N$	Dimethylaniline	194.15	Nonazeotrope		255
9021	$C_8H_{16}O_3$	Isoamyl lactate	202.4	Nonazeotrope		255
9022	$C_8H_{18}O$	sec-Octyl alcohol	180.4	Nonazeotrope		255
9023	$C_9H_{12}O$	Benzyl ethyl ether	185.0	Nonazeotrope		239
9024	$C_9H_{12}O$	Phenyl propyl ether	190.5	Nonazeotrope		255
9025	$C_9H_{13}N$	N,N-Dimethyl-o-toluidine	185.3	Nonazeotrope		231
9026	$C_9H_{13}N$	N,N-Dimethyl-p-toluidine	210.2	Nonazeotrope		231
9027	$C_9H_{14}O$	Phorone	197.8	Nonazeotrope		232
9028	$C_{10}H_{20}O_2$	Isoamyl isovalerate	192.7	Nonazeotrope		255
A =	$C_6H_4Br_2$	**p-Dibromobenzene**	**220.25**			
9029	$C_6H_4ClNO_2$	m-Chloronitrobenzene	235.5	Nonazeotrope		234
9030	$C_6H_4ClNO_2$	p-Chloronitrobenzene	239.1	Nonazeotrope		234
9031	C_6H_5ClO	p-Chlorophenol	219.75	215.05	65	254
9032	$C_6H_5NO_2$	Nitrobenzene	210.75	210.45	22.5	234
9033	$C_6H_5NO_3$	o-Nitrophenol	217.2	215.15	48	244
9034	C_6H_6O	Phenol	182.2	Nonazeotrope		215
9035	$C_6H_6O_2$	Pyrocatechol	245.9	218.15	90	218
9036	$C_6H_6O_2$	Resorcinol	281.4	Nonazeotrope		222
9037	$C_6H_{12}O_2$	Caproic acid	205.15	203.4	42	244
9038	$C_7H_5Cl_3$	α,α,α-Trichlorotoluene	220.9	219.6	72	229
9039	$C_7H_6O_2$	Benzoic acid	250.5	219.5	96.2	218
9040	C_7H_7BrO	o-Bromoanisole	217.7	<217.4	<12	255
9041	$C_7H_7NO_2$	m-Nitrotoluene	230.8	Nonazeotrope		234
9042	$C_7H_7NO_2$	o-Nitrotoluene	221.75	218.0	73	234
9043	$C_7H_7NO_2$	p-Nitrotoluene	238.9	Nonazeotrope		234
9044	C_7H_8O	Benzyl alcohol	205.2	204.2	34.5	254
9045	C_7H_8O	m-Cresol	202.1	201.9	7	221
9046	C_7H_8O	o-Cresol	191.1	Nonazeotrope		218
9047	C_7H_8O	p-Cresol	201.7	Nonazeotrope		222
9048	$C_7H_8O_2$	Guaiacol	205.05	Nonazeotrope		236
9049	$C_7H_8O_2$	m-Methoxyphenol	244	Nonazeotrope		215
9050	C_7H_9N	m-Toluidine	203.1	Nonazeotrope		231
9051	C_7H_9N	o-Toluidine	200.35	Nonazeotrope		231
9052	C_7H_9N	p-Toluidine	200.55	Nonazeotrope		231
9053	C_7H_9NO	o-Anisidine	219.0	217.5	....	255
9054	$C_7H_{14}O_2$	Enanthic acid	220.0	215.5	70	242
9055	$C_7H_{16}O_4$	2-[2-(2-Methoxyethoxy)ethoxy]-ethanol	245.25	Nonazeotrope		255
9056	$C_8H_8O_2$	α-Toluic acid	266.5	Nonazeotrope		255
9057	$C_8H_8O_3$	Methyl salicylate	222.35	219.4	75	254
9058	C_8H_9BrO	p-Bromophenetole	234.5	Nonazeotrope		255
9059	$C_8H_{10}O$	3,4-Xylenol	226.8	218.65	75	250
9060	$C_8H_{10}O$	p-Ethylphenol	218.8	216.0	50	242
9061	$C_8H_{10}O$	Phenethyl alcohol	219.4	215.0	67.5	254
9062	$C_8H_{10}O$	2,4-Xylenol	210.5	209.8	10	255
9063	$C_8H_{10}O_2$	m-Dimethoxybenzene	214.7	Nonazeotrope		215
9064	$C_8H_{10}O_2$	o-Ethoxyphenol	216.5	214.0	32	255
9065	$C_8H_{10}O_2$	2-Phenoxyethanol	245.2	Nonazeotrope		255
9066	$C_8H_{11}N$	Ethylaniline	205.5	Nonazeotrope		231
9067	$C_8H_{11}N$	3,4-Xylidine	225.5	<219.9	<89	255
9068	$C_8H_{11}NO$	o-Phenetidine	232.5	Nonazeotrope		228
9069	$C_8H_{12}O_4$	Ethyl fumarate	217.85	<216.5	<47	255
9070	$C_8H_{14}O_4$	Ethyl succinate	217.25	<215.0	>25	227
9071	$C_8H_{14}O_4$	Propyl oxalate	214	<213	<32	255
9072	$C_8H_{16}O_2$	Caprylic acid	237.5	218.8	~90	221
9073	$C_8H_{18}O$	Octyl alcohol	195.2	Nonazeotrope		255
9074	$C_8H_{18}O_3$	2-(2-Butoxyethoxy)ethanol	231.2	Nonazeotrope		255
9075	C_9H_7N	Quinoline	237.3	Nonazeotrope		233

No.	B-Component Formula	Name	B.P., ° C.	Azeotropic Data B.P., ° C.	Wt. % A	Ref.
A =	$C_6H_4Br_2$	***p*-Dibromobenzene (*continued*)**	**220.25**			
9076	$C_9H_{10}O$	*p*-Methylacetophenone	226.35	220.15	95	*232*
9077	$C_9H_{10}O$	Propiophenone	217.7	Nonazeotrope		*232*
9078	$C_9H_{10}O_2$	Benzyl acetate	214.9	Nonazeotrope		*218*
9079	$C_9H_{10}O_2$	Ethyl benzoate	212.6	Nonazeotrope		*215*
9080	$C_9H_{10}O_3$	Ethyl salicylate	234.0	Nonazeotrope		*228*
9081	$C_9H_{12}O$	3-Phenylpropanol	220.25	<219.9	>85	*255*
9082	$C_9H_{13}N$	*N*,*N*-Dimethyl-*p*-toluidine	210.2	Nonazeotrope		*231*
9083	$C_9H_{18}O_2$	Pelargonic acid	254.0	Nonazeotrope		*255*
9084	$C_{10}H_8$	Naphthalene	218.05	Nonazeotrope		*254*
9085	$C_{10}H_{12}O$	Estragole	215.6	Nonazeotrope		*215*
9086	$C_{10}H_{12}O_2$	Ethyl *α*-toluate	228.75	Nonazeotrope		*227*
9087	$C_{10}H_{12}O_2$	Propyl benzoate	230.85	Nonazeotrope		*255*
9088	$C_{10}H_{14}O$	Carvacrol	237.85	Nonazeotrope		*255*
9089	$C_{10}H_{14}O$	Carvone	231.0	Nonazeotrope		*232*
9090	$C_{10}H_{14}O$	Thymol	232.9	Nonazeotrope		*222*
9091	$C_{10}H_{14}O_2$	*m*-Diethoxybenzene	235.0	Nonazeotrope		*239*
9092	$C_{10}H_{15}N$	Diethylaniline	217.05	Nonazeotrope		*231*
9093	$C_{10}H_{16}O$	Pulegone	223.8	Nonazeotrope		*232*
9094	$C_{10}H_{18}O$	Borneol	213.4	213.3	~18	*215*
9095	$C_{10}H_{18}O$	Geraniol	229.6	220.2	97	*215*
9096	$C_{10}H_{18}O$	*α*-Terpineol	217.8	Reacts		*215*
9097	$C_{10}H_{20}O$	Citronellol	224.5	Nonazeotrope		*215*
			224.5	218.5	....	*213*
9098	$C_{10}H_{20}O$	Menthol	216.4	215.4	43	*254*
9099	$C_{10}H_{20}O_2$	Methyl pelargonate	213.8	Nonazeotrope		*255*
9100	$C_{10}H_{22}O$	Decyl alcohol	~232.9	220.2	98	*215*
9101	$C_{11}H_{16}O$	Methyl thymol ether	216.5	Nonazeotrope		*239*
9102	$C_{11}H_{20}O$	Terpineol methyl ether	216.3	Nonazeotrope		*228*
9103	$C_{11}H_{22}O_3$	Isoamyl carbonate	232.2	Nonazeotrope		*227*
9104	$C_{12}H_{18}$	1,3,5-Triethylbenzene	215.5	Nonazeotrope		*255*
9105	$C_{12}H_{20}O_2$	Bornyl acetate	227.6	Nonazeotrope		*218*
A =	$C_6H_4ClNO_2$	***m*-Chloronitrobenzene**	**235.5**			
9106	$C_6H_6O_2$	Pyrocatechol	245.9	Nonazeotrope		*234*
9107	$C_6H_{14}O_3$	Dipropylene glycol	229.2	<227.0	....	*234*
9108	$C_7H_5Cl_3$	*α*,*α*,*α*-Trichlorotoluene	220.8	Nonazeotrope		*234*
9109	$C_7H_7NO_2$	*m*-Nitrotoluene	230.8	Nonazeotrope		*234*
9110	$C_7H_7NO_2$	*p*-Nitrotoluene	238.9	Nonazeotrope		*255*
9111	C_7H_9NO	*o*-Anisidine	219.0	Nonazeotrope		*255*
9112	$C_7H_{14}O_2$	Enanthic acid	222.0	<221.5	....	*234*
9113	$C_8H_8O_3$	Methyl salicylate	222.95	Nonazeotrope		*234*
9114	$C_8H_{10}O$	*p*-Ethylphenol	220.0	Nonazeotrope		*234*
9115	$C_8H_{10}O$	3,4-Xylenol	226.8	Nonazeotrope		*234*
9116	$C_8H_{11}NO$	*o*-Phenetidine	232.5	Nonazeotrope		*231*
9117	$C_8H_{11}NO$	*p*-Phenetidine	249.9	Nonazeotrope		*231*
9118	C_9H_7N	Quinoline	237.3	Nonazeotrope		*234*
9119	$C_9H_{10}O$	*p*-Methylacetophenone	226.35	Nonazeotrope		*255*
9120	$C_9H_{10}O$	Cinnamyl alcohol	257.0	Nonazeotrope		*234*
9121	$C_9H_{10}O_3$	Ethyl salicylate	233.8	Nonazeotrope		*234*
9122	$C_{10}H_8$	Naphthalene	218.0	Nonazeotrope		*234*
9123	$C_{10}H_{12}O_2$	Propyl benzoate	230.85	Nonazeotrope		*234*
9124	$C_{10}H_{14}O$	Carvacrol	237.85	<235.4	....	*234*
9125	$C_{10}H_{14}O$	Carvone	231.0	Nonazeotrope		*255*
9126	$C_{10}H_{14}O$	Thymol	232.9	Nonazeotrope		*234*
9127	$C_{10}H_{22}S$	Isoamyl sulfide	214.3	Nonazeotrope		*255*
9128	$C_{11}H_{10}$	1-Methylnaphthalene	244.6	Nonazeotrope		*234*
9129	$C_{11}H_{22}O_3$	Isoamyl carbonate	232.2	<231.8	....	*234*
9130	$C_{12}H_{20}O_2$	Bornyl acetate	227.6	Nonazeotrope		*237*
A =	$C_6H_4ClNO_2$	***o*-Chloronitrobenzene**	**246.0**			
9131	$C_6H_6O_2$	Pyrocatechol	245.9	243.5	....	*234*
9132	$C_6H_6O_2$	Resorcinol	281.4	Nonazeotrope		*234*
9133	$C_6H_{14}O_4$	Triethylene glycol	288.7	Nonazeotrope		*234*
9134	$C_7H_6O_2$	Benzoic acid	250.8	243.0	67	*234*
9135	$C_7H_7NO_2$	*p*-Nitrotoluene	238.9	Nonazeotrope		*234*
9136	C_7H_8O	*m*-Cresol	202.2	Nonazeotrope		*224*
9137	$C_7H_{14}O_2$	Enanthic acid	222.0	Nonazeotrope		*234*

No.	B-Component Formula	Name	B.P., ° C.	Azeotropic Data B.P., ° C.	Wt. % A	Ref.
A =	$C_6H_4ClNO_2$	**o-Chloronitrobenzene** (*continued*)	**246.0**			
9138	$C_8H_{11}NO$	o-Phenetidine	232.5	Nonazeotrope		231
9139	$C_8H_{11}NO$	p-Phenetidine	249.9	Nonazeotrope		231
9140	C_9H_7N	Quinoline	237.3	Nonazeotrope		233
9141	$C_{10}H_7Cl$	1-Chloronaphthalene	262.7	Nonazeotrope		234
9142	$C_{10}H_{10}O_2$	Isosafrol	252.0	Nonazeotrope		234
9143	$C_{10}H_{10}O_2$	Safrole	235.9	Nonazeotrope		234
9144	$C_{10}H_{14}O$	Carvacrol	237.85	Nonazeotrope		234
9145	$C_{10}H_{14}O$	Thymol	232.9	Nonazeotrope		234
9146	$C_{11}H_{10}$	2-Methylnaphthalene	241.15	Nonazeotrope		234
9147	$C_{11}H_{14}O_2$	Butyl benzoate	249.5	Nonazeotrope		234
9148	$C_{11}H_{14}O_2$	Isobutyl benzoate	241.9	Nonazeotrope		234
9149	$C_{12}H_{16}O_3$	Isoamyl salicylate	277.5	Nonazeotrope		234
A =	$C_6H_4ClNO_2$	**p-Chloronitrobenzene**	**239.1**			
9150	$C_6H_6O_2$	Pyrocatechol	247.9	238.6	82.5	234
9151	$C_6H_6O_2$	Resorcinol	281.4	Nonazeotrope		234
9152	$C_6H_{14}O_3$	Dipropylene glycol	229.2	<228.3	<89	234
9153	$C_7H_6O_2$	Benzoic acid	250.8	237.75	84	234
9154	$C_7H_7NO_2$	p-Nitrotoluene	238.9	238.85	33	234
9155	C_7H_8O	Benzyl alcohol	205.25	Nonazeotrope		234
9156	$C_7H_{16}O_4$	2-[2-(2-Methoxyethoxy)ethoxy]-ethanol	245.25	<234.0	....	234
9157	$C_8H_8O_2$	Anisaldehyde	249.5	Nonazeotrope		255
9158	$C_8H_{10}O$	3,4-Xylenol	226.8	Nonazeotrope		234
9159	$C_8H_{11}NO$	o-Phenetidine	232.5	Nonazeotrope		231
9160	$C_8H_{11}NO$	p-Phenetidine	249.9	Nonazeotrope		231
9161	$C_8H_{16}O_2$	Caprylic acid	238.5	<235.5	....	231
9162	C_9H_7N	Quinoline	237.3	Nonazeotrope		233
9163	C_9H_8O	Cinnamyl aldehyde	253.5	Nonazeotrope		234
9164	$C_9H_{10}O$	Cinnamyl alcohol	257.0	Nonazeotrope		234
9165	$C_9H_{10}O_3$	Ethyl salicylate	233.8	Nonazeotrope		223
9166	$C_{10}H_9N$	Quinaldine	246.5	Nonazeotrope		234
9167	$C_{10}H_{10}O_2$	Safrole	235.9	Nonazeotrope		234
9168	$C_{10}H_{12}O_2$	Ethyl α-toluate	228.75	Nonazeotrope		234
9169	$C_{10}H_{12}O_2$	Propyl benzoate	230.85	Nonazeotrope		233
9170	$C_{10}H_{14}O$	Carvacrol	237.85	237.4	....	234
9171	$C_{10}H_{14}O$	Thymol	232.9	Nonazeotrope		255
9172	$C_{10}H_{14}O$	Carvone	231.0	Nonazeotrope		234
9173	$C_{11}H_{10}$	1-Methylnaphthalene	244.6	Nonazeotrope		207
9174	$C_{11}H_{10}$	2-Methylnaphthalene	241.15	Nonazeotrope		234
9175	$C_{11}H_{14}O_2$	Butyl benzoate	249.5	Nonazeotrope		234
9176	$C_{11}H_{14}O_2$	Isobutyl benzoate	241.9	Nonazeotrope		234
9177	$C_{11}H_{22}O_3$	Isoamyl carbonate	232.2	232.1	5?	234
9178	$C_{12}H_{10}$	Biphenyl	256.1	Nonazeotrope		234
9179	$C_{12}H_{20}O_2$	Bornyl acetate	227.6	Nonazeotrope		234
A =	$C_6H_4Cl_2$	**o-Dichlorobenzene**	**179.5**			
9180	C_6H_5Br	Bromobenzene	156.1	Nonazeotrope		255
9181	C_6H_5ClO	o-Chlorophenol	176.8	173.6	52	242
9182	$C_6H_5NO_2$	Nitrobenzene	210.75	Nonazeotrope		234
9183	C_6H_6O	Phenol	182.2	173.7	65	242
9184	C_6H_7N	Aniline	184.35	177.4	70	231
9185	$C_6H_8O_4$	Methyl fumarate	193.25	Nonazeotrope		207
9186	$C_6H_{10}O_3$	Ethyl acetoacetate	180.4	175.5	58	232
9187	$C_6H_{10}O_4$	Ethylidene diacetate	168.5	Nonazeotrope		207
9188	$C_6H_{10}O_4$	Ethyl oxalate	185.65	<178.2	<82	255
9189	$C_6H_{12}O$	Cyclohexanol	160.8	Nonazeotrope		255
9190	$C_6H_{12}O_2$	Caproic acid	205.15	179.0	92	244
9191	$C_6H_{12}O_2$	Isocaproic acid	199.5	178.5	94	255
9192	$C_6H_{14}O$	Hexyl alcohol	157.85	Nonazeotrope		255
9193	$C_6H_{14}O_2$	2-Butoxyethanol	171.15	170.0	27	236
9194	C_7H_6O	Benzaldehyde	179.2	<178.5	>48	255
9195	C_7H_8O	Benzyl alcohol	205.25	Nonazeotrope		255
9196	C_7H_8O	m-Cresol	202.2	Nonazeotrope		255
9197	C_7H_8O	o-Cresol	191.1	179.1	85	255
9198	C_7H_8O	p-Cresol	201.7	Nonazeotrope		255
9199	C_7H_9N	Methylaniline	196.25	Nonazeotrope		231

No.	B-Component Formula	Name	B.P., ° C.	Azeotropic Data B.P., ° C.	Wt. % A	Ref.
A =	$C_6H_4Cl_2$	**o-Dichlorobenzene** (*continued*)	**179.5**			
9200	$C_7H_{14}O_2$	Isoamyl acetate	142.1	Nonazeotrope		*255*
9201	$C_7H_{14}O_3$	1,3-Butanediol methyl ether acetate	171.75	Nonazeotrope		*255*
9202	$C_7H_{16}O$	Heptyl alcohol	176.15	173.5	45	*247*
9203	$C_8H_8O_2$	Phenyl acetate	195.7	Nonazeotrope		*255*
9204	$C_8H_{10}O$	*p*-Methylanisole	177.05	179.6	~5	*239*
9205	$C_8H_{10}O$	Phenetole	170.45	Nonazeotrope		*239*
9206	$C_8H_{11}N$	Dimethylaniline	194.15	Nonazeotrope		*231*
9207	$C_8H_{16}O_2$	Butyl butyrate	166.4	Nonazeotrope		*255*
9208	$C_8H_{18}O$	Octyl alcohol	195.2	Nonazeotrope		*255*
9209	$C_8H_{18}O$	*sec*-Octyl alcohol	180.4	177.7	58	*247*
9210	$C_8H_{20}SiO_4$	Ethyl silicate	168.8	Nonazeotrope		*255*
9211	C_9H_8	Indene	182.6	> 183.0	....	*255*
9212	C_9H_{12}	Pseudocumene	168.2	Nonazeotrope		*255*
9213	$C_9H_{12}O$	Benzyl ethyl ether	185.0	Nonazeotrope		*239*
9214	$C_9H_{13}N$	*N,N*-Dimethyl-*o*-toluidine	185.3	Nonazeotrope		*231*
9215	$C_9H_{18}O_2$	Isobutyl isovalerate	171.2	Nonazeotrope		*255*
9216	$C_{10}H_{16}$	Dipentene	177.7	177.5	>20	*255*
9217	$C_{10}H_{16}$	Nopinene	163.8	Nonazeotrope		*255*
9218	$C_{10}H_{16}$	α-Terpinene	173.4	Nonazeotrope		*255*
9219	$C_{10}H_{18}O$	Cineole	176.35	Nonazeotrope		*239*
9220	$C_{10}H_{18}O$	Linaloöl	198.6	Nonazeotrope		*255*
9221	$C_{10}H_{19}N$	Bornylamine	199.8	Nonazeotrope		*255*
9222	$C_{10}H_{20}O_2$	Isoamyl isovalerate	192.7	Nonazeotrope		*255*
9223	$C_{10}H_{22}O$	Amyl ether	187.5	Nonazeotrope		*239*
9224	$C_{10}H_{22}O$	Isoamyl ether	173.2	Nonazeotrope		*239*
A =	$C_6H_4Cl_2$	***p*-Dichlorobenzene**	**174.4**			
9225	C_6H_5BrO	*o*-Bromophenol	195.0	Nonazeotrope		*255*
9226	C_6H_5ClO	*o*-Chlorophenol	176.8	171.0	65	*242*
9227	C_6H_6O	Phenol	182.2	171.05	74.8	*235*
9228	C_6H_6S	Benzenethiol	169.5	<168.2	<29	*255*
9229	C_6H_7N	Aniline	184.35	173.95	88	*231*
9230	$C_6H_{10}O_3$	Ethyl acetoacetate	180.4	172.65	71	*232*
9231	$C_6H_{10}O_4$	Ethyl oxalate	185.65	174.25?	~5	*215*
9232	$C_6H_{12}O$	Cyclohexanol	160.8	160.2	....	*251*
9233	$C_6H_{12}O_2$	Caproic acid	205.2	Nonazeotrope		*221*
9234	$C_6H_{12}O_2$	Isocaproic acid	199.5	174.2	98	*255*
9235	$C_6H_{12}O_3$	2-Ethoxyethyl acetate	156.8	Nonazeotrope		*206*
9236	$C_6H_{12}O_3$	Propyl lactate	171.7	<170.0	<38	*247*
9237	$C_6H_{14}O$	Hexyl alcohol	157.85	157.65	....	*251*
9238	$C_6H_{14}O_2$	2-Butoxyethanol	171.2	168.3	48	*207*
9239	$C_6H_{14}O_2$	Pinacol	174.35	<167.0	<70	*247*
9240	C_7H_5N	Benzonitrile	191.1	Nonazeotrope		*245*
9241	C_7H_6O	Benzaldehyde	179.2	174.1	83	*216*
9242	C_7H_8O	Benzyl alcohol	205.2	Nonazeotrope		*215*
9243	C_7H_8O	*o*-Cresol	191.1	Nonazeotrope		*216*
9244	C_7H_8O	*p*-Cresol	201.7	Nonazeotrope		*222*
9245	C_7H_9N	Methylaniline	196.25	Nonazeotrope		*231*
9246	$C_7H_{14}O$	2-Methylcyclohexanol	168.5	167.3	43	*247*
9247	$C_7H_{14}O_3$	Isobutyl lactate	182.15	Nonazeotrope		*218*
9248	$C_7H_{14}O_3$	1,3-Butanediol methyl ether acetate	171.75	Nonazeotrope		*207, 236*
9249	$C_7H_{16}O$	Heptyl alcohol	176.15	171.2	65	*247*
9250	$C_8H_{10}O$	Benzyl methyl ether	167.8	Nonazeotrope		*239*
9251	$C_8H_{10}O$	*p*-Methylanisole	177.65	Nonazeotrope		*239*
9252	$C_8H_{10}O$	*p*-Methylanisole	177.05	177.07	~6	*221*
9253	$C_8H_{10}O$	Phenetole	170.45	Nonazeotrope		*218*
9254	$C_8H_{11}N$	Dimethylaniline	194.15	Nonazeotrope		*231*
9255	$C_8H_{14}O$	Methylheptenone	173.2	Nonazeotrope		*232*
9256	$C_8H_{16}O$	2-Octanone	172.85	Nonazeotrope		*232*
9257	$C_8H_{16}O_2$	Butyl butyrate	166.4	Nonazeotrope		*227*
9258	$C_8H_{16}O_2$	Ethyl caproate	167.7	Nonazeotrope		*255*
9259	$C_8H_{16}O_2$	Hexyl acetate	171.5	171.4	....	*227*
9260	$C_8H_{16}O_2$	Isoamyl propionate	164.4	Nonazeotrope		*227*
9261	$C_8H_{18}O$	*n*-Octyl alcohol	195.15	Nonazeotrope		*210*
9262	$C_8H_{18}O$	*sec*-Octyl alcohol	180.4	173.85	78	*244*

No.	B-Component Formula	Name	B.P., ° C.	Azeotropic Data B.P., ° C.	Wt. % A	Ref.
A =	$C_6H_4Cl_2$	**p-Dichlorobenzene** (*continued*)	**174.4**			
9263	$C_8H_{18}O_3$	Bis(2-ethoxyethyl) ether	186.0	Nonazeotrope		255
9264	$C_8H_{18}S$	Butyl sulfide	185.0	Nonazeotrope		255
9265	$C_8H_{18}S$	Isobutyl sulfide	172.0	<171.0	<42	246
9266	$C_8H_{20}SiO_4$	Ethyl silicate	168.8	Nonazeotrope		244
9267	C_9H_8	Indene	183.0	Nonazeotrope		221
9268	C_9H_{12}	Cumene	152.8	Nonazeotrope		255
9269	C_9H_{12}	Mesitylene	164.6	Nonazeotrope		255
9270	C_9H_{12}	Pseudocumene	168.2	Nonazeotrope		221
9271	$C_9H_{12}O$	Benzyl ethyl ether	185.0	Nonazeotrope		239
9272	$C_9H_{13}N$	*N,N*-Dimethyl-*o*-toluidine	185.3	Nonazeotrope		231
9273	$C_9H_{18}O$	2,6-Dimethyl-4-heptanone	168.0	Nonazeotrope		232
9274	$C_9H_{18}O_2$	Isoamyl butyrate	178.5	Nonazeotrope		227
9275	$C_9H_{18}O_2$	Isoamyl isobutyrate	170.0	Nonazeotrope		225
9276	$C_9H_{18}O_2$	Isobutyl isovalerate	171.4	Nonazeotrope		218
9277	$C_9H_{18}O_3$	Isobutyl carbonate	190.3	Nonazeotrope		227
9278	$C_{10}H_{14}$	Butylbenzene	183.1	Nonazeotrope		255
9279	$C_{10}H_{14}$	Cymene	176.7	Nonazeotrope		255
9280	$C_{10}H_{16}$	Camphene	159.6	Nonazeotrope		218
9281	$C_{10}H_{16}$	*d*-Limonene	177.8	174.2	86	210
9282	$C_{10}H_{16}$	Nopinene	163.8	Nonazeotrope		255
9283	$C_{10}H_{16}$	α-Pinene	155.8	Nonazeotrope		218
9284	$C_{10}H_{16}$	α-Terpinene	173.4	173.15	50	207
9285	$C_{10}H_{16}$	γ-Terpinene	183	Nonazeotrope		255
9286	$C_{10}H_{16}$	Terpinene	181.5	Nonazeotrope		218
9287	$C_{10}H_{16}$	Terpinolene	184.6	Nonazeotrope		255
9288	$C_{10}H_{16}$	Thymene	179.7	Nonazeotrope		215
9289	$C_{10}H_{18}O$	Cineole	176.4	174.1	~80	239
9290	$C_{10}H_{22}O$	Amyl ether	187.5	Nonazeotrope		239
9291	$C_{10}H_{22}O$	Isoamyl ether	172.6	172.1	36.5	235
A =	C_6H_5Br	**Bromobenzene**	**132**			
9292	C_6H_5Cl	Chlorobenzene	156	Nonazeotrope		243
9293	C_6H_5ClO	*o*-Chlorophenol	176.8	Nonazeotrope		255
9294	$C_6H_5NO_2$	Nitrobenzene	210.75	Nonazeotrope		234
9295	C_6H_6O	Phenol	182.2	Nonazeotrope		222
9296	C_6H_7N	Aniline	184.35	Nonazeotrope		231
9297	$C_6H_{10}O$	Cyclohexanone	155.7	Nonazeotrope		232
9298	$C_6H_{10}O_3$	Ethyl acetoacetate	156.1	Nonazeotrope		232
9299	$C_6H_{10}O_4$	Ethylidene diacetate	168.5	155.95	92.5	207
9300	$C_6H_{10}O_4$	Ethyl oxalate	185.65	Nonazeotrope		207
9301	$C_6H_{10}S$	Allyl sulfide	139.35	Nonazeotrope		246
9302	$C_6H_{11}ClO_2$	Isobutyl chloroacetate	174.5	Nonazeotrope		255
9303	$C_6H_{12}O$	Cyclohexanol	160.65	153.6	66.5	243
9304	$C_6H_{12}O_3$	2-Ethoxyethyl acetate	156.8	155.45	63	236
9305	$C_6H_{13}ClO_2$	Chloroacetal	156.8	~156	....	243
9306	$C_6H_{14}O$	Hexyl alcohol	157.95	151.6	66	218
9307	$C_6H_{14}O_2$	2-Butoxyethanol	171.15	155.85	93.5	236
9308	$C_6H_{14}O_2$	Pinacol	174.3	153.2	~85	212
			171.5	152	~86	243
9309	$C_6H_{14}S$	Propyl sulfide	141.5	Nonazeotrope		255
9310	C_7H_7Cl	*o*-Chlorotoluene	159.2	Nonazeotrope		229
9311	C_7H_8	Toluene	110.7	Nonazeotrope		243
9312	C_7H_8O	Anisole	153.85	Nonazeotrope		243
9313	C_7H_8O	*o*-Cresol	190.8	Nonazeotrope		243
9314	$C_7H_{14}O_2$	Ethyl valerate	145.45	Nonazeotrope		255
9315	$C_7H_{14}O_2$	Isoamyl acetate	142.1	Nonazeotrope		227
9316	$C_7H_{14}O_2$	Methyl caproate	151.0	Nonazeotrope		227
9317	$C_7H_{14}O_2$	Propyl butyrate	143.7	Nonazeotrope		227
9318	$C_7H_{14}O_3$	1,3-Butanediol methyl ether acetate	171.75	Nonazeotrope		255
9319	$C_7H_{16}O$	Heptyl alcohol	176.15	Nonazeotrope		255
9320	$C_7H_{16}O_3$	Ethyl orthoformate	145.75	Nonazeotrope		239
9321	C_8H_8	Styrene	145.8	Nonazeotrope		215
9322	C_8H_{10}	Ethylbenzene	136.15	Nonazeotrope		243
9323	C_8H_{10}	*m*-Xylene	139	Nonazeotrope		207, 243
9324	$C_8H_{10}O$	Benzyl methyl ether	167.8	Nonazeotrope		239
9325	$C_8H_{16}O_2$	Butyl butyrate	166.4	Nonazeotrope		227

No.	Formula	Name (B-Component)	B.P., ° C. (B-Component)	B.P., ° C. (Azeotropic Data)	Wt. % A (Azeotropic Data)	Ref.
A =	**C_6H_5Br**	**Bromobenzene** (*continued*)	**132**			
9326	$C_8H_{16}O_2$	Isoamyl propionate	~160.3	~155.2	~73	243
9327	$C_8H_{16}O_2$	Isobutyl butyrate	156.8	155.2	....	225
9328	$C_8H_{16}O_2$	Isobutyl isobutyrate	147.3	Nonazeotrope		253
9329	$C_8H_{16}O_2$	Propyl isovalerate	155.7	154.5	57	253
9330	$C_8H_{18}O$	Butyl ether	142.4	Nonazeotrope		239
9331	$C_8H_{18}O$	*sec*-Octyl alcohol	178.7	Nonazeotrope		243
9332	$C_8H_{20}SiO_4$	Ethyl silicate	168.8	Nonazeotrope		255
9333	C_9H_{12}	Cumene	152.8	Nonazeotrope		255
9334	C_9H_{12}	Mesitylene	164.0	Nonazeotrope		243
9335	C_9H_{12}	Propylbenzene	159.3	Nonazeotrope		255
9336	$C_9H_{18}O_2$	Isobutyl isovalerate	171.35	Nonazeotrope		221
9337	$C_{10}H_{16}$	Camphene	159.5	155.0	~56	208
9338	$C_{10}H_{16}$	Nopinene	163.8	<155.9	>72	255
9339	$C_{10}H_{16}$	α-Pinene	155.8	153.4	50	243
9340	$C_{10}H_{22}$	2,7-Dimethyloctane	160.25	155.9	~87	243
A =	**C_6H_5BrO**	***o*-Bromophenol**	**195.0**			
9341	$C_6H_5NO_3$	*o*-Nitrophenol	217.2	Nonazeotrope		255
9342	C_7H_7Br	*p*-Bromotoluene	185.0	183.8	20	255
9343	C_7H_7ClO	*p*-Chloroanisole	197.8	Nonazeotrope		255
9344	C_7H_8O	*o*-Cresol	191.1	189.8	25	255
9345	C_7H_8O	*p*-Cresol	201.7	194.0	20	255
9346	C_8H_8O	Acetophenone	202.0	212.5	52	255
9347	$C_8H_8O_2$	Methyl benzoate	199.4	206.2	42	242
9348	$C_8H_8O_2$	Phenyl acetate	195.7	205.0	50	242
9349	$C_8H_{16}O$	2-Octanone	172.85	198.5	....	255
9350	$C_8H_{16}O_2$	Butyl butyrate	166.4	Nonazeotrope		255
9351	$C_8H_{18}O$	Octyl alcohol	195.2	204.0	50	255
9352	$C_8H_{18}O$	*sec*-Octyl alcohol	180.8	Nonazeotrope		255
9353	$C_8H_{18}S$	Butyl sulfide	185.0	Nonazeotrope		255
9354	C_9H_8	Indene	182.6	Nonazeotrope		255
9355	$C_9H_{10}O_2$	Ethyl benzoate	212.5	214.2	15?	255
9356	$C_9H_{12}O$	Benzyl ethyl ether	185.0	Nonazeotrope		255
9357	$C_9H_{18}O_2$	Isoamyl butyrate	181.05	197.5	72	255
9358	$C_{10}H_{12}O_2$	Ethyl α-toluate	228.75	Nonazeotrope		255
9359	$C_{10}H_{12}O_2$	Propyl benzoate	230.85	Nonazeotrope		255
9360	$C_{10}H_{14}$	Butylbenzene	183.1	Nonazeotrope		255
9361	$C_{10}H_{16}O$	Camphor	209.1	216.5	40	255
9362	$C_{10}H_{20}O_2$	Isoamyl isovalerate	192.7	203.0	54	42
9363	$C_{10}H_{22}O$	Isoamyl ether	173.2	Nonazeotrope		255
9364	$C_{10}H_{22}S$	Isoamyl sulfide	214.8	Nonazeotrope		255
9365	$C_{11}H_{20}O$	Isobornyl methyl ether	192.4	<192.2	<25	255
9366	$C_{12}H_{20}O_2$	Bornyl acetate	227.6	Nonazeotrope		255
A =	**C_6H_5Cl**	**Chlorobenzene**	**131.75**			
9367	$C_6H_5NO_2$	Nitrobenzene	210.75	Nonazeotrope		234
9368	C_6H_6	Benzene	80.2	Nonazeotrope		243
9369	C_6H_6O	Phenol	181.5	Nonazeotrope		243
9370	C_6H_7N	Aniline, 95–380 mm.	....	Nonazeotrope, V-l.		83
			184.35	Nonazeotrope		231
9371	$C_6H_{10}O$	Cyclohexanone	155.7	Nonazeotrope		232
9372	$C_6H_{10}O$	Mesityl oxide	129.45	Nonazeotrope		207
9373	$C_6H_{10}S$	Allyl sulfide	139.35	Nonazeotrope		246
9374	C_6H_{12}	Cyclohexane	80.75	Nonazeotrope		255
9375	$C_6H_{12}O_2$	Butyl acetate	124.8	Nonazeotrope		207
9376	$C_6H_{12}O_2$	Ethyl butyrate	121.5	Nonazeotrope		255
9377	$C_6H_{12}O_3$	Paraldehyde	124	Nonazeotrope		243
9378	$C_6H_{14}O$	Hexyl alcohol	157.85	Nonazeotrope		255
9379	$C_6H_{14}O_2$	2-Butoxyethanol	171.25	Nonazeotrope		206
9380	$C_6H_{14}O_2$	Pinacol	174.35	Nonazeotrope		255
9381	$C_6H_{14}S$	Propyl sulfide	141.5	Nonazeotrope		255
9382	C_7H_8	Toluene	110.7	Nonazeotrope		243
9383	C_7H_{14}	Methylcyclohexane	101.15	Nonazeotrope		255
9384	$C_7H_{14}O$	4-Heptanone	143.55	Nonazeotrope		232
9385	$C_7H_{14}O_2$	Ethyl isovalerate	134.7	Nonazeotrope		227
9386	$C_7H_{14}O_2$	Isoamyl acetate	~138.8	Nonazeotrope		243
9387	$C_7H_{14}O_2$	Isobutyl propionate	136.9	Nonazeotrope		227

No.	B-Component Formula	Name	B.P., ° C.	Azeotropic Data B.P., ° C.	Wt. % A	Ref.
A =	**C_6H_5Cl**	**Chlorobenzene** (*continued*)	**131.75**			
9388	$C_7H_{14}O_2$	Propyl butyrate	143	Nonazeotrope		*243*
9389	C_7H_{16}	Heptane	98.4	Nonazeotrope		*207*
9390	C_8H_{10}	Ethylbenzene	136.15	Nonazeotrope		*243*
9391	C_8H_{10}	*m*-Xylene	139.0	Nonazeotrope		*207*
9392	C_8H_{10}	*p*-Xylene	138.2	Nonazeotrope		*243*
9393	C_8H_{16}	1,3-Dimethylcyclohexane	120.7	Nonazeotrope		*255*
9394	C_8H_{18}	Octane	125.8	Nonazeotrope		*243*
9395	$C_8H_{18}O$	Butyl ether	142.2	Nonazeotrope		*228*
9396	$C_8H_{18}O$	Isobutyl ether	122.3	Nonazeotrope		*239*
A =	**C_6H_5ClO**	***o*-Chlorophenol**	**176.8**			
9397	C_6H_5I	Iodobenzene	188.45	<176.0	<78	*255*
9398	C_6H_6O	Phenol	182.2	174.5	25	*242*
9399	C_6H_7N	Aniline	184.35	Nonazeotrope		*243*
9400	C_6H_7N	3-Picoline	144	178–184	....	*327*
9401	C_6H_7N	4-Picoline	145	178–184	....	*327*
9402	$C_6H_{12}O$	Cyclohexanol	160.8	Nonazeotrope		*255*
9403	$C_6H_{13}ClO_2$	Chloroacetal	157.4	Nonazeotrope		*255*
9404	C_7H_7Br	*α*-Bromotoluene	~198.5	Reacts		*243*
9405	C_7H_7Br	*o*-Bromotoluene	181.75	171.5	~68	*243*
9406	C_7H_7Br	*p*-Bromotoluene	185.0	<175.5	>64	*242*
9407	C_7H_7Cl	*α*-Chlorotoluene	179.35	Reacts		*243*
9408	C_7H_7ClO	*o*-Chloroanisole	195.7	Nonazeotrope		*255*
9409	C_7H_8O	*o*-Cresol	191.1	Nonazeotrope		*255*
9410	C_7H_9N	2,6-Lutidine	144	178–184	....	*327*
9411	$C_7H_{14}O_2$	Isoamyl acetate	142.1	Nonazeotrope		*255*
9412	C_8H_8O	Acetophenone	202.0	>204.5	....	*255*
9413	$C_8H_8O_2$	Benzyl formate	203.0	Nonazeotrope		*255*
9414	$C_8H_8O_2$	Phenyl acetate	195.7	197.0	12	*255*
9415	$C_8H_{10}O$	Phenetole	170.45	Nonazeotrope		*255*
9416	$C_8H_{16}O$	2-Octanone	173	177	~75	*243*
9417	$C_8H_{18}O$	Octyl alcohol	195.2	Nonazeotrope		*255*
9418	$C_8H_{18}O$	*sec*-Octyl alcohol	180.4	183.5	25	*255*
9419	$C_8H_{18}S$	Butyl sulfide	185.0	175.0	82	*246*
9420	$C_8H_{18}S$	Isobutyl sulfide	172.0	169.5	....	*246*
9421	C_9H_8	Indene	182.4	Min. b.p.		*117*
9422	$C_9H_{10}O_2$	Ethyl benzoate	212.5	Nonazeotrope		*255*
9423	C_9H_{12}	Mesitylene	164.6	Nonazeotrope		*255*
9424	C_9H_{12}	Propylbenzene	159.3	Nonazeotrope		*255*
9425	$C_9H_{18}O_2$	Isoamyl butyrate	181.05	188.0	38	*242*
9426	$C_9H_{18}O_2$	Isobutyl isovalerate	171.2	182.8	57	*242*
9427	$C_{10}H_{14}$	Cymene	175.3	173.5	~50	*243*
9428	$C_{10}H_{16}$	*d*-Limonene	177.8	<175	....	*243*
9429	$C_{10}H_{16}$	*α*-Pinene	155.8	<155.2	>5	*255*
9430	$C_{10}H_{16}$	*α*-Terpinene	173.4	<169.5	>28	*255*
9431	$C_{10}H_{22}O$	Isoamyl ether	173.2	171.0	30	*255*
A =	**C_6H_5ClO**	***p*-Chlorophenol**	**219.75**			
9432	$C_6H_5NO_2$	Nitrobenzene	210.75	219.9	8	*234*
9433	$C_6H_5NO_3$	*o*-Nitrophenol	217.2	<217.05	>7	*255*
9434	$C_6H_8O_4$	Methyl fumarate	193.25	>221.0	<92	*255*
9435	$C_6H_8O_4$	Methyl maleate	204.05	223.0	68	*242*
9436	$C_6H_{10}O_4$	Ethyl oxalate	185.65	>221.5	>88	*255*
9437	$C_6H_{10}O_4$	Methyl succinate	195.5	222.5	<90	*228*
9438	$C_7H_5Cl_3$	*α,α,α*-Trichlorotoluene	220.9	Reacts		*215*
9439	$C_7H_6Cl_2$	*α,α*-Dichlorotoluene	205.1	Reacts		*243*
9440	C_7H_7BrO	*o*-Bromoanisole	217.7	Nonazeotrope		*255*
9441	C_7H_7I	*p*-Iodotoluene	214.5	212.0	22	*242*
9442	$C_7H_7NO_2$	*m*-Nitrotoluene	230.8	Nonazeotrope		*234*
9443	$C_7H_7NO_2$	*o*-Nitrotoluene	221.75	223.2	43	*234*
9444	C_7H_8O	Benzyl alcohol	205.2	Nonazeotrope		*255*
9445	C_7H_8O	*p*-Cresol	201.7	Nonazeotrope		*255*
9446	C_7H_8O	*m*-Methoxyphenol	243.8	Nonazeotrope		*255*
9447	$C_7H_8O_2$	Guaiacol	205.05	Nonazeotrope		*215*
9448	C_8H_8O	Acetophenone	202.0	224.5	85	*255*
9449	$C_8H_8O_2$	Benzyl formate	202.3	221.4	75	*228*
9450	$C_8H_8O_2$	Methyl benzoate	199.45	220.75	79	*216*

No.	B-Component Formula	Name	B.P., ° C.	Azeotropic Data B.P., ° C.	Wt. % A	Ref.
A =	**C_6H_5ClO**	***p*-Chlorophenol (*continued*)**	**219.75**			
9451	$C_8H_8O_2$	Phenyl acetate	195.7	220.2	~90	228
9452	C_8H_9BrO	*p*-Bromophenetole	234.2	Nonazeotrope		255
9453	$C_8H_{10}O$	Phenethyl alcohol	219.4	227.7	52.5	254
9454	$C_8H_{10}O$	2,4-Xylenol	210.5	<210.0	....	255
9455	$C_8H_{10}O$	3,4-Xylenol	226.8	219.0	89	255
9456	$C_8H_{10}O_2$	Veratrol	206.8	Nonazeotrope		255
9457	$C_8H_{10}O_2$	*m*-Dimethoxybenzene	214.7	Nonazeotrope		255
9458	$C_8H_{10}O_2$	*o*-Ethoxyphenol	216.5	222.0	70	255
9459	$C_8H_{12}O_4$	Ethyl fumarate	217.85	>230.5	<54	255
9460	$C_8H_{12}O_4$	Ethyl maleate	223.3	232.5	53	242
9461	$C_8H_{14}O_4$	Ethyl succinate	217.25	~231.8	....	209
9462	$C_8H_{18}O$	Octyl alcohol	195.15	Nonazeotrope		215
9463	$C_9H_{10}O$	*p*-Methylacetophenone	226.35	235.4	52	232
9464	$C_9H_{10}O$	Propiophenone	217.7	230.2	....	232
9465	$C_9H_{10}O_2$	Benzyl acetate	214.9	226.5	~55	209
9466	$C_9H_{10}O_2$	Ethyl benzoate	212.6	224.9	60	254
9467	$C_9H_{12}O$	Mesitol	220.5	217.2	58	242
9468	$C_9H_{12}O$	3-Phenylpropanol	235.6	Nonazeotrope		218
9469	$C_9H_{18}O_2$	Ethyl enanthate	188.7	Nonazeotrope		255
9470	$C_9H_{18}O_3$	Isobutyl carbonate	190.3	>220.5	....	255
9471	$C_{10}H_8$	Naphthalene	218.05	216.3	36.5	254
9472	$C_{10}H_{10}O_2$	Methyl cinnamate	261.9	Nonazeotrope		255
9473	$C_{10}H_{10}O_2$	Safrole	235.9	Nonazeotrope		236
9474	$C_{10}H_{12}O$	Anethole	235.7	Nonazeotrope		255
9475	$C_{10}H_{12}O_2$	Ethyl α-toluate	228.75	233.0	27	215
9476	$C_{10}H_{12}O_2$	Propyl benzoate	230.85	234.5	25	228
9477	$C_{10}H_{14}O$	Carvone	231.0	238.3	<45	232
9478	$C_{10}H_{14}O$	Thymol	232.9	Nonazeotrope		255
9479	$C_{10}H_{14}O_2$	*m*-Diethoxybenzene	235.4	Nonazeotrope		255
9480	$C_{10}H_{16}O$	Camphor	209.1	227.5	>75	232
9481	$C_{10}H_{17}Cl$	Bornyl chloride	~210	~206.5	....	243
9482	$C_{10}H_{18}O$	Borneol	213.2	222.5	52.5	209
9483	$C_{10}H_{18}O$	Geraniol	229.7	~230.7	~10	218
9484	$C_{10}H_{18}O$	Linaloöl	198.6	Nonazeotrope		215
9485	$C_{10}H_{18}O$	α-Terpineol	217.4	225.7	49.8	209
9486	$C_{10}H_{18}O$	β-Terpineol	210.5	Nonazeotrope		255
9487	$C_{10}H_{20}O$	Citronellol	224	~227.5	~30	215
9488	$C_{10}H_{20}O$	Menthol	216.4	223.5	57.5	209
9489	$C_{10}H_{20}O_2$	Ethyl caprylate	208.35	223.2	65	242
9490	$C_{10}H_{20}O_2$	Isoamyl isovalerate	192.7	Nonazeotrope ?		228
9491	$C_{10}H_{22}S$	Isoamyl sulfide	214.8	212.5	28	246
9492	$C_{11}H_{10}$	2-Methylnaphthalene	241.15	Nonazeotrope		255
9493	$C_{11}H_{14}O_2$	Butyl benzoate	249.5	Nonazeotrope		228
9494	$C_{11}H_{14}O_2$	Isobutyl benzoate	241.9	242.7	7	228
9495	$C_{11}H_{20}O$	Methyl α-terpineol ether	216.2	<215.9	<15	255
9496	$C_{11}H_{22}O_3$	Isoamyl carbonate	232.2	235.3	22	228
9497	$C_{12}H_{10}$	Biphenyl	256.1	Nonazeotrope		255
9498	$C_{12}H_{18}$	1,3,5-Triethylbenzene	215.4	214.7	18	228
9499	$C_{12}H_{20}O_2$	Bornyl acetate	227.7	232.7	28	209
9500	$C_{13}H_{28}$	Tridecane	234.0	Nonazeotrope		255
A =	**C_6H_5F**	**Fluorobenzene**	**85.2**			
9501	C_6H_5I	Iodobenzene	188.55	Vapor pressure data		243
9502	C_6H_6	Benzene	80.15	Nonazeotrope		255
9503	C_6H_{12}	Cyclohexane	80.75	Nonazeotrope		255
9504	C_6H_{12}	Methylcyclopentane	72.0	Nonazeotrope		255
9505	C_6H_{14}	Hexane	68.8	Nonazeotrope		255
A =	**C_6H_5I**	**Iodobenzene**	**188.55**			
9506	$C_6H_5NO_2$	Nitrobenzene	210.75	Nonazeotrope		234
9507	C_6H_6O	Phenol	181.5	177.7	53	243
9508	C_6H_7N	Aniline	184.35	181.6	>40	231
9509	$C_6H_8O_4$	Methyl fumarate	193.25	186.2	70	207
9510	$C_6H_{10}O_3$	Ethyl acetoacetate	180.4	178.0	52	232
9511	$C_6H_{10}O_4$	Ethyl oxalate	185.65	181.0	48	218
9512	$C_6H_{10}O_4$	Glycol diacetate	186.3	<183.5	>42	242
9513	$C_6H_{10}O_4$	Methyl succinate	195	~186.5	....	243

	B-Component			Azeotropic Data		
No.	Formula	Name	B.P., ° C.	B.P., ° C.	Wt. % A	Ref.
A =	**C_6H_5I**	**Iodobenzene** (*continued*)	**188.55**			
9514	$C_6H_{11}ClO_2$	Butyl chloroacetate	181.8	<181.2	>82	*255*
9515	$C_6H_{11}ClO_2$	Isobutyl chloroacetate	174.5	Nonazeotrope		*255*
9516	$C_6H_{12}O$	Cyclohexanol	160.65	Nonazeotrope		*253*
9517	$C_6H_{12}O_2$	Caproic acid	205.15	186.8	88	*244*
9518	$C_6H_{12}O_2$	Isocaproic acid	199.5	185.5	85	*242*
9519	$C_6H_{14}O$	Hexyl alcohol	157.85	Nonazeotrope		*255*
9520	$C_6H_{14}O_2$	2-Butoxyethanol	171.17	<170.8	....	*255*
9521	C_7H_5N	Benzonitrile	191.1	<187.0	....	*245*
9522	C_7H_6O	Benzaldehyde	179.2	Nonazeotrope		*255*
9523	C_7H_7Br	*m*-Bromotoluene	184.3	Nonazeotrope		*229*
9524	C_7H_8O	Benzyl alcohol	205.2	187.75	88	*215*
9525	C_7H_8O	*o*-Cresol	190.8	185	~32 ~53	*243*
9526	C_7H_8O	*p*-Cresol	201.7	188.1	90	*222*
9527	C_7H_9N	Methylaniline	196.25	Nonazeotrope		*231*
9528	C_7H_9N	*m*-Toluidine	203.1	Nonazeotrope		*231*
9529	C_7H_9N	*o*-Toluidine	200.35	Nonazeotrope		*231*
9530	C_7H_9N	*p*-Toluidine	200.55	Nonazeotrope		*231*
9531	$C_7H_{12}O_4$	Ethyl malonate	199.2	<188	>80	*227*
9532	$C_7H_{14}O_3$	Isobutyl lactate	182.15	180.5	30	*247*
9533	$C_8H_8O_2$	Methyl benzoate	199.45	Nonazeotrope		*227*
9534	$C_8H_8O_2$	Phenyl acetate	195.7	<188.3	....	*255*
9535	$C_8H_{10}O$	*p*-Methylanisole	177.05	Nonazeotrope		*239*
9536	$C_8H_{10}O$	Phenetole	170.45	Nonazeotrope		*239*
9537	$C_8H_{11}N$	*N*,*N*-Dimethylaniline	194.05	186.7	75	*215*
9538	$C_8H_{11}N$	Ethylaniline	205.5	Nonazeotrope		*231*
9539	$C_8H_{16}O_3$	Isoamyl lactate	202.4	Nonazeotrope		*255*
9540	$C_8H_{18}O$	*n*-Octyl alcohol	195.15	187.5	....	*211*
9541	$C_8H_{18}O$	*sec*-Octyl alcohol	179.0	178.4	....	*211*
9542	C_9H_8	Indene	182.6	Nonazeotrope		*255*
9543	$C_9H_{12}O$	Benzyl ethyl ether	185.0	Nonazeotrope		*239*
9544	$C_9H_{13}N$	*N*,*N*-Dimethyl-*o*-toluidine	185.3	Nonazeotrope		*231*
9545	$C_9H_{14}O$	Phorone	197.8	Nonazeotrope		*232*
9546	$C_9H_{18}O_2$	Butyl isovalerate	177.6	Nonazeotrope		*227*
9547	$C_9H_{18}O_2$	Isoamyl butyrate	178.5	Nonazeotrope		*218*
9548	$C_9H_{18}O_3$	Isobutyl carbonate	190.3	185.5	~65	*243*
9549	$C_{10}H_{14}$	Butylbenzene	183.1	Nonazeotrope		*255*
9550	$C_{10}H_{14}$	Cymene	176.7	Nonazeotrope		*255*
9551	$C_{10}H_{16}$	Dipentene	177.7	Nonazeotrope		*255*
9552	$C_{10}H_{16}$	α-Terpinene	173.4	Nonazeotrope		*255*
9553	$C_{10}H_{16}$	Terpinene	181.5	Nonazeotrope		*218*
9554	$C_{10}H_{16}O$	Fenchone	193	Nonazeotrope		*243*
9555	$C_{10}H_{18}O$	Linaloöl	198.6	Nonazeotrope		*212*
9556	$C_{10}H_{20}O_2$	Isoamyl isovalerate	192.7	<188.3	>87	*255*
A =	**$C_6H_5NO_2$**	**Nitrobenzene**	**210.75**			
9557	$C_6H_5NO_3$	*o*-Nitrophenol	217.2	Nonazeotrope		*234*
9558	C_6H_6	Benzene	80.15	Nonazeotrope		*234*
9559	C_6H_7N	Aniline	184.35	Nonazeotrope, V-l.		*231*, 335*
9560	$C_6H_8O_4$	Methyl maleate	204.05	203.9	7	*207*
9561	$C_6H_{12}O_2$	Caproic acid	205.15	<202.5	<35	*234*
9562	C_6H_{14}	*n*-Hexane	68.8	Nonazeotrope		*234*
9563	$C_6H_{14}O$	*n*-Hexanol	157.85	Nonazeotrope		*234*
9564	$C_6H_{14}O_2$	2-Butoxyethanol	171.15	Nonazeotrope		*234*
9565	$C_6H_{14}O_2$	Pinacol	174.35	Nonazeotrope		*256*
9566	$C_7H_5Cl_3$	α,α,α-Trichlorotoluene	220.8	Nonazeotrope		*234*
9567	$C_7H_6Cl_2$	α,α-Dichlorotoluene	205.2	Nonazeotrope		*234*
9568	C_7H_6O	Benzaldehyde	179.2	Nonazeotrope		*234*
9569	C_7H_7Br	*o*-Bromotoluene	181.75	Nonazeotrope		*243*
9570	C_7H_7Cl	α-Chlorotoluene	179.35	Nonazeotrope		*243*
9571	C_7H_7I	*p*-Iodotoluene	214.5	<208.8	....	*234*
9572	C_7H_8	Toluene	110.7	Nonazeotrope		*234*
9573	C_7H_8O	Benzyl alcohol	205.25	204.2	38	*234*
9574	C_7H_8O	*m*-Cresol	202.2	Nonazeotrope		*234*
9575	C_7H_8O	*o*-Cresol	191.1	Nonazeotrope		*234*
9576	C_7H_8O	*p*-Cresol	201.7	Nonazeotrope		*234*
9577	$C_7H_8O_2$	Guaiacol	205.05	Nonazeotrope		*234*

No.	B-Component Formula	Name	B.P., ° C.	Azeotropic Data B.P., ° C.	Wt. % A	Ref.
A =	$C_6H_5NO_2$	**Nitrobenzene** (*continued*)	**210.75**			
9578	C_7H_9N	Benzylamine	185.0	Nonazeotrope		*231*
9579	C_7H_9N	Methylaniline	196.25	Nonazeotrope		*231*
9580	C_7H_9N	*m*-Toluidine	203.1	Nonazeotrope		*231*
9581	C_7H_9N	*o*-Toluidine	200.35	Nonazeotrope		*231*
9582	C_7H_9N	*p*-Toluidine	200.55	Nonazeotrope		*231*
9583	C_7H_9NO	*o*-Anisidine	219.0	Nonazeotrope		*255*
9584	$C_7H_{12}O_4$	Ethyl malonate	199.35	Nonazeotrope		*234*
9585	$C_7H_{14}O_2$	Enanthic acid	222.0	<209.5	<88	*234*
9586	$C_7H_{16}O_4$	2-[2-(2-Methoxyethoxy)ethoxy]-ethanol	245.25	Nonazeotrope		*234*
9587	C_8H_8O	Acetophenone	202.0	Nonazeotrope		*232*
9588	$C_8H_8O_2$	Benzyl formate	203.0	Nonazeotrope		*234*
9589	$C_8H_8O_2$	Methyl benzoate	199.4	Nonazeotrope		*255*
9590	$C_8H_8O_2$	Phenyl acetate	215.3	Nonazeotrope		*234*
9591	$C_8H_8O_3$	Methyl salicylate	222.95	Nonazeotrope		*234*
9592	$C_8H_{10}O$	*p*-Ethylphenol	220.0	Nonazeotrope		*234*
9593	$C_8H_{10}O$	Phenethyl alcohol	219.4	210.6	92	*234*
9594	$C_8H_{10}O$	3,4-Xylenol	226.8	Nonazeotrope		*234*
9595	$C_8H_{10}O_2$	*m*-Dimethoxybenzene	214.7	207.5	>62	*234*
9596	$C_8H_{10}O_2$	*o*-Ethoxyphenol	216.5	Nonazeotrope		*234*
9597	$C_8H_{10}O_2$	Veratrol	206.8	<203.8	....	*234*
9598	$C_8H_{11}N$	Dimethylaniline	194.15	Nonazeotrope		*231*
9599	$C_8H_{11}N$	Ethylaniline	205.5	Nonazeotrope		*231*
9600	$C_8H_{11}N$	2,4-Xylidine	214.0	Nonazeotrope		*231*
9601	$C_8H_{11}N$	3,4-Xylidine	225.5	Nonazeotrope		*231*
9602	$C_8H_{12}O_4$	Ethyl fumarate	217.85	Nonazeotrope		*234*
9603	$C_8H_{12}O_4$	Ethyl maleate	223.3	Nonazeotrope		*234*
9604	$C_8H_{14}O_4$	Ethyl succinate	217.25	<210.6	....	*234*
9605	$C_8H_{14}O_4$	Propyl oxalate	214.2	210.0	....	*234*
9606	$C_8H_{16}O_2$	Caprylic acid	238.5	Nonazeotrope		*234*
9607	$C_8H_{16}O_3$	Isoamyl lactate	202.4	Nonazeotrope		*234*
9608	$C_8H_{18}O$	*n*-Octyl alcohol	195.2	Nonazeotrope		*234*
9609	$C_9H_{10}O$	Cinnamyl alcohol	257.0	Nonazeotrope		*234*
9610	$C_9H_{10}O$	Propiophenone	217.7	Nonazeotrope		*232*
9611	$C_9H_{10}O_2$	Benzyl acetate	215.0	Nonazeotrope		*234*
9612	$C_9H_{10}O_2$	Ethyl benzoate	212.5	210.6	81	*234*
9613	$C_9H_{12}O$	3-Phenylpropanol	235.6	Nonazeotrope		*234*
9614	$C_9H_{13}N$	*N,N*-Dimethyl-*o*-toluidine	185.3	Nonazeotrope		*255*
9615	$C_9H_{13}N$	*N,N*-Dimethyl-*p*-toluidine	210.2	<210	....	*231*
9616	$C_9H_{14}O$	Phorone	197.8	Nonazeotrope		*232*
9617	$C_{10}H_8$	Naphthalene	218.0	Nonazeotrope		*234*
9618	$C_{10}H_{14}O$	Thymol	232.9	Nonazeotrope		*234*
9619	$C_{10}H_{15}N$	Diethylaniline	217.05	210.72	97	*231*
9620	$C_{10}H_{16}O$	Camphor	208.9	208.4	35	*243*
9621	$C_{10}H_{16}O$	Fenchone	193.6	Nonazeotrope		*255*
9622	$C_{10}H_{16}O$	Pulegone	223.8	Nonazeotrope		*232*
9623	$C_{10}H_{17}Cl$	Bornyl chloride	207.5	205.0	....	*234*
9624	$C_{10}H_{18}O$	Borneol	215.0	207.8	58	*234*
9625	$C_{10}H_{18}O$	Citronellal	208.0	207.0	22	*234*
9626	$C_{10}H_{18}O$	Geraniol	229.6	Nonazeotrope		*234*
9627	$C_{10}H_{18}O$	Linaloöl	198.6	Nonazeotrope		*234*
9628	$C_{10}H_{18}O$	Menthone	206.5	Nonazeotrope		*243*
9629	$C_{10}H_{18}O$	α-Terpineol	218.85	209.7	78	*234*
9630	$C_{10}H_{18}O$	β-Terpineol	210.5	204.8	50	*234*
9631	$C_{10}H_{20}O$	Citronellol	224.5	Min. b.p.		*254*
9632	$C_{10}H_{20}O$	Menthol	216.3	208.35	67.3	*234*
9633	$C_{10}H_{22}O$	*n*-Decyl alcohol	232.8	Nonazeotrope		*234*
9634	$C_{10}H_{22}S$	Isoamyl sulfide	214.8	209.5	<93	*234*
9635	$C_{11}H_{16}O$	Methyl thymol ether	216.5	<209.2	<82	*234*
9636	$C_{11}H_{20}O$	Methyl α-terpineol ether	216.2	208.6	75?	*234*
9637	$C_{11}H_{24}O_2$	Diisoamyloxymethane	210.8	206.5	>42	*234*
9638	$C_{12}H_{18}$	1,3,5-Triethylbenzene	215.5	Nonazeotrope		*234*
9639	$C_{12}H_{22}O$	Ethyl bornyl ether	204.9	203.0	30	*234*
9640	$C_{12}H_{22}O$	Ethyl isobornyl ether	203.8	202.5?	25?	*234*

No.	B-Component Formula	Name	B.P., ° C.	Azeotropic Data B.P., ° C.	Wt. % A	Ref.
A =	$C_6H_5NO_3$	**o-Nitrophenol**	**217.25**			
9641	$C_6H_6O_2$	Pyrocatechol	245.9	Nonazeotrope		222
9642	$C_6H_8O_4$	Methyl maleate	204.05	Nonazeotrope		207
9643	$C_6H_{14}O_2$	Pinacol	174.35	Nonazeotrope		255
9644	$C_6H_{14}O_3$	Dipropylene glycol	229.2	215.0?	....	255
9645	C_7H_7BrO	*o*-Bromoanisole	217.7	Nonazeotrope		255
9646	C_7H_7ClO	*p*-Chloroanisole	197.8	Nonazeotrope		255
9647	C_7H_7I	*p*-Iodotoluene	214.5	212.0	18	255
9648	$C_7H_7NO_2$	*o*-Nitrotoluene	221.75	Nonazeotrope		234
9649	C_7H_8O	Benzyl alcohol	205.25	Nonazeotrope		255
9650	C_7H_8O	*m*-Cresol	202.2	Nonazeotrope		222
9651	C_7H_8O	*o*-Cresol	191.1	Nonazeotrope		255
9652	C_7H_8O	*p*-Cresol	201.7	Nonazeotrope		224
9653	C_7H_9NO	*o*-Anisidine	219.0	Nonazeotrope		255
9654	$C_7H_{14}O$	2-Methylcyclohexano	168.5	Nonazeotrope		255
9655	$C_7H_{16}O$	Heptyl alcohol	176.16	Nonazeotrope		255
9656	C_8H_8O	Acetophenone	202.0	Nonazeotrope		232
9657	$C_8H_8O_2$	Benzyl formate	202.3	Nonazeotrope		228
9658	$C_8H_8O_2$	Methyl benzoate	199.4	Nonazeotrope		255
9659	$C_8H_8O_3$	Methyl salicylate	222.95	Nonazeotrope		255
9660	C_8H_9BrO	*p*-Bromophenetole	234.2	Nonazeotrope		255
9661	$C_8H_{10}O$	Phenethyl alcohol	219.4	214.0	59	247
9662	$C_8H_{10}O$	3,4-Xylenol	226.8	Nonazeotrope		255
9663	$C_8H_{10}O_2$	*m*-Dimethoxybenzene	214.7	Nonazeotrope		255
9664	$C_8H_{10}O_2$	Veratrole	206.8	Nonazeotrope		255
9665	$C_8H_{11}NO$	*o*-Phenetidine	232.5	Nonazeotrope		255
9666	$C_8H_{12}O_4$	Ethyl fumarate	217.85	Nonazeotrope		206
9667	$C_8H_{12}O_4$	Ethyl maleate	223.3	Nonazeotrope		255
9668	$C_8H_{14}O_4$	Ethyl succinate	217.25	<216.9	<54	255
9669	$C_8H_{18}O$	Octyl alcohol	195.2	Nonazeotrope		255
9670	$C_8H_{18}O$	*sec*-Octyl alcohol	180.4	Nonazeotrope		255
9671	$C_8H_{18}S$	Butyl sulfide	185.0	Nonazeotrope		255
9672	C_9H_7N	Quinoline	237.3	Nonazeotrope		255
9673	$C_9H_{10}O$	Cinnamyl alcohol	257.0	Nonazeotrope		255
9674	$C_9H_{10}O$	*p*-Methylacetophenone	226.35	Nonazeotrope		232
9675	$C_9H_{10}O_2$	Benzyl acetate	215.0	Nonazeotrope		255
9676	$C_9H_{10}O_2$	Ethyl benzoate	212.6	Nonazeotrope		222
9677	$C_9H_{12}O$	3-Phenylpropanol	235.6	Nonazeotrope		255
9678	$C_9H_{14}O$	Phorone	197.8	Nonazeotrope		232
9679	$C_{10}H_8$	Naphthalene	218.05	215.75	60	222
9680	$C_{10}H_{12}O_2$	Ethyl α-toluate	228.75	Nonazeotrope		228
9681	$C_{10}H_{12}O_2$	Propyl benzoate	230.85	Nonazeotrope		228
9682	$C_{10}H_{14}O$	Carvacrol	237.85	Nonazeotrope		255
9683	$C_{10}H_{14}O$	Thymol	232.9	Nonazeotrope		222
9684	$C_{10}H_{14}O_2$	*m*-Diethoxybenzene	235.4	Nonazeotrope		255
9685	$C_{10}H_{16}O$	Camphor	209.1	Nonazeotrope		232
9686	$C_{10}H_{16}O$	Fenchone	193.6	Nonazeotrope		255
9687	$C_{10}H_{18}O$	Borneol	213.4	211.9	~40	222
9688	$C_{10}H_{18}O$	Menthone	209.5	Nonazeotrope		255
9689	$C_{10}H_{18}O$	α-Terpineol	218.85	213.9	58	247
9690	$C_{10}H_{18}O$	β-Terpineol	210.5	209.0	22	247
9691	$C_{10}H_{20}O$	Citronellol	224.4	214.5	78	255
9692	$C_{10}H_{20}O$	Menthol	216.4	212.2	46	244
9693	$C_{10}H_{20}O_2$	Ethyl caprylate	208.35	Nonazeotrope		255
9694	$C_{10}H_{20}O_2$	Methyl pelargenate	213.8	Nonazeotrope		255
9695	$C_{10}H_{22}O$	Decyl alcohol	232.8	216.5	90	255
9696	$C_{10}H_{22}S$	Isoamyl sulfide	214.8	212.5	30	246
9697	$C_{11}H_{10}$	1-Methylnaphthalene	244.6	Nonazeotrope		255
9698	$C_{11}H_{10}$	2-Methylnaphthalene	241.15	Nonazeotrope		255
9699	$C_{11}H_{20}O$	Methyl α-terpineol ethe	216.2	215.9	28	255
9700	$C_{12}H_{18}$	1,3,5-Triethylbenzene	215.4	~214.3	<45	228
9701	$C_{12}H_{20}O_2$	Bornyl acetate	227.7	Nonazeotrope		228
9702	$C_{13}H_{28}$	Tridecane	234.0	<215.0	<94	255
A =	C_6H_6	**Benzene**	**80.15**			
9703	C_6H_7N	Aniline	184.35	Nonazeotrope		231
9704	C_6H_8	1,3-Cyclohexadiene	80.4	<79.9	....	241

No.	Formula	B-Component Name	B.P., ° C.	Azeotropic Data B.P., ° C.	Wt. % A	Ref.
A =	C_6H_6	**Benzene (*continued*)**	**80.15**			
9705	C_6H_8	1,4-Cyclohexadiene	85.6	Nonazeotrope		*242*
9706	C_6H_{10}	Cyclohexene	82.1	78.9	64.7, V-l.	*153, 243**
9707	C_6H_{12}	Cyclohexane, 40° C.	184.5	206.1	48, V-l.	*346*
		70° C.	543.6	600	48, V-l.	*346*
			80.6	77.7	51.8	*269*
			80.60	77.4	49.7, V-l.	*325*
		1204 mm.	....	....	53.65	
		93 mm.	....	....	46.70	*35, 241**
9708	C_6H_{12}	Methylcyclopentane	71.8	71.5	9.4, V-l.	*145*
		5 lb./sq. inch gage	....	....	9	*283*
		150 lb./sq. inch gage	....	....	14	*203*, 241*, 283*
9709	$C_6H_{12}O$	Cyclohexanol	160.65	Nonazeotrope		*243*
9710	$C_6H_{12}O$	Pinacolone	106.2	Nonazeotrope		*232*
9711	$C_6H_{12}O_2$	Ethyl isobutyrate	110.1	Nonazeotrope		*255*
9712	C_6H_{14}	Hexane	68.7	Nonazeotrope, V-l.		*399*
			69.0	68.5	4.7	*175*, 241*, 269, 432**
9713	$C_6H_{14}O$	Hexyl alcohol	155	Nonazeotrope		*93*
9714	$C_6H_{14}O$	Isopropyl ether	68.3	Nonazeotrope		*238*
9715	$C_6H_{14}O$	Propyl ether	90.55	Nonazeotrope		*218*
9716	$C_6H_{14}O_2$	Acetal	104.5	Nonazeotrope		*243*
9717	$C_6H_{15}N$	Triethylamine	89.35	Nonazeotrope		*231*
9718	$C_6H_{15}NO$	2-(Diethylamino)ethanol	162.2	Nonazeotrope		*255*
9719	C_7H_8	Toluene	110.68	Nonazeotrope, b.p. curve		*432*
9720	C_7H_{16}	2,2-Dimethylpentane	79.1	75.85	46.3	*28*
9721	C_7H_{16}	2,3-Dimethylpentane	89.8	79.2	79.5	*269*
9722	C_7H_{16}	2,4-Dimethylpentane	80.8	75.2	48.3, V-l.	*28*, 269*, 325*
9723	C_7H_{16}	Heptane	98.4	80.1	99.3	*269*
			98.45	Nonazeotrope		*207*
9724	C_7H_{16}	2,2,3-Trimethylbutane, 736 mm.	79.9	75.6	50.5, V-l.	*153*
			....	76.6	49.7	*269*
9725	C_8H_{18}	2,2,4-Trimethylpentane	99.2	80.1	97.7	*269*
9726	$C_9H_{10}O_2$	Ethyl benzoate	213	Vapor pressure data		*243*
A =	C_6H_6O	**Phenol**	**182.2**			
9727	C_6H_7N	Aniline	184.35	186.2	42	*231*
9728	C_6H_7N	3-Picoline	143.0	185.5	76, V-l.	*291*
		600 mm.	135.3	178.0	74, V-l.	*291*
		400 mm.	121.0	166.3	71, V-l.	*291*
		200 mm.	99.9	146.2	32, V-l.	*291, 326**
9729	C_6H_7N	4-Picoline	144.8	190	67.5, V-l.	*291*
		600 mm.	136.0	181.2	66, V-l.	*291*
		400 mm.	122.6	167.5	65, V-l.	*291*
		200 mm.	101.5	147.0	64.5, V-l.	*291, 326**
9730	$C_6H_8O_4$	Methyl fumarate	193.25	194.85	23	*206*
9731	$C_6H_8O_4$	Methyl maleate	204.05	Nonazeotrope		*207*
9732	$C_6H_{10}O$	Cyclohexanone	....	184.5	72	*116*
			Composition independent of pressure			*116*
			155.7	Nonazeotrope		*232*
9733	$C_6H_{10}O_3$	Ethyl acetoacetate	180.7	188?	Reacts	*243*
9734	$C_6H_{10}O_4$	Ethylidene diacetate	168.5	>182.5	<18	*207*
9735	$C_6H_{10}O_4$	Ethyl oxalate	185.65	189.5	41	*222*
9736	$C_6H_{10}O_4$	Glycol diacetate	186.3	189.9	40	*243*
9737	$C_6H_{10}O_4$	Methyl succinate	195	~197	....	*243*
9738	$C_6H_{12}O$	Cyclohexanol	160.7	183.0	87	*254*
			....	Nonazeotrope, V-l.		*2, 116**
9739	$C_6H_{12}O_2$	Isocaproic acid	199.5	Nonazeotrope		*255*
9740	$C_6H_{12}O_3$	2-Ethoxyethyl acetate	156.8	184.9	72	*236*
9741	$C_6H_{12}O_3$	Ethyl α-hydroxy isobutyrate	150	Nonazeotrope		*255*
9742	$C_6H_{12}O_3$	Isopropyl lacetate	167.5	184.8	73	*222*
9743	$C_6H_{12}O_3$	Propyl lactate	171.7	~185	~78	*243*
9744	$C_6H_{13}Br$	1-Bromohexane	156.5	Nonazeotrope		*255*
9745	$C_6H_{14}O$	*n*-Hexyl alcohol	157.8	Nonazeotrope		*216*
9746	$C_6H_{14}O_2$	2-Butoxyethanol	171.25	186.35	63	*236*

No.	B-Component Formula	Name	B.P., ° C.	Azeotropic Data B.P., ° C.	Wt. % A	Ref.
A =	C_6H_6O	**Phenol** (*continued*)	**182.2**			
9747	$C_6H_{14}O_2$	Pinacol	174.35	185.5	71	*253*
9748	$C_6H_{14}O_3$	2-(2-Ethoxyethoxy)ethanol	201.9	208.0	36	*247*
9749	C_7H_5N	Benzonitrile	191.1	192.0	80	*245*
9750	$C_7H_6Cl_2$	α,α-Dichlorotoluene	205.1	Reacts		*243*
9751	C_7H_6O	Benzaldehyde	179.2	185.6	51	*243*
9752	C_7H_7Br	α-Bromotoluene	198.5	Reacts		*243*
9753	C_7H_7Br	*m*-Bromotoluene	183.8	175.7	43	*207*
9754	C_7H_7Br	*o*-Bromotoluene	181.75	174.35	40	*243*
9755	C_7H_7Br	*p*-Bromotoluene	185	176.2	44	*235*
9756	C_7H_7Cl	α-Chlorotoluene	179.35	Reacts		*243*
9757	C_7H_7Cl	*o*-Chlorotoluene	159.2	159.0	3	*255*
9758	C_7H_7Cl	*p*-Chlorotoluene	162.4	161.5	~12	*218*
9759	C_7H_7ClO	*o*-Chloroanisole	195.7	Nonazeotrope		*255*
9760	C_7H_7I	*p*-Iodotoluene	215.0	Nonazeotrope		*222*
9761	C_7H_8	Toluene	110.75	Nonazeotrope		*255*
9762	C_7H_8O	Anisole	153.85	Nonazeotrope		*224*
9763	C_7H_8O	Benzyl alcohol	205.15	Nonazeotrope		*253*
9764	C_7H_8O	*m*-Cresol	202.2	Nonazeotrope		*328*
9765	C_7H_8O	*o*-Cresol	191.1	Nonazeotrope		*328*
9766	C_7H_8O	*p*-Cresol	201.7	Nonazeotrope		*328*
9767	C_7H_9N	Benzylamine	185.0	196.8	45	*231*
9768	C_7H_9N	2,6-Lutidine	143.3	185.5	72.5, V-l.	*291*
		600 mm.	134.5	178.5	71, V-l.	*291*
		400 mm.	121.0	163.5	67, V-l.	*291*
		200 mm.	100.8	143.5	64.5, V-l.	*291, 326**
9769	C_7H_9N	Methylaniline	196.25	Nonazeotrope		*231*
9770	C_7H_9N	*m*-Toluidine	203.1	Nonazeotrope		*231*
9771	C_7H_9N	*o*-Toluidine	200.35	Nonazeotrope		*231*
9772	C_7H_9N	*p*-Toluidine	200.55	Nonazeotrope		*231*
9773	$C_7H_{12}O_4$	Ethyl malonate	198.6	Reacts		*243*
9774	$C_7H_{14}O$	2-Methylcyclohexanol	168.5	183.1	80	*255*
9775	$C_7H_{14}O_3$	Isobutyl lactate	182.15	189.05	~46	*243*
9776	$C_7H_{14}O_3$	1,3-Butanediol methyl ether acetate	171.75	187.0	55	*207*
9777	C_7H_{16}	Heptane	98.4	Nonazeotrope		*255*
9778	$C_7H_{16}O$	Heptyl alcohol	176.15	185.0	72	*250*
9779	C_8H_8	Styrene	145.8	Nonazeotrope		*255*
9780	C_8H_8O	Acetophenone	202.0	202.0	7.8	*232*
9781	$C_8H_8O_2$	Benzyl formate	202.4	Nonazeotrope		*222*
9782	$C_8H_8O_2$	Methyl benzoate	199.55	Nonazeotrope		*243*
9783	$C_8H_8O_2$	Phenyl acetate	195.7	196.6	~12	*253*
9784	C_8H_{10}	Ethylbenzene	136.15	Nonazeotrope		*255*
9785	C_8H_{10}	*m*-Xylene	139.0	Nonazeotrope		*207*
9786	C_8H_{10}	*o*-Xylene	142.6	Nonazeotrope		*243*
9787	$C_8H_{10}O$	Benzyl methyl ether	167.8	Nonazeotrope		*255*
9788	$C_8H_{10}O$	*p*-Methylanisole	177.05	177.02	~3	*221*
9789	$C_8H_{10}O$	Phenetole	170.45	Nonazeotrope		*222, 236*
9790	$C_8H_{10}O_2$	Veratrol	206.8	Nonazeotrope		*255*
9791	$C_8H_{11}N$	Dimethylaniline	194.15	Nonazeotrope		*231*
9792	$C_8H_{11}N$	Ethylaniline	205.5	Nonazeotrope		*231*
9793	$C_8H_{14}O$	Methylheptenone	173.2	184.6	67	*232*
9794	$C_8H_{16}O$	2-Octanone	172.85	184.5	68	*232*
9795	$C_8H_{16}O_2$	Butyl butyrate	166.4	Nonazeotrope		*255*
9796	$C_8H_{16}O_2$	Ethyl caproate	167.85	Nonazeotrope		*222*
9797	$C_8H_{16}O_2$	Isoamyl propionate	160.3	Nonazeotrope		*211*
9798	$C_8H_{16}O_3$	Isoamyl lactate	202.4	~203.5	12	*222*
9799	C_8H_{18}	Octane	125.75	Nonazeotrope		*255*
9800	$C_8H_{18}O$	Butyl ether	142.4	Nonazeotrope		*236*
9801	$C_8H_{18}O$	*n*-Octyl alcohol	195.15	195.4	13	*253*
9802	$C_8H_{18}O$	*sec*-Octyl alcohol	179.0	184.5	50	*215*
9803	$C_8H_{18}S$	Butyl sulfide	172.0	<170.5	<28	*246*
9804	$C_8H_{18}S$	Isobutyl sulfide	172	<170.5	<28	*235*
9805	$C_8H_{20}SiO_4$	Ethyl silicate	165	Nonazeotrope		*243*
9806	C_9H_8	Indene	182.2	173.2	45	*253*
			183.0	177.8	47	*221*
9807	$C_9H_{10}O$	Propiophenone	217.7	Nonazeotrope		*232*

No.	Formula	B-Component Name	B.P., ° C.	Azeotropic Data B.P., ° C.	Wt. % A	Ref.
A =	C_6H_6O	**Phenol** (*continued*)	**182.2**			
9808	C_9H_{12}	Cumene	152.8	Nonazeotrope		*255*
9809	C_9H_{12}	Mesitylene	164.6	163.5	21	*255*
9810	C_9H_{12}	Propylbenzene	158.9	158.0	~4	*222*
9811	C_9H_{12}	Pseudocumene	168.2	166.0	25	*222*
9812	$C_9H_{12}O$	Benzyl ethyl ether	185.0	<181.9	<93	*255*
9813	$C_9H_{12}O$	Phenyl propyl ether	190.2	Nonazeotrope		*222*
9814	$C_9H_{13}N$	*N,N*-Dimethyl-*o*-toluidine	185.35	180.6	69.5	*231*
9815	$C_9H_{14}O$	Phorone	197.8	198.8	18	*232*
9816	$C_9H_{18}O$	2,6-Dimethyl-4-heptanone	168.0	183.4	80	*232*
9817	$C_9H_{18}O_2$	Butyl isovalerate	177.6	184.0	70	*242*
9818	$C_9H_{18}O_2$	Ethyl enanthate	188.7	190.0	12	*242*
9819	$C_9H_{18}O_2$	Isoamyl butyrate	178.5	185.0	~58	*253*
9820	$C_9H_{18}O_2$	Isoamyl isobutyrate	169.8	Nonazeotrope		*255*
9821	$C_9H_{18}O_2$	Isobutyl isovalerate	168.7	182.8	92	*253*
			171.2	Nonazeotrope		*244*
9822	$C_9H_{18}O_2$	Isobutyl valerate	171.35	Nonazeotrope		*222*
9823	$C_9H_{18}O_3$	Isobutyl carbonate	190.3	192.5	26	*243*
9824	$C_{10}H_8$	Naphthalene	218.1	Nonazeotrope		*243*
9825	$C_{10}H_{10}O_2$	Safrole	235.9	Nonazeotrope		*255*
9826	$C_{10}H_{14}$	Butylbenzene	183.1	175.0	46	*242*
9827	$C_{10}H_{14}$	Cymene	176.7	~170.5	37	*222*
9828	$C_{10}H_{16}$	Camphene	159.6	156.1	22	*210*
9829	$C_{10}H_{16}$	*d*-Limonene	177.8	169.0	40.5	*243*
9830	$C_{10}H_{16}$	Nopinene	163.8	~159	~25	*243*
9831	$C_{10}H_{16}$	α-Phellandrene	171.5	165	35	*243*
9832	$C_{10}H_{16}$	α-Pinene	155.8	152.75	19	*243*
9833	$C_{10}H_{16}$	α-Terpinene	173.4	166.7	36	*242*
9834	$C_{10}H_{16}$	Terpinene	181.5	171.5	45	*222*
9835	$C_{10}H_{16}$	Terpinolene	185	173	~62	*243*
9836	$C_{10}H_{16}$	Terpinolene	184.6	172.8	46	*242*
9837	$C_{10}H_{16}$	Thymene	179.7	172.25	40	*210*
9838	$C_{10}H_{16}O$	Camphor	209.1	Nonazeotrope		*232*
9839	$C_{10}H_{16}O$	Carvenone	234.5	Max. b.p.		*243*
9840	$C_{10}H_{16}O$	Fenchone	193.6	196.2	25	*232*
9841	$C_{10}H_{18}$	Menthene	170.5	~164	~33	*243*
9842	$C_{10}H_{18}O$	Borneol	211.8	Nonazeotrope		*243*
9843	$C_{10}H_{18}O$	Cineole	176.4	182.85	72	*208*
9844	$C_{10}H_{18}O$	1,4-Cineole, 100 mm.	105–106	119.3–120	88.7	*178*
9845	$C_{10}H_{18}O$	1,8-Cineole, 100 mm.	107.9	121–121.2	67	*178*
9846	$C_{10}H_{18}O$	Linaloöl	198.6	Nonazeotrope		*215*
9847	$C_{10}H_{18}O$	Menthone	~206	Nonazeotrope		*243*
9848	$C_{10}H_{18}O$	α-Terpineol	218.85	Nonazeotrope		*255*
9849	$C_{10}H_{18}O$	β-Terpineol	210.5	Nonazeotrope		*255*
9850	$C_{10}H_{20}O$	Citronellol	224.4	Nonazeotrope		*255*
9851	$C_{10}H_{20}O$	Menthol	212	Nonazeotrope		*243*
9852	$C_{10}H_{20}O_2$	Isoamyl isovalerate	193.5	Nonazeotrope		*244*
9853	$C_{10}H_{22}$	Decane	173.3	168.0	35	*242*
9854	$C_{10}H_{22}$	2,7-Dimethyloctane	160.25	159.5	6	*224*
9855	$C_{10}H_{22}O$	Amyl ether	187.5	180.2	78	*242*
9856	$C_{10}H_{22}O$	Isoamyl ether	173.2	172.2	15	*236*
9857	$C_{10}H_{22}S$	Isoamyl sulfide	214.8	Nonazeotrope		*246*
9858	$C_{11}H_{20}O$	Isobornyl methyl ether	192.4	Nonazeotrope		*236*
9859	$C_{12}H_{18}$	1,3,5-Triethylbenzene	216	Nonazeotrope		*243*
A =	$C_6H_6O_2$	**Pyrocatechol**	**245.9**			
9860	$C_6H_6O_2$	Resorcinol	281.4	Nonazeotrope		*255*
9861	$C_6H_{14}O_3$	Dipropylene glycol	229.2	253.0	~88	*255*
9862	$C_7H_6Cl_2$	α,α-Dichlorotoluene	205.2	Reacts		*222*
9863	$C_7H_6O_2$	Benzoic acid	250.5	245.85	98	*218*
9864	C_7H_7BrO	*o*-Bromoanisole	217.7	Nonazeotrope		*255*
9865	C_7H_7I	*p*-Iodotoluene	215.0	214.0	7	*222*
9866	$C_7H_7NO_2$	*m*-Nitrotoluene	230.8	Nonazeotrope		*234*
9867	$C_7H_7NO_2$	*o*-Nitrotoluene	221.75	Nonazeotrope		*234*
9868	$C_7H_7NO_2$	*p*-Nitrotoluene	238.9	238.7	11	*234*
9869	$C_7H_8O_2$	*m*-Methoxyphenol	243.8	241.5	....	*222*
9870	C_8H_7N	Indole	253.5	255.0	15	*255*

No.	Formula	Name (B-Component)	B.P., ° C. (B-Component)	B.P., ° C. (Azeotropic Data)	Wt. % A (Azeotropic Data)	Ref.
A =	$C_6H_6O_2$	**Pyrocatechol** *(continued)*	**245.9**			
9871	$C_8H_8O_2$	Anisaldehyde	249.5	253	25	*236*
9872	$C_8H_8O_2$	α-Toluic acid	266.5	Nonazeotrope		*255*
9873	C_8H_9BrO	*p*-Bromophenetole	234.2	231.5	20	*255*
9874	$C_8H_{10}O$	3,4-Xylenol	226.8	Nonazeotrope		*229*
9875	$C_8H_{11}NO$	*o*-Phenetidine	232.5	246.0	92	*231*
9876	$C_8H_{11}NO$	*p*-Phenetidine	249.9	253.8	34	*231*
9877	$C_8H_{12}O_4$	Ethyl maleate	223.3	Nonazeotrope		*255*
9878	$C_8H_{16}O_2$	Caprylic acid	238.5	Nonazeotrope		*255*
9879	C_9H_7N	Quinoline	237.4	257.9	61	*244*
9880	C_9H_8O	Cinnamaldehyde	253.5	Nonazeotrope		*225*
9881	$C_9H_{10}O$	Cinnamyl alcohol	257.0	Nonazeotrope		*255*
9882	$C_9H_{10}O$	*p*-Methylacetophenone	226.35	246.3	87.5	*232*
9883	$C_9H_{10}O_3$	Ethyl salicylate	234.0	Nonazeotrope		*218*
9884	$C_9H_{12}O$	3-Phenylpropanol	235.6	Nonazeotrope		*255*
9885	$C_9H_{18}O_2$	Pelargonic acid	254.0	Nonazeotrope		*255*
9886	$C_{10}H_7Br$	1-Bromonaphthalene	281.8	245.5	~80	*222*
9887	$C_{10}H_7Cl$	1-Chloronaphthalene	262.7	241.0	59	*222*
9888	$C_{10}H_8$	Naphthalene	218.05	217.45	11.5	*218*
9889	$C_{10}H_9N$	Quinaldine	246.5	252.5	48	*255*
9890	$C_{10}H_{10}O_2$	Isasafrole	252.0	243.0	70	*224*
9891	$C_{10}H_{10}O_2$	Methyl cinnamate	261.9	Nonazeotrope		*222*
9892	$C_{10}H_{10}O_2$	Safrole	235.9	233.55	23	*216*
9893	$C_{10}H_{12}O$	Anethole	235.7	233.0	25	*242*
9894	$C_{10}H_{12}O_2$	Ethyl α-toluate	228.75	Nonazeotrope		*253*
9895	$C_{10}H_{12}O_2$	Eugenol	254.8	245.85	98.5	*218*
9896	$C_{10}H_{12}O_2$	Propyl benzoate	230.9	Nonazeotrope		*218*
9897	$C_{10}H_{14}O$	Carvacrol	237.85	236.7	30	*255*
9898	$C_{10}H_{14}O$	Carvone	231.0	248.3	71	*232*
9899	$C_{10}H_{14}O$	Thymol	232.9	232.2	17	*229*
9900	$C_{10}H_{14}O_2$	*m*-Diethoxybenzene	235.4	<233.5	<29	*255*
9901	$C_{10}H_{16}$	Terpinolene	184.6	Nonazeotrope		*255*
9902	$C_{10}H_{16}O$	Pulegone	223.8	246.5	90	*232*
9903	$C_{10}H_{18}O$	Geraniol	229.7	Reacts		
				Nonazeotrope		*222*
9904	$C_{10}H_{20}O_2$	Capric acid	268.8	Nonazeotrope		*255*
9905	$C_{10}H_{22}O$	Decyl alcohol	232.9	Nonazeotrope		*253*
9906	$C_{11}H_{10}$	1-Methylnaphthalene	244.9	235.1	40	*216*
9907	$C_{11}H_{10}$	2-Methylnaphthalene	241.15	233.25	37	*207*
9908	$C_{11}H_{12}O_2$	Ethyl cinnamate	272.0	Nonazeotrope		*255*
9909	$C_{11}H_{14}O_2$	1-Allyl-3,4-dimethoxybenzene	255.0	Nonazeotrope		*218*
9910	$C_{11}H_{14}O_2$	Butyl benzoate	249.8	Nonazeotrope		*222*
9911	$C_{11}H_{14}O_2$	1,2-Dimethoxy-4-propenylbenzene	270.5	Nonazeotrope		*222*
9912	$C_{11}H_{14}O_2$	Isobutyl benzoate	241.9	Nonazeotrope		*218*
9913	$C_{11}H_{16}O$	Methyl thymyl ether	216.5	Nonazeotrope		*255*
9914	$C_{11}H_{20}O$	α-Terpineol methyl ether	216.2	Nonazeotrope		*222*
9915	$C_{11}H_{22}O_3$	Isoamyl carbonate	232.2	Nonazeotrope		*222*
9916	$C_{12}H_{10}$	Acenaphthene	277.9	245.25	84	*222*
9917	$C_{12}H_{10}$	Biphenyl	255.9	239.85	56.5	*222*
9918	$C_{12}H_{10}O$	Phenyl ether	259.3	242.0	59.3	*218*
9919	$C_{12}H_{16}O_2$	Isoamyl benzoate	262.0	Nonazeotrope		*222*
9920	$C_{12}H_{18}$	1,3,5-Triethylbenzene	215.5	214.7	....	*222*
9921	$C_{12}H_{20}O_2$	Bornyl acetate	227.7	Nonazeotrope		*222*
9922	$C_{12}H_{22}O_4$	Isoamyl oxalate	268.0	Nonazeotrope		*224*
9923	$C_{13}H_{10}$	Fluorene	295	Nonazeotrope		*255*
9924	$C_{13}H_{12}$	Diphenyl methane	265.6	243.05	65	*216*
9925	$C_{13}H_{12}O$	Benzyl phenyl ether	286.5	Nonazeotrope		*255*
9926	$C_{13}H_{28}$	Tridecane	234.0	229.7	30	*222*
9927	$C_{14}H_{14}$	1,2-Diphenylethane	284.9	Nonazeotrope		*222*
A =	$C_6H_6O_2$	**Resorcinol**	**281.4**			
9928	$C_6H_6O_3$	Pyrogallol	309	Nonazeotrope		*255*
9929	$C_7H_7NO_2$	*p*-Nitrotoluene	238.9	Nonazeotrope		*255*
9930	$C_8H_8O_2$	α-Toluic acid	266.5	Nonazeotrope		*221*
9931	$C_8H_{11}NO$	*o*-Phenetidine	232.5	Nonazeotrope		*231*
9932	$C_8H_{11}NO$	*p*-Phenetidine	249.9	Nonazeotrope		*224*
9933	$C_9H_{10}O$	Cinnamyl alcohol	257.0	Nonazeotrope		*255*

No.	Formula	B-Component Name	B.P., ° C.	Azeotropic Data B.P., ° C.	Wt. % A	Ref.
A =	$C_6H_6O_2$	**Resorcinol** (*continued*)	**281.4**			
9934	$C_9H_{12}O$	3-Phenylpropanol	235.6	Nonazeotrope		*224*
9935	$C_{10}H_7Br$	1-Bromonaphthalene	281.8	266.3	45	*222*
9936	$C_{10}H_7Cl$	1-Chloronaphthalene	262.7	255.8	26	*222*
9937	$C_{10}H_8$	Naphthalene	218.05	Nonazeotrope		*218*
9938	$C_{10}H_8O$	1-Naphthol	288.0	280.2	70	*255*
9939	$C_{10}H_8O$	2-Naphthol	295	280.8	85	*255*
9940	$C_{10}H_{10}O_2$	Isosafrole	252.0	Nonazeotrope		*222*
9941	$C_{10}H_{10}O_2$	Methyl cinnamate	261.9	Nonazeotrope		*218*
9942	$C_{10}H_{10}O_4$	Methyl phthalate	283.7	287.5	38	*224*
9943	$C_{10}H_{12}O_2$	Eugenol	254.8	Nonazeotrope		*222*
9944	$C_{10}H_{12}O_2$	Isoeugenol	268.5	Nonazeotrope		*222*
9945	$C_{10}H_{18}O_4$	Propyl succinate	250.5	Nonazeotrope		*255*
9946	$C_{10}H_{20}O$	Citronellol	224.4	Nonazeotrope		*255*
9947	$C_{10}H_{20}O_2$	Capric acid	268.8	Nonazeotrope		*255*
9948	$C_{11}H_{10}$	1-Methylnaphthalene	244.6	243.1	14.5	*218*
9949	$C_{11}H_{10}$	2-Methylnaphthalene	241.15	240.05	10.5	*207*
9950	$C_{11}H_{12}O_2$	Ethyl cinnamate	271.5	Nonazeotrope		*222*
9951	$C_{11}H_{14}O_2$	1-Allyl-3,4-dimethoxybenzene	255.0	Nonazeotrope		*222*
9952	$C_{11}H_{14}O_2$	1,2-Dimethoxy-4-propenylbenzene	270.5	Nonazeotrope		*224*
9953	$C_{11}H_{16}O$	*p-tert*-Amylphenol	266.5	265.8	15	*255*
9954	$C_{12}H_{10}$	Acenaphthene	277.9	266.2	41	*222*
9955	$C_{12}H_{10}$	Biphenyl	255.9	252.15	21	*222*
9956	$C_{12}H_{10}O$	Phenyl ether	259.3	255.65	23	*236*
9957	$C_{12}H_{16}O_2$	Isoamyl benzoate	262.0	Nonazeotrope		*218*
9958	$C_{12}H_{18}$	1,3,5-Triethylbenzene	215.5	Nonazeotrope		*222*
9959	$C_{12}H_{22}O_4$	Isoamyl oxalate	268.0	282.5	85	*224*
9960	$C_{13}H_{10}$	Fluorene	295.0	274.0	48	*242*
9961	$C_{13}H_{12}$	Diphenylmethane	265.6	258.95	26	*216*
9962	$C_{13}H_{12}O$	Benzyl phenyl ether	286.5	<275.0	<83	*242*
9963	$C_{13}H_{28}$	Tridecane	234.0	233.25	12	*222*
9964	$C_{14}H_{12}$	Stilbene	306.5	277.5	56	*242*
9965	$C_{14}H_{14}$	1,2-Diphenylethane	284.9	269.7	47	*222*
A =	$C_6H_6O_3$	**Pyrogallol**	**309**			
9966	$C_{10}H_8O$	2-Naphthol	295.0	293.5	78	*255*
9967	$C_{11}H_{10}$	2-Methylnaphthalene	241.15	<240.6	<6	*255*
9968	$C_{12}H_{10}$	Acenaphthene	277.9	272.8	20	*242*
9969	$C_{12}H_{10}$	Biphenyl	256.1	253.5	10	*242*
9970	$C_{13}H_{12}$	Diphenylmethane	265.4	<263.5	>11	*242*
9971	$C_{13}H_{12}O$	Benzyl phenyl ether	286.5	<283.5	<20	*255*
A =	C_6H_6S	**Benzenethiol**	**169.5**			
9972	C_7H_7Cl	*p*-Chlorotoluene	162.4	<161.5	79	*246*
9973	$C_8H_{16}O_2$	Isobutyl butyrate	157	~155	~15?	*243*
9974	$C_{10}H_{16}$	Camphene	~158	Reacts		*243*
9975	$C_{10}H_{16}$	*α*-Phellandrene	171.5	Reacts		*243*
9976	$C_{10}H_{16}$	*α*-Pinene	155.8	Reacts		*243*
9977	$C_{10}H_{18}$	Menthene	170.8	Reacts		*243*
A =	C_6H_7N	**Aniline**	**184.35**			
9978	C_nH_{2n-6}	Aromatic hydrocarbons	160–175	Min. b.p.		*89*
9979	C_nH_{2n+2}	Paraffins	160–175	Min. b.p.		*89*
9980	$C_6H_{10}O$	Cyclohexanone	155.7	Nonazeotrope		*231*
9981	$C_6H_{10}O_4$	Ethyl oxalate	185.0	~181.5	~40	*243*
9982	$C_6H_{11}NO_2$	Nitrocyclohexane	205.4	Nonazeotrope		*231*
9983	C_6H_{12}	Cyclohexane	80.75	Nonazeotrope		*231*
9984	$C_6H_{12}O$	Cyclohexanol	160.8	Nonazeotrope		*231*
9985	C_6H_{14}	*n*-Hexane	68.8	Nonazeotrope		*231*
9986	$C_6H_{14}O$	*n*-Hexyl alcohol	157.85	Nonazeotrope		*231*
9987	$C_6H_{14}O_2$	2-Butoxyethanol	171.15	Nonazeotrope		*231*
9988	$C_6H_{14}O_2$	Pinacol	174.35	172.0	45	*231*
9989	$C_6H_{14}O_3$	2-(2-Ethoxyethoxy)ethanol	201.9	Nonazeotrope		*255*
9990	$C_6H_{15}NO$	2-Diethylaminoethanol	162.2	Nonazeotrope		*231*
9991	C_7H_5N	Benzonitrile	191.1	Nonazeotrope		*245*
9992	C_7H_6O	Benzaldehyde	179.2	Reacts		*243*
9993	C_7H_7Br	*α*-Bromotoluene	198.5	Reacts		*243*
9994	C_7H_7Br	*m*-Bromotoluene	184.3	179.9	39	*231*

No.	B-Component Formula	Name	B.P., ° C.	Azeotropic Data B.P., ° C.	Wt. % A	Ref.
A =	C_6H_7N	**Aniline** (*continued*)	**184.35**			
9995	C_7H_7Br	*o*-Bromotoluene	181.5	178.45	35	*231*
9996	C_7H_7Br	*p*-Bromotoluene	185.0	180.2	44	*231*
9997	C_7H_7Cl	α-Chlorotoluene	179.35	Reacts		*243*
9998	C_7H_7Cl	*o*-Chlorotoluene	159.2	Nonazeotrope		*231*
9999	C_7H_7Cl	*p*-Chlorotoluene	162.4	Nonazeotrope		*231*
10000	$C_7H_7NO_2$	*o*-Nitrotoluene	221.75	Nonazeotrope		*231*
10001	C_7H_8	Toluene	110.75	Nonazeotrope		*231*
10002	C_7H_8O	Anisole	153.85	Nonazeotrope		*231*
10003	C_7H_8O	Benzyl alcohol	205.25	Nonazeotrope		*231*
10004	C_7H_8O	*m*-Cresol	202.2	Nonazeotrope		*231*
10005	C_7H_8O	*o*-Cresol	191.1	191.25	8	*231*
10006	C_7H_8O	*p*-Cresol	201.7	Nonazeotrope		*231*
10007	$C_7H_8O_2$	Guaiacol	205.05	Nonazeotrope		*231*
10008	C_7H_9N	Benzylamine	185.0	185.55	44	*248*
10009	C_7H_{14}	Methylcyclohexane	101.15	Nonazeotrope		*231*
10010	$C_7H_{14}O$	2-Methylcyclohexanol	168.5	168	....	*256*
10011	$C_7H_{14}O_3$	Isobutyl lactate	182.15	~180	....	*243*
10012	C_7H_{16}	Heptane	98.4	Nonazeotrope		*207*
10013	$C_7H_{16}O$	*n*-Heptyl alcohol	176.15	175.4	22	*231*
10014	C_8H_8	Styrene	145.8	Nonazeotrope		*231*
10015	C_8H_8O	Acetophenone	202.0	Nonazeotrope		*231*
10016	C_8H_{10}	Ethylbenzene	136.15	Nonazeotrope		*231*
10017	C_8H_{10}	*m*-Xylene	139.2	Nonazeotrope		*207*
10018	C_8H_{10}	*o*-Xylene	144.3	Nonazeotrope		*231*
10019	C_8H_{10}	*p*-Xylene	138.45	Nonazeotrope		*231*
10020	$C_8H_{10}O$	Benzyl methyl ether	167.8	Nonazeotrope		*231*
10021	$C_8H_{10}O$	*p*-Methylanisole	177.05	Nonazeotrope		*231*
10022	$C_8H_{10}O$	Phenetole	170.45	Nonazeotrope		*231*
10023	$C_8H_{10}O_2$	*o*-Ethoxyphenol	216.5	Nonazeotrope		*231*
10024	$C_8H_{10}O_2$	Veratrole	206.8	Nonazeotrope		*231*
10025	$C_8H_{14}O$	Methylheptenone	173.2	Reacts		*215*
10026	C_8H_{16}	1,3-Dimethylcyclohexane	120.7	Nonazeotrope		*231*
10027	$C_8H_{16}O$	2-Octanone	~173	Nonazeotrope		*243*
10028	C_8H_{18}	Octane	125.75	Nonazeotrope		*231*
10029	$C_8H_{18}O$	Butyl ether	142.4	Nonazeotrope		*231*
10030	$C_8H_{18}O$	Isobutyl ether	122.3	Nonazeotrope		*231*
10031	$C_8H_{18}O$	*n*-Octyl alcohol	195.2	183.95	83	*231*
10032	$C_8H_{18}O$	*sec*-Octyl alcohol	180.4	179.0	36	*231*
10033	C_9H_8	Indene	182.6	179.75	41.5	*231*
10034	C_9H_{12}	Cumene	152.8	Nonazeotrope		*231*
10035	C_9H_{12}	Mesitylene	164.6	Nonazeotrope		*89**, *231*
10036	C_9H_{12}	Propylbenzene	159.3	Nonazeotrope		*231*
10037	C_9H_{12}	Pseudocumene	168.2	<167.8	<13	*231*
10038	$C_9H_{12}O$	Benzyl ethyl ether	185.0	179.8	51	*231*
10039	$C_9H_{12}O$	Phenyl propyl ether	190.5	<183.5	<82	*231*
10040	$C_9H_{13}N$	Dimethyl-*o*-toluidine	185.3	180.55	51.5	*229*
10041	$C_{10}H_8$	Naphthalene	218.0	Nonazeotrope		*231*
10042	$C_{10}H_{14}$	Butylbenzene	183.1	177.8	46	*231*
10043	$C_{10}H_{14}$	Cymene	176.7	173.5	27	*231*
10044	$C_{10}H_{16}$	Camphene	159.6	157.5	13	*231*
10045	$C_{10}H_{16}$	Dipentene	177.7	171.3	39	*231*
10046	$C_{10}H_{16}$	*d*-Limonene	177.8	171.35	38.8	*243*
10047	$C_{10}H_{16}$	Nopinene	163.8	161.8	23	*231*
10048	$C_{10}H_{16}$	α-Phellandrene	171.5	167	~30	*243*
10049	$C_{10}H_{16}$	α-Pinene	155.8	155.25	15	*231*
10050	$C_{10}H_{16}$	α-Terpinene	173.4	169.5	32	*231*
10051	$C_{10}H_{16}$	γ-Terpinene	181.5	174	~42	*218*
10052	$C_{10}H_{16}$	Terpinolene	184.6	175.8	52	*231*
10053	$C_{10}H_{16}$	Thymene	179.7	173.5	41	*212*
10054	$C_{10}H_{16}O$	Camphor	209.1	Nonazeotrope		*231*
10055	$C_{10}H_{16}O$	Fenchone	193	Nonazeotrope		*243*
10056	$C_{10}H_{18}$	*d*-Menthene	170.8	<167.5	<34	*231*
10057	$C_{10}H_{18}O$	Cineole	176.35	174.65	30	*231*
10058	$C_{10}H_{18}O$	Linaloöl	198.6	Nonazeotrope		*231*
10059	$C_{10}H_{18}O$	β-Terpineol	210.75	Nonazeotrope		*231*
10060	$C_{10}H_{22}$	*n*-Decane	173.3	<169.5	<36	*231*

No.	Formula	B-Component Name	B.P., ° C.	Azeotropic Data B.P., ° C.	Wt. % A	Ref.
A =	C_6H_8N	**Aniline** (*continued*)	**184.35**			
10061	$C_{10}H_{22}$	2,7-Dimethyloctane	160.1	<159.5	<22	*231*
10062	$C_{10}H_{22}O$	Amyl ether	187.5	177.5	55	*231*
10063	$C_{10}H_{22}O$	Isoamyl ether	173.2	169.35	28	*231*
10064	$C_{11}H_{10}$	2-Methylnaphthalene	241.15	Nonazeotrope		*207, 231**
10065	$C_{11}H_{20}O$	Isobornyl methyl ether	192.4	<183.8	<80	*231*
			192.2	Nonazeotrope		*243*
10066	$C_{12}H_{18}$	1,3,5-Triethylbenzene	215.5	Nonazeotrope		*230*
10067	$C_{12}H_{22}O$	Ethyl isobornyl ether	203.8	Nonazeotrope		*255*
A =	C_6H_7N	**Picolines**	....			
10068	C_8H_8	Styrene	145	Min. b.p.		*99*
10069	C_8H_{10}	Ethylbenzene	136	Min. b.p.		*99*
10070	C_8H_{10}	Xylenes	140	Min. b.p.		*99*
A =	C_6H_7N	**2-Picoline**	**130.7**			
10071	$C_6H_{10}S$	Allyl sulfide	139.35	<130.2	<95	*255*
10072	$C_6H_{14}S$	Propyl sulfide	141.5	129.8	90	*255*
10073	C_8H_{18}	2,2,4-Trimethylpentane	99.3	Nonazeotrope		*255*
A =	C_6H_7N	**3-Picoline**	**144.0**			
10074	$C_6H_{10}S$	Allyl sulfide	139.35	135.5	30	*255*
10075	C_7H_8	Toluene	110.7	Nonazeotrope		*82*
10076	C_8H_{18}	2,3,4-Trimethylpentane	113.4	Nonazeotrope		*82*
A =	C_6H_7N	**4-Picoline**	**145.3**			
10077	C_7H_8	Toluene	110.7	Nonazeotrope		*82*
10078	C_8H_{18}	2,3,4-Trimethylpentane	113.4	Nonazeotrope		*82*
A =	C_6H_8	**1,3-Cyclohexadiene**	**80.8**			
10079	C_6H_{10}	Cyclohexene	82.75	Nonazeotrope		*243*
10080	C_6H_{12}	Cyclohexane	80.75	79.0	45	*241*
A =	$C_6H_8N_2$	***o*-Phenylenediamine**	**258.6**			
10081	$C_7H_7NO_2$	*m*-Nitrotoluene	230.8	Nonazeotrope		*231*
10082	$C_7H_7NO_2$	*p*-Nitrotoluene	238.9	Nonazeotrope		*207*
10083	$C_7H_8O_2$	*m*-Methoxyphenol	243.8	Nonazeotrope		*231*
10084	$C_8H_{10}O$	Phenethyl alcohol	219.4	Nonazeotrope		*207*
10085	$C_9H_{12}O$	3-Phenylpropanol	235.6	Nonazeotrope		*207*
10086	$C_{10}H_8O$	1-Naphthol	288.0	Nonazeotrope		*207*
10087	$C_{10}H_{10}O_2$	Isosafrole	252.0	249.2	30	*207*
10088	$C_{10}H_{10}O_2$	Safrole	235.9	Nonazeotrope		*207*
10089	$C_{10}H_{12}O$	Anethole	235.7	Nonazeotrope		*207*
10090	$C_{10}H_{12}O_2$	Eugenol	254.8	Nonazeotrope		*231*
10091	$C_{10}H_{12}O_2$	Isoeugenol	268.8	Nonazeotrope		*255*
10092	$C_{10}H_{20}O$	Menthol	216.3	Nonazeotrope		*207*
A =	$C_6H_8N_2$	***o*-Phenylenediamine**	**258.6**			
10093	$C_{11}H_{10}$	1-Methylnaphthalene	244.6	<243.0	<17	*207*
10094	$C_{11}H_{14}O_2$	1-Allyl-3,4-dimethylbenzene	254.7	250.5	38	*207*
10095	$C_{11}H_{14}O_2$	1,2-Dimethoxy-4-propenylbenzene	270.5	Nonazeotrope		*231*
10096	$C_{12}H_{10}$	Acenaphthene	277.9	<258.0	....	*207*
10097	$C_{12}H_{10}$	Biphenyl	256.1	249.7	37	*207*
10098	$C_{12}H_{10}O$	Phenyl ether	259.0	251.2	46	*207*
10099	$C_{13}H_{12}$	Diphenylmethane	265.4	254.0	70	*207*
10100	$C_{14}H_{14}$	1,2-Diphenylethane	284.5	Nonazeotrope		*207*
A =	$C_6H_8O_4$	**Methyl Fumarate**	**193.25**			
10101	$C_6H_8O_4$	Methyl maleate	264.05	Nonazeotrope		*207*
10102	$C_6H_{10}O_4$	Ethyl oxalate	185.65	Nonazeotrope		*207*
10103	$C_6H_{10}O_4$	Glycol diacetate	186.3	Nonazeotrope		*229*
10104	$C_6H_{12}O_2$	Caproic acid	205.15	Nonazeotrope		*255*
10105	$C_6H_{14}O_2$	2-Butoxyethanol	171.15	Nonazeotrope		*207*
10106	C_7H_7Br	α-Bromotoluene	198.5	<192.3	....	*255*
10107	C_7H_7Br	*m*-Bromotoluene	184.3	183.65	16	*207*
10108	C_7H_7Br	*o*-Bromotoluene	181.5	Nonazeotrope		*207*
10109	C_7H_7Cl	α-Chlorotoluene	179.3	Nonazeotrope		*207*
10110	C_7H_8O	*m*-Cresol	202.2	204.3	72	*206*
10111	C_7H_8O	*o*-Cresol	191.1	197.8	60	*250*
10112	C_7H_8O	*p*-Cresol	201.7	204.0	29	*207*
10113	$C_7H_{12}O_4$	Ethyl malonate	199.35	Nonazeotrope		*207*

No.	Formula	B-Component Name	B.P., ° C.	Azeotropic Data B.P., ° C.	Wt. % A	Ref.
A =	**$C_6H_8O_4$**	**Methyl Fumarate** (*continued*)	**193.25**			
10114	$C_8H_8O_2$	Methyl benzoate	199.4	Nonazeotrope		*207, 229*
10115	$C_8H_{10}O$	*p*-Methylanisole	177.05	Nonazeotrope		*207*
10116	$C_8H_{18}O$	*n*-Octyl alcohol	195.2	<190.1	<72	*207*
10117	C_9H_8	Indene	182.6	Nonazeotrope		*255*
10118	$C_9H_{12}O$	Benzyl ethyl ether	185.0	183.5	32	*207*
10119	$C_9H_{18}O_2$	Methyl caprylate	192.9	189.4	46	*207*
10120	$C_{10}H_8$	Naphthalene	218.0	Nonazeotrope		*255*
10121	$C_{10}H_{14}$	Butylbenzene	183.1	Nonazeotrope		*255*
10122	$C_{10}H_{16}$	Dipentene	177.7	172.5	70	*242*
10123	$C_{10}H_{16}$	α-Pinene	155.8	Nonazeotrope		*255*
10124	$C_{10}H_{16}$	α-Terpinene	173.4	170.5	75	*242*
10125	$C_{10}H_{18}O$	Borneol	215	Nonazeotrope		*255*
10126	$C_{10}H_{18}O$	Cineole	176.35	175.75	15	*237*
10127	$C_{10}H_{18}O$	Citronellal	208.0	Nonazeotrope		*255*
10128	$C_{10}H_{20}O_2$	Ethyl caprylate	208.35	Nonazeotrope		*255*
10129	$C_{10}H_{20}O_2$	Isoamyl isovalerate	192.7	189.3	95	*250*
			192.7	189.3	43	*229*
10130	$C_{10}H_{22}O$	Isoamyl ether	173.2	172.35	16	*207*
10131	$C_{11}H_{20}O$	Isobornyl methyl ether	192.4	185.5	48	*207*
10132	$C_{12}H_{22}O$	Bornyl ethyl ether	204.9	191.2	80	*237*
10133	$C_{12}H_{22}O$	Ethyl isobornyl ether	203.8	<191.5	<81	*237*
A =	**$C_6H_8O_4$**	**Methyl Maleate**	**204.05**			
10134	$C_6H_{10}O_4$	Methyl succinate	195.5	Nonazeotrope		*207*
10135	$C_6H_{12}O_2$	Caproic acid	205.15	201.5	63	*242*
10136	$C_6H_{12}O_2$	Isocaproic acid	199.5	198.3	40	*242*
10137	C_7H_7Br	α-Bromotoluene	198.5	197.7	12	*255*
10138	C_7H_8O	Benzyl alcohol	205.25	Reacts		*207*
10139	C_7H_8O	*m*-Cresol	202.2	208.75	55	*207*
10140	C_7H_8O	*o*-Cresol	191.1	204.65	78	*207*
10141	C_7H_8O	*p*-Cresol	201.7	208.6	56	*249, 250*
10142	$C_7H_8O_2$	Guaiacol	205.05	205.15	20	*207*
10143	$C_7H_{12}O_4$	Ethyl malonate	199.35	Nonazeotrope		*207*
10144	C_8H_8O	Acetophenone	202.0	201.0	39	*250*
10145	$C_8H_8O_2$	Methyl benzoate	199.4	198.95	25	*207*
10146	$C_8H_8O_2$	Phenyl acetate	195.7	Nonazeotrope		*207*
10147	$C_8H_{10}O$	3,4-Xylenol	226.8	Nonazeotrope		*207*
10148	$C_8H_{10}O_2$	*m*-Dimethoxybenzene	214.7	<202.8	>55	*237*
10149	$C_8H_{10}O_2$	*o*-Ethoxyphenol	216.5	Nonazeotrope		*255*
10150	$C_8H_{10}O_2$	Veratrole	206.8	<200.9	....	*237*
10151	$C_8H_{14}O_4$	Propyl oxalate	214	Nonazeotrope		*255*
10152	$C_8H_{16}O_3$	Isoamyl lactate	202.4	200.0	45	*255*
10153	$C_8H_{18}O$	Octyl alcohol	195.2	193.55	32	*250*
10154	$C_9H_{10}O_2$	Ethyl benzoate	212.5	Nonazeotrope		*207*
10155	$C_{10}H_8$	Naphthalene	218.0	203.7	87	*207*
10156	$C_{10}H_{12}O$	Estragol	215.6	Nonazeotrope		*237*
10157	$C_{10}H_{18}O$	Borneol	215.0	202.95	78	*207*
10158	$C_{10}H_{18}O$	Citronellal	208.0	Nonazeotrope		*255*
10159	$C_{10}H_{18}O$	Geraniol	229.6	Nonazeotrope		*255*
10160	$C_{10}H_{18}O$	Linaloöl	198.6	<197.2	<40	*255*
10161	$C_{10}H_{18}O$	α-Terpineol	218.85	<203.8	....	*255*
10162	$C_{10}H_{20}O_2$	Isoamyl isovalerate	192.7	190.65	25	*207*
10163	$C_{10}H_{22}S$	Isoamyl sulfide	214.8	203.0	82	*246*
10164	$C_{11}H_{10}$	2-Methylnaphthalene	241.15	Nonazeotrope		*207*
10165	$C_{11}H_{16}O$	Methyl thymol ether	216.5	Nonazeotrope		*237*
10166	$C_{12}H_{18}$	Triethylbenzene	215.5	<202.8	>72	*207*
10167	$C_{12}H_{22}O$	Ethyl isobornyl ether	203.8	<197.8	....	*237*
A =	**C_6H_{10}**	**Biallyl**	**60.1**			
10168	C_6H_{14}	2,3-Dimethylbutane	58.0	<57.5	42	*241*
A =	**C_6H_{10}**	**Cyclohexene**	**82.2/741 mm.**			
10169	C_6H_{12}	Cyclohexane	80.0	Nonazeotrope, V-l.		*153*
10170	C_6H_{12}	Cyclohexane	80.75	<80.6	>10	*241*
10171	C_6H_{14}	Hexane	68.95	Nonazeotrope		*243*
10172	$C_6H_{14}O$	Propyl ether	90.55	Nonazeotrope		*228*
10173	$C_6H_{14}O_2$	Acetal	103.55	Nonazeotrope		*238*

No.	Formula	Name	B.P., ° C.	Azeotropic Data B.P., ° C.	Wt. % A	Ref.
A =	C_6H_{10}	**Cyclohexene** (*continued*)	**82.2/741 mm.**			
10174	C_7H_{14}	Methylcyclohexane	101.15	Nonazeotrope		*255*
10175	C_7H_{16}	Heptane	98.4	Nonazeotrope		*255*
A =	C_6H_{10}	**Methylcyclopentene**	**75.85**			
10176	C_6H_{14}	Hexane	68.8	<68.6	>7	*241*
A =	$C_6H_{10}O$	**Cyclohexanone**	**155.7**			
10177	$C_6H_{12}O$	Cyclohexanol	160.8	Nonazeotrope		*116*, 232*
10178	$C_6H_{12}O_3$	Propyl lactate	171.7	Nonazeotrope		*232*
10179	$C_6H_{13}ClO_2$	Chloroacetal	157.4	155.3	....	*232*
10180	$C_6H_{14}O$	Hexyl alcohol	157.85	155.65	94	*232*
10181	$C_6H_{14}S$	Propyl sulfide	141.5	Nonazeotrope		*255*
10182	C_7H_7Cl	*o*-Chlorotoluene	159.2	Nonazeotrope		*232*
10183	C_7H_7Cl	*p*-Chlorotoluene	162.4	Nonazeotrope		*232*
10184	C_7H_8O	Anisole	153.85	Nonazeotrope		*232*
10185	$C_7H_{14}O$	2-Methylcyclohexanol	168.5	Nonazeotrope		*232*
10186	$C_7H_{14}O_2$	Methyl caproate	149.7	Nonazeotrope		*232*
10187	C_8H_{10}	*o*-Xylene	144.3	Nonazeotrope		*232*
10188	$C_8H_{16}O_2$	Butyl butyrate	166.4	Nonazeotrope		*232*
10189	$C_8H_{16}O_2$	Isoamyl propionate	160.7	Nonazeotrope		*232*
10190	$C_8H_{16}O_2$	Isobutyl butyrate	156.9	155.3	60	*232*
10191	$C_8H_{16}O_2$	Propyl isovalerate	155.7	155.2	45	*232*
10192	C_9H_{12}	Cumene	152.8	152.0	65	*232*
10193	C_9H_{12}	Mesitylene	164.6	Nonazeotrope		*232*
10194	C_9H_{12}	Pseudocumene	168.2	Nonazeotrope		*255*
10195	$C_{10}H_{16}$	Camphene	159.6	150.55	57.5	*232*
10196	$C_{10}H_{16}$	Nopinene	163.8	152.2	65	*232*
10197	$C_{10}H_{16}$	α-Pinene	155.8	149.8	40	*232*
10198	$C_{10}H_{16}$	α-Terpinene	173.4	Nonazeotrope		*232*
10199	$C_{10}H_{22}$	2,7-Dimethyloctane	160.1	151.5	55	*232*
A =	$C_6H_{10}O$	**Mesityl Oxide**	**130.5**			
10200	$C_6H_{10}S$	Allyl sulfide	139.35	Nonazeotrope		*246*
10201	$C_6H_{12}O_2$	Butyl acetate	126.0	Nonazeotrope		*207*
10202	$C_6H_{12}O_2$	Isoamyl formate	123.8	Nonazeotrope		*207*
10203	$C_6H_{12}O_2$	Propyl propionate	123.0	Nonazeotrope		*207*
10204	$C_6H_{12}O_3$	Paraldehyde	124.35	Nonazeotrope		*232*
10205	C_7H_8	Toluene	110.75	Nonazeotrope		*207*
10206	C_7H_{14}	Methylcyclohexane	101.15	Nonazeotrope		*232*
10207	$C_7H_{14}O_2$	Ethyl isovalerate	134.7	Nonazeotrope		*207*
10208	$C_7H_{14}O_2$	Isobutyl propionate	134.0	Nonazeotrope		*232*
10209	$C_7H_{14}O_2$	Propyl isobutyrate	133.9	Nonazeotrope		*211*
10210	C_8H_{10}	Ethylbenzene	136.15	Nonazeotrope		*207*
10211	C_8H_{10}	*m*-Xylene	139.2	Nonazeotrope		*207*
10212	C_8H_{16}	1,3-Dimethylcyclohexane	120.7	118.0	25	*232*
10213	$C_8H_{16}O_2$	Propyl isovalerate	134.7	Nonazeotrope		*232*
10214	C_8H_{18}	Octane	125.75	121.0	35	*207*
10215	$C_8H_{18}O$	Butyl ether	142.4	Nonazeotrope		*232*
10216	$C_8H_{18}O$	Isobutyl ether	122.3	Nonazeotrope		*232*
10217	$C_8H_{19}N$	Diisobutylamine	138.5	<128.5	>25	*255*
A =	$C_6H_{10}O_2$	**2,5-Hexanedione**	**192.2**			
10218	C_7H_8O	*m*-Cresol	202.4	....	36.3, V-l.	*292*
10219	C_7H_8O	*p*-Cresol	202.0	....	32.2, V-l.	*292*
10220	C_8H_9Cl	*o,m,p*-Chloroethylbenzene, 10 mm.	67.5	66.0	24	*24*
10221	$C_8H_{18}O$	Octyl alcohol	195.2	190.0	65	*355*
10222	$C_8H_{18}O$	*sec*-Octyl alcohol	180.4	<179.0	>18	*255*
A =	$C_6H_{10}O_3$	**Ethyl Acetoacetate**	**180.4**			
10223	$C_6H_{10}O_4$	Ethyl oxalate	185.65	Nonazeotrope		*207*
10224	$C_6H_{12}O_2$	Isocaproic acid	199.5	Nonazeotrope		*232*
10225	$C_7H_6Cl_2$	α,α-Dichlorotoluene	205.1	Nonazeotrope		*243*
10226	C_7H_6O	Benzoic acid	179.2	Reacts		*243*
10227	C_7H_7Br	α-Bromotoluene	198.5	Azeotrope doubtful		*243*
10228	C_7H_7Br	*m*-Bromotoluene	184.3	176.5	55	*207*
10229	C_7H_7Br	*o*-Bromotoluene	181.5	174.7	51	*232*
10230	C_7H_7Br	*p*-Bromotoluene	185	176.5	55	*232*
10231	C_7H_7Cl	α-Chlorotoluene	179.3	175	35	*232*

	B-Component			Azeotropic Data		
No.	Formula	Name	B.P., ° C.	B.P., ° C.	Wt. % A	Ref.
A =	$C_6H_{10}O_3$	**Ethyl Acetoacetate** (*continued*)	**180.4**			
10232	C_7H_7Cl	*o*-Chlorotoluene	159.2	Nonazeotrope		232
10233	C_7H_7Cl	*p*-Chlorotoluene	162.4	Nonazeotrope		232
10234	C_7H_8O	Anisole	153.85	Nonazeotrope		232
10235	C_7H_8O	*o*-Cresol	190.8	Reacts		243
10236	C_8H_8	Styrene	145.8	Nonazeotrope		232
10237	C_8H_8O	Acetophenone	202.0	Nonazeotrope		232
10238	$C_8H_8O_2$	Phenyl acetate	195.7	Nonazeotrope		232
10239	C_8H_{10}	*m*-Xylene	139	Nonazeotrope		244
10240	C_8H_{10}	*o*-Xylene	144.3	Nonazeotrope		232
10241	C_8H_{10}	*p*-Xylene	138.4	Nonazeotrope		244
10242	$C_8H_{10}O$	*p*-Methylanisole	177.05	175.7	....	251
10243	$C_8H_{10}O$	Phenetole	170.45	169.8	24	232
10244	$C_8H_{10}O_2$	Veratrole	206.8	Nonazeotrope		232
10245	$C_8H_{14}O$	Methylheptenone	173.2	173.0	30?	232
10246	$C_8H_{16}O_2$	Butyl butyrate	166.4	Nonazeotrope		232
10247	$C_8H_{16}O_2$	Isoamyl propionate	160.7	Nonazeotrope		232
10248	$C_8H_{18}O$	Butyl ether	142.4	Nonazeotrope		232
10249	$C_8H_{18}O$	*sec*-Octyl alcohol	179.0	Nonazeotrope		252
10250	$C_8H_{18}S$	Butyl sulfide	185.0	<178.5	<78	246
10251	$C_8H_{18}S$	Isobutyl sulfide	172.0	171.0	10	247
10252	C_9H_8	Indene	182.6	177.15	68	232
10253	C_9H_{12}	Mesitylene	164.6	162.5	32	232
10254	C_9H_{12}	Propylbenzene	159.3	158.3	24	232
10255	C_9H_{12}	Pseudocumene	168.2	165.2	37	232
10256	$C_9H_{12}O$	Benzyl ethyl ether	185.0	175.5	>75	232
10257	$C_9H_{18}O$	2,6-Dimethyl-4-heptanone	168.0	Nonazeotrope		232
10258	$C_9H_{18}O_2$	Isoamyl butyrate	181.05	174.5	60	244
10259	$C_9H_{18}O_2$	Isoamyl isobutyrate	169.8	169.0	20	232
10260	$C_9H_{18}O_2$	Isobutyl isovalerate	171.2	170.2	25	232
10261	$C_9H_{18}O_2$	Methyl caprylate	192.9	180.0	80	255
10262	$C_{10}H_8$	Naphthalene	218.0	Nonazeotrope		232
10263	$C_{10}H_{14}$	Butylbenzene	183.1	174.0	52	232
10264	$C_{10}H_{14}$	Cymene	176.7	170.5	41	232
10265	$C_{10}H_{16}$	Camphene	159.6	156.15	30	232
10266	$C_{10}H_{16}$	Dipentene	177.7	169.05	43	232
10267	$C_{10}H_{16}$	*d*-Limonene	177.8	169.05	43	243
10268	$C_{10}H_{16}$	Nopinene	163.8	159.3	<35	232
10269	$C_{10}H_{16}$	α-Phellandrene	171.5	165	~40	243
10270	$C_{10}H_{16}$	α-Pinene	155.8	153.35	22	232
10271	$C_{10}H_{16}$	α-Terpinene	173.4	166.6	40	232
10272	$C_{10}H_{16}$	Terpinene	181.5	171.0	50	225
10273	$C_{10}H_{16}$	Terpinolene	184.6	172.2	55	232
10274	$C_{10}H_{16}O$	Fenchone	193.6	Nonazeotrope		232
10275	$C_{10}H_{18}$	*m*-Menthene-8	170.8	164.9	....	232
10276	$C_{10}H_{18}O$	Cineol	176.35	168.75	43	232
10277	$C_{10}H_{20}O_2$	Isoamyl isovalerate	192.7	179.5	77	232
10278	$C_{10}H_{22}$	2,7-Dimethyloctane	160.1	156.0	24	232
10279	$C_{10}H_{22}O$	Amyl ether	187.5	174.5	70	232
10280	$C_{10}H_{22}O$	Isoamyl ether	173.2	167.4	40	232
10281	$C_{11}H_{20}O$	Isobornyl methyl ether	192.4	<179.0	....	232
10282	$C_{12}H_{18}$	1,3,5-Triethylbenzene	216	Nonazeotrope		243
10283	$C_{12}H_{22}O$	Ethyl isobornyl ether	203.8	Nonazeotrope		232
A =	$C_6H_{10}O_4$	**Ethylidene Diacetate**	**168.5**			
10284	$C_6H_{12}O_3$	2-Ethoxyethyl acetate	156.8	Nonazeotrope		207
10285	$C_6H_{14}O$	Hexyl alcohol	157.85	<157.3	....	255
10286	$C_6H_{14}O_2$	2-Butoxyethanol	171.15	166.7	64	207
10287	$C_6H_{14}O_2$	Pinacol	174.35	<167.0	....	255
10288	C_7H_7Br	*m*-Bromotoluene	184.3	Nonazeotrope		207
10289	C_7H_7Br	*o*-Bromotoluene	181.5	Nonazeotrope		255
10990	C_7H_7Cl	α-Chlorotoluene	179.3	Nonazeotrope		255
10291	C_7H_7Cl	*p*-Chlorotoluene	162.4	<161.0	>70	207
10292	C_7H_8O	Anisole	153.85	Nonazeotrope		207
10293	C_7H_8O	*o*-Cresol	191.1	Nonazeotrope		207
10294	$C_7H_{14}O$	2-Methylcyclohexanol	168.5	<165.8	<57	255

No.	B-Component Formula	Name	B.P., ° C.	Azeotropic Data B.P., ° C.	Wt. % A	Ref.
A =	**$C_6H_{10}O_4$**	**Ethylidene Diacetate** (*continued*)	**168.5**			
10295	$C_7H_{14}O_3$	1,3-Butanediol methyl ether acetate	171.75	Nonazeotrope		*207*
10296	C_8H_{10}	*m*-Xylene	139.2	Nonazeotrope		*207*
10297	C_8H_{10}	*o*-Xylene	144.3	Nonazeotrope		*207*
10298	$C_8H_{10}O$	Benzyl methyl ether	167.8	164.0	48	*207*
10299	$C_8H_{10}O$	*p*-Methylanisole	177.05	<168.3	>62	*237*
10300	$C_8H_{10}O$	Phenetole	170.45	164.5	56	*207*
10301	$C_8H_{14}O$	Methylheptenone	173.2	Nonazeotrope		*232*
10302	$C_8H_{16}O$	2-Octanone	172.85	Nonazeotrope		*232*
10303	$C_8H_{16}O_2$	Butyl butyrate	166.4	163.5	37	*207*
10304	$C_8H_{16}O_2$	Ethyl caproate	167.7	164.0	45	*229*
10305	$C_8H_{16}O_2$	Hexyl acetate	171.5	<166.5	<67	*207*
10306	$C_8H_{16}O_2$	Isoamyl propionate	160.7	159.3	23	*229*
10307	$C_8H_{18}O$	*sec*-Octyl alcohol	180.4	168.3	93.5	*207*
10308	$C_9H_{18}O_2$	Butyl isovalerate	177.6	167.5	....	*255*
10309	$C_9H_{18}O_2$	Isoamyl isobutyrate	169.8	165.0	60	*207*
10310	$C_9H_{18}O_2$	Isobutyl isovalerate	171.2	165.5	65	*207*
10311	$C_{10}H_{14}$	Cymene	176.7	165.5	>62	*242*
10312	$C_{10}H_{16}$	Camphene	159.6	<157.0	>32	*207*
10313	$C_{10}H_{16}$	α-Pinene	155.8	<154.0	>25	*207*
10314	$C_{10}H_{18}O$	Cineole	176.35	164.95	66	*207*
10315	$C_{10}H_{22}O$	Isoamyl ether	173.2	161.5	57	*207*
A =	**$C_6H_{10}O_4$**	**Ethyl Oxalate**	**185.65**			
10316	$C_6H_{10}O_4$	Methyl succinate	195.5	Nonazeotrope		*207*
10317	$C_6H_{12}O_2$	Isocaproic acid	199.7	Nonazeotrope		*207*
10318	$C_6H_{12}O_3$	2-Ethoxyethyl acetate	156.8	Nonazeotrope		*206*
10319	$C_6H_{13}Br$	1-Bromohexane	156.5	Nonazeotrope		*255*
10320	$C_6H_{14}O_2$	2-Butoxyethanol	171.25	Reacts		*206*
10321	C_7H_5N	Benzonitrile	191.1	Nonazeotrope		*245*
10322	C_7H_6O	Benzaldehyde	179.2	Nonazeotrope		*243*
10323	C_7H_7Br	*m*-Bromotoluene	184.3	179.0	46	*207*
10324	C_7H_7Br	*o*-Bromotoluene	181.75	177.40	38	*207*
10325	C_7H_7Br	*p*-Bromotoluene	185	<180.2	<49	*208*
10326	C_7H_7Cl	α-Chlorotoluene	179.35	Nonazeotrope		*243*
10327	C_7H_7Cl	*o*-Chlorotoluene	159.2	Nonazeotrope		*207*
10328	C_7H_7Cl	*p*-Chlorotoluene	162.4	Nonazeotrope		*207*
10329	C_7H_8O	Anisole	153.85	Nonazeotrope		*207*
10330	C_7H_8O	*m*-Cresol	202.2	202.3	~3	*222*
10331	C_7H_8O	*o*-Cresol	191.1	194.1	36	*222*
10332	C_7H_8O	*p*-Cresol	201.7	202.0	6.5	*222*
10333	C_7H_9N	Methylaniline	196.1	Reacts		*243*
10334	$C_7H_{13}ClO_2$	Isoamyl chloroacetate	190.5	181.5	~65	*244*
10335	$C_7H_{14}O$	2-Methylcyclohexanol	168.5	Nonazeotrope		*255*
10336	$C_7H_{14}O_3$	1,3-Butanediol methyl ether acetate	171.75	Nonazeotrope		*207*
10337	$C_7H_{16}O$	Heptyl alcohol	176.15	175.5	....	*207*
10338	C_8H_8	Styrene	145.8	Nonazeotrope		*255*
10339	$C_8H_8O_2$	Phenyl acetate	195.7	Nonazeotrope		*207*
10340	$C_8H_{10}O$	Benzyl methyl ether	167.8	Nonazeotrope		*207, 237*
10341	$C_8H_{10}O$	*p*-Methylanisole	177.05	<176.3	....	*237*
10342	$C_8H_{10}O$	Phenetole	171.5	Nonazeotrope		*207*
10343	$C_8H_{10}O_2$	Veratrol	205.5	Nonazeotrope		*237*
10344	$C_8H_{16}O_2$	Hexyl acetate	171.5	Nonazeotrope		*255*
10345	$C_8H_{18}O$	Octyl alcohol	195.15	Reacts		*215*
10346	$C_8H_{18}O$	*sec*-Octyl alcohol	180.4	178.85	33	*247*
10347	C_9H_8	Indene	182.6	<181.0	<43	*255*
10348	C_9H_{12}	Cumene	152.8	Nonazeotrope		*255*
10349	C_9H_{12}	Mesitylene	164.6	Nonazeotrope		*226*
10350	C_9H_{12}	Pseudocumene	168.2	167.95	~6	*221*
10351	$C_9H_{12}O$	Benzyl ethyl ether	185.0	<181.8	<50	*207*
10352	$C_9H_{18}O_2$	Butyl isovalerate	177.6	176.3	25	*207*
10353	$C_9H_{18}O_2$	Ethyl enanthate	188.7	183.0	60	*229*
10354	$C_9H_{18}O_2$	Isoamyl butyrate	181.05	179.45	32.5	*248*
10355	$C_9H_{18}O_2$	Isobutyl isovalerate	185.65	Nonazeotrope		*207*
10356	$C_9H_{18}O_2$	Methyl caprylate	192.9	184.2	70	*229*
10357	$C_{10}H_8$	Naphthalene	218.0	Nonazeotrope		*255*

No.	B-Component Formula	Name	B.P., ° C.	Azeotropic Data B.P., ° C.	Wt. % A	Ref.
A =	$C_6H_{10}O_4$	**Ethyl Oxalate** (*continued*)	**185.65**			
10358	$C_{10}H_{14}$	Butylbenzene	183.1	<180.0	<44	242
10359	$C_{10}H_{14}$	Cymene	175.3	~173	~15	243
10360	$C_{10}H_{16}$	Camphene	159.6	158.5	16	254
10361	$C_{10}H_{16}$	Dipentene	177.7	172.2	40	255
10362	$C_{10}H_{16}$	*d*-Limonene	177.8	172.2	41	243
10363	$C_{10}H_{16}$	Nopinene	163.8	161.5	27	226
10364	$C_{10}H_{16}$	α-Pinene	155.8	154.8	20	217
10365	$C_{10}H_{16}$	α-Terpinene	173.3	170.5	30	226
10366	$C_{10}H_{16}$	γ-Terpinene	181.5	173.5	45	218
10367	$C_{10}H_{16}$	Terpinolene	185	173	~50	243
10368	$C_{10}H_{16}$	Thymene	179.7	~176.0	40.5	217
10369	$C_{10}H_{18}$	*m*-Menthene-8	170.8	168.0	28	255
10370	$C_{10}H_{18}O$	Cineole	176.35	173.5	28	237
10371	$C_{10}H_{18}O$	Linaloöl	198.6	Nonazeotrope		255
10372	$C_{10}H_{18}O$	Linaloöl	198.6	185.6	~97	254
10373	$C_{10}H_{20}O_2$	Isoamyl isovalerate	192.7	184.1	69	207
10374	$C_{10}H_{22}$	2,7-Dimethyloctane	160.1	188.5	28	242
10375	$C_{10}H_{22}O$	Amyl ether	187.5	177.7	54	207
10376	$C_{10}H_{22}O$	Isoamyl ether	173.2	170.15	29	207
10377	$C_{10}H_{22}O$	Isoamyl ether	172.6	Nonazeotrope		215
10378	$C_{11}H_{20}O$	Methyl isobornyl ether	192.2	181.15	88?	237
10379	$C_{12}H_{18}$	1,3,5-Triethylbenzene	215.5	Nonazeotrope		255
10380	$C_{12}H_{22}O$	Ethyl isobornyl ether	203.8	Nonazeotrope		237
A =	$C_6H_{10}O_4$	**Glycol Diacetate**	**186.3**			
10381	$C_6H_{12}O_3$	2-Ethoxyethyl acetate	156.8	Nonazeotrope		255
10382	$C_6H_{14}O_2$	2-Butoxyethanol	171.15	Nonozeotrope		255
10383	C_7H_7Br	*o*-Bromotoluene	181.5	<179.8	<32	255
10384	C_7H_7Br	*p*-Bromotoluene	185.0	<182.0	<45	255
10385	C_7H_8O	*m*-Cresol	202.4	....	24, V-l.	292
10386	C_7H_8O	*o*-Cresol	191.1	194.5	35	242
10387	C_7H_8O	*p*-Cresol	202.0	....	23, V-l.	292
10388	$C_7H_{14}O_3$	1,3-Butanediol methyl ether acetate	171.75	Nonazeotrope		207
10389	$C_8H_8O_2$	Phenyl acetate	195.7	Nonazeotrope		255
10390	$C_8H_{10}O$	Benzyl methyl ether	167.8	Nonazeotrope		237
10391	$C_8H_{10}O$	Phenetole	170.45	Nonazeotrope		237
10392	$C_8H_{10}O_2$	Veratrole	206.8	Nonazeotrope		237
10393	$C_8H_{18}O$	Octyl alcohol	195.2	<186.0	....	255
10394	$C_8H_{18}O$	*sec*-Octyl alcohol	180.4	179.2	....	247
10395	C_9H_{12}	Mesitylene	164.6	Nonazeotrope		255
10396	C_9H_{12}	Propylbenzene	159.3	Nonazeotrope		255
10397	$C_9H_{12}O$	Benzyl ethyl ether	185.0	<181.2	....	237
10398	$C_9H_{18}O_2$	Butyl isovalerate	177.6	<177.0	>15	229
10399	$C_9H_{18}O_2$	Isoamyl butyrate	181.05	179.0	38	229
10400	$C_{10}H_{14}$	Butylbenzene	183.1	<181.2	<42	255
10401	$C_{10}H_{16}$	Dipentene	177.7	<173.5	<37	255
10402	$C_{10}H_{20}O_2$	Isoamyl isovalerate	192.7	184.6	75	229
10403	$C_{10}H_{22}O$	Amyl ether	187.5	<179.0	<60	237
10404	$C_{10}H_{22}O$	Isoamyl ether	173.2	170.1	....	237
10405	$C_{11}H_{20}O$	Isobornyl methyl ether	192.4	<183.5	<82	237
A =	$C_6H_{10}O_4$	**Methyl Succinate**	**195.5**			
10406	$C_6H_{12}O_2$	Caproic acid	205.15	Nonazeotrope		255
10407	$C_6H_{12}O_2$	Isocaproic acid	199.5	<194.2	<80	242
10408	C_7H_5N	Benzonitrile	191.1	Nonazeotrope		245
10409	$C_7H_6Cl_2$	α,α-Dichlorotoluene	205.2	Nonazeotrope		227
10410	C_7H_7Br	α-Bromotoluene	198.5	<192.5	>55	255
10411	C_7H_7Br	*m*-Bromotoluene	184.3	182.6	<21	255
10412	C_7H_7Br	*o*-Bromotoluene	181.5	<181.0	<10	255
10413	C_7H_7Br	*p*-Bromotoluene	185.0	180.0	....	227
10414	C_7H_8O	*o*-Cresol	190.8	198.8	~60	243
10415	C_7H_8O	*p*-Cresol	201.8	204.7	....	243
10416	$C_7H_{12}O_4$	Ethyl malonate	199.35	Nonazeotrope		255
10417	C_8H_8O	Acetophenone	202.0	Nonazeotrope		232
10418	$C_8H_8O_2$	Methyl benzoate	199.4	Nonazeotrope		255
10419	$C_8H_8O_2$	Phenyl acetate	195.5	Nonazeotrope		252

No.	B-Component Formula	Name	B.P., ° C.	Azeotropic Data B.P., ° C.	Wt. % A	Ref.
A =	$C_6H_{10}O_4$	**Methyl Succinate** (*continued*)	**195.5**			
10420	$C_8H_{10}O$	*p*-Methylanisole	177.05	Nonazeotrope		*237*
10421	$C_8H_{18}O$	*n*-Octyl alcohol	195.15	192.5	50	*252*
10422	C_9H_8	Indene	182.6	Nonazeotrope		*255*
10423	C_9H_{12}	Mesitylene	164.6	Nonazeotrope		*226*
10424	C_9H_{12}	Propylbenzene	159.3	Nonazeotrope		*255*
10425	C_9H_{12}	Pseudocumene	168.2	Nonazeotrope		*255*
10426	$C_9H_{14}O$	Phorone	197.8	Nonazeotrope		*232*
10427	$C_9H_{18}O_3$	Isobutyl carbonate	190.3	Nonazeotrope		*229*
10428	$C_{10}H_8$	Naphthalene	218.1	Nonazeotrope		*226*
10429	$C_{10}H_{16}$	Camphene	159.6	~159.0	10	*226*
10430	$C_{10}H_{16}$	*d*-Limonene	177.8	175.5	26	*209*
10431	$C_{10}H_{16}$	α-Pinene	155.8	155.5	<10	*226*
10432	$C_{10}H_{16}$	α-Terpinene	173.4	172.5	19	*242*
10433	$C_{10}H_{16}$	γ-Terpinene	181.5	178.0	32	*218*
10434	$C_{10}H_{16}$	Terpinolene	185	~178	~28	*243*
10435	$C_{10}H_{16}$	Thymene	179.7	178.2	~32	*210*
10436	$C_{10}H_{17}Cl$	Bornyl chloride	207.5	<195.2	....	*255*
10437	$C_{10}H_{18}O$	Cineole	176.35	<176.0	<95	*237*
10438	$C_{10}H_{18}O$	Linaloöl	198.6	Reacts		*216*
10439	$C_{10}H_{20}O$	Menthol	212	Nonazeotrope ?		*243*
10440	$C_{10}H_{20}O_2$	Ethyl caprylate	208.35	Nonazeotrope		*229*
10441	$C_{10}H_{20}O_2$	Isoamyl isovalerate	192.7	191.0	30	*229*
10442	$C_{10}H_{22}O$	Isoamyl ether	173.2	<172.5	....	*237*
10443	$C_{51}H_{20}O$	Isobornyl methyl ether	192.4	186.4	....	*237*
10444	$C_{12}H_{18}$	1,3,5-Triethylbenzene	216	Nonazeotrope		*226*
10445	$C_{12}H_{22}O$	Ethyl isobornyl ether	203.8	193.0	75	*237*
A =	$C_6H_{10}S$	**Allyl Sulfide**	**139.35**			
10446	$C_6H_{12}O$	Cyclohexanol	160.8	Nonazeotrope		*246*
10447	$C_6H_{12}O$	2-Hexanone	127.2	Nonazeotrope		*246*
10448	$C_6H_{12}O$	4-Methyl-2-pentanone	116.05	Nonazeotrope		*246*
10449	$C_6H_{12}O_2$	Butyl acetate	126.0	Nonazeotrope		*246*
10450	$C_6H_{12}O_2$	Ethyl butyrate	121.5	Nonazeotrope		*246*
			119.9	~117.5	~15	*243*
10451	$C_6H_{12}O_2$	Isoamyl formate	123.6	~120	~20	*243*
10452	$C_6H_{14}O$	Hexyl alcohol	157.85	Nonazeotrope		*246*
10453	$C_7H_{14}O$	4-Heptanone	143.55	138.2	75	*246*
10454	$C_7H_{16}O_2$	Dipropoxymethane	137.2	<135.5	>68	*242*
10455	C_8H_{10}	Ethylbenzene	136.15	<136.0	>11	*246*
10456	C_8H_{10}	*m*-Xylene	139.2	<138.3	>52	*246*
10457	C_8H_{16}	1,3-Dimethylcyclohexane	120.7	Nonazeotrope		*246*
10458	$C_8H_{18}O$	Butyl ether	142.4	<139.0	70	*246*
A =	$C_6H_{11}BrO_2$	**Ethyl α-bromoisobutyrate**	**178**			
10459	C_7H_6O	Benzaldehyde	179.2	Azeotrope doubtful		*243*
10460	C_7H_7Cl	α-Chlorotoluene	179.3	~173.5	~60	*212*
10461	$C_8H_{18}O$	*sec*-Octyl alcohol	178.7	~175	....	*243*
10462	$C_{10}H_{16}$	*d*-Limonene	177.8	174	~55	*243*
A =	$C_6H_{11}ClO_2$	**Butyl Chloroacetate**	**181.8**			
10463	C_7H_7Br	*o*-Bromotoluene	181.5	179.5	45	*242*
10464	$C_8H_{10}O$	Benzyl methyl ether	167.8	Nonazeotrope		*255*
10465	$C_8H_{10}O$	Phenetole	170.45	Nonazeotrope		*255*
10466	$C_8H_{18}O$	Octyl alcohol	195.2	Nonazeotrope		*255*
10467	$C_{10}H_{14}$	Butylbenzene	183.1	<179.5	<70	*242*
10468	$C_{10}H_{14}$	Cymene	176.7	175.4	25	*255*
10469	$C_{10}H_{16}$	Dipentene	177.7	175.0	32	*242*
10470	$C_{10}H_{22}O$	Isoamyl ether	173.2	Nonazeotrope		*255*
A =	$C_6H_{11}ClO_2$	**Isobutyl Chloroacetate**	**174.5**			
10471	C_7H_7Cl	*p*-Chlorotoluene	162.4	Nonazeotrope		*255*
10472	$C_8H_{10}O$	Phenetole	170.45	170.0	12	*255*
10473	C_9H_{12}	Propylbenzene	159.3	Nonazeotrope		*255*
10474	$C_{10}H_{14}$	Cymene	176.7	172.2	65	*242*
10475	$C_{10}H_{16}$	Camphene	159.6	Nonazeotrope		*255*
10476	$C_{10}H_{16}$	α-Pinene	155.8	Nonazeotrope		*255*
10477	$C_{10}H_{18}O$	Cineole	176.35	173.2	70	*242*
10478	$C_{10}H_{18}O$	Linaloöl	198.6	Nonazeotrope		*255*

No.	Formula	B-Component Name	B.P., ° C.	Azeotropic Data B.P., ° C.	Wt. % A	Ref.
A =	**$C_6H_{11}ClO_2$**	**Isobutyl Chloroacetate** (*continued*)	**174.5**			
10479	$C_{10}H_{22}O$	Amyl ether	187.5	Nonazeotrope		*255*
10480	$C_{10}H_{22}O$	Isoamyl ether	173.2	172.0	38	*242*
A =	**$C_6H_{11}N$**	**Capronitrile**	**163.9**			
10481	$C_6H_{12}O$	Cyclohexanol	160.8	158.0	36	*247*
10482	$C_6H_{14}O$	Hexyl alcohol	157.85	<156.6	>19	*247*
10483	$C_6H_{14}O_2$	2-Butoxyethanol	171.15	Nonazeotrope		*255*
10484	C_8H_{10}	*m*-Xylene	139.2	Nonazeotrope		*255*
10485	C_9H_{12}	Cumene	152.8	150.8	18	*255*
10486	$C_{10}H_{16}$	Camphene	159.6	143.0	35	*242*
10487	$C_{10}H_{16}$	α-Pinene	155.8	142.0	30	*242*
A =	**$C_6H_{11}NO_2$**	**Nitrocyclohexane**	**205.3**			
10488	$C_6H_{15}NO$	2-(Diethylamino)ethanol	162.2	Nonazeotrope		*255*
10489	C_7H_6O	Benzaldehyde	179.2	Nonazeotrope		*234*
10490	C_7H_9N	Methylaniline	196.25	Nonazeotrope		*231*
10491	C_7H_9N	*m*-Toluidine	203.1	<203.0	>4	*231*
10492	C_7H_9N	*o*-Toluidine	200.35	Nonazeotrope		*231*
10493	$C_7H_{14}O_3$	Isobutyl lactate	182.15	Nonazeotrope		*255*
10494	$C_8H_{11}N$	Dimethylaniline	194.15	Nonazeotrope		*231*
10495	$C_8H_{11}N$	Ethylaniline	205.5	<204.8	....	*231*
10496	$C_8H_{16}O_3$	Isoamyl lactate	202.4	<201.0	>28	*255*
10496a	$C_8H_{18}S$	Butyl sulfide	185.0	Nonazeotrope		*255*
10497	$C_9H_{13}N$	*N,N*-Dimethyl-*o*-toluidine	185.3	Nonazeotrope		*231*
A =	**C_6H_{12}**	**Cyclohexane**	**80.75**			
10498	$C_6H_{12}O$	4-Methyl-2-pentanone	116.05	Nonazeotrope		*207*
10499	$C_6H_{12}O$	Pinacolone	106.2	Nonazeotrope		*232*
10500	$C_6H_{12}O_2$	Ethyl isobutyrate	110.1	Nonazeotrope		*255*
10501	C_6H_{14}	Hexane	68.95	Nonazeotrope		*243*
10502	$C_6H_{14}O$	Propyl ether	90.55	Nonazeotrope		*228*
10503	$C_6H_{14}O_2$	Acetal	103.55	Nonazeotrope		*218*
10504	C_7H_8	Toluene	110.7	Nonazeotrope		*243*
10505	C_7H_{14}	Methylcyclohexane	100.80	Nonazeotrope, V-l.		*325*
10506	C_7H_{16}	2,2,3-Trimethylbutane, 744 mm.	80.1	79.45	47.8, V-l.	*153*
			80.75	Nonazeotrope		*255*
10507	C_8H_{18}	2,5-Dimethylhexane	109.4	Nonazeotrope		*255*
A =	**C_6H_{12}**	**Methylcyclopentane**	**71.95**			
10508	C_6H_{14}	Hexane	68.8	<67.9	>25	*175*, 241*
10509	$C_6H_{14}O$	Isopropyl ether	68.3	<68.0	<20	*238*
10510	$C_6H_{15}N$	Triethylamine	89.35	Nonazeotrope		*231*
A =	**$C_6H_{12}O$**	**Cyclohexanol**	**160.8**			
10511	$C_6H_{12}O_3$	Isopropyl lactate	166.8	<160.7	....	*255*
10512	$C_6H_{12}O_3$	Paraldehyde	124.35	Nonazeotrope		*255*
10513	$C_6H_{12}O_3$	Propyl lactate	171.7	Nonazeotrope		*255*
10514	$C_6H_{13}Br$	1-Bromohexane	156.5	<153.7	<34	*255*
10515	$C_6H_{13}ClO_2$	Chloroacetal	156.8	155.6	15	*243*
10516	$C_6H_{14}O$	Hexyl alcohol	157.95	Nonazeotrope		*218*
10517	$C_6H_{14}O_2$	2-Butoxyethanol	171.15	Nonazeotrope		*255*
10518	C_7H_6O	Benzaldehyde	179.2	Nonazeotrope		*255*
10519	C_7H_7Br	*m*-Bromotoluene	184.3	Nonazeotrope		*207*
10520	C_7H_7Br	*o*-Bromotoluene	181.45	160.6?	~98	*210*
10521	C_7H_7Br	*p*-Bromotoluene	185.0	Nonazeotrope		*255*
10522	C_7H_7Cl	α-Chlorotoluene	179.35	Nonazeotrope		*243*
10523	C_7H_7Cl	*o*-Chlorotoluene	159.3	155.5	38	*253*
10524	C_7H_7Cl	*p*-Chlorotoluene	162.4	156.5	55	*211*
10525	C_7H_8	Toluene	110.75	Nonazeotrope		*221*
10526	C_7H_8O	Anisole	153.85	152.45	30	*209*
10527	C_7H_8O	*o*-Cresol	191.1	Nonazeotrope		*222*
10528	C_7H_{14}	Methylcyclohexane	101.1	Nonazeotrope		*217*
10529	$C_7H_{14}O_2$	Methyl caproate	149.8	Nonazeotrope		*255*
10530	$C_7H_{14}O_3$	1,3-Butanediol methyl ether acetate	144.6	Nonazeotrope		*255*
10531	C_7H_{16}	Heptane	98.45	Nonazeotrope		*221*
10532	C_8H_8	Styrene	145.8	144	....	*217*
10533	C_8H_{10}	*m*-Xylene	139.0	138.9	5	*243*
10534	C_8H_{10}	*o*-Xylene	143.6	143.0	14	*217*

No.	Formula	B-Component Name	B.P., ° C.	Azeotropic Data B.P., ° C.	Wt. % A	Ref.
A =	$C_6H_{12}O$	**Cyclohexanol** (*continued*)	**160.8**			
10535	C_8H_{10}	*p*-Xylene	138.2	Nonazeotrope		*221*
10536	$C_8H_{10}O$	Benzyl methyl ether	167.8	159.0	62	*236, 360**
10537	$C_8H_{10}O$	Phenetole	170.35	159.2	~72	*209*
10538	$C_8H_{10}O$	*p*-Methylanisole	177.05	160.5	92	*244*
10539	$C_8H_{11}N$	Dimethylaniline	194.05	Nonazeotrope		*231*
10540	$C_8H_{14}O$	Methylheptenone	173.2	Nonazeotrope		*232*
10541	C_8H_{16}	1,3-Dimethylcyclohexane	120.7	Nonazeotrope		*255*
10542	$C_8H_{16}O$	2-Octanone	172.85	Nonazeotrope		*232*
10543	$C_8H_{16}O_2$	Butyl butyrate	166.4	<160.5	....	*255*
10544	$C_8H_{16}O_2$	Isoamyl propionate	~160.3	157.7	~63	*243*
10545	$C_8H_{16}O_2$	Isobutyl butyrate	156.8	156	~20	*217*
10546	$C_8H_{16}O_2$	Isobutyl isobutyrate	147.3	Nonazeotrope		*217*
10547	$C_8H_{16}O_2$	Propyl isovalerate	155.7	155.1	17	*255*
10548	$C_8H_{18}O$	Butyl ether	142.1	Nonazeotrope		*256*
10549	$C_8H_{18}O$	Isobutyl ether	122.3	Nonazeotrope		*255*
10550	$C_8H_{18}S$	Butyl sulfide	185.0	Nonazeotrope		*246*
10551	C_9H_8	Indene	181.7	160	75	*217*
10552	C_9H_{12}	Cumene	152.8	150.0	28	*247*
10553	C_9H_{12}	Mesitylene	164.0	156.3	~50	*243*
10554	C_9H_{12}	Propylbenzene	158.8	153.8	40	*217*
10555	C_9H_{12}	Pseudocumene	169	158	~60	*243*
10556	$C_9H_{12}O$	Benzyl ethyl ether	185.0	Nonazeotrope		*255*
10557	$C_9H_{13}N$	*N,N*-Dimethyl-*o*-toluidine	185.3	Nonazeotrope		*231*
10558	$C_9H_{18}O$	2,6-Dimethyl-4-heptanone	168.0	Nonazeotrope		*232*
10559	$C_9H_{18}O_2$	Isobutyl isovalerate	168.7	Nonazeotrope		*216*
10560	$C_{10}H_8$	Naphthalene	218.05	Nonazeotrope		*220*
10561	$C_{10}H_{14}$	Butylbenzene	183.1	Nonazeotrope		*255*
10562	$C_{10}H_{14}$	Cymene	176.7	159.5	72	*217*
10563	$C_{10}H_{16}$	Camphene	159.5	151.9	41	*208*
10564	$C_{10}H_{16}$	*d*-Limonene	177.8	159.25	73.5	*221*
10565	$C_{10}H_{16}$	α-Phellandrene	171.5	158	65	*243*
10566	$C_{10}H_{16}$	α-Pinene	155.8	149.9	35.5	*243*
10567	$C_{10}H_{16}$	α-Terpinene	173.4	158.3	65	*247*
10568	$C_{10}H_{16}$	γ-Terpinene	183	160.3	83	*255*
10569	$C_{10}H_{16}$	Terpinene	181	159.8	....	*243*
10570	$C_{10}H_{16}$	Terpinolene	184.6	160.5	87	*255*
10571	$C_{10}H_{16}$	Thymene	179.7	159.8	78	*253*
10572	$C_{10}H_{18}$	*d*-Menthene	170.8	~157.5	~62	*243*
10573	$C_{10}H_{18}O$	Cineole	176.35	160.55	92	*254*
10574	$C_{10}H_{22}$	2,7-Dimethyloctane	160.2	153.0	~62	*217*
10575	$C_{10}H_{22}O$	Amyl ether	187.5	Nonazeotrope		*236*
10576	$C_{10}H_{22}O$	Isoamyl ether	172.6	158.8	78	*254*
A =	$C_6H_{12}O$	**2-Hexanone**	**127.2**			
10577	$C_6H_{12}O_2$	Butyl acetate	126.0	125.4	32	*207*
10578	$C_6H_{12}O_2$	Isoamyl formate	123.8	Nonazeotrope		*232*
10579	$C_7H_{14}O_2$	Propyl isobutyrate	134.0	Nonazeotrope		*232*
A =	$C_6H_{12}O$	**3-Hexanone**	**123.3**			
10580	$C_6H_{12}O_2$	Butyl acetate	126.0	123.1	....	*232*
10581	$C_6H_{12}O_2$	Ethyl butyrate	121.5	Nonazeotrope		*232*
10582	$C_6H_{12}O_2$	Isoamyl formate	123.8	123.0	50	*232*
10583	$C_6H_{12}O_2$	Isobutyl acetate	117.4	Nonazeotrope		*232*
10584	$C_6H_{12}O_2$	Methyl isovalerate	116.5	Nonazeotrope		*232*
10585	$C_6H_{12}O_2$	Propyl propionate	123.0	122.5	40	*232*
10586	$C_6H_{14}S$	Isopropyl sulfide	120.5	119.0	32	*235*
10587	$C_6H_{15}BO_3$	Ethyl borate	118.6	116.7	28	*232*
10588	$C_6H_{15}N$	Dipropylamine	109.2	Nonazeotrope		*231*
10589	C_7H_8	Toluene	110.75	Nonazeotrope		*232*
10590	C_7H_{16}	*n*-Heptane	98.4	Nonazeotrope		*207*
10591	C_8H_{10}	Ethylbenzene	136.15	Nonazeotrope		*255*
10592	C_8H_{10}	*m*-Xylene	139.2	Nonazeotrope		*207*
10593	C_8H_{16}	1,3-Dimethylcyclohexane	120.7	116.0	37	*232*
10594	$C_8H_{19}N$	Diisobutylamine	138.5	Nonazeotrope		*255*
A =	$C_6H_{12}O$	**4-Methyl-2-pentanone**	**116.05**			
10595	$C_6H_{12}O_2$	Ethyl butyrate	121.5	Nonazeotrope		*207*

No.	B-Component Formula	Name	B.P., ° C.	Azeotropic Data B.P., ° C.	Wt. % A	Ref.
A =	**$C_6H_{12}O$**	**4-Methyl-2-pentanone** (*continued*)	**116.05**			
10596	$C_6H_{12}O_2$	Ethyl isobutyrate	110.1	Nonazeotrope		*207*
10597	$C_6H_{12}O_2$	Isobutyl acetate	117.4	115.6	....	*232*
10598	$C_6H_{12}O_2$	Isopropyl propionate	110.5	Nonazeotrope		*232*
10599	$C_6H_{12}O_2$	Methyl isovalerate	116.5	115.6	55	*207*
10600	$C_6H_{14}S$	Isopropyl sulfide	120.5	114.9	72	*235*
10601	$C_6H_{15}N$	Dipropylamine	109.2	<105.5	<32	*231*
10602	C_7H_8	Toluene	110.75	110.7	3	*207*
10603	C_7H_{14}	Methylcyclohexane	101.15	<100.1	<20	*207*
10604	C_7H_{16}	Heptane	98.4	97.5	13	*232*
10605	C_8H_{10}	Ethylbenzene	136.15	Nonazeotrope		*207*
10606	C_8H_{16}	1,3-Dimethylcyclohexane	120.7	112.0	53	*232*
10607	C_8H_{18}	*n*-Octane	125.75	113.4	65	*207*
10608	$C_8H_{18}O$	Isobutyl ether	122.3	Nonazeotrope		*255*
10609	$C_8H_{19}N$	Diisobutylamine	138.5	Nonazeotrope		*255*
A =	**$C_6H_{12}O$**	**Pinacolone**	**106.2**			
10610	$C_6H_{12}O_2$	Ethyl isobutyrate	110.1	Nonazeotrope		*232*
10611	$C_6H_{12}O_2$	Isopropyl propionate	110.5	Nonazeotrope		*232*
10612	C_6H_{14}	Hexane	68.8	Nonazeotrope		*232*
10613	$C_6H_{14}O_2$	Acetal	103.55	Nonazeotrope		*255*
10614	$C_6H_{15}N$	Dipropylamine	109.2	<104.5	....	*255*
10615	C_7H_8	Toluene	110.75	106.0	85	*232*
10616	C_7H_{14}	Methylcyclohexane	101.15	97.0	32	*232*
10617	C_7H_{16}	Heptane	98.4	95.5	28	*232*
10618	C_8H_{16}	1,3-Dimethylcyclohexane	120.7	104.0	75	*232*
A =	**$C_6H_{12}O_2$**	**Butyl Acetate**	**126.0**			
10619	$C_6H_{12}O_2$	Isoamyl formate	123.8	Nonazeotrope		*255*
10620	$C_6H_{12}O_2$	Propyl propionate	123.0	Nonazeotrope		*255*
10621	$C_6H_{12}O_3$	2-Ethoxyethyl acetate	156.8	Nonazeotrope		*255*
10622	$C_6H_{12}O_3$	Paraldehyde	124.35	124.25	9	*207*
10623	$C_6H_{14}S$	Propyl sulfide	141.5	Nonazeotrope		*255*
10624	C_7H_8	Toluene	110.75	Nonazeotrope		*207*
10625	$C_7H_{14}O_2$	Propyl isobutyrate	134.0	Nonazeotrope		*255*
10626	$C_7H_{16}O_2$	Dipropoxymethane	137.2	Nonazeotrope		*237*
10627	C_8H_{10}	Ethylbenzene	136.1	Nonazeotrope		*207*
10628	C_8H_{10}	*m*-Xylene	139.0	Nonazeotrope		*207*
10629	C_8H_{10}	*p*-Xylene	138.45	Nonazeotrope		*207*
10630	C_8H_{16}	1,3-Dimethylcyclohexane	120.7	<118.0	<37	*255*
10631	C_8H_{18}	Octane	125.8	119	52	*218*
10632	$C_8H_{18}O$	Isobutyl ether	122.3	Nonazeotrope		*237*
10633	$C_{10}H_{16}$	Camphene	159.6	Nonazeotrope		*255*
10634	$C_{10}H_{16}$	Nopinene	163.8	Nonazeotrope		*207*
10635	$C_{10}H_{16}$	α-Pinene	155.8	Nonazeotrope		*255*
A =	**$C_6H_{12}O_2$**	**Caproic Acid**	**205.3**			
10636	$C_7H_6Cl_2$	α,α-Dichlorotoluene	205.2	199.0	36	*222*
10637	C_7H_7Br	α-Bromotoluene	198.5	~196.5	77	*243*
10638	C_7H_7Br	*o*-Bromotoluene	181.5	180.8	6	*221*
10639	C_7H_7Br	*p*-Bromotoluene	185.0	184.0	8	*221*
10640	C_7H_7BrO	*o*-Bromoanisole	217.7	Nonazeotrope		*255*
10641	C_7H_7Cl	α-Chlorotoluene	179.3	179.0	~3	*221*
10642	C_7H_7Cl	*m*-Chlorotoluene	162.3	Nonazeotrope		*244*
10643	C_7H_7Cl	*o*-Chlorotoluene	159.2	Nonazeotrope		*244*
10644	C_7H_7Cl	*p*-Chlorotoluene	162.4	Nonazeotrope		*244*
10645	C_7H_7I	*p*-Iodotoluene	214.5	202.2	50	*242*
10646	$C_7H_7NO_2$	*o*-Nitrotoluene	221.85	~205.0	~96	*222*
10647	$C_7H_7NO_2$	*p*-Nitrotoluene	238.9	Nonazeotrope		*234*
10648	C_7H_8O	*m*-Cresol	202.2	201.9	13	*244*
10649	C_7H_8O	*o*-Cresol	190.8	Nonazeotrope		*243*
10650	C_7H_8O	*p*-Cresol	201.7	201.5	11	*244*
10651	C_7H_8O	*p*-Cresol	201.8	Nonazeotrope		*243*
10652	$C_7H_8O_2$	Guaiacol	205.05	200.8	42	*236*
10653	$C_7H_{12}O_4$	Ethyl malonate	199.35	198.5	12	*242*
10654	$C_7H_{13}ClO_2$	Isoamyl chloroacetate	190.5	Nonazeotrope		*255*
10655	C_8H_8O	Acetophenone	202.0	200.5	32	*232*
10656	$C_8H_8O_2$	Benzyl formate	203.0	<202.2	20	*255*

No.	B-Component Formula	Name	B.P., ° C.	Azeotropic Data B.P., ° C.	Wt. % A	Ref.
A =	$C_6H_{12}O_2$	**Caproic Acid** (*continued*)	**205.3**			
10657	$C_8H_8O_2$	Phenyl acetate	195.7	Nonazeotrope		*221*
10658	$C_8H_{10}O$	*p*-Ethylphenol	218.8	Nonazeotrope		*255*
10659	$C_8H_{10}O$	3,4-Xylenol	226.8	Nonazeotrope		*244*
10660	$C_8H_{10}O_2$	*m*-Dimethoxybenzene	216.2	Nonazeotrope		*223*
10661	$C_8H_{10}O_2$	*o*-Ethoxyphenol	216.5	Nonazeotrope		*255*
10662	$C_8H_{10}O_2$	Veratrole	206.5	~202.5	~42	*217*
10663	$C_8H_{14}O_4$	Propyl oxalate	214	Nonazeotrope		*255*
10664	$C_8H_{16}O_4$	2-(2-Ethoxyethoxy)ethyl acetate	218.5	Nonazeotrope		*255*
10665	C_9H_8	Indene	182.6	Nonazeotrope		*255*
10666	$C_9H_{10}O$	Propiophenone	217.7	Nonazeotrope		*232*
10667	$C_9H_{10}O_2$	Benzyl acetate	215.0	Nonazeotrope		*255*
10668	$C_9H_{10}O_2$	Ethyl benzoate	212.5	Nonazeotrope		*255*
10669	C_9H_{12}	Mesitylene	164.6	Nonazeotrope		*244*
10670	C_9H_{12}	Pseudocumene	168.2	Nonazeotrope		*223*
10671	$C_9H_{12}O$	Benzyl ethyl ether	185.0	Nonazeotrope		*255*
10672	$C_9H_{12}O$	Phenyl propyl ether	190.5	Nonazeotrope		*255*
10673	$C_9H_{14}O$	Phorone	197.8	Nonazeotrope		*232*
10674	$C_9H_{18}O_2$	Methyl caprylate	192.9	Nonazeotrope		*255*
10675	$C_9H_{18}O_3$	Isobutyl carbonate	190.3	Nonazeotrope		*255*
10676	$C_{10}H_7Cl$	1-Chloronaphthalene	262.7	Nonazeotrope		*244*
10677	$C_{10}H_8$	Naphthalene	218.05	203.75	71	*244*
10678	$C_{10}H_{14}$	Cymene	176.7	Nonazeotrope		*223*
10679	$C_{10}H_{16}$	*d*-Limonene	177.8	177.0	~5	*221*
10680	$C_{10}H_{16}$	Nopinene	163.8	Nonazeotrope		*255*
10681	$C_{10}H_{16}$	Terpinolene	185	Azeotrope doubtful		*243*
10682	$C_{10}H_{16}$	Thymene	179.7	179.0	~3	*221*
10683	$C_{10}H_{16}O$	Camphor	209.1	204.0	....	*232*
10684	$C_{10}H_{17}Cl$	Bornyl chloride	207.5	200.0	38	*242*
10685	$C_{10}H_{18}O$	Citronellal	207.8	~203.5	....	*221*
10686	$C_{10}H_{20}O_2$	Isoamyl isovalerate	192.7	Nonazeotrope		*255*
10687	$C_{10}H_{20}O_2$	Methyl pelargonate	213.8	Nonazeotrope		*255*
10688	$C_{10}H_{22}S$	Isoamyl sulfide	214.8	<204.5	<95	*246*
10689	$C_{11}H_{10}$	1-Methylnaphthalene	244.6	Nonazeotrope		*255*
10690	$C_{11}H_{10}$	2-Methylnaphthalene	241.15	Nonazeotrope		*207*
10691	$C_{11}H_{20}O$	Isobornyl methyl ether	192.4	Nonazeotrope		*255*
10692	$C_{12}H_{18}$	1,3,5-Triethylbenzene	215.5	202.0	63	*244*
10693	$C_{12}H_{22}O$	Ethyl isobornyl ether	203.5	<201.5	>30	*243*
A =	$C_6H_{12}O_2$	**Ethyl Butyrate**	**121.5**			
10694	$C_6H_{12}O_2$	Isoamyl formate	123.8	Nonazeotrope		*255*
10695	$C_6H_{12}O_2$	Isobutyl acetate	117.4	Nonazeotrope		*255*
10696	$C_6H_{12}O_2$	Methyl isovalerate	116.5	Nonazeotrope		*255*
10697	$C_6H_{12}O_2$	Propyl propionate	123.0	Nonazeotrope		*255*
10698	$C_6H_{12}O_3$	Paraldehyde	124	Nonazeotrope		*237*
10699	$C_6H_{14}S$	Isopropyl sulfide	120.5	<120.0	<42	*246*
10700	$C_6H_{15}BO_3$	Ethyl borate	118.6	117.6	35	*229*
10701	C_7H_8	Toluene	110.7	Nonazeotrope		*243*
10702	C_7H_{14}	Methylcyclohexane	101.1	Nonazeotrope		*226*
10703	$C_7H_{14}O_2$	Isoamyl acetate	137.5	Nonazeotrope		*162*
10704	C_7H_{16}	Heptane	98.5	Nonazeotrope		*207*
10705	C_8H_{10}	Ethylbenzene	136.15	Nonazeotrope		*255*
10706	C_8H_{16}	1,3-Dimethylcyclohexane	120.7	116.7	<50	*242*
10707	C_8H_{18}	Octane	125.8	Nonazeotrope		*243*
			125.8	118.0	>60	*226*
10708	$C_8H_{18}O$	Isobutyl ether	122.3	120.5	20	*237*
A =	$C_6H_{12}O_2$	**Ethyl Isobutyrate**	**110.1**			
10709	$C_6H_{12}O_2$	Methyl isovalerate	116.5	Nonazeotrope		*255*
10710	$C_6H_{14}O_2$	Acetal	103.55	Nonazeotrope		*237*
10711	$C_6H_{14}O_2$	Ethoxypropoxymethane	113.7	Nonazeotrope		*237*
10712	$C_6H_{14}S$	Isopropyl sulfide	120.5	Nonazeotrope		*246*
10713	C_7H_8	Toluene	110.75	109.8	....	*253*
10714	C_7H_{14}	Methylcyclohexane	101.1	100.1	<20	*226*
10715	C_7H_{16}	Heptane	98.5	97.0	17	*207*
10716	C_8H_{16}	1,3-Dimethylcyclohexane	120.7	<109.5	<88	*255*
10717	C_8H_{18}	Octane	125.75	<109.8	<96	*255*
10718	$C_8H_{18}O$	Isobutyl ether	122.2	Nonazeotrope		*237*

No.	Formula	B-Component Name	B.P., ° C.	Azeotropic Data B.P., ° C.	Wt. % A	Ref.
A =	**$C_6H_{12}O_2$**	**4-Hydroxy-4-methyl-2-pentanone**	**61.6/10 mm.**			
10719	C_8H_9Cl	*o,m,p*-Chloroethylbenzene, 10 mm.	67.5	59.0	58	*24*
A =	**$C_6H_{12}O_2$**	**Isoamyl Formate**	**123.8**			
10720	$C_6H_{12}O_2$	Propyl propionate	122.5	Nonazeotrope		*225*
10721	$C_6H_{12}O_3$	Paraldehyde	124.1	123.0	56	*237*
10722	C_7H_8	Toluene	110.7	Nonazeotrope		*243*
10723	C_8H_{10}	Ethylbenzene	136.15	Nonazeotrope		*253*
10724	C_8H_{18}	Octane	125.8	<116.5	~55	*243*
10725	$C_8H_{18}O$	Isobutyl ether	122.3	121.5	65	*237*
A =	**$C_6H_{12}O_2$**	**Isobutyl Acetate**	**117.2**			
10726	$C_6H_{12}O_2$	Methyl isovalerate	116.5	Nonazeotrope		*229*
10727	$C_6H_{12}O_3$	Paraldehyde	124	Nonazeotrope		*237*
10728	$C_6H_{14}O_2$	Acetal	103.55	Nonazeotrope		*237*
10729	$C_6H_{14}S$	Isopropyl sulfide	120.5	115.2	57	*246*
10730	$C_6H_{15}BO_3$	Ethyl borate	118.6	117.0	63	*229*
10731	C_7H_8	Toluene	110.6	Nonazeotrope		*252*
10732	C_7H_{16}	Heptane	98.5	Nonazeotrope		*226*
10733	C_8H_{10}	Ethylbenzene	136.15	Nonazeotrope		*255*
10734	C_8H_{16}	1,3-Dimethylcyclohexane	120.7	<114.0	<62	*242*
10735	C_8H_{18}	Octane	125.8	114.5	>70	*226*
10736	$C_8H_{18}O$	Isobutyl ether	122.3	Nonazeotrope		*237*
A =	**$C_6H_{12}O_2$**	**Isocaproic Acid**	**199.5**			
10737	C_7H_6O	Benzaldehyde	179.2	Nonazeotrope		*255*
10738	$C_7H_6O_2$	Salicylaldehyde	196.7	<196.4	....	*255*
10739	C_7H_7Br	*α*-Bromotoluene	198.5	193.0	32	*242*
10740	C_7H_7Br	*m*-Bromotoluene	184.3	183.0	10	*242*
10741	C_7H_7Br	*o*-Bromotoluene	181.5	180.5	9	*255*
10742	C_7H_7Br	*p*-Bromotoluene	185.0	183.0	12	*255*
10743	C_7H_7Cl	*α*-Chlorotoluene	179.3	178.0	8	*255*
10744	C_7H_7Cl	*o*-Chlorotoluene	159.2	Nonazeotrope		*255*
10745	C_7H_7Cl	*p*-Chlorotoluene	162.4	Nonazeotrope		*255*
10746	C_7H_8O	*o*-Cresol	191.1	Nonazeotrope		*255*
10747	C_7H_8O	*p*-Cresol	201.7	199.1	80?	*255*
10748	$C_7H_8O_2$	Guaiacol	205.05	<198.5	>80	*255*
10749	$C_7H_{12}O_4$	Ethyl malonate	199.35	196.5	42	*242*
10751	C_8H_8O	Acetophenone	202.0	<199.2	....	*255*
10752	$C_8H_8O_2$	Benzyl formate	203.0	198.8	62	*255*
10753	$C_8H_{10}O$	Benzyl methyl ether	167.8	Nonazeotrope		*255*
10754	$C_8H_{10}O$	*p*-Methylanisole	177.05	Nonazeotrope		*255*
10755	$C_8H_{10}O$	Phenetole	170.45	Nonazeotrope		*255*
10756	C_9H_8	Indene	182.6	Nonazeotrope		*255*
10757	C_9H_{12}	Mesitylene	164.6	Nonazeotrope		*255*
10758	$C_9H_{12}O$	Benzyl ethyl ether	185.0	Nonazeotrope		*255*
10759	$C_9H_{12}O$	Phenyl propyl ether	190.5	190.0	10	*255*
10760	$C_{10}H_8$	Naphthalene	218.0	199.0	75	*242*
10761	$C_{10}H_{14}$	Cymene	176.7	<176.2	>3	*255*
10762	$C_{10}H_{16}$	Dipentene	177.7	176.5	10	*242*
10763	$C_{10}H_{16}$	Limonene	177.7	176.5	10	*255*
10764	$C_{10}H_{16}O$	Camphor	209.1	Nonazeotrope		*255*
10765	$C_{10}H_{18}O$	Cineole	176.35	Nonazeotrope		*255*
10766	$C_{10}H_{20}O_2$	Isoamyl isovalerate	192.7	Nonazeotrope		*255*
10767	$C_{10}H_{22}O$	Amyl ether	187.5	<186.5	>8	*255*
10768	$C_{10}H_{22}O$	Isoamyl ether	172.6	Nonazeotrope		*244*
10769	$C_{10}H_{22}S$	Isoamyl sulfide	214.8	Nonazeotrope		*246*
A =	**$C_6H_{12}O_2$**	**Methyl Isovalerate**	**116.5**			
10770	$C_6H_{12}O_3$	Paraldehyde	124.35	Nonazeotrope		*237*
10771	$C_6H_{14}O_2$	Acetal	103.55	Nonazeotrope		*237*
10772	C_7H_8	Toluene	110.75	Nonazeotrope		*253*
10773	C_7H_{14}	Methylcyclohexane	101.15	Nonazeotrope		*255*
10774	C_7H_{16}	Heptane	98.5	Nonazeotrope		*207*
10775	C_8H_{16}	1,3-Dimethylcyclohexane	120.7	<115.0	<75	*255*
10776	C_8H_{18}	Octane	125.75	<115.5	<88	*255*
10777	$C_8H_{18}O$	Isobutyl ether	122	Nonazeotrope		*237*

No.	B-Component Formula	B-Component Name	B.P., ° C.	Azeotropic Data B.P., ° C.	Azeotropic Data Wt. % A	Ref.
A =	**$C_6H_{12}O_2$**	**Propyl Propionate**	**122.5**			
10778	C_7H_8	Toluene	110.75	Nonazeotrope		*218*
10779	C_8H_{10}	Ethylbenzene	136.15	Nonazeotrope		*218*
10780	C_8H_{18}	Octane	125.8	118.2	60	*218*
A =	**$C_6H_{12}O_3$**	**2-Ethoxyethyl Acetate**	**156.8**			
10781	$C_6H_{12}O_3$	Isopropyl lactate	166.8	Nonazeotrope		*255*
10782	$C_6H_{13}Br$	1-Bromohexane	156.5	<155.0	<49	*255*
10783	$C_6H_{14}O$	Hexyl alcohol	157.85	<156.0	<63	*255*
10784	$C_6H_{14}O_2$	2-Butoxyethanol	171.15	Nonazeotrope		*236*
10785	C_7H_6O	Benzaldehyde	179.2	Nonazeotrope		*206*
10786	C_7H_7Cl	*o*-Chlorotoluene	159.2	156.6	90	*206*
10787	C_7H_7Cl	*p*-Chlorotoluene	162.4	Nonazeotrope		*255*
10788	C_7H_8O	Anisole	153.85	Nonazeotrope		*236*
10789	C_7H_8O	*m*-Cresol	202.2	Nonazeotrope		*206*
10790	C_7H_8O	*o*-Cresol	191.1	191.5	10	*236*
10791	C_7H_8O	*p*-Cresol	201.7	Nonazeotrope		*206*
10792	$C_7H_{14}O$	2-Heptanone	143.55	Nonazeotrope		*255*
10793	$C_7H_{14}O$	2-Methylcyclohexanol	168.5	Nonazeotrope		*255*
10794	$C_7H_{14}O$	5-Methyl-2-hexanone	144.2	Nonazeotrope		*255*
10795	$C_7H_{14}O_2$	Ethyl isovalerate	134.7	Nonazeotrope		*255*
10796	$C_7H_{14}O_2$	Isoamyl acetate	142.1	Nonazeotrope		*255*
10797	$C_7H_{14}O_2$	Propyl butyrate	143.7	Nonazeotrope		*255*
10798	$C_7H_{16}O$	Heptyl alcohol	176.15	Nonazeotrope		*255*
10799	$C_7H_{16}O_3$	Ethyl orthoformate	145.75	Nonazeotrope		*236*
10800	C_8H_8	Styrene	145.8	Nonazeotrope		*255*
10801	C_8H_{10}	Ethylbenzene	136.15	Nonazeotrope		*206*
10802	C_8H_{10}	*m*-Xylene	139.2	Nonazeotrope		*207*
10803	C_8H_{10}	*o*-Xylene	144.3	Nonazeotrope		*206*
10804	C_8H_{10}	*p*-Xylene	138.45	Nonazeotrope		*206*
10805	$C_8H_{10}O$	Benzyl methyl ether	167.8	Nonazeotrope		*255*
10806	$C_8H_{10}O$	*p*-Methylanisole	177.05	Nonazeotrope		*255*
10807	$C_8H_{10}O$	Phenetole	170.45	Nonazeotrope		*206*
10808	$C_8H_{16}O$	2-Octanone	172.85	Nonazeotrope		*255*
10809	$C_8H_{16}O_2$	Ethyl caproate	167.7	Nonazeotrope		*255*
10810	$C_8H_{16}O_2$	Hexyl acetate	171.5	Nonazeotrope		*255*
10811	$C_8H_{16}O_2$	Isoamyl propionate	160.7	156.5	90	*206*
10812	$C_8H_{16}O_2$	Isobutyl butyrate	156.9	156.0	52	*206*
10813	$C_8H_{16}O_2$	Isobutyl isobutyrate	148.6	Nonazeotrope		*255*
10814	$C_8H_{16}O_2$	Propyl isovalerate	155.7	<155.0	<35	*255*
10815	$C_8H_{18}O$	Butyl ether	142.4	141.7	88	*206*
10816	$C_8H_{18}O$	*sec*-Octyl alcohol	180.4	Nonazeotrope		*206*
10817	C_9H_{12}	Cumene	152.8	152.0	15	*255*
10818	C_9H_{12}	Mesitylene	164.6	Nonazeotrope		*255*
10819	C_9H_{12}	Propylbenzene	159.3	<156.0	>70	*255*
10820	$C_9H_{18}O$	2,6-Dimethyl-4-heptanone	168.0	Nonazeotrope		*255*
10821	$C_9H_{18}O_2$	Isoamyl butyrate	181.05	Nonazeotrope		*255*
10822	$C_9H_{18}O_2$	Isobutyl isovalerate	171.3	Nonazeotrope		*206*
10823	$C_{10}H_{14}$	Butylbenzene	183.1	Nonazeotrope		*206*
10824	$C_{10}H_{14}$	Cymene	176.7	Nonazeotrope		*255*
10825	$C_{10}H_{16}$	Camphene	159.6	153.2	68	*206*
10826	$C_{10}H_{16}$	Nopinene	163.8	154.0	80	*242*
10827	$C_{10}H_{16}$	*α*-Pinene	155.8	151.0	50	*206*
10828	$C_{10}H_{16}$	*α*-Terpinene	173.4	<156.5	<93	*255*
10829	$C_{10}H_{16}$	Terpinolene	184.6	Nonazeotrope		*255*
10830	$C_{10}H_{18}O$	Cineole	176.35	Nonazeotrope		*236*
10831	$C_{10}H_{22}$	2,7-Dimethyloctane	160.1	153.0	75	*242*
10832	$C_{10}H_{22}O$	Isoamyl ether	173.2	156.45	94	*207, 236*
A =	**$C_6H_{12}O_3$**	**Isopropyl Lactate**	**166.8**			
10833	$C_6H_{14}O$	Hexyl alcohol	157.85	Nonazeotrope		*255*
10834	C_7H_8O	*o*-Cresol	191.1	Nonazeotrope		*255*
10835	C_7H_8O	*p*-Cresol	201.7	Nonazeotrope		*255*
10836	$C_7H_{14}O$	2-Methylcyclohexanol	168.5	165.5	67	*255*
10837	$C_7H_{16}O$	Heptyl alcohol	176.15	Nonazeotrope		*255*
10838	C_9H_{12}	Mesitylene	164.6	159.5	60	*247*
10839	$C_{10}H_{16}$	Camphene	159.6	154.2	30	*247*
10840	$C_{10}H_{16}$	Nopinene	163.8	157.5	38	*247*

	B-Component			Azeotropic Data		
No.	Formula	Name	B.P., ° C.	B.P., ° C.	Wt. % A	Ref.
A =	$C_6H_{12}O_3$	**Isopropyl Lactate** (*continued*)	**166.8**			
10841	$C_{10}H_{16}$	α-Pinene	155.8	152.5	22	255
A =	$C_6H_{12}O_3$	**Paraldehyde**	**124.35**			
10842	$C_6H_{14}O$	Hexyl alcohol	157.85	Nonazeotrope		255
10843	$C_6H_{15}BO_3$	Ethyl borate	118.6	Nonazeotrope		228
10844	C_7H_8	Toluene	110.7	Nonazeotrope		243
10845	$C_7H_{14}O_2$	Ethyl isovalerate	134.7	Nonazeotrope		237
10846	$C_7H_{14}O_2$	Isobutyl propionate	137.5	Nonazeotrope		237
10847	$C_7H_{14}O_2$	Propyl isobutyrate	134.0	Nonazeotrope		237
10848	C_8H_{10}	Ethylbenzene	136.15	Nonazeotrope		243
10849	C_8H_{10}	*m*-Xylene	139.0	Nonazeotrope		243
10850	C_8H_{10}	*p*-Xylene	138.4	Nonazeotrope		228
A =	$C_6H_{12}O_3$	**Propyl Lactate**	**171.7**			
10851	$C_6H_{13}ClO_2$	Chloroacetal	157.4	Nonazeotrope		255
10852	$C_6H_{14}O$	Hexyl alcohol	157.85	Nonazeotrope		255
10853	$C_6H_{14}O_2$	2-Butoxyethanol	171.25	>170.75	>55	255
10854	$C_6H_{14}O_2$	Pinacol	171.5	~168	~37	243
10855	C_7H_6O	Benzaldehyde	179.2	Nonazeotrope		243
10856	C_7H_7Br	*o*-Bromotoluene	181.5	171.0	~15	255
10857	C_7H_7Cl	α-Chlorotoluene	179.35	171.2	~78	243
10858	C_7H_7Cl	*o*-Chlorotoluene	159.2	<159.0	....	255
10859	C_7H_7Cl	*p*-Chlorotoluene	162.4	160.5	18	247
10860	C_7H_8O	Anisole	153.85	Nonazeotrope		236
10861	C_7H_8O	*m*-Cresol	202.2	Nonazeotrope		255
10862	C_7H_8O	*o*-Cresol	191.1	Nonazeotrope		224
10863	C_7H_8O	*p*-Cresol	201.7	Nonazeotrope		224
10864	$C_7H_{14}O$	2-Methylcyclohexanol	168.5	<167.8	<34	255
10865	$C_7H_{16}O$	Heptyl alcohol	176.15	<171.55	<90	255
10866	C_8H_8	Styrene	145.8	Nonazeotrope		255
10867	$C_8H_{10}O$	Benzyl methyl ether	167.8	165.5	25	255
10868	$C_8H_{10}O$	*p*-Methylanisole	177.05	<171.0	>82	255
10869	$C_8H_{10}O$	Phenetole	171.5	167.1	50	236
10870	$C_8H_{16}O$	2-Octanone	172.85	<171.4	<75	232
10871	$C_8H_{18}O$	*sec*-Octyl alcohol	179.8	Nonazeotrope		255
10872	$C_8H_{18}S$	Isobutyl sulfide	172.0	169.0	48	246
10873	C_9H_{12}	Cumene	152.8	Nonazeotrope		255
10874	C_9H_{12}	Mesitylene	164.6	160.5	28	218
10875	C_9H_{12}	Pseudocumene	108.2	103.5	38	247
10876	$C_9H_{12}O$	Benzyl ethyl ether	185.0	Nonazeotrope		255
10877	$C_9H_{18}O_2$	Isoamyl isobutyrate	169.8	167.5	40	255
10878	$C_9H_{18}O_2$	Isobutyl isovalerate	171.2	<169.0	<52	207
10879	$C_{10}H_{14}$	Cymene	176.7	~167.0	60	218
10880	$C_{10}H_{16}$	Camphene	159.6	~156.2	17	218
10881	$C_{10}H_1$	*d*-Limonene	177.8	166.35	63	243
10882	$C_{10}H_{16}$	Nopinene	163.8	159.0	33	247
10883	$C_{10}H_{16}$	α-Phellandrene	171.5	~162.5	~50	243
10884	$C_{10}H_{16}$	α-Pinene	155.8	<154.5	....	255
10885	$C_{10}H_{16}$	α-Terpinene	173.3	~164.0	50	228
10886	$C_{10}H_{18}O$	Cineole	176.3	~169	~73	243
10887	$C_{10}H_{22}O$	Isoamyl ether	173.2	167.5	53	236
A =	$C_6H_{13}Br$	**1-Bromohexane**	**156.5**			
10888	$C_6H_{14}O$	Hexyl alcohol	157.85	150.5	60	255
10889	$C_6H_{14}O_2$	2-Butoxyethanol	171.15	<156.0	....	255
10890	C_7H_8O	*o*-Cresol	191.1	Nonazeotrope		255
10891	$C_7H_{14}O_2$	Isoamyl acetate	142.1	Nonazeotrope		255
10892	$C_7H_{16}O$	Heptyl alcohol	176.15	Nonazeotrope		255
10893	$C_8H_{1c}O$	Benzyl methyl ether	167.8	Nonazeotrope		239
10894	$C_8H_{16}O_2$	Isobutyl isobutyrate	148.6	Nonazeotrope		255
10895	$C_8H_{16}O_2$	Propyl isovalerate	155.7	<155.2	>28	255
10896	$C_8H_{18}O$	Butyl ether	142.4	Nonazeotrope		239
10897	$C_8H_{18}O$	*sec*-Octyl alcohol	180.4	Nonazeotrope		255
10898	$C_9H_{18}O_2$	Isobutyl isovalerate	171.2	Nonazeotrope		255
A =	$C_6H_{13}ClO_2$	**Chloroacetal**	**157.4**			
10899	$C_6H_{14}O$	Hexyl alcohol	157.85	<154.5	<58	255
10900	$C_6H_{14}O_2$	Pinacol	171.5	155.5	<90	243

No.	B-Component Formula	Name	B.P., ° C.	Azeotropic Data B.P., ° C.	Wt. % A	Ref.
A =	**$C_6H_{13}ClO_2$**	**Chloroacetal** (*continued*)	**157.4**			
10901	C_7H_8O	Anisole	153.85	Nonazeotrope		228
10902	$C_7H_{14}O$	4-Heptanone	143.55	Nonazeotrope		255
10903	C_8H_8	Styrene	145.8	Nonazeotrope		228
10904	C_8H_{10}	*m*-Xylene	139.2	Nonazeotrope		255
10905	C_8H_{10}	*o*-Xylene	143.6	Nonazeotrope		228
10906	$C_8H_{10}O$	Phenetole	170.45	Nonazeotrope		255
10907	$C_8H_{16}O$	2-Octanone	172.85	Nonazeotrope		232
10908	$C_8H_{16}O_2$	Isoamyl propionate	160.3	Nonazeotrope		211
10909	$C_8H_{16}O_2$	Propyl isovalerate	155.8	154.7	~43	243
10910	C_9H_{12}	Cumene	152.8	<152.0	<10	255
10911	C_9H_{12}	Propylbenzene	159.2	<156.0	<75	228
10912	$C_9H_{18}O$	2,6-Dimethyl-4-heptanone	168.0	Nonazeotrope		255
10913	$C_9H_{18}O_2$	Isobutyl isovalerate	171.35	Nonazeotrope		225
10914	$C_{10}H_{14}$	Cymene	176.7	Nonazeotrope		211
10915	$C_{10}H_{16}$	Camphene	159.5	~155.2	56	236
10916	$C_{10}H_{16}$	*d*-Limonene	177.8	Nonazeotrope		211
10917	$C_{10}H_{16}$	Nopinene	163.8	156.2	23	236
10918	$C_{10}H_{16}$	α-Pinene	155.8	153.0	43	236
10919	$C_{10}H_{16}$	α-Terpinene	173.3	Nonazeotrope		228
10920	$C_{10}H_{22}$	2,7-Dimethyloctane	160.2	155.5	35	236
10921	$C_{10}H_{22}O$	Isoamyl ether	173.4	Nonazeotrope		228
A =	**C_6H_{14}**	**Hexane**	**68.8**			
10923	$C_6H_{14}O$	Isopropyl ether	68.3	67.5	47	238
10924	$C_6H_{15}N$	Triethylamine	89.35	Nonazeotrope		231
10925	C_7H_{16}	Heptane	98.45	Vapor pressure data		369
10926	C_8H_{18}	Octane	125.8	Nonazeotrope (b.p. curve)		432
A =	**$C_6H_{14}O$**	**2-Ethylbutanol**	**55.6/10 mm.**			
10927	C_8H_9Cl	*o,m,p*-Chloroethylbenzene, 10 mm.	67.5	54.9	74	24
A =	**$C_6H_{14}O$**	**Hexyl Alcohol**	**157.8**			
10928	$C_6H_{14}O$	Isopropyl ether	69.0	Nonazeotrope		93
10929	$C_6H_{14}O_2$	2-Butoxyethanol	171.25	Nonazeotrope		206
10930	C_7H_6O	Benzaldehyde	179.2	Nonazeotrope		255
10931	C_7H_7Br	*o*-Bromotoluene	181.5	Nonazeotrope		255
10932	C_7H_7Cl	α-Chlorotoluene	179.3	Nonazeotrope		255
10933	C_7H_7Cl	*o*-Chlorotoluene	159.2	153.5	44	247
10934	C_7H_7Cl	*p*-Chlorotoluene	166.4	<154.0	<54	247
10935	C_7H_8	Toluene	110.75	Nonazeotrope		217
10936	C_7H_8O	Anisole	153.85	151.0	36.5	218
10937	C_7H_8O	*o*-Cresol	191.1	Nonazeotrope		255
10938	C_7H_{14}	Methylcyclohexane	101.1	Nonazeotrope		220
10939	$C_7H_{14}O$	5-Methyl-2-hexanone	144.2	Nonazeotrope		232
10940	$C_7H_{14}O_2$	Propyl butyrate	142.8	Nonazeotrope		216
10941	$C_7H_{14}O_3$	1,3-Butanediol methyl ether acetate	171.75	Nonazeotrope		255
10942	C_7H_{16}	Heptane	98.45	Nonazeotrope		221
10943	C_8H_8	Styrene	145.8	144	23	221
10944	C_8H_9Cl	*o,m,p*-Chloroethylbenzene, 10 mm.	67.5	62.0	43	24
10945	C_8H_{10}	Ethylbenzene	136.15	Nonazeotrope		217
10946	C_8H_{10}	*m*-Xylene	139.0	138.3	15	217
10947	C_8H_{10}	*o*-Xylene	143.6	142.3	~18	217
10948	C_8H_{10}	*p*-Xylene	138.2	~137.7	13	221
10949	$C_8H_{10}O$	Benzyl methyl ether	167.8	156.7	73	255
10950	$C_8H_{10}O$	*p*-Methylanisole	177.05	Nonazeotrope		255
10951	$C_8H_{10}O$	Phenetole	170.45	157.65	81	218
10952	$C_8H_{11}N$	Dimethylaniline	194.05	Nonazeotrope		231
10953	$C_8H_{16}O$	2-Octanone	172.85	Nonazeotrope		232
10954	$C_8H_{16}O_2$	Butyl butyrate	166.4	Nonazeotrope		255
10955	$C_8H_{16}O_2$	Isoamyl propionate	160.7	156.7	60	247
10956	$C_8H_{16}O_2$	Isobutyl butyrate	156.8	~155.0	40	216
10957	$C_8H_{16}O_2$	Isobutyl isobutyrate	147.3	Nonazeotrope		216
10958	$C_8H_{16}O_2$	Propyl isovalerate	155.7	~154.2	33	216
10959	C_8H_{18}	Octane	125.75	Nonazeotrope		255
10960	$C_8H_{18}O$	Isobutyl ether	122.3	Nonazeotrope		236
10961	$C_8H_{18}S$	Butyl sulfide	185.0	Nonazeotrope		246
10962	$C_8H_{18}S$	Isobutyl sulfide	172.0	Nonazeotrope		246

No.	B-Component Formula	B-Component Name	B.P., ° C.	Azeotropic Data B.P., ° C.	Azeotropic Data Wt. % A	Ref.
A =	**$C_6H_{14}O$**	**Hexyl Alcohol (*continued*)**	**157.8**			
10963	C_9H_8	Indene	182.6	Nonazeotrope		*255*
10964	C_9H_{12}	Cumene	152.8	149.5	35	*247*
10965	C_9H_{12}	Mesitylene	164.6	153.5	55	*217*
10966	C_9H_{12}	Pseudocumene	168.2	156.3	68	*221*
10967	C_9H_{12}	Propylbenzene	158.8	152.5	45	*220*
10968	$C_9H_{12}O$	Benzyl ethyl ether	185.0	Nonazeotrope		*255*
10969	$C_9H_{13}N$	*N,N*-Dimethyl-*o*-toluidine	185.3	Nonazeotrope		*231*
10970	$C_9H_{18}O$	2,6-Dimethyl-4-heptanone	168.0	Nonazeotrope		*232*
10971	$C_9H_{18}O_2$	Isobutyl isovalerate	171.2	Nonazeotrope		*255*
10972	$C_{10}H_{14}$	Butylbenzene	183.1	Nonazeotrope		*255*
10973	$C_{10}H_{16}$	Camphene	159.6	~150.8	~48	*253*
10974	$C_{10}H_{16}$	*d*-Limonene	177.8	155.5	~79	*217*
10975	$C_{10}H_{16}$	Nopinene	163.8	153.0	52	*247*
10976	$C_{10}H_{16}$	α-Pinene	155.8	150.8	40	*217*
10977	$C_{10}H_{16}$	α-Terpinene	173.4	156.5	72	*247*
10978	$C_{10}H_{18}O$	Cineole	176.35	Nonazeotrope		*236*
10979	$C_{10}H_{22}$	2,7-Dimethyloctane	160.2	152.5	47	*217*
10980	$C_{10}H_{22}O$	Isoamyl ether	173.4	Nonazeotrope		*256*
			173.4	157	89	*236*
A =	**$C_6H_{14}O$**	**Propyl Ether**	**90.1**			
10981	$C_6H_{15}N$	Dipropylamine	109.2	Nonazeotrope		*231*
10982	$C_6H_{15}N$	Triethylamine	89.35	<88.5	....	*231*
10983	C_7H_8	Toluene	110.75	Nonazeotrope		*238*
10984	C_7H_{14}	Methylcyclohexane	101.1	Nonazeotrope		*253*
10985	C_7H_{16}	Heptane	98.45	Nonazeotrope		*207*
10986	C_8H_{18}	2,5-Dimethylhexane	109.4	Nonazeotrope		*238*
A =	**$C_6H_{14}O_2$**	**Acetal**	**103.55**			
10987	$C_6H_{14}S$	Isopropyl sulfide	120.5	Nonazeotrope		*246*
10988	$C_6H_{15}N$	Dipropylamine	109.2	Nonazeotrope		*231*
10989	$C_6H_{15}N$	Triethylamine	89.35	Nonazeotrope		*231*
10990	C_7H_8	Toluene	110.75	Nonazeotrope		*253*
10991	C_7H_{14}	Methylcyclohexane	101.15	99.65	40	*238*
10992	C_7H_{16}	*n*-Heptane	98.45	97.75	28	*238*
10993	C_8H_{18}	2,5-Dimethylhexane	109.3	103.0	75	*228*
10994	C_8H_{18}	Octane	125.75	Nonazeotrope		*238*
A =	**$C_6H_{14}O_2$**	**2-Butoxyethanol**	**171.15**			
10995	$C_6H_{15}NO$	2-Diethylaminoethanol	162.2	Nonazeotrope		*231*
10996	C_7H_5N	Benzonitrile	191.1	Nonazeotrope		*236*
10997	C_7H_6O	Benzaldehyde	179.2	170.95	91	*236*
10998	C_7H_7Br	*o*-Bromotoluene	181.5	169.7	65	*206*
10999	C_7H_7Cl	*o*-Chlorotoluene	159.2	158.0	12	*206*
11000	C_7H_7Cl	*p*-Chlorotoluene	162.4	160.5	20	*236*
11001	C_7H_7ClO	*o*-Chloroanisole	195.7	Nonazeotrope		*255*
11002	C_7H_8O	Anisole	153.85	Nonazeotrope		*236*
11003	C_7H_8O	*m*-Cresol	202.2	Nonazeotrope		*206*
11004	C_7H_8O	*o*-Cresol	191.1	191.55	15	*236*
11005	C_7H_8O	*p*-Cresol	201.7	Nonazeotrope		*236*
11006	C_7H_9N	Benzylamine	185.0	Nonazeotrope		*231*
11007	C_7H_9N	Methylaniline	196.25	Nonazeotrope		*231*
11008	$C_7H_{13}ClO_2$	Isoamyl chloroacetate	190.5	Nonazeotrope		*255*
11009	$C_7H_{14}O$	2-Methylcyclohexanol	168.5	Nonazeotrope		*255*
11010	$C_7H_{14}O_3$	1,3-Butanediol methyl ether acetate	171.75	170.1	53	*236*
11011	$C_7H_{14}O_3$	Isobutyl lactate	182.15	Nonazeotrope		*255*
11012	$C_7H_{16}O$	Heptyl alcohol	176.15	Nonazeotrope		*206*
11013	$C_8H_8O_2$	Methyl benzoate	199.4	Nonazeotrope		*236*
11014	$C_8H_8O_2$	Phenyl acetate	195.7	Nonazeotrope		*255*
11015	C_8H_9Cl	*o,m,p*-Chloroethylbenzene, 10 mm.	67.5	62.5	37	*24*
11016	C_8H_{10}	*m*-Xylene	139.2	Nonazeotrope		*255*
11017	C_8H_{10}	*o*-Xylene	144.3	Nonazeotrope		*236*
11018	$C_8H_{10}O$	Benzyl methyl ether	167.8	165.0	43	*206*
11019	$C_8H_{10}O$	*p*-Methylanisole	177.05	169.3	62	*206*
11020	$C_8H_{10}O$	Phenetole	170.45	167.1	52	*236*
11021	$C_8H_{11}N$	Dimethylaniline	194.15	Nonazeotrope		*231*
11022	$C_8H_{16}O_2$	Butyl butyrate	166.4	164.7	20	*206*

No.	Formula	Name	B.P., ° C.	Azeotropic Data B.P., ° C.	Wt. % A	Ref.
A =	$C_6H_{14}O_2$	**2-Butoxyethanol** (*continued*)	**171.15**			
11023	$C_8H_{16}O_2$	Ethyl caproate	167.7	166.0	25	*247*
11024	$C_8H_{16}O_2$	Hexyl acetate	171.5	167.7	45	*247*
11025	$C_8H_{16}O_2$	Isoamyl propionate	160.7	Nonazeotrope		*255*
11026	$C_8H_{16}O_2$	Isobutyl butyrate	156.9	Nonazeotrope		*255*
11027	$C_8H_{16}O_2$	Propyl isovalerate	155.7	Nonazeotrope		*255*
11028	$C_8H_{16}O_4$	2-(2-Ethoxyethoxy)ethyl acetate	218.5	Nonazeotrope		*255*
11029	$C_8H_{18}O$	Butyl ether	142.4	Nonazeotrope		*255*
11030	$C_8H_{18}O$	*sec*-Octyl alcohol	180.4	Nonazeotrope		*206*
11031	$C_8H_{18}S$	Isobutyl sulfide	172	163.8	42	*235*
11032	C_9H_7N	Quinoline	237.3	Nonazeotrope		*233*
11033	C_9H_{12}	Mesitylene	164.6	162.0	32	*236*
11034	C_9H_{12}	Propylbenzene	159.3	158.0	....	*206*
11035	C_9H_{12}	Pseudocumene	168.2	164.5	38	*255*
11036	$C_9H_{13}N$	*N,N*-Dimethyl-*o*-toluidine	185.3	170.95	88	*231*
11037	$C_9H_{18}O_2$	Isoamyl butyrate	181.05	170.85	86	*236*
11038	$C_9H_{18}O_2$	Isoamyl isobutyrate	169.8	166.5	36	*247*
11039	$C_9H_{18}O_2$	Isobutyl isovalerate	171.2	167.75	43	*207*
11040	$C_{10}H_{14}$	Butylbenzene	183.0	170.2	80	*206*
11041	$C_{10}H_{14}$	Cymene	176.7	168.0	60	*236*
11042	$C_{10}H_{16}$	Camphene	159.6	154.5	30	*206*
11043	$C_{10}H_{16}$	Dipentene	177.7	164.0	53	*247*
11044	$C_{10}H_{16}$	Nopinene	163.8	158.0	37	*206*
11045	$C_{10}H_{16}$	α-Pinene	155.8	151.5	25	*247*
11046	$C_{10}H_{16}$	α-Terpinene	173.4	164.0	50	*206*
11047	$C_{10}H_{18}O$	Cineole	176.35	168.9	58.5	*207*
11048	$C_{10}H_{18}O$	Citronellal	207.8	Nonazeotrope		*206*
11049	$C_{10}H_{18}O$	Linaloöl	198.6	Nonazeotrope		*255*
11050	$C_{10}H_{22}O$	Amyl ether	187.5	169.0	67	*236*
11051	$C_{10}H_{22}O$	Isoamyl ether	173.2	164.95	54	*250*
11052	$C_{10}H_{22}O_2$	Acetaldehyde dibutyl acetal	188.8	170.6	42	*62*
11053	$C_{11}H_{20}O$	Isobornyl methyl ether	192.4	Nonazeotrope		*236*
11054	$C_{12}H_{18}$	Triethylbenzene	215.5	Nonazeotrope		*206*
A =	$C_6H_{14}O_2$	**Pinacol**	**174.35**			
11055	C_7H_7Cl	*o*-Chlorotoluene	159.2	<157.0	....	*255*
11056	C_7H_7Cl	*p*-Chlorotoluene	162.4	158.0	>13	*247*
11057	C_7H_8	Toluene	110.7	Nonazeotrope		*220*
11058	C_7H_8O	Anisole	174.35	153.5	....	*225*
11059	C_7H_8O	*m*-Cresol	202.2	Nonazeotrope		*224*
11060	C_7H_8O	*o*-Cresol	191.1	191.5	8	*255*
11061	C_7H_8O	*p*-Cresol	201.7	Nonazeotrope		*255*
11062	C_7H_{14}	Methylcyclohexane	101.1	Nonazeotrope		*217*
11063	C_7H_{16}	Heptane	98.45	Nonazeotrope		*217*
11064	C_8H_{10}	*m*-Xylene	139.0	Nonazeotrope		*217*
11065	$C_8H_{10}O$	Benzyl methyl ether	167.8	163.5?	28?	*255*
11066	$C_8H_{10}O$	*p*-Methylanisole	177.05	168.7	44	*256*
11067	$C_8H_{10}O$	Phenetole	170.4	165.2	33	*252*
11068	$C_8H_{11}N$	Dimethylaniline	194.05	<169.5	>60	*231*
11069	$C_8H_{14}O$	Methylheptenone	173.2	171.7	40	*232*
11070	$C_8H_{16}O$	2-Octanone	172.85	171.5	35	*232*
11071	C_8H_{18}	2,5-Dimethylhexane	109.4	Nonazeotrope		*255*
11072	C_8H_{18}	Octane	125.75	Nonazeotrope		*255*
11073	C_9H_{12}	Mesitylene	164.6	160.2	35	*252*
11074	C_9H_{12}	Propylbenzene	159.3	156.3	28	*247*
11075	C_9H_{12}	Pseudocumene	168.2	162.9	38	*247*
11076	$C_9H_{12}O$	Benzyl ethyl ether	185.0	<171.5	>62	*255*
11077	$C_9H_{18}O_2$	Isobutyl isovalerate	171.2	<169.8	>10	*255*
11078	$C_9H_{18}O_2$	Isoamyl butyrate	181.05	<173.9	....	*255*
11079	$C_{10}H_8$	Naphthalene	218.05	Nonazeotrope		*217*
11080	$C_{10}H_{14}$	Cymene	176.7	167.7	50	*247*
11081	$C_{10}H_{16}$	Camphene	159.6	155.5	~28	*217*
11082	$C_{10}H_{16}$	Dipentene	177.7	166.7	~50	*255*
11083	$C_{10}H_{16}$	*d*-Limonene	177.8	171	~45	*217*
11084	$C_{10}H_{16}$	α-Pinene	155.8	152.5	....	*217*
11085	$C_{10}H_{18}O$	Cineole	176.35	168.5	45	*247*
11086	$C_{10}H_{22}$	2,7-Dimethyloctane	160.25	~144?	....	*243*

No.	B-Component Formula	Name	B.P., ° C.	Azeotropic Data B.P., ° C.	Wt. % A	Ref.
A =	**$C_6H_{14}O_2$**	**Pinacol (*continued*)**	**174.35**			
11087	$C_{10}H_{22}O$	Isoamyl ether	173.4	167.2	40	*256*
A =	**$C_6H_{14}O_3$**	**Dipropylene Glycol**	**229.2**			
11088	C_7H_7BrO	*o*-Bromoanisole	217.7	212.0	30	*255*
11089	$C_7H_7NO_2$	*o*-Nitrotoluene	221.75	216.9	>21	*234*
11090	$C_7H_7NO_2$	*p*-Nitrotoluene	238.9	225.0	62?	*234*
11091	C_7H_8O	Benzyl alcohol	205.25	Nonazeotrope		*255*
11092	C_7H_8O	*p*-Cresol	201.7	Nonazeotrope		*255*
11093	$C_8H_8O_2$	Anisaldehyde	249.5	Nonazeotrope		*255*
11094	$C_8H_8O_3$	Methyl salicylate	222.95	213.0	35	*255*
11095	C_8H_9BrO	*p*-Bromophenetole	234.2	221.0	45	*255*
11096	C_9H_7N	Quinoline	237.3	<228.0	<72	*255*
11097	$C_9H_{10}O_3$	Ethyl salicylate	233.8	218.2	55	*255*
11098	$C_{10}H_9N$	Quinaldine	246.5	Nonazeotrope		*255*
11099	$C_{10}H_{10}O_2$	Isosafrole	252.0	225.5	60	*247*
11100	$C_{10}H_{10}O_2$	Safrole	235.9	222.0	50	*247*
11101	$C_{10}H_{12}O$	Anisole	235.7	221.5	48	*247*
11102	$C_{10}H_{18}O$	Cineole	176.35	Nonazeotrope		*255*
11103	$C_{10}H_{22}O$	Isoamyl ether	173.2	Nonazeotrope		*255*
11104	$C_{11}H_{14}O_2$	1-Allyl-3,4-dimethoxybenzene	254.7	226.5	65	*255*
11105	$C_{11}H_{16}O$	Methyl thymyl ether	216.5	211.0	30	*255*
11106	$C_{11}H_{20}O$	Methyl α-terpineol ether	216.2	<211.5	>24	*255*
11107	$C_{12}H_{10}O$	Phenyl ether	259.0	<228.0	<77	*255*
11108	$C_{12}H_{16}O_3$	Isoamyl salicylate	277.5	Nonazeotrope		*255*
11109	$C_{13}H_{12}O$	Benzyl phenyl ether	286.5	Nonazeotrope		*255*
11110	$C_{14}H_{14}O$	Benzyl ether	297.0	Nonazeotrope		*255*
A =	**$C_6H_{14}O_3$**	**2-(2-Ethoxyethoxy)ethanol**	**195.0**			
11111	C_7H_8O	*m*-Cresol	202.4	....	36.8, V-l.	*292*
11112	C_7H_8O	*o*-Cresol	191.1	205.5	70	*255*
11113	C_7H_8O	*p*-Cresol	202.0	....	38, V-l.	*292*
			202.0	209.0	50	*247*
11114	$C_7H_{16}O_4$	2-[2-(2-Methoxyethoxy)ethoxy]-ethanol	245.25	Nonazeotrope		*255*
11115	$C_8H_8O_3$	Methyl salicylate	222.95	Nonazeotrope		*255*
11116	$C_8H_{10}O$	3,4-Xylenol	226.8	Nonazeotrope		*255*
11117	$C_8H_{11}N$	Dimethylaniline	194.15	<193.0	>10	*255*
11118	$C_8H_{16}O_3$	Isoamyl lactate	202.4	<201.0	>38	*255*
11119	C_9H_7N	Quinoline	237.3	Nonazeotrope		*255*
11120	$C_9H_{13}N$	Dimethyl-*o*-toluidine	185.3	Nonazeotrope		*255*
11121	$C_9H_{13}N$	Dimethyl-*p*-toluidine	210.2	199.5	....	*255*
11122	$C_{10}H_8$	Naphthalene	218.0	200.5	....	*255*
11123	$C_{10}H_{12}O$	Estragole	215.6	201.0	87	*255*
11124	$C_{10}H_{14}$	Butylbenzene	183.1	181.3	18	*255*
11125	$C_{10}H_{15}N$	Diethylaniline	217.05	<200.5	>85	*255*
11126	$C_{10}H_{16}$	Dipentene	177.7	173.0	23	*255*
11127	$C_{10}H_{18}O$	Cineole	176.35	<175.5	....	*255*
11128	$C_{10}H_{22}O$	Amyl ether	187.5	<183.0	....	*255*
11129	$C_{11}H_{10}$	2-Methylnaphthalene	241.15	Nonazeotrope		*255*
11130	$C_{11}H_{20}O$	Isobornyl methyl ether	192.4	190.5	25	*247*
11131	$C_{12}H_{22}O$	Ethyl isobornyl ether	203.8	198.5	55	*247*
A =	**$C_6H_{14}O_4$**	**Triethylene Glycol**	**288.7**			
11132	$C_9H_{10}O_3$	Ethyl salicylate	233.8	Nonazeotrope		*255*
11133	$C_{10}H_7Br$	1-Bromonaphthalene	281.2	273.4	33	*207*
11134	$C_{10}H_7Cl$	1-Chloronaphthalene	262.7	261.5	5	*207*
11135	$C_{10}H_{10}O_2$	Isosafrole	252.0	Nonazeotrope		*236*
11136	$C_{10}H_{10}O_2$	Methyl cinnamate	261.9	Nonazeotrope		*206*
11137	$C_{10}H_{10}O_2$	Safrole	235.9	Nonazeotrope		*206*
11138	$C_{10}H_{10}O_4$	Methyl phthalate	283.2	277.0	33	*206*
11139	$C_{10}H_{12}O$	Anethole	235.7	Nonazeotrope		*255*
11140	$C_{11}H_{10}$	1-Methylnaphthalene	244.6	Nonazeotrope		*206*
11141	$C_{11}H_{10}$	2-Methylnaphthalene	241.15	Nonazeotrope		*207*
11142	$C_{11}H_{12}O_2$	Ethyl cinnamate	272.0	<271.5	>7	*255*
11143	$C_{11}H_{14}O_2$	1-Allyl-3,4-dimethoxybenzene	254.7	Nonazeotrope		*206*
11144	$C_{11}H_{14}O_2$	Butyl benzoate	249.0	Nonazeotrope		*206*
11145	$C_{12}H_{10}$	Acenaphthene	277.9	271.5	35	*207*

No.	B-Component Formula	Name	B.P., ° C.	Azeotropic Data B.P., ° C.	Wt. % A	Ref.
A =	**$C_6H_{14}O_4$**	**Triethylene Glycol (*continued*)**	**288.7**			
11146	$C_{12}H_{10}$	Biphenyl	256.1	255.3	10	*236*
11147	$C_{12}H_{10}O$	Phenyl ether	259.0	258.7	3	*236*
11148	$C_{12}H_{14}O_4$	Ethyl phthalate	298.5	<285.5	>58	*255*
11149	$C_{12}H_{16}O_2$	Isoamyl benzoate	262.0	261.4	14	*207*
11150	$C_{12}H_{16}O_3$	Isoamyl salicylate	277.5	269.0	30	*255*
11151	$C_{12}H_{22}O_4$	Isoamyl oxalate	268.0	Reacts		*206*
11152	$C_{13}H_{10}O_2$	Phenyl benzoate	315	286.0	80	*206*
11153	$C_{13}H_{12}$	Diphenylmethane	265.4	263.0	20	*236*
11154	$C_{13}H_{12}O$	Benzyl phenyl ether	286.5	280.0	40	*206*
11155	$C_{14}H_{12}$	Stilbene	306.5	284.5	60	*206*
11156	$C_{14}H_{14}$	1,2-Diphenylmethane	284.5	275.5	42	*206*
A =	**$C_6H_{14}S$**	**Isopropyl Sulfide**	**120.5**			
11157	C_7H_8	Toluene	110.75	Nonazeotrope		*255*
11158	C_7H_{14}	Methylcyclohexane	101.15	Nonazeotrope		*255*
11159	C_7H_{16}	Heptane	98.4	Nonazeotrope		*255*
11160	$C_8H_{18}O$	Isobutyl ether	122.3	<119.8	>64	*246*
A =	**$C_6H_{14}S$**	**Propyl Sulfide**	**141.5**			
11161	$C_7H_{14}O$	5-Methyl-2-hexanone	144.2	<140.7	>65	*246*
11162	$C_7H_{14}O_2$	Ethyl isovalerate	134.7	~134.0	~10	*212*
11163	C_8H_{10}	*m*-Xylene	139.0	~137.5	....	*211*
11164	C_8H_{10}	*p*-Xylene	138.45	<138.2	>7	*255*
11165	$C_8H_{18}O$	Butyl ether	142.4	140.3	62	*242*
A =	**$C_6H_{15}BO_3$**	**Ethyl Borate**	**118.6**			
11166	C_7H_8	Toluene	110.75	Nonazeotrope		*210*
11167	C_7H_{14}	Methylcyclohexane	101.1	Nonazeotrope		*226*
11168	C_7H_{16}	Heptane	98.5	Nonazeotrope		*226*
11169	$C_8H_{18}O$	Butyl ether	122.3	<116.8	....	*237*
A =	**$C_6H_{15}N$**	**Dipropylamine**	**109.2**			
11170	C_7H_8	Toluene	110.75	<108.5	>53	*231*
11171	C_7H_{16}	*n*-Heptane	98.4	Nonazeotrope		*207*
11172	C_8H_{16}	1.3-Dimethylcyclohexane	120.7	Nonazeotrope		*231*
11173	C_8H_{18}	2,4-Dimethylhexane	109.4	<108.0	<54	*231*
11174	$C_8H_{18}O$	Isobutyl ether	122.3	Nonazeotrope		*231*
A =	**$C_6H_{15}N$**	**Isohexylamine**	**123.5**			
11175	C_7H_8	Toluene	110.75	Nonazeotrope		*255*
11176	C_8H_{16}	1,3-Dimethylcyclohexane	120.7	<120.0	....	*255*
11177	$C_8H_{18}O$	Isobutyl ether	122.3	<121.8	....	*255*
A =	**$C_6H_{14}N$**	**Triethylamine**	**89.35**			
11178	C_7H_{14}	Methylcyclohexane	101.15	Nonazeotrope		*231*
11179	C_7H_{16}	*n*-Heptane	98.4	Nonazeotrope		*231*
A =	**$C_6H_{15}NO$**	**2-(Diethylamino)ethanol**	**162.2**			
11180	C_7H_8	Toluene	110.75	Nonazeotrope		*255*
11181	C_7H_8O	Anisole	153.85	<148.0	>19	*231*
11182	C_7H_8O	*o*-Cresol	191.1	Nonazeotrope		*231*
11183	C_7H_9N	Methylaniline	196.25	Nonazeotrope		*231*
11184	C_7H_{16}	Heptane	98.4	Nonazeotrope		*255*
11185	C_8H_9Cl	*o,m,p*-Chloroethylbenzene, 10 mm.	67.5	57.0	91	*24*
11186	C_8H_{10}	*m*-Xylene	139.2	<136.0	>8	*255*
11187	$C_8H_{11}N$	Dimethylaniline	194.15	<160.5	>58	*231*
11188	$C_8H_{18}O$	Isobutyl ether	122.3	Nonazeotrope		*231*
11189	$C_{10}H_{16}$	Camphene	159.6	<146.5	....	*255*
11190	$C_{10}H_{18}O$	Cineole	176.35	<158.0	....	*255*
11191	$C_{10}H_{22}O$	Isoamyl ether	173.2	<156.5	>58	*231*
A =	**$C_7H_5Cl_3$**	**α,α,α-Trichlorotoluene**	**220.8**			
11192	$C_7H_7NO_2$	*m*-Nitrotoluene	230.8	Nonazeotrope		*234*
11193	$C_7H_7NO_2$	*o*-Nitrotoluene	221.75	219.45	75.5	*234*
11194	$C_7H_7NO_2$	*p*-Nitrotoluene	238.9	Nonazeotrope		*234*
11195	C_7H_8O	Benzyl alcohol	205.2	Reacts		*215*
11196	$C_7H_8O_2$	Guaiacol	205.05	Reacts		*215*
11197	C_7H_9N	*o*-Toluidine	200.3	Nonazeotrope		*218*
11198	$C_8H_8O_2$	Benzyl formate	202.3	Nonazeotrope		*227*

No.	B-Component Formula	B-Component Name	B.P., ° C.	Azeotropic Data B.P., ° C.	Azeotropic Data Wt. % A	Ref.
A =	**$C_7H_5Cl_3$**	**α,α,α-Trichlorotoluene** *(continued)*	**220.8**			
11199	$C_8H_8O_3$	Methyl salicylate	222.35	220.75	~97	*218*
11200	C_8H_9BrO	*p*-Bromophenetole	234.5	Nonazeotrope		*255*
11201	$C_8H_{10}O_2$	*m*-Dimethoxybenzene	214.7	Nonazeotrope		*215*
11202	$C_9H_{10}O$	*p*-Methylacetophenone	226.35	Nonazeotrope		*232*
11203	$C_9H_{10}O$	Propiophenone	217.7	Nonazeotrope		*232*
11204	$C_9H_{10}O_2$	Benzyl acetate	214.9	Nonazeotrope		*215*
11205	$C_9H_{10}O_2$	Ethyl benzoate	212.6	Nonazeotrope		*254*
11206	$C_9H_{10}O_3$	Ethyl salicylate	234.0	Nonazeotrope		*218*
11207	$C_{10}H_7Cl$	1-Chloronaphthalene	262.7	Nonazeotrope		*225*
11208	$C_{10}H_8$	Naphthalene	218.05	Nonazeotrope		*254*
11209	$C_{10}H_{12}O$	Estragole	215.6	Nonazeotrope		*215*
11210	$C_{10}H_{12}O_2$	Ethyl α-toluate	228.75	Nonazeotrope		*218*
11211	$C_{10}H_{12}O_2$	Propyl benzoate	230.85	Nonazeotrope		*218*
11212	$C_{10}H_{14}O$	Carvone	231.0	Nonazeotrope		*231*
11213	$C_{10}H_{14}O$	Thymol	232.9	Reacts		*222*
11214	$C_{10}H_{15}N$	Diethylaniline	217.05	Nonazeotrope		*218*
11215	$C_{11}H_{22}O_3$	Isoamyl carbonate	232.2	Nonazeotrope		*227*
11216	$C_{12}H_{18}$	1,3,5-Triethylbenzene	215.5	Nonazeotrope		*255*
11217	$C_{12}H_{20}O_2$	Bornyl acetate	~227.7	Nonazeotrope		*215*
A =	**C_7H_5N**	**Benzonitrile**	**191.1**			
11218	C_7H_7Br	*m*-Bromotoluene	184.3	183.8	11.5	*250*
11219	C_7H_7Br	*o*-Bromotoluene	181.5	181.4	....	*245*
11220	C_7H_7Br	*p*-Bromotoluene	185.0	184.3	15	*245*
11221	C_7H_7Br	*p*-Bromotoluene	185	~181	....	*243*
11222	C_7H_7Cl	*p*-Chlorotoluene	162.4	Nonazeotrope		*245*
11223	C_7H_8O	Benzyl alcohol	205.25	Nonazeotrope		*245*
11224	C_7H_8O	*m*-Cresol	202.2	202.5	11	*207*
11225	C_7H_8O	*o*-Cresol	191.1	195.95	49	*250*
11226	C_7H_8O	*p*-Cresol	201.7	202.1	14	*207*
11227	C_7H_9N	Methylaniline	196.25	Nonazeotrope		*255*
11228	C_7H_9N	*o*-Toluidine	200.35	Nonazeotrope		*255*
11229	$C_7H_{12}O_4$	Ethyl malonate	199.35	Nonazeotrope		*255*
11230	$C_7H_{16}O$	Heptyl alcohol	176.15	Nonazeotrope		*245*
11231	$C_8H_8O_2$	Phenyl acetate	195.7	<189.5	>51	
11232	$C_8H_{10}O$	Benzyl methyl ether	167.8	Nonazeotrope		*245*
11233	$C_8H_{10}O$	Phenetole	170.45	Nonazeotrope		*245*
11234	$C_8H_{11}N$	Dimethylaniline	194.15	Nonazeotrope		*255*
11235	$C_8H_{11}N$	Ethylaniline	205.5	Nonazeotrope		*255*
11236	$C_8H_{18}O$	*n*-Octyl alcohol	195.2	<189.2	<70	*207*
11237	$C_8H_{18}O$	*sec*-Octyl alcohol	180.4	180.05	11	*250*
11238	$C_8H_{18}S$	Butyl sulfide	185.0	<184.5	<12	*255*
11239	$C_8H_{18}S$	Isobutyl sulfide	172.0	Nonazeotrope		*246*
11240	$C_9H_{12}O$	Benzyl ethyl ether	185.0	182.5	27	*245*
11241	$C_9H_{18}O_2$	Butyl isovalerate	177.6	Nonazeotrope		*245*
11242	$C_9H_{18}O_2$	Isoamyl butyrate	181.05	180.85	8	*207*
11243	$C_9H_{18}O_2$	Isoamyl isobutyrate	169.8	Nonazeotrope		*245*
11244	$C_9H_{18}O_2$	Isobutyl isovalerate	171.2	Nonazeotrope		*245*
11245	$C_{10}H_{18}O$	Cineole	176.35	175.6	14	*207*
11246	$C_{10}H_{20}O_2$	Isoamyl isovalerate	192.7	<189.0	>42	*207*
11247	$C_{10}H_{22}O$	Amyl ether	187.5	180.5	42	*207*
11248	$C_{10}H_{22}O$	Isoamyl ether	173.2	171.4	16	*207*
11249	$C_{11}H_{20}O$	Isobornyl methyl ether	192.4	<186.0	....	*245*
A =	**C_7H_5NO**	**Phenyl Isocyanate**	**162.8**			
11250	$C_8H_{18}S$	Butyl sulfide	185.0	Nonazeotrope		*255*
11251	$C_8H_{18}S$	Isobutyl sulfide	172.0	Nonazeotrope		*255*
A =	**$C_7H_6Cl_2$**	**α,α-Dichlorotoluene**	**205.2**			
11252	$C_7H_6O_2$	Benzoic acid	250.8	Nonazeotrope		*255*
11253	$C_7H_7NO_2$	*o*-Nitrotoluene	221.75	Nonazeotrope		*255*
11254	C_7H_8O	Benzyl alcohol	205.5	182?	....	*243*
11255	C_7H_8O	*m*-Cresol	202.8	Reacts		*243*
11256	C_7H_8O	*o*-Cresol	190.8	Reacts		*243*
11257	C_7H_8O	*p*-Cresol	201.8	Reacts		*243*
11258	C_7H_9N	Methylaniline	196.1	Reacts		*243*

No.	B-Component Formula	Name	B.P., ° C.	Azeotropic Data B.P., ° C.	Wt. % A	Ref.
A =	**$C_7H_6Cl_2$**	**α,α-Dichlorotoluene** (*continued*)	**205.2**			
11259	C_7H_9N	*o*-Toluidine	200.3	Nonazeotrope		218
11260	C_7H_9N	*p*-Toluidine	200.3	Reacts		243
11261	$C_7H_{12}O_4$	Ethyl malonate	198.9	Nonazeotrope		243
11262	C_8H_8O	Acetophenone	202	Nonazeotrope		243
11263	$C_8H_8O_2$	Benzyl formate	202.3	Nonazeotrope		218
11264	$C_8H_8O_2$	Methyl benzoate	199.55	Nonazeotrope		243
11265	$C_8H_8O_2$	Phenyl acetate	195.5	Nonazeotrope		243
11266	$C_8H_{11}N$	Dimethylaniline	194.15	Nonazeotrope		231
11267	$C_8H_{11}N$	Ethylaniline	206.3	Reacts		243
11268	$C_8H_{14}O_4$	Ethyl succinate	217.25	Nonazeotrope		227
11269	$C_8H_{14}O_4$	Propyl oxalate	212	Nonazeotrope		227
11270	$C_8H_{16}O_3$	Isoamyl lactate	202.4	201.3	45	243
11271	$C_8H_{18}O$	*n*-Octyl alcohol	195.15	194.5	~10	211
11272	$C_9H_{10}O_2$	Benzyl acetate	214.9	Nonazeotrope		218
11273	$C_9H_{10}O_2$	Ethyl benzoate	213	Nonazeotrope		243
11274	$C_{10}H_8$	Naphthalene	218.05	Nonazeotrope		243
11275	$C_{10}H_{16}O$	Camphor	209.1	209.7	25	231
11276	$C_{10}H_{18}O$	Borneol	213.4	205.0	~85	218
11277	$C_{10}H_{18}O$	Citronellal	~207.8	Nonazeotrope		218
11278	$C_{10}H_{18}O$	Menthone	207	Azeotrope doubtful		243
11279	$C_{10}H_{18}O$	Menthone	209.5	Nonazeotrope		255
11280	$C_{10}H_{20}O$	Menthol	216.3	Nonazeotrope		255
11281	$C_{10}H_{20}O_2$	Isoamyl isovalerate	192.7	Nonazeotrope		255
11282	$C_{12}H_{18}$	1,3,5-Triethylbenzene	215.5	Nonazeotrope		218
A =	**C_7H_6O**	**Benzaldehyde**	**179.2**			
11283	C_7H_7Br	*m*-Bromotoluene	184.3	<179.0	<92	255
11284	C_7H_7Br	*o*-Bromotoluene	181.5	178.5	....	225
11285	C_7H_7Br	*p*-Bromotoluene	185.0	Nonazeotrope		225
11286	C_7H_7Cl	α-Chlorotoluene	179.35	177.9	50	243
11287	C_7H_7Cl	*o*-Chlorotoluene	159.15	Nonazeotrope		228
11288	C_7H_7Cl	*p*-Chlorotoluene	162.4	Nonazeotrope		225
11289	C_7H_7ClO	*o*-Chloroanisole	195.7	Nonazeotrope		255
11290	C_7H_8O	Anisole	153.85	Nonazeotrope		255
11291	C_7H_8O	*m*-Cresol	202.2	Nonazeotrope		255
11292	C_7H_8O	*o*-Cresol	191.1	192.0	23	218
11293	C_7H_8O	*p*-Cresol	201.7	Nonazeotrope		225
11294	$C_7H_{14}O_3$	Isobutyl lactate	182.15	<178.8	<92	255
11295	$C_7H_{16}O$	Heptyl alcohol	176.15	<174.5	<45	255
11296	C_8H_8	Styrene	145.8	Nonazeotrope		255
11297	C_8H_9Cl	*o,m,p*-Chloroethylbenzene, 10 mm.	67.5	63.5	57	24
11298	C_8H_{10}	*o*-Xylene	144.3	Nonazeotrope		255
11299	$C_8H_{10}O$	Benzyl methyl ether	167.8	<167.0	....	255
11300	$C_8H_{10}O$	*p*-Ethylphenol	218.8	Nonazeotrope		255
11301	$C_8H_{10}O$	*p*-Methylanisole	177.05	<175.5	....	255
11302	$C_8H_{10}O$	Phenetole	170.45	<169.8	<12	255
11303	$C_8H_{11}N$	Dimethylaniline	194.05	Reacts		243
11304	$C_8H_{14}O$	Methylheptenone	173.2	Nonazeotrope		232
11305	$C_8H_{16}O$	2-Octanone	172.85	Nonazeotrope		232
11306	$C_8H_{16}O_2$	Butyl butyrate	166.4	Nonazeotrope		255
11307	$C_8H_{16}O_2$	Ethyl caproate	167.7	Nonazeotrope		255
11308	$C_8H_{16}O_2$	Hexyl acetate	171.5	<171.3	....	255
11309	$C_8H_{18}O$	Butyl ether	142.6	Nonazeotrope		255
11310	$C_8H_{18}O$	Octyl alcohol	195.2	Nonazeotrope		255
11311	$C_8H_{18}O$	*sec*-Octyl alcohol	178.7	174	~25	243
11312	C_9H_{12}	Cumene	152.8	Nonazeotrope		255
11313	$C_9H_{12}O$	Benzyl ethyl ether	185.0	<117.5	<92	255
11314	$C_9H_{14}O$	Phorone	197.8	Nonazeotrope		232
11315	$C_9H_{18}O$	2,6-Dimethyl-4-heptanone	168.0	Nonazeotrope		232
11316	$C_9H_{18}O_2$	Isoamyl butyrate	178.5	~176.3	38	216
11317	$C_9H_{18}O_2$	Isoamyl isobutyrate	169.8	Nonazeotrope		255
11318	$C_9H_{18}O_2$	Isobutyl isovalerate	171.2	170.85	10	255
11319	$C_9H_{18}O_2$	Isobutyl isovalerate	171.35	Nonazeotrope		225
11320	$C_9H_{18}O_3$	Isobutyl carbonate	190.3	Nonazeotrope		255
11321	$C_{10}H_8$	Naphthalene	218.0	Nonazeotrope		255
11322	$C_{10}H_{14}$	Butylbenzene	183.1	<176.5	<65	255

No.	Formula	B-Component Name	B.P., ° C.	Azeotropic Data B.P., ° C.	Wt. % A	Ref.
A =	C_7H_6O	**Benzaldehyde** (*continued*)	**179.2**			
11323	$C_{10}H_{14}$	Cymene	175.3	171	28	243
11324	$C_{10}H_{16}$	Camphene	159.6	158.45	15.5	228
11325	$C_{10}H_{16}$	*d*-Limonene	177.8	171.2	43	243
11326	$C_{10}H_{16}$	Nopinene	163.8	<162.0	<25	228
11327	$C_{10}H_{16}$	α-Phellandrene	171.5	170	....	243
11328	$C_{10}H_{16}$	α-Pinene	155.8	Nonazeotrope		255
11329	$C_{10}H_{16}$	α-Pinene	155.8	~155.0	~10	228
11330	$C_{10}H_{16}$	α-Terpinene	173.4	<170.0	<38	255
11331	$C_{10}H_{16}$	γ-Terpinene	179.9	~173.0	~48	228
11332	$C_{10}H_{16}$	Terpinolene	185	<176.5	>70	243
11333	$C_{10}H_{16}O$	Fenchone	193.6	Nonazeotrope		232
11334	$C_{10}H_{18}O$	Cineole	176.35	172.05	36	236
			176.3	Nonazeotrope		243
11335	$C_{10}H_{22}$	2,7-Dimethyloctane	160.2	<159.5	....	255
11336	$C_{10}H_{22}O$	Amyl ether	187.5	175.2	....	236
11337	$C_{10}H_{22}O$	Isoamyl ether	173.2	168.6	37.5	207
11338	$C_{11}H_{20}O$	Isobornyl methyl ether	192.4	178.0	92?	255
11339	$C_{12}H_{18}$	1,3,5-Triethylbenzene	215.5	Nonazeotrope		255
11340	$C_{12}H_{22}O$	Bornyl ethyl ether	204.9	Nonazeotrope		255
11341	$C_{12}H_{22}O$	Ethyl isobornyl ether	203.8	Nonazeotrope		255
A =	$C_7H_6O_2$	**Benzoic Acid**	**250.8**			
11342	$C_7H_7NO_2$	*m*-Nitrotoluene	230.8	Nonazeotrope		234
11343	$C_7H_7NO_2$	*o*-Nitrotoluene	221.75	Nonazeotrope		234
11344	$C_7H_7NO_2$	*p*-Nitrotoluene	238.9	237.4	11	234
11345	$C_7H_8O_2$	*m*-Methoxyphenol	243.8	Nonazeotrope		255
11346	$C_8H_8O_2$	Anisaldehyde	249.5	Nonazeotrope		218
11347	$C_8H_{10}O$	3,4-Xylenol	226.8	Nonazeotrope		255
11348	$C_8H_{11}NO$	*p*-Phenetidine	249.9	Nonazeotrope		221
11349	C_9H_8O	Cinnamaldehyde	253.5	~250.2	~90	218
11350			253.5	Nonazeotrope		255
11351	$C_9H_{10}O$	*p*-Methylacetophenone	226.35	Nonazeotrope		232
11352	$C_9H_{10}O_3$	Ethyl salicylate	234.0	233.85	6	218
11353	$C_{10}H_7Br$	1-Bromonaphthalene	281.8	249.9	~95	221
			281.8	Nonazeotrope		244
11354	$C_{10}H_7Cl$	1-Chloronaphthalene	262.7	247.8	57	221
11355	$C_{10}H_8$	Naphthalene	218.05	217.7	5	218
11356	$C_{10}H_{10}O_2$	Isosafrole	252.0	246.5	53.5	236
11357	$C_{10}H_{10}O_2$	Methyl cinnamate	261.9	Nonazeotrope		221
11358	$C_{10}H_{10}O_2$	Safrole	235.9	Nonazeotrope		217
			235.9	234.75	12.5	236
11359	$C_{10}H_{12}O$	Anethole	235.7	234.6	12	242
11360	$C_{10}H_{12}O_2$	Eugenol	254.8	Nonazeotrope		255
11361	$C_{10}H_{12}O_2$	Eugenol	254.8	250.4	96.5	218
11362	$C_{10}H_{12}O_2$	Propyl benzoate	230.85	Nonazeotrope		222
11363	$C_{10}H_{14}O$	Carvone	231.0	Nonazeotrope		232
11364	$C_{10}H_{14}O$	Carvacrol	237.85	<237.75	....	255
11365	$C_{10}H_{14}O$	Thymol	232.9	Nonazeotrope		255
11366	$C_{10}H_{14}O$	Thymol	232.9	232.85?	1.5?	218
11367	$C_{10}H_{14}O_2$	*m*-Diethoxybenzene	235.0	Nonazeotrope		221
11368	$C_{10}H_{18}O_4$	Propyl succinate	250.5	248.0	43	255
11369	$C_{10}H_{20}O_4$	2-(2-Butoxyethoxy)ethyl acetate	245.3	251.8	70	242
11370	$C_{11}H_{10}$	1-Methylnaphthalene	244.6	239.6	27	218
11371	$C_{11}H_{10}$	2-Methylnaphthalene	241.15	237.25	25	207
11372	$C_{11}H_{14}O_2$	1-Allyl-3,4-dimethoxybenzene	254.7	Nonazeotrope		217
			255.0	250.3	89	218
11373	$C_{11}H_{14}O_2$	Butyl benzoate	249.0	245.5	35	242
11374	$C_{11}H_{14}O_2$	1,2-Dimethoxy-4-propenylbenzene	270.5	Nonazeotrope		221
11375	$C_{11}H_{14}O_2$	Isobutyl benzoate	241.9	241.15	~12	218
11376	$C_{11}H_{16}O$	Methyl thymol ether	216.5	Nonazeotrope		255
11377	$C_{11}H_{20}O$	Methyl α-terpineol ether	216.2	Nonazeotrope		255
11378	$C_{11}H_{22}O_3$	Isoamyl carbonate	232.2	Nonazeotrope		255
11379	$C_{12}H_{10}$	Acenaphthene	277.9	~250.0	....	221
11380	$C_{12}H_{10}$	Biphenyl	277.9	246.05	50.5	221
11381	$C_{12}H_{10}O$	Phenyl ether	257	Nonazeotrope		242
			259.3	247.3	59	236

No.	Formula	B-Component Name	B.P., ° C.	Azeotropic Data B.P., ° C.	Wt. % A	Ref.
A =	**$C_7H_6O_2$**	**Benzoic Acid** (*continued*)	**250.8**			
11382	$C_{12}H_{16}O_3$	Isoamyl salicylate	277.5	Nonazeotrope		*255*
11383	$C_{12}H_{18}$	1,3,5-Triethylbenzene	215.5	Nonazeotrope		*223*
11384	$C_{12}H_{22}O_4$	Isoamyl oxalate	268.0	Nonazeotrope		*221*
11385	$C_{13}H_{10}$	Fluorene	295	Nonazeotrope		*255*
11386	$C_{13}H_{12}$	Diphenylmethane	265.6	248.95	82	*218*
11387	$C_{13}H_{12}O$	Benzyl phenyl ether	286.5	Nonazeotrope		*255*
11388	$C_{14}H_{12}$	Stilbene	306.5	Nonazeotrope		*255*
11389	$C_{14}H_{14}$	1,2-Diphenylethane	284	Nonazeotrope		*223*
A =	**C_7H_7Br**	**α-Bromotoluene**	**198.5**			
11390	C_7H_8O	*o*-Cresol	190.8	Reacts		*243*
11391	C_7H_8O	*p*-Cresol	201.8	Reacts		*243*
11392	C_7H_9N	Methylaniline	196.1	Reacts		*243*
11393	C_7H_9N	*p*-Toluidine	200.3	Reacts		*243*
11394	$C_7H_{12}O_4$	Ethyl malonate	198.9	197.3	58	*243*
11395	C_8H_8O	Acetophenone	202	Nonazeotrope		*243*
11396	$C_8H_8O_2$	Benzyl formate	203.0	<198.0	....	*255*
11397	$C_8H_8O_2$	Methyl benzoate	199.45	Nonazeotrope		*255*
	$C_8H_8O_2$	Methyl benzoate	199.55	~197.5	~59	*243*
11398	$C_8H_8O_2$	Phenyl acetate	195.5	194.5	~43	*243*
11399	$C_8H_{11}N$	Dimethylaniline	194.05	Reacts		*243*
11400	$C_8H_{14}O_4$	Propyl oxalate	214.5	Nonazeotrope		*255*
11401	$C_8H_{16}O_3$	Isoamyl lactate	202.4	197.6	~73	*243*
11402	$C_8H_{18}O$	Octyl alcohol	195.2	193.5	68	*255*
11403	$C_8H_{18}O$	*sec*-Octyl alcohol	180.4	Nonazeotrope		*255*
11404	$C_9H_{12}O$	Phenyl propyl ether	190.5	Nonazeotrope		*255*
11405	$C_9H_{18}O_2$	Isoamyl butyrate	181.05	Nonazeotrope		*255*
11406	$C_9H_{18}O_3$	Isobutyl carbonate	190.3	Nonazeotrope		*227*
11407	$C_{10}H_{16}O$	Fenchone	193	Nonazeotrope		*243*
11408	$C_{10}H_{18}O$	Citronellal	208.0	Nonazeotrope (reacts)		*255*
11409	$C_{10}H_{18}O$	Menthone	~207	Nonazeotrope		*243*
11410	$C_{10}H_{20}O_2$	Ethyl caprylate	208.35	Nonazeotrope		*255*
11411	$C_{10}H_{20}O_2$	Isoamyl isovalerate	192.7	Nonazeotrope		*227*
11412	$C_{12}H_{22}O$	Bornyl ethyl ether	204.9	Nonazeotrope		*239*
A =	**C_7H_7Br**	***m*-Bromotoluene**	**184.3**			
11413	C_7H_8O	Benzyl alcohol	205.25	<184.15	....	*255*
11414	C_7H_8O	*o*-Cresol	191.1	183.05	78	*207*
11415	C_7H_9N	Methylaniline	196.25	Nonazeotrope		*207*
11416	C_7H_9N	*o*-Toluidine	200.35	Nonazeotrope		*207*
11417	$C_7H_{14}O_2$	Enanthic acid	221.3	Nonazeotrope		*207*
11418	$C_7H_{14}O_3$	Isobutyl lactate	182.15	180.4	40	*247*
11419	$C_8H_{11}N$	Dimethylaniline	194.15	Nonazeotrope		*207*
11420	$C_8H_{16}O$	2-Octanone	172.85	Nonazeotrope		*207*
11421	$C_8H_{16}O_3$	Isoamyl lactate	202.4	Nonazeotrope		*255*
11422	$C_8H_{18}O$	Octyl alcohol	195.2	184.05	91	*207*
11423	$C_8H_{18}O$	*sec*-Octyl alcohol	180.4	178.9	43	*207*
11424	$C_9H_{12}O$	Phenyl propyl ether	190.5	Nonazeotrope		*239*
11425	$C_9H_{13}N$	*N,N*-Dimethyl-*o*-toluidine	185.3	184.25	87	*244*
11426	$C_9H_{13}N$	*N,N*-Dimethyl-*o*-toluidine	185.3	Nonazeotrope		*231*
11427	$C_9H_{18}O_2$	Isobutyl isovalerate	171.2	Nonazeotrope		*255*
11428	$C_9H_{18}O_3$	Isobutyl carbonate	190.3	182.8	75	*242*
11429	$C_{10}H_{14}$	Butylbenzene	183.1	Nonazeotrope		*255*
11430	$C_{10}H_{16}$	Dipentene	177.7	Nonazeotrope		*207*
11431	$C_{10}H_{16}$	α-Terpinene	173.4	Nonazeotrope		*207*
11432	$C_{10}H_{18}O$	Cineole	176.35	Nonazeotrope		*207*
A =	**C_7H_7Br**	***o*-Bromotoluene**	**181.75**			
11433	C_7H_7Cl	α-Chlorotoluene	179.35	Nonazeotrope		*243*
11434	C_7H_8O	Benzyl alcohol	205.15	181.25	93?	*211*
11435	C_7H_8O	*m*-Cresol	202.2	Nonazeotrope		*224*
11436	C_7H_8O	*o*-Cresol	191.1	180.3	81	*222*
11437	C_7H_8O	*p*-Cresol	201.8	Nonazeotrope		*222*
11438	C_7H_9N	*m*-Toluidine	200.55	Nonazeotrope		*231*
11439	C_7H_9N	*o*-Toluidine	200.35	Nonazeotrope		*231*
11440	C_7H_9N	*p*-Toluidine	200.55	Nonazeotrope		*231*
11441	$C_7H_{14}O_3$	1,3-Butanediol methyl ether acetate	171.75	Nonazeotrope		*255*

No.	Formula	B-Component Name	B.P., ° C.	Azeotropic Data B.P., ° C.	Wt. % A	Ref.
A =	**C_7H_7Br**	**o-Bromotoluene (*continued*)**	**181.75**			
11442	$C_7H_{14}O_3$	Isobutyl lactate	182.15	180	56	*243*
11443	$C_7H_{16}O$	Heptyl alcohol	176.15	174.0	33	*247*
11444	$C_8H_{10}O$	p-Methylanisole	177.05	Nonazeotrope		*228*
11445	$C_8H_{10}O$	Phenetole	170.35	Nonazeotrope		*253*
11446	$C_8H_{11}N$	Dimethylaniline	194.15	Nonazeotrope		*231*
11447	$C_8H_{14}O$	Methylheptenone	173.2	Nonazeotrope		*232*
11448	$C_8H_{16}O$	2-Octanone	172.85	Nonazeotrope		*232*
11449	$C_8H_{18}O$	*n*-Octyl alcohol	195.15	181.0	....	*209*
11450	$C_8H_{18}O$	*sec*-Octyl alcohol	179.0	177.0	48	*252*
11451	$C_8H_{20}SiO_4$	Ethyl silicate	168.8	Nonazeotrope		*255*
11452	C_9H_8	Indene	182.3	<180.5	....	*243*
11453	$C_9H_{13}N$	*N,N*-Dimethyl-*o*-toluidine	185.3	Nonazeotrope		*231*
11454	$C_9H_{18}O_2$	Butyl isovalerate	177.6	Nonazeotrope		*227*
11455	$C_9H_{18}O_2$	Ethyl enanthate	188.7	Nonazeotrope		*255*
11456	$C_9H_{18}O_2$	Isoamyl butyrate	178.5	Nonazeotrope		*227*
11457	$C_9H_{18}O_2$	Isoamyl isobutyrate	170.0	Nonazeotrope		*227*
11458	$C_9H_{18}O_2$	Isobutyl isovalerate	168.7	Nonazeotrope		*243*
11459	$C_9H_{18}O_3$	Isobutyl carbonate	190.3	180.5	~90	*243*
			190.3	Nonazeotrope		*227*
11460	$C_{10}H_{14}$	Cymene	176.7	Nonazeotrope		*218*
11461	$C_{10}H_{16}$	*d*-Limonene	177.8	Nonazeotrope		*215*
			177.8	177.3	~17	*243*
11462	$C_{10}H_{16}$	α-Terpinene	173.4	Nonazeotrope		*255*
11463	$C_{10}H_{16}$	γ-Terpinene	181.5	181.0	....	*218*
11464	$C_{21}H_{16}$	Terpinolene	184.6	Nonazeotrope		*255*
11465	$C_{10}H_{16}$	Thymene	179.7	179.55	~15	*253*
11466	$C_{10}H_{18}O$	Cineole	176.4	Nonazeotrope		*208*
11467	$C_{10}H_{18}O$	Linaloöl	198.6	Nonazeotrope		*209*
11468	$C_{10}H_{19}N$	Bornylamine	199.8	Nonazeotrope		*255*
11469	$C_{10}H_{20}O_2$	Isoamyl isovalerate	192.7	Nonazeotrope		*227*
11470	$C_{10}H_{22}O$	Isoamyl ether	173.5	Nonazeotrope		*228*
A =	**C_7H_7Br**	**p-Bromotoluene**	**185.0**			
11471	C_7H_8O	Benzyl alcohol	205.2	~184.5	~92	*215*
11472	C_7H_8O	*m*-Cresol	202.2	184.8	~95	*222*
11473	C_7H_8O	*o*-Cresol	191.1	182.7	72	*218*
11474	C_7H_8O	*p*-Cresol	201.7	184.8	~93	*222*
11475	C_7H_9N	*o*-Toluidine	200.35	Nonazeotrope		*231*
11476	C_7H_9N	*p*-Toluidine	200.55	Nonazeotrope		*231*
11477	$C_7H_{12}O_4$	Ethyl malonate	199.2	Nonazeotrope		*227*
11478	$C_7H_{14}O_3$	Isobutyl lactate	182.15	180.2	38	*247*
11479	$C_8H_8O_2$	Phenyl acetate	195.7	Nonazeotrope		*227*
11480	$C_8H_{10}O$	2,4-Xylenol	210.5	Nonazeotrope		*255*
11481	$C_8H_{11}N$	Dimethylaniline	194.15	Nonazeotrope		*231*
			194.05	184.2	85	*215*
11482	$C_8H_{18}O$	Octyl alcohol	195.2	184.6	90	*255*
11483	$C_9H_{14}O$	Phorone	197.8	Nonazeotrope		*232*
11484	$C_9H_{18}O_2$	Butyl isovalerate	177.6	Nonazeotrope		*255*
11485	$C_9H_{18}O_2$	Isoamyl butyrate	178.5	Nonazeotrope		*227*
11486	$C_9H_{18}O_3$	Isobutyl carbonate	190.3	182.9	~35	*243*
11487	$C_{10}H_{14}$	Butylbenzene	183.1	Nonazeotrope		*255*
11488	$C_{10}H_{14}$	Cymene	176.7	Nonazeotrope		*255*
11489	$C_{10}H_{16}$	*d*-Limonene	177.8	Nonazeotrope		*215*
11490	$C_{10}H_{16}$	α-Terpinene	173.4	Nonazeotrope		*255*
11491	$C_{10}H_{16}$	γ-Terpinene	183	182.8	15	*255*
11492	$C_{10}H_{16}$	Terpinolene	185	~183	....	*243*
11493	$C_{10}H_{16}$	Thymene	179.7	Nonazeotrope		*215*
11494	$C_{10}H_{16}O$	Fenchone	193.6	Nonazeotrope		*255*
11495	$C_{10}H_{18}O$	Cineole	176.35	Nonazeotrope		*253*
11496	$C_{10}H_{18}O$	Linaloöl	198.6	Nonazeotrope		*212*
11497	$C_{10}H_{20}O_2$	Isoamyl isovalerate	192.7	Nonazeotrope		*227*
A =	**C_7H_7BrO**	**o-Bromoanisole**	**217.7**			
11498	C_7H_7I	*p*-Iodotoluene	214.5	<214.3	<10	*255*
11499	C_7H_8O	*m*-Cresol	202.2	Nonazeotrope		*255*
11500	$C_8H_{10}O$	3,4-Xylenol	226.8	Nonazeotrope		*255*

No.	Formula	B-Component Name	B.P., ° C.	Azeotropic Data B.P., ° C.	Wt. % A	Ref.
A =	**C_7H_7BrO**	**o-Bromoanisole** (*continued*)	**217.7**			
11501	C_9H_7N	Quinoline	237.3	Nonazeotrope		*255*
11502	$C_{10}H_8$	Naphthalene	218.0	<216.5	>55	*242*
11503	$C_{10}H_{12}O$	Estragole	215.6	Nonazeotrope		*228*
11504	$C_{10}H_{18}O$	Citronellal	208.0	Nonazeotrope		*255*
11505	$C_{11}H_{20}O$	Terpineol methyl ether	216.2	~215.0	>15	*228*
A =	**C_7H_7BrO**	**p-Bromoanisole**	**217.7**			
11506	$C_9H_{10}O$	p-Methylacetophenone	226.25	Nonazeotrope		*255*
11507	$C_9H_{10}O$	Propiophenone	217.7	<217.4	>54	*255*
11508	$C_{10}H_{16}O$	Pulegone	223.8	Nonazeotrope		*255*
A =	**C_7H_7Cl**	**α-Chlorotoluene**	**179.3**			
11509	C_7H_8O	Benzyl alcohol	205.15	Nonazeotrope		*210*
11510	C_7H_8O	o-Cresol	190.8	Reacts		*243*
11511	$C_7H_{14}O$	2-Methylcyclohexanol	168.5	<168.2	<34	*255*
11512	$C_7H_{14}O_2$	Enanthic acid	222.0	204.0	88	*255*
11513	$C_7H_{14}O_3$	Isobutyl lactate	182.15	178.0	~70	*243*
11514	$C_7H_{16}O$	Heptyl alcohol	176.15	<173.5	<51	*255*
11515	C_8H_8O	Acetophenone	202.0	Nonazeotrope		*232*
11516	$C_8H_{10}O$	Phenetole	170.35	Nonazeotrope		*210*
11517	$C_8H_{11}N$	Dimethylaniline	194.05	Reacts		*243*
11518	$C_8H_{14}O$	Methylheptenone	173.2	Nonazeotrope		*232*
11519	$C_8H_{16}O$	2-Octanone	172.85	Nonazeotrope		*232*
11520	$C_8H_{16}O_2$	Butyl butyrate	166.4	Nonazeotrope		*227*
11521	$C_8H_{16}O_2$	Ethyl caproate	167.7	Nonazeotrope		*255*
11522	$C_8H_{16}O_2$	Hexyl acetate	171.5	Nonazeotrope		*255*
11523	$C_8H_{16}O_2$	Isoamyl propionate	160.4	Nonazeotrope		*227*
11525	$C_8H_{18}O$	n-Octyl alcohol	195.15	Nonazeotrope		*210*
11526	$C_8H_{18}O$	sec-Octyl alcohol	179.0	165.7	....	*211*
11527	C_9H_{12}	Mesitylene	164.6	Nonazeotrope		*255*
11528	C_9H_{12}	Propylbenzene	159.3	Nonazeotrope		*255*
11529	C_9H_{12}	Pseudocumene	169	Nonazeotrope		*243*
11530	$C_9H_{18}O_2$	Butyl isovalerate	177.6	Nonazeotrope		*227*
11531	$C_9H_{18}O_2$	Isoamyl butyrate	178.5	~178.2	30?	*210*
11532	$C_9H_{18}O_2$	Isoamyl isobutyrate	170.0	Nonazeotrope		*227*
11533	$C_9H_{18}O_2$	Isobutyl isovalerate	171.35	Nonazeotrope		*218*
11534	$C_9H_{18}O_3$	Isobutyl carbonate	190.3	Nonazeotrope		*227*
11535	$C_{10}H_{14}$	Cymene	175.3	174	<20	*243*
11536	$C_{10}H_{16}$	Camphene	159.6	Nonazeotrope		*255*
11537	$C_{10}H_{16}$	d-Limonene	177.8	174.8	46	*243*
11538	$C_{10}H_{16}$	Nopinene	163.8	Nonazeotrope		*255*
11539	$C_{10}H_{16}$	α-Phellandrene	171.5	170?	....	*243*
11540	$C_{10}H_{16}$	α-Terpinene	173.4	173.0	....	*242*
11541	$C_{10}H_{16}$	γ-Terpinene	181.5	176.9	~70	*218*
11542	$C_{10}H_{16}$	Terpinolene	185	~177.5	....	*243*
11543	$C_{10}H_{16}$	Thymene	179.7	177.2	~52	*211*
11544	$C_{10}H_{18}$	m-Menthene-8	170.8	<170.0	<15	*242*
11545	$C_{10}H_{18}O$	Cineol	176.3	175.5	~19	*243*
11546	$C_{10}H_{18}O$	Linaloöl	198.6	Nonazeotrope		*212*
11547	$C_{10}H_{22}O$	Isoamyl ether	172.6	Nonazeotrope		*253*
A =	**C_7H_7Cl**	**o-Chlorotoluene**	**159.15**			
11548	C_7H_8O	Anisole	153.85	Nonazeotrope		*228*
11549	C_7H_8O	o-Cresol	191.1	Nonazeotrope		*255*
11550	$C_7H_{14}O$	2-Methylcyclohexanol	168.5	158.4	....	*255*
11551	$C_7H_{14}O_2$	Methyl caproate	151.0	Nonazeotrope		*227*
11552	$C_8H_{10}O$	Benzyl methyl ether	167.8	Nonazeotrope		*239*
11553	$C_8H_{10}O$	Phenetole	170.45	Nonazeotrope		*239*
11554	$C_8H_{14}O$	Methylheptenone	173.2	Nonazeotrope		*232*
11555	$C_8H_{16}O_2$	Butyl butyrate	166.4	Nonazeotrope		*227*
11556	$C_8H_{16}O_2$	Isoamyl propionate	160.3	158.0	>65	*218*
11557	$C_8H_{16}O_2$	Isobutyl butyrate	157	155.5	<50	*243*
			156.8	Nonazeotrope		*227*
11558	$C_8H_{16}O_2$	Isobutyl isobutyrate	147.3	Nonazeotrope		*227*
11559	$C_8H_{16}O_2$	Propyl isovalerate	155.7	Nonazeotrope		*227*
11560	$C_8H_{18}O$	sec-Octyl alcohol	180.4	Nonazeotrope		*255*
11561	$C_8H_{20}SiO_4$	Ethyl silicate	168.8	Nonazeotrope		*255*

No.	B-Component Formula	Name	B.P., ° C.	Azeotropic Data B.P., ° C.	Wt. % A	Ref.
A =	**C_7H_7Cl**	***o*-Chlorotoluene** (*continued*)	**159.15**			
11562	C_9H_{12}	Cumene	152.8	Nonazeotrope		255
11563	C_9H_{12}	Mesitylene	164.6	Nonazeotrope		218
11564	C_9H_{12}	Pseudocumene	168.2	Nonazeotrope		255
11565	$C_9H_{18}O$	2,6-Dimethyl-4-heptanone	168.0	Nonazeotrope		232
11566	$C_9H_{18}O_2$	Isobutyl isovalerate	171.35	Nonazeotrope		218
11567	$C_{10}H_{16}$	Camphene	159.6	~158.0	....	218
11568	$C_{10}H_{16}$	Nopinene	163.8	<158.5	>63	242
11569	$C_{10}H_{16}$	α-Pinene	155.8	154.5	....	242
11570	$C_{10}H_{16}$	α-Terpinene	173.4	Nonazeotrope		255
A =	**C_7H_7Cl**	***p*-Chlorotoluene**	**161.3**			
11571	C_7H_8O	Anisole	153.85	Nonazeotrope		243
11572	C_7H_8O	*o*-Cresol	191.1	Nonazeotrope		255
11573	$C_7H_{14}O$	2-Methylcyclohexanol	168.5	161.1	75	247
11574	$C_7H_{14}O_3$	1,3-Butanediol methyl ether acetate	171.75	Nonazeotrope		255
11575	$C_7H_{16}O$	Heptyl alcohol	176.15	161.9	~92	255
11576	$C_8H_{10}O$	Phenetole	170.35	Nonazeotrope		253
11577	$C_8H_{14}O$	Methylheptenone	173.2	Nonazeotrope		232
11578	$C_8H_{16}O$	2-Octanone	172.85	Nonazeotrope		232
11579	$C_8H_{16}O_2$	Butyl butyrate	166.4	Nonazeotrope		227
11580	$C_8H_{16}O_2$	Ethyl caproate	167.9	Nonazeotrope		227
11581	$C_8H_{16}O_2$	Isoamyl propionate	160.3	159.5	....	227
11582	$C_8H_{18}O$	*sec*-Octyl alcohol	179.0	Nonazeotrope		253
11583	$C_8H_{18}S$	Isobutyl sulfide	172.0	Nonazeotrope		246
11584	$C_8H_{20}SiO_4$	Ethyl silicate	168.8	Nonazeotrope		255
11585	C_9H_{12}	Cumene	152.8	Nonazeotrope		255
11586	C_9H_{12}	Mesitylene	164.0	160.5	~72	243
11587	C_9H_{12}	Pseudocumene	168.2	Nonazeotrope		218
11588	$C_9H_{13}N$	*N,N*-Dimethyl-*o*-toluidine	185.3	Nonazeotrope		231
11589	$C_9H_{18}O$	2,6-Dimethyl-4-heptanone	168.0	Nonazeotrope		232
11590	$C_9H_{18}O_2$	Isoamyl butyrate	181.05	Nonazeotrope		255
11591	$C_9H_{18}O_2$	Isobutyl isovalerate	171.2	Nonazeotrope		255
11592	$C_{10}H_{14}$	Cymene	176.7	Nonazeotrope		255
11593	$C_{10}H_{16}$	Camphene	159.6	~158.0	....	215
11594	$C_{10}H_{16}$	Dipentene	177.7	Nonazeotrope		255
11595	$C_{10}H_{16}$	Nopinene	163.8	160.2	....	243
11596	$C_{10}H_{16}$	α-Pinene	155.8	<155.5	<20	255
11597	$C_{10}H_{16}$	α-Terpinene	173.4	Nonazeotrope		255
11598	$C_{10}H_{18}$	*m*-Menthene-8	170.8	Nonazeotrope		255
11599	$C_{10}H_{18}O$	Cineole	176.35	Nonazeotrope		239
11600	$C_{10}H_{22}$	2,7-Dimethyloctane	160.25	158.5	~50	243
A =	**C_7H_7ClO**	***m*-Chloroanisole**	**193.3**			
11601	$C_7H_{14}O_3$	1,3-Butanediol methyl ether acetate	171.75	Nonazeotrope		255
11602	$C_8H_{18}S$	Butyl sulfide	185.0	Nonazeotrope		255
A =	**C_7H_7ClO**	***o*-Chloroanisole**	**195.7**			
11603	C_7H_8O	*o*-Cresol	191.1	<189.8	>20	242
A =	**C_7H_7ClO**	***p*-Chloroanisole**	**193.3**			
11604	C_8H_8O	Acetophenone	202.0	Nonazeotrope		255
11605	$C_8H_{18}S$	Butyl sulfide	185.0	Nonazeotrope		255
11606	$C_9H_{12}O$	Benzyl ethyl ether	185.0	Nonazeotrope		255
11607	$C_9H_{14}O$	Phorone	197.8	<197.4	....	255
11608	$C_{10}H_8$	Naphthalene	218.0	Nonazeotrope		255
11609	$C_{10}H_{16}O$	Camphor	209.1	Nonazeotrope		255
11610	$C_{10}H_{16}O$	Fenchone	193.6	Nonazeotrope		255
11611	$C_{12}H_{18}$	1,3,5-Triethylbenzene	215.5	Nonazeotrope		255
A =	**C_7H_7I**	***p*-Iodotoluene**	**214.5**			
11612	$C_7H_7NO_2$	*o*-Nitrotoluene	221.75	Nonazeotrope		234
11613	C_7H_8O	Benzyl alcohol	205.15	~203.0	25?	209
11614	C_7H_8O	*m*-Cresol	202.2	201.6	25	222
11615	C_7H_8O	*o*-Cresol	190.8	Nonazeotrope		243

No.	Formula	B-Component Name	B.P., ° C.	Azeotropic Data B.P., ° C.	Wt. % A	Ref.
A =	C_7H_7I	*p*-Iodotoluene (*continued*)	214.5			
11616	C_7H_8O	*p*-Cresol	201.7	201.0	23	*222*
11617	C_7H_9N	*m*-Toluidine	203.1	Nonazeotrope		*231*
11618	C_7H_9N	*o*-Toluidine	200.35	Nonazeotrope		*231*
11619	C_7H_9N	*p*-Toluidine	200.55	Nonazeotrope		*231*
11620	C_7H_9NO	*o*-Anisidine	219.0	213.0	70?	*255*
11621	$C_7H_{12}O_4$	Ethyl malonate	199.35	<198.8	>8	*255*
11622	$C_7H_{14}O_2$	Enanthic acid	222.0	211.5	83	*242*
11623	$C_8H_8O_2$	Methyl benzoate	199.4	Nonazeotrope		*255*
11624	$C_8H_8O_3$	Methyl salicylate	222.95	Nonazeotrope		*255*
11625	$C_8H_{10}O$	*p*-Ethylphenol	218.8	212.0	72	*242*
11626	$C_8H_{10}O$	Phenethyl alcohol	219.4	<211.5	....	*255*
11627	$C_8H_{10}O$	2,4-Xylenol	210.5	207.5	38	*255*
11628	$C_8H_{10}O$	3,4-Xylenol	226.8	214.0	85	*255*
11629	$C_8H_{10}O_2$	*m*-Dimethoxybenzene	214.7	Nonazeotrope		*215*
11630	$C_8H_{10}O_2$	Veratrole	205.5	Nonazeotrope		*215*
11631	$C_8H_{11}N$	Dimethylaniline	194.15	Nonazeotrope		*231*
11632	$C_8H_{11}N$	2,4-Xylidine	214.0	<212.5	....	*255*
11633	$C_8H_{14}O_4$	Propyl oxalate	214	<209.2	>53	*255*
11634	$C_8H_{16}O_3$	Isoamyl lactate	202.4	Nonazeotrope		*255*
11635	$C_8H_{18}O$	Octyl alcohol	195.2	Nonazeotrope		*255*
11636	$C_8H_{18}O_3$	2-(2-Butoxyethoxy)ethanol	231.2	Nonazeotrope		*255*
11637	C_9H_7N	Quinoline	237.3	Nonazeotrope		*233*
11638	$C_9H_{10}O$	Propiophenone	217.7	Nonazeotrope		*232*
11639	$C_9H_{10}O_2$	Ethyl benzoate	212.5	<212.3	>14	*255*
11640	$C_{10}H_{20}O$	Menthol	216.3	<213.0	....	*255*
11641	$C_{10}H_{20}O_2$	Ethyl caprylate	208.35	Nonazeotrope		*255*
11642	$C_{10}H_{22}S$	Isoamyl sulfide	214.8	<213.3	>42	*242*
A =	$C_7H_7NO_2$	*m*-Nitrotoluene	230.8			
11643	C_7H_8O	Benzyl alcohol	205.25	Nonazeotrope		*234*
11644	C_7H_9NO	*o*-Anisidine	219.0	Nonazeotrope		*255*
11645	$C_7H_{14}O_2$	Enanthic acid	222.0	220.0	30	*234*
11646	$C_7H_{16}O_4$	2-[2-(2-Methoxyethoxy)ethoxy]-ethanol	245.25	226.4	77	*234*
11647	$C_8H_8O_3$	Methyl salicylate	222.95	Nonazeotrope		*234*
11648	$C_8H_{10}O$	3,4-Xylenol	226.8	Nonazeotrope		*234*
11649	$C_8H_{10}O$	*p*-Ethylphenol	220.0	Nonazeotrope		*234*
11650	$C_8H_{11}NO$	*o*-Phenetidine	232.5	233.0	30	*231*
11651	$C_8H_{11}NO$	*p*-Phenetidine	249.9	Nonazeotrope		*231*
11652	$C_8H_{12}O_4$	Ethyl fumarate	217.85	Nonazeotrope		*234*
11653	$C_8H_{12}O_4$	Ethyl maleate	223.3	Nonazeotrope		*234*
11654	$C_8H_{14}O_4$	Ethyl succinate	217.25	Nonazeotrope		*234*
11655	$C_8H_{16}O_2$	Caprylic acid	238.5	<229.8	<80	*234*
11656	$C_8H_{18}O_3$	2-(2-Butoxyethoxy)ethanol	231.2	<229.0	<70	*234*
11657	C_9H_7N	Quinoline	237.6	Nonazeotrope		*234*
11658	$C_9H_{10}O$	Cinnamyl alcohol	257.0	Nonazeotrope		*234*
11659	$C_9H_{10}O$	*p*-Methylacetophenone	226.35	Nonazeotrope		*255*
11660	$C_9H_{10}O$	Propiophenone	217.7	Nonazeotrope		*255*
11661	$C_9H_{10}O_2$	Benzyl acetate	215.0	Nonazeotrope		*234*
11662	$C_9H_{10}O_3$	Ethyl salicylate	253.8	Nonazeotrope		*234*
11663	$C_9H_{12}O$	3-Phenylpropanol	235.6	229.5	68	*234*
11664	$C_9H_{18}O_2$	Pelargonic acid	254.0	Nonazeotrope		*255*
11665	$C_{10}H_8$	Naphthalene	218.0	Nonazeotrope		*234*
11666	$C_{10}H_{10}O_2$	Safrol	232	227	55	*243*
11667	$C_{10}H_{12}O_2$	Propyl benzoate	230.85	230.0	48	*234*
11668	$C_{10}H_{14}O$	Carvacrol	237.85	Nonazeotrope		*234*
11669	$C_{10}H_{14}O$	Carvone	231.0	230.5	....	*225*
11670	$C_{10}H_{14}O$	Thymol	232.9	Nonazeotrope		*234*
11671	$C_{10}H_{15}N$	Diethylaniline	217.05	Nonazeotrope		*231*
11672	$C_{10}H_{16}O$	Pulegone	223.8	Nonazeotrope		*255*
11673	$C_{10}H_{18}O$	Borneol	213.4	Nonazeotrope		*256*
11674	$C_{10}H_{18}O$	Geraniol	229.6	227.3	49	*234*
11675	$C_{10}H_{18}O$	α-Terpineol	218.85	218.65	8	*234*
11676	$C_{10}H_{20}O$	Citronellol	224.4	223.2	>26	*234*
11677	$C_{10}H_{20}O$	Menthol	216.3	<216.2	....	*234*
11678	$C_{10}H_{22}O$	*n*-Decanol	232.8	228.2	60	*234*

	B-Component			Azeotropic Data		
No.	Formula	Name	B.P., ° C.	B.P., ° C.	Wt. % A	Ref.
A =	**$C_7H_7NO_2$**	***m*-Nitrotoluene (*continued*)**	**230.8**			
11679	$C_{11}H_{10}$	1-Methylnaphthalene	244.6	Nonazeotrope		*234*
11680	$C_{11}H_{10}$	2-Methylnaphthalene	241.15	Nonazeotrope		*234*
11681	$C_{11}H_{14}O_2$	Ethyl *β*-phenylpropionate	248.1	Nonazeotrope		*234*
11682	$C_{11}H_{14}O_2$	Isobutyl benzoate	241.9	Nonazeotrope		*234*
11683	$C_{11}H_{17}N$	Isoamylaniline	256.0	Nonazeotrope		*231*
11684	$C_{11}H_{22}O_3$	Isoamyl carbonate	232.2	<230.2	>56	*234*
11685	$C_{12}H_{20}O_2$	Bornyl acetate	227.6	<226.5	>28	*234*
A =	**$C_7H_7NO_2$**	***o*-Nitrotoluene**	**221.75**			
11686	C_7H_8O	Benzyl alcohol	202.25	Nonazeotrope		*234*
			205.2	204.75	9	*216*
11687	C_7H_8O	*m*-Cresol	202.2	Nonazeotrope		*234*
11688	C_7H_9N	Methylaniline	196.25	Nonazeotrope		*231*
11689	C_7H_9N	*o*-Toluidine	200.35	Nonazeotrope		*231*
11690	C_7H_9N	*p*-Toluidine	200.55	Nonazeotrope		*231*
11691	$C_7H_{14}O_2$	Enanthic acid	222.0	<218.0	<60	*234*
11692	$C_7H_{16}O_4$	2-[2-(2-Methoxyethoxy)ethoxy]-ethanol	245.25	<220.8	88	*234*
11693	$C_8H_8O_2$	Phenyl acetate	228.75	Nonazeotrope		*234*
11694	$C_8H_8O_3$	Methyl salicylate	222.95	221.65	86	*234*
11695	$C_8H_{10}O$	2-Phenethyl alcohol	219.4	217.6	43	*234*
11696	$C_8H_{10}O$	2,4-Xylenol	210.5	Nonazeotrope		*255*
11697	$C_8H_{10}O$	3,4-Xylenol	226.8	Nonazeotrope		*234*
11698	$C_8H_{10}O_2$	*m*-Dimethoxybenzene	214.7	Nonazeotrope		*217*
11699	$C_8H_{10}O_2$	*o*-Ethoxyphenol	216.5	Nonazeotrope		*234*
11700	$C_8H_{10}O_2$	Veratrol	206.5	Nonazeotrope		*217*
11701	$C_8H_{11}N$	Dimethylaniline	194.15	Nonazeotrope		*231*
11702	$C_8H_{11}N$	Ethylaniline	205.5	Nonazeotrope		*231*
11703	$C_8H_{11}N$	2,4-Xylidine	214.0	Nonazeotrope		*231*
11704	$C_8H_{11}N$	3,4-Xylidine	225.5	Nonazeotrope		*231*
11705	$C_8H_{11}NO$	*o*-Phenetidine	232.5	Nonazeotrope		*231*
11706	$C_8H_{12}O_4$	Ethyl fumarate	217.85	Nonazeotrope		*234*
11707	$C_8H_{12}O_4$	Ethyl maleate	223.3	221.0	62	*234*
11708	$C_8H_{14}O_4$	Ethyl succinate	217.25	<217.1	....	*234*
11709	$C_8H_{16}O_2$	Caprylic acid	237.5	221.5	~95	*221*
11710	$C_8H_{18}O$	*n*-Octyl alcohol	195.2	Nonazeotrope		*234*
11711	C_9H_7N	Quinoline	237.3	Nonazeotrope		*234*
11712	$C_9H_{10}O$	Cinnamyl alcohol	257.0	Nonazeotrope		*234*
11713	$C_9H_{10}O$	*p*-Methylacetophenone	226.35	Nonazeotrope		*232*
11714	$C_9H_{10}O$	Propiophenone	217.7	Nonazeotrope		*232*
11715	$C_9H_{10}O_2$	Benzyl acetate	215.0	Nonazeotrope		*234*
11716	$C_9H_{10}O_2$	Ethyl benzoate	212.5	Nonazeotrope		*234*
11717	$C_9H_{10}O_3$	Ethyl salicylate	233.8	Nonazeotrope		*234*
11718	$C_9H_{12}O$	3-Phenylpropanol	235.6	Nonazeotrope		*234*
			235.6	235.3	92	*225*
11719	$C_9H_{13}N$	*N,N*-Dimethyl-*p*-toluidine	210.2	Nonazeotrope		*231*
11720	$C_{10}H_8$	Naphthalene	218.0	Nonazeotrope		*234*
11721	$C_{10}H_{10}O_2$	Safrole	235.9	Nonazeotrope		*234*
11722	$C_{10}H_{12}O_2$	Propyl benzoate	230.85	Nonazeotrope		*234*
11723	$C_{10}H_{14}O$	Carvacrol	237.85	Nonazeotrope		*234*
11724	$C_{10}H_{14}O$	Thymol	232.9	Nonazeotrope		*234*
11725	$C_{10}H_{15}N$	Diethylaniline	217.05	216.85	12	*231*
11726	$C_{10}H_{16}O$	Camphor	209.1	Nonazeotrope		*232*
11727	$C_{10}H_{16}O$	Pulegone	223.8	Nonazeotrope		*232*
11728	$C_{10}H_{17}Cl$	Bornyl chloride	207.5	Nonazeotrope		*234*
11729	$C_{10}H_{18}O$.	Borneol	215.0	213.5	25	*234*
11730	$C_{10}H_{18}O$	Citronellal	208.0	Nonazeotrope		*234*
11731	$C_{10}H_{18}O$	Geraniol	229.6	220.7	81	*234*
17732	$C_{10}H_{18}O$	Linaloöl	198.6	Nonazeotrope		*234*
11733	$C_{10}H_{18}O$	*α*-Terpineol	218.85	217.1	38	*234*
11734	$C_{10}H_{18}O$	*β*-Terpineol	210.5	209.7	10	*234*
11735	$C_{10}H_{20}O$	Citronellol	224.4	219.8	62	*234*
11736	$C_{10}H_{20}O$	Menthol	216.3	214.65	34	*234*
11737	$C_{10}H_{20}O_2$	Methyl pelargonate	213.8	Nonazeotrope		*234*
11738	$C_{10}H_{22}O$	*n*-Decyl alcohol	232.8	221.0	85	*234*
11739	$C_{10}H_{22}S$	Isoamyl sulfide	214.8	Nonazeotrope		*255*

No.	B-Component Formula	B-Component Name	B.P., ° C.	Azeotropic Data B.P., ° C.	Azeotropic Data Wt. % A	Ref.
A =	**$C_7H_7NO_2$**	**o-Nitrotoluene (*continued*)**	**221.75**			
11740	$C_{11}H_{10}$	1-Methylnaphthalene	244.6	Nonazeotrope		*234*
11741	$C_{11}H_{10}$	2-Methylnaphthalene	241.15	Nonazeotrope		*234*
11742	$C_{11}H_{20}O$	Methyl α-terpineol ether	216.2	215.0	15?	*234*
11743	$C_{11}H_{22}O_3$	Isoamyl carbonate	232.2	Nonazeotrope		*234*
11744	$C_{12}H_{18}$	1,3,5-Triethylbenzene	215.5	Nonazeotrope		*234*
11745	$C_{12}H_{20}O_2$	Bornyl acetate	227.6	221.15	73	*234*
A =	**$C_7H_7NO_2$**	**p-Nitrotoluene**	**238.9**			
11746	C_7H_8O	Benzyl alcohol	202.25	Nonazeotrope		*234*
11747	$C_7H_{16}O_4$	2-[2-(2-Methoxyethoxy)ethoxy]-ethanol	245.25	231.2	61	*234*
11748	$C_8H_8O_2$	Anisaldehyde	249.5	Nonazeotrope		*218*
11749	$C_8H_8O_2$	α-Toluic acid	266.8	Nonazeotrope		*234*
11750	$C_8H_{10}O$	3,4-Xylenol	226.8	Nonazeotrope		*234*
11751	$C_8H_{10}O$	2-Phenylethanol	219.4	Nonazeotrope		*234*
11752	$C_8H_{11}NO$	o-Phenetidine	232.5	Nonazeotrope		*231*
11753	$C_8H_{11}NO$	p-Phenetidine	249.9	Nonazeotrope		*231*
11754	$C_8H_{16}O_2$	Caprylic acid	238.5	<235.0	<38	*234*
11755	C_9H_7N	Quinoline	237.3	237.2	8	*233*
11756	C_9H_8O	Cinnamyl aldehyde	253.5	Nonazeotrope		*234*
11757	$C_9H_{10}O_3$	Ethyl salicylate	233.8	Nonazeotrope		*234*
11758	$C_9H_{12}O$	3-Phenylpropanol	235.6	234.0	38	*234*
11759	$C_9H_{12}O_2$	2-Benzyloxyethanol	265.2	Nonazeotrope		*234*
11760	$C_{10}H_7Cl$	1-Chloronaphthalene	262.7	Nonazeotrope		*234*
11761	$C_{10}H_{10}O_2$	Isosafrole	252.1	Nonazeotrope		*234*
11762	$C_{10}H_{10}O_2$	Safrole	235.9	234.5	18	*234*
11763	$C_{10}H_{12}O_2$	Eugenol	254.8	Nonazeotrope		*234*
11764	$C_{10}H_{12}O_2$	Ethyl α-toluate	228.75	Nonazeotrope		*234*
11765	$C_{10}H_{12}O_2$	Propyl benzoate	230.85	Nonazeotrope		*234*
11766	$C_{10}H_{14}O$	Carvacrol	237.85	237.7	>25	*234*
11767	$C_{10}H_{14}O$	Carvone	231.0	Nonazeotrope		*232*
11768	$C_{10}H_{14}O$	Thymol	232.9	Nonazeotrope		*234*
11769	$C_{10}H_{18}O$	Borneol	215.0	Nonazeotrope		*234*
11770	$C_{10}H_{18}O$	Geraniol	229.6	228.8	25	*234*
11771	$C_{10}H_{18}O$	α-Terpineol	217.8	~217.6	5	*216*
			218.0	Nonazeotrope		*225*
11772	$C_{10}H_{18}O$	β-Terpineol	210.5	Nonazeotrope		*234*
11773	$C_{10}H_{20}O$	Menthol	216.3	Nonazeotrope		*234*
			216.4	216.3	3	*216*
11774	$C_{10}H_{22}O$	n-Decyl alcohol	232.8	231.5	33	*234*
11775	$C_{11}H_{10}$	1-Methylnaphthalene	244.6	Nonazeotrope		*234*
11776	$C_{11}H_{10}$	2-Methylnaphthalene	241.15	Nonazeotrope		*207*
11777	$C_{11}H_{14}O_2$	Butyl benzoate	249.5	Nonazeotrope		*234*
11778	$C_{11}H_{14}O_2$	Ethyl β-phenylpropionate	248.1	Nonazeotrope		*234*
11779	$C_{11}H_{14}O_2$	Isobutyl benzoate	241.9	238.6	70	*234*
11780	$C_{11}H_{17}N$	Isoamylaniline	256.0	Nonazeotrope		*231*
11781	$C_{12}H_{10}$	Biphenyl	256.1	Nonazeotrope		*234*
11782	$C_{12}H_{10}O$	Phenyl ether	259.0	Nonazeotrope		*234*
11783	$C_{12}H_{16}O_3$	Isoamyl salicylate	277.5	Nonazeotrope		*234*
11784	$C_{12}H_{20}O_2$	Bornyl acetate	227.6	227.45	10	*234*
A =	**C_7H_8**	**Toluene**	**110.7**			
11785	C_7H_9N	2,6-Lutidine	144	Nonazeotrope		*242*
11786	C_7H_{14}	Ethylcyclopentane	103.5	103.0	7	*203**, *270*
11787	C_7H_{14}	Methylcyclohexane	100.85	Nonazeotrope, V-l.		*311*
11788	$C_7H_{14}O$	2-Methylcyclohexanol	168.5	Nonazeotrope		*255*
11789	$C_7H_{14}O_2$	Isopropyl isobutyrate	120.8	Nonazeotrope		*255*
11790	C_7H_{16}	n-Heptane	98.4	Nonazeotrope, V-l.		*44*, *379**
11791	$C_7H_{16}O$	Heptyl alcohol	176.15	Nonazeotrope		*255*
11792	C_8H_{10}	Ethylbenzene	136.18	Nonazeotrope (b.p. curve)		*432*
11793	C_8H_{16}	1,3-Dimethylcyclohexane	120.7	Nonazeotrope		*255*
11794	C_8H_{16}	cis-1,3-Dimethylcyclohexane	120.1	110.6	96	*270*
11795	C_8H_{16}	1,1,3-Trimethylcyclopentane	104.9	103.8	16	*270*
11796	C_8H_{16}	cis-trans-cis-1,2,3-Trimethylcyclopentane	110.4	108.0	39	*270*
11797	C_8H_{16}	cis-trans-cis-1,2,4-Trimethylcyclopentane	109.3	107.0	39	*270*

No.	Formula	B-Component Name	B.P., ° C.	Azeotropic Data B.P., ° C.	Wt. % A	Ref.
A =	**C_7H_8**	**Toluene** (*continued*)	**110.7**			
11798	C_8H_{16}	2,3,4-Trimethyl-2-pentene	116	110	82	270
11799	C_8H_{18}	2,5-Dimethylhexane	109.4	107.0	35	270
11800	C_8H_{18}	2-Methylheptane	117.6	110.3	82	270
11801	C_8H_{18}	*n*-Octane	125.4	Nonazeotrope, V-l.		44
11802	C_8H_{18}	2,3,4-Trimethylpentane	113.5	109.5	60	270
11803	$C_8H_{18}O$	Isobutyl ether	122	Nonazeotrope		217
11804	$C_8H_{18}O$	*sec*-Octyl alcohol	180.4	Nonazeotrope		255
A =	**C_7H_8O**	**Anisole**	**153.85**			
11805	$C_7H_{14}O$	4-Heptanone	143.3	Nonazeotrope		225
11806	$C_7H_{14}O$	2-Methylcyclohexanol	168.5	Nonazeotrope		256
11807	$C_7H_{14}O_2$	Butyl propionate	146.5	Nonazeotrope		237
11808	$C_7H_{14}O_2$	Isoamyl acetate	142.1	Nonazeotrope		237
11809	$C_7H_{14}O_2$	Propyl butyrate	143.7	Nonazeotrope		237
11810	$C_7H_{14}O_3$	1,3-Butanediol methyl ether acetate	171.75	Nonazeotrope		207
11811	$C_7H_{16}O$	Heptyl alcohol	176.15	Nonazeotrope		236
11812	$C_7H_{16}O_3$	Ethyl orthoformate	145.75	Nonazeotrope		229
11813	C_8H_8	Styrene	145.8	Nonazeotrope		253
11814	C_8H_{10}	*m*-Xylene	139.2	Nonazeotrope		207
11815	C_8H_{10}	*o*-Xylene	143.6	Nonazeotrope		228
11816	$C_8H_{16}O$	2-Octanone	172.85	Nonazeotrope		232
11817	$C_8H_{16}O_2$	Butyl butyrate	166.4	Nonazeotrope		237
11818	$C_8H_{16}O_2$	Isoamyl propionate	160.4	Nonazeotrope		237
11819	$C_8H_{16}O_2$	Isobutyl butyrate	156.8	Nonazeotrope		237
			157	151	67	243
11820	$C_8H_{16}O_2$	Isobutyl isobutyrate	148.0	Nonazeotrope		237
11821	$C_8H_{16}O_2$	Propyl isovalerate	155.7	<153.6	....	237
11822	$C_8H_{18}O$	Butyl ether	142.4	Nonazeotrope		229
11823	$C_8H_{19}N$	Diisobutylamine	138.5	Nonazeotrope		231
11824	$C_8H_{20}SiO_4$	Ethyl silicate	168.8	Nonazeotrope		237
11825	C_9H_{12}	Cumene	152.8	<152.0	>30	238
11826	C_9H_{12}	Mesitylene	164.6	Nonazeotrope		238
11827	$C_9H_{18}O_2$	Isobutyl isovalerate	171.2	Nonazeotrope		237
11828	$C_{10}H_{16}$	Camphene	159.5	151.85	63	252
11829	$C_{10}H_{16}$	Nopinene	163.8	152.3	74	238
11830	$C_{10}H_{16}$	α-Pinene	155.8	150.45	56	243
11831	$C_{10}H_{16}$	α-Terpinene	173.4	Nonazeotrope		238
11832	$C_{10}H_{22}$	2,7-Dimethyloctane	160.1	153.2	66	238
11833	$C_{10}H_{22}$	2,7-Dimethyloctane	160.25	Nonazeotrope		243
A =	**C_7H_8O**	**Benzyl Alcohol**	**205.2**			
11834	C_7H_8O	*m*-Cresol	202.2	207.1	61	222
11835	C_7H_8O	*o*-Cresol	191.1	Nonazeotrope		215
			190.8	206	....	243
11836	C_7H_8O	*p*-Cresol	201.7	206.8	62	222
11837	$C_7H_8O_2$	Guaiacol	205.05	204.25	43	236
11838	C_7H_9N	Methylaniline	196.25	195.8	30	231
			196.1	Nonazeotrope		225
11839	C_7H_9N	*m*-Toluidine	203.1	Nonazeotrope		231
			203.2	203.1	47	228
11840	C_7H_9N	*o*-Toluidine	200.35	Nonazeotrope		231
11841	C_7H_9N	*p*-Toluidine	200.55	Nonazeotrope		231
11842	C_7H_9NO	*o*-Anisidine	219.0	Nonazeotrope		231
11843	$C_7H_{13}ClO_2$	Isoamyl chloroacetate	195.0	Nonazeotrope		255
11844	C_8H_8O	Acetophenone	202.0	Nonazeotrope		251
			202	~201	....	243
11845	$C_8H_8O_2$	Benzyl formate	~202.3	~202.0	....	215
11846	$C_8H_8O_2$	Methyl benzoate	199.2	Nonazeotrope		209
11847	$C_8H_8O_2$	Phenyl acetate	195.7	Nonazeotrope		215
11848	$C_8H_8O_3$	Methyl salicylate	205.2	Nonazeotrope		225
11849	$C_8H_{10}O$	*p*-Ethylphenol	218.8	Nonazeotrope		255
11850	$C_8H_{10}O$	3,4-Xylenol	226.8	Nonazeotrope		255
11851	$C_8H_{10}O_2$	*m*-Dimethoxybenzene	214.7	Min. b.p. ?		256
11852	$C_8H_{10}O_2$	*o*-Ethoxyphenol	216.5	Nonazeotrope		255
11853	$C_8H_{10}O_2$	2-Phenoxyethanol	245.2	Nonazeotrope		255
11854	$C_8H_{10}O_2$	Veratrole	206.5	202.5	50	225

No.	B-Component Formula	Name	B.P., ° C.	Azeotropic Data B.P., ° C.	Wt. % A	Ref.
A =	C_7H_8O	**Benzyl Alcohol** (*continued*)	**205.2**			
11855	$C_8H_{11}N$	Dimethylaniline	194.05	193.9	6.5	*231*
11856	$C_8H_{11}N$	Ethylaniline	205.5	202.8	50	*231*
11857	$C_8H_{11}N$	2,4-Xylidine	214.0	Nonazeotrope		*231*
11858	$C_8H_{11}N$	3,4-Xylidine	225.5	Nonazeotrope		*231*
11859	$C_8H_{11}NO$	*o*-Phenetidine	232.5	Nonazeotrope		*231*
11860	$C_8H_{16}O_4$	2-(2-Ethoxyethoxy)ethyl acetate	218.5	Nonazeotrope		*255*
11861	C_9H_7N	Quinoline	237.3	Nonazeotrope		*233*
11862	$C_9H_{10}O$	Propiophenone	217.7	Nonazeotrope		*232*
11863	$C_9H_{10}O_2$	Benzyl acetate	214.9	Nonazeotrope		*209*
11864	$C_9H_{10}O_2$	Ethyl benzoate	213	Nonazeotrope		*243*
11865	$C_9H_{10}O_2$	Methyl α-toluate	215.3	Nonazeotrope		*255*
11866	C_9H_{12}	Mesitylene	164.6	Nonazeotrope		*220*
11867	$C_9H_{12}O$	Phenyl propyl ether	190.5	Nonazeotrope		*255*
11868	$C_9H_{13}N$	*N,N*-Dimethyl-*o*-toluidine	185.3	185.2	7	*231*
			185.3	Nonazeotrope		*225*
11869	$C_9H_{13}N$	*N,N*-Dimethyl-*p*-toluidine	210.2	202.8	58	*231*
11870	$C_9H_{18}O_3$	Isobutyl carbonate	190.3	Nonazeotrope		*255*
11871	$C_{10}H_8$	Naphthalene	218.05	204.1	60	*221*
11872	$C_{10}H_{10}O_2$	Safrole	235.9	Nonazeotrope		*236*
11873	$C_{10}H_{12}O$	Anethole	235.7	Nonazeotrope		*255*
11874	$C_{10}H_{14}$	Cymene	176.7	Nonazeotrope		*217*
11875	$C_{10}H_{14}O$	Thymol	232.9	Nonazeotrope		*255*
11876	$C_{10}H_{15}N$	Diethylaniline	217.05	204.2	72	*231*
11877	$C_{10}H_{16}$	Camphene	159.6	Nonazeotrope		*217*
11878	$C_{10}H_{16}$	*d*-Limonene	177.8	176.4	11	*221*
11879	$C_{10}H_{16}$	α-Pinene	155.8	Nonazeotrope		*243*
11880	$C_{10}H_{16}$	α-Terpinene	173.4	Nonazeotrope		*255*
11881	$C_{10}H_{16}$	Terpinene	180.5	179	13?	*243*
11882	$C_{10}H_{16}$	Terpinolene	184.6	182.5	15	*255*
11883	$C_{10}H_{16}$	Thymene	179.7	179.0	14	*210*
11884	$C_{10}H_{16}O$	Camphor	209.1	Nonazeotrope		*232*
			208.9	205.45?	....	*243*
11885	$C_{10}H_{18}O$	Borneol	215.0	205.07	85.8	*229*
11886	$C_{10}H_{18}O$	Citronellal	207.8	202.9	56	*209*
11887	$C_{10}H_{18}O$	Menthone	209.5	Nonazeotrope		*232*
			207	~204.8	....	*243*
11888	$C_{10}H_{18}O$	α-Terpineol	217.8	Nonazeotrope		*212*
11889	$C_{10}H_{20}O$	Menthol	216.4	Nonazeotrope		*225*
11890	$C_{10}H_{20}O_2$	Ethyl caprylate	208.35	<204.8	<82	*255*
11891	$C_{10}H_{20}O_2$	Isoamyl isovalerate	192.7	Nonazeotrope		*255*
11892	$C_{10}H_{22}S$	Isoamyl sulfide	214.8	Nonazeotrope		*246*
11893	$C_{11}H_{10}$	1-Methylnaphthalene	244.9	Nonazeotrope		*217*
11894	$C_{11}H_{10}$	2-Methylnaphthalene	241.15	Nonazeotrope		*255*
11895	$C_{11}H_{16}O$	Methyl thymyl ether	216.5	Nonazeotrope		*255*
11896	$C_{11}H_{20}O$	Isobornyl methyl ether	192.4	Nonazeotrope		*236*
11897	$C_{11}H_{20}O$	Isobornyl methyl ether	192.2	Min. b.p. ?		*256*
11898	$C_{11}H_{20}O$	Terpineol methyl ether	216.2	Nonazeotrope		*225*
11899	$C_{11}H_{24}O_2$	Diisoamyloxymethane	207.5	198.7	~50	*243*
11900	$C_{12}H_{18}$	1,3,5-Triethylbenzene	215.5	203.2	57	*217*
11901	$C_{12}H_{22}O$	Ethyl isobornyl ether	203.5	201	39	*236*
11902	$C_{12}H_{22}O$	Bornyl ethyl ether	204.9	<203.0	<50	*255*
A =	C_7H_8O	***m*-Cresol**	**202.2**			
11903	C_7H_8O	*o*-Cresol	191.1	Nonazeotrope		*328*
11904	C_7H_8O	*p*-Cresol	200.9	Nonazeotrope		*134*
11905	$C_7H_8O_2$	Guaiacol	205.05	Nonazeotrope		*222*
11906	C_7H_9N	Benzylamine	185.0	<207.2	<94	*231*
11907	C_7H_9N	Methylaniline	196.25	Nonazeotrope		*231*
11908	C_7H_9N	*m*-Toluidine	203.1	205.5	53	*231*
11909	C_7H_9N	*o*-Toluidine	200.35	203.65	61.5	*231*
11910	C_7H_9N	*p*-Toluidine	200.55	204.3	62	*231*
11911	$C_7H_{14}O_2$	Enanthic acid	222.0	Nonazeotrope		*255*
11912	$C_7H_{14}O_3$	Isobutyl lactate	182.15	Max. b.p.		*224*
11913	$C_7H_{16}O_3$	2-Ethoxyethyl 2-methoxyethyl ether	194.2	....	63.6, V-l.	*292*
11914	C_8H_8O	Acetophenone	202.0	208.45	47.2	*232*
11915	$C_8H_8O_2$	Benzyl formate	202.4	207.1	46	*222*

No.	Formula	B-Component Name	B.P., ° C.	Azeotropic Data B.P., ° C.	Wt. % A	Ref.
A =	C_7H_8O	***m*-Cresol (*continued*)**	**202.2**			
11916	$C_8H_8O_2$	Methyl benzoate	199.45	204.6	63	*222*
11917	$C_8H_8O_2$	Phenyl acetate	195.7	204.4	70	*222*
11918	$C_8H_{10}O$	Phenethyl alcohol	219.4	Nonazeotrope		*222*
11919	$C_8H_{10}O$	2,4-Xylenol	210.5	Nonazeotrope		*255*
11920	$C_8H_{10}O_2$	*m*-Dimethoxybenzene	214.7	Nonazeotrope		*224*
11921	$C_8H_{10}O_2$	Veratrole	206.5	Nonazeotrope		*222*
11922	$C_8H_{11}N$	Dimethylaniline	194.15	Nonazeotrope		*231*
11923	$C_8H_{11}N$	Ethylaniline	205.5	Nonazeotrope		*231*
11924	$C_8H_{12}O_4$	Ethyl fumarate	217.85	Nonazeotrope		*255*
11925	$C_8H_{12}O_4$	Ethyl maleate	223.3	Nonazeotrope		*255*
11926	$C_8H_{16}O_2$	2-Ethylcaproic acid	227	Nonazeotrope, V-l.		*292*
11927	$C_8H_{16}O_3$	Isoamyl lactate	202.4	207.6	50	*243*
11928	$C_8H_{18}O$	Octyl alcohol	195.15	203.3	62	*222*
11929	$C_8H_{18}O$	*sec*-Octyl alcohol	179.0	Nonazeotrope		*222*
11930	$C_8H_{18}O_3$	Bis(2-ethoxyethyl) ether	188.9	....	62, V-l.	*292*
11931	C_9H_8	Indene	182.6	Nonazeotrope		*222*
11932	$C_9H_{10}O$	*p*-Methylacetophenone	226.35	Nonazeotrope		*232*
11933	$C_9H_{10}O$	Propiophenone	217.7	218.6	17	*232*
11934	$C_9H_{10}O_2$	Benzyl acetate	215.0	Nonazeotrope		*255*
11935	$C_9H_{10}O_2$	Benzyl acetate	214.9	215.5	12	*222*
11936	$C_9H_{10}O_2$	Ethyl benzoate	212.6	212.75	~9	*222*
11937	$C_9H_{12}O$	Phenyl propyl ether	190.5	Nonazeotrope		*255*
11938	$C_9H_{13}N$	*N,N*-Dimethyl-*o*-toluidine	185.35	Nonazeotrope		*231*
11939	$C_9H_{13}N$	*N,N*-Dimethyl-*p*-toluidine	210.2	Nonazeotrope		*231*
11940	$C_9H_{14}O$	Phorone	197.8	206.5	55	*232*
11941	$C_9H_{18}O_2$	Isoamyl butyrate	181.05	Nonazeotrope		*255*
11942	$C_9H_{18}O_3$	Isobutyl carbonate	190.3	Nonazeotrope		*224*
11943	$C_{10}H_7Cl$	1-Chloronaphthalene	262.7	Nonazeotrope		*224*
11944	$C_{10}H_8$	Naphthalene	218.05	202.08	2.8?	*221*
11945	$C_{10}H_{12}O$	Estragole	215.6	Nonazeotrope		*222*
11946	$C_{10}H_{12}O_2$	Ethyl α-toluate	228.75	Nonazeotrope		*255*
11947	$C_{10}H_{14}$	Butylbenzene	183.1	Nonazeotrope		*255*
11948	$C_{10}H_{14}$	Cymene	176.7	Nonazeotrope		*224*
11949	$C_{10}H_{14}O$	Carvone	231.0	Nonazeotrope		*232*
11950	$C_{10}H_{15}N$	Diethylaniline	217.05	Nonazeotrope		*231*
11951	$C_{10}H_{16}$	*d*-Limonene	177.9	Nonazeotrope		*224*
11952	$C_{10}H_{16}$	Nopinene	163.8	Nonazeotrope		*255*
11953	$C_{10}H_{16}$	α-Terpinene	173.4	Nonazeotrope		*255*
11954	$C_{10}H_{16}$	Thymene	179.7	Nonazeotrope		*222*
11955	$C_{10}H_{16}O$	Camphor	209.1	213.35	36.5	*232*
11956	$C_{10}H_{18}O$	Borneol	213.4	Nonazeotrope		*222*
11957	$C_{10}H_{18}O$	Citronellal	207.8	211.0	30	*225*
11958	$C_{10}H_{18}O$	Geraniol	229.6	Nonazeotrope		*255*
11959	$C_{10}H_{18}O$	Linaloöl	198.6	Reacts		*222*
11960	$C_{10}H_{20}O$	Menthol	216.4	Nonazeotrope		*224*
11961	$C_{10}H_{20}O_2$	Isoamyl isovalerate	192.7	Nonazeotrope		*222*
11962	$C_{10}H_{20}O_2$	Methyl pelargonate	213.8	Nonazeotrope		*255*
11963	$C_{10}H_{22}O$	Isoamyl ether	173.35	Nonazeotrope		*244*
11964	$C_{11}H_{10}$	2-Methylnaphthalene	241.1	Nonazeotrope, V-l.		*292*
11965	$C_{11}H_{20}O$	α-Terpineol methyl ether	216.2	Nonazeotrope		*222*
11966	$C_{12}H_{12}$	1-Ethylnaphthalene	254.2	Nonazeotrope, V-l.		*292*
11967	$C_{12}H_{18}$	1,3,5-Triethylbenzene	215.5	Nonazeotrope		*222*
11968	$C_{12}H_{20}O_2$	Bornyl acetate	227.7	Nonazeotrope		*224*
11969	$C_{13}H_{14}$	2-Isopropylnaphthalene	266.5	Nonazeotrope, V-l.		*292*
11970	$C_{14}H_{30}O$	Tetradecanol	260.0	Nonazeotrope, V-l.		*292*
11971	$C_{15}H_{18}$	2-Amylnaphthalene	292.3	Nonazeotrope, V-l.		*292*
11972	$C_{16}H_{20}$	Diisopropylnaphthalene	305	Nonazeotrope, V-l.		*292*
A =	C_7H_8O	***o*-Cresol**	**191.1**			
11973	C_7H_8O	*p*-Cresol	201.7	Nonazeotrope		*225*
11974	C_7H_9N	Benzylamine	185.0	201.45	67	*231*
11975	C_7H_9N	Methylaniline	196.25	Nonazeotrope		*231*
			196.1	196.7	~10	*243*
11976	C_7H_9N	*m*-Toluidine	203.1	Nonazeotrope		*231*
11977	C_7H_9N	*o*-Toluidine	200.35	Nonazeotrope		*231*
11978	C_7H_9N	*p*-Toluidine	200.55	Nonazeotrope		*231*

No.	B-Component Formula	Name	B.P., ° C.	Azeotropic Data B.P., ° C.	Wt. % A	Ref.
A =	C_7H_8O	*o*-Cresol (*continued*)	191.1			
11979	C_7H_9NO	*o*-Anisidine	219.0	Nonazeotrope		255
11980	$C_7H_{12}O_4$	Ethyl malonate	198.9	Reacts		243
11981	$C_7H_{14}O$	2-Methylcyclohexanol	168.5	Nonazeotrope		255
11982	$C_7H_{14}O_3$	1,3-Butanediol methyl ether acetate	171.75	194.1	68	236
11983	$C_7H_{14}O_3$	Isobutyl lactate	182.15	193.3	69	222
11984	$C_7H_{16}O$	Heptyl alcohol	176.16	Nonazeotrope		255
11985	C_8H_8	Styrene	145.8	Nonazeotrope		255
11986	C_8H_8O	Acetophenone	202.0	203.75	26	232
11987	$C_8H_8O_2$	Benzyl formate	202.3	~203.0	~15	254
11988	$C_8H_8O_2$	Methyl benzoate	199.45	200.3	21	222
11989	$C_8H_8O_2$	Phenyl acetate	195.7	198.5	36	222
11990	C_8H_{10}	*o*-Xylene	144.3	Nonazeotrope		255
11991	$C_8H_{10}O$	*p*-Methylanisole	177.05	Nonazeotrope		222
11992	$C_8H_{10}O$	Phenetole	170.45	Nonazeotrope		236
11993	$C_8H_{10}O_2$	Veratrole	206.5	Nonazeotrope		224
11994	$C_8H_{11}N$	Dimethylaniline	194.15	Nonazeotrope		231
			194.05	195.6	<30	243
11995	$C_8H_{11}N$	Ethylaniline	205.5	Nonazeotrope		231
11996	$C_8H_{11}N$	2,4-Xylidine	214.0	Nonazeotrope		231
11997	$C_8H_{12}O_4$	Ethyl fumarate	217.85	Nonazeotrope		255
11998	$C_8H_{12}O_4$	Ethyl maleate	223.3	Nonazeotrope		255
11999	$C_8H_{14}O$	Methylheptenone	173.2	191.9	85	232
12000	$C_8H_{14}O_4$	Ethyl succinate	216.5	Nonazeotrope		243
12001	$C_8H_{16}O$	2-Octanone	172.85	192.05	76	207
12002	$C_8H_{16}O_3$	Isoamyl lactate	202.4	204.2	18	222
12003	$C_8H_{18}O$	Octyl alcohol	195.15	196.9	38	254
12004	$C_8H_{18}O$	*sec*-Octyl alcohol	179.0	191.4	~92	215
12005	$C_8H_{18}S$	Butyl sulfide	185.0	183.8	25	246
12006	$C_8H_{18}S$	Isobutyl sulfide	172.0	Nonazeotrope		246
12007	$C_8H_{20}SiO_4$	Ethyl silicate	168.8	Nonazeotrope		255
12008	C_9H_8	Indene	183.0	182.9	9	221
12009	$C_9H_{10}O$	Propiophenone	217.7	Nonazeotrope		232
12010	$C_9H_{10}O_2$	Benzyl acetate	215.0	Nonazeotrope		255
12011	$C_9H_{10}O_2$	Ethyl benzoate	212.9	Nonazeotrope		243
12012	C_9H_{12}	Mesitylene	164.0	Nonazeotrope		243
12013	C_9H_{12}	Cumene	152.8	Nonazeotrope		255
12014	C_9H_{12}	Propylbenzene	159.3	Nonazeotrope		255
12015	C_9H_{12}	Pseudocumene	168.2	Nonazeotrope		255
12016	$C_9H_{12}O$	Benzyl ethyl ether	185.0	Nonazeotrope		255
12017	$C_9H_{13}N$	*N,N*-Dimethyl-*o*-toluidine	185.35	185.3	5	231
12018	$C_9H_{13}N$	*N,N*-Dimethyl-*p*-toluidine	210.2	Nonazeotrope		255
12019	$C_9H_{14}O$	Phorone	197.8	201.3	35	232
12020	$C_9H_{18}O$	2,6-Dimethyl-4-heptanone	168.0	Nonazeotrope		232
12021	$C_9H_{18}O_2$	Butyl isovalerate	177.6	Nonazeotrope		255
12022	$C_9H_{18}O_2$	Ethyl enanthate	188.7	193.7	60	242
12023	$C_9H_{18}O_2$	Isoamyl butyrate	178.5	191.6	~83	253
12024	$C_9H_{18}O_2$	Isobutyl isovalerate	168.7	Nonazeotrope		243
12025	$C_9H_{18}O_2$	Methyl caprylate	192.9	195.8	33	242
12026	$C_9H_{18}O_3$	Isobutyl carbonate	190.3	194.5	49	222
12027	$C_{10}H_8$	Naphthalene	218.05	Nonazeotrope		218
12028	$C_{10}H_{14}$	Cymene	175.3	~175	....	243
12029	$C_{10}H_{15}N$	Diethylaniline	217.05	Nonazeotrope		231
12030	$C_{10}H_{16}$	Camphene	159.6	Nonazeotrope		222
12031	$C_{10}H_{16}$	*d*-Limonene	177.8	175.35	25	243
12032	$C_{10}H_{16}$	Nopinene	163.8	Azeotrope doubtful (reacts)		243
12033	$C_{10}H_{16}$	α-Phellandrene	171.5	171?	....	243
12034	$C_{10}H_{16}$	α-Pinene	155.8	Nonazeotrope		243
12035	$C_{10}H_{16}$	α-Terpinene	173.4	172.0	16	242
12036	$C_{10}H_{16}$	Terpinene	181.5	177.8	28	222
12037	$C_{10}H_{16}$	Terpinolene	184.6	179.5	34	242
12038	$C_{10}H_{16}$	Thymene	179.7	176.6	73	253
12039	$C_{10}H_{16}O$	Camphor	209.1	209.85	15	232
12040	$C_{10}H_{16}O$	Fenchone	193.6	199.6	43	232
12041	$C_{10}H_{17}Cl$	Bornyl chloride	~210	Nonazeotrope		243

No.	Formula	B-Component Name	B.P., ° C.	Azeotropic Data B.P., ° C.	Wt. % A	Ref.
A =	**C_7H_8O**	**o-Cresol** (*continued*)	**191.1**			
12042	$C_{10}H_{18}O$	Borneol	211.8	Nonazeotrope		*243*
12043	$C_{10}H_{18}O$	Cineole	176.35	Nonazeotrope		*236*
12044	$C_{10}H_{18}O$	Citronellal	208.0	Nonazeotrope		*255*
12045	$C_{10}H_{18}O$	Linaloöl	198.6	199.0	~20	*215*
			198.6	Nonazeotrope		*218*
12046	$C_{10}H_{18}O$	α-Terpineol	218.85	Nonazeotrope		*255*
12047	$C_{10}H_{18}O$	β-Terpineol	210.5	Nonazeotrope		*255*
12048	$C_{10}H_{20}O$	Menthol	216.4	Nonazeotrope		*222*
12049	$C_{10}H_{20}O_2$	Ethyl caprylate	208.35	Nonazeotrope		*255*
12050	$C_{10}H_{20}O_2$	Isoamyl isovalerate	192.7	195.45	33	*250*
12051	$C_{10}H_{22}$	2,7-Dimethyloctane	160.1	Nonazeotrope		*255*
12052	$C_{10}H_{22}O$	Amyl ether	187.5	186.2	....	*236*
12053	$C_{10}H_{22}O$	Isoamyl ether	173.4	Nonazeotrope		*222, 236*
12054	$C_{10}H_{22}S$	Isoamyl sulfide	214.8	Nonazeotrope		*246*
12055	$C_{11}H_{20}O$	Isobornyl methyl ether	192.4	189.7	68	*242*
12056	$C_{12}H_{18}$	1,3,5-Triethylbenzene	216	Nonazeotrope		*222*
12057	$C_{12}H_{22}O$	Ethyl isobornyl ether	204.9	Nonazeotrope		*255*
A =	**C_7H_8O**	***p*-Cresol**	**201.6**			
12058	$C_7H_8O_2$	Guaiacol	205.1	Nonazeotrope		*208*
12059	C_7H_9N	Benzylamine	185.0	>206.5	<95	*231*
12060	C_7H_9N	Methylaniline	196.25	Nonazeotrope		*231*
			196.1	~202.2	~93	*243*
12061	C_7H_9N	*m*-Toluidine	203.1	204.9	47	*231*
12062	C_7H_9N	*o*-Toluidine	200.35	203.5	57	*231*
12063	C_7H_9N	*p*-Toluidine	200.55	204.05	57	*231*
12064	C_7H_9NO	*o*-Anisidine	219.0	Nonazeotrope		*255*
12065	$C_7H_{12}O_4$	Ethyl malonate	198.9	Reacts		*243*
12066	$C_7H_{14}O$	2-Methylcyclohexanol	168.5	Nonazeotrope		*255*
12067	$C_7H_{14}O_2$	Enanthic acid	222.0	Nonazeotrope		*255*
12068	$C_7H_{14}O_3$	1,3-Butanediol methyl ether acetate	171.75	203.3	82	*207*
12069	$C_7H_{14}O_3$	Isobutyl lactate	182.15	Nonazeotrope		*222*
12070	$C_7H_{16}O_3$	2-Ethoxyethyl 2-methoxyethyl ether	194.2	64.7	V-l.	*292*
12071	C_8H_8O	Acetophenone	202.0	208.4	46.5	*232*
12072	$C_8H_8O_2$	Benzyl formate	202.4	207.0	42	*222*
12073	$C_8H_8O_2$	Methyl benzoate	199.4	204.35	40	*207*
12074	$C_8H_8O_2$	Phenyl acetate	195.7	204.3	68	*253*
12075	$C_8H_{10}O$	Phenethyl alcohol	219.4	Nonazeotrope		*222*
12076	$C_8H_{10}O_2$	*m*-Dimethoxybenzene	214.7	Nonazeotrope		*218*
12077	$C_8H_{10}O_2$	*o*-Ethoxyphenol	216.5	Nonazeotrope		*222*
12078	$C_8H_{10}O_2$	Veratrole	206.5	Nonazeotrope		*222*
12079	$C_8H_{11}N$	Dimethylaniline	194.15	Nonazeotrope		*231*
12080	$C_8H_{11}N$	2,4-Xylidine	214.0	Nonazeotrope		*231*
12081	$C_8H_{11}N$	Ethylaniline	205.5	Nonazeotrope		*231*
			206.05	207.2	<20	*242*
12082	$C_8H_{12}O_4$	Ethyl fumarate	217.85	Nonazeotrope		*206*
12083	$C_8H_{12}O_4$	Ethyl maleate	223.3	Nonazeotrope		*206*
12084	$C_8H_{14}O_4$	Ethyl succinate	216.5	Reacts		*243*
12085	$C_8H_{16}O_2$	2-Ethylcaproic acid	227	Nonazeotrope, V-l.		*292*
12086	$C_8H_{16}O_3$	Isoamyl lactate	202.4	207.25	48	*243*
12087	$C_8H_{18}O$	Octyl alcohol	195.2	202.25	70	*244*
12088	$C_8H_{18}O$	*sec*-Octyl alcohol	178.5	Nonazeotrope		*243*
12089	$C_8H_{18}O_3$	Bis(2-ethoxyethyl) ether	188.9	....	63, V-l.	*292*
12090	$C_8H_{18}S$	Butyl sulfide	185.0	Nonazeotrope		*246*
12091	C_9H_8	Indene	182.6	Nonazeotrope		*222*
12092	$C_9H_{10}O$	*p*-Methylacetophenone	226.35	Nonazeotrope		*232*
12093	$C_9H_{10}O$	Propiophenone	217.7	218.5	16.2	*232*
12094	$C_9H_{10}O_2$	Benzyl acetate	214.9	~215.2	10	*222*
			215.6	Nonazeotrope		*243*
12095	$C_9H_{10}O_2$	Ethyl benzoate	212.6	Nonazeotrope		*222*
12096	$C_9H_{12}O$	Phenyl propyl ether	190.5	Nonazeotrope		*255*
12097	$C_9H_{13}N$	*N,N*-Dimethyl-*o*-toluidine	185.35	Nonazeotrope		*231*
12098	$C_9H_{13}N$	*N,N*-Dimethyl-*p*-toluidine	210.2	Nonazeotrope		*231*
12099	$C_9H_{14}O$	Phorone	197.8	206.0	55	*232*
12100	$C_9H_{18}O_2$	Butyl isovalerate	177.6	Nonazeotrope		*255*

No.	Formula	B-Component Name	B.P., ° C.	Azeotropic Data B.P., ° C.	Wt. % A	Ref.
A =	C_7H_8O	*p*-Cresol (*continued*)	201.6			
12101	$C_9H_{18}O_2$	Ethyl enanthate	188.7	Nonazeotrope		255
12102	$C_9H_{18}O_2$	Isoamyl butyrate	178.5	Nonazeotrope		222
12103	$C_9H_{18}O_2$	Methyl caprylate	192.9	Nonazeotrope		255
12104	$C_9H_{18}O_3$	Isobutyl carbonate	190.3	203.2	~80	243
12105	$C_{10}H_8$	Naphthalene	218.05	Nonazeotrope		222
12106	$C_{10}H_{12}O_2$	Ethyl α-toluate	228.75	Nonazeotrope		255
12107	$C_{10}H_{12}O_2$	Propyl benzoate	230.85	Nonazeotrope		255
12108	$C_{10}H_{14}$	Butylbenzene	183.1	Nonazeotrope		255
12109	$C_{10}H_{14}$	Cymene	176.7	Nonazeotrope		222
12110	$C_{10}H_{14}O$	Carvone	231.0	Nonazeotrope		232
12111	$C_{10}H_{15}N$	Diethylaniline	217.05	Nonazeotrope		231
12112	$C_{10}H_{16}$	*d*-Limonene	177.8	177.6	4	222
12113	$C_{10}H_{16}$	Nopinene	163.8	Nonazeotrope		255
12114	$C_{10}H_{16}$	α-Pinene	155.8	Nonazeotrope		255
12115	$C_{10}H_{16}$	α-Terpinene	173.4	Nonazeotrope		255
12116	$C_{10}H_{16}$	γ-Terpinene	183	181.8	13	255
12117	$C_{10}H_{16}$	Terpinene	180.5	~179	....	243
12118	$C_{10}H_{16}$	Terpinolene	184.6	183	16	255
12119	$C_{10}H_{16}$	Thymene	179.7	Nonazeotrope		224
12120	$C_{10}H_{16}O$	Camphor	209.1	213.5	30.5	232
12121	$C_{10}H_{16}O$	Fenchone	193.6	205.5	72	232
12122	$C_{10}H_{16}O$	Pulegone	223.8	224.2	97	232
12123	$C_{10}H_{17}Cl$	Bornyl chloride	~210	200.5	70	243
12124	$C_{10}H_{18}O$	Borneol	213.4	213.6	~10	215
12125	$C_{10}H_{18}O$	Cineole	176.35	Nonazeotrope		236
12126	$C_{10}H_{18}O$	Citronellal	207.8	210.5	....	225
12127	$C_{10}H_{18}O$	Geraniol	229.5	Nonazeotrope		255
12128	$C_{10}H_{18}O$	Linaloöl	198.6	204	~55	215
12129	$C_{10}H_{18}O$	Menthone	~206	211	~38	243
12130	$C_{10}H_{18}O$	α-Terpineol	218.0	Nonazeotrope		222
12131	$C_{10}H_{18}O$	β-Terpineol	210.5	Nonazeotrope		255
12132	$C_{10}H_{20}O$	Citronellol	224.4	Nonazeotrope		255
12133	$C_{10}H_{20}O$	Menthol	216.4	Nonazeotrope		215
			212	212	....	243
12134	$C_{10}H_{20}O_2$	Ethyl caprylate	208.35	209.5	25	255
12135	$C_{10}H_{20}O_2$	Isoamyl isovalerate	~193.5	~203.5	~74	253
			192.7	Nonazeotrope		222
12136	$C_{10}H_{22}O$	Amyl ether	187.5	Nonazeotrope		236
12137	$C_{10}H_{22}O$	Isoamyl ether	173.35	Nonazeotrope		244
12138	$C_{11}H_{10}$	2-Methylnaphthalene	241.1	Nonazeotrope, V-l.		207*, 292
12139	$C_{11}H_{20}O$	Isobornyl methyl ether	192.4	Nonazeotrope		255
12140	$C_{11}H_{22}O_3$	Isoamyl carbonate	232.2	Nonazeotrope		255
12141	$C_{12}H_{12}$	1-Ethylnaphthalene	254.2	Nonazeotrope, V-l.		292
12142	$C_{12}H_{18}$	1,3,5-Triethylbenzene	216	201.5	~96	243
12143	$C_{12}H_{20}O_2$	Bornyl acetate	227.7	Nonazeotrope		224
12144	$C_{13}H_{14}$	2-Isopropylnaphthalene	266.5	Nonazeotrope, V-l.		292
12145	$C_{14}H_{30}O$	Tetradecanol	260.0	Nonazeotrope, V-l.		292
12146	$C_{15}H_{18}$	2-Amylnaphthalene	292.3	Nonazeotrope, V-l.		292
12147	$C_{16}H_{20}$	Diisopropylnaphthalene	305	Nonazeotrope, V-l.		292
A =	$C_7H_8O_2$	Guaiacol	205.05			
12148	C_7H_9N	Methylaniline	196.25	Nonazeotrope		231
12149	C_7H_9N	*m*-Toluidine	203.1	Nonazeotrope		231
12150	C_7H_9N	*o*-Toluidine	200.35	Nonazeotrope		231
12151	C_7H_9N	*p*-Toluidine	200.55	Nonazeotrope		231
12152	$C_7H_{12}O_4$	Ethyl malonate	198.9	Nonazeotrope		243
12153	C_8H_8O	Acetophenone	202.0	205.25	67.5	232
12154	$C_8H_8O_2$	Benzyl formate	202.3	206.2	~90	254
12155	$C_8H_8O_2$	Methyl benzoate	199.45	Nonazeotrope		236
12156	$C_8H_8O_2$	Phenyl acetate	195.5	Nonazeotrope		243
12157	$C_8H_8O_3$	Methyl salicylate	222.95	Nonazeotrope		255
12158	$C_8H_{10}O$	Phenethyl alcohol	219.4	Nonazeotrope		215
12159	$C_8H_{10}O$	2,4-Xylenol	210.5	Nonazeotrope		255
12160	$C_8H_{10}O_2$	*m*-Dimethoxybenzene	214.7	Nonazeotrope		215
12161	$C_8H_{11}N$	Dimethylaniline	194.15	Nonazeotrope		231
12162	$C_8H_{11}N$	Ethylaniline	205.5	204.4	55	231

	B-Component			Azeotropic Data		
No.	Formula	Name	B.P., ° C.	B.P., ° C.	Wt. % A	Ref.
A =	$C_7H_8O_2$	**Guaiacol** (*continued*)	**205.05**			
12163	$C_8H_{11}N$	2,4-Xylidine	214.0	Nonazeotrope		*231*
12164	$C_8H_{16}O_3$	Isoamyl lactate	202.4	Nonazeotrope		*243*
12165	$C_8H_{18}O$	Octyl alcohol	195.2	Nonazeotrope		*255*
12166	$C_8H_{18}S$	Butyl sulfide	185.0	Nonazeotrope		*246*
12167	$C_9H_{10}O$	Propiophenone	217.7	Nonazeotrope		*255*
12168	$C_9H_{10}O_2$	Benzyl acetate	215.0	Nonazeotrope		*225*
12169	$C_9H_{10}O_2$	Ethyl benzoate	212.6	Nonazeotrope		*236*
12170	$C_9H_{13}N$	*N,N*-Dimethyl-*o*-toluidine	185.35	Nonazeotrope		*231*
12171	$C_9H_{14}O$	Phorone	197.8	Nonazeotrope		*255*
12172	$C_{10}H_8$	Naphthalene	218.05	Nonazeotrope		*215*
12173	$C_{10}H_{12}O$	Estragole	215.6	Nonazeotrope		*215*
12174	$C_{10}H_{15}N$	Diethylaniline	217.05	Nonazeotrope		*231*
12175	$C_{10}H_{16}O$	Camphor	209.1	Nonazeotrope		*232*
12176	$C_{10}H_{16}O$	Fenchone	193.6	Nonazeotrope		*255*
12177	$C_{10}H_{18}O$	Borneol	211.8	Nonazeotrope		*236*
12178	$C_{10}H_{18}O$	Citronellal	207.8	204.55	86.5	*236*
12179	$C_{10}H_{18}O$	Geraniol	229.6	Nonazeotrope		*255*
12180	$C_{10}H_{18}O$	Linaloöl	198.6	Nonazeotrope		*225*
12181	$C_{10}H_{18}O$	α-Terpineol	217.8	Nonazeotrope		*215*
12182	$C_{10}H_{20}O$	Menthol	216.4	Nonazeotrope		*215*
12183	$C_{10}H_{20}O_2$	Ethyl caprylate	208.35	208.9	15	*255*
12184	$C_{10}H_{20}O_2$	Methyl pelargonate	213.8	Nonazeotrope		*255*
12185	$C_{10}H_{22}S$	Isoamyl sulfide	214.8	Nonazeotrope		*246*
12186	$C_{12}H_{18}$	1,3,5-Triethylbenzene	215.5	Nonazeotrope		*215*
12187	$C_{13}H_{28}$	Tridecane	234.0	Nonazeotrope		*255*
A =	$C_7H_8O_2$	***m*-Methoxyphenol**	**243.8**			
12188	C_8H_7N	Indole	253.5	Nonazeotrope		*255*
12189	C_9H_7N	Quinoline	237.3	Nonazeotrope		*255*
12190	C_9H_8O	Cinnamaldehyde	253.7	Nonazeotrope		*255*
12191	$C_9H_{10}O_3$	Ethyl salicylate	233.8	Nonazeotrope		*255*
12192	$C_9H_{12}O$	3-Phenylpropanol	235.6	Nonazeotrope		*255*
12193	$C_{10}H_8$	Naphthalene	218.0	Nonazeotrope		*255*
12194	$C_{10}H_{10}O_2$	Isosafrole	252.1	Nonazeotrope		*215*
12195	$C_{10}H_{10}O_2$	Safrole	235.9	Nonazeotrope		*255*
12196	$C_{10}H_{14}O$	Carvacrol	237.85	Nonazeotrope		*255*
12197	$C_{10}H_{14}O$	Thymol	232.9	Nonazeotrope		*224*
12198	$C_{10}H_{14}O_2$	*m*-Diethoxybenzene	235.0	Nonazeotrope		*215*
12199	$C_{11}H_{10}$	1-Methylnaphthalene	245.1	243	....	*215*
12200	$C_{11}H_{10}$	2-Methylnaphthalene	241.15	240.2	25	*255*
12201	$C_{11}H_{14}O_2$	1-Allyl-3,4-dimethoxybenzene	255.2	Nonazeotrope		*215*
12202	$C_{11}H_{14}O_2$	Isobutyl benzoate	242.15	245.5	~60	*215*
12203	$C_{11}H_{17}N$	Isoamylaniline	256.0	Nonazeotrope		*231*
12204	$C_{12}H_{10}$	Biphenyl	256.1	Nonazeotrope		*255*
A =	C_7H_8S	**α-Toluenethiol**	**194.8**			
12205	$C_{10}H_{16}$	Terpinolene	185	Reacts		*243*
A =	C_7H_9N	**Benzylamine**	**185.0**			
12206	$C_8H_{10}O$	Benzyl methyl ether	167.8	Nonazeotrope		*231*
12207	$C_8H_{10}O$	*p*-Methylanisole	177.05	Nonazeotrope		*231*
12208	$C_8H_{10}O$	Phenetole	170.45	Nonazeotrope		*231*
12209	$C_9H_{12}O$	Benzyl ethyl ether	185.0	<181.5	....	*255*
12210	$C_{10}H_{18}O$	Cineole	176.35	175.6	16.5	*207*
12211	$C_{10}H_{22}O$	Amyl ether	187.5	<180.0	<67	*231*
12212	$C_{10}H_{22}O$	Isoamyl ether	173.2	170.4	23	*231*
12213	$C_{11}H_{20}O$	Isobornyl methyl ether	192.4	<184.2	....	*255*
A =	C_7H_9N	**2,6-Lutidine**	**144**			
12214	C_8H_8	Styrene	145	Min. b.p.		*99*
12215	C_8H_{10}	Ethylbenzene	136	Min. b.p.		*99*
12216	C_8H_{10}	Xylenes	140	Min. b.p.		*99*
12217	C_8H_{18}	2,3,4-Trimethylpentane	113.4	Nonazeotrope		*82*
A =	C_7H_9N	**Methylaniline**	**196.25**			
12218	C_7H_9N	*o*-Toluidine	200.3	Nonazeotrope		*229*
12219	$C_7H_{16}O$	*n*-Heptyl alcohol	176.75	Nonazeotrope		*231*

No.	Formula	B-Component Name	B.P., ° C.	Azeotropic Data B.P., ° C.	Wt. % A	Ref.
A =	C_7H_9N	**Methylaniline** (*continued*)	**196.25**			
12220	C_8H_8O	Acetophenone	202.25	Nonazeotrope		*225*
12221	$C_8H_{10}O$	*p*-Methylanisole	177.05	Nonazeotrope		*231*
12222	$C_8H_{10}O_2$	*o*-Ethoxyphenol	216.5	Nonazeotrope		*231*
12223	$C_8H_{11}N$	Dimethylaniline	194.15	Nonazeotrope		*229*
12224	$C_8H_{18}O$	*n*-Octyl alcohol	195.2	193.0	45	*231*
12225	$C_8H_{18}O$	*sec*-Octyl alcohol	180.4	Nonazeotrope		*231*
12226	C_9H_8	Indene	182.6	Nonazeotrope		*231*
12227	C_9H_{12}	Mesitylene	164.6	Nonazeotrope		*231*
12228	$C_{10}H_8$	Naphthalene	218.0	Nonazeotrope		*231*
12229	$C_{10}H_{14}$	Cymene	176.7	Nonazeotrope		*231*
12230	$C_{10}H_{16}$	Camphene	159.6	Nonazeotrope		*231*
12231	$C_{10}H_{16}$	Dipentene	177.7	<177.2	<11	*231*
12232	$C_{10}H_{16}$	*d*-Limonene	177.8	174.5	13	*243*
12233	$C_{10}H_{16}$	Nopinene	163.8	Nonazeotrope		*231*
12234	$C_{10}H_{16}$	α-Pinene	155.8	Nonazeotrope		*231*
12235	$C_{10}H_{16}$	α-Terpinene	173.4	Nonazeotrope		*231*
12236	$C_{10}H_{16}$	Terpinolene	185	180	~32	*243*
12237	$C_{10}H_{18}O$	Borneol	215.0	Nonazeotrope		*231*
12238	$C_{10}H_{18}O$	Cineole	176.35	Nonazeotrope		*231*
12239	$C_{10}H_{18}O$	Linaloöl	198.6	195.6	70	*231*
12240	$C_{10}H_{18}O$	Menthone	209.5	Nonazeotrope		*255*
12241	$C_{10}H_{18}O$	β-Terpineol	210.5	Nonazeotrope		*231*
12242	$C_{10}H_{20}O$	Menthol	216.3	Nonazeotrope		*231*
12243	$C_{10}H_{22}O$	Isoamyl ether	173.2	Nonazeotrope		*231*
12244	$C_{12}H_{18}$	1,3,5-Triethylbenzene	215.5	Nonazeotrope		*231*
12245	$C_{12}H_{22}O$	Ethyl isobornyl ether	203.8	Nonazeotrope		*231*
A =	C_7H_9N	***m*-Toluidine**	**203.1**			
12246	$C_8H_{10}O$	*p*-Ethylphenol	218.8	Nonazeotrope		*231*
12247	$C_8H_{10}O$	3,4-Xylenol	226.8	Nonazeotrope		*231*
12248	$C_8H_{10}O_2$	*o*-Ethoxyphenol	216.5	Nonazeotrope		*231*
12249	$C_8H_{11}N$	Ethylaniline	205.5	202.95	89	*244*
12250	$C_8H_{18}O$	*n*-Octyl alcohol	195.2	Nonazeotrope		*231*
12251	$C_8H_{18}O$	*sec*-Octyl alcohol	180.4	Nonazeotrope		*231*
12252	$C_{10}H_8$	Naphthalene	218.0	Nonazeotrope		*231*
12253	$C_{10}H_{14}$	Butylbenzene	183.1	Nonazeotrope		*231*
12254	$C_{10}H_{16}O$	Camphor	209.1	Nonazeotrope		*231*
12255	$C_{10}H_{16}O$	Pulegone	223.8	Nonazeotrope		*231*
12256	$C_{10}H_{18}O$	Borneol	215.0	Nonazeotrope		*231*
12257	$C_{10}H_{18}O$	Menthone	209.5	Nonazeotrope		*255*
12258	$C_{10}H_{18}O$	α-Terpineol	218.85	Nonazeotrope		*231*
12259	$C_{10}H_{18}O$	β-Terpineol	210.5	Nonazeotrope		*255*
12260	$C_{10}H_{20}O$	Menthol	216.3	Nonazeotrope		*231*
12261	$C_{11}H_{16}O$	Methyl thymyl ether	216.5	Nonazeotrope		*255*
12262	$C_{11}H_{20}O$	Methyl α-terpineol ether	216.2	Nonazeotrope		*231*
12263	$C_{12}H_{22}O$	Ethyl isobornyl ether	203.8	<201.0	<60	*231*
A =	C_7H_9N	***o*-Toluidine**	**200.7**			
12264	$C_7H_{12}O_4$	Ethyl malonate	198.9	Reacts		*243*
12265	$C_7H_{16}O$	*n*-Heptyl alcohol	176.15	Nonazeotrope		*231*
12266	C_8H_8O	Acetophenone	202.0	203.65	32	*231*
12267	$C_8H_{10}O$	Phenethyl alcohol	219.4	Nonazeotrope		*231*
12268	$C_8H_{10}O_2$	*m*-Dimethoxybenzene	214.7	Nonazeotrope		*217*
12269	$C_8H_{18}O$	*n*-Octyl alcohol	195.2	194.7	23	*244*
12270	$C_8H_{18}O$	*sec*-Octyl alcohol	180.4	Nonazeotrope		*231*
12271	C_9H_8	Indene	182.6	Nonazeotrope		*231*
12272	$C_9H_{10}O$	Propiophenone	217.7	Nonazeotrope		*231*
12273	$C_9H_{13}N$	*N*-Dimethyl-*o*-toluidine	185.3	Nonazeotrope		*229*
12274	$C_{10}H_8$	Naphthalene	218.0	Nonazeotrope		*231*
12275	$C_{10}H_{14}$	Butylbenzene	183.1	Nonazeotrope		*231*
12276	$C_{10}H_{14}$	Cymene	176.7	Nonazeotrope		*231*
12277	$C_{10}H_{16}O$	Camphor	209.1	Nonazeotrope		*231*
12278	$C_{10}H_{18}O$	Borneol	215.0	Nonazeotrope		*231*
12279	$C_{10}H_{18}O$	Cineole	176.35	Nonazeotrope		*255*
12280	$C_{10}H_{18}O$	Linaloöl	198.6	198.3	30	*231*
12281	$C_{10}H_{18}O$	α-Terpineol	218.85	Nonazeotrope		*255*
12282	$C_{10}H_{18}O$	β-Terpineol	210.75	Nonazeotrope		*231*

No.	Formula	B-Component Name	B.P., ° C.	Azeotropic Data B.P., ° C.	Wt. % A	Ref.
A =	**C_7H_9N**	***o*-Toluidine (*continued*)**	**200.7**			
12283	$C_{10}H_{20}O$	Menthol	216.3	Nonazeotrope		231
12284	$C_{11}H_{20}O$	Isobornyl methyl ether	192.4	<192.0	....	255
12285	$C_{11}H_{20}O$	Terpineol methyl ether	216.0	Nonazeotrope		217
12286	$C_{12}H_{18}$	1,3,5-Triethylbenzene	215.5	Nonazeotrope		231
12287	$C_{12}H_{22}O$	Ethyl isobornyl ether	203.8	<198.5	....	255
A =	**C_7H_9N**	***p*-Toluidine**	**200.5**			
12288	C_8H_8O	Acetophenone	202.0	203.65	32	231
12289	C_8H_8O	Acetophenone	202	~199	....	243
12290	$C_8H_{18}O$	*n*-Octyl alcohol	195.2	194.65	23	231
12291	$C_8H_{18}O$	*n*-Octyl alcohol	195.15	194.4	33	225
12292	$C_8H_{18}O$	*sec*-Octyl alcohol	180.4	Nonazeotrope		231
12293	C_9H_8	Indene	182.6	Nonazeotrope		231
12294	$C_9H_{10}O$	Propiophenone	217.7	Nonazeotrope		231
12295	$C_{10}H_8$	Naphthalene	218.0	Nonazeotrope		231
12296	$C_{10}H_{16}$	Terpinolene	184.6	<183.5	....	231
12297	$C_{10}H_{16}O$	Camphor	209.1	Nonazeotrope		231
12298	$C_{10}H_{18}O$	Borneol	215.0	Nonazeotrope		231
12299	$C_{10}H_{18}O$	Menthone	~207	Nonazeotrope		243
12300	$C_{10}H_{20}O$	Menthol	216.3	Nonazeotrope		231
A =	**C_7H_9NO**	***o*-Anisidine**	**219.0**			
12301	C_8H_8O	Acetophenone	202.0	Nonazeotrope		255
12302	$C_8H_8O_3$	Methyl salicylate	222.95	Nonazeotrope		255
12303	$C_8H_{10}O$	3,4-Xylenol	226.8	Nonazeotrope		255
12304	$C_9H_{10}O$	*p*-Methylacetophenone	226.35	Nonazeotrope		255
12305	$C_9H_{10}O$	Propiophenone	217.7	219.7	~65	255
12306	$C_9H_{10}O_3$	Ethyl salicylate	233.8	Nonazeotrope		255
12307	$C_9H_{14}O$	Phorone	197.8	Nonazeotrope		255
12308	$C_{10}H_8$	Naphthalene	218.0	217.0	50	255
12309	$C_{10}H_{14}O$	Thymol	232.9	Nonazeotrope		255
12310	$C_{10}H_{20}O$	Menthol	216.3	<216.0	....	231
12311	$C_{11}H_{10}$	2-Methylnaphthalene	241.15	Nonazeotrope		255
12312	$C_{11}H_{20}O$	Methyl α-terpineol ether	216.2	215.2	35	255
12313	$C_{12}H_{18}$	1,3,5-Triethylbenzene	215.5	214.5	35	255
A =	**$C_7H_{12}O_4$**	**Ethyl Malonate**	**198.6**			
12314	C_8H_8O	Acetophenone	202.0	Nonazeotrope		232
12315	$C_8H_8O_2$	Benzyl formate	203.0	<198.2	....	229
12316	$C_8H_8O_2$	Methyl benzoate	199.55	198.2	~54	208
12317	$C_8H_8O_2$	Methyl benzoate	199.4	198.7	56	207
12318	$C_8H_8O_2$	Phenyl acetate	195.7	Nonazeotrope		209
12319	$C_8H_{10}O_2$	*m*-Dimethoxybenzene	214.7	Nonazeotrope		237
12320	$C_8H_{14}O_4$	Propyl oxalate	214	Nonazeotrope		255
12321	$C_8H_{16}O$	2-Octanone	172.85	Nonazeotrope		232
12322	$C_8H_{16}O_3$	Isoamyl lactate	202.4	Nonazeotrope		255
12323	$C_8H_{18}O$	Octyl alcohol	195.15	Reacts		216
12324	$C_9H_{10}O_2$	Ethyl benzoate	212.5	Nonazeotrope		255
12325	C_9H_{12}	Mesitylene	164.6	Nonazeotrope		255
12326	C_9H_{12}	Propylbenzene	159.3	Nonazeotrope		255
12327	$C_9H_{12}O$	Benzyl ethyl ether	185.0	Nonazeotrope		237
12328	$C_9H_{14}O$	Phorone	197.8	<197.65	<47	232
12329	$C_9H_{18}O_2$	Methyl caprylate	192.9	191.9	26	229
12330	$C_9H_{18}O_3$	Isobutyl carbonate	190.3	Nonazeotrope		229
12331	$C_{10}H_8$	Naphthalene	218.1	Nonazeotrope		243
12332	$C_{10}H_{14}$	Cymene	176.7	Nonazeotrope		255
12333	$C_{10}H_{16}$	Camphene	159.6	Nonazeotrope		217
12334	$C_{10}H_{16}$	Dipentene	177.7	Nonazeotrope		255
12335	$C_{10}H_{16}$	*d*-Limonene	177.8	177.5	10	217
12336	$C_{10}H_{16}$	Nopinene	163.8	Nonazeotrope		255
12337	$C_{10}H_{16}$	α-Pinene	155.8	Nonazeotrope		226
12338	$C_{10}H_{16}$	α-Terpinene	173.4	Nonazeotrope		255
12339	$C_{10}H_{16}$	Terpinene	181.5	178.0	22	218
12340	$C_{10}H_{16}O$	Camphor	209.1	Nonazeotrope		232
12341	$C_{10}H_{17}Cl$	Bornyl chloride	207.5	<198.0	<82	255

No.	B-Component Formula	Name	B.P., ° C.	Azeotropic Data B.P., ° C.	Wt. % A	Ref.
A =	**$C_7H_{12}O_4$**	**Ethyl Malonate (*continued*)**	**198.6**			
12342	$C_{10}H_{18}O$	Linaloöl	199	~198	~60	243
12343	$C_{10}H_{20}O_2$	Isoamyl isovalerate	192.7	191.75	30	207
12344	$C_{11}H_{16}O$	Methyl thymol ether	216.5	Nonazeotrope		237
12345	$C_{11}H_{20}O$	Methyl *α*-terpineol ether	216.2	Nonazeotrope		237
12346	$C_{11}H_{24}O_2$	Diisoamyloxymethane	207.5	Azeotrope doubtful		243
			....	Nonazeotrope		237
12347	$C_{12}H_{18}$	1,3,5-Triethylbenzene	215.5	Nonazeotrope		255
12348	$C_{12}H_{22}O$	Bornyl ethyl ether	204.9	<196.0	<71	237
12349	$C_{12}H_{22}O$	Ethyl isobornyl ether	203.8	<196.2	<70	237
A =	**$C_7H_{13}ClO_2$**	**Isoamyl Chloroacetate**	**190.5**			
12350	$C_7H_{14}O_3$	Isobutyl lactate	182.15	Nonazeotrope		255
12351	C_8H_8O	Acetophenone	202.0	Nonazeotrope		255
12352	$C_8H_8O_2$	Methyl benzoate	199.55	Nonazeotrope		243
12353	$C_8H_{16}O$	2-Octanone	172.85	Nonazeotrope		255
12354	$C_8H_{18}O$	Octyl alcohol	195.2	<193.5	<62	255
12355	$C_8H_{18}O$	*sec*-Octyl alcohol	180.4	Nonazeotrope		255
12356	$C_{10}H_{16}$	*d*-Limonene	177.8	Nonazeotrope		243
12357	$C_{10}H_{18}O$	Linaloöl	198.6	<194.2	<82	255
A =	**C_7H_{14}**	**3-Heptene**	**94.8**			
12358	C_7H_{16}	Heptane	98.4	Nonazeotrope		255
A =	**C_7H_{14}**	**Methylcyclohexane**	**100.8**			
12359	C_7H_{16}	*n*-Heptane	98.4	Nonazeotrope, V-l.		44
			98.45	98.3	10	160*, 252
12360	C_8H_{18}	2,5-Dimethylhexane	109.4	Nonazeotrope		255
12361	C_8H_{18}	2,2,4-Trimethylpentane, 741 mm.	98.2	Nonazeotrope, V-l.		153
12362	$C_8H_{18}O$	Isobutyl ether	122.3	Nonazeotrope		238
A =	**$C_7H_{14}O$**	**4-Heptanone**	**143.55**			
12363	$C_7H_{14}O_2$	Butyl propionate	146.8	Nonazeotrope		232
12364	$C_7H_{14}O_2$	Ethyl *n*-valerate	145.15	Nonazeotrope		232
12365	$C_7H_{14}O_2$	Isoamyl acetate	142.1	141.7	25	232
12366	$C_7H_{14}O_2$	Isobutyl propionate	137.5	Nonazeotrope		232
12367	$C_7H_{14}O_2$	Propyl butyrate	143.7	143.0	47	232
12368	C_8H_{10}	Ethylbenzene	136.15	Nonazeotrope		232
12369	C_8H_{10}	*m*-Xylene	139.2	139.0	10	232
12370	C_8H_{10}	*o*-Xylene	144.3	142.4	42	232
12371	$C_8H_{19}N$	Diisobutylamine	138.5	<137.0	<32	255
12372	C_9H_{12}	Cumene	152.8	Nonazeotrope		232
12373	C_9H_{12}	Propylbenzene	159.3	Nonazeotrope		232
12374	$C_{10}H_{16}$	Camphene	159.6	142.5	95	232
12375	$C_{10}H_{16}$	*α*-Pinene	155.8	142.0	80	223
A =	**$C_7H_{14}O$**	**2-Methylcyclohexanol**	**168.5**			
12376	$C_7H_{14}O_3$	Isobutyl lactate	182.15	Nonazeotrope		255
12377	C_8H_{10}	Ethylbenzene	136.15	Nonazeotrope		255
12378	C_8H_{10}	*m*-Xylene	139.2	Nonazeotrope		255
12379	$C_8H_{10}O$	Benzyl methyl ether	167.8	165.0	46	255
12380	$C_8H_{10}O$	*p*-Methylanisole	177.05	167.5	71	256
12381	$C_8H_{10}O$	Phenetole	170.45	165.7	50	256
12382	$C_8H_{11}N$	Dimethylaniline	194.05	Nonazeotrope		231
12383	$C_8H_{14}O$	Methylheptenone	173.2	Nonazeotrope		232
12384	$C_8H_{16}O$	2-Octanone	172.85	Nonazeotrope		232
12385	$C_8H_{16}O_2$	Isoamyl propionate	160.7	Nonazeotrope		255
12386	$C_8H_{16}O_2$	Isobutyl isobutyrate	156.9	Nonazeotrope		255
12387	C_9H_{12}	Cumene	152.8	151.7	12	255
12388	C_9H_{12}	Mesitylene	164.6	160.5	34	247
12389	C_9H_{12}	Pseudocumene	168.2	<164.0	<48	255
12390	$C_9H_{12}O$	Benzyl ethyl ether	185.0	Nonazeotrope		255
12391	$C_9H_{13}N$	*N,N*-Dimethyl-*o*-toluidine	185.3	Nonazeotrope		231
12392	$C_9H_{18}O$	2,6-Dimethyl-4-heptanone	168.0	167.5	40	232
12393	$C_9H_{18}O_2$	Isobutyl isovalerate	171.2	167.5	62	255
12394	$C_{10}H_{14}$	Butylbenzene	183.1	<168.0	>70	255
12395	$C_{10}H_{14}$	Cymene	176.7	<166.5	<68	255

No.	Formula	B-Component Name	B.P., ° C.	Azeotropic Data B.P., ° C.	Wt. % A	Ref.
A =	**$C_7H_{14}O$**	**2-Methylcyclohexanol** (*continued*)	**168.5**			
12396	$C_{10}H_{16}$	Camphene	159.6	155.5	25	*247*
12397	$C_{10}H_{16}$	Dipentene	177.7	165.3	60	*247*
12398	$C_{10}H_{16}$	α-Pinene	155.8	152.8	20	*247*
12399	$C_{10}H_{16}$	α-Terpinene	173.4	163.7	52	*247*
12400	$C_{10}H_{18}O$	Cineole	176.35	167.2	70	*256*
12401	$C_{10}H_{22}$	2,7-Dimethyloctane	160.1	155.8	27	*247*
12402	$C_{10}H_{22}O$	Amyl ether	187.5	Nonazeotrope		*255*
12403	$C_{10}H_{22}O$	Isoamyl ether	173.4	166.2	60	*225*
A =	**$C_7H_{14}O$**	**3-Methylcyclohexanol**	**172**			
12404	$C_8H_{10}O$	Phenetole, 770 mm.	170.5	167.2	46.5	*199*
		13 mm.	....	60	24	*199*
		2 mm.	....	28.8	18.7	*199*
A =	**$C_7H_{14}O$**	**5-Methyl-2-hexanone**	**144.2**			
12405	$C_7H_{14}O_2$	Butyl propionate	146.8	Nonazeotrope		*232*
12406	$C_7H_{14}O_2$	Isoamyl acetate	142.1	141.8	18	*232*
12407	$C_7H_{14}O_2$	Isobutyl propionate	137.5	Nonazeotrope		*232*
12408	$C_7H_{14}O_2$	Propyl butyrate	143.7	143.3	35	*232*
12409	C_8H_{10}	Ethylbenzene	136.15	Nonazeotrope		*232*
12410	C_8H_{10}	o-Xylene	144.3	143.0	42	*232*
12411	$C_8H_{16}O_2$	Isobutyl isobutyrate	148.6	Nonazeotrope		*232*
12412	$C_8H_{19}N$	Diisobutylamine	138.5	136.3	30	*255*
12413	C_9H_{12}	Cumene	152.8	Nonazeotrope		*232*
12414	$C_{10}H_{16}$	α-Pinene	155.8	142.0	75	*232*
A =	**$C_7H_{14}O_2$**	**Amyl Acetate**	**148.8**			
12415	$C_7H_{14}O_2$	Butyl propionate	146.8	Nonazeotrope		*255*
12416	$C_7H_{14}O_2$	Isoamyl acetate	142.1	Nonazeotrope		*255*
12417	$C_7H_{14}O_2$	Propyl butyrate	143.7	Nonazeotrope		*255*
12418	C_8H_{10}	o-Xylene	143.6	Nonazeotrope		*226*
12419	$C_8H_{16}O_2$	Isobutyl isobutyrate	148.6	<148.5	>10	*229*
12420	$C_8H_{18}O$	Butyl ether	142.4	Nonazeotrope		*237*
12421	$C_{10}H_{16}$	α-Pinene	155.8	<148.0	75	*226*
A =	**$C_7H_{14}O_2$**	**Butyl Propionate**	**146.8**			
12422	$C_7H_{14}O_2$	Isoamyl acetate	142.1	Nonazeotrope		*255*
12423	$C_7H_{14}O_2$	Propyl butyrate	143.7	Nonazeotrope		*255*
12424	C_8H_8	Styrene	146	145.5	....	*226*
12425	C_8H_{10}	o-Xylene	143.6	Nonazeotrope		*226*
12426	$C_8H_{18}O$	Butyl ether	142.4	Nonazeotrope		*237*
12427	C_9H_{12}	Cumene	152.8	Nonazeotrope		*255*
12428	$C_{10}H_{16}$	α-Pinene	155.8	<145.8	>85	*226*
A =	**$C_7H_{14}O_2$**	**Enanthic Acid**	**222.0**			
12429	C_8H_8O	Acetophenone	202.0	Nonazeotrope		*232*
12430	$C_8H_{10}O$	3,4-Xylenol	226.8	Nonazeotrope		*255*
12431	$C_8H_{10}O_2$	o-Ethoxyphenol	216.5	<215.2	>15	*255*
12432	$C_8H_{12}O_4$	Ethyl fumarate	217.85	216.4	22	*242*
12433	$C_8H_{12}O_4$	Ethyl maleate	223.3	220.0	50	*242*
12434	$C_8H_{14}O_4$	Ethyl succinate	217.25	216.0	20	*242*
12435	$C_8H_{14}O_4$	Propyl oxalate	214	<213.8	>7	*255*
12436	$C_8H_{16}O_4$	2-(2-Ethoxyethoxy)ethyl acetate	218.5	224.5	58	*242*
12437	C_9H_8	Indene	182.6	Nonazeotrope		*255*
12438	$C_9H_{10}O$	p-Methylacetophenone	226.35	<221.2	>70	*232*
12439	$C_9H_{10}O$	Propiophenone	217.7	216.5	20	*232*
12440	$C_9H_{10}O_2$	Benzyl acetate	215.0	Nonazeotrope		*255*
12441	$C_9H_{10}O_2$	Ethyl benzoate	212.5	Nonazeotrope		*255*
12442	$C_{10}H_7Cl$	1-Chloronaphthalene	262.7	Nonazeotrope		*255*
12443	$C_{10}H_8$	Naphthalene	218.0	214.2	30	*242*
12444	$C_{10}H_{10}O_2$	Safrole	235.9	<221.7	>85	*255*
12445	$C_{10}H_{12}O_2$	Ethyl α-toluate	228.75	Nonazeotrope		*255*
12446	$C_{10}H_{14}O$	Carvacrol	237.85	Nonazeotrope		*255*
12447	$C_{10}H_{14}O$	Carvone	231.0	Nonazeotrope		*232*
12448	$C_{11}H_{16}O$	Methyl thymol ether	216.5	215.0	25	*255*
12449	$C_{11}H_{20}O$	Methyl α-terpineol ether	216.2	<215.3	<30	*255*

No.	B-Component Formula	Name	B.P., ° C.	Azeotropic Data B.P., ° C.	Wt. % A	Ref.
A =	$C_7H_{14}O_2$	**Enanthic Acid** (*continued*)	**222.0**			
12450	$C_{12}H_{10}$	Biphenyl	256.1	Nonazeotrope		255
12451	$C_{12}H_{18}$	1,3,5-Triethylbenzene	215.5	211.0	27	242
12452	$C_{12}H_{20}O_2$	Bornyl acetate	227.6	Nonazeotrope		255
12453	$C_{13}H_{28}$	Tridecane	234.0	<219.2	>55	242
A =	$C_7H_{14}O_2$	**Ethyl Isovalerate**	**134.7**			
12454	$C_7H_{16}O_3$	Ethyl orthoformate	145.75	Nonazeotrope		237
12455	C_8H_8	Styrene	145.8	Nonazeotrope		255
12456	C_8H_{10}	Ethylbenzene	136.15	Nonazeotrope		211
12457	C_8H_{10}	*m*-Xylene	139.0	Nonazeotrope		207
12458	C_8H_{10}	*p*-Xylene	138.45	Nonazeotrope		255
12459	$C_8H_{18}O$	Butyl ether	142.4	Nonazeotrope		237
12460	$C_8H_{18}O$	Isobutyl ether	122.3	Nonazeotrope		237
A =	$C_7H_{14}O_2$	**Ethyl Valerate**	**145.45**			
12461	$C_7H_{14}O_2$	Isoamyl acetate	142.1	Nonazeotrope		255
12462	C_8H_8	Styrene	145.8	<145.0	>48	255
12463	C_8H_{10}	*m*-Xylene	139.2	Nonazeotrope		207
12464	C_8H_{10}	*o*-Xylene	144.3	Nonazeotrope		255
12465	$C_8H_{18}O$	Butyl ether	142.4	Nonazeotrope		237
A =	$C_7H_{14}O_2$	**Isoamyl Acetate**	**142.1**			
12466	$C_7H_{14}O_2$	Isobutyl propionate	137.5	Nonazeotrope		255
12467	$C_7H_{14}O_2$	Propyl butyrate	142.8	Nonazeotrope		252
12468	$C_7H_{16}O_3$	Ethyl orthoformate	145.75	Nonazeotrope		237
12469	C_8H_{10}	Ethylbenzene	136.15	Nonazeotrope		252
12470	C_8H_{10}	*m*-Xylene	139.0	Nonazeotrope		207
			139.0	136	50	243
12471	C_8H_{10}	*o*-Xylene	143.6	Nonazeotrope		226
12472	C_8H_{10}	*p*-Xylene	138.3	Nonazeotrope		226
12473	C_8H_{16}	1,3-Dimethylcyclohexane	120.7	Nonazeotrope		255
12474	$C_8H_{18}O$	Butyl ether	142.2	<141.2	<55	237
12475	C_9H_{12}	Cumene	152.8	Nonazeotrope		255
12476	$C_{10}H_{16}$	Camphene	158	Nonazeotrope		226
12477	$C_{10}H_{16}$	Nopinene	163.8	Nonazeotrope		255
12478	$C_{10}H_{16}$	α-Pinene	155.8	142.05	97.5	217
A =	$C_7H_{14}O_2$	**Isobutyl Propionate**	**136.9**			
12479	C_8H_8	Styrene, 60 mm.	68	Nonazeotrope		26
12480	C_8H_{10}	Ethylbenzene	136.15	135.8	~30	253
		60 mm.	60.5	60	13	26
12881	C_8H_{10}	*m*-Xylene	139.0	Nonazeotrope		253
			139.0	134.5	....	243
12482	C_8H_{10}	*o*-Xylene	143.6	Nonazeotrope		226
12483	C_8H_{10}	*p*-Xylene	138.3	136.8	85	226
12484	$C_8H_{18}O$	Butyl ether	142.4	Nonazeotrope		237
A =	$C_7H_{14}O_2$	**Isopropyl Isobutyrate**	**120.8**			
12485	C_7H_{16}	Heptane	98.4	Nonazeotrope		255
A =	$C_7H_{14}O_2$	**Methyl Caproate**	**149.6**			
12486	C_8H_{10}	*m*-Xylene	139.0	Nonazeotrope		243
12487	C_8H_{10}	*o*-Xylene	144.3	Nonazeotrope		255
12488	$C_8H_{16}O_2$	Isobutyl isobutyrate	149.75	Nonazeotrope		255
12489	$C_8H_{16}O_2$	Propyl isovalerate	155.7	Nonazeotrope		255
12490	C_9H_{12}	Cumene	152.8	Nonazeotrope		255
A =	$C_7H_{14}O_2$	**Propyl Butyrate**	**143.7**			
12491	C_8H_8	Styrene	146	Nonazeotrope		226
12492	C_8H_8	Styrene	145.8	<143.5	<68	255
12493	C_8H_{10}	*m*-Xylene	139.0	Nonazeotrope		207
			139.0	138.7	....	243
12494	C_8H_{10}	*o*-Xylene	143.6	143.2	55	226
12495	$C_8H_{18}O$	Butyl ether	142.4	<142.0	<45	237
12496	C_9H_{12}	Cumene	152.8	Nonazeotrope		255
12497	$C_{10}H_{16}$	α-Pinene	155.8	<143.4	<88	255
12498	$C_{10}H_{16}$	α-Pinene	155.8	Nonazeotrope		243

No.	Formula	B-Component Name	B.P., ° C.	Azeotropic Data B.P., ° C.	Wt. % A	Ref.
A =	**$C_7H_{14}O_2$**	**Propyl Isobutyrate**	**134.0**			
12499	$C_7H_{16}O_2$	Dipropoxymethane	137.2	Nonazeotrope		*237*
12500	C_8H_8	Styrene	146	Nonazeotrope		*226*
12501	C_8H_{10}	Ethylbenzene	136.15	Nonazeotrope		*255*
12502	C_8H_{10}	*m*-Xylene	139.0	Nonazeotrope		*207*
12503	C_8H_{10}	*p*-Xylene	138.2	Nonazeotrope		*253*
12504	$C_8H_{18}O$	Butyl ether	142.2	Nonazeotrope		*237*
12505	$C_{10}H_{16}$	α-Pinene	155.8	Nonazeotrope		*226*
A =	**$C_7H_{14}O_3$**	**1,3-Butanediol Methyl Ether Acetate**	**171.75**			
12506	$C_7H_{16}O$	Heptyl alcohol	176.15	Nonazeotrope		*255*
12507	$C_8H_{10}O$	*p*-Methylanisole	177.05	Nonazeotrope		*255*
12508	$C_8H_{10}O$	Phenetole	170.45	170.0	22	*207*
12509	$C_8H_{16}O$	2-Octanone	172.85	171.3	35	*255*
12510	$C_8H_{16}O_2$	Ethyl caproate	167.7	167.4	~10	*255*
12511	$C_8H_{16}O_2$	Hexyl acetate	171.5	170.7	49	*242*
12512	$C_8H_{16}O_2$	Isoamyl propionate	160.7	Nonazeotrope		*207*
12513	$C_8H_{16}O_2$	Isobutyl butyrate	156.9	Nonazeotrope		*255*
12514	$C_8H_{18}O$	Octyl alcohol	195.2	Nonazeotrope		*255*
12515	$C_8H_{18}O$	*sec*-Octyl alcohol	180.4	Nonazeotrope		*255*
12516	C_9H_{12}	Mesitylene	164.6	Nonazeotrope		*255*
12517	C_9H_{12}	Propylbenzene	159.3	Nonazeotrope		*255*
12518	$C_9H_{12}O$	Benzyl ethyl ether	185.0	Nonazeotrope		*255*
12519	$C_9H_{18}O$	2,6-Dimethyl-4-heptanone	168.0	Nonazeotrope		*255*
12520	$C_9H_{18}O_2$	Isoamyl butyrate	181.05	Nonazeotrope		*207*
12521	$C_9H_{18}O_2$	Isobutyl isovalerate	171.2	170.35	47	*250*
12522	$C_9H_{18}O_3$	Isobutyl carbonate	190.3	Nonazeotrope		*255*
12523	$C_{10}H_{14}$	Cymene	176.7	Nonazeotrope		*255*
12524	$C_{10}H_{16}$	Camphene	159.6	<159.45	>5	*255*
12525	$C_{10}H_{16}$	Dipentene	177.7	169.6	78	*242*
12526	$C_{10}H_{16}$	Nopinene	163.8	162.0	20	*242*
12527	$C_{10}H_{16}$	α-Terpinene	173.4	168.9	65	*242*
12528	$C_{10}H_{18}O$	Cineole	176.35	170.9	64	*207*
12529	$C_{10}H_{20}O_2$	Isoamyl isovalerate	192.7	Nonazeotrope		*207*
12530	$C_{10}H_{22}O$	Amyl ether	187.5	Nonazeotrope		*255*
12531	$C_{10}H_{22}O$	Isoamyl ether	173.2	<170.0	>52	*207*
A =	**$C_7H_{14}O_3$**	**Isobutyl Lactate**	**182.15**			
12532	$C_8H_{10}O$	Benzyl methyl ether	167.8	Nonazeotrope		*255*
12533	$C_8H_{10}O$	Phenetole	171.5	Nonazeotrope		*243*
12534	$C_8H_{10}O$	2,4-Xylenol	210.5	Nonazeotrope		*255*
12535	$C_8H_{18}O$	Octyl alcohol	195.2	Nonazeotrope		*255*
12536	$C_8H_{18}O$	*sec*-Octyl alcohol	178.5	117.3	....	*243*
12537	$C_8H_{18}S$	Butyl sulfide	185.0	<181.3	<78	*246*
12538	C_9H_8	Indene	182.8	177	48	*228*
12539	C_9H_{12}	Mesitylene	164.6	Nonazeotrope		*255*
12540	$C_9H_{12}O$	Benzyl ethyl ether	185.0	181.0	75?	*255*
12541	$C_9H_{18}O_2$	Isoamyl butyrate	181.05	<178.5	>28	*207*
12542	$C_{10}H_{14}$	Cymene	175.3	171.5	~35	*243*
12543	$C_{10}H_{16}$	Camphene	159.6	Nonazeotrope		*218*
12544	$C_{10}H_{16}$	*d*-Limonene	177.8	172.5	40	*243*
12545	$C_{10}H_{16}$	Nopinene	163.8	Nonazeotrope		*255*
12546	$C_{10}H_{16}$	α-Pinene	155.8	Nonazeotrope		*255*
12547	$C_{10}H_{16}$	Terpinene	180.5	172.5	~46	*243*
12548	$C_{10}H_{16}$	Terpinolene	185	175	55	*243*
12549	$C_{10}H_{18}O$	Cineole	176.35	174.0	32	*236*
12550	$C_{10}H_{18}O$	Linaloöl	198.6	Nonazeotrope		*255*
12551	$C_{10}H_{22}O$	Isoamyl ether	173.2	<172.0	>13	*255*
A =	**C_7H_{16}**	**2,4-Dimethylpentane, 505 mm.**	**67.58**			
12552	C_7H_{16}	2,2,3-Trimethylbutane, 505 mm.	67.58	67.71	~50	
			Nonazeotropic below 55° C.			*59*
			Nonazeotropic above 75° C.			*59*
A =	**$C_7H_{16}O$**	**2-Heptanol, 10 mm.**	**65.4**			
12553	C_8H_9Cl	*o,m,p*-Chloroethylbenzene, 10 mm.	67.5	61.4	43	*24*

No.	Formula	B-Component Name	B.P., ° C.	Azeotropic Data B.P., ° C.	Wt. % A	Ref
A =	$C_7H_{16}O$	**Heptyl Alcohol**	**176.15**			
12554	C_8H_{10}	*m*-Xylene	139.2	Nonazeotrope		255
12555	$C_8H_{10}O$	Benzyl methyl ether	167.8	167.0	20	255
12556	$C_8H_{10}O$	*p*-Methylanisole	177.05	173.3	52	247
12557	$C_8H_{10}O$	Phenetole	170.45	169.0	28	225
12558	$C_8H_{11}N$	Dimethylaniline	194.05	Nonazeotrope		231
12559	$C_8H_{14}O$	Methylheptenone	173.2	Nonazeotrope		232
12560	$C_8H_{16}O_2$	Ethyl caproate	167.7	Nonazeotrope		255
12561	$C_8H_{16}O_2$	Isoamyl propionate				
12562	$C_8H_{18}O$	*sec*-Octyl alcohol	180.4	Nonazeotrope		255
12563	C_9H_{12}	Cumene	152.8	Nonazeotrope		255
12564	$C_9H_{13}N$	*N,N*-Dimethyl-*o*-toluidine	185.3	175.5	82	231
12565	$C_9H_{18}O_2$	Isobutyl isovalerate	171.2	<171.0	>8	255
12566	$C_{10}H_{14}$	Cymene	176.0	172.5	47	247
12567	$C_{10}H_{15}N$	Diethylaniline	217.05	Nonazeotrope		231
12568	$C_{10}H_{16}$	Camphene	159.6	<159.3	>10	255
12569	$C_{10}H_{16}$	Dipentene	177.7	171.7	50	247
12570	$C_{10}H_{16}$	Nopinene	163.8	<162.6	>15	255
12571	$C_{10}H_{16}$	α-Terpinene	173.4	169.7	40	247
12572	$C_{10}H_{18}O$	Cineole	176.35	173.0	48	236
12573	$C_{10}H_{22}O$	Isoamyl ether	173.35	170.35	37	244
A =	$C_7H_{16}O_3$	**Ethyl Orthoformate**	**145.75**			
12574	C_8H_8	Styrene	145.8	<145.0	<45	238
12575	C_8H_{10}	*m*-Xylene	139.2	Nonazeotrope		207
12576	$C_8H_{16}O_2$	Propyl isovalerate	155.7	Nonazeotrope		237
12577	C_9H_{12}	Cumene	152.8	Nonazeotrope		238
12578	C_9H_{12}	Propylbenzene	159.3	Nonazeotrope		238
12579	$C_{10}H_{16}$	Camphene	159.6	Nonazeotrope		238
12580	$C_{10}H_{16}$	Nopinene	163.8	Nonazeotrope		238
A =	$C_7H_{16}O_4$	**2-[2-(2-Methoxyethoxy)ethoxy] Ethanol**	**245.25**			
12581	$C_8H_8O_2$	Methyl benzoate	199.4	Nonazeotrope		255
12582	$C_8H_8O_3$	Methyl salicylate	222.95	222.0	8	255
12583	$C_8H_{10}O_2$	2-Phenoxyethanol	245.2	<244.0	>55	255
12584	$C_8H_{12}O_4$	Ethyl fumarate	217.85	Nonazeotrope		255
12585	$C_8H_{12}O_4$	Ethyl maleate	223.3	Nonazeotrope		255
12586	C_9H_7N	Quinoline	237.3	235.55	22	233
12587	$C_9H_{10}O_2$	Benzyl acetate	215.0	Nonazeotrope		255
12588	$C_9H_{10}O_2$	Ethyl benzoate	212.5	Nonazeotrope		255
12589	$C_9H_{10}O_3$	Ethyl salicylate	233.8	227.7	28	236
12590	$C_9H_{12}O_2$	2-Benzyloxyethanol	265.2	Nonazeotrope		255
12591	$C_{10}H_7Br$	1-Bromonaphthalene	281.2	Nonazeotrope		255
12592	$C_{10}H_7Cl$	1-Chloronaphthalene	262.7	Nonazeotrope		255
12593	$C_{10}H_8$	Naphthalene	218.0	214.8	20	236
12594	$C_{10}H_8O$	1-Naphthol	288.5	Nonazeotrope		236
12595	$C_{10}H_9N$	Quinaldine	246.5	<243.0	....	255
12596	$C_{10}H_{10}O_2$	Isosafrole	252.0	241.5	65	247
12597	$C_{10}H_{10}O_2$	Methyl cinnamate	261.9	242.3	70	247
12598	$C_{10}H_{10}O_2$	Safrole	235.9	233.5	31	247
12599	$C_{10}H_{10}O_4$	Methyl phthalate	283.2	Nonazeotrope		255
12600	$C_{10}H_{12}O$	Anethole	235.7	233.0	30	247
12601	$C_{10}H_{12}O_2$	Propyl benzoate	230.85	226.0	32	247
12602	$C_{11}H_{10}$	1-Methylnaphthalene	244.6	232.0	46	247
12603	$C_{11}H_{10}$	2-Methylnaphthalene	241.15	229.4	44	236
12604	$C_{11}H_{14}O_2$	Butyl benzoate	249.0	235.0	52	247
12605	$C_{11}H_{14}O_2$	Isobutyl benzoate	241.9	231.2	40	247
12606	$C_{11}H_{16}O$	Methyl thymyl ether	216.5	Nonazeotrope		255
12607	$C_{11}H_{20}O$	Methyl α-terpineol ether	216.2	Nonazeotrope		255
12608	$C_{12}H_{10}$	Acenaphthene	277.9	242.5	71	236
12609	$C_{12}H_{10}$	Biphenyl	256.1	236.0	50	247
12610	$C_{12}H_{10}O$	Phenyl ether	259.0	243.0	80	247
12611	$C_{12}H_{16}O_2$	Isoamyl benzoate	262.0	239.4	60	236
12612	$C_{12}H_{16}O_3$	Isoamyl salicylate	277.5	Nonazeotrope		255
12613	$C_{12}H_{18}$	1,3,5-Triethylbenzene	215.5	212.0	18	247
12614	$C_{13}H_{12}$	Diphenylmethane	265.4	239.0	56	247
12615	$C_{14}H_{14}$	1,2-Diphenylethane	284.5	243.8	80	255

No.	Formula	B-Component Name	B.P., ° C.	Azeotropic Data B.P., ° C.	Wt. % A	Ref.
A =	**C_8H_7N**	**Indole**	**253.5**			
12616	C_8H_9BrO	*p*-Bromophenetole	234.2	Nonazeotrope		*255*
12617	$C_9H_{10}O$	Cinnamyl alcohol	257.0	Nonazeotrope		*255*
12618	$C_{10}H_{10}O_2$	Safrole	235.9	Nonazeotrope		*255*
12619	$C_{10}H_{12}O_2$	Eugenol	254.8	<251.8	>35	*255*
12620	$C_{10}H_{12}O_2$	Isoeugenol	268.8	Nonazeotrope		*255*
12621	$C_{10}H_{14}O$	Carvacrol	237.85	254.5	88	*255*
12622	$C_{11}H_{14}O_2$	1-Allyl-3,4-dimethoxybenzene	254.7	<251.8	>55	*255*
12623	$C_{11}H_{14}O_2$	1,2-Dimethyl-4-propenylbenzene	270.5	Nonazeotrope		*255*
12624	$C_{11}H_{16}O$	*p-tert*-Amylphenol	266.5	268.0	12	*255*
12625	$C_{12}H_{10}O$	Phenyl ether	259.0	Nonazeotrope		*255*
A =	**C_8H_7N**	**α-Toluonitrile**	**232**			
12626	$C_{10}H_{18}O$	Geraniol	229.5	~226	....	*243*
A =	**C_8H_8**	**Styrene**	**145.8**			
12627	C_8H_{10}	Ethylbenzene	136.15	Nonazeotrope		*241*
12628	C_8H_{10}	*m*-Xylene	139.2	Nonazeotrope		*241*
12629	C_8H_{10}	*o*-Xylene	142.6	Nonazeotrope		*243*
12630	$C_8H_{16}O_2$	Isobutyl isobutyrate	148.6	<145.5	>60	*255*
12631	$C_8H_{16}O_2$	Propyl isovalerate	155.7	Nonazeotrope		*255*
12632	C_9H_{20}	Nonane	149.5	144.0	75	*241*
A =	**C_8H_8O**	**Acetophenone**	**202.0**			
12633	$C_8H_8O_2$	Benzyl formate	203.0	Nonazeotrope		*232*
12634	$C_8H_8O_2$	Methyl benzoate	199.4	Nonazeotrope		*232*
12635	$C_8H_8O_2$	Phenyl acetate	195.7	Nonazeotrope		*232*
12636	$C_8H_{10}O$	*p*-Ethylphenol	218.8	219.5	15	*232*
12637	$C_8H_{10}O$	2,4-Xylenol	210.5	213.0	30	*255*
12638	$C_8H_{10}O$	3,4-Xylenol	226.8	Nonazeotrope		*232*
12639	$C_8H_{10}O_2$	*o*-Ethoxyphenol	216.5	Nonazeotrope		*232*
12640	$C_8H_{10}O_2$	Veratrol	205.5	Nonazeotrope		*254*
12641	$C_8H_{11}N$	Dimethylaniline	194.15	Nonazeotrope		*231*
12642	$C_8H_{11}N$	Ethylaniline	205.5	Nonazeotrope		*231*
12643	$C_8H_{11}N$	2,4-Xylidine	214.0	Nonazeotrope		*231*
12644	$C_8H_{14}O_4$	Propyl oxalate	214.2	Nonazeotrope		*232*
12645	$C_8H_{16}O_3$	Isoamyl lactate	202.4	<201.7	48	*232*
12646	$C_8H_{16}O_4$	2-(2-Ethoxyethoxy)ethyl acetate	218.5	Nonazeotrope		*255*
12647	$C_8H_{18}O$	Octyl alcohol	195.2	194.95	12.5	*232*
12648	$C_8H_{18}O$	*sec*-Octyl alcohol	180.4	Nonazeotrope		*232*
12649	$C_9H_{10}O_2$	Benzyl acetate	215.0	Nonazeotrope		*232*
12650	$C_9H_{10}O_2$	Ethyl benzoate	212.5	Nonazeotrope		*232*
12651	$C_9H_{13}N$	*N,N*-Dimethyl-*o*-toluidine	185.3	Nonazeotrope		*231*
12652	$C_9H_{13}N$	*N,N*-Dimethyl-*p*-toluidine	210.2	Nonazeotrope		*255*
12653	$C_{10}H_8$	Naphthalene	218.0	Nonazeotrope		*232*
12654	$C_{10}H_{14}O$	Thymol	232.9	Nonazeotrope		*232*
12655	$C_{10}H_{15}N$	Diethylaniline	217.05	Nonazeotrope		*231*
12656	$C_{10}H_{18}O$	Borneol	215.0	Nonazeotrope		*232*
12657	$C_{10}H_{18}O$	Citronellal	208.0	201.95	95	*232*
12658	$C_{10}H_{18}O$	Linaloöl	198.6	198.0	14	*232*
12659	$C_{10}H_{18}O$	β-Terpineol	210.5	Nonazeotrope		*232*
12660	$C_{10}H_{20}O$	Menthol	216.3	Nonazeotrope		*232*
12661	$C_{10}H_{20}O_2$	Methyl pelargonate	213.8	Nonazeotrope		*232*
12662	$C_{10}H_{22}S$	Isoamyl sulfide	214.8	Nonazeotrope		*246*
12663	$C_{11}H_{20}O$	Isobornyl methyl ether	192.4	Nonazeotrope		*255*
12664	$C_{12}H_{18}$	1,3,5-Triethylbenzene	215.5	Nonazeotrope		*232*
12665	$C_{12}H_{22}O$	Bornyl ethyl ether	204.9	Nonazeotrope		*255*
A =	**$C_8H_8O_2$**	**Anisaldehyde**	**249.5**			
12666	C_8H_9BrO	*p*-Bromophenetole	234.2	Nonazeotrope		*255*
12667	$C_9H_{10}O$	Cinnamyl alcohol	257.0	<248.0	....	*255*
12668	$C_{10}H_7Cl$	1-Chloronaphthalene	262.7	Nonazeotrope		*255*
12669	$C_{10}H_{10}O_2$	Isosafrole	252.0	248.6	60	*236*
12670	$C_{10}H_{10}O_2$	Methyl cinnamate	261.9	Nonazeotrope		*228*
12671	$C_{10}H_{10}O_2$	Safrole	235.9	Nonazeotrope		*236*
12672	$C_{10}H_{14}O$	Carvacrol	237.85	Nonazeotrope		*255*

No.	B-Component Formula	Name	B.P., ° C.	Azeotropic Data B.P., ° C.	Wt. % A	Ref.
A =	$C_8H_8O_2$	**Anisaldehyde** (*continued*)	**249.5**			
12673	$C_{10}H_{14}O$	Thymol	232.9	Nonazeotrope		*255*
12674	$C_{10}H_{20}O$	Citronellol	224.5	Nonazeotrope		*255*
12675	$C_{11}H_{14}O_2$	1-Allyl-3,4-dimethoxybenzene	255.0	Nonazeotrope		*236*
12676	$C_{11}H_{14}O_2$	Butyl benzoate	249.5	<248.8	~50	*228*
12677	$C_{11}H_{14}O_2$	1,2-Dimethoxy-4-propenylbenzene	270.5	Nonazeotrope		*255*
12678	$C_{11}H_{14}O_2$	Isobutyl benzoate	241.9	Nonazeotrope		*218*
12679	$C_{12}H_{10}O$	Phenyl ether	259.3	Nonazeotrope		*236*
12680	$C_{12}H_{16}O_2$	Isoamyl benzoate	262.0	Nonazeotrope		*228*
A =	$C_8H_8O_2$	**Benzyl Formate**	**203.0**			
12681	$C_8H_8O_2$	Methyl benzoate	199.4	Nonazeotrope		*229*
12682	$C_8H_8O_2$	Phenyl acetate	195.7	Nonazeotrope		*255*
12683	$C_8H_{10}O$	3,4-Xylenol	226.8	Nonazeotrope		*255*
12684	$C_8H_{10}O_2$	*m*-Dimethoxybenzene	214.7	Nonazeotrope		*217*
12685	$C_8H_{18}O$	Octyl alcohol	195.2	Nonazeotrope		*255*
12686	$C_8H_{18}O$	Octyl alcohol	195.15	195.0	3	*216*
12687	$C_{10}H_8$	Naphthalene	218.05	Nonazeotrope		*217*
12688	$C_{10}H_{16}$	*d*-Limonene	177.9	Nonazeotrope		*226*
12689	$C_{10}H_{16}$	γ-Terpinene	179.7	Nonazeotrope		*226*
12690	$C_{10}H_{16}O$	Camphor	209.1	Nonazeotrope		*228*
12691	$C_{10}H_{18}O$	Borneol	213.4	Nonazeotrope		*215*
12692	$C_{10}H_{18}O$	Citronellal	208.0	Nonazeotrope		*255*
12693	$C_{10}H_{18}O$	Linaloöl	198.6	197.5	....	*215*
12694	$C_{10}H_{18}O$	α-Terpineol	217.8	Nonazeotrope		*216*
12695	$C_{10}H_{20}O$	Menthol	216.4	Nonazeotrope		*215*
12696	$C_{10}H_{20}O_2$	Isoamyl isovalerate	192.7	Nonazeotrope		*255*
12697	$C_{11}H_{16}O$	Methyl thymol ether	216.5	Nonazeotrope		*237*
12698	$C_{12}H_{18}$	1,3,5-Triethylbenzene	216	Nonazeotrope		*226*
A =	$C_8H_8O_2$	**Methyl Benzoate**	**199.4**			
12699	$C_8H_{10}O$	2,4-Xylenol	210.5	Nonazeotrope		*255*
12700	$C_8H_{10}O_2$	Veratrol	205.5	Nonazeotrope		*237*
12701	$C_8H_{14}O_4$	Propyl oxalate	214	Nonazeotrope		*255*
12702	$C_8H_{16}O_3$	Isoamyl lactate	202.4	<198.8	....	*255*
12703	$C_8H_{16}O_3$	Isoamyl lactate	202.4	Nonazeotrope		*243*
12704	$C_8H_{16}O_4$	2-(2-Ethoxyethoxy)ethyl acetate	218.5	Nonazeotrope		*255*
12705	$C_8H_{18}O$	*n*-Octyl alcohol	195.2	194.4	35	*250*
12706	C_9H_8	Indene	182.6	Nonazeotrope		*255*
12707	$C_9H_{10}O_2$	Ethyl benzoate	212.5	Nonazeotrope		*255*
12708	$C_9H_{12}O$	Benzyl ethyl ether	185.0	Nonazeotrope		*237*
12709	$C_9H_{14}O$	Phorone	197.8	Nonazeotrope		*232*
12710	$C_9H_{18}O_3$	Isobutyl carbonate	190.3	Nonazeotrope		*255*
12711	$C_{10}H_8$	Naphthalene	218.0	Nonazeotrope		*255*
12712	$C_{10}H_{14}$	Cymene	176.7	Nonazeotrope		*255*
12713	$C_{10}H_{16}$	*d*-Limonene	177.8	Nonazeotrope		*210*
12714	$C_{10}H_{16}$	α-Terpinene	173.4	Nonazeotrope		*255*
12715	$C_{10}H_{16}$	γ-Terpinene	179.7	Nonazeotrope		*226*
12716	$C_{10}H_{16}O$	Camphor	209.1	Nonazeotrope		*232*
12717	$C_{10}H_{17}Cl$	Bornyl chloride	207.5	Nonazeotrope		*255*
12718	$C_{10}H_{18}O$	Borneol	213.4	Nonazeotrope		*216*
12719	$C_{10}H_{18}O$	Citronellal	~207.8	Nonazeotrope		*209*
12720	$C_{10}H_{18}O$	Linaloöl	198.7	197.8	~42	*208*
12721	$C_{10}H_{18}O$	β-Terpineol	210.5	Nonazeotrope		*255*
12722	$C_{10}H_{20}O$	Menthol	216.3	Nonazeotrope		*255*
12723	$C_{10}H_{20}O_2$	Ethyl caprylate	208.35	Nonazeotrope		*255*
12724	$C_{10}H_{20}O_2$	Isoamyl isovalerate	192.7	Nonazeotrope		*229*
12725	$C_{11}H_{16}O$	Methyl thymol ether	216.5	Nonazeotrope		*237*
12726	$C_{11}H_{24}O_2$	Diisoamyloxymethane	210.8	Nonazeotrope		*237*
12727	$C_{12}H_{18}$	1,3,5-Triethylbenzene	215.5	Nonazeotrope		*255*
A =	$C_8H_8O_2$	**Phenyl Acetate**	**195.7**			
12728	$C_8H_{10}O$	2,4-Xylenol	210.5	Nonazeotrope		*255*
12729	$C_8H_{10}O_2$	Veratrole	205.5	Nonazeotrope		*237*
12730	$C_8H_{18}O$	*n*-Octyl alcohol	195.15	192.4	53	*252*
12731	C_9H_8	Indene	182.6	Nonazeotrope		*255*
12732	C_9H_{12}	Pseudocumene	168.2	Nonazeotrope		*255*

No.	B-Component Formula	Name	B.P., ° C.	Azeotropic Data B.P., ° C.	Wt. % A	Ref.
A =	$C_8H_8O_2$	**Phenyl Acetate** (*continued*)	**195.7**			
12733	$C_9H_{12}O$	Benzyl ethyl ether	185.0	Nonazeotrope		237
12734	$C_9H_{14}O$	Phorone	198.2	Nonazeotrope		253
			197.8	<195.6	<90	232
12735	$C_9H_{18}O_3$	Isobutyl carbonate	190.3	Nonazeotrope		255
12736	$C_{10}H_8$	Naphthalene	218.05	Nonazeotrope		217
12737	$C_{10}H_{14}$	Cymene	176.7	Nonazeotrope		217
12738	$C_{10}H_{16}$	Camphene	158	Nonazeotrope		226
12739	$C_{10}H_{16}$	*d*-Limonene	177.8	177.5	7	218
12740	$C_{10}H_{16}$	Nopinene	163.8	Nonazeotrope		255
12741	$C_{10}H_{16}$	α-Terpinene	173.4	Nonazeotrope		255
12742	$C_{10}H_{16}$	γ-Terpinene	181.5	180.3	15	218
12743	$C_{10}H_{16}$	Thymene	179.7	179.3	18	210
12744	$C_{10}H_{18}O$	Borneol	213.2	Nonazeotrope		210
12745	$C_{10}H_{18}O$	Cineole	176.35	Nonazeotrope		237
12746	$C_{10}H_{18}O$	Citronellal	208.0	Nonazeotrope		255
12747	$C_{10}H_{18}O$	Linaloöl	198.6	193.5	61	209
12748	$C_{10}H_{18}O$	β-Terpineol	210.5	Nonazeotrope		255
12749	$C_{10}H_{20}O_2$	Ethyl caprylate	208.35	Nonazeotrope		255
12750	$C_{10}H_{22}O$	Isoamyl ether	173.2	Nonazeotrope		237
12751	$C_{11}H_{20}O$	Isobornyl methyl ether	192.4	Nonazeotrope		237
12752	$C_{11}H_{24}O_2$	Diisoamyloxymethane	210.8	Nonazeotrope		237
12753	$C_{12}H_{18}$	1,3,5-Triethylbenzene	216	Nonazeotrope		226
12754	$C_{12}H_{22}O$	Bornyl ethyl ether	204.9	Nonazeotrope		237
12755	$C_{12}H_{22}O$	Ethyl isobornyl ether	203.8	Nonazeotrope		237
A =	$C_8H_8O_2$	**α-Toluic Acid**	**266.5**			
12756	C_9H_8O	Cinnamaldehyde	253.5	Nonazeotrope		221
12757	$C_{10}H_7Br$	1-Bromonaphthalene	281.8	264.0	53.5	221
12758	$C_{10}H_7Cl$	1-Chloronaphthalene	262.7	255.9	30	221
12759	$C_{10}H_8$	Naphthalene	218.05	Nonazeotrope		221
12760	$C_{10}H_8O$	1-Naphthol	288.5	Nonazeotrope		221
12761	$C_{10}H_{10}O_2$	Isosafrole	252.0	251.5	11	221
12762	$C_{10}H_{10}O_2$	Methyl cinnamate	261.9	261.8	3	221
12763	$C_{10}H_{10}O_4$	Methyl phthalate	283.7	Nonazeotrope		221
12764	$C_{10}H_{12}O$	Anethole	235.7	Nonazeotrope		236
12765	$C_{10}H_{12}O_2$	Eugenol	254.8	Nonazeotrope		255
12766	$C_{10}H_{12}O_2$	Isoeugenol	268.8	<266.2	>58	255
12767	$C_{10}H_{18}O_4$	Propyl succinate	250.5	Nonazeotrope		255
12768	$C_{11}H_{10}$	1-Methylnaphthalene	244.6	243.2	~12	221
12769	$C_{11}H_{10}$	2-Methylnaphthalene	241.15	239.95	12	207
12770	$C_{11}H_{12}O_2$	Ethyl cinnamate	271.5	Nonazeotrope		221
12771	$C_{11}H_{14}O_2$	1-Allyl-3,4-dimethoxybenzene	255.0	Nonazeotrope		221
12772	$C_{11}H_{14}O_2$	Butyl benzoate	249.8	Nonazeotrope		221
12773	$C_{11}H_{14}O_2$	1,2-Dimethoxy-4-propenylbenzene	270.5	265.4	60	221
12774	$C_{11}H_{14}O_2$	Ethyl β-phenylpropionate	248.1	Nonazeotrope		255
12775	$C_{12}H_{10}$	Acenaphthene	277.9	262.2	71	221
12776	$C_{12}H_{10}$	Biphenyl	255.9	252.15	23.3	221
12777	$C_{12}H_{10}O$	Phenyl ether	259.3	255.05	27.8	236
12778	$C_{12}H_{16}O_2$	Isoamyl benzoate	262.0	259.85	26	221
12779	$C_{12}H_{18}$	1,3,5-Triethyl benzene	215.5	Nonazeotrope		255
12780	$C_{12}H_{22}O_4$	Isoamyl oxalate	268.0	262.35	50	221
12781	$C_{13}H_{10}$	Fluorene	295	265.8	90	255
12782	$C_{13}H_{12}$	Diphenylmethane	265.4	258.7	35	221
12783	$C_{13}H_{12}O$	Benzyl phenyl ether	286.5	<266.0	>90	255
12784	$C_{14}H_{12}$	Stilbene	306.5	Nonazeotrope		255
12785	$C_{14}H_{14}$	1,2-Diphenylethane	284.5	264.3	~90	221
A =	$C_8H_8O_3$	**Methyl Salicylate**	**222.95**			
12786	$C_8H_{10}O$	*p*-Ethylphenol	218.8	Nonazeotrope		255
12787	$C_8H_{10}O$	Phenethyl alcohol	219.4	218.0	43	209
12788	$C_8H_{10}O$	3,4-Xylenol	226.8	Nonazeotrope		244
12789	$C_8H_{10}O_2$	*m*-Dimethoxybenzene	214.7	Nonazeotrope		255
12790	$C_8H_{10}O_2$	*o*-Ethoxyphenol	216.5	Nonazeotrope		255
12791	$C_8H_{10}O_2$	2-Phenoxyethanol	245.2	Nonazeotrope		255
12792	$C_8H_{11}NO$	*o*-Phenetidine	232.5	Nonazeotrope		232

	B-Component			Azeotropic Data		
No.	Formula	Name	B.P., ° C.	B.P., ° C.	Wt. % A	Ref.
A =	**$C_8H_8O_3$**	**Methyl Salicylate** (*continued*)	**222.95**			
12793	$C_8H_{12}O_4$	Ethyl fumarate	217.85	Nonazeotrope		*255*
12794	$C_8H_{12}O_4$	Ethyl maleate	223.3	221.95	60	*250*
12795	$C_8H_{18}O_3$	2-(2-Butoxyethoxy)ethanol	231.2	220.7	78	*255*
12796	C_9H_7N	Quinoline	237.3	Nonazeotrope		*233*
12797	$C_9H_{10}O$	*p*-Methylacetophenone	226.35	Nonazeotrope		*232*
12798	$C_9H_{10}O$	Propiophenone	217.7	Nonazeotrope		*232*
12799	$C_9H_{10}O_2$	Benzyl acetate	215.0	Nonazeotrope		*225*
12800	$C_9H_{10}O_2$	Ethyl benzoate	212.6	Nonazeotrope		*225*
12801	$C_9H_{10}O_2$	Methyl α-toluate	215.3	Nonazeotrope		*255*
12802	$C_9H_{12}O$	3-Phenylpropanol	235.6	Nonazeotrope		*225*
12803	$C_{10}H_8$	Naphthalene	218.05	Nonazeotrope		*208*
12804	$C_{10}H_{10}O_2$	Safrole	234.5	Nonazeotrope		*236*
12805	$C_{10}H_{12}O_2$	Ethyl α-toluate	228.75	Nonazeotrope		*209*
12806	$C_{10}H_{12}O_2$	Propyl benzoate	230.85	Nonazeotrope		*228*
12807	$C_{10}H_{14}O$	Carvone	231.0	Nonazeotrope		*232*
12808	$C_{10}H_{14}O$	Thymol	232.9	Nonazeotrope		*216*
12809	$C_{10}H_{14}O_2$	*m*-Diethoxybenzene	235.4	Nonazeotrope		*255*
12810	$C_{10}H_{16}O$	Pulegone	223.8	Nonazeotrope		*232*
12811	$C_{10}H_{18}O$	Borneol	213.4	Nonazeotrope		*216*
12812	$C_{10}H_{18}O$	Geraniol	229.7	222.2	97	*216*
12813	$C_{10}H_{18}O$	Linaloöl	198.6	Nonazeotrope		*255*
12814	$C_{10}H_{18}O$	α-Terpineol	217.8	216.0	~37	*208*
12815	$C_{10}H_{20}O$	Citronellol	224.5	220.5	....	*216*
12816	$C_{10}H_{20}O$	Menthol	216.4	216.25	15	*209*
12817	$C_{10}H_{20}O_2$	Ethyl caprylate	208.35	Nonazeotrope		*255*
12818	$C_{10}H_{22}O$	Decyl alcohol	232.9	Nonazeotrope		*216*
12819	$C_{11}H_{10}$	1-Methylnaphthalene	244.6	Nonazeotrope		*255*
12820	$C_{11}H_{10}$	2-Methylnaphthalene	241.15	Nonazeotrope		*255*
12821	$C_{11}H_{20}O$	Methyl α-terpineol ether	216.2	Nonazeotrope		*255*
12822	$C_{11}H_{22}O_3$	Isoamyl carbonate	232.2	Nonazeotrope		*228*
12823	$C_{12}H_{18}$	1,3,5-Triethylbenzene	215.5	Nonazeotrope		*218*
12824	$C_{12}H_{20}O_2$	Bornyl acetate	227.7	222.3	10?	*210*
12825	$C_{13}H_{28}$	Tridecane	234.0	Nonazeotrope		*255*
A =	**C_8H_9BrO**	***p*-Bromophenetole**	**234.2**			
12826	$C_8H_{10}O$	3,4-Xylenol	226.8	226.0	12	*255*
12827	C_9H_7N	Isoquinoline	240.8	Nonazeotrope		*255*
12828	C_9H_8O	Cinnamaldehyde	253.7	Nonazeotrope		*255*
12829	$C_9H_{10}O$	*p*-Methylacetophenone	226.25	Nonazeotrope		*255*
12830	$C_{10}H_8$	Naphthalene	218.0	Nonazeotrope		*255*
12831	$C_{10}H_{10}O_2$	Safrole	235.9	233.5	78	*255*
12832	$C_{10}H_{12}O$	Anethole	235.7	233.0	70	*242*
12833	$C_{10}H_{14}N_2$	Nicotine	247.5	Nonazeotrope		*255*
12834	$C_{10}H_{14}O$	Carvone	231.0	Nonazeotrope		*255*
12835	$C_{11}H_{10}$	2-Methylnaphthalene	241.15	Nonazeotrope		*255*
A =	**C_8H_{10}**	**Ethylbenzene**	**136.15**			
12836	C_8H_{10}	*m*-Xylene	139.2	Nonazeotrope		*241*
12837	C_8H_{10}	*p*-Xylene	138.2	Nonazeotrope		*243*
12838	C_8H_{18}	Octane	125.75	<125.6	<12	*241*
12839	$C_8H_{18}O$	Butyl ether	142.2	Nonazeotrope		*243*
12840	$C_8H_{18}O$	Isobutyl ether	122.3	Nonazeotrope		*238*
12841	$C_8H_{19}N$	Diisobutylamine	138.5	<135.5	<62	*255*
A =	**C_8H_{10}**	***m*-Xylene**	**139.2**			
12842	C_8H_{10}	*o*-Xylene	144.3	Nonazeotrope		*255*
12843	C_8H_{10}	*p*-Xylene	138.2	Nonazeotrope		*243*
12844	$C_8H_{16}O_2$	Isobutyl isobutyrate	147.3	Nonazeotrope		*207*
12845	$C_8H_{18}O$	Butyl ether	142.2	Nonazeotrope		*228*
12846	$C_8H_{18}O$	Octyl alcohol	195.2	Nonazeotrope		*255*
12847	$C_8H_{18}O$	*sec*-Octyl alcohol	179.0	Nonazeotrope		*217*
12848	$C_8H_{19}N$	Diisobutylamine	138.5	<137.5	<49	*231*
A =	**C_8H_{10}**	***o*-Xylene**	**143.6**			
12849	$C_8H_{18}O$	Butyl ether	142.4	<142.0	<22	*238*

No.	Formula	B-Component Name	B.P., ° C.	Azeotropic Data B.P., ° C.	Wt. % A	Ref.
A =	**$C_8H_{10}O$**	**Benzyl Methyl Ether**	**167.8**			
12850	$C_8H_{14}O$	Methylheptenone	173.2	Nonazeotrope		*255*
12851	$C_8H_{16}O$	2-Octanone	172.85	Nonazeotrope		*255*
12852	$C_8H_{16}O_2$	Butyl butyrate	166.4	166.0	30	*237*
12853	$C_8H_{16}O_2$	Isoamyl propionate	160.7	Nonazeotrope		*237*
12954	$C_8H_{18}O$	*sec*-Octyl alcohol	180.4	Nonazeotrope		*255*
12855	$C_8H_{20}SiO_4$	Ethyl silicate	168.8	<165.5	....	*237*
12856	C_9H_{12}	Mesitylene	164.6	<163.5	>15	*238*
12857	$C_9H_{18}O_2$	Isoamyl butyrate	181.05	Nonazeotrope		*237*
12858	$C_9H_{18}O_2$	Isobutyl isovalerate	171.2	Nonazeotrope		*237*
12859	$C_{10}H_{16}$	Camphene	159.6	158.0	<30	*238*
12860	$C_{10}H_{16}$	Nopinene	163.8	161.2	35	*238*
12861	$C_{10}H_{16}$	α-Terpinene	173.4	166.4	65	*238*
A =	**$C_8H_{10}O$**	***o*-Ethylphenol**	**216.5**			
12862	$C_{10}H_{18}O$	Citronellal	208.0	Nonazeotrope		*255*
A =	**$C_8H_{10}O$**	***p*-Ethylphenol**	**218.8**			
12863	$C_8H_{10}O$	Phenethyl alcohol	219.4	>220.5	>55	*255*
12864	$C_8H_{10}O$	2,4-Xylenol	210.5	Nonazeotrope		*255*
12865	$C_8H_{10}O_2$	Veratrole	206.8	Nonazeotrope		*255*
12866	$C_8H_{10}O_2$	2-Phenoxyethanol	245.2	Nonazeotrope		*255*
12867	$C_8H_{11}N$	Ethylaniline	217.05	214.0	60	*231*
12868	$C_8H_{11}NO$	*o*-Phenetidine	232.5	Nonazeotrope		*231*
12869	$C_8H_{12}O_4$	Ethyl fumarate	217.85	223.0	48	*242*
12870	$C_8H_{12}O_4$	Ethyl maleate	223.3	226.3	38	*255*
12871	$C_8H_{18}O$	Octyl alcohol	195.2	Nonazeotrope		*255*
12872	C_9H_7N	Quinoline	237.3	<239.5	>11	*255*
12873	$C_9H_{10}O$	*p*-Methylacetophenone	226.35	229.5	30	*232*
12874	$C_9H_{10}O$	Propiophenone	217.7	224.5	....	*232*
12875	$C_9H_{10}O_2$	Benzyl acetate	215.0	221.0	60	*242*
12876	$C_9H_{10}O_2$	Ethyl benzoate	212.5	219.8	80	*255*
12877	$C_9H_{13}N$	*N,N*-Dimethyl-*p*-toluidine	210.2	Nonazeotrope		*231*
12878	$C_{10}H_8$	Naphthalene	218.0	215.0	45	*242*
12879	$C_{10}H_{12}O_2$	Propyl benzoate	230.85	Nonazeotrope		*255*
12880	$C_{10}H_{15}N$	Diethylaniline	217.05	214.0	60	*231*
12881	$C_{10}H_{18}O$	Citronellal	208.0	Nonazeotrope		*255*
12882	$C_{10}H_{18}O$	α-Terpineol	218.85	<219.7	>58	*255*
12883	$C_{10}H_{22}O$	Decyl alcohol	232.8	Nonazeotrope		*255*
12884	$C_{10}H_{22}S$	Isoamyl sulfide	214.8	<213.5	>23	*246*
12885	$C_{11}H_{16}O$	Methyl thymyl ether	216.5	<216.3	>20	*255*
12886	$C_{11}H_{20}O$	Methyl α-terpineol ether	216.2	<215.9	>14	*255*
12887	$C_{11}H_{22}O_3$	Isoamyl carbonate	232.2	Nonazeotrope		*255*
12888	$C_{12}H_{16}O_2$	Isoamyl benzoate	241.9	Nonazeotrope		*255*
12889	$C_{12}H_{18}$	1,3,5-Triethylbenzene	215.5	212.0	40	*242*
A =	**$C_8H_{10}O$**	***p*-Methylanisole**	**177.05**			
12890	$C_8H_{11}N$	Dimethylaniline	194.15	Nonazeotrope		*231*
12891	$C_8H_{16}O$	2-Octanone	172.85	Nonazeotrope		*255*
12892	$C_8H_{16}O_2$	Butyl butyrate	166.4	Nonazeotrope		*237*
12893	$C_8H_{16}O_2$	Isoamyl propionate	160.7	Nonazeotrope		*237*
12894	$C_8H_{18}O$	Octyl alcohol	195.15	Nonazeotrope		*256*
12895	$C_8H_{18}O$	*sec*-Octyl alcohol	180.4	176.3	79	*256*
12896	$C_8H_{18}S$	Butyl sulfide	185.0	Nonazeotrope		*255*
12897	C_9H_8	Indene	183.0	Nonazeotrope		*221*
12898	C_9H_{12}	Pseudocumene	~168.2	Nonazeotrope		*221*
12899	$C_9H_{13}N$	Dimethyl-*o*-toluidine	185.35	Nonazeotrope		*231*
12900	$C_9H_{18}O_2$	Butyl isovalerate	177.6	176.4	58	*237*
12901	$C_9H_{18}O_2$	Isoamyl butyrate	181.05	Nonazeotrope		*237*
12902	$C_9H_{18}O_2$	Isoamyl isobutyrate	169.8	Nonazeotrope		*237*
12903	$C_9H_{18}O_2$	Isobutyl isovalerate	171.35	Nonazeotrope		*237*
12904	$C_{10}H_{14}$	Butylbenzene	183.2	Nonazeotrope		*228*
12905	$C_{10}H_{14}$	Cymene	176.7	Nonazeotrope?		*228*
12906	$C_{10}H_{16}$	α-Terpinene	173.4	Nonazeotrope		*238*
12907	$C_{10}H_{16}$	Terpinolene	184.6	Nonazeotrope		*238*
12908	$C_{10}H_{18}O$	Cineole	176.35	175.35	35	*207*
12909	$C_{10}H_{20}O_2$	Isoamyl isovalerate	192.7	Nonazeotrope		*237*
12910	$C_{10}H_{22}O$	Isoamyl ether	173.2	172.5	29.5	*229*
12911	$C_{10}H_{23}N$	Diisoamylamine	188.2	Nonazeotrope		*231*

No.	B-Component Formula	Name	B.P., ° C.	Azeotropic Data B.P., ° C.	Wt. % A	Ref.
A =	$C_8H_{10}O$	**Phenethyl Alcohol**	**219.4**			
12912	$C_8H_{10}O$	3,4-Xylenol	226.8	Nonazeotrope		255
12913	$C_8H_{10}O_2$	2-Phenoxyethanol	245.2	Nonazeotrope		255
12914	$C_8H_{11}N$	Dimethylaniline	194.05	Nonazeotrope		231
12915	$C_8H_{11}N$	Ethylaniline	205.5	Nonazeotrope		225
12916	$C_8H_{11}N$	2,4-Xylidine	214.0	Nonazeotrope		231
12917	$C_8H_{11}N$	3,4-Xylidine	225.5	Nonazeotrope		231
12918	$C_8H_{11}NO$	*o*-Phenetidine	232.5	Nonazeotrope		231
12919	$C_8H_{12}O_4$	Ethyl fumarate	217.85	Nonazeotrope		255
12920	$C_8H_{12}O_4$	Ethyl maleate	223.3	Nonazeotrope		255
12921	$C_8H_{16}O_3$	Isoamyl lactate	202.4	Nonazeotrope		255
12922	$C_8H_{18}O_3$	2-(2-Butoxyethoxy)ethanol	231.2	<219.0	<92	255
12923	$C_9H_{10}O$	*p*-Methylacetophenone	226.35	Nonazeotrope		232
12924	$C_9H_{10}O$	Propiophenone	217.7	Nonazeotrope		232
12925	$C_9H_{10}O_2$	Benzyl acetate	214.9	Nonazeotrope		209
12926	$C_9H_{10}O_2$	Ethyl benzoate	212.6	Nonazeotrope		215
12927	$C_9H_{10}O_3$	Ethyl salicylate	233.7	Nonazeotrope		216
12928	$C_9H_{13}N$	*N,N*-Dimethyl-*p*-toluidine	210.2	208.5	30	231
12929	$C_{10}H_8$	Naphthalene	218.05	214.2	44	208
12930	$C_{10}H_{10}O_2$	Safrole	235.9	Nonazeotrope		255
12931	$C_{10}H_{12}O$	Anethole	235.7	Nonazeotrope		255
12932	$C_{10}H_{12}O_2$	Ethyl *α*-toluate	228.75	Nonazeotrope		215
12933	$C_{10}H_{12}O_2$	Propyl benzoate	230.85	Nonazeotrope		255
12934	$C_{10}H_{14}O$	Carvacrol	237.85	Nonazeotrope		255
12935	$C_{10}H_{14}O$	Carvone	231.0	Nonazeotrope		232
12936	$C_{10}H_{14}O$	Thymol	232.8	Nonazeotrope		210
12937	$C_{10}H_{15}N$	Diethylaniline	217.05	213.95	40	231
12938	$C_{10}H_{16}O$	Pulegone	223.8	Nonazeotrope		232
12939	$C_{10}H_{18}O$	Borneol	213.4	213.0	20	225
12940	$C_{10}H_{18}O$	Citronellal	208.0	Nonazeotrope		255
12941	$C_{10}H_{18}O$	*α*-Terpineol	218.85	217.85	33	229
12942	$C_{10}H_{20}O$	Menthol	216.3	215.05	30	229
12943	$C_{11}H_{10}$	1-Methylnaphthalene	244.9	Nonazeotrope		217
12944	$C_{11}H_{16}O$	Methyl thymyl ether	216.5	~215.0	....	255
12945	$C_{11}H_{17}N$	Isoamylaniline	256.0	Nonazeotrope		231
12946	$C_{11}H_{20}O$	*α*-Terpineol methyl ether	216.2	215.5	....	225
12947	$C_{12}H_{10}$	Biphenyl	254.9	Nonazeotrope		217
12948	$C_{12}H_{18}$	1,3,5-Triethylbenzene	215.5	212.5	....	217
12949	$C_{12}H_{20}O_2$	Bornyl acetate	227.6	Nonazeotrope		215
A =	$C_8H_{10}O$	**Phenetole**	**170.45**			
12950	$C_8H_{11}N$	Dimethylaniline	194.15	Nonazeotrope		231
12951	$C_8H_{14}O$	Methylheptenone	173.2	170.1	90?	232
12952	$C_8H_{16}O$	2-Octanone	172.85	170.0	92	232
12953	$C_8H_{16}O_2$	Butyl butyrate	166.4	Nonazeotrope		237
12954	$C_8H_{16}O_2$	Hexyl acetate	171.5	169.9	<75	237
12955	$C_8H_{16}O_2$	Isoamyl propionate	160.3	Nonazeotrope		237
12956	$C_8H_{18}O$	*sec*-Octyl alcohol	179.0	Nonazeotrope		236
12957	$C_8H_{18}S$	Butyl sulfide	185.0	Nonazeotrope		246
12958	$C_8H_{20}SiO_4$	Ethyl silicate	168.8	<166.0	....	237
12959	C_9H_8	Indene	182.8	Nonazeotrope		228
12960	C_9H_{12}	Cumene	168.2	168.15	<10	238
12961	C_9H_{12}	Mesitylene	164.6	Nonazeotrope		210
12962	C_9H_{12}	Propylbenzene	159.3	Nonazeotrope		238
12963	C_9H_{12}	Pseudocumene	168.2	168.15	<10	228
12964	$C_9H_{13}N$	Dimethyl-*o*-toluidine	185.35	Nonazeotrope		231
12965	$C_9H_{18}O_2$	Butyl isovalerate	177.6	Nonazeotrope		237
12966	$C_9H_{18}O_2$	Isoamyl butyrate	178.5	Nonazeotrope		237
12967	$C_9H_{18}O_2$	Isoamyl isobutyrate	169.8	169.2	40?	237
12968	$C_9H_{18}O_2$	Isobutyl isovalerate	171.4	170.1	65	237
12969	$C_9H_{18}O_3$	Isobutyl carbonate	190.3	Nonazeotrope		237
12970	$C_{10}H_{14}$	Cymene	176.7	Nonazeotrope		228
12971	$C_{10}H_{16}$	Camphene	159.6	Nonazeotrope		228
12972	$C_{10}H_{16}$	Dipentene	177.7	Nonazeotrope		238
12973	$C_{10}H_{16}$	*d*-Limonene	177.8	170.35	97?	228
12974	$C_{10}H_{16}$	Nopinene	163.8	Nonazeotrope		238

No.	Formula	B-Component Name	B.P., ° C.	Azeotropic Data B.P., ° C.	Wt. % A	Ref.
A =	$C_8H_{10}O$	**Phenetole** (*continued*)	**170.45**			
12975	$C_{10}H_{16}$	α-Pinene	155.8	Nonazeotrope		*228*
12976	$C_{10}H_{16}$	α-Terpinene	173.4	170.0	86	*238*
12977	$C_{10}H_{16}$	γ-Terpinene	179.9	Nonazeotrope		*228*
12978	$C_{10}H_{18}O$	Cineole	176.35	Nonazeotrope		*225*
12979	$C_{10}H_{20}O_2$	Isoamyl isovalerate	192.7	Nonazeotrope		*237*
12980	$C_{10}H_{22}O$	Isoamyl ether	173.2	169.2	65	*229*
12981	$C_{10}H_{23}N$	Diisoamylamine	188.2	Nonazeotrope		*231*
A =	$C_8H_{10}O$	**2,4-Xylenol**	**210.5**			
12982	$C_8H_{12}O_4$	Ethyl fumarate	217.85	219.65	32	*255*
12983	$C_8H_{12}O_4$	Ethyl maleate	223.3	223.7	....	*255*
12984	$C_8H_{16}O_3$	Isoamyl lactate	202.4	>212.2	<30	*255*
12985	C_9H_7N	Quinoline	237.3	239.0	8	*255*
12986	$C_9H_{10}O$	*p*-Methylacetophenone	226.35	227.0	85	*255*
12987	$C_9H_{10}O$	Propiophenone	217.7	221.0	65	*255*
12988	$C_9H_{10}O_2$	Benzyl acetate	215.0	216.8	36	*255*
12989	$C_9H_{10}O_2$	Ethyl benzoate	212.5	>214.5	>32	*255*
12990	$C_{10}H_{16}O$	Camphor	209.1	217.0	50	*255*
12991	$C_{10}H_{20}O_2$	Isoamyl isovalerate	192.7	Nonazeotrope		*255*
12992	$C_{10}H_{22}S$	Isoamyl sulfide	214.8	<209.5	<88	*255*
12993	$C_{12}H_{20}O_2$	Bornyl acetate	227.6	Nonazeotrope		*255*
A =	$C_8H_{10}O$	**3,4-Xylenol**	**226.8**			
12994	$C_8H_{10}O_2$	*o*-Ethoxyphenol	216.5	Nonazeotrope		*255*
12995	$C_8H_{10}O_2$	2-Phenoxyethanol	245.2	Nonazeotrope		*255*
12996	$C_8H_{11}N$	2,4-Xylidine	214.0	Nonazeotrope		*231*
12997	$C_8H_{11}N$	Ethylaniline	205.5	Nonazeotrope		*231*
12998	$C_8H_{11}NO$	*o*-Phenetidine	232.5	232.65	8	*231*
12999	$C_8H_{11}NO$	*p*-Phenetidine	249.9	Nonazeotrope		*231*
13000	$C_8H_{12}O_4$	Ethyl fumarate	217.85	228.2	65	*1*, 206*
13001	$C_8H_{12}O_4$	Ethyl maleate	223.3	230.0	55	*207*
13002	$C_8H_{16}O_2$	Caprylic acid	238.5	Nonazeotrope		*255*
13003	$C_8H_{16}O_3$	Isoamyl lactate	202.4	Nonazeotrope		*255*
13004	$C_8H_{18}O$	Octyl alcohol	195.2	Nonazeotrope		*255*
13005	C_9H_7N	Quinoline	237.3	241.95	35	*248*
13006	$C_9H_{10}O$	Cinnamyl alcohol	257.0	Nonazeotrope		*255*
13007	$C_9H_{10}O$	*p*-Methylacetophenone	226.35	231.35	51	*248*
13008	$C_9H_{10}O$	Propiophenone	217.7	228.5	67	*232*
13009	$C_9H_{10}O_2$	Benzyl acetate	215.0	Nonazeotrope		*255*
13010	$C_9H_{10}O_2$	Ethyl benzoate	212.5	Nonazeotrope		*255*
13011	$C_9H_{10}O_3$	Ethyl salicylate	233.8	Nonazeotrope		*255*
13012	$C_9H_{12}O$	Mesitol	220.5	Nonazeotrope		*255*
13013	$C_9H_{12}O$	3-Phenylpropanol	235.6	Nonazeotrope		*255*
13014	$C_9H_{13}N$	*N,N*-Dimethyl-*p*-toluidine	210.2	Nonazeotrope		*231*
13015	$C_{10}H_8$	Naphthalene	218.0	217.6	16	*244*
13016	$C_{10}H_9N$	Quinaldine	246.5	>248.0	20	*255*
13017	$C_{10}H_{12}O_2$	Ethyl α-toluate	228.75	230.8	42	*242*
13018	$C_{10}H_{12}O_2$	Propyl benzoate	230.85	231.9	33	*255*
13019	$C_{10}H_{14}O$	Thymol	232.9	Nonazeotrope		*229*
13020	$C_{10}H_{15}N$	Diethylaniline	217.05	217.0	8	*231*
13021	$C_{10}H_{16}O$	Camphor	209.1	227.55	73	*248*
13022	$C_{10}H_{18}O$	Borneol	215.0	Nonazeotrope		*255*
13023	$C_{10}H_{18}O$	Citronellal	208.0	Nonazeotrope		*255*
13024	$C_{10}H_{18}O$	Linaloöl	198.6	Nonazeotrope		*255*
13025	$C_{10}H_{18}O$	α-Terpineol	218.85	Nonazeotrope		*255*
13026	$C_{10}H_{20}O$	Menthol	216.3	Nonazeotrope		*255*
13027	$C_{10}H_{20}O_2$	Ethyl caprylate	208.35	Nonazeotrope		*255*
13028	$C_{10}H_{22}S$	Isoamyl sulfide	214.8	Nonazeotrope		*246*
13029	$C_{11}H_{14}O_2$	Isobutyl benzoate	241.9	Nonazeotrope		*255*
13030	$C_{11}H_{16}O$	Methyl thymyl ether	216.5	Nonazeotrope		*255*
13031	$C_{11}H_{20}O$	Methyl α-terpineol ether	216.2	Nonazeotrope		*255*
13032	$C_{11}H_{22}O_3$	Isoamyl carbonate	232.2	Nonazeotrope		*255*
13033	$C_{12}H_{18}$	1,3,5-Triethylbenzene	215.5	Nonazeotrope		*255*
13034	$C_{12}H_{20}O_2$	Bornyl acetate	227.6	>229.8	>37	*255*
13035	$C_{13}H_{28}$	Tridecane	234.0	223.5	58	*242*

No.	Formula	B-Component Name	B.P., ° C.	Azeotropic Data B.P., ° C.	Wt. % A	Ref.
A =	$C_8H_{10}O_2$	***m*-Dimethoxybenzene**	**214.7**			
13036	$C_8H_{11}N$	2,4-Xylidine	214.0	<211.8	<56	255
13037	$C_8H_{11}N$	3,4-Xylidine	225.5	Nonazeotrope		255
13038	$C_8H_{12}O_4$	Ethyl fumarate	217.85	211.2	....	237
13039	$C_8H_{12}O_4$	Ethyl maleate	223.3	<212.5	>82	255
13040	$C_9H_{10}O_2$	Benzyl acetate	215.0	<214.0	<60	255
13041	$C_9H_{10}O_2$	Ethyl benzoate	212.5	<212.35	....	237
13042	$C_{10}H_{18}O$	Borneol	213.4	213.0	....	256
13043	$C_{10}H_{18}O$	α-Terpineol	218.85	<214.0	>70	255
13044	$C_{10}H_{18}O$	α-Terpineol	218.0	Nonazeotrope		256
13045	$C_{10}H_{20}O$	Menthol	216.4	214.2	....	256
13046	$C_{10}H_{22}S$	Isoamyl sulfide	214.8	<213.5	>44	255
13047	$C_{11}H_{20}O$	Terpineol methyl ether	216.2	Nonazeotrope		217
13048	$C_{12}H_{20}O_2$	Bornyl acetate	227.6	Nonazeotrope		237
A =	$C_8H_{10}O_2$	***m*-Ethoxyphenol**	**243.8**			
13049	$C_{11}H_{14}O_2$	Butyl benzoate	249.0	Nonazeotrope		255
A =	$C_8H_{10}O_2$	***o*-Ethoxyphenol**	**216.5**			
13050	$C_8H_{10}O_2$	2-Phenoxyethanol	245.2	Nonazeotrope		255
13051	$C_8H_{11}N$	Dimethylaniline	194.15	Nonazeotrope		231
13052	$C_8H_{11}N$	Ethylaniline	205.5	Nonazeotrope		231
13053	$C_8H_{11}N$	2,4-Xylidine	214.0	Nonazeotrope		231
13054	$C_8H_{12}O_4$	Ethyl maleate	223.3	Nonazeotrope		255
13055	$C_8H_{14}O_4$	Ethyl succinate	216.5	Azeotropic		243
13056	$C_8H_{18}O_3$	2-(2-Butoxyethoxy)ethanol	231.2	Nonazeotrope		255
13057	$C_9H_{10}O$	Propiophenone	217.7	218.3	....	232
13058	$C_9H_{10}O_2$	Benzyl acetate	~214.9	218	....	215
13059	$C_9H_{10}O_2$	Ethyl benzoate	212.6	Nonazeotrope		228
13060	$C_9H_{12}O$	Mesitol	220.5	Nonazeotrope		255
13061	$C_9H_{13}N$	*N,N*-Dimethyl-*p*-toluidine	210.2	Nonazeotrope		231
13062	$C_{10}H_8$	Naphthalene	218.0	<215.5	>72	255
13063	$C_{10}H_{14}O$	Thymol	232.9	Nonazeotrope		222
13064	$C_{10}H_{15}N$	Diethylaniline	217.05	<216.2	>57	231
13065	$C_{10}H_{16}O$	Camphor	209.1	Nonazeotrope		255
13066	$C_{10}H_{16}O$	Pulegone	223.8	Nonazeotrope		232
13067	$C_{10}H_{18}O$	Borneol	211.8	Nonazeotrope		243
13068	$C_{10}H_{20}O$	Menthol	216.3	<216.0	....	255
13069	$C_{10}H_{20}O_2$	Ethyl caprylate	208.35	Nonazeotrope		255
13070	$C_{10}H_{22}S$	Isoamyl sulfide	214.8	<214.2	....	246
13071	$C_{12}H_{18}$	1,3,5-Triethylbenzene	215.5	<214.5	>30	255
13072	$C_{12}H_{20}O_2$	Bornyl acetate	227.6	Nonazeotrope		215
A =	$C_8H_{10}O_2$	**2-Phenoxyethanol**	**245.2**			
13073	$C_9H_{10}O$	Cinnamyl alcohol	257.0	Nonazeotrope		255
13074	$C_9H_{10}O_3$	Ethyl salicylate	233.8	Nonazeotrope		255
13075	$C_9H_{12}O$	γ-Phenylpropanol	235.6	Nonazeotrope		255
13076	$C_{10}H_7Cl$	1-Chloronaphthalene	262.7	Nonazeotrope		255
13077	$C_{10}H_8$	Naphthalene	218.0	Nonazeotrope		255
13078	$C_{10}H_{10}O_2$	Isosafrole	252.0	<244.5	>68	255
13079	$C_{10}H_{18}O$	Geraniol	229.6	Nonazeotrope		255
13080	$C_{11}H_{10}$	1-Methylnaphthalene	244.6	<243.0	>43	255
13081	$C_{11}H_{10}$	2-Methylnaphthalene	241.15	239.5	30	255
13082	$C_{12}H_{10}$	Acenaphthene	277.9	Nonazeotrope		255
13083	$C_{12}H_{10}O$	Phenyl ether	259.0	Nonazeotrope		255
13084	$C_{13}H_{12}$	Diphenylmethane	265.4	Nonazeotrope		255
A =	$C_8H_{10}O_2$	**Veratrole**	**206.8**			
13085	$C_8H_{11}N$	Dimethylaniline	194.15	Nonazeotrope		231
13086	$C_8H_{11}N$	Ethylaniline	205.5	<203.0	....	255
13087	$C_8H_{12}O_4$	Ethyl fumarate	217.85	<205.9	>69	237
13088	$C_9H_{10}O_2$	Benzyl acetate	215.0	Nonazeotrope		237
13089	$C_9H_{10}O_2$	Ethyl benzoate	212.6	Nonazeotrope		237
13090	$C_9H_{13}N$	Dimethyl-*o*-toluidine	185.35	Nonazeotrope		231
13091	$C_{10}H_8$	Naphthalene	218.05	Nonazeotrope		253
13092	$C_{10}H_{15}N$	Diethylaniline	217.05	Nonazeotrope		231
13093	$C_{10}H_{18}O$	Borneol	213.4	Nonazeotrope		253

		B-Component		Azeotropic Data		
No.	Formula	Name	B.P., ° C.	B.P., ° C.	Wt. % A	Ref.
A =	**$C_8H_{10}O_2$**	**Veratrole (*continued*)**	**206.8**			
13094	$C_{10}H_{20}O_2$	Isoamyl isovalerate	192.7	Nonazeotrope		*237*
13095	$C_{12}H_{18}$	1,3,5-Triethylbenzene	215.5	Nonazeotrope		*217*
A =	**$C_8H_{11}N$**	**Dimethylaniline**	**194.05**			
13096	$C_8H_{18}O$	Octyl alcohol	195.2	191.75	49.5	*231*
13097	$C_8H_{18}O$	*sec*-Octyl alcohol	180.4	Nonazeotrope		*231*
			180.4	180.0	....	*225*
13098	C_9H_8	Indene	182.6	Nonazeotrope		*231*
13099	$C_9H_{10}O$	Propiophenone	217.7	Nonazeotrope		*231*
13100	C_9H_{12}	Mesitylene	164.6	Nonazeotrope		*231*
13101	C_9H_{12}	Propylbenzene	159.3	Nonazeotrope		*231*
13102	$C_9H_{12}O$	Benzyl ethyl ether	185.0	Nonazeotrope		*255*
13103	$C_{10}H_8$	Naphthalene	218.0	Nonazeotrope		*231*
13104	$C_{10}H_{14}$	Cymene	176.7	Nonazeotrope		*231*
13105	$C_{10}H_{16}$	Camphene	159.6	Nonazeotrope		*231*
13106	$C_{10}H_{16}$	Dipentene	177.7	Nonazeotrope		*231*
13107	$C_{10}H_{16}$	*d*-Limonene	177.8	Nonazeotrope		*225*
			177.8	174	27	*243*
13108	$C_{10}H_{16}$	Nopinene	163.8	Nonazeotrope		*231*
13109	$C_{10}H_{16}$	α-Pinene	155.8	Nonazeotrope		*231*
13110	$C_{10}H_{16}$	α-Terpinene	173.4	Nonazeotrope		*231*
13111	$C_{10}H_{16}$	Terpinolene	185	~179	~35	*243*
13112	$C_{10}H_{16}$	Thymene	179.7	Nonazeotrope		*212*
13113	$C_{10}H_{16}O$	Camphor	209.1	Nonazeotrope		*231*
13114	$C_{10}H_{16}O$	Fenchone	193	191	~35	*243*
13115	$C_{10}H_{18}O$	Borneol	215.0	Nonazeotrope		*231*
13116	$C_{10}H_{18}O$	Cineole	176.35	Nonazeotrope		*231*
13117	$C_{10}H_{18}O$	Linaloöl	198.6	193.9	85	*231*
13118	$C_{10}H_{18}O$	α-Terpineol	218.85	Nonazeotrope		*231*
13119	$C_{10}H_{20}O$	Citronellol	224.4	Nonazeotrope		*231*
13120	$C_{10}H_{20}O$	Menthol	216.3	Nonazeotrope		*231*
13121	$C_{10}H_{22}O$	Amyl ether	187.5	<187.0	<27	*231*
13122	$C_{10}H_{22}O$	Isoamyl ether	173.2	Nonazeotrope		*231*
13123	$C_{12}H_{22}O$	Bornyl ethyl ether	204.9	Nonazeotrope		*231*
A =	**$C_8H_{11}N$**	**Ethylaniline**	**205.5**			
13124	$C_8H_{18}O$	*n*-Octyl alcohol	195.2	194.9	15	*231*
13125	$C_8H_{18}O$	*sec*-Octyl alcohol	180.4	Nonazeotrope		*231*
13126	$C_9H_{10}O$	Propiophenone	217.7	Nonazeotrope		*231*
13127	$C_9H_{12}O$	Phenyl propyl ether	190.5	Nonazeotrope		*255*
13128	$C_{10}H_8$	Naphthalene	218.0	Nonazeotrope		*231*
			218.1	205	~10	*243*
13129	$C_{10}H_{14}O$	Thymol	232.9	Nonazeotrope		*231*
13130	$C_{10}H_{16}$	Terpinolene	184.6	Nonazeotrope		*231*
13131	$C_{10}H_{16}O$	Camphor	209.1	Nonazeotrope		*231*
13132	$C_{10}H_{18}O$	Borneol	215.0	Nonazeotrope		*231*
13133	$C_{10}H_{18}O$	Geraniol	229.6	Nonazeotrope		*255*
13134	$C_{10}H_{18}O$	Linaloöl	198.6	Nonazeotrope		*231*
13135	$C_{10}H_{18}O$	Menthone	207	<205	~60	*243*
13136	$C_{10}H_{18}O$	Menthone	209.5	Nonazeotrope		*255*
13137	$C_{10}H_{18}O$	α-Terpineol	218.85	Nonazeotrope		*231*
13138	$C_{10}H_{20}O$	Citronellol	244.4	Nonazeotrope		*231*
13139	$C_{10}H_{20}O$	Menthol	216.3	Nonazeotrope		*231*
13140	$C_{10}H_{22}O$	*n*-Decyl alcohol	232.8	Nonazeotrope		*231*
13141	$C_{11}H_{16}O$	Methyl thymyl ether	216.5	Nonazeotrope		*255*
13142	$C_{11}H_{20}O$	Isobornyl methyl ether	192.4	Nonazeotrope		*231*
13143	$C_{11}H_{20}O$	Methyl α-terpineol ether	216.3	Nonazeotrope		*243*
13144	$C_{11}H_{24}O_2$	Diisoamyloxymethane	207.3	204	58	*243*
13145	$C_{12}H_{22}O$	Bornyl ethyl ether	204.9	<203.0	<48	*231*
A =	**$C_8H_{11}N$**	***s*-Collidine**	**170.0**			
13146	C_8H_{18}	2,2,4-Trimethylpentane	99.3	Nonazeotrope		*255*
A =	**$C_8H_{11}N$**	**2,4-Xylidine**	**214.0**			
13147	$C_8H_{18}O$	*n*-Octyl alcohol	195.2	Nonazeotrope		*231*
13148	$C_9H_{10}O$	Propiophenone	217.7	Nonazeotrope		*231*
13149	$C_{10}H_{14}O$	Thymol	232.9	Nonazeotrope		*231*

No.	Formula	B-Component Name	B.P., ° C.	Azeotropic Data B.P., ° C.	Wt. % A	Ref.
A =	**$C_8H_{11}N$**	**2,4-Xylidine (*continued*)**	**214.0**			
13150	$C_{10}H_{16}O$	Camphor	209.1	Nonazeotrope		*231*
13151	$C_{10}H_{20}O$	Menthol	216.3	213.5	70	*231*
13152	$C_{11}H_{16}O$	Methyl thymyl ether	216.5	<212.5	....	*255*
13153	$C_{12}H_{18}$	1,3,5-Triethylbenzene	215.5	<212.5	>51	*231*
13154	$C_{12}H_{22}O$	Ethyl bornyl ether	204.9	Nonazeotrope		*255*
A =	**$C_8H_{11}N$**	**3,4-Xylidine**	**225.5**			
13155	$C_9H_{12}O$	3-Phenylpropanol	235.6	Nonazeotrope		*231*
13156	$C_{10}H_8$	Naphthalene	218.0	Nonazeotrope		*231*
13157	$C_{10}H_{14}O$	Carvacrol	237.85	Nonazeotrope		*255*
13158	$C_{10}H_{20}O$	Citronellol	224.4	223.5	40	*231*
13159	$C_{11}H_{10}$	2-Methylnaphthalene	241.15	Nonazeotrope		*207, 231*
13160	$C_{12}H_{22}O$	Bornyl ethyl ether	204.9	Nonazeotrope		*255*
A =	**$C_8H_{11}NO$**	***o*-Phenetidine**	**232.5**			
13161	$C_8H_{18}O_3$	2-(2-Butoxyethoxy)ethanol	231.2	226.0	52	*255*
13162	$C_9H_{10}O$	*p*-Methylacetophenone	226.35	Nonazeotrope		*231*
13163	$C_9H_{10}O_3$	Ethyl salicylate	233.8	232.2	82	*231*
13164	$C_9H_{12}O$	3-Phenylpropanol	235.6	Nonazeotrope		*231*
13165	$C_{10}H_8$	Naphthalene	218.0	Nonazeotrope		*231*
13166	$C_{10}H_{10}O_2$	Isosafrole	252.0	Nonazeotrope		*231*
13167	$C_{10}H_{10}O_2$	Safrole	235.9	232.38	86.5	*231*
13168	$C_{10}H_{12}O$	Anethole	235.7	232.25	75	*231*
13169	$C_{10}H_{14}O$	Carvacrol	237.85	238.0	13	*231*
13170	$C_{10}H_{14}O$	Carvone	231.0	>232.8	<74	*231*
13171	$C_{10}H_{14}O$	Thymol	232.9	234.3	45.5	*231*
13172	$C_{10}H_{16}O$	Carvenone	234.5	235.0	30	*231*
13173	$C_{10}H_{16}O$	Pulegone	223.8	Nonazeotrope		*231*
13174	$C_{10}H_{18}O$	α-Terpineol	218.85	Nonazeotrope		*231*
13175	$C_{10}H_{20}O$	Menthol	216.3	Nonazeotrope		*231*
13176	$C_{10}H_{22}O$	*n*-Decyl alcohol	232.8	232.0	>52	*231*
13177	$C_{11}H_{10}$	1-Methylnaphthalene	244.6	Nonazeotrope		*231*
			244.6	Nonazeotrope		*228*
13178	$C_{11}H_{10}$	2-Methylnaphthalene	241.15	Nonazeotrope		*207, 231*
13179	$C_{12}H_{18}$	1,3,5-Triethylbenzene	215.5	Nonazeotrope		*231*
A =	**$C_8H_{11}NO$**	***p*-Phenetidine**	**249.9**			
13180	$C_9H_{10}O$	Cinnamyl alcohol	257.0	Nonazeotrope		*231*
13181	$C_9H_{10}O_3$	Ethyl salicylate	233.8	Nonazeotrope		*231*
13182	$C_9H_{12}O$	3-Phenylpropanol	235.6	Nonazeotrope		*231*
13183	$C_9H_{12}O_2$	Benzyloxyethanol	265.2	Nonazeotrope		*255*
13184	$C_{10}H_7Cl$	1-Chloronaphthalene	262.7	249.7	90	*231*
13185	$C_{10}H_{10}O_2$	Isosafrole	252.0	248.8	64	*231*
13186	$C_{10}H_{10}O_2$	Safrole	235.9	Nonazeotrope		*231*
13187	$C_{10}H_{12}O$	Anethole	235.7	Nonazeotrope		*231*
13188	$C_{10}H_{14}O$	Carvacrol	237.85	Nonazeotrope		*231*
13189	$C_{10}H_{14}O$	Carvone	231.0	Nonazeotrope		*231*
13190	$C_{10}H_{14}O$	Thymol	232.9	Nonazeotrope		*231*
13191	$C_{10}H_{16}O$	Carvenone	234.5	Nonazeotrope		*231*
13192	$C_{11}H_{10}$	1-Methylnaphthalene	244.6	243.95	27	*231*
13193	$C_{11}H_{10}$	2-Methylnaphthalene	241.15	240.85	15	*207*
13194	$C_{11}H_{14}O_2$	1-Allyl-3,4-dimethoxybenzene	254.7	249.4	75	*231*
13195	$C_{11}H_{14}O_2$	1,2-Dimethoxy-4-propenylbenzene	270.5	Nonazeotrope		*231*
13196	$C_{12}H_{10}$	Biphenyl	256.1	249.5	90	*231*
13197	$C_{12}H_{10}O$	Phenyl ether	259.0	249.75	85	*231*
13198	$C_{12}H_{16}O_3$	Isoamyl salicylate	277.5	Nonazeotrope		*231*
13199	$C_{13}H_{12}$	Diphenylmethane	265.4	Nonazeotrope		*231*
A =	**$C_8H_{12}O_4$**	**Ethyl Fumarate**	**217.85**			
13200	$C_8H_{14}O_4$	Propyl oxalate	214	Nonazeotrope		*255*
13201	$C_8H_{16}O_2$	Caprylic acid	238.5	Nonazeotrope		*255*
13202	$C_8H_{16}O_4$	2-(2-Ethoxyethoxy)ethyl acetate	218.5	217.0	62	*242*
13203	$C_9H_{10}O$	*p*-Methylacetophenone	226.35	Nonazeotrope		*232*
13204	$C_9H_{10}O$	Propiophenone	217.7	216.8	53	*232*
13205	$C_9H_{10}O_2$	Benzyl acetate	215.0	Nonazeotrope		*229*
13206	$C_9H_{10}O_2$	Ethyl benzoate	212.5	Nonazeotrope		*255*
13207	$C_{10}H_8$	Naphthalene	218.0	216.7	58	*207*
13208	$C_{10}H_{10}O_2$	Safrole	235.9	Nonazeotrope		*237*

No.	Formula	B-Component Name	B.P., ° C.	Azeotropic Data B.P., ° C.	Wt. % A	Ref.
A =	**$C_8H_{12}O_4$**	**Ethyl Fumarate** (*continued*)	**217.85**			
13209	$C_{10}H_{12}O$	Anethole	235.7	Nonazeotrope		*237*
13210	$C_{10}H_{12}O_2$	Ethyl α-toluate	228.75	Nonazeotrope		*255*
13211	$C_{10}H_{14}O$	Thymol	232.9	233.35	12.5	*242*
13212	$C_{10}H_{14}O_2$	*m*-Diethoxybenzene	235.0	Nonazeotrope		*237*
13213	$C_{10}H_{16}O$	Camphor	209.1	Nonazeotrope		*232*
13214	$C_{10}H_{16}O$	Pulegone	223.8	Nonazeotrope		*232*
13215	$C_{10}H_{18}O$	Borneol	215.0	Nonazeotrope		*206*
13216	$C_{10}H_{18}O$	Citronellal	208.0	Nonazeotrope		*255*
13217	$C_{10}H_{18}O$	Geraniol	229.6	Nonazeotrope		*255*
13218	$C_{10}H_{18}O$	α-Terpineol	218.85	Nonazeotrope		*255*
13219	$C_{10}H_{20}O$	Menthol	216.3	216.0	30	*206*
13220	$C_{10}H_{20}O_2$	Methyl pelargonate	213.8	Nonazeotrope		*229*
13221	$C_{11}H_{10}$	2-Methylnaphthalene	241.15	Nonazeotrope		*207*
13222	$C_{11}H_{16}O$	Methyl thymol ether	216.5	<212.8	....	*237*
13223	$C_{11}H_{20}O$	Methyl α-terpineol ether	216.2	209.5	43	*237*
13224	$C_{11}H_{22}O_2$	Ethyl pelargonate	227	Nonazeotrope		*255*
13225	$C_{12}H_{18}$	1,3,5-Triethylbenzene	215.5	<215.0	<43	*255*
13226	$C_{12}H_{20}O_2$	Bornyl acetate	227.6	Nonazeotrope		*229*
A =	**$C_8H_{12}O_4$**	**Ethyl Maleate**	**223.3**			
13227	$C_8H_{14}O_4$	Propyl oxalate	214	Nonazeotrope		*255*
13228	$C_8H_{16}O_2$	Caprylic acid	238.5	Nonazeotrope		*255*
13229	$C_9H_{10}O$	*p*-Methylacetophenone	226.35	223.15	88	*232*
13230	$C_9H_{10}O$	Propiophenone	217.7	Nonazeotrope		*239*
13231	$C_9H_{10}O_2$	Benzyl acetate	215.0	Nonazeotrope		*225*
13232	$C_9H_{10}O_2$	Ethyl benzoate	212.5	Nonazeotrope		*252*
13233	$C_9H_{10}O_3$	Ethyl salicylate	233.8	Nonazeotrope		*257*
13234	$C_{10}H_8$	Naphthalene	218.0	217.65	23	*205*
13235	$C_{10}H_{10}O_2$	Safrole	235.9	Nonazeotrope		*236*
13236	$C_{10}H_{12}O$	Anethole	235.7	Nonazeotrope		*237*
13237	$C_{10}H_{12}O_2$	Propyl benzoate	230.85	Nonazeotrope		*255*
13238	$C_{10}H_{14}O$	Carvacrol	237.85	238.7	12	*255*
13239	$C_{10}H_{14}O$	Carvone	231.0	Nonazeotrope		*232*
13240	$C_{10}H_{14}O$	Thymol	232.9	234.9	27	*242*
13242	$C_{10}H_{16}O$	Pulegone	223.8	221.8	53	*232*
13243	$C_{10}H_{18}O$	Citronellal	208.0	Nonazeotrope		*255*
13244	$C_{10}H_{18}O$	α-Terpineol	218.85	218.3	20	*206*
13245	$C_{10}H_{20}O$	Citronellol	224.4	<222.3	<50	*255*
13246	$C_{10}H_{22}O$	Decyl alcohol	232.8	Nonazeotrope		*255*
13247	$C_{11}H_{10}$	2-Methylnaphthalene	241.15	Nonazeotrope		*207*
13248	$C_{11}H_{16}O$	Methyl thymyl ether	216.5	<215.9	<12	*255*
13249	$C_{11}H_{20}O$	Methyl terpineol ether	216.2	<214.8	<18	*255*
13250	$C_{11}H_{22}O_3$	Isoamyl carbonate	232.2	Nonazeotrope		*255*
13251	$C_{12}H_{18}$	1,3,5-Triethylbenzene	215.5	Nonazeotrope		*255*
A =	**$C_8H_{14}O$**	**Methylheptenone**	**173.2**			
13252	$C_8H_{18}O$	Octyl alcohol	195.2	Nonazeotrope		*232*
13253	$C_8H_{18}O$	*sec*-Octyl alcohol	180.4	Nonazeotrope		*232*
13254	$C_8H_{18}S$	Butyl sulfide	185.0	Nonazeotrope		*246*
13255	C_9H_8	Indene	182.6	Nonazeotrope		*232*
13256	C_9H_{12}	Mesitylene	164.6	Nonazeotrope		*232*
13257	C_9H_{12}	Propylbenzene	159.3	Nonazeotrope		*255*
13258	$C_9H_{18}O_2$	Isoamyl butyrate	181.05	Nonazeotrope		*232*
13259	$C_9H_{18}O_2$	Isoamyl isobutyrate	169.8	Nonazeotrope		*232*
13260	$C_9H_{18}O_2$	Isobutyl isovalerate	171.2	Nonazeotrope		*232*
13261	$C_{10}H_{14}$	Butylbenzene	183.1	Nonazeotrope		*232*
13262	$C_{10}H_{14}$	Cymene	176.7	172.7	72	*232*
13263	$C_{10}H_{16}$	Camphene	159.6	157.5	12	*232*
			159.6	Nonazeotrope		*225*
13264	$C_{10}H_{16}$	Dipentene	177.7	170.9	52.5	*232*
13265	$C_{10}H_{16}$	*d*-Limonene	177.8	170.9	52.5	*209*
13266	$C_{10}H_{16}$	α-Pinene	155.8	Nonazeotrope		*253*
13267	$C_{10}H_{16}$	α-Terpinene	173.4	170.0	42	*232*
13268	$C_{10}H_{18}O$	Cineole	176.35	171.9	52	*232*
13269	$C_{10}H_{22}$	Decane	173.3	169.0	42	*232*
13270	$C_{10}H_{22}O$	Isoamyl ether	172.6	~171.5	....	*254*

No.	B-Component Formula	B-Component Name	B.P., ° C.	Azeotropic Data B.P., ° C.	Azeotropic Data Wt. % A	Ref.
A =	**$C_8H_{14}O_4$**	**Ethyl Succinate**	**217.25**			
13271	$C_8H_{16}O_2$	Caprylic acid	238.5	Nonazeotrope		*255*
13272	C_9H_8	Indene	182.6	Nonazeotrope		*255*
13273	$C_9H_{10}O$	*p*-Methylacetophenone	226.35	Nonazeotrope		*232*
13274	$C_9H_{10}O$	Propiophenone	217.7	216.7	67	*232*
13275	$C_9H_{10}O_2$	Ethyl benzoate	212.4	Nonazeotrope		*209*
13276	$C_{10}H_8$	Naphthalene	218.05	216.3	61.5	*209*
13277	$C_{10}H_{10}O_2$	Safrole	235.9	Nonazeotrope		*237*
13278	$C_{10}H_{12}O_2$	Ethyl α-toluate	228.75	Nonazeotrope		*229*
13279	$C_{10}H_{14}O$	Thymol	232.9	>233.0	....	*255*
13280	$C_{10}H_{16}$	*d*-Limonene	177.8	Nonazeotrope		*218*
13281	$C_{10}H_{16}$	γ-Terpinene	179.9	Nonazeotrope		*226*
13282	$C_{10}H_{16}$	Thymene	179.7	Nonazeotrope		*218*
13283	$C_{10}H_{16}O$	Camphor	209.1	Nonazeotrope		*232*
13284	$C_{10}H_{16}O$	Pulegone	~223.8	Nonazeotrope		*232*
13285	$C_{10}H_{18}O$	Borneol	213.4	Nonazeotrope		*215*
13286	$C_{10}H_{18}O$	Geraniol	229.7	Reacts		*215*
13287	$C_{10}H_{20}O$	Menthol	216.4	215	....	*215*
13288	$C_{10}H_{20}O_2$	Methyl pelargonate	213.8	212.5	....	*229*
13289	$C_{11}H_{10}$	1-Methylnaphthalene	245.1	Nonazeotrope		*226*
13290	$C_{11}H_{10}$	2-Methylnaphthalene	241.15	Nonazeotrope		*207*
13291	$C_{11}H_{16}O$	Methyl thymyl ether	216.5	<213.5	>38	*255*
13292	$C_{11}H_{20}O$	Methyl α-terpineol ether	216.2	<212	18?	*237*
13293	$C_{11}H_{22}O_2$	Ethyl pelargonate	227	Nonazeotrope		*229*
13294	$C_{11}H_{24}O_2$	Diisoamyloxymethane	210.8	<210.4	....	*237*
13295	$C_{12}H_{18}$	1,3,5-Triethylbenzene	215.5	<214.0	<46	*242*
13296	$C_{12}H_{20}O_2$	Bornyl acetate	227.6	Nonazeotrope		*229*
A =	**$C_8H_{14}O_4$**	**Propyl Oxalate**	**214**			
13297	$C_9H_{10}O_2$	Benzyl acetate	215.0	<212.5	....	*229*
13298	$C_{10}H_8$	Naphthalene	218.1	Nonazeotrope		*226*
13299	$C_{10}H_{14}O$	Thymol	232.9	Nonazeotrope		*255*
13300	$C_{10}H_{16}$	*d*-Limonene	177.9	Nonazeotrope		*226*
13301	$C_{10}H_{16}$	α-Pinene	155.8	Nonazeotrope		*226*
13302	$C_{10}H_{17}Cl$	Bornyl chloride	207.5	205.5	25	*255*
13303	$C_{12}H_{18}$	1,3,5-Triethylbenzene	216	<210	>70	*226*
A =	**$C_8H_{15}N$**	**Caprylonitrile**	**205.2**			
13304	$C_8H_{18}O$	Octyl alcohol	195.2	Nonazeotrope		*255*
A =	**C_8H_{16}**	**1,3-Dimethylcyclohexane**	**120.7**			
13305	C_8H_{18}	Octane	125.75	Nonazeotrope		*241*
13306	$C_8H_{18}O$	Isobutyl ether	122.3	120.0	72	*238*
A =	**$C_8H_{16}O$**	**2-Octanone**	**172.85**			
13307	$C_8H_{16}O_2$	Butyl butyrate	166.4	Nonazeotrope		*232*
13308	$C_8H_{16}O_2$	Ethyl caproate	167.7	Nonazeotrope		*232*
13309	$C_8H_{16}O_2$	Hexyl acetate	171.5	171.4 ?	....	*232*
13310	$C_8H_{18}O$	*sec*-Octyl alcohol	180.4	Nonazeotrope		*232*
13311	$C_8H_{18}S$	Butyl sulfide	185.0	Nonazeotrope		*255*
13312	$C_8H_{18}S$	Isobutyl sulfide	172.0	169.8	50	*246*
13313	C_9H_8	Indene	182.6	Nonazeotrope		*255*
13314	C_9H_{12}	Mesitylene	164.6	Nonazeotrope		*232*
13315	C_9H_{12}	Propylbenzene	159.3	Nonazeotrope		*232*
13316	C_9H_{12}	Pseudocumene	168.2	168.0	....	*232*
13317	$C_9H_{18}O_2$	Isoamyl butyrate	181.05	Nonazeotrope		*232*
13318	$C_9H_{18}O_2$	Isobutyl isovalerate	171.2	Nonazeotrope		*232*
13319	$C_{10}H_{14}$	Butylbenzene	183.2	Nonazeotrope		*228*
13320	$C_{10}H_{14}$	Cymene	176.7	172.5	75	*232*
			175.3	Nonazeotrope		*243*
13321	$C_{10}H_{16}$	Camphene	159.6	158.0	13	*232*
13322	$C_{10}H_{16}$	Dipentene	177.7	170.0	55	*232*
13323	$C_{10}H_{16}$	*d*-Limonene	177.8	170	~57	*253*
13324	$C_{10}H_{16}$	α-Pinene	155.8	Nonazeotrope		*232*
13325	$C_{10}H_{16}$	α-Terpinene	173.4	169.0	42	*232*
13326	$C_{10}H_{16}$	γ-Terpinene	183	171.0	75	*232*
13327	$C_{10}H_{18}O$	Cineole	176.35	172.0	55	*232*

No.	Formula	B-Component Name	B.P., ° C.	Azeotropic Data B.P., ° C.	Wt. % A	Ref.
A =	**$C_8H_{16}O_2$**	**Butyl Butyrate**	**166.4**			
13328	$C_8H_{16}O_2$	Ethyl caproate	167.7	Nonazeotrope		*255*
13329	$C_8H_{16}O_2$	Isoamyl propionate	160.7	Nonazeotrope		*255*
13330	$C_8H_{16}O_2$	Isobutyl butyrate	156.9	Nonazeotrope		*255*
13331	$C_8H_{20}SiO_4$	Ethyl silicate	168.8	Nonazeotrope		*229*
13332	C_9H_8	Indene	182.6	Nonazeotrope		*255*
13333	C_9H_{12}	Mesitylene	164.6	Nonazeotrope		*226*
13334	C_9H_{12}	Propylbenzene	159.3	Nonazeotrope		*255*
13335	$C_9H_{18}O$	2,6-Dimethyl-4-heptanone	168.0	Nonazeotrope		*232*
13336	$C_9H_{18}O_2$	Isoamyl isobutyrate	169.8	Nonazeotrope		*255*
13337	$C_9H_{18}O_2$	Isobutyl isovalerate	171.2	Nonazeotrope		*255*
13338	$C_{10}H_{14}$	Cymene	176.7	Nonazeotrope		*255*
13339	$C_{10}H_{16}$	Camphene	159.6	158.0	30	*242*
13340	$C_{10}H_{16}$	*d*-Limonene	177.9	Nonazeotrope		*226*
13341	$C_{10}H_{16}$	Nopinene	163.8	160.5	40	*242*
13342	$C_{10}H_{16}$	α-Pinene	155.8	<155.0	<20	*255*
13343	$C_{10}H_{16}$	α-Pinene	155.8	Nonazeotrope		*226*
13344	$C_{10}H_{16}$	α-Terpinene	173.4	<165.0	<74	*255*
13345	$C_{10}H_{18}O$	Cineole	176.35	Nonazeotrope		*237*
13346	$C_{10}H_{22}O$	Isoamyl ether	173.4	Nonazeotrope		*237*
A =	**$C_8H_{16}O_2$**	**Caprylic Acid**	**238.5**			
13347	$C_9H_{10}O$	*p*-Methylacetophenone	226.35	Nonazeotrope		*255*
13348	$C_{10}H_7Cl$	1-Chloronaphthalene	262.7	Nonazeotrope		*255*
13349	$C_{10}H_7Cl$	1-Chloronaphthalene	262.7	237.0	....	*223*
13350	$C_{10}H_8$	Naphthalene	218.05	216.2	6	*221*
13351	$C_{10}H_{10}O_2$	Safrole	235.9	232.5	~45	*221*
13352	$C_{10}H_{12}O$	Anethole	235.7	<234.0	>35	*242*
13353	$C_{10}H_{12}O_2$	Ethyl α-toluate	228.75	Nonazeotrope		*255*
13354	$C_{10}H_{14}O$	Carvacrol	237.85	237.6	25	*255*
13355	$C_{10}H_{14}O$	Thymol	232.9	<232.8	....	*255*
13356	$C_{11}H_{10}$	1-Methylnaphthalene	244.6	233.5	52	*222*
13357	$C_{11}H_{10}$	2-Methylnaphthalene	241.15	235.0	48	*207*
13358	$C_{11}H_{16}O$	Methyl thymol ether	216.5	Nonazeotrope		*255*
13359	$C_{11}H_{20}O$	Methyl α-terpineol ether	216.2	Nonazeotrope		*223*
13360	$C_{11}H_{22}O_3$	Isoamyl carbonate	232.2	<231.8	>10	*255*
13361	$C_{12}H_{18}$	1,3,5-Triethylbenzene	215.5	~214.3	4	*221*
13362	$C_{12}H_{20}O_2$	Bornyl acetate	227.6	Nonazeotrope		*255*
A =	**$C_8H_{16}O_2$**	**Ethyl Caproate**	**167.7**			
13363	$C_8H_{18}S$	Isobutyl sulfide	172.0	Nonazeotrope		*255*
13364	C_9H_{12}	Mesitylene	164.6	Nonazeotrope		*255*
13365	C_9H_{12}	Propylbenzene	158.9	Nonazeotrope		*226*
13366	C_9H_{12}	Pseudocumene	168.2	167.6	....	*226*
13367	$C_9H_{18}O$	2,6-Dimethyl-4-heptanone	168.0	167.5	60	*232*
13368	$C_9H_{18}O_2$	Isobutyl isovalerate	171.2	Nonazeotrope		*255*
13369	$C_{10}H_{16}$	Camphene	158	159	15	*226*
13370	$C_{10}H_{16}$	α-Pinene	155.8	Nonazeotrope		*226*
13371	$C_{10}H_{16}$	α-Terpinene	173.4	Nonazeotrope		*255*
13372	$C_{10}H_{18}O$	Cineole	176.35	Nonazeotrope		*237*
13373	$C_{10}H_{22}O$	Isoamyl ether	173.2	Nonazeotrope		*237*
A =	**$C_8H_{16}O_2$**	**Hexyl Acetate**	**171.5**			
13374	$C_8H_{18}O$	*sec*-Octyl alcohol	180.4	Nonazeotrope		*255*
13375	$C_9H_{18}O_2$	Isoamyl butyrate	181.05	Nonazeotrope		*255*
13376	$C_{10}H_{18}O$	Cineole	176.35	Nonazeotrope		*237*
13377	$C_{10}H_{22}O$	Isoamyl ether	173.4	~171.2	>80	*237*
A =	**$C_8H_{16}O_2$**	**Isoamyl Propionate**	**160.7**			
13378	$C_8H_{16}O_2$	Isobutyl butyrate	156.9	Nonazeotrope		*255*
13379	$C_8H_{16}O_2$	Propyl isovalerate	155.7	Nonazeotrope		*255*
13380	$C_8H_{18}O$	*sec*-Octyl alcohol	160.3	Nonazeotrope		*216*
13381	$C_8H_{18}S$	Isobutyl sulfide	172.0	Nonazeotrope		*255*
13382	$C_8H_{20}SiO_4$	Ethyl silicate	168.8	Nonazeotrope		*255*
13383	C_9H_{12}	Mesitylene	164.6	Nonazeotrope		*226*
13384	$C_9H_{18}O$	2,6-Dimethyl-4-heptanone	168.0	Nonazeotrope		*232*
13385	$C_9H_{20}O_2$	Diisobutoxymethane	163.8	Nonazeotrope		*237*

No.	B-Component Formula	Name	B.P., ° C.	Azeotropic Data B.P., ° C.	Wt. % A	Ref.
A =	**$C_8H_{16}O_2$**	**Isoamyl Propionate (*continued*)**	**160.7**			
13386	$C_{10}H_{14}$	Cymene	176.7	Nonazeotrope		255
13387	$C_{10}H_{16}$	Camphene	159.6	155.5	46	250
			~158	~155.5	<50	243
13388	$C_{10}H_{16}$	Nopinene	163.8	157.0	57	242
13389	$C_{10}H_{16}$	α-Pinene	155.8	154	~25	243
13390	$C_{10}H_{18}O$	Cineole	176.35	Nonazeotrope		237
13391	$C_{10}H_{22}$	2,7-Dimethyloctane	160.25	157	~49	243
13392	$C_{10}H_{22}O$	Isoamyl ether	173.2	Nonazeotrope		237
A =	**$C_8H_{16}O_2$**	**Isobutyl Butyrate**	**156.9**			
13393	$C_8H_{20}SiO_4$	Ethyl silicate	168.8	Nonazeotrope		255
13394	C_9H_{12}	Mesitylene	164.6	Nonazeotrope		253
13395	$C_{10}H_{16}$	Nopinene	163.8	<155.4	<75	255
13396	$C_{10}H_{16}$	α-Pinene	155.8	<153.0	<50	226
13397	$C_{10}H_{16}$	α-Terpinene	173.3	Nonazeotrope		226
A =	**$C_8H_{16}O_2$**	**Isobutyl Isobutyrate**	**148.6**			
13398	$C_8H_{18}O$	Butyl ether	142.4	Nonazeotrope		237
13399	C_9H_{12}	Cumene	152.8	Nonazeotrope		255
13400	$C_{10}H_{16}$	Camphene	158	153	63	226
13401	$C_{10}H_{16}$	α-Pinene	155.8	Nonazeotrope		226
A =	**$C_8H_{16}O_2$**	**Propyl Isovalerate**	**155.7**			
13402	$C_8H_{18}O$	Butyl ether	142.4	Nonazeotrope		237
13403	$C_8H_{20}SiO_4$	Ethyl silicate	168.8	Nonazeotrope		255
13404	C_9H_{12}	Cumene	152.8	Nonazeotrope		255
13405	C_9H_{12}	Mesitylene	164.6	Nonazeotrope		253
13406	C_9H_{12}	Propylbenzene	158.9	Nonazeotrope		226
13407	$C_9H_{20}O_2$	Diisobutoxymethane	163.8	Nonazeotrope		237
13408	$C_{10}H_{16}$	Camphene	159.6	145	65	225
13409	$C_{10}H_{16}$	Nopinene	163.8	155.0	75	242
13410	$C_{10}H_{16}$	α-Pinene	155.8	144.0	53	225
13411	$C_{10}H_{16}$	α-Terpinene	173.4	Nonazeotrope		255
13412	$C_{10}H_{22}$	2,7-Dimethyloctane	160.25	152	57	253
A =	**$C_8H_{16}O_3$**	**Isoamyl Lactate**	**202.4**			
13413	$C_8H_{18}O$	Octyl alcohol	195.2	Nonazeotrope		255
13414	$C_9H_{14}O$	Phorone	197.8	Nonazeotrope		232
13415	$C_{10}H_8$	Naphthalene	218.05	Nonazeotrope		218
13416	$C_{10}H_{14}O$	Carvacrol	237.85	Nonazeotrope		255
13417	$C_{10}H_{14}O$	Thymol	232.9	Nonazeotrope		222
13418	$C_{10}H_{16}O$	Camphor	209.1	Nonazeotrope		232
13419	$C_{10}H_{17}Cl$	Bornyl chloride	207.2	201.8	....	255
13420	$C_{10}H_{18}O$	Citronellal	208.0	<202.2	....	255
13421	$C_{10}H_{18}O$	Linaloöl	198.6	<198.5	....	255
13422	$C_{10}H_{20}O_2$	Ethyl caprylate	208.35	<202.0	....	255
13423	$C_{10}H_{22}S$	Isoamyl sulfide	214.8	Nonazeotrope		245
13424	$C_{12}H_{18}$	1,3,5-Triethylbenzene	215.5	Nonazeotrope		256
A =	**$C_8H_{16}O_4$**	**2-(2-Ethoxyethoxy) Ethyl Acetate**	**218.5**			
13425	$C_9H_{10}O$	p-Methylacetophenone	226.35	Nonazeotrope		255
13426	$C_9H_{10}O_2$	Benzyl acetate	215.0	<214.8	>9	255
13427	$C_9H_{10}O_2$	Ethyl benzoate	212.5	212.3	8	255
13428	$C_9H_{12}O$	3-Phenylpropanol	235.6	Nonazeotrope		255
13429	$C_{10}H_{18}O$	Borneol	215	Nonazeotrope		255
13430	$C_{10}H_{18}O$	Geraniol	229.6	Nonazeotrope		255
13431	$C_{10}H_{18}O$	α-Terpineol	218.85	<218.0	>53	255
13432	$C_{10}H_{20}O$	Citronellol	224.4	Nonazeotrope		255
13433	$C_{10}H_{20}O_2$	Ethyl caprylate	208.35	Nonazeotrope		255
13434	$C_{10}H_{22}O$	Decyl alcohol	232.8	Nonazeotrope		255
13435	$C_{12}H_{20}O_2$	Bornyl acetate	227.6	Nonazeotrope		255
A =	**C_8H_{18}**	***n*-Octane**	**125.4**			
13436	C_8H_{18}	2,2,4-Trimethylpentane	99.2	Nonazeotrope, V-l.		44
13437	$C_8H_{18}O$	Isobutyl ether	122.3	122.0	90	238
13438	$C_8H_{18}O$	Isobutyl ether	122.2	Nonazeotrope ?		228

No.	B-Component Formula	Name	B.P., ° C.	Azeotropic Data B.P., ° C.	Wt. % A	Ref.
A =	**$C_8H_{18}O$**	**Butyl Ether**	**142.4**			
13439	C_9H_{12}	Cumene	152.8	Nonazeotrope		*238*
13440	$C_{10}H_{16}$	α-Pinene	155.8	Nonazeotrope		*238*
A =	**$C_8H_{18}O$**	**Isobutyl Ether**	**122.3**			
13441	$C_8H_{19}N$	Diisobutylamine	138.5	Nonazeotrope		*231*
A =	**$C_8H_{18}O$**	**Octyl Alcohol**	**195.2**			
13442	C_9H_8	Indene	182.6	182.4	12	*207*
13443	$C_9H_{10}O_2$	Ethyl benzoate	212.6	Nonazeotrope		*216*
13444	C_9H_{12}	Mesitylene	164.6	Nonazeotrope		*255*
13445	C_9H_{12}	Propylbenzene	159.3	Nonazeotrope		*255*
13446	$C_9H_{12}O$	Benzyl ethyl ether	185.0	Nonazeotrope		*225*
13447	$C_9H_{12}O$	Phenyl propyl ether	190.2	190.0	....	*218*
13448	$C_9H_{13}N$	*N,N*-Dimethyl-*o*-toluidine	185.3	184.8	20	*231*
13449	$C_9H_{14}O$	Phorone	197.8	<193.5	<80	*232*
			197.8	Nonazeotrope		*228*
13450	$C_9H_{18}O_2$	Ethyl enanthate	188.7	Nonazeotrope		*255*
13451	$C_9H_{18}O_3$	Isobutyl carbonate	190.3	~189.5	20	*216*
13452	$C_{10}H_8$	Naphthalene	218.05	Nonazeotrope		*217*
13453	$C_{10}H_{14}$	Cymene	176.7	Nonazeotrope		*217*
13454	$C_{10}H_{14}O$	Thymol	232.9	Nonazeotrope		*255*
13455	$C_{10}H_{15}N$	Diethylaniline	217.05	Nonazeotrope		*231*
13456	$C_{10}H_{16}$	Camphene	159.6	Nonazeotrope		*255*
13457	$C_{10}H_{16}$	*d*-Limonene	177.8	177.45	~8	*209*
13458	$C_{10}H_{16}$	Nopinene	163.8	Nonazeotrope		*255*
13459	$C_{10}H_{16}$	α-Pinene	155.8	Nonazeotrope		*255*
13460	$C_{10}H_{16}$	α-Terpinene	173.4	Nonazeotrope		*255*
13461	$C_{10}H_{16}$	γ-Terpinene	183	182.5	>10	*255*
13462	$C_{10}H_{16}$	Thymene	179.7	179.6	~7	*210*
13463	$C_{10}H_{16}O$	Camphor	209.1	Nonazeotrope		*232*
13464	$C_{10}H_{18}O$	Cineole	176.35	Nonazeotrope		*236*
13465	$C_{10}H_{18}O$	Citronellal	208.0	Nonazeotrope		*255*
13466	$C_{10}H_{18}O$	Linaloöl	198.7	Nonazeotrope		*208*
13467	$C_{10}H_{18}O$	Menthone	209.5	Nonazeotrope		*232*
13468	$C_{10}H_{20}O_2$	Ethyl caprylate	208.35	Nonazeotrope		*255*
13469	$C_{10}H_{20}O_2$	Isoamyl isovalerate	192.7	192.55	15	*244*
13470	$C_{10}H_{22}O$	Isoamyl ether	173.2	Nonazeotrope		*236*
13471	$C_{10}H_{22}S$	Isoamyl sulfide	214.8	Nonazeotrope		*246*
13472	$C_{11}H_{20}O$	Isobornyl methyl ether	192.2	191.9	30	*236*
A =	**$C_8H_{18}O$**	***sec*-Octyl Alcohol**	**179.0**			
13473	C_9H_8	Indene	181.7	176	~60	*217*
13474	C_9H_{12}	Cumene	152.8	Nonazeotrope		*255*
13475	C_9H_{12}	Mesitylene	164.6	Nonazeotrope		*221*
13476	C_9H_{12}	Propylbenzene	159.3	Nonazeotrope		*255*
13477	$C_9H_{12}O$	Benzyl ethyl ether	185.0	180.0	....	*225*
13478	$C_9H_{12}O$	Phenyl propyl ether	190.2	Nonazeotrope		*256*
13479	$C_9H_{13}N$	*N,N*-Dimethyl-*o*-toluidine	185.3	179.0	70	*231*
13480	$C_9H_{13}N$	*N,N*-Dimethyl-*p*-toluidine	210.2	Nonazeotrope		*231*
13481	$C_9H_{18}O_2$	Butyl isovalerate	137.6	177.4	11	*255*
13482	$C_9H_{18}O_2$	Isoamyl butyrate	181.05	180.3	72	*244*
13483	$C_9H_{18}O_2$	Isoamyl isobutyrate	169.8	Nonazeotrope		*255*
13484	$C_9H_{18}O_2$	Isobutyl isovalerate	168.7	Nonazeotrope		*216*
13485	$C_9H_{18}O_3$	Isobutyl carbonate	190.3	<180.0	....	*255*
13486	$C_9H_{18}O_3$	Isobutyl carbonate	190.3	Nonazeotrope		*216*
13487	$C_{10}H_{14}$	Butylbenzene	183.1	178.2	50	*247*
13488	$C_{10}H_{14}$	Cymene	176.7	174	44	*217*
13489	$C_{10}H_{15}N$	Diethylaniline	217.05	Nonazeotrope		*231*
13490	$C_{10}H_{16}$	Camphene	159.6	159.55?	....	*217*
13491	$C_{10}H_{16}$	*d*-Limonene	177.8	174.5	~45	*217*
13492	$C_{10}H_{16}$	Nopinene	163.8	163.5	~5	*255*
13493	$C_{10}H_{16}$	α-Phellandrene	171.5	~170	....	*243*
13494	$C_{10}H_{16}$	α-Pinene	155.8	Nonazeotrope		*243*
13495	$C_{10}H_{16}$	α-Terpinene	173.4	171.8	27	*247*
13496	$C_{10}H_{16}$	Terpinene	180.5	~175.5	....	*243*
13497	$C_{10}H_{16}$	Terpinolene	184.6	179.0	57	*247*

No.	Formula	B-Component Name	B.P., ° C.	Azeotropic Data B.P., ° C.	Wt. % A	Ref.
A =	**$C_8H_{18}O$**	***sec*-Octyl Alcohol (*continued*)**	**179.0**			
13498	$C_{10}H_{16}$	Thymene	179.7	176	52	217
13499	$C_{10}H_{18}O$	Cineole	176.35	175.85	26.5	252
13500	$C_{10}H_{22}$	2,7-Dimethyloctane	160.1	Nonazeotrope		255
13501	$C_{10}H_{22}O$	Amyl ether	187.5	179.8	86	236
13502	$C_{10}H_{22}O$	Isoamyl ether	173.2	172.65	17	207
13503	$C_{10}H_{22}O$	Isoamyl ether	173.4	Nonazeotrope		256
A =	**$C_8H_{18}O_3$**	**Bis(2-ethoxyethyl) Ether**	**186.0**			
13504	C_9H_8	Indene	182.5	Nonazeotrope		238
13505	$C_{10}H_{16}$	Dipentene	177.7	Nonazeotrope		238
A =	**$C_8H_{18}O_3$**	**2-(2-Butoxyethoxy) Ethanol**	**231.2**			
13506	C_9H_7N	Quinoline	237.3	<229.5	>56	233
13507	$C_9H_{10}O$	Cinnamyl alcohol	257.0	Nonazeotrope		255
13508	$C_9H_{10}O_3$	Ethyl salicylate	233.8	225.2	54	255
13509	$C_{10}H_7Cl$	1-Chloronaphthalene	262.7	Nonazeotrope		255
13510	$C_{10}H_9N$	Quinaldine	246.5	Nonazeotrope		255
13511	$C_{10}H_{18}O$	Geraniol	229.6	<228.5	....	255
13512	$C_{10}H_{22}O$	Decyl alcohol	232.8	<230.5	<85	255
A =	**$C_8H_{18}S$**	**Butyl Sulfide**	**185.0**			
13513	C_9H_{12}	Mesitylene	164.6	Nonazeotrope		246
13514	$C_9H_{12}O$	Benzyl ethyl ether	185.0	<184.2	>53	246
13515	$C_9H_{18}O$	2,6-Dimethyl-4-heptanone	168.0	Nonazeotrope		246
13516	$C_9H_{18}O_2$	Butyl isovalerate	177.6	Nonazeotrope		246
13517	$C_9H_{18}O_2$	Isobutyl isovalerate	171.2	Nonazeotrope		246
13518	$C_{10}H_{14}$	Butylbenzene	183.1	182.0	40	246
13519	$C_{10}H_{18}O$	Cineole	176.35	Nonazeotrope		246
13520	$C_{10}H_{22}O$	Isoamyl ether	173.2	Nonazeotrope		246
A =	**$C_8H_{18}S$**	**Isobutyl Sulfide**	**172.0**			
13521	C_9H_{12}	Mesitylene	164.6	Nonazeotrope		246
13522	$C_9H_{18}O$	2,6-Dimethyl-4-heptanone	168.0	<167.2	....	246
13523	$C_{10}H_{16}$	Camphene	159.6	Nonazeotrope		246
13524	$C_{10}H_{16}$	α-Pinene	155.8	Nonazeotrope		246
13525	$C_{10}H_{22}O$	Isoamyl ether	172.6	171.0	62	235
A =	**$C_8H_{20}SiO_4$**	**Ethyl Silicate**	**168.8**			
13526	$C_9H_{18}O_2$	Butyl isovalerate	177.6	Nonazeotrope		255
13527	$C_9H_{18}O_2$	Isoamyl isobutyrate	169.8	168.2	....	255
13528	$C_9H_{18}O_2$	Isobutyl isovalerate	171.2	168.75	93	229
13529	$C_{10}H_{16}$	Camphene	~158	~150	~37	243
13530	$C_{10}H_{16}$	α-Pinene	155.8	<149	<35	243
13531	$C_{10}H_{22}O$	Isoamyl ether	173.2	<165.5	....	237
A =	**C_9H_7N**	**Quinoline**	**237.3**			
13532	$C_9H_{10}O$	*p*-Methylacetophenone	226.35	Nonazeotrope		255
13533	$C_9H_{10}O_3$	Ethyl salicylate	233.8	Nonazeotrope		233
13534	$C_9H_{12}O$	Mesitol	220.5	240.4	85	255
13535	$C_9H_{12}O_2$	2-Benzyloxyethanol	265.2	Nonazeotrope		233
13536	$C_{10}H_8$	Naphthalene	237.3	Nonazeotrope		233
13537	$C_{10}H_{10}O_2$	Isosafrole	252.0	Nonazeotrope		233
13538	$C_{10}H_{10}O_2$	Safrole	235.9	235.15	27	233
13539	$C_{10}H_{12}O$	Anethole	235.7	234.7	30	233
13540	$C_{10}H_{12}O_2$	Eugenol	154.8	Nonazeotrope		255
13541	$C_{10}H_{14}O$	Carvacrol	237.85	244.3	48	255
13542	$C_{10}H_{14}O$	Thymol	232.9	243.1	55	244
13543	$C_{10}H_{14}O_2$	*m*-Diethoxybenzene	235.4	235.0	22	255
13544	$C_{10}H_{18}O$	α-Terpineol	218.85	Nonazeotrope		255
13545	$C_{10}H_{20}O$	Menthol	216.3	Nonazeotrope		233
13546	$C_{11}H_{10}$	1-Methylnaphthalene	244.6	Nonazeotrope		233
13547	$C_{11}H_{10}$	2-Methylnaphthalene	241.15	237.25	93	233
			....	237.25	93	207
13548	$C_{11}H_{14}O_2$	1-Allyl-3,4-dimethylbenzene	254.7	Nonazeotrope		255
13549	$C_{11}H_{16}O$	Methyl thymyl ether	216.5	Nonazeotrope		255
13550	$C_{11}H_{16}O$	*p-tert*-Amylphenol	266.5	267.5	6	255

No.	Formula	B-Component Name	B.P., ° C.	Azeotropic Data B.P., ° C.	Wt. % A	Ref.
A =	C_9H_7N	**Quinoline** (*continued*)	**237.3**			
13551	$C_{11}H_{20}O$	Methyl α-terpineol ether	216.2	Nonazeotrope		*255*
13552	$C_{12}H_{10}$	Biphenyl	256.1	Nonazeotrope		*233*
13553	$C_{12}H_{16}O_3$	Isoamyl salicylate	277.5	Nonazeotrope		*233*
A =	C_9H_8	**Indene**	**182.6**			
13554	$C_9H_{12}O$	Benzyl ethyl ether	185.0	Nonazeotrope		*238*
13555	$C_9H_{13}N$	*N,N*-Dimethyl-*o*-toluidine	185.3	Nonazeotrope		*231*
13556	$C_9H_{14}O$	Phorone	197.8	Nonazeotrope		*228*
13557	$C_9H_{18}O_2$	Ethyl enanthate	188.7	Nonazeotrope		*255*
13558	$C_9H_{18}O_2$	Isoamyl butyrate	178.5	178.0	....	*226*
13559	$C_9H_{18}O_2$	Isobutyl isovalerate	171.35	Nonazeotrope		*221*
13560	$C_9H_{18}O_3$	Isobutyl carbonate	190.3	Nonazeotrope		*255*
13561	$C_{10}H_{14}$	Cymene	176.7	Nonazeotrope		*241*
13562	$C_{10}H_{16}$	Dipentene	177.7	Nonazeotrope		*255*
13563	$C_{10}H_{16}$	Limonene	177.7	Nonazeotrope		*241*
13564	$C_{10}H_{18}O$	Borneol	215	Nonazeotrope		*255*
13565	$C_{10}H_{18}O$	Cineole	176.35	Nonazeotrope		*238*
13566	$C_{10}H_{18}O$	Linaloöl	198.6	Nonazeotrope		*255*
13567	$C_{10}H_{18}O$	β-Terpineol	210.5	Nonazeotrope		*255*
13568	$C_{10}H_{20}O$	Menthol	216.3	Nonazeotrope		*255*
13569	$C_{10}H_{20}O_2$	Isoamyl isovalerate	192.7	Nonazeotrope		*226*
13570	$C_{10}H_{22}O$	Amyl ether	187.5	Nonazeotrope		*238*
13571	$C_{10}H_{22}O$	Isoamyl ether	173.2	Nonazeotrope		*238*
13572	$C_{10}H_{23}N$	Diisoamylamine	188.2	Nonazeotrope		*231*
A =	C_9H_8O	**Cinnamaldehyde**	**253.5**			
13573	$C_9H_{10}O$	Cinnamyl alcohol	257.0	<252.3	....	*255*
13574	$C_9H_{12}O$	3-Phenylpropanol	235.6	Nonazeotrope		*255*
13575	$C_{10}H_7Cl$	1-Chloronaphthalene	262.7	Nonazeotrope		*225*
13576	$C_{10}H_8$	Naphthalene	218.0	Nonazeotrope		*255*
13577	$C_{10}H_{10}O_2$	Isosafrole	252.0	251.3	23	*236*
13578	$C_{10}H_{10}O_2$	Methyl cinnamate	261.9	Nonazeotrope		*225*
13579	$C_{10}H_{10}O_2$	Safrole	235.9	Nonazeotrope		*228*
13580	$C_{10}H_{12}O$	Anethole	235.7	Nonazeotrope		*255*
13581	$C_{10}H_{12}O_2$	Isoeugenol	268.8	Nonazeotrope		*255*
13582	$C_{10}H_{14}O$	Carvacrol	237.85	Nonazeotrope		*255*
13583	$C_{10}H_{14}O$	Thymol	232.9	Nonazeotrope		*255*
13584	$C_{11}H_{10}$	1-Methylnaphthalene	244.6	Nonazeotrope		*255*
13585	$C_{11}H_{10}$	1-Methylnaphthalene	244.6	~244.4	~5	*218*
13586	$C_{11}H_{10}$	2-Methylnaphthalene	241.15	Nonazeotrope		*207*
13587	$C_{11}H_{14}O_2$	1-Allyl-3,4-dimethoxybenzene	255.0	253.0	80?	*218*
13588	$C_{11}H_{14}O_2$	Butyl benzoate	249.5	Nonazeotrope		*228*
13589	$C_{11}H_{14}O_2$	1,2-Dimethoxy-4-propenylbenzene	270.5	Nonazeotrope		*255*
13590	$C_{11}H_{14}O_2$	Isobutyl benzoate	241.9	Nonazeotrope		*228*
13591	$C_{12}H_{10}$	Acenaphthene	277.9	Nonazeotrope		*255*
13592	$C_{12}H_{10}$	Biphenyl	255.0	~250.0	~40	*228*
13593	$C_{12}H_{10}O$	Phenyl ether	259.0	253.0	65	*236*
13594	$C_{12}H_{16}O_2$	Isoamyl benzoate	262.0	Nonazeotrope		*228*
13595	$C_{12}H_{18}$	1,3,5-Triethylbenzene	215.5	Nonazeotrope		*255*
13596	$C_{13}H_{12}$	Diphenylmethane	265.4	Nonazeotrope		*228*
A =	C_9H_9N	**2-Methylindole**	**268**			
13597	$C_{11}H_{16}O$	*p-tert*-Amylphenol	266.5	272.0	56	*255*
A =	$C_9H_{10}O$	**Cinnamyl Alcohol**	**257.0**			
13598	$C_9H_{12}O_2$	2-Benzyloxyethanol	265.2	Nonazeotrope		*255*
13599	$C_{10}H_8$	Naphthalene	218.0	Nonazeotrope		*255*
13600	$C_{10}H_{10}O_2$	Isosafrole	252.0	<251.6	....	*255*
13601	$C_{10}H_{10}O_2$	Methyl cinnamate	261.9	Nonazeotrope		*255*
13602	$C_{10}H_{10}O_2$	Safrole	235.9	Nonazeotrope		*255*
13603	$C_{10}H_{12}O_2$	Isoeugenol	268.8	Nonazeotrope		*255*
13604	$C_{10}H_{14}O$	Carvone	231.0	Nonazeotrope		*232*
13605	$C_{10}H_{14}O$	Thymol	232.9	Nonazeotrope		*255*
13606	$C_{10}H_{15}N$	Diethylaniline	217.05	Nonazeotrope		*231*
13607	$C_{10}H_{20}O_4$	2-(2-Butoxyethoxy)ethyl acetate	245.3	Nonazeotrope		*255*
13608	$C_{11}H_{10}$	1-Methylnaphthalene	244.6	<244.3	>12	*255*

No.	B-Component Formula	B-Component Name	B.P., ° C.	Azeotropic Data B.P., ° C.	Azeotropic Data Wt. % A	Ref.
A =	**$C_9H_{10}O$**	**Cinnamyl Alcohol** (*continued*)	**257.0**			
13609	$C_{11}H_{12}O_2$	Ethyl cinnamate	272.0	Nonazeotrope		*255*
13610	$C_{11}H_{14}O_2$	Butyl benzoate	249.0	Nonazeotrope		*255*
13611	$C_{11}H_{14}O_2$	Ethyl β-phenylpropionate	248.1	Nonazeotrope		*255*
13612	$C_{11}H_{14}O_2$	Isobutyl benzoate	241.9	Nonazeotrope		*255*
13613	$C_{11}H_{22}O_3$	Isoamyl carbonate	232.2	Nonazeotrope		*255*
13614	$C_{12}H_{10}$	Acenaphthene	277.9	Nonazeotrope		*255*
13615	$C_{12}H_{10}$	Biphenyl	256.1	253.0	~45	*255*
13616	$C_{12}H_{10}O$	Phenyl ether	259.0	<256.0	....	*255*
13617	$C_{12}H_{16}O_2$	Isoamyl benzoate	262.0	Nonazeotrope		*255*
13618	$C_{12}H_{22}O_4$	Isoamyl oxalate	268.0	<256.7	....	*255*
13619	$C_{13}H_{12}$	Diphenylmethane	265.4	<256.2	>62	*255*
13620	$C_{13}H_{28}$	Tridecane	234.0	Nonazeotrope		*255*
A =	**$C_9H_{10}O$**	***p*-Methylacetophenone**	**226.35**			
13621	$C_9H_{10}O_3$	Ethyl salicylate	233.8	Nonazeotrope		*232*
13622	$C_9H_{12}O$	3-Phenylpropanol	235.6	Nonazeotrope		*232*
13623	$C_{10}H_8$	Naphthalene	218.0	Nonazeotrope		*232*
13624	$C_{10}H_{10}O_2$	Safrole	235.9	Nonazeotrope		*232*
13625	$C_{10}H_{12}O$	Anethole	235.7	Nonazeotrope		*232*
13626	$C_{10}H_{12}O_2$	Ethyl α-toluate	228.75	226.2	75	*232*
13627	$C_{10}H_{12}O_2$	Propyl benzoate	230.85	Nonazeotrope		*232*
13628	$C_{10}H_{14}O$	Thymol	232.9	234.9	32	*232*
13629	$C_{10}H_{14}O_2$	*m*-Diethoxybenzene	235	Nonazeotrope		*217*
13630	$C_{10}H_{15}N$	Diethylaniline	217.05	Nonazeotrope		*231*
13631	$C_{10}H_{18}O$	Geraniol	229.6	226.25	95	*232*
13632	$C_{10}H_{18}$	α-Terpineol	218.85	Nonazeotrope		*232*
13633	$C_{10}H_{20}O$	Citronellol	224.4	223.7	32	*232*
13634	$C_{10}H_{20}O$	Menthol	216.4	Nonazeotrope		*215*
13635	$C_{10}H_{22}O$	Decyl alcohol	232.8	Nonazeotrope		*232*
13636	$C_{11}H_{10}$	2-Methylnaphthalene	241.15	Nonazeotrope		*207*
13637	$C_{11}H_{20}O$	Methyl terpenyl ether	216.2	Nonazeotrope		*232*
13638	$C_{11}H_{22}O_3$	Isoamyl carbonate	232.2	Nonazeotrope		*232*
13639	$C_{12}H_{20}O_2$	Bornyl acetate	227.6	225.8	60	*232*
A =	**$C_9H_{10}O$**	**Propiophenone**	**217.7**			
13640	$C_9H_{10}O_2$	Benzyl acetate	215.0	Nonazeotrope		*232*
13641	$C_9H_{10}O_2$	Ethyl benzoate	212.5	Nonazeotrope		*232*
13642	$C_9H_{13}N$	*N,N*-Dimethyl-*p*-toluidine	210.2	Nonazeotrope		*255*
13643	$C_{10}H_8$	Naphthalene	218.0	Nonazeotrope		*232*
13644	$C_{10}H_{14}O$	Carvacrol	237.85	Nonazeotrope		*255*
13645	$C_{10}H_{14}O$	Thymol	232.9	>233.2	>13	*232*
13646	$C_{10}H_{15}N$	Diethylaniline	217.05	<216.6	<47	*231*
13647	$C_{10}H_{18}O$	Borneol	215.0	Nonazeotrope		*232*
13648	$C_{10}H_{20}O_2$	Methyl pelargonate	213.8	Nonazeotrope		*232*
13649	$C_{12}H_{18}$	1,3,5-Triethylbenzene	215.5	215.4	25	*232*
13650	$C_{20}H_{20}O_2$	Bornyl acetate	227.6	Nonazeotrope		*232*
A =	**$C_9H_{10}O_2$**	**Benzyl Acetate**	**214.9**			
13651	$C_9H_{10}O_2$	Ethyl benzoate	212.4	212.35	2	*209*
			212.5	Nonazeotrope		*229*
13652	$C_{10}H_8$	Naphthalene	218.05	214.65	~72	*209*
13653	$C_{10}H_{14}O$	Thymol	232.8	Nonazeotrope		*211*
13654	$C_{10}H_{16}$	γ-Terpinene	179.7	Nonazeotrope		*226*
13655	$C_{10}H_{16}O$	Camphor	209.1	Nonazeotrope		*232*
13656	$C_{10}H_{16}O$	Pulegone	223.8	Nonazeotrope		*232*
13657	$C_{10}H_{17}Cl$	Bornyl chloride	207.5	Nonazeotrope		*255*
13658	$C_{10}H_{18}O$	Borneol	213.2	212.8	~36	*209*
13659	$C_{10}H_{18}O$	Citronellal	208.0	Nonazeotrope		*255*
13660	$C_{10}H_{18}O$	α-Terpineol	217.8	214.5	~65	*209*
13661	$C_{10}H_{18}O$	β-Terpineol	210.5	210.2	22	*255*
13662	$C_{10}H_{20}O$	Citronellol	224.4	Nonazeotrope		*255*
13663	$C_{10}H_{20}O$	Menthol	216.4	~213.5	73.5	*209*
13664	$C_{11}H_{10}$	2-Methylnaphthalene	241.15	Nonazeotrope		*207*
13665	$C_{11}H_{20}O$	Methyl α-terpineol ether	216.2	214.7	72	*237*
13666	$C_{11}H_{24}O_2$	Diisoamyloxymethane	207.5	Nonazeotrope		*237*
13667	$C_{12}H_{18}$	1,3,5-Triethylbenzene	216	214.5	50	*226*

No.	Formula	B-Component Name	B.P., ° C.	Azeotropic Data B.P., ° C.	Wt. % A	Ref.
A =	**$C_9H_{10}O_2$**	**Ethyl Benzoate**	**212.5**			
13668	$C_9H_{10}O_2$	Methyl α-toluate	215.3	Nonazeotrope		*229*
13669	$C_{10}H_8$	Naphthalene	218.05	Nonazeotrope		*243*
13670	$C_{10}H_{12}O$	Estragol	215.6	Nonazeotrope		*237*
13671	$C_{10}H_{14}O$	Thymol	232.8	Nonazeotrope		*211*
13672	$C_{10}H_{15}N$	Diethylaniline	216.1	Reacts		*243*
13673	$C_{10}H_{16}O$	Camphor	209.1	Nonazeotrope		*232*
13674	$C_{10}H_{17}Cl$	Bornyl chloride	207.5	Nonazeotrope		*255*
13675	$C_{10}H_{17}Cl$	Bornyl chloride	~210	~209.5	....	*243*
13676	$C_{10}H_{18}O$	Borneol	213.2	212.2	90	*209*
13677	$C_{10}H_{18}O$	Citronellal	~207.8	Nonazeotrope		*212*
13678	$C_{10}H_{18}O$	Linaloöl	198.6	Nonazeotrope		*215*
13679	$C_{10}H_{18}O$	α-Terpineol	218.85	Nonazeotrope		*255*
13680	$C_{10}H_{18}O$	α-Terpineol	~217.8	212.55	~98	*216*
13681	$C_{10}H_{18}O$	β-Terpineol	210.5	<209.8	<48	*255*
13682	$C_{10}H_{20}O$	Menthol	216.4	212.3	95	*209*
13683	$C_{11}H_{20}O$	Terpineol methyl ether	216	<212.3	<78	*237*
13684	$C_{11}H_{24}O_2$	Diisoamyloxymethane	210.8	<210.6	15?	*237*
13685	$C_{12}H_{18}$	1,3,5-Triethylbenzene	216.0	Nonazeotrope		*226*
A =	**$C_9H_{10}O_2$**	**Methyl α-Toluate**	**215.3**			
13686	$C_{10}H_{16}O$	Pulegone	223.8	Nonazeotrope		*232*
13687	$C_{10}H_{18}O$	Borneol	215.0	<214.3	<52	*255*
13668	$C_{10}H_{18}O$	α-Terpineol	218.85	<215.0	>75	*255*
13689	$C_{10}H_{20}O$	Menthol	216.3	<214.5	>63	*255*
A =	**$C_9H_{10}O_3$**	**Ethyl Salicylate**	**233.8**			
13690	$C_{10}H_{10}O_2$	Isosafrole	252.0	Nonazeotrope		*255*
13691	$C_{10}H_{10}O_2$	Safrole	235.9	233.65	88	*216*
			235.9	Nonazeotrope		*236*
13692	$C_{10}H_{12}O_2$	Ethyl α-toluate	234.0	Nonazeotrope		*218*
13693	$C_{10}H_{12}O_2$	Propyl benzoate	230.85	Nonazeotrope		*228*
13694	$C_{10}H_{14}O$	Carvacrol	237.85	Nonazeotrope		*255*
13695	$C_{10}H_{14}O$	Carvone	231.0	Nonazeotrope		*232*
13696	$C_{10}H_{14}O$	Thymol	232.9	235	~65	*216*
13697	$C_{10}H_{16}O$	Pulegone	223.8	Nonazeotrope		*232*
13698	$C_{10}H_{18}O$	Borneol	213.4	Nonazeotrope		*225*
13699	$C_{10}H_{18}O$	Geraniol	229.7	228.5	40	*216*
13700	$C_{10}H_{18}O$	α-Terpineol	~217.8	Nonazeotrope		*216*
13701	$C_{10}H_{20}O$	Citronellol	224.5	Nonazeotrope		*225*
13702	$C_{10}H_{20}O$	Menthol	216.4	Nonazeotrope		*216*
13703	$C_{10}H_{22}O$	Decyl alcohol	232.9	230.5	48	*216*
13704	$C_{11}H_{10}$	1-Methylnaphthalene	244.9	Nonazeotrope		*216*
13705	$C_{11}H_{10}$	2-Methylnaphthalene	241.15	Nonazeotrope		*207*
13706	$C_{11}H_{14}O_2$	Ethyl β-phenylpropionate	248.1	Nonazeotrope		*255*
13707	$C_{11}H_{14}O_2$	Isobutyl benzoate	241.9	Nonazeotrope		*218*
13708	$C_{11}H_{22}O_2$	Ethyl pelargonate	227	Nonazeotrope		*255*
13709	$C_{11}H_{22}O_3$	Isoamyl carbonate	232.2	<232.0	<28	*255*
13710	$C_{12}H_{10}$	Biphenyl	256.1	Nonazeotrope		*255*
13711	$C_{12}H_{20}O_2$	Bornyl acetate	227.6	Nonazeotrope		*218*
A =	**C_9H_{12}**	**Cumene**	**152.8**			
13712	C_9H_{20}	Nonane	149.5	148.0	23	*241*
13713	$C_{10}H_{16}$	α-Pinene	155.8	151.8	80	*241*
A =	**C_9H_{12}**	**Mesitylene**	**164.6**			
13714	C_9H_{12}	Propylbenzene	159.3	Nonazeotrope		*241*
13715	C_9H_{12}	Pseudocumene	169.0	Nonazeotrope		*243*
13716	$C_9H_{13}N$	*N,N*-Dimethyl-*o*-toluidine	185.3	Nonazeotrope		*231*
13717	$C_9H_{18}O_2$	Isoamyl butyrate	181.05	Nonazeotrope		*255*
13718	$C_9H_{18}O_2$	Isoamyl isobutyrate	169.8	Nonazeotrope		*255*
13719	$C_9H_{18}O_2$	Isobutyl isovalerate	168.7	163	....	*243*
			168.7	Nonazeotrope		*226*
13720	$C_9H_{18}O_3$	Isobutyl carbonate	190.3	Nonazeotrope		*255*
13721	$C_{10}H_{14}$	Cymene	176.7	Nonazeotrope		*241*
13722	$C_{10}H_{16}$	Camphene	159.6	Nonazeotrope		*241*
13723	$C_{10}H_{16}$	Nopinene	163.8	162.7	40	*241*

No.	B-Component Formula	Name	B.P., ° C.	Azeotropic Data B.P., ° C.	Wt. % A	Ref.
A =	C_9H_{12}	**Mesitylene** (*continued*)	**164.6**			
13724	$C_{10}H_{16}$	α-Pinene	155.8	Nonazeotrope		*241*
13725	$C_{10}H_{16}$	α-Terpinene	173.4	Nonazeotrope		*241*
13726	$C_{10}H_{18}O$	Linaloöl	198.6	Nonazeotrope		*220*
13727	$C_{10}H_{22}$	2,7-Dimethyloctane	160.1	158.6	28	*241*
13728	$C_{10}H_{22}O$	Isoamyl ether	173.4	Nonazeotrope		*228*
A =	C_9H_{12}	**Propylbenzene**	**159**			
13729	$C_9H_{13}N$	*N,N*-Dimethyl-*o*-toluidine	185.3	Nonazeotrope		*255*
13730	$C_{10}H_{16}$	Camphene	159.6	158.0	47	*241*
13731	$C_{10}H_{16}$	Nopinene	163.8	<159.0	>85	*241*
13732	$C_{10}H_{16}$	α-Pinene	155.8	155.0	17	*241*
A =	C_9H_{12}	**Pseudocumene**	**168.2**			
13733	$C_9H_{13}N$	*N,N*-Dimethyl-*o*-toluidine	185.3	Nonazeotrope		*231*
13734	$C_9H_{18}O_2$	Isobutyl isovalerate	171.35	Nonazeotrope		*221*
			168.7	<166.5	~49	*243*
13735	$C_{10}H_{14}$	Cymene	176.7	Nonazeotrope		*241*
13736	$C_{10}H_{18}$	Menthene	170.8	167.5	>85	*241*
13737	$C_{10}H_{18}O$	Cineole	176.35	Nonazeotrope		*238*
13738	$C_{10}H_{22}$	Decane	173.3	166.5	75	*241*
13739	$C_{10}H_{22}O$	Isoamyl ether	173.2	Nonazeotrope		*238*
A =	$C_9H_{12}O$	**Benzyl Ethyl Ether**	**185.0**			
13740	$C_9H_{18}O_2$	Butyl isovalerate	177.6	Nonazeotrope		*237*
13741	$C_9H_{18}O_2$	Isoamyl butyrate	181.05	Nonazeotrope		*237*
13742	$C_{10}H_{14}$	Cymene	176.7	Nonazeotrope		*238*
13743	$C_{10}H_{16}$	Dipentene	177.7	Nonazeotrope		*238*
13744	$C_{10}H_{16}O$	Fenchone	193.6	Nonazeotrope		*255*
13745	$C_{10}H_{18}O$	Citronellal	208.0	Nonazeotrope		*255*
13746	$C_{10}H_{18}O$	Linaloöl	198.6	Nonazeotrope		*255*
13747	$C_{10}H_{20}O_2$	Isoamyl isovalerate	192.7	Nonazeotrope		*237*
A =	$C_9H_{12}O$	**Mesitol**	**230.5**			
13748	$C_{10}H_8$	Naphthalene	218.0	215.5	37	*242*
13749	$C_{12}H_{18}$	1,3,5-Triethylbenzene	215.5	213.0	30	*242*
A =	$C_9H_{12}O$	**3-Phenylpropanol**	**235.6**			
13750	$C_9H_{12}O_2$	2-Benzyloxyethanol	265.2	Nonazeotrope		*255*
13751	$C_{10}H_8$	Naphthalene	218.05	217.8	~20	*217*
13752	$C_{10}H_{10}O_2$	Isosafrole	252.0	Nonazeotrope		*255*
13753	$C_{10}H_{10}O_2$	Safrole	235.9	233.8	47	*225*
13754	$C_{10}H_{12}O$	Anethole	235.7	234.0	48	*247*
13755	$C_{10}H_{12}O_2$	Ethyl α-toluate	228.75	Nonazeotrope		*216*
13756	$C_{10}H_{12}O_2$	Eugenol	254.8	Nonazeotrope		*255*
13757	$C_{10}H_{12}O_2$	Propyl benzoate	230.85	Nonazeotrope		*216*
13758	$C_{10}H_{14}O$	Carvacrol	237.85	>238.5	<42	*255*
13759	$C_{10}H_{14}O$	Carvone	231.0	Nonazeotrope		*232*
13760	$C_{10}H_{14}O$	Thymol	232.9	237.5	~62	*222*
13761	$C_{10}H_{14}O_2$	*m*-Diethoxybenzene	235.4	<234.8	>43	*255*
13762	$C_{10}H_{15}N$	Diethylaniline	217.05	216.9	7	*231*
			217.05	Nonazeotrope		*228*
13763	$C_{10}H_{18}O$	Geraniol	229.7	Nonazeotrope		*225*
13764	$C_{10}H_{20}O$	Citronellol	224.4	Nonazeotrope		*229*
13765	$C_{10}H_{20}O_4$	2-(2-Butoxyethoxy)ethyl acetate	245.3	Nonazeotrope		*255*
13766	$C_{10}H_{22}O$	Decyl alcohol	232.9	232.0	....	*225*
13767	$C_{11}H_{10}$	1-Methylnaphthalene	244.6	234	~60	*221*
13768	$C_{11}H_{10}$	2-Methylnaphthalene	241.15	233.7	....	*255*
13769	$C_{11}H_{14}O_2$	Ethyl β-phenylpropionate	248.1	Nonazeotrope		*255*
13770	$C_{11}H_{14}O_2$	Isobutyl benzoate	241.9	Nonazeotrope		*215*
13771	$C_{11}H_{16}O$	Methyl thymyl ether	216.5	Nonazeotrope		*255*
13772	$C_{11}H_{17}N$	Isoamylaniline	256.0	Nonazeotrope		*231*
13773	$C_{11}H_{22}O_3$	Isoamyl carbonate	232.2	<231.8	>5	*255*
13774	$C_{12}H_{10}$	Biphenyl	254.9	235.4	....	*217*
13775	$C_{12}H_{16}O_3$	Isoamyl salicylate	277.5	Nonazeotrope		*255*
13776	$C_{12}H_{20}O_2$	Bornyl acetate	227.6	Nonazeotrope		*255*
13777	$C_{13}H_{12}$	Diphenylmethane	265.6	Nonazeotrope		*217*

No	Formula	B-Component Name	B.P., ° C.	Azeotropic Data B.P., ° C.	Wt. % A	Ref.
A =	$C_9H_{12}O$	**Phenyl Propyl Ether**	**190.5**			
13778	$C_9H_{13}N$	Dimethyl-*o*-toluidine	185.35	Nonazeotrope		255
13779	$C_{10}H_{18}O$	Linaloöl	198.6	Nonazeotrope		225
A =	$C_9H_{12}O_2$	**2-Benzyloxyethanol**	**265.2**			
13780	$C_{10}H_7Cl$	1-Chloronaphthalene	262.7	<261.5	....	255
13781	$C_{10}H_8$	Naphthalene	218.0	Nonazeotrope		255
13782	$C_{10}H_{10}O_2$	Isosafrole	252.0	Nonazeotrope		255
13783	$C_{10}H_{10}O_2$	Methyl cinnamate	261.9	Nonazeotrope		255
13784	$C_{10}H_{10}O_2$	Safrole	235.9	Nonazeotrope		255
13785	$C_{10}H_{12}O_2$	Eugenol	254.8	Nonazeotrope		255
13786	$C_{11}H_{10}$	1-Methylnaphthalene	244.6	Nonazeotrope		255
13787	$C_{11}H_{10}$	2-Methylnaphthalene	241.15	Nonazeotrope		255
13788	$C_{11}H_{12}O_2$	Ethyl cinnamate	272.0	Nonazeotrope		255
13789	$C_{11}H_{14}O_2$	Butyl benzoate	249.0	Nonazeotrope		255
13790	$C_{11}H_{14}O_2$	Ethyl β-phenylpropionate	248.1	Nonazeotrope		255
13791	$C_{12}H_{10}O$	Phenyl ether	259.0	<258.2	>15	255
13792	$C_{12}H_{16}O_2$	Isoamyl benzoate	262.0	261.0	~15	255
13793	$C_{12}H_{16}O_3$	Isoamyl salicylate	277.5	Nonazeotrope		255
13794	$C_{13}H_{12}$	Diphenylmethane	265.4	262.5	46	255
13795	$C_{14}H_{14}$	1,2-Diphenylethane	284.5	Nonazeotrope		255
A =	$C_9H_{13}N$	***N,N*-Dimethyl-*o*-toluidine**	**185.3**			
13796	$C_{10}H_8$	Naphthalene	218.0	Nonazeotrope		231
13797	$C_{10}H_{14}$	Cymene	176.7	Nonazeotrope		231
13798	$C_{10}H_{16}$	Camphene	159.6	Nonazeotrope		231
13799	$C_{10}H_{16}$	α-Pinene	155.8	Nonazeotrope		231
13800	$C_{10}H_{16}O$	Camphor	209.1	Nonazeotrope		231
13801	$C_{10}H_{18}O$	Borneol	215.0	Nonazeotrope		231
13802	$C_{10}H_{18}O$	Cineole	176.35	Nonazeotrope		231
13803	$C_{10}H_{18}O$	Linaloöl	198.6	Nonazeotrope		231
13804	$C_{10}H_{18}O$	β-Terpineol	210.5	Nonazeotrope		231
13805	$C_{11}H_{20}O$	Isobornyl methyl ether	192.4	Nonazeotrope		231
13806	$C_{12}H_{18}$	1,3,5-Triethylbenzene	215.5	Nonazeotrope		255
A =	$C_9H_{13}N$	***N,N*-Dimethyl-*p*-toluidine**	**210.2**			
13807	$C_{10}H_8$	Naphthalene	218.0	Nonazeotrope		255
13808	$C_{10}H_{18}O$	Geraniol	229.6	Nonazeotrope		231
13809	$C_{10}H_{22}O$	*n*-Decyl alcohol	232.8	Nonazeotrope		231
13810	$C_{11}H_{20}O$	Methyl α-terpineol ether	216.2	Nonazeotrope		255
13811	$C_{12}H_{18}$	1,3,5-Triethylbenzene	215.5	Nonazeotrope		255
13812	$C_{12}H_{22}O$	Ethyl isobornyl ether	203.8	Nonazeotrope		255
A =	$C_9H_{14}O$	**Phorone**	**197.8**			
13813	$C_9H_{18}O_2$	Methyl caprylate	192.9	Nonazeotrope		232
13814	$C_9H_{18}O_3$	Isobutyl carbonate	190.3	Nonazeotrope		232
13815	$C_{10}H_{14}$	Butylbenzene	183.1	Nonazeotrope		255
13816	$C_{10}H_{14}O$	Thymol	232.9	Nonazeotrope		255
13817	$C_{10}H_{15}N$	Diethylaniline	217.05	Nonazeotrope		255
13818	$C_{10}H_{20}O_2$	Isoamyl isovalerate	192.7	Nonazeotrope		232
13819	$C_{10}H_{22}S$	Isoamyl sulfide	214.8	Nonazeotrope		246
13820	$C_{11}H_{20}O$	Isobornyl methyl ether	192.4	Nonazeotrope		255
13821	$C_{12}H_{22}O$	Bornyl ethyl ether	204.9	Nonazeotrope		255
A =	$C_9H_{18}O$	**2,6-Dimethyl-4-heptanone**	**168.0**			
13822	$C_9H_{18}O_2$	Isoamyl isobutyrate	169.8	Nonazeotrope		232
13823	$C_9H_{18}O_2$	Isobutyl isovalerate	171.2	Nonazeotrope		232
A =	$C_9H_{18}O_2$	**Butyl Isovalerate**	**177.6**			
13824	$C_9H_{18}O_2$	Isoamyl butyrate	181.05	Nonazeotrope		255
13825	$C_9H_{18}O_2$	Isobutyl isovalerate	171.2	Nonazeotrope		255
13826	$C_{10}H_{16}$	Camphene	158	Nonazeotrope		226
13827	$C_{10}H_{16}$	*d*-Limonene	177.9	176	55	226
13828	$C_{10}H_{16}$	Nopinene	164	Nonazeotrope		226
13829	$C_{10}H_{16}$	α-Pinene	155.8	Nonazeotrope		255
13830	$C_{10}H_{18}O$	Cineole	176.35	<176.2	<75	237
13831	$C_{10}H_{22}O$	Amyl ether	187.5	Nonazeotrope		237
13832	$C_{10}H_{22}O$	Isoamyl ether	173.2	Nonazeotrope		237

No.	B-Component Formula	Name	B.P., ° C.	Azeotropic Data B.P., ° C.	Wt. % A	Ref.
A =	**$C_9H_{18}O_2$**	**Ethyl Enanthate**	**188.7**			
13833	$C_{10}H_{14}$	Butylbenzene	183.1	Nonazeotrope		255
13834	$C_{10}H_{16}$	Dipentene	177.7	Nonazeotrope		255
13835	$C_{10}H_{16}$	α-Pinene	155.8	Nonazeotrope		255
A =	**$C_9H_{18}O_2$**	**Isoamyl Butyrate**	**181.05**			
13836	$C_9H_{18}O_2$	Isobutyl isovalerate	171.2	Nonazeotrope		255
13837	$C_{10}H_{14}$	Butylbenzene	183.2	Nonazeotrope		226
13838	$C_{10}H_{14}$	Cymene	176.7	Nonazeotrope		255
13839	$C_{10}H_{14}$	Cymene	175.3	<173	....	243
13840	$C_{10}H_{16}$	Camphene	158	Nonazeotrope		226
13841	$C_{10}H_{16}$	*d*-Limonene	177.8	~176.5	~45	208
13842	$C_{10}H_{16}$	Nopinene	163.8	Nonazeotrope		255
13843	$C_{10}H_{16}$	α-Terpinene	173.4	Nonazeotrope		255
13844	$C_{10}H_{16}$	γ-Terpinene	179.9	177.5	57	226
13845	$C_{10}H_{16}$	Terpinolene	185	~177	....	243
			185.2	Nonazeotrope		226
13846	$C_{10}H_{18}O$	Cineole	176.35	Nonazeotrope		237
13847	$C_{10}H_{18}O$	Cineole	176.35	<175.9	~25	252
13848	$C_{10}H_{18}O$	Linaloöl	198.6	Nonazeotrope		216
13849	$C_{10}H_{22}O$	Amyl ether	187.5	Nonazeotrope		237
13850	$C_{10}H_{22}O$	Isoamyl ether	173.2	Nonazeotrope		237
13851	$C_{11}H_{20}O$	Isobornyl methy lether	192.4	Nonazeotrope		237
A =	**$C_9H_{18}O_2$**	**Isoamyl Isobutyrate**	**168.8**			
13852	$C_9H_{18}O_2$	Isobutyl isovalerate	168.7	168.4?	....	253
13853	$C_{10}H_{14}$	Cymene	176.7	Nonazeotrope		255
13854	$C_{10}H_{16}$	Camphene	159.6	<159.5	<22	255
13855	$C_{10}H_{16}$	Dipentene	177.7	Nonazeotrope		255
13856	$C_{10}H_{16}$	α-Pinene	155.8	<155.6	<16	255
13857	$C_{10}H_{18}O$	Cineole	176.35	Nonazeotrope		237
A =	**$C_9H_{18}O_2$**	**Isobutyl Isovalerate**	**171.2**			
13858	$C_{10}H_{14}$	Butylbenzene	183.1	Nonazeotrope		255
13859	$C_{10}H_{14}$	Cymene	176.7	Nonazeotrope		226
13860	$C_{10}H_{16}$	Camphene	159.6	Nonazeotrope		255
13861	$C_{10}H_{16}$	*d*-Limonene	177.9	Nonazeotrope		226
13862	$C_{10}H_{16}$	α-Pinene	155.8	Nonazeotrope		226
13863	$C_{10}H_{16}$	α-Terpinene	173.3	170.5	65	226
13864	$C_{10}H_{16}$	γ-Terpinene	183	Nonazeotrope		255
13865	$C_{10}H_{16}$	Terpinolene	185.2	Nonazeotrope		226
13866	$C_{10}H_{18}$	*m*-Menthene-8	170.8	<170.5	<92	255
13867	$C_{10}H_{18}O$	Cineole	176.35	Nonazeotrope		237
13868	$C_{10}H_{22}$	2,7-Dimethyloctane	160.2	159	12	226
13869	$C_{10}H_{22}O$	Amyl ether	187.5	Nonazeotrope		237
13870	$C_{10}H_{22}O$	Isoamyl ether	173.2	170.95	90	237
A =	**$C_9H_{18}O_2$**	**Methyl Caprylate**	**192.9**			
13871	$C_{10}H_{14}$	Butylbenzene	183.1	Nonazeotrope		255
13872	$C_{10}H_{16}$	Dipentene	177.7	Nonazeotrope		255
13873	$C_{10}H_{20}O_2$	Isoamyl isovalerate	192.7	192.5	47	229
A =	**$C_9H_{18}O_2$**	**Pelargonic Acid**	**254.0**			
13874	$C_{10}H_7Br$	1-Bromonaphthalene	281.2	Nonazeotrope		255
13875	$C_{10}H_7Cl$	1-Chloronaphthalene	262.7	252.5	>50	255
13876	$C_{10}H_8$	Naphthalene	218.0	Nonazeotrope		255
13877	$C_{10}H_{10}O_2$	Isosafrole	252.0	249.5	35	236
13878	$C_{10}H_{10}O_2$	Safrole	235.9	Nonazeotrope		255
13879	$C_{10}H_{12}O_2$	Eugenol	254.8	250.5	52	255
13880	$C_{10}H_{14}O$	Thymol	232.9	Nonazeotrope		255
13881	$C_{10}H_{18}O_4$	Propyl succinate	250.5	<249.8	20	255
13882	$C_{11}H_{10}$	1-Methylnaphthalene	244.6	243.0	18	242
13883	$C_{11}H_{10}$	2-Methylnaphthalene	241.15	240.2	10	207
13884	$C_{11}H_{14}O_2$	1,2-Dimethoxy-4-propenylbenzene	270.5	Nonazeotrope		255
13885	$C_{12}H_{10}$	Biphenyl	256.1	250	45	242
13886	$C_{12}H_{10}O$	Phenyl ether	259.0	250.5	55	236

No.	Formula	B-Component Name	B.P., ° C.	Azeotropic Data B.P., ° C.	Wt. % A	Ref.
A =	**$C_9H_{18}O_2$**	**Pelargonic Acid** (*continued*)	**254.0**			
13887	$C_{12}H_{18}$	1,3,5-Triethylbenzene	215.5	Nonazeotrope		*255*
13888	$C_{12}H_{22}O_4$	Isoamyl oxalate	268.0	Nonazeotrope		*255*
13889	$C_{13}H_{12}$	Diphenylmethane	265.4	252.7	75	*243*
A =	**$C_9H_{18}O_3$**	**Isobutyl Carbonate**	**190.3**			
13890	$C_{10}H_{16}$	Camphene	158	Nonazeotrope		*226*
13891	$C_{10}H_{16}$	Dipentene	177.7	<174.5	<33	*255*
13892	$C_{10}H_{16}$	*d*-Limonene	177.9	Nonazeotrope		*226*
13893	$C_{10}H_{16}$	α-Pinene	155.8	Nonazeotrope		*226*
13894	$C_{10}H_{18}O$	Cineole	176.35	<176.0	>18	*237*
13895	$C_{10}H_{18}O$	Cineole	176.35	Nonazeotrope		*228*
13896	$C_{10}H_{18}O$	Linaloöl	198.6	<189.8	<96	*255*
13897	$C_{10}H_{18}O$	Linaloöl	198.6	Nonazeotrope		*215*
13898	$C_{10}H_{22}O$	Isoamyl ether	173.2	<172.5	....	*237*
13899	$C_{11}H_{10}$	1-Methylnaphthalene	244.6	Nonazeotrope		*218*
A =	**$C_{10}H_7Br$**	**1-Bromonaphthalene**	**281.2**			
13900	$C_{10}H_8O$	1-Naphthol	288	281	....	*224*
13901	$C_{10}H_8O$	2-Naphthol	295	Nonazeotrope		*255*
13902	$C_{10}H_{10}O_2$	Methyl cinnamate	261.9	Nonazeotrope		*227*
13903	$C_{10}H_{10}O_4$	Methyl phthalate	283.7	278.85	61	*221*
13904	$C_{11}H_{12}O_2$	Ethyl cinnamate	271.5	Nonazeotrope		*221*
13905	$C_{11}H_{14}O_2$	1,2-Dimethoxy-4-propenylbenzene	270.5	Nonazeotrope		*239*
13906	$C_{11}H_{16}O_3$	Isoamyl salicylate	277.5	Nonazeotrope		*255*
13907	$C_{12}H_{10}$	Acenaphthene	277.9	Nonazeotrope		*222*
13908	$C_{12}H_{16}O_2$	Isoamyl benzoate	262.0	Nonazeotrope		*227*
13909	$C_{12}H_{22}O_4$	Isoamyl oxalate	268.0	Nonazeotrope		*222*
13910	$C_{13}H_{10}$	Fluorene	295	Nonazeotrope		*255*
13911	$C_{13}H_{12}$	Diphenylmethane	265.4	Nonazeotrope		*255*
13912	$C_{13}H_{12}O$	Benzyl phenyl ether	286.5	Nonazeotrope		*239*
13913	$C_{14}H_{14}$	1,2-Diphenylethane	284.5	Nonazeotrope		*225*
A =	**$C_{10}H_7Cl$**	**1-Chloronaphthalene**	**262.7**			
13914	$C_{10}H_8O$	1-Naphthol	288	Nonazeotrope		*222*
13915	$C_{10}H_8O$	2-Naphthol	295	Nonazeotrope		*222*
13916	$C_{10}H_{10}O_2$	Isosafrole	252.0	Nonazeotrope		*221*
13917	$C_{10}H_{10}O_2$	Methyl cinnamate	261.9	260.7	55	*222*
13918	$C_{10}H_{10}O_4$	Methyl phthalate	283.7	Nonazeotrope		*227*
13919	$C_{10}H_{12}O_2$	Eugenol	254.8	Nonazeotrope		*255*
13920	$C_{10}H_{12}O_2$	Isoeugenol	268.8	<262.4	<92	*255*
13921	$C_{10}H_{14}O$	Carvacrol	237.85	Nonazeotrope		*255*
13922	$C_{10}H_{14}O$	Thymol	232.9	Nonazeotrope		*224*
13923	$C_{10}H_{18}O_4$	Propyl succinate	250.5	Nonazeotrope		*227*
13924	$C_{10}H_{20}O_2$	Capric acid	268.8	<261.5	<88	*255*
13925	$C_{11}H_{10}$	1-Methylnaphthalene	244.6	Nonazeotrope		*255*
13926	$C_{11}H_{10}$	2-Methylnaphthalene	241.15	Nonazeotrope		*207*
13927	$C_{11}H_{12}O_2$	Ethyl cinnamate	271.5	Nonazeotrope		*221*
13928	$C_{11}H_{14}O_2$	1-Allyl-3,4-dimethoxybenzene	255.0	Nonazeotrope		*221*
13929	$C_{11}H_{14}O_2$	Butyl benzoate	249.5	Nonazeotrope		*227*
13930	$C_{11}H_{14}O_2$	1,2-Dimethoxy-4-propenylbenzene	270.5	Nonazeotrope		*239*
13931	$C_{12}H_{10}$	Acenaphthene	277.9	Nonazeotrope		*255*
13932	$C_{12}H_{10}$	Biphenyl	254.8	Nonazeotrope		*225*
13933	$C_{12}H_{10}O$	Phenyl ether	259.3	258.92	~6	*239*
13934	$C_{12}H_{16}O_2$	Isoamyl benzoate	262.0	261.65	23	*222*
13935	$C_{12}H_{16}O_3$	Isoamyl salicylate	277.5	Nonazeotrope		*255*
13936	$C_{12}H_{22}O_4$	Isoamyl oxalate	268.0	262.5	~92	*222*
13937	$C_{13}H_{12}$	Diphenylmethane	265.4	262.55	93	*221*
A =	**$C_{10}H_8$**	**Naphthalene**	**218.05**			
13938	$C_{10}H_{10}O_2$	Safrole	235.9	Nonazeotrope		*228*
13939	$C_{10}H_{12}O$	Anethole	235.7	Nonazeotrope		*238*
13940	$C_{10}H_{12}O_2$	Ethyl α-toluate	228.75	Nonazeotrope		*209*
13941	$C_{10}H_{12}O_2$	Propyl benzoate	231.2	Nonazeotrope		*243*
13942	$C_{10}H_{14}O$	Carvacrol	237.85	Nonazeotrope		*255*
13943	$C_{10}H_{14}O$	Carvone	231.0	Nonazeotrope		*232*
13944	$C_{10}H_{14}O$	Thymol	232.8	Nonazeotrope		*210*

No.	B-Component Formula	Name	B.P., ° C.	Azeotropic Data B.P., ° C.	Wt. % A	Ref.
A =	$C_{10}H_8$	**Naphthalene** (*continued*)	**218.05**			
13945	$C_{10}H_{15}N$	Diethylaniline	217.05	Nonazeotrope		*231*
			216.5	213	....	*243*
13946	$C_{10}H_{16}O$	Camphor	209.1	Nonazeotrope		*232*
13947	$C_{10}H_{16}O$	Citral	226	Nonazeotrope		*243*
13948	$C_{10}H_{16}O$	Pulegone	~224	Nonazeotrope		*209*
13949	$C_{10}H_{17}Cl$	Bornyl chloride	207.5	Nonazeotrope		*255*
13950	$C_{10}H_{18}O$	Borneol	213.4	213.0	35	*254*
13951	$C_{10}H_{18}O$	Geraniol	229.6	Nonazeotrope		*221*
			229.5	218.0?	....	*243*
13952	$C_{10}H_{18}O$	Linaloöl	198.6	Nonazeotrope		*212*
13953	$C_{10}H_{18}O$	α-Terpineol	217.8	212	~45	*208*
13954	$C_{10}H_{18}O$	β-Terpineol	210.5	Nonazeotrope		*255*
13955	$C_{10}H_{18}O_4$	Propyl succinate	250.5	Nonazeotrope		*226*
13956	$C_{10}H_{20}O$	Citronellol	224.5	217.8	70	*217*
13957	$C_{10}H_{20}O$	Menthol	216.4	215.15	25.5	*209*
13958	$C_{10}H_{20}O_2$	Capric acid	268.8	Nonazeotrope		*255*
13959	$C_{10}H_{20}O_2$	Ethyl caprylate	208.35	Nonazeotrope		*255*
13960	$C_{10}H_{20}O_2$	Isoamyl isovalerate	192.7	Nonazeotrope		*255*
13961	$C_{10}H_{22}O$	*n*-Decyl alcohol	232.9	Nonazeotrope		*209*
13962	$C_{10}H_{22}S$	Isoamyl sulfide	214.8	Nonazeotrope		*255*
13963	$C_{11}H_{14}O_2$	Isobutyl benzoate	241.9	Nonazeotrope		*255*
13964	$C_{11}H_{20}O$	Terpineol methyl ether	216	Nonazeotrope		*243*
13965	$C_{11}H_{22}O_2$	Ethyl pelargonate	227	Nonazeotrope		*255*
13966	$C_{11}H_{22}O_3$	Isoamyl carbonate	228.8	Nonazeotrope		*211*
13967	$C_{12}H_{18}$	1,3,5-Triethylbenzene	215.5	<214.8	<20	*241*
13968	$C_{12}H_{20}O_2$	Bornyl acetate	227.7	Nonazeotrope		*209*
13969	$C_{12}H_{22}O$	Bornyl ethyl ether	204.9	Nonazeotrope		*238*
13970	$C_{13}H_{28}$	Tridecane	234.0	Nonazeotrope		*241*
A =	$C_{10}H_8O$	**1-Naphthol**	**288.0**			
13971	$C_{10}H_9N$	1-Naphthylamine	300.8	Nonazeotrope		*231*
13972	$C_{10}H_9N$	2-Naphthylamine	306.1	Nonazeotrope		*231*
13973	$C_{10}H_{10}O_2$	Methyl cinnamate	261.9	Nonazeotrope		*255*
13974	$C_{11}H_{10}$	1-Methylnaphthalene	244.6	Nonazeotrope		*222*
13975	$C_{11}H_{10}$	2-Methylnaphthalene	241.15	Nonazeotrope		*207*
13976	$C_{11}H_{12}O_2$	Ethyl cinnamate	271.5	Nonazeotrope		*222*
13977	$C_{11}H_{14}O_2$	1,2-Dimethoxy-4-propenylbenzene	270.5	Nonazeotrope		*222*
13978	$C_{12}H_{10}$	Acenaphthene	277.9	Nonazeotrope		*255*
13979	$C_{12}H_{10}$	Acenaphthene	177.9	174.0	20	*224*
13980	$C_{12}H_{10}$	Biphenyl	255.9	Nonazeotrope		*222*
13981	$C_{12}H_{10}O$	Phenyl ether	259.0	Nonazeotrope		*236*
13982	$C_{12}H_{11}N$	Diphenylamine	275	Azeotropic		*243*
13983	$C_{12}H_{16}O_2$	Isoamyl benzoate	262.0	Nonazeotrope		*255*
13984	$C_{12}H_{16}O_3$	Isoamyl salicylate	277.5	Nonazeotrope		*255*
13985	$C_{12}H_{22}O_4$	Isoamyl oxalate	268.0	Nonazeotrope		*222*
13986	$C_{13}H_{10}$	Fluorene	295	Nonazeotrope		*255*
13987	$C_{13}H_{12}$	Diphenylmethane	265.4	Nonazeotrope		*255*
13988	$C_{13}H_{12}$	Diphenylmethane	265.6	265	10	*224*
13989	$C_{14}H_{12}$	1,2-Diphenylethylene	308.5	Nonazeotrope		*255*
A =	$C_{10}H_8O$	**2-Naphthol**	**295.0**			
13990	$C_{10}H_{10}O_4$	Methyl phthalate	283.2	>296.0	>82	*255*
13991	$C_{11}H_{12}O_2$	Ethyl cinnamate	272.0	Nonazeotrope		*255*
13992	$C_{12}H_{10}$	Acenaphthene	277.9	Nonazeotrope		*255*
13993	$C_{12}H_{10}$	Acenaphthene	277.9	277.0	10	*224*
13994	$C_{12}H_{10}$	Biphenyl	255.9	Nonazeotrope		*222*
13995	$C_{13}H_{12}$	Diphenylmethane	265.5	Nonazeotrope		*222*
13996	$C_{14}H_{12}$	Stilbene	308.5	Nonazeotrope		*255*
13997	$C_{14}H_{14}$	1,2-Diphenylethane	285.5	Nonazeotrope		*255*
13998	$C_{14}H_{14}$	1,2-Diphenylethane	284	283.5	....	*224*
A =	$C_{10}H_9N$	**1-Naphthylamine**	**300.8**			
13999	$C_{12}H_{10}$	Acenaphthene	277.9	Nonazeotrope		*231*
14000	$C_{13}H_{12}O$	Benzyl phenyl ether	286.5	Nonazeotrope		*231*
14001	$C_{14}H_{14}$	1,2-Diphenylethane	284.5	Nonazeotrope		*231*
14002	$C_{14}H_{14}O$	Benzyl ether	297	<296	....	*255*

No.	B-Component Formula	Name	B.P., ° C.	Azeotropic Data B.P., ° C.	Wt. % A	Ref.
A =	**$C_{10}H_9N$**	**2-Naphthylamine**	**306.1**			
14003	$C_{13}H_{12}O$	Benzyl phenyl ether	286.5	Nonazeotrope		*255*
14004	$C_{14}H_{14}O$	Benzyl ether	297	Nonazeotrope		*255*
A =	**$C_{10}H_9N$**	**Quinaldine**	**246.5**			
14005	$C_{10}H_{10}O_2$	Safrole	235.9	Nonazeotrope		*255*
14006	$C_{10}H_{14}O$	Carvacrol	237.85	250.8	67	*255*
14007	$C_{10}H_{14}O$	Thymol	232.9	250.0	80	*255*
A =	**$C_{10}H_{10}O_2$**	**Isosafrol**	**252.1**			
14008	$C_{10}H_{10}O_2$	Methyl cinnamate	261.6	Nonazeotrope		*211, 237*
14009	$C_{10}H_{12}O_2$	Eugenol	255.0	252.05?	~92	*254*
14010	$C_{10}H_{14}O$	Thymol	232.9	Nonazeotrope		*222*
14011	$C_{10}H_{18}O_4$	Propyl succinate	250.5	<249.0	<70	*237*
14012	$C_{10}H_{20}O_2$	Capric acid	268.8	Nonazeotrope		*255*
14013	$C_{11}H_{10}$	1-Methylnaphthalene	244.6	Nonazeotrope		*228*
14014	$C_{11}H_{10}$	2-Methylnaphthalene	241.15	Nonazeotrope		*207*
14015	$C_{11}H_{14}O_2$	1-Allyl-3,4-dimethoxybenzene	254.7	Nonazeotrope		*229*
14016	$C_{11}H_{14}O_2$	Butyl benzoate	249.5	Nonazeotrope		*237*
14017	$C_{11}H_{14}O_2$	Isobutyl benzoate	241.9	Nonazeotrope		*237*
14018	$C_{11}H_{17}N$	Isoamylaniline	256.0	<250.0	>64	*231*
14019	$C_{12}H_{10}$	Biphenyl	255.0	Nonazeotrope		*228*
14020	$C_{12}H_{10}O$	Phenyl ether	259.0	Nonazeotrope		*229*
14021	$C_{12}H_{16}O_2$	Isoamyl benzoate	262.05	Nonazeotrope		*237*
14022	$C_{12}H_{22}O_4$	Isoamyl oxalate	268.0	Nonazeotrope		*237*
14023	$C_{13}H_{12}$	Diphenylmethane	265.6	Nonazeotrope		*215*
14024	$C_{15}H_{33}BO_3$	Isoamyl borate	255	<250.8	....	*237*
A =	**$C_{10}H_{10}O_2$**	**Methyl Cinnamate**	**261.95**			
14025	$C_{10}H_{12}O_2$	Eugenol	255.0	Nonazeotrope		*236*
14026	$C_{10}H_{12}O_2$	Isoeugenol	268.8	Nonazeotrope		*215*
14027	$C_{10}H_{14}O$	Thymol	232.9	Nonazeotrope		*255*
14028	$C_{10}H_{20}O_2$	Capric acid	~268.8	Nonazeotrope		*255*
14029	$C_{10}H_{20}O_4$	2-(2-Butoxyethoxy)ethyl acetate	245.3	Nonazeotrope		*255*
14030	$C_{11}H_{10}$	1-Methylnaphthalene	245.1	Nonazeotrope		*226*
14031	$C_{11}H_{10}$	2-Methylnaphthalene	241.15	Nonazeotrope		*207*
14032	$C_{11}H_{14}O_2$	1-Allyl-3,4-dimethoxybenzene	255.2	Nonazeotrope		*237*
14033	$C_{11}H_{14}O_2$	1,2-Dimethoxy-4-propenylbenzene	270.5	Nonazeotrope		*237*
14034	$C_{12}H_{10}$	Acenaphthene	277.9	Nonazeotrope		*226*
14035	$C_{12}H_{10}$	Biphenyl	255.9	Nonazeotrope		*222*
14036	$C_{12}H_{10}O$	Phenyl ether	259.3	258.8	17?	*237*
14037	$C_{12}H_{16}O_2$	Isoamyl benzoate	262.0	260.5	47.5	*229*
14038	$C_{12}H_{16}O_3$	Isoamyl salicylate	277.5	Nonazeotrope		*255*
14039	$C_{12}H_{22}O_4$	Isoamyl oxalate	268.0	Nonazeotrope		*255*
14040	$C_{13}H_{12}$	Diphenylmethane	265.6	261.55	~95	*253*
A =	**$C_{10}H_{10}O_2$**	**Safrole**	**235.9**			
14041	$C_{10}H_{12}O$	Anethole	235.7	234.65	60	*207*
14042	$C_{10}H_{12}O_2$	Ethyl α-toluate	228.75	Nonazeotrope		*237*
14043	$C_{10}H_{12}O_2$	Propyl benzoate	230.85	Nonazeotrope		*237*
			231.2	228	40	*243*
14044	$C_{10}H_{14}N_2$	Nicotine	247.5	Nonazeotrope		*255*
14045	$C_{10}H_{14}O$	Carvacrol	237.85	Nonazeotrope		*236*
14046	$C_{10}H_{14}O$	Carvone	231.0	Nonazeotrope		*232*
14047	$C_{10}H_{14}O$	Thymol	232.8	Nonazeotrope		*209*
14048	$C_{10}H_{15}N$	Diethylaniline	217.05	Nonazeotrope		*231*
14049	$C_{10}H_{16}O$	Menthenone	222.5	Nonazeotrope		*244*
14050	$C_{10}H_{16}O$	Pulegone	223.8	Nonazeotrope		*255*
14051	$C_{10}H_{18}O$	Borneol	215.0	Nonazeotrope		*255*
14052	$C_{10}H_{18}O$	Geraniol	235.9	Nonazeotrope		*225*
14053	$C_{10}H_{18}O$	α-Terpineol	218.85	Nonazeotrope		*255*
14054	$C_{10}H_{18}O_4$	Propyl succinate	250.5	Nonazeotrope		*237*
14055	$C_{10}H_{20}O$	Citronellol	224.4	Nonazeotrope		*225*
14056	$C_{10}H_{22}O$	Decyl alcohol	235.9	Nonazeotrope		*225*
14057	$C_{11}H_{10}$	1-Methylnaphthalene	244.9	Nonazeotrope		*217*
14058	$C_{11}H_{10}$	2-Methylnaphthalene	241.15	Nonazeotrope		*207*
14059	$C_{11}H_{14}O_2$	1-Allyl-3,4-dimethoxybenzene	255.2	Nonazeotrope		*215*

No.	B-Component Formula	B-Component Name	B.P., ° C	Azeotropic Data B.P., ° C.	Azeotropic Data Wt. % A	Ref.
A =	**$C_{10}H_{10}O_2$**	**Safrole (*continued*)**	**235.9**			
14060	$C_{11}H_{14}O_2$	Butyl benzoate	249.0	Nonazeotrope		*237*
14061	$C_{11}H_{14}O_2$	Ethyl β-phenylpropionate	248.1	Nonazeotrope		*237*
14062	$C_{11}H_{14}O_2$	Isobutyl benzoate	241.9	Nonazeotrope		*237*
14063	$C_{11}H_{17}N$	Isoamylaniline	256.0	Nonazeotrope		*231*
14064	$C_{11}H_{22}O_3$	Isoamyl carbonate	232.2	<231.8	....	*237*
14065	$C_{11}H_{22}O_3$	Isoamyl carbonate	232.2	Nonazeotrope		*228*
14066	$C_{12}H_{20}O_2$	Bornyl acetate	227.6	Nonazeotrope		*237*
A =	**$C_{10}H_{10}O_4$**	**Methyl Phthalate**	**283.2**			
14067	$C_{11}H_{12}O_2$	Ethyl cinnamate	272.0	Nonazeotrope		*229*
14068	$C_{11}H_{14}O_2$	1,2-Dimethoxy-4-propenylbenzene	270.5	Nonazeotrope		*237*
14069	$C_{12}H_{10}$	Acenaphthene	277.9	276.35	33.5	*222*
14070	$C_{12}H_{10}$	Biphenyl	255.9	Nonazeotrope		*226*
14071	$C_{12}H_{10}O$	Phenyl ether	259.0	Nonazeotrope		*237*
14072	$C_{12}H_{16}O_3$	Isoamyl salicylate	277.5	Nonazeotrope		*255*
14073	$C_{13}H_{12}$	Diphenylmethane	265.6	Nonazeotrope		*226*
14074	$C_{13}H_{12}O$	Benzyl phenyl ether	286.5	<282.5	....	*237*
14075	$C_{14}H_{14}$	1,2-Diphenylethane	284	280.5	53	*226*
14076	$C_{14}H_{14}O$	Benzyl ether	297	Nonazeotrope		*237*
A =	**$C_{10}H_{12}O$**	**Anethole**	**235.7**			
14077	$C_{10}H_{12}O_2$	Propyl benzoate	230.85	Nonazeotrope		*237*
14078	$C_{10}H_{14}O$	Carvacrol	237.85	Nonazeotrope		*236*
14079	$C_{10}H_{14}O$	Carvone	231.0	Nonazeotrope		*232*
14080	$C_{10}H_{14}O$	Thymol	232.9	Nonazeotrope		*255*
14081	$C_{10}H_{15}N$	Diethylaniline	217.05	Nonazeotrope		*231*
14082	$C_{10}H_{16}O$	Pulegone	223.8	Nonazeotrope		*255*
14083	$C_{10}H_{18}O$	α-Terpineol	218.85	Nonazeotrope		*255*
14084	$C_{10}H_{20}O$	Citronellol	224.4	Nonazeotrope		*255*
14085	$C_{10}H_{20}O$	Menthol	216.3	Nonazeotrope		*255*
14086	$C_{10}H_{22}O$	Decyl alcohol	232.8	<232.6	<78	*255*
14087	$C_{11}H_{10}$	1-Methylnaphthalene	244.6	Nonazeotrope		*238*
14088	$C_{11}H_{10}$	2-Methylnaphthalene	241.15	Nonazeotrope		*207*
14089	$C_{11}H_{14}O_2$	Isobutyl benzoate	241.9	Nonazeotrope		*237*
A =	**$C_{10}H_{12}O$**	**Estragole**	**215.6**			
14090	$C_{10}H_{16}O$	Camphor	209.1	Nonazeotrope		*255*
A =	**$C_{10}H_{12}O_2$**	**Ethyl α-toluate**	**228.75**			
14091	$C_{10}H_{12}O_2$	Propyl benzoate	230.9	228.7	97	*209*
			230.85	Nonazeotrope		*229*
14092	$C_{10}H_{14}O$	Carvacrol	237.85	238.3	20	*255*
14093	$C_{10}H_{14}O$	Carvone	231.0	228.6	93	*232*
14094	$C_{10}H_{14}O$	Thymol	232.8	235.75	37.5	*209*
14095	$C_{10}H_{14}O_2$	*m*-Diethoxybenzene	235.0	Nonazeotrope		*237*
14096	$C_{10}H_{16}O$	Carvenone	234.5	Nonazeotrope		*232*
14097	$C_{10}H_{16}O$	Pulegone	223.8	Nonazeotrope		*232*
14098	$C_{10}H_{18}O$	Geraniol	229.6	228.1	70	*209*
14099	$C_{10}H_{18}O$	α-Terpineol	217.8	Nonazeotrope		*216*
14100	$C_{10}H_{20}O$	Citronellol	224.5	Nonazeotrope		*216*
14101	$C_{10}H_{20}O$	Menthol	216.3	Nonazeotrope		*255*
14102	$C_{10}H_{20}O_4$	2-(2-Butoxyethoxy)ethyl acetate	245.3	Nonazeotrope		*255*
14103	$C_{10}H_{22}O$	Decyl alcohol	232.9	228.55	94	*209*
14104	$C_{11}H_{10}$	1-Methylnaphthalene	244.9	Nonazeotrope		*217*
14105	$C_{11}H_{12}$	2-Methylnaphthalene	241.15	Nonazeotrope		*255*
14106	$C_{11}H_{14}O_2$	Isobutyl benzoate	241.9	Nonazeotrope		*255*
14107	$C_{11}H_{16}O$	Methyl thymol ether	216.5	Nonazeotrope		*237*
14108	$C_{11}H_{22}O_3$	Isoamyl carbonate	228.5	227.9	....	*253*
14109	$C_{12}H_{20}O_2$	Bornyl acetate	227.6	226.6	44	*229*
A =	**$C_{10}H_{12}O_2$**	**Eugenol**	**254.8**			
14110	$C_{10}H_{14}O$	Carvone	231.0	Nonazeotrope		*255*
14111	$C_{10}H_{16}O$	Menthenone	222.5	Nonazeotrope		*255*
14112	$C_{10}H_{20}O$	Citronellol	224.4	Nonazeotrope		*255*
14113	$C_{11}H_{10}$	1-Methylnaphthalene	244.6	Nonazeotrope		*236*
14114	$C_{11}H_{10}$	2-Methylnaphthalene	241.15	Nonazeotrope		*207*
14115	$C_{11}H_{14}O_2$	1-Allyl-3,4-dimethoxybenzene	255.2	255.3	~45	*254*

No.	B-Component Formula	Name	B.P., ° C	Azeotropic Data B.P., ° C.	Wt. % A	Ref.
A =	$C_{10}H_{12}O_2$	**Eugenol** (*continued*)	**254.8**			
14116	$C_{11}H_{14}O_2$	Butyl benzoate	249.5	Nonazeotrope		*228*
14117	$C_{11}H_{14}O_2$	Isobutyl benzoate	242.15	Nonazeotrope		*215*
14118	$C_{11}H_{16}O$	*p-tert*-Amylphenol	266.5	Nonazeotrope		*255*
14119	$C_{11}H_{17}N$	Isoamylaniline	256.0	<254.5	....	*231*
14120	$C_{12}H_{10}$	Biphenyl	255.0	253.5	50?	*236*
14121	$C_{12}H_{10}O$	Phenyl ether	259.3	254.9	~97	*254*
14122	$C_{12}H_{16}O_2$	Isoamyl benzoate	262.05	Nonazeotrope		*236, 254*
14123	$C_{13}H_{12}$	Diphenylmethane	265.4	Nonazeotrope		*236*
A =	$C_{10}H_{12}O_2$	**Isoeugenol**	**268.8**			
14124	$C_{11}H_{10}$	2-Methylnaphthalene	241.15	Nonazeotrope		*255*
14125	$C_{11}H_{12}O_2$	Ethyl cinnamate	272.5	Nonazeotrope		*228*
14126	$C_{11}H_{14}O_2$	1,2-Dimethoxy-4-propenylbenzene	270.5	Nonazeotrope		*215*
14127	$C_{11}H_{16}O$	*p-tert*-Amylphenol	266.5	Nonazeotrope		*255*
14128	$C_{11}H_{17}N$	Isoamylaniline	256.0	Nonazeotrope		*255*
14129	$C_{12}H_{10}$	Acenaphthene	277.9	Nonazeotrope		*236*
14130	$C_{12}H_{10}$	Biphenyl	255.0	Nonazeotrope		*236*
14131	$C_{12}H_{10}O$	Phenyl ether	259.3	Nonazeotrope		*251*
14132	$C_{12}H_{16}O_2$	Isoamyl benzoate	262.05	Nonazeotrope		*215*
14133	$C_{12}H_{16}O_3$	Isoamyl salicylate	277.5	Nonazeotrope		*255*
14134	$C_{13}H_{12}$	Diphenylmethane	265.5	264.7	20?	*236*
14135	$C_{14}H_{14}$	1,2-Diphenylethane	284.5	Nonazeotrope		*255*
A =	$C_{10}H_{12}O_2$	**Propyl Benzoate**	**230.85**			
14136	$C_{10}H_{14}O$	Carvacrol	237.85	238.85	18	*242*
14137	$C_{10}H_{14}O$	Carvone	231.0	231.5?	50	*232*
14138	$C_{10}H_{14}O$	Thymol	232.8	235.5	45	*209*
14139	$C_{10}H_{16}O$	Carvenone	234.5	Nonazeotrope		*232*
14140	$C_{10}H_{16}O$	Citral	226	Nonazeotrope		*243*
14141	$C_{10}H_{16}O$	Pulegone	223.8	Nonazeotrope		*232*
14142	$C_{10}H_{18}O$	Geraniol	229.5	228.0	~45	*243*
14143	$C_{10}H_{18}O$	α-Terpineol	218.85	Nonazeotrope		*255*
14144	$C_{10}H_{20}O$	Citronellol	224.5	Nonazeotrope		*216*
14145	$C_{10}H_{20}O$	Menthol	216.3	Nonazeotrope		*255*
14146	$C_{10}H_{20}O_4$	2-(2-Butoxyethoxy)ethyl acetate	245.3	Nonazeotrope		*255*
14147	$C_{10}H_{22}O$	*n*-Decyl alcohol	232.5	230.7	~75	*208*
14148	$C_{11}H_{10}$	1-Methylnaphthalene	244.9	Nonazeotrope		*217*
14149	$C_{11}H_{10}$	2-Methylnaphthalene	241.15	Nonazeotrope		*207*
14150	$C_{11}H_{22}O_3$	Isoamyl carbonate	232.2	<230.8	....	*229*
A =	$C_{10}H_{14}$	**Butylbenzene**	**183.1**			
14151	$C_{10}H_{14}$	Cymene	176.7	Nonazeotrope		*241*
14152	$C_{10}H_{16}$	α-Terpinene	173.4	Nonazeotrope		*241*
14153	$C_{10}H_{16}$	Terpinolene	184.6	182.2	65	*241*
14154	$C_{10}H_{18}O$	Borneol	215	Nonazeotrope		*255*
14155	$C_{10}H_{18}O$	Cineole	176.35	Nonazeotrope		*228*
14156	$C_{10}H_{18}O$	Citronellal	208.0	Nonazeotrope		*255*
14157	$C_{10}H_{18}O$	Linaloöl	198.6	Nonazeotrope		*255*
14158	$C_{10}H_{20}O$	Menthol	216.3	Nonazeotrope		*255*
14159	$C_{10}H_{22}O$	Amyl ether	187.5	Nonazeotrope		*238*
14160	$C_{11}H_{20}O$	Isobornyl methyl ether	192.4	Nonazeotrope		*238*
A =	$C_{10}H_{14}$	**Cymene**	**176.7**			
14161	$C_{10}H_{16}$	Camphene	159.6	Nonazeotrope		*241*
14162	$C_{10}H_{16}$	Dipentene	177.7	175.8	60	*241*
14163	$C_{10}H_{16}$	*d*-Limonene	177.8	174.5	75	*243*
14164	$C_{10}H_{16}$	Nopinene	163.8	Nonazeotrope		*241*
14165	$C_{10}H_{16}$	α-Terpinene	173.4	173.0	20	*241*
14166	$C_{10}H_{18}O$	Cineole	176.35	176.2	45	*238*
14167	$C_{10}H_{18}O$	Linaloöl	198.6	Nonazeotrope		*217*
14168	$C_{10}H_{18}O$	α-Terpineol	218.85	Nonazeotrope		*255*
14169	$C_{10}H_{22}O$	Isoamyl ether	172.6	Nonazeotrope		*217*
14170	$C_{10}H_{23}N$	Diisoamylamine	188.2	Nonazeotrope		*231*
A =	$C_{10}H_{14}$	**Isobutylbenzene**	**241.9**			
14171	$C_{10}H_{14}O_2$	*m*-Diethoxybenzene	235.0	Nonazeotrope		*237*

No.	B-Component Formula	Name	B.P., °C.	Azeotropic Data B.P., °C.	Wt. % A	Ref.
A =	$C_{10}H_{14}N_2$	**Nicotine**	**247.5**			
14171a	$C_{10}H_{14}O$	Thymol	232.9	>250.2	>79	255
14171b	$C_{10}H_{14}O_2$	*m*-Diethoxybenzene	235.4	Nonazeotrope		255
A =	$C_{10}H_{14}O$	**Carvacrol**	**237.85**			
14172	$C_{10}H_{14}O$	Carvone	231.0	242.2	>58	232
14173	$C_{10}H_{14}O$	Thymol	232.9	Nonazeotrope		255
14174	$C_{10}H_{15}N$	Diethylaniline	217.05	Nonazeotrope		231
14175	$C_{10}H_{16}O$	Carvenone	234.5	243.0	55	255
14176	$C_{10}H_{16}O$	Menthenone	222.5	239.5	75	255
14177	$C_{10}H_{16}O$	Pulegone	223.8	238.4	....	232
14178	$C_{10}H_{18}O$	Geraniol	229.6	>238.2	>85	255
14179	$C_{10}H_{18}O$	Menthone	209.5	Nonazeotrope		255
14180	$C_{10}H_{18}O$	α-Terpineol	218.85	Nonazeotrope		255
14181	$C_{10}H_{18}O_4$	Propyl succinate	250.5	251.5	25	255
14182	$C_{10}H_{22}O$	Decyl alcohol	232.8	Nonazeotrope		255
14183	$C_{11}H_{10}$	1-Methylnaphthalene	244.6	Nonazeotrope		255
14184	$C_{11}H_{14}O_2$	Butyl benzoate	249.0	Nonazeotrope		255
14185	$C_{11}H_{14}O_2$	Isobutyl benzoate	241.9	243.85	33	242
14186	$C_{11}H_{17}N$	Isoamylaniline	256.0	Nonazeotrope		231
14187	$C_{11}H_{22}O_3$	Isoamyl carbonate	232.2	>239.0	>62	255
14188	$C_{12}H_{10}$	Biphenyl	256.1	Nonazeotrope		255
14189	$C_{12}H_{20}O_2$	Bornyl acetate	227.6	238.8	75	242
A =	$C_{10}H_{14}O$	**Carvone**	**230.95**			
14190	$C_{10}H_{14}O$	Thymol	232.9	238.65	48	232
14191	$C_{10}H_{14}O_2$	*m*-Diethoxybenzene	235	Nonazeotrope		217
14192	$C_{10}H_{15}N$	Diethylaniline	217.05	Nonazeotrope		231
14193	$C_{10}H_{18}O$	Borneol	215.0	Nonazeotrope		232
14194	$C_{10}H_{18}O$	Geraniol	229.6	229.2	40	232
14195	$C_{10}H_{20}O$	Citronellol	224.4	Nonazeotrope		232
14196	$C_{10}H_{20}O$	Menthol	216.3	Nonazeotrope		232
14197	$C_{10}H_{22}O$	*n*-Decyl alcohol	232.8	230.85	81	232
14198	$C_{11}H_{10}$	1-Methylnaphthalene	244.6	Nonazeotrope		232
14199	$C_{11}H_{10}$	2-Methylnaphthalene	241.15	Nonazeotrope		207
14200	$C_{11}H_{14}O_2$	Isobutyl benzoate	241.9	Nonazeotrope		232
14201	$C_{11}H_{16}O$	*p*-*tert*-Amylphenol	265	Nonazeotrope		255
14202	$C_{11}H_{17}N$	*N*-Isoamylaniline	256.0	Nonazeotrope		255
14203	$C_{11}H_{22}O_3$	Isoamyl carbonate	228.5	Nonazeotrope		253
			232.2	230.5	60	232
14204	$C_{12}H_{20}O_2$	Bornyl acetate	227.6	Nonazeotrope		232
A =	$C_{10}H_{14}O$	**Thymol**	**232.9**			
14206	$C_{10}H_{14}O_2$	*m*-Diethoxybenzene	235.0	Nonazeotrope		222
14207	$C_{10}H_{15}N$	Diethylaniline	217.05	Nonazeotrope		231
14208	$C_{10}H_{16}O$	Camphor	209.1	233.3	84	232
			209.1	Nonazeotrope		222
14209	$C_{10}H_{16}O$	Carvenone	234.5	241.0	50	255
14210	$C_{10}H_{16}O$	Pulegone	223.8	235.3	65	232
14211	$C_{10}H_{18}O$	Borneol	213.4	Nonazeotrope		222
14212	$C_{10}H_{18}O$	Geraniol	229.6	235.6	57.5	209
14213	$C_{10}H_{18}O$	Linaloöl	198.6	Nonazeotrope		255
14214	$C_{10}H_{18}O$	Menthone	209.5	233.2	92	255
14215	$C_{10}H_{18}O$	α-Terpineol	217.8	Nonazeotrope		209
14216	$C_{10}H_{18}O_4$	Propyl succinate	250.5	Nonazeotrope		255
14217	$C_{10}H_{20}O$	Citronellol	224	233.8	~85	253
14218	$C_{10}H_{20}O$	Menthol	216.4	Nonazeotrope		222
14219	$C_{10}H_{20}O_2$	Methyl pelargonate	213.8	Nonazeotrope		255
14220	$C_{10}H_{22}O$	*n*-Decyl alcohol	232.5	~234.5	~60	209
14221	$C_{11}H_{10}$	1-Methylnaphthalene	242	Nonazeotrope		253
14222	$C_{11}H_{10}$	2-Methylnaphthalene	241.15	Nonazeotrope		207
14223	$C_{11}H_{14}O_2$	1-Allyl-3,4-dimethoxybenzene	254.7	Nonazeotrope		255
14224	$C_{11}H_{14}O_2$	Butyl benzoate	249.8	Nonazeotrope		222
14225	$C_{11}H_{14}O_2$	Isobutyl benzoate	242.15	243.2	20	253
14226	$C_{11}H_{16}O$	Methyl thymyl ether	216.5	Nonazeotrope		255
14227	$C_{11}H_{20}O$	Methyl α-terpineol ether	216.2	Nonazeotrope		224
14228	$C_{11}H_{22}O_3$	Isoamyl carbonate	232.2	236.25	~48	232
14229	$C_{12}H_{10}$	Biphenyl	255.9	Nonazeotrope		222

No.	B-Component Formula	B-Component Name	B-Component B.P., ° C.	Azeotropic Data B.P., ° C.	Azeotropic Data Wt. % A	Ref.
A =	**$C_{10}H_{14}O$**	**Thymol (*continued*)**	**232.9**			
14230	$C_{12}H_{10}O$	Phenyl ether	259.0	Nonazeotrope		*255*
14231	$C_{12}H_{18}$	1,3,5-Triethylbenzene	216	Nonazeotrope		*224*
14232	$C_{12}H_{22}O_2$	Bornyl acetate	227.7	235.6	60	*209*
A =	**$C_{10}H_{14}O_2$**	***m*-Diethoxybenzene**	**235.4**			
14234	$C_{10}H_{15}N$	Diethylaniline	217.05	Nonazeotrope		*255*
14235	$C_{10}H_{18}O$	Geraniol	229.7	Nonazeotrope		*256*
14236	$C_{10}H_{20}O$	Citronellol	224.4	Nonazeotrope		*255*
14237	$C_{10}H_{22}O$	Decyl alcohol	232.8	232.2	....	*256*
14238	$C_{11}H_{22}O_3$	Isoamyl carbonate	232.2	<231.0	>33	*237*
14239	$C_{12}H_{20}O_2$	Bornyl acetate	227.6	Nonazeotrope		*237*
=	**$C_{10}H_{15}N$**	**Diethylaniline**	**217.05**			
14240	$C_{10}H_{16}O$	Camphor	209.1	Nonazeotrope		*231*
14241	$C_{10}H_{16}O$	Citral	226	Reacts		*243*
14242	$C_{10}H_{16}O$	Pulegone	223.8	Nonazeotrope		*231*
14243	$C_{10}H_{18}O$	Borneol	215.0	<214.8	<20	*231*
			213.5	Nonazeotrope		*222*
14244	$C_{10}H_{18}O$	Geraniol	229.6	Nonazeotrope		*231*
14245	$C_{10}H_{18}O$	Linaloöl	198.6	Nonazeotrope		*231*
14246	$C_{10}H_{18}O$	α-Terpineol	218.85	215.5	56	*231*
14247	$C_{10}H_{18}O$	β-Terpineol	210.5	Nonazeotrope		*231*
14248	$C_{10}H_{20}O$	Citronellol	224.4	Nonazeotrope		*231*
14249	$C_{10}H_{20}O$	Menthol	216.3	215.3	43.5	*231*
14250	$C_{10}H_{22}O$	Decyl alcohol	232.8	Nonazeotrope		*231*
14251	$C_{11}H_{10}$	2-Methylnaphthalene	241.5	Nonazeotrope		*207*
14252	$C_{11}H_{16}O$	Methyl thymyl ether	216.5	<216.0	<49	*255*
14253	$C_{11}H_{20}O$	Methyl α-terpinyl ether	216.2	<215.0	<48	*231*
14254	$C_{11}H_{24}O_2$	Diisoamyloxymethane	210.8	Nonazeotrope		*231*
14255	$C_{12}H_{22}O$	Ethyl isobornyl ether	203.8	Nonazeotrope		*231*
A =	**$C_{10}H_{16}$**	**Camphene**	**159.6**			
14256	$C_{10}H_{16}$	Dipentene	177.7	Nonazeotrope		*241*
14257	$C_{10}H_{16}$	Nopinene	163.8	Nonazeotrope		*241*
14258	$C_{10}H_{16}$	α-Pinene	155.8	Nonazeotrope		*241*
14259	$C_{10}H_{18}O$	Linaloöl	198.6	Nonazeotrope		*217*
14260	$C_{10}H_{22}$	2,7-Dimethyloctane	160.25	158	62	*241*
14261	$C_{10}H_{23}N$	Diisoamylamine	188.2	Nonazeotrope		*231*
14262	$C_{12}H_{20}O_2$	Isobornyl acetate	225.8	Nonazeotrope		*255*
A =	**$C_{10}H_{16}$**	**Dipentene**	**177.7**			
14263	$C_{10}H_{16}$	α-Pinene	155.8	Nonazeotrope		*241*
14264	$C_{10}H_{16}$	α-Terpinene	173.4	Nonazeotrope		*255*
14265	$C_{10}H_{22}O$	Amyl ether	187.5	Nonazeotrope		*238*
14266	$C_{10}H_{23}N$	Diisoamylamine	188.2	Nonazeotrope		*231*
14267	$C_{12}H_{20}O_2$	Isobornyl acetate	225.8	Nonazeotrope		*255*
A =	**$C_{10}H_{16}$**	***d*-Limonene**	**177.8**			
14268	$C_{10}H_{16}$	Terpinene	180.5	Nonazeotrope		*243*
14269	$C_{10}H_{18}O$	Borneol	213.4	Nonazeotrope		*217*
14270	$C_{10}H_{18}O$	Cineole	176.35	Nonazeotrope		*209*
14271	$C_{10}H_{18}O$	Linaloöl	198.6	Nonazeotrope		*217*
14272	$C_{10}H_{20}O$	Menthol	216.4	Nonazeotrope		*217*
14273	$C_{10}H_{20}O_2$	Isoamyl isovalerate	~193.5	Nonazeotrope		*253*
14274	$C_{10}H_{22}O$	Isoamyl ether	172.7	Nonazeotrope		*243*
A =	**$C_{10}H_{16}$**	**Nopinene**	**163.8**			
14275	$C_{10}H_{16}$	α-Terpinene	173.4	Nonazeotrope		*241*
14276	$C_{10}H_{22}O$	Isoamyl ether	173.2	Nonazeotrope		*238*
A =	**$C_{10}H_{16}$**	**α-Phellandrene**	**171.5**			
14277	$C_{10}H_{18}O$	Cineole	176.3	Nonazeotrope		*243*
A =	**$C_{10}H_{16}$**	**α-Pinene**	**155.8**			
14278	$C_{10}H_{16}$	α-Terpinene	173.4	Nonazeotrope		*241*
14279	$C_{10}H_{18}O$	Borneol	155.8	Nonazeotrope		*217*
14280	$C_{10}H_{22}$	2,7-Dimethyloctane	160.1	<155.5	<89	*241*

	B-Component			Azeotropic Data		
No.	Formula	Name	B.P., ° C.	B.P., ° C.	Wt. % A	Ref.
A =	**$C_{10}H_{16}$**	**α-Terpinene**	**173.4**			
14281	$C_{10}H_{18}O$	Cineole	176.35	Nonazeotrope		238
14282	$C_{10}H_{18}O$	Linaloöl	198.6	Nonazeotrope		255
14283	$C_{10}H_{22}$	Decane	173.3	<171.5	<50	241
14284	$C_{10}H_{22}O$	Isoamyl ether	173.2	172.0	50	238
A =	**$C_{10}H_{16}$**	**γ-Terpinene**	**180.5**			
14285	$C_{10}H_{18}O$	Cineole	176.3	Nonazeotrope		243
14286	$C_{10}H_{20}O_2$	Isoamyl isovalerate	192.7	Nonazeotrope		226
14287	$C_{10}H_{22}O$	Isoamyl ether	173.4	Nonazeotrope		228
A =	**$C_{10}H_{16}$**	**Terpinolene**	**184.6**			
14288	$C_{10}H_{20}O_2$	Isoamyl isovalerate	192.7	Nonazeotrope		255
14289	$C_{11}H_{20}O$	Isobornyl methyl ether	192.4	Nonazeotrope		238
A =	**$C_{10}H_{16}$**	**Thymene**	**179.7**			
14290	$C_{10}H_{18}O$	Borneol	213.4	Nonazeotrope		217
14291	$C_{10}H_{18}O$	Cineole	176.35	Nonazeotrope		217
14292	$C_{10}H_{18}O$	Linaloöl	198.6	Nonazeotrope		254
14293	$C_{10}H_{18}O$	α-Terpineol	~217.8	Nonazeotrope		217
14294	$C_{10}H_{20}O$	Menthol	216.4	Nonazeotrope		220
14295	$C_{10}H_{20}O_2$	Isoamyl isovalerate	193.5	Nonazeotrope		253
A =	**$C_{10}H_{16}O$**	**Camphor**	**208.9**			
14296	$C_{10}H_{17}Cl$	Bornyl chloride	~210	Nonazeotrope		243
14297	$C_{10}H_{18}O$	Borneol	215.0	Nonazeotrope		232
14298	$C_{10}H_{18}O$	Citronellal	208.0	207.5	....	232
14299	$C_{10}H_{18}O$	Linaloöl	198.6	Nonazeotrope		232
14300	$C_{10}H_{18}O$	Menthone	207	Nonazeotrope		243
14301	$C_{10}H_{20}O$	Menthol	216.3	Nonazeotrope		232
14302	$C_{10}H_{22}S$	Isoamyl sulfide	214.8	<208.8	....	246
14303	$C_{11}H_{16}O$	Methyl thymyl ether	216.5	Nonazeotrope		255
14304	$C_{11}H_{20}O$	Methyl terpenyl ether	216.2	Nonazeotrope		232
14305	$C_{12}H_{18}$	1,3,5-Triethylbenzene	215.5	Nonazeotrope		232
A =	**$C_{10}H_{16}O$**	**Carvenone**	**234.5**			
14306	$C_{11}H_{14}O_2$	Isobutyl benzoate	241.9	Nonazeotrope		232
14307	$C_{11}H_{22}O_3$	Isoamyl carbonate	232.2	Nonazeotrope		232
A =	**$C_{10}H_{16}O$**	**Citral**	**226**			
14308	$C_{10}H_{18}O$	Geraniol	229	Nonazeotrope		243
14309	$C_{12}H_{18}$	1,3,5-Triethylbenzene	215.5	Nonazeotrope		256
A =	**$C_{10}H_{16}O$**	**Fenchone**	**193**			
14310	$C_{11}H_{20}O$	Methyl isobornyl ether	192.2	191	....	243
A =	**$C_{10}H_{16}O$**	**Pulegone**	**223.8**			
14311	$C_{10}H_{17}Cl$	Bornyl chloride	207.5	Nonazeotrope		232
14312	$C_{10}H_{18}O$	Borneol	215.0	Nonazeotrope		232
14313	$C_{10}H_{18}O$	α-Terpineol	218.85	Nonazeotrope		232
14314	$C_{10}H_{20}O$	Menthol	216.3	Nonazeotrope		232
14315	$C_{11}H_{16}O$	Methyl thymyl ether	216.5	Nonazeotrope		255
14316	$C_{11}H_{20}O$	Terpineol methyl ether	216.3	Nonazeotrope		243
14317	$C_{11}H_{22}O_3$	Isoamyl carbonate	232.2	Nonazeotrope		232
14318	$C_{12}H_{18}$	1,3,5-Triethylbenzene	215.5	Nonazeotrope		255
14319	$C_{12}H_{20}O_2$	Bornyl acetate	227.6	Nonazeotrope		232
A =	**$C_{10}H_{17}Cl$**	**Bornyl Chloride**	**207.5**			
14320	$C_{10}H_{22}S$	Isoamyl sulfide	214.8	Nonazeotrope		255
A =	**$C_{10}H_{18}O$**	**Borneol**	**211.8**			
14321	$C_{10}H_{18}O$	Menthone	207	Nonazeotrope		243
14322	$C_{10}H_{18}O$	α-Terpineol	218.0	Nonazeotrope		225
14323	$C_{10}H_{20}O$	Menthol	216.4	Nonazeotrope		225
14324	$C_{11}H_{16}O$	Methyl thymyl ether	216.5	<214.0	<62	256
14325	$C_{11}H_{20}O$	Methyl α-terpineol ether	216.2	214.0	55	256
14326	$C_{11}H_{20}O$	Methyl α-terpineol ether	216	Nonazeotrope		243

No.	Formula	B-Component Name	B.P., ° C	Azeotropic Data B.P., ° C.	Wt. % A	Ref.
A =	$C_{10}H_{18}O$	**Borneol** (*continued*)	**211.8**			
14327	$C_{12}H_{18}$	1,3,5-Triethylbenzene	215.5	212.2	62	*225*
14328	$C_{12}H_{22}O$	Ethyl isobornyl ether	204.9	Nonazeotrope		*255*
A =	$C_{10}H_{18}O$	**Cineole**	**176.35**			
14329	$C_{10}H_{18}O$	α-Terpineol	218.85	Nonazeotrope		*255*
14330	$C_{10}H_{20}O_2$	Isoamyl isovalerate	192.7	Nonazeotrope		*237*
14331	$C_{10}H_{22}O$	Isoamyl ether	173.2	Nonazeotrope		*229*
14332	$C_{10}H_{23}N$	Diisoamylamine	188.2	Nonazeotrope		*231*
A =	$C_{10}H_{18}O$	**Citronellal**	**208.0**			
14333	$C_{10}H_{18}O$	α-Terpineol	218.85	Nonazeotrope		*255*
14334	$C_{10}H_{20}O$	Citronellol	224.4	Nonazeotrope		*255*
14335	$C_{10}H_{20}O$	Menthol	216.3	Nonazeotrope		*255*
14336	$C_{11}H_{20}O$	Isobornyl methyl ether	192.4	Nonazeotrope		*255*
A =	$C_{10}H_{18}O$	**Geraniol**	**229.6**			
14337	$C_{10}H_{18}O$	α-Terpineol	218.85	Nonazeotrope		*255*
14338	$C_{10}H_{22}O$	Decyl alcohol	232.9	Nonazeotrope		*255*
14339	$C_{11}H_{10}$	1-Methylnaphthalene	244.9	Nonazeotrope		*217*
14340	$C_{11}H_{16}O$	Methyl thymyl ether	216.5	Nonazeotrope		*255*
14341	$C_{11}H_{20}O$	Methyl α-terpineol ether	216.2	Nonazeotrope		*255*
14342	$C_{11}H_{22}O_3$	Isoamyl carbonate	232.2	<229.2	>65	*247*
14343	$C_{12}H_{18}$	1,3,5-Triethylbenzene	215.5	Nonazeotrope		*255*
14344	$C_{12}H_{20}O_2$	Bornyl acetate	228	Nonazeotrope		*208*
A =	$C_{10}H_{18}O$	**Linaloöl**	**198.6**			
14345	$C_{10}H_{20}O_2$	Isoamyl isovalerate	192.7	<192.4	....	*255*
14346	$C_{11}H_{20}O$	Isobornyl methyl ether	192.2	Nonazeotrope		*256*
14347	$C_{12}H_{18}$	1,3,5-Triethylbenzene	215.5	Nonazeotrope		*217*
A =	$C_{10}H_{18}O$	**α-Terpineol**	**217.8**			
14348	$C_{10}H_{20}O$	Menthol	216.4	Nonazeotrope		*209*
14350	$C_{11}H_{10}$	1-Methylnaphthalene	244.9	Nonazeotrope		*220*
14351	$C_{11}H_{10}$	2-Methylnaphthalene	241.15	Nonazeotrope		*207*
14352	$C_{11}H_{16}O$	Methyl thymyl ether	216.5	<215.5	....	*255*
14353	$C_{11}H_{20}O$	Methyl terpineol ether	216.2	Min. b.p. ?		*256*
14354	$C_{12}H_{20}O_2$	Bornyl acetate	227.7	Nonazeotrope		*209*
A =	$C_{10}H_{18}O$	**β-Terpineol**	**210.5**			
14355	$C_{11}H_{20}O$	Isobornyl methyl ether	192.4	Nonazeotrope		*255*
14356	$C_{11}H_{20}O$	Methyl terpineol ether	216.2	<210	>82	*255*
14357	$C_{12}H_{18}$	1,3,5-Triethylbenzene	215.5	210.0	....	*255*
A =	$C_{10}H_{18}O_4$	**Propyl Succinate**	**250.5**			
14358	$C_{11}H_{10}$	1-Methylnaphthalene	245.1	Nonazeotrope		*226*
14359	$C_{11}H_{10}$	2-Methylnaphthalene	241.15	Nonazeotrope		*255*
14360	$C_{11}H_{14}O_2$	1-Allyl-3,4-dimethoxybenzene	254.7	Nonazeotrope		*255*
14361	$C_{11}H_{14}O_2$	Butyl benzoate	249.0	Nonazeotrope		*229*
14362	$C_{11}H_{14}O_2$	Isobutyl benzoate	241.9	Nonazeotrope		*255*
14363	$C_{12}H_{10}$	Biphenyl	256.1	Nonazeotrope		*255*
14364	$C_{12}H_{10}O$	Phenyl ether	259.0	<250.0	....	*237*
A =	$C_{10}H_{20}O$	**Citronellol**	**224.4**			
14365	$C_{11}H_{10}$	2-Methylnaphthalene	241.15	Nonazeotrope		*255*
14366	$C_{11}H_{20}O$	Methyl terpineol ether	216.2	Nonazeotrope		*256*
14367	$C_{11}H_{22}O_3$	Isoamyl carbonate	232.2	<224.2	....	*255*
14368	$C_{12}H_{18}$	1,3,5-Triethylbenzene	215.5	<215.3	....	*255*
14369	$C_{12}H_{20}O_2$	Bornyl acetate	227.6	Nonazeotrope		*255*
A =	$C_{10}H_{20}O$	**Menthol**	**216.3**			
14370	$C_{10}H_{20}O_2$	Ethyl caprylate	208.35	Nonazeotrope		*255*
14371	$C_{11}H_{10}$	1-Methylnaphthalene	244.9	Nonazeotrope		*217*
14372	$C_{11}H_{10}$	2-Methylnaphthalene	241.15	Nonazeotrope		*255*
14373	$C_{11}H_{20}O$	Terpineol methyl ether	216.2	215.3	50	*225*
14374	$C_{11}H_{22}O_2$	Ethyl pelargonate	227	Nonazeotrope		*255*
14375	$C_{12}H_{18}$	1,3,5-Triethylbenzene	215.5	214	~55	*217*
14376	$C_{12}H_{20}O_2$	Bornyl acetate	227.6	Nonazeotrope		*215*

No.	Formula	B-Component Name	B.P., ° C.	Azeotropic Data B.P., ° C.	Wt. % A	Ref.
A =	$C_{10}H_{20}O_2$	**Capric Acid**	**268.8**			
14377	$C_{11}H_{10}$	1-Methylnaphthalene	244.6	Nonazeotrope		*255*
14378	$C_{11}H_{10}$	2-Methylnaphthalene	241.15	Nonazeotrope		*207*
14379	$C_{12}H_{10}O$	Phenyl ether	259.0	<258.0	>12	*255*
14380	$C_{12}H_{22}O_4$	Isoamyl oxalate	268.0	<266.0	>35	*255*
14381	$C_{13}H_{12}$	Diphenylmethane	265.4	262.5	28	*242*
A =	$C_{10}H_{20}O_2$	**Ethyl Caprylate**	**208.35**			
14382	$C_{10}H_{22}S$	Isoamyl sulfide	214.8	Nonazeotrope		*59*
14383	$C_{11}H_{20}O$	Methyl α-terpineol ether	216.2	Nonazeotrope		*237*
14384	$C_{12}H_{18}$	1,3,5-Triethylbenzene	215.5	Nonazeotrope		*255*
A =	$C_{10}H_{20}O_2$	**Isoamyl Isovalerate**	**192.7**			
14385	$C_{10}H_{22}O$	Isoamyl ether	173.2	Nonazeotrope		*237*
14386	$C_{11}H_{20}O$	Isobornyl methyl ether	192.4	<192	<55	*237*
14387	$C_{12}H_{18}$	1,3,5-Triethylbenzene	215.5	Nonazeotrope		*255*
14388	$C_{12}H_{22}O$	Bornyl ethyl ether	204.9	Nonazeotrope		*237*
14389	$C_{12}H_{22}O$	Ethyl isobornyl ether	203.8	Nonazeotrope		*237*
A =	$C_{10}H_{20}O_2$	**Methyl Pelargonate**	**213.8**			
14390	$C_{12}H_{18}$	1,3,5-Triethylbenzene	215.5	Nonazeotrope		*255*
A =	$C_{10}H_{20}O_4$	**2-(2-Butoxyethoxy) Ethyl Acetate**	**245.3**			
14391	$C_{11}H_{14}O_2$	Ethyl β-phenylpropionate	248.1	<245.0	>82	*255*
14392	$C_{11}H_{14}O_2$	Isobutyl benzoate	241.9	<241.7	>10	*255*
14393	$C_{11}H_{22}O_3$	Isoamyl carbonate	232.2	Nonazeotrope		*255*
14394	$C_{12}H_{20}O_2$	Bornyl acetate	227.6	Nonazeotrope		*255*
A =	$C_{10}H_{22}O$	**Decyl Alcohol**	**~232.9**			
14395	$C_{11}H_{10}$	1-Methylnaphthalene	244.9	Nonazeotrope		*217*
14396	$C_{11}H_{14}O_2$	Isobutyl benzoate	241.9	Nonazeotrope		*216*
14397	$C_{11}H_{16}O$	Methyl thymyl ether	216.5	Nonazeotrope		*255*
14398	$C_{11}H_{20}O$	Methyl terpineol ether	216.0	Nonazeotrope		*255*
14399	$C_{11}H_{22}O_3$	Isoamyl carbonate	232.2	<230.9	>36	*247*
14400	$C_{12}H_{10}$	Biphenyl	254.8	Nonazeotrope		*220*
14401	$C_{12}H_{18}$	1,3,5-Triethylbenzene	215.5	Nonazeotrope		*217*
14402	$C_{12}H_{20}O_2$	Bornyl acetate	228	Nonazeotrope		*208*
14403	$C_{13}H_{12}$	Diphenylmethane	265.6	Nonazeotrope		*217*
A =	$C_{10}H_{22}O$	**Isoamyl Ether**	**173.2**			
14404	$C_{10}H_{23}N$	Diisoamylamine	188.2	Nonazeotrope		*231*
A =	$C_{10}H_{22}S$	**Isoamyl Sulfide**	**214.8**			
14405	$C_{11}H_{20}O$	Methyl α-terpineol ether	216.2	213.8	70	*246*
14406	$C_{12}H_{18}$	1,3,5-Triethylbenzene	215.5	214.0	65	*255*
14407	$C_{12}H_{22}O$	Ethyl isobornyl ether	203.8	Nonazeotrope		*246*
A =	$C_{11}H_{10}$	**1-Methylnaphthalene**	**244.6**			
14408	$C_{11}H_{10}$	2-Methylnaphthalene	241.15	Nonazeotrope		*241*
14409	$C_{11}H_{14}O_2$	1-Allyl-3,4-dimethoxybenzene	254.7	Nonazeotrope		*228*
14410	$C_{11}H_{14}O_2$	Butyl benzoate	249.5	Nonazeotrope		*226*
14411	$C_{11}H_{14}O_2$	Ethyl β-phenylpropionate	248.1	Nonazeotrope		*255*
14412	$C_{11}H_{14}O_2$	Isobutyl benzoate	242.15	Nonazeotrope		*212*
14413	$C_{11}H_{16}O$	*p-tert*-Amylphenol	266.5	Nonazeotrope		*255*
14414	$C_{11}H_{17}N$	Isoamylaniline	256.0	Nonazeotrope		*255*
14415	$C_{11}H_{22}O_3$	Isoamyl carbonate	232.2	Nonazeotrope		*226*
14416	$C_{12}H_{10}$	Biphenyl	256.1	Nonazeotrope		*241*
14417	$C_{12}H_{10}O$	Phenyl ether	259.0	Nonazeotrope		*238*
14418	$C_{12}H_{16}O_2$	Isoamyl benzoate	262.0	Nonazeotrope		*255*
14419	$C_{12}H_{20}O_2$	Bornyl acetate	227.7	Nonazeotrope		*215*
14420	$C_{13}H_{12}$	Diphenylmethane	265.4	Nonazeotrope		*241*
A =	$C_{11}H_{10}$	**2-Methylnaphthalene**	**241.15**			
14421	$C_{11}H_{14}O_2$	Butyl benzoate	249.0	Nonazeotrope		*207*
14422	$C_{11}H_{14}O_2$	Ethyl β-phenylpropionate	248.1	Nonazeotrope		*255*
14423	$C_{11}H_{14}O_2$	Isobutyl benzoate	241.9	240.8	60	*207*
14424	$C_{11}H_{17}N$	Isoamylaniline	256.0	Nonazeotrope		*255*

No.	Formula	B-Component Name	B.P., ° C.	Azeotropic Data B.P., ° C.	Wt. % A	Ref.
A =	**$C_{11}H_{10}$**	**2-Methylnaphthalene** (*continued*)	**241.15**			
14425	$C_{11}H_{22}O_3$	Isoamyl carbonate	232.2	Nonazeotrope		*255*
14426	$C_{12}H_{20}O_2$	Bornyl acetate	227.6	Nonazeotrope		*255*
A =	**$C_{11}H_{12}O_2$**	**Ethyl Cinnamate**	**272.0**			
14427	$C_{11}H_{14}O_2$	1,2-Dimethyl-4-propenylbenzene	270.5	Nonazeotrope		*237*
14428	$C_{11}H_{14}O_2$	1,2-Dimethoxy-4-propenylbenzene	270.5	270.4	~7	*221*
14429	$C_{12}H_{10}$	Acenaphthene	277.9	Nonazeotrope		*226*
14430	$C_{12}H_{10}$	Biphenyl	256.1	Nonazeotrope		*255*
14431	$C_{12}H_{10}O$	Phenyl ether	259.3	Nonazeotrope		*237*
14432	$C_{12}H_{16}O_2$	Isoamyl benzoate	262.0	Nonazeotrope		*225*
14433	$C_{12}H_{16}O_3$	Isoamyl salicylate	277.5	Nonazeotrope		*255*
14434	$C_{12}H_{22}O_4$	Isoamyl oxalate	268.0	<267.5	>21	*229*
14435	$C_{13}H_{12}$	Diphenylmethane	265.6	Nonazeotrope		*226*
14436	$C_{14}H_{14}$	1,2-Diphenylethane	284	Nonazeotrope		*226*
A =	**$C_{11}H_{14}O_2$**	**1-Allyl-3,4-dimethoxybenzene**	**~249.8**			
14437	$C_{11}H_{14}O_2$	Butyl benzoate	254.7	Nonazeotrope		*237*
14438	$C_{11}H_{14}O_2$	Isobutyl benzoate	242.15	Nonazeotrope		*237*
14439	$C_{11}H_{17}N$	Isoamylaniline	256.0	250.5	58	*231*
14440	$C_{12}H_{10}$	Biphenyl	255.0	254.5	70	*238*
14441	$C_{12}H_{10}O$	Phenyl ether	259.0	Nonazeotrope		*229*
14442	$C_{12}H_{16}O_2$	Isoamyl benzoate	262.05	Nonazeotrope		*237*
14443	$C_{13}H_{12}$	Diphenylmethane	265.6	Nonazeotrope		*215*
A =	**$C_{11}H_{14}O_2$**	**Butyl Benzoate**	**249.8**			
14444	$C_{12}H_{10}$	Biphenyl	255.9	Nonazeotrope		*226*
14445	$C_{12}H_{10}O$	Phenyl ether	259.3	Nonazeotrope		*217, 237*
14446	$C_{15}H_{33}BO_3$	Isoamyl borate	255	Nonazeotrope		*255*
A =	**$C_{11}H_{14}O_2$**	**1,2-Dimethoxy-4-propenylbenzene**	**270.5**			
14447	$C_{11}H_{17}N$	Isoamylaniline	256.0	Nonazeotrope		*255*
14448	$C_{12}H_{10}$	Acenaphthene	277.9	Nonazeotrope		*228*
14449	$C_{12}H_{10}O$	Phenyl ether	259.3	Nonazeotrope		*215*
14450	$C_{12}H_{16}O_2$	Isoamyl benzoate	262.05	Nonazeotrope		*215, 237*
14451	$C_{12}H_{16}O_3$	Isoamyl salicylate	277.5	Nonazeotrope		*255*
14452	$C_{12}H_{22}O_4$	Isoamyl oxalate	268.0	Nonazeotrope		*237*
14453	$C_{12}H_{22}O_4$	Isoamyl oxalate	268.0	267.95	4	*221*
14454	$C_{13}H_{12}$	Diphenylmethane	265.6	Nonazeotrope		*215*
A =	**$C_{11}H_{14}O_2$**	**Ethyl β-phenylpropionate**	**248.1**			
14455	$C_{11}H_{14}O_2$	Isobutyl benzoate	241.9	Nonazeotrope		*255*
14456	$C_{12}H_{10}$	Biphenyl	256.1	Nonazeotrope		*255*
14457	$C_{12}H_{10}O$	Phenyl ether	259.0	Nonazeotrope		*237*
A =	**$C_{11}H_{16}O$**	***p-tert*-Amylphenol**	**266.5**			
14458	$C_{12}H_{10}$	Acenaphthene	277.9	Nonazeotrope		*255*
14459	$C_{12}H_{16}O_3$	Isoamyl salicylate	277.5	Nonazeotrope		*255*
14460	$C_{13}H_{10}$	Fluorene	295	Nonazeotrope		*255*
14461	$C_{13}H_{12}$	Diphenylmethane	265.4	263.0	40	*255*
14462	$C_{14}H_{14}$	1,2-Diphenylethane	284.5	Nonazeotrope		*255*
A =	**$C_{11}H_{16}O$**	**Methyl Thymol Ether**	**216.5**			
14463	$C_{12}H_{20}O_2$	Bornyl acetate	227.6	Nonazeotrope		*237*
A =	**$C_{11}H_{17}N$**	**Isoamylaniline**	**256.0**			
14464	$C_{12}H_{10}$	Biphenyl	256.1	<255.0	....	*255*
14465	$C_{12}H_{10}O$	Phenyl ether	259.0	<252.5	....	*255*
A =	**$C_{11}H_{20}O$**	**Methyl α-Terpineol Ether**	**216.2**			
14466	$C_{12}H_{18}$	1,3,5-Triethylbenzene	215.5	Nonazeotrope		*238*
14467	$C_{12}H_{20}O_2$	Bornyl acetate	227.6	Nonazeotrope		*237*

No.	Formula	B-Component Name	B.P., °C.	Azeotropic Data B.P., °C.	Wt. % A	Ref.
A =	**$C_{11}H_{22}O_3$**	**Isoamyl Carbonate**	**232.2**			
14468	$C_{12}H_{16}O_2$	Isoamyl benzoate	241.9	Nonazeotrope		255
14469	$C_{12}H_{20}O_2$	Bornyl acetate	227.6	Nonazeotrope		222
A =	**$C_{12}H_{10}$**	**Acenaphthene**	**277.9**			
14470	$C_{12}H_{14}O_4$	Ethyl phthalate	277.9	Nonazeotrope		255
14471	$C_{12}H_{16}O_2$	Isoamyl benzoate	262.0	Nonazeotrope		226
14472	$C_{12}H_{22}O_4$	Isoamyl oxalate	268.0	Nonazeotrope		222
14473	$C_{13}H_{12}$	Diphenylmethane	265.4	Nonazeotrope		241
14474	$C_{13}H_{12}O$	Benzyl phenyl ether	286.5	Nonazeotrope		238
14475	$C_{14}H_{14}$	1,2-Diphenylethane	284.5	Nonazeotrope		241
A =	**$C_{12}H_{10}$**	**Biphenyl**	**255.9**			
14476	$C_{12}H_{10}O$	Phenyl ether	259.3	Nonazeotrope		222
14477	$C_{12}H_{14}O_4$	Ethyl phthalate	298.5	Nonazeotrope		255
14478	$C_{12}H_{16}O_2$	Isoamyl benzoate	262.0	Nonazeotrope		226
14479	$C_{12}H_{16}O_3$	Isoamyl salicylate	277.5	Nonazeotrope		255
14480	$C_{12}H_{22}O_4$	Isoamyl oxalate	268.0	Nonazeotrope		226
14481	$C_{13}H_{12}$	Diphenylmethane	265.4	Nonazeotrope		241
A =	**$C_{12}H_{14}O$**	**Phenyl Ether**	**259**			
14482	$C_{12}H_{14}O_4$	Ethyl phthalate	298.5	Nonazeotrope		237
14483	$C_{12}H_{16}O_2$	Isoamyl benzoate	262.05	258.9	90	237
14484	$C_{12}H_{16}O_3$	Isoamyl salicylate	277.5	Nonazeotrope		255
14485	$C_{12}H_{22}O_4$	Isoamyl oxalate	268.0	Nonazeotrope		221
14486	$C_{13}H_{12}$	Diphenylmethane	265.6	Nonazeotrope		209
14487	$C_{14}H_{14}O$	Benzyl ether	297	Nonazeotrope		255
A =	**$C_{12}H_{14}O_4$**	**Ethyl Phthalate**	**298.5**			
14488	$C_{13}H_{12}$	Diphenylmethane	265.4	Nonazeotrope		255
A =	**$C_{12}H_{16}O_2$**	**Isoamyl Benzoate**	**262.0**			
14489	$C_{12}H_{16}O_3$	Isoamyl salicylate	277.5	Nonazeotrope		255
14490	$C_{12}H_{22}O_4$	Isoamyl oxalate	268.0	Nonazeotrope		221
14491	$C_{13}H_{12}$	Diphenylmethane	265.6	Nonazeotrope		215
A =	**$C_{12}H_{16}O_3$**	**Isoamyl Salicylate**	**277.5**			
14492	$C_{13}H_{12}$	Diphenylmethane	265.4	Nonazeotrope		255
14493	$C_{13}H_{12}O$	Benzyl phenyl ether	286.5	Nonazeotrope		255
14494	$C_{14}H_{14}$	1,2-Diphenylethane	284.5	Nonazeotrope		255
A =	**$C_{12}H_{13}$**	**1,3,5-Triethylbenzene**	**215.5**			
14495	$C_{12}H_{20}O_2$	Bornyl acetate	227.2	Nonazeotrope		217
14496	$C_{12}H_{22}O$	Bornyl ethyl ether	204.9	Nonazeotrope		238
A =	**$C_{12}H_{22}O_4$**	**Isoamyl Oxalate**	**268.0**			
14497	$C_{13}H_{12}$	Diphenylmethane	265.4	265.25	14	225
14498	$C_{14}H_{14}$	1,2-Diphenylethane	284	Nonazeotrope		226
A =	**$C_{13}H_{10}O_2$**	**Phenyl Benzoate**	**315**			
14499	$C_{14}H_{12}$	Stilbene	306.5	Nonazeotrope		255
14500	$C_{14}H_{14}O$	Benzyl ether	297	Nonazeotrope		237
A =	**$C_{13}H_{12}O$**	**Benzyl Phenyl Ether**	**286.5**			
14501	$C_{14}H_{14}$	1,2-Diphenylethane	284.5	Nonazeotrope		238

Table II. Ternary Systems

	A-Component			B-Component			C-Component			Azeotropic Data				
No.	Formula	Name	B.P., ° C.	Formula	Name	B.P., ° C.	Formula	Name	B.P., ° C.	B.P., ° C.	Wt. % A	Wt. % B	Wt. % C	Ref.
14502	BCl_3	Boron chloride	11.5	B_2H_6	Boron hydride	−92.5	ClH	Hydrogen chloride	−80		Nonazeotrope			*263*
14503	BrH	Hydrobromic acid	−67	H_2O	Water	100	C_6H_5Cl	Chlorobenzene	131.8	105	10.4	11.0	78.6	*93*
	BrH	Hydrobromic acid	...	H_2O	Water	...	C_6H_5Cl	Chlorobenzene, 100 mm.	...	56.4	12.2	12.3	75.5	*93*
14504	ClH	Hydrochloric acid	−80	H_2O	Water	100	C_6H_5Cl	Chlorobenzene	131.8	96.9	5.3	20.2	74.5	*308*
	ClH	Hydrochloric acid	...	H_2O	Water	...	C_6H_5Cl	Chlorobenzene, 100 mm.	...	49.5	4.8	15.9	79.3	*93*
14505	ClH	Hydrochloric acid	−80	H_2O	Water	100	C_6H_6O	Phenol	182	107.33	15.8	64.8	19.4	*308*
14506	FH	Hydrofluoric acid	19.4	H_2O	Water	100	C_2H_6O	Ethyl alcohol	78.3	103	30	10	60	*66*
14507	FH	Hydrofluoric acid	19.4	F_6H_2Si	Fluosilicic acid	...	H_2O	Water	100	116.1	10	36	54	*275*
14508	FH	Hydrofluoric acid	19.4	SO_2	Sulfur dioxide	−10	CCl_2F_2	Dichlorodifluoromethane	...	−36	...	...	...	*21*
	FH	Hydrofluoric acid	...	SO_2	Sulfur dioxide	...	CCl_2F_2	Dichlorodifluoromethane, 44 lb./sq. inch gage	...	4	3.5	12	84	*21*
14509	HNO_3	Nitric acid	86	H_2O	Water	100	SO_3	Sulfur trioxide	47		Vapor pressure data			*243*
14510	H_2O	Water	100	CCl_4	Carbon tetrachloride	71.75	C_2H_3N	Acetonitrile	81.6	60	...	...	...	*309*
14511	H_2O	Water	100	CCl_4	Carbon tetrachloride	76.75	C_2H_6O	Ethyl alcohol	78.3	62	4.5	85.5	10	*243*
	H_2O	Water	...	CCl_4	Carbon tetrachloride	...	C_2H_6O	Ethyl alcohol	...	61.8	3.4	86.3	10.3	*161*
14512	H_2O	Water	100	CCl_4	Carbon tetrachloride	76.75	C_3H_6O	Acetone	57		Nonazeotrope			*10*
14513	H_2O	Water	100	CCl_4	Carbon tetrachloride	76.75	C_3H_6O	Allyl alcohol	96.95	65.15	5	84	11	*243*
	H_2O	Water	...	CCl_4	Carbon tetrachloride	...	C_3H_6O	Allyl alcohol	...	65.4	4.13	90.43	5.44	*149*

14514	H_2O	Water	100	CCl_4	Carbon tetrachloride	76.75	C_3H_8O	Propyl alcohol	97.2	65.4	5	84	11	*243*
14515	H_2O	Water	100	CCl_4	Carbon tetrachloride	76.75	C_4H_8O	2-Butanone	79.6	65.7	3	74.8	22.2	*10*
14516	H_2O	Water	100	CCl_4	Carbon tetrachloride	76.75	$C_4H_{10}O$	*tert*-Butyl alcohol	82.5	64.7	3.1	85.0	11.9	*10*
14517	H_2O	Water	100	CS_2	Carbon disulfide	46.25	CH_4O	Methanol	64.7		Nonazeotrope			*10*
14518	H_2O	Water	100	CS_2	Carbon disulfide	46.25	C_2H_3N	Acetonitrile	81.6	39	...	...	...	*309*
14519	H_2O	Water	100	CS_2	Carbon disulfide	46.25	C_2H_6O	Ethyl alcohol	78.3	41.3	1.6	3.4	5.0	*131*
14520	H_2O	Water	100	CS_2	Carbon disulfide	46.25	C_3H_6O	Acetone	56.4	38.042	0.81	75.21	23.98	*389*
14521	H_2O	Water	100	CS_2	Carbon disulfide	46.25	$C_4H_8O_2$	Dioxane	101.4		Nonazeotrope			*90*
14522	H_2O	Water	100	$CHBrCl_2$	Bromodichloromethane	90.2	C_2H_6O	Ethyl alcohol	78.3	72.0	7.5	>70	<22.5	*243*
14523	H_2O	Water	100	$CHBrCl_2$	Bromodichloromethane	90.2	C_3H_6O	Allyl alcohol	96.95	76	...	...	...	*243*
14524	H_2O	Water	100	$CHBrCl_2$	Bromodichloromethane	90.2	C_3H_8O	Isopropyl alcohol	82.45	~74.5	...	...	...	*243*
14525	H_2O	Water	100	$CHBrCl_2$	Bromodichloromethane	90.2	$C_4H_{10}O$	Isobutyl alcohol	108	77.5	...	...	...	*243*
14526	H_2O	Water	100	$CHCl_3$	Chloroform	61	C_2H_3N	Acetonitrile	81.6		Minimum b.p.			*309*
14527	H_2O	Water	100	$CHCl_3$	Chloroform	61.2	C_2H_6O	Ethyl alcohol	78.3	55.4	3.5	92.5	4	*409*
14528	H_2O	Water	100	$CHCl_3$	Chloroform	61	$C_3H_6O_3$	Acetone	56.4	60.4?	40	57.6	38.4	*323*
14529	H_2O	Water	100	CH_2Cl_2	Dichloromethane	41.5	C_2H_6O	Ethyl alcohol	78.3		Nonazeotrope			*15*
14530	H_2O	Water	100	CH_2O_2	Formic acid	100.75	C_8H_{10}	*m*-Xylene	139	97.5?	10.6	40.4	49.0	*323*
14531	H_2O	Water	100	CH_3NO_2	Nitromethane	101.0	C_3H_8O	Isopropyl alcohol	82.0	78	6	32	62	*353*
	H_2O	Water	...	CH_3NO_2	Nitromethane	...	C_3H_8O	Isopropyl alcohol	...	Liquid-vapor equilibrium				*353*
14532	H_2O	Water	100	CH_3NO_2	Nitromethane	101	C_3H_8O	Propyl alcohol	97.2	82.3	17.5	55.9	26.6, V-l.	*120*
14533	H_2O	Water	100	CH_3NO_2	Nitromethane	101.2	$C_5H_{10}O$	3-Pentanone	102.2	82.4	18?	17?	65?	*243*
14534	H_2O	Water	100	CH_4O	Methanol	64.7	$C_3H_5ClO_2$	Methyl chloroacetate	131.4	67.85	5.26	81.20	13.54	*58*
14535	H_2O	Water	100	CH_4O	Methanol	64.7	$C_3H_6O_2$	Methyl acetate	57		Nonazeotrope			*150*
14536	H_2O	Water	100	CH_4O	Methanol	64.7	$C_3H_8O_2$	Methylal	42.3		Nonazeotrope			*131*
14537	H_2O	Water	100	CH_4O	Methanol	64.7	$C_4H_{10}O$	Isobutyl alcohol	108		Nonazeotrope			*176*
14538	H_2O	Water	100	CH_4O	Methanol	64.7	$C_4H_{10}O_2$	Acetaldehyde dimethylacetal	64.3		Nonazeotrope			*20*
14539	H_2O	Water	100	CH_4O	Methanol	64.7	$C_4H_{10}O_2$	Ethoxymethoxymethane	65.90		Nonazeotrope			*429*

	A-Component			B-Component			C-Component			Azeotropic Data				
No.	Formula	Name	B.P., ° C.	Formula	Name	B.P., ° C.	Formula	Name	B.P., ° C.	B.P., ° C.	Wt. % A	Wt. % B	Wt. % C	Ref.
14540	H_2O	Water	100	CH_4O	Methanol	64.7	C_5H_6O	2-Methylfuran	63.7	51.2	...	...	...	*310*
14541	H_2O	Water	100	CH_4O	Methanol	64.7	C_6H_6	Benzene	80.2		Nonazeotrope			*431*
14542	H_2O	Water	100	CH_4O	Methanol	64.7	C_6H_8	1,3-Cyclohexadiene	80.8		Nonazeotrope			*243*
14543	H_2O	Water	100	CH_4O	Methanol	64.7	C_6H_{10}	Biallyl	60.2		Nonazeotrope			*243*
14544	H_2O	Water	100	CH_4O	Methanol	64.7	C_6H_{10}	Cyclohexene	82.75		Nonazeotrope			*243*
14545	H_2O	Water	100	CH_4O	Methanol	64.7	C_6H_{12}	Cyclohexane	80.75		Nonazeotrope			*243*
14546	H_2O	Water	100	CH_4O	Methanol	64.7	C_6H_{14}	Hexane	68.95		Nonazeotrope			*243*
14547	H_2O	Water	100	CH_4O	Methanol	64.7	C_7H_8	Toluene	110.7		Nonazeotrope			*243*
14548	H_2O	Water	100	C_2Cl_4	Tetrachloroethylene	120.8	C_2H_3N	Acetonitrile	81.6	72	...	...	...	*309*
14549	H_2O	Water	100	C_2Cl_4	Tetrachloroethylene	120.8	C_3H_8O	Propyl alcohol	97.2	88	...	...	...	*243*
14550	H_2O	Water	100	C_2HCl_3	Trichloroethylene	86.95	C_2H_3N	Acetonitrile	81.6	67	6.4	73.1	20.5	*309*
	H_2O	Water	...	C_2HCl_3	Trichloroethylene	...	C_2H_3N	Acetonitrile	...	Liquid-vapor equilibrium				*309*
14551	H_2O	Water	100	C_2HCl_3	Trichloroethylene	86.95	C_2H_5ClO	2-Chloroethanol	128		Nonazeotrope			*276*
	H_2O	Water	...	C_2HCl_3	Trichloroethylene	...	C_2H_5ClO	2-Chloroethanol	...	70.8–71.5	...	...	...	*102*
14552	H_2O	Water	100	C_2HCl_3	Trichloroethylene	86.95	C_2H_6O	Ethyl alcohol, 118 mm.	...	25.1	3.4	85.1	11.5	*259*
	H_2O	Water	...	C_2HCl_3	Trichloroethylene	...	C_2H_6O	Ethyl alcohol, 509 mm.	...	52.5	5.2	79.6	15.2	*259, 323**
	H_2O	Water	...	C_2HCl_3	Trichloroethylene	...	C_2H_6O	Ethyl alcohol, 760 mm.	...	67	5.5	78.4	16.1	*76, 259*
	H_2O	Water	...	C_2HCl_3	Trichloroethylene	...	C_2H_6O	Ethyl alcohol, 2060 mm.	...	96	7.1	72.3	20.6	*259*
	H_2O	Water	...	C_2HCl_3	Trichloroethylene	...	C_2H_6O	Ethyl alcohol, 5660 mm.	...	131	8.3	70.5	21.2	*259*
14553	H_2O	Water	100	C_2HCl_3	Trichloroethylene	86.95	C_3H_6O	Allyl alcohol	96.95	71.6	6.55	84.7	8.75	*149, 243**
14554	H_2O	Water	100	C_2HCl_3	Trichloroethylene	86.95	C_3H_8O	Isopropyl alcohol	82.45	~70	...	...	...	*243*

14555	H_2O	Water	100	C_2HCl_3	Trichloroethylene	86.95	C_3H_8O	Propyl alcohol	97.2	71.55	7	81	12	*243*
14556	H_2O	Water	100	C_2HCl_3	Trichloroethylene	86.95	$C_4H_{10}O$	Isobutyl alcohol	108	72.7	...	...	...	*243*
14557	H_2O	Water	100	$C_2H_2Cl_2$	*cis*-1,2-Dichloroethylene	60.25	C_2H_6O	Ethyl alcohol	78.3	53.8	2.85	90.5	6.65	*71*
14558	H_2O	Water	100	$C_2H_2Cl_2$	*trans*-1,2-Dichloroethylene	48.35	C_2H_6O	Ethyl alcohol	78.3	44.4	1.1	94.5	4.4	*71*
14559	H_2O	Water	100	$C_2H_2Cl_4$	1,1,2,2-Tetrachloroethane	146.35	C_2H_3N	Acetonitrile	81.6		Nonazeotrope			*309*
14560	H_2O	Water	100	C_2H_3N	Acetonitrile	81.6	C_3H_6O	Acetone	56.4		Nonazeotrope, V-l.			*309*
14561	H_2O	Water	100	C_2H_3N	Acetonitrile	81.6	$C_4H_8O_2$	Ethyl acetate	77	70	...	...	...	*309*
14562	H_2O	Water	100	C_2H_3N	Acetonitrile	81.6	$C_5H_{10}O_2$	Propyl acetate	101.6	74	...	...	...	*309*
14563	H_2O	Water	100	C_2H_3N	Acetonitrile	81.6	C_6H_6	Benzene	80.2	66	8.2	23.3	68.5	*309*
14564	H_2O	Water	100	C_2H_3N	Acetonitrile	81.6	$C_6H_{12}O_2$	Butyl acetate	124.8		Nonazeotrope			*309*
14565	H_2O	Water	100	C_2H_3N	Acetonitrile	81.6	C_7H_8	Toluene	110.7	73	...	...	...	*309*
14566	H_2O	Water	100	$C_2H_4Cl_2$	1,2-Dichloroethane	83.7	C_2H_5ClO	2-Chloroethanol	128		Nonazeotrope			*276*
	H_2O	Water	...	$C_2H_4Cl_2$	1,2-Dichloroethane	...	C_2H_5ClO	2-Chloroethanol	...	69.6	...	...	...	*102*
14567	H_2O	Water	100	$C_2H_4Cl_2$	1,2-Dichloroethane	83.7	C_2H_6O	Ethyl alcohol	78.3	66.7	5	78	17	*243*
14568	H_2O	Water	100	$C_2H_4O_2$	Acetic acid	118.5	C_7H_8	Toluene	110.7		Nonazeotrope			*243*
14569	H_2O	Water	100	$C_2H_4O_2$	Acetic acid	118.1	C_8H_{10}	Ethylbenzene	136		Minimum b.p.			*30*
14570	H_2O	Water	100	$C_2H_4O_2$	Acetic acid	118.1	C_8H_{10}	Xylenes	140		Minimum b.p.			*30*
14571	H_2O	Water	100	C_2H_5Br	Bromoethane	38.4	C_2H_6O	Ethyl alcohol	78.3		Azeotropic ?			*243*
14572	H_2O	Water	100	C_2H_5ClO	2-Chloroethanol	128	$C_4H_8Cl_2O$	Bis(2-chloroethyl) ether	178		Minimum b.p.			*276*
14573	H_2O	Water	100	C_2H_5ClO	2-Chloroethanol	128	C_6H_6	Benzene	80.1		Nonazeotrope			*276*
	H_2O	Water	...	C_2H_5ClO	2-Chloroethanol	...	C_6H_6	Benzene	...	67.0	...	...	...	*102*
14574	H_2O	Water	100	C_2H_5I	Iodoethane	72.3	C_2H_6O	Ethyl alcohol	78.3	61	~5	~86	~9	*243*
14575	H_2O	Water	100	C_2H_6O	Ethyl alcohol	78.3	C_3H_5Br	*cis*-1-Bromopropene	57.8	54?	3	6	91	*243*
14576	H_2O	Water	100	C_2H_6O	Ethyl alcohol	78.3	C_3H_5Br	*trans*-1-Bromopropene	63.25	54.5	4	87.5	7.5	*243*
14577	H_2O	Water	100	C_2H_6O	Ethyl alcohol	78.3	C_3H_5Br	2-Bromopropene	48.35	43.3?	1	4	95	*243*
14578	H_2O	Water	100	C_2H_6O	Ethyl alcohol	78.3	C_3H_5I	3-Iodopropene	102	72	...	...	...	*243*
14579	H_2O	Water	100	C_2H_6O	Ethyl alcohol	78.3	C_3H_7Br	1-Bromopropane	71.0	60	5	12	83	*243*
14580	H_2O	Water	100	C_2H_6O	Ethyl alcohol	78.3	$C_4H_6O_2$	Biacetyl	88		Nonazeotrope ?			*264*

	A-Component			B-Component			C-Component			Azeotropic Data				
No.	Formula	Name	B.P., ° C.	Formula	Name	B.P., ° C.	Formula	Name	B.P., ° C.	B.P., ° C.	Wt. % A	Wt. % B	Wt. % C	Ref.
14581	H_2O	Water	100	C_2H_6O	Ethyl alcohol	78.3	$C_4H_7ClO_2$	Ethyl chloroacetate	143.5	81.35	17.5	61.7	20.8	*58*
14584	H_2O	Water	100	C_2H_6O	Ethyl alcohol	78.3	$C_4H_8O_2$	Ethyl acetate	77.05		Nonazeotrope			*10*
	H_2O	Water	...	C_2H_6O	Ethyl alcohol	...	$C_4H_8O_2$	Ethyl acetate, 25 mm.	...	−1.40	4.0	4.0	92.0	*273*
	H_2O	Water	...	C_2H_6O	Ethyl alcohol	...	$C_4H_8O_2$	Ethyl acetate, 760 mm.	...	70.23	9.0	8.4	82.6	*273*
	H_2O	Water	...	C_2H_6O	Ethyl alcohol	...	$C_4H_8O_2$	Ethyl acetate, 1446 mm.	...	88.96	10.3	12.1	77.6	*273*
14585	H_2O	Water	100	C_2H_6O	Ethyl alcohol	78.3	C_4H_9Br	1-Bromo-2-methylpropane	91.6	69.5	~8	~25	~65	*243*
14586	H_2O	Water	100	C_2H_6O	Ethyl alcohol	78.3	C_4H_9Cl	1-Chloro-2-methylpropane	68.85	58.62	4.5	13	82.5	*243*
14587	H_2O	Water	100	C_2H_6O	Ethyl alcohol	78.3	$C_4H_{10}O$	Ethyl ether	34.5		Nonazeotrope			*427*
14588	H_2O	Water	100	C_2H_6O	Ethyl alcohol	78.3	$C_4H_{10}O_2$	2-Ethoxyethanol	133		Nonazeotrope			*14*
14589	H_2O	Water	100	C_2H_6O	Ethyl alcohol	78.3	$C_4H_{10}O_2$	Ethoxymethoxymethane	65.90		Nonazeotrope			*429*
14590	H_2O	Water	100	C_2H_6O	Ethyl alcohol	78.3	$C_5H_{12}O_2$	Diethoxymethane	87.5	73.2	12.8	18.4	69.5	*131*
14591	H_2O	Water	100	C_2H_6O	Ethyl alcohol	78.3	C_6H_5Cl	Chlorobenzene	131.8	75.0	...	...	13	*93*
14592	H_2O	Water	100	C_2H_6O	Ethyl alcohol	78.3	C_6H_6	Benzene	80.2	64.86	7.4	18.5	74.1	*433*
	H_2O	Water	...	C_2H_6O	Ethyl alcohol	...	C_6H_6	Benzene	Effect of pressure, 1–19 atmospheres					*181*
14593	H_2O	Water	100	C_2H_6O	Ethyl alcohol	78.3	C_6H_8	1,3-Cyclohexadiene	80.8	63.6	7	20	73	*243*
14594	H_2O	Water	100	C_2H_6O	Ethyl alcohol	78.3	C_6H_8	1,4-Cyclohexadiene	85.6	~65.5	...	...	...	*243*
14595	H_2O	Water	100	C_2H_6O	Ethyl alcohol	78.3	C_6H_{10}	Biallyl	60.2	~52	...	...	...	*243*
14596	H_2O	Water	100	C_2H_6O	Ethyl alcohol	78.3	C_6H_{10}	Cyclohexene	82.75	64.05	7	20	73	*243*
14597	H_2O	Water	100	C_2H_6O	Ethyl alcohol	78.3	C_6H_{10}	1-Hexyne	70.2	59.9	...	...	...	*157*
14598	H_2O	Water	100	C_2H_6O	Ethyl alcohol	78.3	C_6H_{10}	3-Hexyne	80.5	64.4	...	...	...	*157*
14599	H_2O	Water	100	C_2H_6O	Ethyl alcohol	78.3	C_6H_{12}	Cyclohexane	80.75	62.1	...	...	...	*243*
14600	H_2O	Water	100	C_2H_6O	Ethyl alcohol	78.3	C_6H_{14}	*n*-Hexane	68.95	56.60	...	...	...	*431*
14601	H_2O	Water	100	C_2H_6O	Ethyl alcohol	78.3	$C_6H_{14}O_2$	Acetal	103.6	77.8	11.4	27.6	61.0	*20*
14602	H_2O	Water	100	C_2H_6O	Ethyl alcohol	78.3	$C_6H_{14}O_2$	Ethoxypropoxymethane	113.7		Nonazeotrope			*429*

14603	H_2O	Water	100	C_2H_6O	Ethyl alcohol	78.3	$C_6H_{15}N$	Triethylamine	89.4	74.7	9	13	78	*404*
14604	H_2O	Water	100	C_2H_6O	Ethyl alcohol	78.3	C_7H_8	Toluene	110.7	74.55	...	...	...	*243*
14605	H_2O	Water	100	C_2H_6O	Ethyl alcohol	78.3	C_7H_{12}	1-Heptyne	99.5	71.0	...	...	...	*157*
14606	H_2O	Water	100	C_2H_6O	Ethyl alcohol	78.3	C_7H_{14}	Methylcyclo-hexane	101.8	~70.5	...	...	...	*243*
14607	H_2O	Water	100	C_2H_6O	Ethyl alcohol	78.3	$C_7H_{14}O_2$	Isoamyl acetate	90.8	69.0	...	...	...	*157*
14608	H_2O	Water	100	C_2H_6O	Ethyl alcohol	78.3	C_7H_{16}	Heptane	98.45	~69.5	...	...	...	*243*
14609	H_2O	Water	100	$C_2H_6O_2$	Glycol	197.4	$C_4H_8O_2$	Dioxane	101.4	Nonazeotrope				*90*
14610	H_2O	Water	100	C_3H_4O	2-Propyn-1-ol	...	C_6H_6	Benzene	80.2	Vapor-liquid equilibrium				*364*
14611	H_2O	Water	100	C_3H_5I	3-Iodopropene	102	C_3H_6O	Allyl alcohol	96.95	77.7	...	...	...	*243*
14612	H_2O	Water	100	C_3H_5I	3-Iodopropene	102	C_3H_8O	Propyl alcohol	97.2	78.15	8	72	20	*243*
14613	H_2O	Water	100	C_3H_6O	Acetone	56.1	C_5H_6O	2-Methylfuran	63.7	55.6	...	...	...	*310*
14614	H_2O	Water	100	C_3H_6O	Acetone	56.4	C_5H_8	Isoprene	34.7	32.5	0.4	7.6	92.0	*296*
14615	H_2O	Water	100	C_3H_6O	Acetone	56.25	C_6H_6O	Phenol	181.5	Nonazeotrope, vapor pressure curve				*351*
14616	H_2O	Water	100	C_3H_6O	Acetone	56.4	$C_6H_{14}O$	Isopropyl ether	69	Minimum b.p.				*128*
14617	H_2O	Water	100	C_3H_6O	Allyl alcohol	96.95	C_6H_6	Benzene	80.2	68.21	8.58	9.16	82.26	*357*, 413*
14618	H_2O	Water	100	C_3H_6O	Allyl alcohol	96.95	C_6H_8	1,3-Cyclohexa-diene	80.8	67.5	...	...	...	*243*
14619	H_2O	Water	100	C_3H_6O	Allyl alcohol	96.95	C_6H_{10}	Cyclohexene	82.75	67.95	8.5	11	80.5	*243*
14620	H_2O	Water	100	C_3H_6O	Allyl alcohol	96.95	$C_6H_{10}O$	Allyl ether	94.8	77.8	12.4	8.7	78.9	*357*
14621	H_2O	Water	100	C_3H_6O	Allyl alcohol	96.95	C_6H_{12}	Cyclohexane	80.75	66.18	8	11	81	*243*
14622	H_2O	Water	100	C_3H_6O	Allyl alcohol	96.95	C_6H_{14}	Hexane	68.95	59.7	5	5	90	*243*
14623	H_2O	Water	100	C_3H_6O	Allyl alcohol	96.95	C_7H_8	Toluene	110.7	80.2	...	...	...	*243*
14624	H_2O	Water	100	$C_3H_6O_3$	Trioxane	114.5	C_6H_{12}	Naphthenes	...	Minimum b.p.				*200*
14625	H_2O	Water	100	$C_3H_6O_3$	Trioxane	114.5	C_6H_{14}	Hexanes	...	Minimum b.p.				*200*
14626	H_2O	Water	100	$C_3H_6O_3$	Trioxane	114.5	C_7H_{14}	Naphthenes	...	Minimum b.p.				*200*
14627	H_2O	Water	100	$C_3H_6O_3$	Trioxane	114.5	C_7H_{16}	Heptanes	...	Minimum b.p.				*200*
14628	H_2O	Water	100	$C_3H_6O_3$	Trioxane	114.5	C_8H_{16}	Naphthenes	...	Minimum b.p.				*200*
14629	H_2O	Water	100	$C_3H_6O_3$	Trioxane	114.5	C_8H_{18}	Octanes	...	Minimum b.p.				*200*
14630	H_2O	Water	100	$C_3H_6O_3$	Trioxane	114.5	C_9H_{20}	Nonanes	...	Minimum b.p.				*200*
14631	H_2O	Water	100	C_3H_7I	1-Iodopropane	102.4	C_3H_8O	Propyl alcohol	97.2	78.25	...	...	...	*243*
14632	H_2O	Water	100	$C_3H_7NO_2$	1-Nitropropane	130.5	C_8H_{10}	Ethylbenzene	136	...	28.8	32.2	39	*25*
14633	H_2O	Water	100	C_3H_8O	Isopropyl alcohol	82.4	C_4H_8O	2-Butanone	79.6	Nonazeotrope				*10*
14634	H_2O	Water	100	C_3H_8O	Isopropyl alcohol	82.45	C_4H_9Cl	1-Chloro-2-methylpropane	68.85	61	...	...	...	*243*

	A-Component			B-Component			C-Component			Azeotropic Data				
No.	Formula	Name	B.P., ° C.	Formula	Name	B.P., ° C.	Formula	Name	B.P., ° C.	B.P., ° C.	Wt. % A	Wt. % B	Wt. % C	Ref.
14635	H_2O	Water	100	C_3H_8O	Isopropyl alcohol	82.4	$C_5H_{10}O$	Allyl ethyl ether	67.6		Azeotropic			*5*
14636	H_2O	Water	100	C_3H_8O	Isopropyl alcohol	82.7	$C_5H_{12}O$	Butyl methyl ether	70.3		Azeotropic			*5*
14637	H_2O	Water	100	C_3H_8O	Isopropyl alcohol	82.4	$C_5H_{12}O$	Ethyl isopropyl ether	54		Azeotropic			*5*
14638	H_2O	Water	100	C_3H_8O	Isopropyl alcohol	82.4	$C_5H_{12}O$	Ethyl propyl ether	64		Azeotropic			*5*
14639	H_2O	Water	100	C_3H_8O	Isopropyl alcohol	82.4	$C_5H_{12}O$	Isobutyl methyl ether	59		Azeotropic			*5*
14640	H_2O	Water	100	C_3H_8O	Isopropyl alcohol	82.45	C_6H_6	Benzene	80.2	66.51	7.5	18.7	73.8	*431*
14641	H_2O	Water	100	C_3H_8O	Isopropyl alcohol	82.45	C_6H_8	1,3-Cyclohexadiene	80.8	65.7	...	...	...	*243*
14642	H_2O	Water	100	C_3H_8O	Isopropyl alcohol	82.45	C_6H_{10}	Cyclohexene	82.75	66.1	7.5	21.5	71	*243*
14643	H_2O	Water	100	C_3H_8O	Isopropyl alcohol	82.45	C_6H_{12}	Cyclohexane	80.75	64.3	7.5	18.5	74	*243*
14644	H_2O	Water	100	C_3H_8O	Isopropyl alcohol	82.45	C_6H_{14}	Hexane	68.95	58.2	...	...	...	*243*
14645	H_2O	Water	100	C_3H_8O	Isopropyl alcohol	82.45	$C_6H_{14}O$	Ethyl *tert*-butyl ether	68–69		Azeotropic			*5*
14646	H_2O	Water	100	C_3H_8O	Isopropyl alcohol	82.45	$C_6H_{14}O$	Isopropyl ether	69.0	61.6	4.7	7.3	88.0	*128*
14647	H_2O	Water	100	C_3H_8O	Isopropyl alcohol	82.45	C_7H_8	Toluene	110.7	76.2	...	...	...	*243*
14648	H_2O	Water	100	C_3H_8O	Propyl alcohol	97.2	C_4H_8O	2-Butanone	79.6		Nonazeotrope			*10*
14649	H_2O	Water	100	C_3H_8O	Propyl alcohol	97.16	$C_4H_8O_2$	Propyl formate	80.9	70.8	13	5	82	*150*
14650	H_2O	Water	100	C_3H_8O	Propyl alcohol	97.2	C_4H_9Cl	1-Chloro-2-methylpropane	68.85	64.2	...	...	...	*243*
14651	H_2O	Water	100	C_3H_8O	Propyl alcohol	97.2	$C_5H_9ClO_2$	Propyl chloroacetate	162.3	88.6	25.25	58.27	16.48	*58*
14652	H_2O	Water	100	C_3H_8O	Propyl alcohol	97,2	$C_5H_{10}O$	3-Pentanone	102.2	~81.2	~20	~20	~60	*243*
16453	H_2O	Water	100	C_3H_8O	Propyl alcohol	97.16	$C_5H_{10}O_2$	Propyl acetate	101.6	82.2	21	19.5	59.5	*150*

14654	H_2O	Water	100	C_3H_8O	Propyl alcohol	97.2	$C_5H_{12}O_2$	Diethoxy-methane	88.0		Nonazeotrope			*429*
14655	H_2O	Water	100	C_3H_8O	Propyl alcohol	97.2	C_6H_6	Benzene	80.2	...	...	...	...	
									740 mm.	67	7.6	10.1	82.3	*259*
									2830 mm.	107	9.5	13.1	77.4	*259*
									4900 mm.	127	10.3	14.2	75.5	*259*
									5930 mm.	135	12.3	15.0	72.7	*259, 431**
14656	H_2O	Water	100	C_3H_8O	Propyl alcohol	97.2	C_6H_8	1,3-Cyclohexa-diene	80.8	67.75	9	12	79	*243*
14657	H_2O	Water	100	C_3H_8O	Propyl alcohol	97.2	C_6H_{10}	Cyclohexene	82.75	63.2	9	11.5	79.5	*243*
14658	H_2O	Water	100	C_3H_8O	Propyl alcohol	97.2	C_6H_{12}	Cyclohexane	80.75	66.55	80.5	10	81.5	*243*
14659	H_2O	Water	100	C_3H_8O	Propyl alcohol	97.2	C_6H_{14}	Hexane	68.95	59.95	...	...	...	*243*
14660	H_2O	Water	100	C_3H_8O	Propyl alcohol	97.2	$C_6H_{14}O$	Propyl ether	91	74.8	11.7	20.2	68.1	*307*
14661	H_2O	Water	100	C_3H_8O	Propyl alcohol	97.2	$C_6H_{14}O_2$	Ethoxypropoxy-methane	113.7	83.8	17.6	22.9	59.5	*429*
14662	H_2O	Water	100	C_3H_8O	Propyl alcohol	97.2	C_7H_8	Toluene	110.7	80.05	...	...	...	*243*
14663	H_2O	Water	100	C_3H_8O	Propyl alcohol	96.90	$C_7H_{16}O_2$	Dipropoxy-methane	137.2	86.4	8	44.8	47.2	*131*
14664	H_2O	Water	100	C_3H_8O	Propyl alcohol	97.2	$C_8H_{18}O_2$	Acetaldehyde dipropylacetal	147.7	87.6	27.4	51.6	21.0	*20*
14665	H_2O	Water	100	$C_3H_8O_2$	2-Methoxy-ethanol	124	C_8H_{10}	Ethylbenzene	136	90	25.4	7.4	67.2	*30*
14666	H_2O	Water	100	$C_3H_8O_2$	2-Methoxy-ethanol	124	C_8H_{10}	Xylenes	140		Minimum b.p.			*30*
14667	H_2O	Water	100	C_4H_6O	Crotonaldehyde	102	C_7H_8	Toluene	110.7	85.3	...	...	...	*385*
14668	H_2O	Water	100	C_4H_6O	Crotonaldehyde	102	C_nH_{2n+2}	Paraffins	...	80–85	...	...	...	*385*
14669	H_2O	Water	100	C_4H_8O	2-Butanone	79.6	$C_4H_{10}O$	*tert*-Butyl alcohol	82.4		Nonazeotrope			*10*
14670	H_2O	Water	100	C_4H_8O	2-Butanone	79.6	C_6H_6	Benzene	80.12	68.9	8.9	17.5	73.6	*358*
14671	H_2O	Water	100	C_4H_8O	2-Butanone	79.6	C_6H_{12}	1-Hexene	82		Minimum b.p.			*31*
14672	H_2O	Water	100	C_4H_8O	2-Butanone	79.6	C_6H_{12}	2-Hexene	...		Minimum b.p.			*31*
14673	H_2O	Water	100	C_4H_8O	2-Butanone	79.6	C_6H_{12}	3-Hexene	...		Minimum b.p.			*31*
14674	H_2O	Water	100	C_4H_8O	2-Butanone	79.6	C_6H_{12}	2-Methyl-1-pentene	...		Minimum b.p.			*31*
14675	H_2O	Water	100	C_4H_8O	2-Butanone	79.6	C_6H_{12}	2-Methyl-2-pentene	...		Minimum b.p.			*31*
14676	H_2O	Water	100	C_4H_8O	2-Butanone	79.6	C_6H_{12}	3-Methyl-2-pentene	...		Minimum b.p.			*31*
14677	H_2O	Water	100	C_4H_8O	2-Butanone	79.6	C_6H_{14}	Hexane	68.95	58.5/742.5	4	22	74	*31*

	A-Component			B-Component			C-Component			Azeotropic Data				
No.	Formula	Name	B.P., ° C.	Formula	Name	B.P., ° C.	Formula	Name	B.P., ° C.	B.P., ° C.	Wt. % A	Wt. % B	Wt. % C	Ref.
14678	H_2O	Water	100	C_4H_8O	2-Butanone	79.6	C_6H_{14}	2-Methylpentane	...		Minimum b.p.			*31*
14679	H_2O	Water	100	C_4H_8O	2-Butanone	79.6	C_6H_{14}	3-Methylpentane	...		Minimum b.p.			*31*
14680	H_2O	Water	100	C_4H_8O	Butyraldehyde	75.7	C_7H_{16}	Heptanes	...	~57	...	...	...	*139*
14681	H_2O	Water	100	C_4H_8O	Isobutyraldehyde	63	C_7H_{16}	Heptanes	...	48	...	...	...	*139*
14682	H_2O	Water	100	C_4H_9Cl	1-Chloro-2-methylpropane	68.85	$C_4H_{10}O$	*tert*-Butyl alcohol	82.55	62	...	...	...	*243*
14683	H_2O	Water	100	$C_4H_{10}O$	Butyl alcohol	117.8	$C_5H_{10}O_2$	Butyl formate	106.6	83.6	21.3	10	68.7	*150*
14684	H_2O	Water	100	$C_4H_{10}O$	Butyl alcohol	116.9	C_6H_{10}	Cyclohexene	82.75	70.22	...	...	...	*243*
14685	H_2O	Water	100	$C_4H_{10}O$	Butyl alcohol	117.4	$C_6H_{11}ClO_2$	Butyl chloroacetate	181.9	93.1	41.8	50.3	7.9	*58*
14686	H_2O	Water	100	$C_4H_{10}O$	Butyl alcohol	117.8	$C_6H_{12}O_2$	Butyl acetate	126.2	89.4	37.3	27.4	35.3	*37**, *137*, *150*
14687	H_2O	Water	100	$C_4H_{10}O$	Butyl alcohol	117.5	$C_8H_{18}O$	Butyl ether	141.9	91	29.3	42.9	27.7	*307*
14688	H_2O	Water	100	$C_4H_{10}O$	Butyl alcohol	117	$C_9H_{20}O_2$	Dibutoxymethane	181.8		Nonazeotrope			*131*
14689	H_2O	Water	100	$C_4H_{10}O$	Butyl alcohol	117	$C_{10}H_{22}O_2$	Acetaldehyde dibutyl acetal	188.8		Nonazeotrope			*20*
14690	H_2O	Water	100	$C_4H_{10}O$	*sec*-Butyl alcohol	99.6	$C_5H_{10}O$	Allyl ethyl ether	67.6		Nonazeotrope			*5*
14691	H_2O	Water	100	$C_4H_{10}O$	*sec*-Butyl alcohol	99.6	$C_5H_{12}O$	Butyl methyl ether	70.3		Nonazeotrope			*5*
14692	H_2O	Water	100	$C_4H_{10}O$	*sec*-Butyl alcohol	99.6	$C_5H_{12}O$	Ethyl isopropyl ether	54		Nonazeotrope			*5*
14693	H_2O	Water	100	$C_4H_{10}O$	*sec*-Butyl alcohol	99.6	$C_5H_{12}O$	Ethyl propyl ether	64		Nonazeotrope			*5*
14694	H_2O	Water	100	$C_4H_{10}O$	*sec*-Butyl alcohol	99.6	$C_5H_{12}O$	Isobutyl methyl ether	59		Nonazeotrope			*5*
14695	H_2O	Water	100	$C_4H_{10}O$	*sec*-Butyl alcohol	99.6	C_6H_6	Benzene	80.2		Azeotrope doubtful			*243*
14696	H_2O	Water	100	$C_4H_{10}O$	*sec*-Butyl alcohol	99.6	C_6H_{12}	Cyclohexane	80.75	~67	...	...	...	*243*
14697	H_2O	Water	100	$C_4H_{10}O$	*sec*-Butyl alcohol	99.6	C_6H_{14}	Hexane	68.95	61.1	...	...	...	*243*
14698	H_2O	Water	100	$C_4H_{10}O$	*sec*-Butyl alcohol	99.6	$C_6H_{14}O$	Ethyl *tert*-butyl ether	68–69		Nonazeotrope			*5*
14699	H_2O	Water	100	$C_4H_{10}O$	*sec*-Butyl alcohol	99.6	$C_6H_{14}O$	Isopropyl ether	69		Nonazeotrope			*5*
14700	H_2O	Water	100	$C_4H_{10}O$	*sec*-Butyl alcohol	99.6	C_8H_{14}	Diisobutylene	...	80.2	...	...	...	*297*
14701	H_2O	Water	100	$C_4H_{10}O$	*sec*-Butyl alcohol	99.6	$C_8H_{18}O$	Butyl ether	141	86.5	...	...	...	*104*

14702	H_2O	Water	100	$C_4H_{10}O$	*sec*-Butyl alcohol	99.53	$C_8H_{18}O$	*sec*-Butyl ether	121	83	...	...	...	*104*
14703	H_2O	Water	100	$C_4H_{10}O$	*tert*-Butyl alcohol	82.55	C_6H_6	Benzene	80.2	67.30	8.1	21.4	70.5	*431*
14704	H_2O	Water	100	$C_4H_{10}O$	*tert*-Butyl alcohol	82.55	C_6H_8	1,3-Cyclohexadiene	80.8	66.7	...	...	...	*243*
14705	H_2O	Water	100	$C_4H_{10}O$	*tert*-Butyl alcohol	82.55	C_6H_{10}	Cyclohexene	82.75	67	...	...	...	*243*
14706	H_2O	Water	100	$C_4H_{10}O$	*tert*-Butyl alcohol	82.55	C_6H_{12}	Cyclohexane	80.75	65	8	21	71	*243*
14707	H_2O	Water	100	$C_4H_{10}O$	*tert*-Butyl alcohol	82.55	C_6H_{14}	Hexane	68.95	58.9	...	...	...	*243*
14708	H_2O	Water	100	$C_4H_{10}O$	Isobutyl alcohol	108.0	$C_5H_{10}O$	3-Pentanone	102.2		Nonazeotrope			*243*
14709	H_2O	Water	100	$C_4H_{10}O$	Isobutyl alcohol	108	$C_5H_{10}O_2$	Isobutyl formate	98.4	80.2	17.3	6.7	76	*150*
14710	H_2O	Water	100	$C_4H_{10}O$	Isobutyl alcohol	108	C_6H_6	Benzene	80.2		Nonazeotrope			*431*
14711	H_2O	Water	100	$C_4H_{10}O$	Isobutyl alcohol	108	C_6H_8	1,3-Cyclohexadiene	80.8		Nonazeotrope			*243*
14712	H_2O	Water	100	$C_4H_{10}O$	Isobutyl alcohol	108	C_6H_{10}	Cyclohexene	82.75	~69.5	...	...	...	*243*
14713	H_2O	Water	100	$C_4H_{10}O$	Isobutyl alcohol	107.4	$C_6H_{11}ClO_2$	Isobutyl chloroacetate	174.4	90.2	33.64	53.1	13.26	*58*
14714	H_2O	Water	100	$C_4H_{10}O$	Isobutyl alcohol	108	C_6H_{12}	Cyclohexane	80.75		Nonazeotrope			*243*
14715	H_2O	Water	100	$C_4H_{10}O$	Isobutyl alcohol	108	$C_6H_{12}O_2$	Isobutyl acetate	117.2	86.8	30.4	23.1	46.5	*137**, *150*
14716	H_2O	Water	100	$C_4H_{10}O$	Isobutyl alcohol	108	C_6H_{14}	Hexane	68.95		Nonazeotrope			*243*
14717	H_2O	Water	100	$C_4H_{10}O$	Isobutyl alcohol	108	C_7H_8	Toluene	110.7	83	...	...	...	*243*
14718	H_2O	Water	100	$C_4H_{10}O$	Isobutyl alcohol	108	C_8H_{10}	Ethylbenzene	136.15	~89.5	...	...	...	*243*
14719	H_2O	Water	100	$C_4H_{10}O$	Isobutyl alcohol	108	$C_8H_{18}O$	Butyl ether	141.9	89	...	...	...	*307*
14720	H_2O	Water	100	$C_4H_{10}O$	Isobutyl alcohol	108	$C_8H_{18}O$	Isobutyl ether	122	85.4	...	...	...	*307*
14721	H_2O	Water	100	$C_4H_{10}O$	Isobutyl alcohol	107.5	$C_9H_{20}O_2$	Diisobutoxymethane	163.8		Nonazeotrope			*131*
14722	H_2O	Water	100	$C_4H_{10}O$	Isobutyl alcohol	107.8	$C_{10}H_{22}O_2$	Acetaldehyde diisobutyl acetal	171.3		Nonazeotrope			*20*
14723	H_2O	Water	100	C_5H_5N	Pyridine	115.5	C_6H_8	1,3-Cyclohexadiene	80.8		Minimum b.p.			*376*
14724	H_2O	Water	100	C_5H_5N	Pyridine	115.5	C_6H_{10}	Cyclohexene	82.75		Minimum b.p.			*376*
14725	H_2O	Water	100	C_5H_5N	Pyridine	115.5	C_6H_{12}	Cyclohexane	80.75		Minimum b.p.			*376*
14726	H_2O	Water	100	C_5H_5N	Pyridine	115.5	C_7H_{10}	Methylcyclohexadiene	...		Minimum b.p.			*376*
14727	H_2O	Water	100	C_5H_5N	Pyridine	115.5	C_7H_{14}	1,1-Dimethylcyclopentane	87.8		Minimum b.p.			*376*

	A-Component			B-Component			C-Component			Azeotropic Data				
No.	Formula	Name	B.P., ° C.	Formula	Name	B.P., ° C.	Formula	Name	B.P., ° C.	B.P., ° C.	Wt. % A	Wt. % B	Wt. % C	Ref.
14728	H_2O	Water	100	C_5H_5N	Pyridine	115.5	C_7H_{14}	1,2-Dimethyl-cyclopentane	...		Minimum b.p.			*376*
14729	H_2O	Water	100	C_5H_5N	Pyridine	115.5	C_7H_{14}	1,3-Dimethyl-cyclopentane	90.8		Minimum b.p.			*376*
14730	H_2O	Water	100	C_5H_5N	Pyridine	115.5	C_7H_{14}	Methylcyclo-hexane	101.2	80.0	...	5	...	*376*
14731	H_2O	Water	100	C_5H_5N	Pyridine	115.5	C_7H_{16}	*n*-Heptane	98.45		Minimum b.p.			*376*
14732	H_2O	Water	100	C_5H_5N	Pyridine	115.5	C_7H_{16}	3-Methylhexane	91.8		Minimum b.p.			*376*
14733	H_2O	Water	100	C_5H_5N	Pyridine	115.5	C_8H_{14}	Diisobutylene	101		Minimum b.p.			
14734	H_2O	Water	100	$C_5H_{12}O$	Amyl alcohol	137.8	$C_6H_{12}O_2$	Amyl formate	132	91.4	37.5	21.5	41	*150*
14735	H_2O	Water	100	$C_5H_{12}O$	Amyl alcohol	137.8	$C_7H_{14}O_2$	Amyl acetate	148.8	94.8	56.2	33.3	10.5	*150, 173**
14736	H_2O	Water	100	$C_5H_{12}O$	Amyl alcohol	138	$C_{10}H_{22}O$	Amyl ether	188	95.94	...	...	...	*427*
14737	H_2O	Water	100	$C_5H_{12}O$	Amyl alcohol	137.2	$C_{11}H_{24}O_2$	Diamyloxy-methane	221.6		Nonazeotrope			*131*
14738	H_2O	Water	100	$C_5H_{12}O$	Amyl alcohol	137.5	$C_{12}H_{26}O_2$	Acetaldehyde diamyl acetal	225.3		Nonazeotrope			*20*
14739	H_2O	Water	100	$C_5H_{12}O$	*tert*-Amyl alcohol	102	C_6H_6	Benzene	80.2		Nonazeotrope			*243*
14740	H_2O	Water	100	$C_5H_{12}O$	*tert*-Amyl alcohol	102	C_6H_{12}	Cyclohexane	80.75		Nonazeotrope			*243*
14741	H_2O	Water	100	$C_5H_{12}O$	*tert*-Amyl alcohol	102	C_7H_8	Toluene	110.7	~82	...	...	...	*243*
14742	H_2O	Water	100	$C_5H_{12}O$	Isoamyl alcohol	131.3	C_6H_6	Benzene	80.2		Nonazeotrope			*431*
14743	H_2O	Water	100	$C_5H_{12}O$	Isoamyl alcohol	131.5	$C_6H_{12}O_2$	Isoamyl formate	124.2	89.8	32.4	19.6	48	*150*
14744	H_2O	Water	100	$C_5H_{12}O$	Isoamyl alcohol	131.3	$C_7H_{13}ClO_2$	Isoamyl chloro-acetate	195.2	95.4	46.2	47.3	6.5	*58*
14745	H_2O	Water	100	$C_5H_{12}O$	Isoamyl alcohol	131.5	$C_7H_{14}O_2$	Isoamyl acetate	142	93.6	44.8	31.2	24	*150, 173**
14746	H_2O	Water	100	$C_5H_{12}O$	Isoamyl alcohol	132	$C_{10}H_{22}O$	Isoamyl ether	171	94.4	...	...	...	*307*
14747	H_2O	Water	100	$C_5H_{12}O$	Isoamyl alcohol	131.6	$C_{12}H_{26}O_2$	Acetaldehyde di-isoamyl acetal	213.6	6	Nonazeotrope			*20*
14748	H_2O	Water	100	C_6H_6O	Phenol	182	C_8H_{10}	Xylene	137	...	Minimum b.p.			*47*
14749	H_2O	Water	100	$C_6H_{12}O$	2-Methyl-2-penten-4-ol	...	$C_8H_{14}O$	2,4,6-Trimethyl-5,6-dihydro-1,2-pyran	...	90.7	27.0	9.7	63.3	*347*
14750	H_3N	Ammonia	−33	C_2H_6O	Methyl ether	−24	C_3H_9N	Trimethylamine	3.5		Nonazeotrope			*158*
14751	H_3N	Ammonia	−33	C_3H_9N	Trimethylamine	3.5	C_4H_8	1-Butene	−6		Nonazeotrope			*158*
14752	H_3N	Ammonia	−33	C_3H_9N	Trimethylamine	3.5	C_4H_8	2-Methylpropene	−6		Nonazeotrope			*158*
14753	H_3N	Ammonia	−33	C_3H_9N	Trimethylamine	3.5	C_4H_{10}	Butane	0		Nonazeotrope			*158*

14754	H_3N	Ammonia	−33	C_3H_9N	Trimethylamine	3.5	C_4H_{10}	2-Methylpropane	−10		Nonazeotrope			*158*
14755	CCl_4	Carbon tetra-chloride	76.75	CH_4O	Methanol	64.7	C_6H_{12}	Cyclohexane	80.75		Nonazeotrope			*243*
14756	CCl_4	Carbon tetra-chloride	76.75	$C_2H_4Br_2$	1,2-Dibromo-ethane	131.5	C_7H_8	Toluene	110.7		Nonazeotrope			*243*
14757	CCl_4	Carbon tetra-chloride	76.75	C_2H_6O	Ethyl alcohol	78.3	C_4H_8O	2-Butanone	79.6		Nonazeotrope			*243*
14758	CCl_4	Carbon tetra-chloride	76.75	C_2H_6O	Ethyl alcohol	78.3	$C_4H_8O_2$	Ethyl acetate	77.05		Nonazeotrope			*243*
14759	CCl_4	Carbon tetra-chloride	76.75	C_2H_6O	Ethyl alcohol	78.3	C_6H_6	Benzene	80.2		Azeotropic ?			*243*
	CCl_4	Carbon tetra-chloride	...	C_2H_6O	Ethyl alcohol	...	C_6H_6	Benzene	...		Nonazeotrope			*60*
14760	CCl_4	Carbon tetra-chloride	76.75	C_4H_8O	2-Butanone	79.6	$C_4H_8O_2$	Methyl propionate	79.7		Nonazeotrope			*243*
14761	CCl_4	Carbon tetra-chloride	76.75	C_4H_8O	2-Butanone	79.6	C_6H_{12}	Cyclohexane	80.75		Nonazeotrope ?			*243*
14762	CCl_4	Carbon tetra-chloride	76.75	$C_4H_8O_2$	Ethyl acetate	77.05	C_6H_{12}	Cyclohexane	80.75		Nonazeotrope			*243*
14763	CS_2	Carbon disulfide	46.25	CH_3I	Iodomethane	42.6	CH_4O	Methanol	64.7	35.95	...	...	< 12	*243*
14764	CS_2	Carbon disulfide	46.25	CH_3I	Iodomethane	42.6	$C_2H_4O_2$	Methyl formate	31.9		Nonazeotrope			*243*
14765	CS_2	Carbon disulfide	46.25	CH_3I	Iodomethane	42.5	$C_3H_8O_2$	Methylal	42.25	37.2?	...	...	...	*243*
14766	CS_2	Carbon disulfide	46.25	CH_4O	Methanol	64.7	C_2H_5Br	Bromoethane	38.4	33.92	~40	~10	~50	*243*
14767	CS_2	Carbon disulfide	46.25	CH_4O	Methanol	64.7	C_3H_6O	Acetone	56.25		Nonazeotrope			*243*
14768	CS_2	Carbon disulfide	46.25	CH_4O	Methanol	64.7	$C_3H_6O_2$	Methyl acetate	57.0	37	...	...	...	*243*
14769	CS_2	Carbon disulfide	46.25	CH_4O	Methanol	64.7	C_3H_7Cl	1-Chloropropane	46.6	37?	...	...	...	*243*
14770	CS_2	Carbon disulfide	46.25	CH_4O	Methanol	64.7	$C_3H_8O_2$	Methylal	42.25	35.55	55	7	38	*243*
14771	CS_2	Carbon disulfide	46.25	CH_4O	Methanol	64.7	C_5H_{10}	2-Methyl-2-butene	37.15		Nonazeotrope			*243*
14772	CS_2	Carbon disulfide	46.25	$C_2H_4O_2$	Methyl formate	31.9	C_2H_5Br	Bromoethane	38.4	24.7?	18?	60?	22?	*243*
14773	CS_2	Carbon disulfide	46.25	$C_2H_4O_2$	Methyl formate	31.9	C_5H_{10}	2-Methyl-2-butene	37.15	~24	...	...	...	*243*
14774	CS_2	Carbon disulfide	46.25	$C_2H_4O_2$	Methyl formate	31.9	C_5H_{12}	Pentane	36.15	21.5?	...	...	...	*243*
14775	CS_2	Carbon disulfide	46.25	C_2H_6O	Ethyl alcohol	78.3	C_4H_8O	2-Butanone	79.6		Nonazeotrope			*243*
14776	CS_2	Carbon disulfide	46.25	C_2H_6O	Ethyl alcohol	78.3	$C_4H_8O_2$	Ethyl acetate	77.05		Nonazeotrope			*243*
14777	CS_2	Carbon disulfide	46.25	C_3H_6O	Acetone	56.25	$C_3H_6O_2$	Methyl acetate	57.0		Nonazeotrope			*243*
14778	CS_2	Carbon disulfide	46.25	$C_3H_6O_2$	Ethyl formate	54.1	C_3H_7Cl	1-Chloropropane	46.6	38.2?	...	...	...	*243*
14779	CS_2	Carbon disulfide	46.25	C_3H_8O	Isopropyl alcohol	82.45	$C_4H_8O_2$	Ethyl acetate	77.05		Nonazeotrope			*243*

	A-Component			B-Component			C-Component			Azeotropic Data				
No.	Formula	Name	B.P., ° C.	Formula	Name	B.P., ° C.	Formula	Name	B.P., ° C.	B.P., ° C.	Wt. % A	Wt. % B	Wt. % C	Ref.
14780	CS_2	Carbon disulfide	46.25	$C_3H_8O_2$	Methylal	42.25	C_5H_{10}	2-Methyl-2-butene	37.15	35.2?	...	...	...	*243*
14781	$CHCl_3$	Chloroform	61	CH_2Cl_2	Dichloromethane	40	C_3H_6O	Acetone	56.4		Nonazeotrope			*110*
14782	$CHCl_3$	Chloroform	61	CH_4O	Methanol	64.7	C_3H_6O	Acetone	56.4	57.5	47	23	30	*110*
14783	$CHCl_3$	Chloroform	61	CH_4O	Methanol	64.7	C_6H_{14}	Hexane	68.95		Nonazeotrope			*243*
14784	$CHCl_3$	Chloroform	61	C_2H_6O	Ethanol	78.3	C_6H_{14}	Hexane	68.95	~58.3	...	...	...	*243*
14785	$CHCl_3$	Chloroform	61	C_3H_6O	Acetone	56.4	C_6H_6	Benzene	80.2		Nonazeotrope, V-l.			*322*
14786	CH_2Cl_2	Dichloromethane	40	CH_4O	Methanol	64.7	C_3H_6O	Acetone	54.6		Nonazeotrope			*110*
14787	CH_3I	Iodomethane	42.6	CH_4O	Methanol	64.7	$C_3H_8O_2$	Methylal	42.25	38.5	...	...	...	*243*
14788	CH_3I	Iodomethane	42.7	$C_2H_4O_2$	Methyl formate	31.9	C_5H_{12}	Pentane	36.15		Nonazeotrope			*243*
14789	CH_3NO_2	Nitromethane	101.2	C_3H_8O	Propyl alcohol	97.2	$C_5H_{10}O$	3-Pentanone	102.2		Azeotropic			*243*
14790	CH_3NO_2	Nitromethane	101.2	$C_5H_{10}O_2$	3-Pentanone	102.2	$C_5H_{10}O_2$	Propyl acetate	101.55	99.0?	...	...	...	*243*
14791	CH_4O	Methanol	64.7	C_2H_5Br	Bromoethane	38.4	C_5H_{10}	2-Methyl-2-butene	37.15	31.4	15	55	30	*243*
14792	CH_4O	Methanol	64.7	C_2H_5Br	Bromoethane	38.4	C_5H_{12}	2-Methylbutane	27.95		Nonazeotrope			*243*
14793	CH_4O	Methanol	64.7	C_2H_5I	Iodoethane	72.3	C_3H_6O	Acetone	56.25		Nonazeotrope ?			*243*
14794	CH_4O	Methanol	64.7	C_2H_5I	Iodoethane	72.3	$C_4H_8O_2$	Ethyl acetate	77.05		Nonazeotrope			*243*
14795	CH_4O	Methanol	64.7	C_3H_6O	Acetone	56.25	$C_3H_6O_2$	Methyl acetate	57.0	53.9	...	...	...	*243*
	CH_4O	Methanol	...	C_3H_6O	Acetone	...	$C_3H_6O_2$	Methyl acetate	...		Nonazeotrope			*127*
14796	CH_4O	Methanol	64.7	C_3H_6O	Acetone	56.25	C_4H_9Cl	1-Chloro-2-methylpropane	68.85	52.0	...	...	...	*243*
14797	CH_4O	Methanol	64.7	C_3H_6O	Acetone	56.4	C_6H_{12}	Cyclohexane	80.75	51.1	16	43.5	40.5	*117*
14798	CH_4O	Methanol	64.7	C_3H_6O	Acetone	56.25	C_6H_{14}	Hexane	68.95		Nonazeotrope			*243*
14799	CH_4O	Methanol	64.7	$C_3H_6O_2$	Methyl acetate	57	C_6H_{12}	Cyclohexane	80.75	50.8	17.8	48.6	33.6	*117*
14800	CH_4O	Methanol	64.7	$C_3H_8O_2$	Methylal	42.25	C_5H_{10}	2-Methyl-2-butene	37.15		Nonazeotrope			*243*
14801	CH_4O	Methanol	64.7	$C_4H_8O_2$	Ethyl acetate	77.05	C_6H_{12}	Cyclohexane	80.75		Nonazeotrope			*243*
14802	CH_4O	Methanol	64.7	C_6H_6	Benzene	80.2	C_6H_{10}	Cyclohexene	82.75		Nonazeotrope			*243*
14803	CH_4O	Methanol	64.7	C_6H_6	Benzene	80.2	C_6H_{12}	Cyclohexane	80.75		Nonazeotrope			*243*
14804	CH_4O	Methanol	64.7	C_6H_8	1,3-Cyclohexadiene	80.8	C_6H_{12}	Cyclohexane	80.75		Nonazeotrope			*243*
14805	C_2Cl_4	Tetrachloroethylene	120.8	$C_2H_4O_2$	Acetic acid	118.5	C_3H_5ClO	Epichlorohydrin	116.45		Nonazeotrope			*243*
14806	C_2Cl_4	Tetrachloroethylene	120.8	C_3H_5ClO	Epichlorohydrin	116.45	C_3H_8O	Propyl alcohol	97.2		Nonazeotrope			*243*

14807	C_2Cl_4	Tetrachloro-ethylene	120.8	C_3H_5ClO	Epichlorohydrin	116.45	C_4H_9I	1-Iodo-2-methyl-propane	120		Azeotrope ?			*243*
14808	C_2Cl_4	Tetrachloro-ethylene	120.8	C_3H_5ClO	Epichlorohydrin	116.45	$C_4H_{10}O$	Isobutyl alcohol	108.0		Nonazeotrope			*243*
14809	C_2Cl_4	Tetrachloro-ethylene	120.8	C_3H_5ClO	Epichlorohydrin	116.45	$C_5H_{12}O$	Isoamyl alcohol	131.8		Nonazeotrope			*243*
14810	C_2Cl_4	Tetrachloro-ethylene	120.8	C_3H_5ClO	Epichlorohydrin	116.45	$C_6H_{12}O_2$	Ethyl butyrate	119.9		Nonazeotrope			*243*
14811	C_2Cl_4	Tetrachloro-ethylene	120.8	$C_5H_{10}O_3$	Ethyl carbonate	126.0	$C_5H_{12}O$	Isoamyl alcohol	131.8	< 116.0?	...	...	...	*243*
14812	C_2Cl_4	Tetrachloro-ethylene	120.8	$C_6H_{12}O_2$	Isoamyl formate	123.6	$C_6H_{12}O_3$	Paraldehyde	124	~117.6	45	25	30	*243*
14813	$C_2H_3ClO_2$	Chloroacetic acid	186.5	C_7H_7Br	*o*-Bromotoluene	181.75	$C_{10}H_{16}$	*d*-Limonene	177.8		Nonazeotrope			*243*
14814	$C_2H_3ClO_2$	Chloroacetic acid	186.5	C_7H_7Cl	α-Chlorotoluene	179.35	$C_{10}H_{16}$	*d*-Limonene	177.8		Nonazeotrope			*243*
14815	$C_2H_4Br_2$	1,2-Dibromo-ethane	131.5	$C_2H_4O_2$	Acetic acid	118.5	C_6H_5Cl	Chlorobenzene	131.8		Nonazeotrope			*243*
14816	$C_2H_4Br_2$	1,2-Dibromo-ethane	131.5	$C_3H_6O_2$	Propionic acid	140.7	C_6H_5Cl	Chlorobenzene	131.8	127.5	...	...	...	*243*
14817	$C_2H_4Br_2$	1,2-Dibromo-ethane	131.5	$C_5H_{12}O$	Isoamyl alcohol	131.8	C_6H_5Cl	Chlorobenzene	131.8		Nonazeotrope			*243*
14818	$C_2H_4Br_2$	1,2-Dibromo-ethane	131.5	$C_5H_{12}O$	Isoamyl alcohol	131.8	C_8H_{10}	Ethylbenzene	136.15		Nonazeotrope			*243*
14819	$C_2H_4O_2$	Acetic acid	118.5	C_3H_5ClO	Epichlorohydrin	116.45	C_7H_8	Toluene	110.7		Nonazeotrope			*243*
14820	$C_2H_4O_2$	Methyl formate	31.9	C_2H_5Br	Bromoethane	38.4	C_5H_8	Isoprene	34.1	< 23	...	...	...	*243*
14821	$C_2H_4O_2$	Methyl formate	31.9	C_2H_5Br	Bromoethane	38.4	C_5H_{10}	2-Methyl-2-butene	37.15	24.1	...	...	...	*243*
14822	$C_2H_4O_2$	Methyl formate	31.9	C_2H_5Br	Bromoethane	38.4	C_5H_{12}	2-Methylbutane	27.95	16.95	~52	~5	~43	*432*
14823	$C_2H_4O_2$	Methyl formate	31.9	C_2H_5Br	Bromoethane	38.4	C_5H_{12}	Pentane	36.15	21.7?	...	...	...	*243*
14824	$C_2H_4O_2$	Methyl formate	31.9	C_2H_6S	Ethanethiol	24.3	C_5H_{10}	2-Methyl-2-butene	37.15	24?	...	...	...	*243*
14825	$C_2H_4O_2$	Methyl formate	31.9	$C_4H_{10}O$	Ethyl ether	34.6	C_5H_{10}	2-Methyl-2-butene	37.15	24	...	...	...	*243*
14826	$C_2H_4O_2$	Methyl formate	31.9	$C_4H_{10}O$	Ethyl ether	34.6	C_5H_{12}	Pentane	36.15	20.4	40	8	52	*243*
14827	$C_2H_4O_2$	Methyl formate	31.9	C_5H_{10}	Cyclopentane	49.3	C_6H_{14}	2,2-Dimethyl-butane	49.7		Nonazeotrope			*315*
14828	C_2H_5I	Iodoethane	72.3	C_2H_6O	Ethyl alcohol	78.3	$C_4H_8O_2$	Ethyl acetate	77.05		Nonazeotrope			*243*
14829	C_2H_6O	Ethyl alcohol	78.3	C_4H_8O	2-Butanone	79.6	$C_4H_8O_2$	Ethyl acetate	77.0		Nonazeotrope			*10*
14830	C_2H_6O	Ethyl alcohol	78.3	C_4H_8O	2-Butanone	79.6	$C_4H_8O_2$	Methyl propionate	79.7		Nonazeotrope			*243*
14831	C_2H_6O	Ethyl alcohol	78.3	C_4H_8O	2-Butanone	79.6	C_6H_6	Benzene	80.2		Nonazeotrope			*243*

	A-Component			B-Component			C-Component			Azeotropic Data				
No.	Formula	Name	B.P., ° C.	Formula	Name	B.P., ° C.	Formula	Name	B.P., ° C.	B.P., ° C.	Wt. % A	Wt. % B	Wt. % C	Ref.
14832	C_2H_6O	Ethyl alcohol	78.3	C_4H_8O	2-Butanone	79.6	C_6H_{12}	Cyclohexane	80.75			Nonazeotrope		243
14833	C_2H_6O	Ethyl alcohol	78.3	$C_4H_8O_2$	Ethyl acetate	77.05	C_6H_{12}	Cyclohexane	80.75	64.3?	...	...	...	243
14834	C_2H_6O	Ethyl alcohol	78.3	C_4H_9Cl	1-Chloro-2-methylpropane	68.95	C_6H_{14}	Hexane	68.95			Azeotropic ?		243
14835	C_2H_6O	Ethyl alcohol	78.3	$C_5H_{14}OSi$	Ethoxytrimethylsilane	75–76	C_6H_6	Benzene	80.2			Minimum b.p.		86
14836	C_2H_6O	Ethyl alcohol	78.3	C_6H_6	Benzene	80.2	C_6H_{12}	Cyclohexane	80.75			Nonazeotrope		243
14837	$C_2H_6O_2$	Glycol	197.4	C_6H_7N	Aniline	184.35	$C_{10}H_{16}$	*d*-Limonene	177.8	162.45	...	...	...	243
14838	C_3H_5ClO	Epichlorohydrin	116.45	C_3H_8O	Propyl alcohol	97.2	C_7H_8	Toluene	110.7			Nonazeotrope		243
14839	C_3H_5ClO	Epichlorohydrin	116.45	C_4H_9I	1-Iodo-2-methylpropane	120	$C_6H_{12}O_2$	Ethyl butyrate	119.9			Nonazeotrope		243
14840	C_3H_5ClO	Epichlorohydrin	116.45	$C_4H_{10}O$	Isobutyl alcohol	108.0	C_7H_8	Toluene	110.7			Nonazeotrope		243
14841	C_3H_5I	3-Iodopropene	102	C_3H_8O	Propyl alcohol	97.2	$C_5H_{10}O$	3-Pentanone	102.2			Nonazeotrope		243
14842	C_3H_5I	3-Iodopropene	102	$C_5H_{10}O$	3-Pentanone	102.2	$C_5H_{10}O_2$	Propyl acetate	101.55			Azeotropic ?		243
14843	C_3H_5I	3-Iodopropene	102	$C_5H_{10}O$	3-Pentanone	102.2	C_7H_{14}	Methylcyclohexane	101.8			Azeotropic ?		243
14844	$C_3H_6Cl_2O$	1,3-Dichloro-2-propanol	174.5	$C_4H_6O_4$	Methyl oxalate	163.3	$C_{10}H_{16}$	*d*-Limonene	177.8			Nonazeotrope		243
14845	$C_3H_6Cl_2O$	1,3-Dichloro-2-propanol	174.5	$C_6H_{12}O_3$	Propyl lactate	171.7	C_7H_7Cl	*α*-Chlorotoluene	179.35			Nonazeotrope		243
14846	$C_3H_6Cl_2O$	1,3-Dichloro-2-propanol	174.5	$C_6H_{12}O_3$	Propyl lactate	171.7	$C_{10}H_{16}$	*d*-Limonene	177.8	165.5?	...	...	...	243
14847	$C_3H_6Cl_2O$	1,3-Dichloro-2-propanol	174.5	C_7H_7C	*α*-Chlorotoluene	179.35	$C_{10}H_{16}$	*d*-Limonene	177.8	165.5?	...	...	...	243
14848	$C_3H_6Cl_2O$	2,3-Dichloro-1-propanol	183	$C_8H_{18}O$	*sec*-Octyl alcohol	178.7	$C_{10}H_{16}$	*d*-Limonene	177.8			Nonazeotrope		243
14849	C_3H_6O	Acetone	56.25	C_4H_9Cl	1-Chloro-2-methylpropane	68.85	C_6H_{14}	Hexane	68.95			Nonazeotrope		243
14850	C_3H_6O	Acetone	56.4	C_7H_8	Toluene	110.4	C_7H_{14}	Methylcyclohexane	100.8			Liquid-vapor equilibrium		44
14851	C_3H_8O	Isopropyl alcohol	82.45	$C_4H_8O_2$	Ethyl acetate	77.05	C_6H_{12}	Cyclohexane	80.75	~68.3	...	...	...	243
14852	C_3H_8O	Propyl alcohol	97.2	$C_5H_{10}O$	3-Pentanone	102.2	$C_5H_{10}O_2$	Propyl acetate	101.55			Nonazeotrope		243
14853	C_3H_8O	Propyl alcohol	97.2	C_6H_6	Benzene	80.2	C_6H_{12}	Cyclohexane	80.75	< 74?	...	...	...	243

14854	$C_3H_8O_2$	Methylal	42.25	C_5H_{10}	2-Methyl-2-butene	37.15	C_5H_{12}	Pentane	36.15		Nonazeotrope			*243*
14855	$C_4H_6O_4$	Methyl oxalate	163.3	$C_5H_4O_2$	2-Furaldehyde	161.5	$C_{10}H_{16}$	α-Pinene	155.8		Nonazeotrope			*243*
14856	$C_4H_6O_4$	Methyl oxalate	163.3	C_6H_5Br	Bromobenzene	156.1	$C_6H_{12}O$	Cyclohexanol	160.65		Nonazeotrope			*243*
14857	$C_4H_6O_4$	Methyl oxalate	163.3	C_6H_5Br	Bromobenzene	156.1	$C_{10}H_{16}$	α-Pinene	155.8		Nonazeotrope			*243*
14858	$C_4H_6O_4$	Methyl oxalate	163.3	$C_6H_{12}O$	Cyclohexanol	160.65	C_9H_{12}	Mesitylene	164	< 154.5	...	...	...	*243*
14859	$C_4H_6O_4$	Methyl oxalate	163.3	$C_6H_{12}O$	Cyclohexanol	160.65	$C_{10}H_{16}$	*d*-Limonene	177.8		Reacts			*243*
14860	$C_4H_6O_4$	Methyl oxalate	163.3	C_9H_{12}	Mesitylene	164.0	$C_{10}H_{16}$	Nopinene	163.8		Nonazeotrope			*243*
14861	$C_4H_7BrO_2$	Ethyl bromoacetate	158.2	C_6H_5Br	Bromobenzene	156.1	$C_{10}H_{16}$	α-Pinene	155.8	< 152.3?	...	...	...	*243*
14862	$C_4H_7BrO_2$	Ethyl bromoacetate	158.2	$C_6H_{12}O$	Cyclohexanol	160.65	$C_{10}H_{16}$	α-Pinene	155.8		Nonazeotrope			*243*
14863	$C_4H_7BrO_2$	Ethyl bromoacetate	158.2	C_7H_8O	Anisole	153.85	$C_{10}H_{16}$	α-Pinene	155.8	< 150.4	...	...	...	*243*
14864	$C_4H_7ClO_2$	Ethyl chloroacetate	143.5	$C_4H_8O_3$	Methyl lactate	144.8	C_8H_{10}	*m*-Xylene	139.0		Nonazeotrope			*243*
14865	$C_4H_7ClO_2$	Ethyl chloroacetate	143.5	$C_7H_{14}O_2$	Propyl butyrate	143	C_8H_{10}	*m*-Xylene	139.0		Nonazeotrope			*243*
14866	C_4H_8O	2-Butanone	79.6	$C_4H_8O_2$	Propyl formate	80.8	C_6H_6	Benzene	80.2		Nonazeotrope			*243*
14867	C_4H_8O	2-Butanone	79.6	C_7H_8	Toluene	110.7	C_7H_{16}	*n*-Heptane	98.45		Nonazeotrope, V-l.			*379*
14868	$C_4H_8O_2$	Ethyl acetate	77.1	$C_4H_{10}O$	Butyl alcohol	117.7	C_7H_8	Toluene	110.7		Nonazeotrope			*261*
14869	$C_4H_8O_2$	Isobutyric acid	154.35	C_6H_5Br	Bromobenzene	156.1	$C_{10}H_{16}$	α-Pinene	155.8	146.4	...	...	...	*243*
14870	$C_4H_8O_2$	Isobutyric acid	154.35	C_7H_8O	Anisole	153.85	$C_{10}H_{16}$	α-Pinene	155.8	143.9	...	...	...	*243*
14871	$C_4H_{10}O$	Ethyl ether	34.6	C_5H_{10}	2-Methyl-2-butene	37.15	C_5H_{12}	Pentane	36.15		Nonazeotrope			*243*
14872	C_5H_5N	Pyridine	115.3	$C_5H_{11}N$	Piperidine	105.8	C_8H_{14}	Diisobutylene	102.5	98.6	...	...	...	*96*
14873	$C_5H_{10}O_2$	Isovaleric acid	176.5	C_7H_6O	Benzaldehyde	179.2	C_7H_7Cl	α-Chlorotoluene	179.35		Nonazeotrope			*243*
14874	$C_5H_{10}O_2$	Isovaleric acid	176.5	C_7H_6O	Benzaldehyde	179.2	$C_{10}H_{16}$	*d*-Limonene	177.8	168.7	...	...	...	*243*
14875	$C_5H_{10}O_2$	Isovaleric acid	176.5	C_7H_7Cl	α-Chlorotoluene	179.35	$C_{10}H_{14}$	Cymene	175.3	167.8?	...	...	...	*243*
14876	$C_5H_{10}O_2$	Isovaleric acid	176.5	C_7H_7Cl	α-Chlorotoluene	179.35	$C_{10}H_{16}$	*d*-Limonene	177.8	168.7?	...	...	...	*243*
14877	$C_5H_{10}O_2$	Isovaleric acid	176.5	C_7H_7Cl	α-Chlorotoluene	179.35	$C_{10}H_{18}O$	Cineole	176.3		Azeotropic ?			*243*
14878	C_6H_5Br	Bromobenzene	156.1	C_6H_6O	Phenol	181.5	$C_{10}H_{16}$	α-Pinene	155.8	152.6?	...	...	...	*243*
14879	C_6H_5Br	Bromobenzene	156.1	$C_6H_{12}O$	Cyclohexanol	160.65	$C_{10}H_{16}$	Camphene	~158	>153.4?	...	...	...	*243*
14880	C_6H_5Br	Bromobenzene	156.1	$C_6H_{12}O$	Cyclohexanol	160.65	$C_{10}H_{16}$	α-Pinene	155.8		Azeotropic ?			*243*
14881	C_6H_5Br	Bromobenzene	156.1	$C_6H_{13}ClO_2$	Chloroacetal	156.8	$C_{10}H_{16}$	α-Pinene	155.8		Nonazeotrope			*243*
14882	C_6H_5ClO	α-Chlorophenol	175.5	C_7H_7Br	*o*-Bromotoluene	181.75	$C_{10}H_{16}$	*d*-Limonene	177.8		Nonazeotrope			*243*
14883	$C_6H_5NO_2$	Nitrobenzene	210.85	C_7H_8O	Benzy alcohol	205.5	$C_{11}H_{24}O_2$	Diisoamyloxymethane	207.5	197?	...	...	...	*243*

	A-Component			B-Component			C-Component			Azeotropic Data				
No.	Formula	Name	B.P., ° C.	Formula	Name	B.P., ° C.	Formula	Name	B.P., ° C.	B.P., ° C.	Wt. % A	Wt. % B	Wt. % C	Ref.
14884	C_6H_6O	Phenol	181.5	C_7H_7Br	*o*-Bromotoluene	181.75	$C_{10}H_{16}$	*d*-Limonene	177.8		Nonazeotrope			*243*
14885	C_6H_7N	Aniline	184.35	$C_6H_{10}O_4$	Ethyl oxalate	178.6	C_7H_7Br	*o*-Bromotoluene	181.75		Reacts			*243*
14886	C_6H_7N	Aniline	184.35	$C_6H_{10}O_4$	Ethyl oxalate	185	C_7H_7Br	*p*-Bromotoluene	185		Reacts			*243*
14887	C_6H_7N	Aniline	184.35	$C_6H_{10}O_4$	Ethyl oxalate	185	$C_{10}H_{16}$	*d*-Limonene	177.8		Reacts			*243*
14888	C_6H_7N	Aniline	184.35	$C_6H_{10}O_4$	Ethyl oxalate	185	$C_{10}H_{16}$	Terpinene	180.5		Reacts			*243*
14889	C_6H_7N	Aniline	184.35	C_7H_7Br	*o*-Bromotoluene	181.75	$C_8H_{18}O$	*sec*-Octyl alcohol	178.7		Nonazeotrope			*243*
14890	C_6H_7N	Aniline	184.35	C_7H_7Br	*o*-Bromotoluene	181.75	$C_{10}H_{16}$	*d*-Limonene	177.8		Nonazeotrope			*243*
14891	C_6H_7N	Aniline	184.35	C_7H_8O	Benzyl alcohol	205.5	$C_{10}H_{16}$	*d*-Limonene	177.8		Nonazeotrope			*243*
14892	C_6H_7N	Aniline	184.35	$C_8H_{18}O$	*sec*-Octyl alcohol	178.7	$C_{10}H_{16}$	*d*-Limonene	177.8		Nonazeotrope			*243*
14893	$C_6H_{10}O$	Cyclohexanone	156.7	C_7H_8O	Anisole	153.85	$C_{10}H_{16}$	α-Pinene	155.8		Nonazeotrope ?			*243*
14894	$C_6H_{10}O_3$	Ethyl aceto-acetate	180.7	C_7H_7Br	*o*-Bromotoluene	181.75	$C_{10}H_{16}$	*d*-Limonene	177.8		Nonazeotrope			*243*
14895	$C_6H_{10}O_3$	Ethyl aceto-acetate	180.7	C_7H_7Cl	α-Chlorotoluene	179.35	$C_{10}H_{16}$	*d*-Limonene	177.8	168.8?	...	...	...	*243*
14896	$C_6H_{10}O_3$	Ethyl aceto-acetate	180.7	C_9H_{12}	Mesitylene	164.0	$C_{10}H_{16}$	Nopinene	163.8		Nonazeotrope			*243*
14897	$C_6H_{10}O_4$	Ethyl oxalate	185	C_7H_7Br	*o*-Bromotoluene	181.75	$C_{10}H_{16}$	*d*-Limonene	177.8		Nonazeotrope			*243*
14898	$C_6H_{12}O$	Cyclohexanol	160.65	C_7H_8O	Anisole	153.85	$C_{10}H_{16}$	α-Pinene	155.8		Nonazeotrope			*243*
14899	$C_6H_{12}O_3$	Propyl lactate	171.7	C_7H_7Cl	α-Chlorotoluene	179.35	$C_{10}H_{16}$	*d*-Limonene	177.8		Nonazeotrope			*243*
14900	$C_6H_{12}O_3$	Propyl lactate	171.7	$C_8H_{10}O$	Phenetole	171.5	$C_{10}H_{18}$	Menthene	170.8	163.0	31	33	36	*243*
14901	C_7H_6O	Benzaldehyde	179.2	C_7H_7Cl	α-Chlorotoluene	179.35	$C_{10}H_{16}$	*d*-Limonene	177.8		Nonazeotrope			*243*
14902	C_7H_6O	Benzaldehyde	179.2	C_7H_7Cl	α-Chlorotoluene	179.35	$C_{10}H_{16}$	Terpinene	180.5		Nonazeotrope			*243*
14903	C_7H_7Cl	α-Chlorotoluene	179.35	$C_7H_{14}O_3$	Isobutyl lactate	182.15	$C_{10}H_{16}$	*d*-Limonene	177.8	172.5	...	...	...	*243*
14904	C_7H_7Cl	α-Chlorotoluene	179.35	$C_7H_{14}O_3$	Isobutyl lactate	182.15	$C_{10}H_{16}$	Terpinene	180.5		Azeotrope doubtful			*243*
14905	C_7H_7Cl	α-Chlorotoluene	179.35	$C_8H_{18}O$	*sec*-Octyl alcohol	178.7	$C_{10}H_{16}$	*d*-Limonene	177.8		Azeotropic ?			*243*
14906	C_7H_8	Toluene	110.4	C_7H_{14}	Methylcyclo-hexane	100.8	C_7H_{16}	*n*-Heptane	98.4		Liquid-vapor equilibrium			*43*
14907	$C_7H_{14}O_3$	Isobutyl lactate	182.15	$C_8H_{18}O$	*sec*-Octyl alcohol	178.7	$C_{10}H_{16}$	*d*-Limonene	177.8		Reacts			*243*
14908	$C_7H_{14}O_3$	Isobutyl lactate	182.15	$C_8H_{18}O$	*sec*-Octyl alcohol	178.7	$C_{10}H_{16}$	Terpinene	180.5		Nonazeotrope			*243*

TABLE III. FORMULA INDEX

The following index lists all compounds appearing in the azeotropic tables, together with the numbers of the systems in which each compound appears.

Formula	Name and System Nos.
A	Argon. B.p., −186 1
$AgCl$	Silver chloride. B.p., 1550 2
BCl_3	Boron chloride. B.p., 11.5 3, 14502
BF_3	Boron fluoride. B.p., −100 4–33
B_2H_6	Boron hydride. B.p., −92.5 3, 4, 31–33, 14502
BrH	Hydrobromic acid. B.p., −73 31, 34–36, 14503, 14504
Br_2	Bromine. B.p., 58.75 37, 38
Br_4Sn	Tin bromide. B.p., 206.7 39–41
C	Graphite. B.p., 2300/0.01 mm. 42
CCl_2O	Phosgene. B.p., 8.2 43, 44
CF_2O	Carbonyl fluoride. 45
CF_4O	Trifluoromethyl hypofluorite. B.p., −94.2 45
CO_2	Carbon dioxide. B.p., −79.1 46–54
ClH	Hydrochloric acid. B.p., −80 32, 46, 55–59, 14502, 14504, 14505
$ClHO_4$	Perchloric acid. B.p., 110 60
Cl_2	Chlorine. B.p., −37.6 47, 61, 62
Cl_2Cu	Cupric chloride. 63, 64
Cl_2O_2S	Thionyl chloride. B.p., 70.5 65
Cl_2Pb	Lead chloride. B.p., 954 2, 63, 66
Cl_2Zn	Zinc chloride. B.p., 732 64
Cl_3OP	Phosphorus oxychloride. B.p., 107.2 65
Cl_3Sb	Antimony trichloride. 67, 68
Cl_4Si	Silicon chloride. B.p., 56.7 69–80
Cl_4Sn	Tin chloride. B.p., 113.85 81–93
Cl_4Ti	Titanium chloride. B.p., 136 69, 81, 94
Cu	Copper. B.p., 2310 95, 96
FH	Hydrofluoric acid. B.p., 19.54 43, 97–102, 14506–14508
F_3Sb	Antimony fluoride. B.p., 319 103
F_5Sb	Antimony pentafluoride. B.p., 155 103
F_6H_2Si	Fluosilicic acid. 14507
HI	Hydriodic acid. B.p., −34 104, 105

Formula	Name and System Nos.
CH_2O_2	Formic acid. B.p., 100.75 7, 120, 526, 589, 665, 775, 835, 920, 1087–1193, 14530
CH_3Br	Bromomethane. B.p., 3.65 1194–1201
CH_3Cl	Chloromethane. B.p., −23.7 51, 1202, 1203
CH_3I	Iodomethane. B.p., 42.55 666, 921, 1030, 1087, 1204–1227, 14763–14765, 14787, 14788
CH_3NO_2	Methyl nitrite. B.p., −16 1228–1232
CH_3NO_2	Nitromethane. B.p., 101 72, 121, 527, 590, 667, 776, 922, 1088, 1233–1341, 14531–14533, 14789, 14790
CH_3NO_3	Methyl nitrate. B.p., 64.8 122, 591, 668, 777, 1031, 1204, 1342–1371
CH_4	Methane. B.p., −164 500
CH_4O	Methanol. B.p., 64.7 8, 123, 528, 592, 669, 778, 923, 989, 992, 993, 1032, 1194, 1205, 1233, 1342, 1372–1550, 14517, 14534–14547, 14755, 14763, 14766–14771, 14782, 14783, 14786, 14787, 14791–14844
CH_4S	Methanethiol. B.p., 6.8 502, 1555–1559
CH_5N	Methylamine. B.p., −6 124, 582, 1560–1574
$C_2Br_2Cl_2$	1,2-Dibromo-1,2-dichloroethylene. B.p., 172 1575, 1576
C_2Cl_3N	Trichloroacetonitrile. 1577
C_2Cl_4	Tetrachloroethylene. B.p., 121.1 529, 593, 1023, 1089, 1234, 1372, 1578–1652, 14548, 14549, 14805–14812
C_2Cl_6	Hexachloroethane. B.p., 184.8 670, 1653–1694
C_2HBrCl_2	*cis*-1-Bromo-1,2-dichloroethylene. B.p., 113.8 1695
C_2HBrCl_2	*trans*-1-Bromo-1,2-dichloroethylene. 1696
C_2HBrCl_2	1-Bromo-2,2-dichloroethylene. B.p., 107 1697
C_2HBr_2Cl	1,2-Dibromo-1-chloroethylene. B.p., 140 1698, 1699
C_2HBr_3O	Bromal. B.p., 174 1700
C_2HClF_4	Chlorotetrafluoroethane. B.p., −10 1701
C_2HCl_3	Trichloroethylene. B.p., 86.2 125, 779, 780, 1090, 1235, 1236, 1373, 1702–1756, 14550–14556
C_2HCl_3O	Chloral. B.p., 97.75 126, 781, 1237, 1578, 1757–1791
$C_2HCl_3O_2$	Trichloroacetic acid. B.p., 196 1653, 1792–1816
C_2HCl_5	Pentachloroethane. B.p., 162.0 127, 1091, 1792, 1817–1912
C_2H_2	Acetylene. B.p., −84 1913, 1914
C_2H_2BrCl	*cis*-1-Bromo-2-chloroethylene. B.p., 106.7 1374, 1915–1918
C_2H_2BrCl	*trans*-1-Bromo-2-chloroethylene. B.p., 75.3 1920
C_2H_2BrI	*cis*-1-Bromo-2-iodoethylene. B.p., 149.05 1921–1924
$C_2H_2Br_2$	*cis*-1,2-Dibromoethylene. B.p., 112.5 1375, 1925
$C_2H_2Br_2$	*trans*-1,2-Dibromoethylene. B.p., 108 1376, 1926
C_2H_2ClI	*cis*-1-Chloro-2-iodoethylene. B.p., 116 1927
C_2H_2ClI	*trans*-1-Chloro-2-iodoethylene. B.p., 113 1929
$C_2H_2Cl_2$	1,1-Dichloroethylene. B.p., 31 1378

Formula	Name and System Nos.
$C_2H_2Cl_2$	*cis*-1,2-Dichloroethylene. B.p., 60.2 128, 1379, 1930, 1931, 14557
$C_2H_2Cl_2$	*trans*-1,2-Dichloroethylene. B.p., 48.35 129, 1932, 14558
$C_2H_2Cl_2O_2$	Dichloroacetic acid. B.p., 190 1933–1940
$C_2H_2Cl_4$	1,1,2,2-Tetrachloroethane. B.p., 146.2 836, 1092, 1941–2018, 14559
C_2H_3Br	Bromoethylene. B.p., 15.8 671, 1093, 1380, 2019–2027
$C_2H_3BrO_2$	Bromoacetic acid. B.p., 205.1 837, 1817, 2028–2052
C_2H_3Cl	Chloroethylene. B.p., −13.6 2053, 2054
$C_2H_3ClO_2$	Chloroacetic acid. B.p., 189.35 838, 1654, 1793, 1818, 1941, 1942, 2055–2141, 14813, 14814
$C_2H_3Cl_3$	1,1,1-Trichloroethane. 1381
$C_2H_3Cl_3$	1,1,2-Trichloroethane. B.p., 113.65 1382, 1579, 2142–2155
$C_2H_3Cl_3O$	Methyl trichloromethyl ether. B.p., 131.2 2156–2161
$C_2H_3Cl_3O_2$	Chloral hydrate. B.p., 97.5 594, 924, 2162–2165
C_2H_3N	Acetonitrile. B.p., 81.6 9, 73, 130, 595, 1033, 1384, 1577, 1702, 2166–2210, 14510, 14518, 14526, 14548, 14550, 14559–14565
C_2H_3NS	Methyl thiocyanate. B.p., 132.5 2212
C_2H_4	Ethylene. B.p., −103.9 503, 1913, 2213
C_2H_4BrCl	1-Bromo-2-chloroethane. B.p., 106.7 1385, 2214–2225
$C_2H_4Br_2$	1,1-Dibromoethane. B.p., 109.5 1386, 2226–2250
$C_2H_4Br_2$	1,2-Dibromoethane. B.p., 131.5 596, 839, 1094, 1388, 2055, 2251–2327, 14756, 14815–14818
$C_2H_4Cl_2$	1,1-Dichloroethane. B.p., 57.4 74, 597, 672, 925, 1095, 1389, 2328–2365
$C_2H_4Cl_2$	1,2-Dichloroethane. B.p., 83.45 44, 75, 131, 598, 926, 1096, 1343, 1390, 1703, 1704, 1757, 2251, 2328, 2366–2413, 14566, 14567
$C_2H_4Cl_2O$	Bis(chloromethyl) ether. B.p., 106 132, 673, 927, 2414–2423
$C_2H_4Cl_2O$	2,2-Dichloroethanol. B.p., 146.2 840, 1580, 1943, 2424–2448
$C_2H_4F_2$	1,1-Difluoroethane. 523
C_2H_4O	Acetaldehyde. B.p., 20.2 133, 1034, 1195, 1391, 2449–2463
C_2H_4O	Ethylene oxide. B.p., 10 134, 1392, 2366, 2449, 2464–2479
C_2H_4OS	Thioacetic acid. B.p., 89.5 2480–2482
$C_2H_4O_2$	Acetic acid. B.p., 118.1 10, 135, 530, 599, 674, 782, 841, 928, 994, 1060, 1097, 1238, 1581, 1705, 1819, 1921, 1944, 2142, 2214, 2226, 2252, 2367, 2483–2622, 14568–14570, 14805, 14815, 14819
$C_2H_4O_2$	Methyl formate. B.p., 31.9 11, 136, 675, 929, 990, 1035, 1196, 1206, 1393, 1555, 1794, 1933, 2019, 2056, 2450, 2464, 2623–2667, 14764, 14772–14774, 14788, 14820–14827
C_2H_4S	Ethylene sulfide. B.p., 55.7 1239, 1394, 2623, 2668–2677
C_2H_5Br	Bromoethane. B.p., 38.4 137, 600, 676, 930, 1036, 1098, 1344, 1395, 2451, 2624, 2668, 2678–2713, 14571, 14766, 14791, 14792, 14820, 14821, 14822, 14823
C_2H_5BrO	2-Bromoethanol. B.p., 150.2 783, 1582, 1706, 1945, 2253, 2714–2744
C_2H_5BrO	Bromomethyl methyl ether. B.p., 87.5 2745, 2746

Formula	Name and System Nos.
C_2H_5Cl	Chloroethane. B.p., 12.4 52, 677, 931, 1099, 1396, 1556, 2020, 2452, 2625, 2747–2754
C_2H_5ClO	2-Chloroethanol. B.p., 127 12, 138, 531, 784, 842, 995, 1240, 1583, 1707, 1708, 1820, 1946, 2227, 2254, 2368, 2755–2868, 14551, 14566, 14572, 14573
C_2H_5ClO	Chloromethyl methyl ether. B.p., 59.5 601, 678, 1037, 1100, 1397, 2329, 2626, 2669, 2678, 2869–2897
C_2H_5I	Iodoethane. B.p., 70 139, 602, 679, 932, 1101, 1241, 1345, 1398, 2166, 2483, 2679, 2898–2927, 14574, 14793, 14794, 14828
C_2H_5IO	2-Iodoethanol. B.p., 176.5 140, 1947, 2928–2941
C_2H_5NO	Acetamide. B.p., 221.2 141, 843, 844, 1399, 1584, 1655, 1821, 1948, 2143, 2228, 2255, 2484, 2755, 2942–3225
$C_2H_5NO_2$	Ethyl nitrite. B.p., 17.4 680, 991, 1197, 1557, 2021, 2627, 2680, 2747, 3226–3239
$C_2H_5NO_2$	Nitroethane. B.p., 114.2 681, 785, 1102, 1400, 1758, 2485, 2756, 3240–3272
$C_2H_5NO_3$	Ethyl nitrate. B.p., 87.68 142, 603, 682, 786, 996, 1242, 1401, 1709, 2369, 2486, 3240, 3273–3316
C_2H_6	Ethane. B.p., −88 33, 53, 57, 501, 504, 1402, 1914, 2213, 3317–3321
$C_2H_6Cl_2Si$	Dichlorodimethylsilane. 3322, 3323
C_2H_6O	Ethyl alcohol. 13, 143, 532, 604, 683, 787, 933, 997, 1038, 1207, 1243, 1346, 1403, 1575, 1585, 1695–1698, 1710, 1759, 1915, 1920, 1925, 1926, 1930, 1932, 2022, 2144, 2167, 2215, 2229, 2256, 2330, 2370, 2453, 2628, 2681, 2748, 2869, 2898, 3241, 3273, 3317, 3324–3512, 14506, 14511, 14519, 14522, 14527, 14529, 14552, 14557, 14558, 14567, 14571, 14574–14608, 14757–14759, 14775, 14776, 14784, 14828–14836
C_2H_6O	Methyl ether. B.p., −23.65 14, 54, 58, 483, 505, 1202, 1711, 3513, 14750
$C_2H_6O_2$	Glycol. B.p., 197.4 144, 788, 845, 1061, 1244, 1586, 1656, 1822, 1949, 2145, 2216, 2230, 2257, 2757, 2942, 3514–3795, 14609, 14837
C_2H_6S	Ethanethiol. B.p., 36.2 1039, 1245, 1404, 2629, 2682, 2870, 3796–3809, 14824
C_2H_6S	Methyl sulfide. B.p., 37.4 684, 1103, 1246, 1405, 2487, 2630, 2683, 2871, 3226, 3324, 3796, 3810–3827
$C_2H_6SO_4$	Methyl sulfate. B.p., 189.1 145, 1657, 1823, 2057, 3828–3848
C_2H_7N	Dimethylamine. B.p., 7.3 146, 484, 1560, 3849–3851
C_2H_7N	Ethylamine. B.p., 16.55 147, 3852–3858
C_2H_7NO	2-Aminoethanol. B.p., 170.8 846, 1062, 1247, 2943, 3514, 3859–3934
$C_2H_8N_2$	Ethylenediamine. B.p., 116 148, 3936–3940
$C_3H_3Cl_3O_2$	Methyl trichloroacetate. B.p., 152.8 3942–3948
C_3H_3N	Acrylonitrile. B.p., 79 76, 149, 605, 1405, 3949–3951
C_3H_4	Propyne. B.p., −23 485, 3952
$C_3H_4Br_2$	*cis*-1,2-Dibromopropene. B.p., 135.2 3953
$C_3H_4Br_2$	*trans*-1,2-Dibromopropene. B.p., 125.95 3954
$C_3H_4Cl_2$	1,2-Dichloro-1-propene. B.p., 76.8 1407
$C_3H_4Cl_4$	1,1,2,2-Tetrachloropropane. B.p., 153 3956–3959
$C_3H_4Cl_4$	1,1,2,2-Tetrachloropropane. B.p., 180 3960, 3961
C_3H_4O	Acrolein. B.p., 52.45 685, 1408, 3962–3965
C_3H_4O	2-Propyn-1-ol. 150, 3966, 14610

Formula	Name and System Nos.
$C_3H_4O_2$	Acrylic acid. B.p., 140.5 3967, 3968
$C_3H_4O_3$	Pyruvic acid (acetyl formic acid). B.p., 166.8 3969–3986
$C_3H_4N_2$	Pyrazole (1,2-diazole). B.p., 187.5 3987–3993
C_3H_5Br	*trans*-1-Bromopropene. B.p., 63.25 1409, 3325, 14576
C_3H_5Br	*cis*-1-Bromopropene. B.p., 57.8 1410, 3326, 14575
C_3H_5Br	2-Bromopropene. B.p., 48.35 1411, 3327, 14577
C_3H_5Br	3-Bromopropene. B.p., 70.5 686, 1104, 1248, 1347, 1412, 2488, 2872, 2899, 3274, 3328, 3994–4013
C_3H_5BrO	Epibromohydrin. B.p., 138.5 1587, 2258, 2489, 4014–4029
$C_3H_5BrO_2$	α-Bromopropionic acid. B.p., 205.8 1824, 4030–4040
$C_3H_5Br_3$	1,2,3-Tribromopropane. B.p., 220 2944, 4041–4060
C_3H_5Cl	*cis*-1-Chloropropene. B.p., 32.8 3329
C_3H_5Cl	*trans*-1-Chloropropene. B.p., 37.4 3330
C_3H_5Cl	2-Chloropropene. B.p., 22.65 1105, 1413, 2631, 3227, 3331, 4061–4067
C_3H_5Cl	3-Chloropropene. B.p., 45.15 687, 1106, 1348, 1414, 2632, 3332, 3873, 3955, 4061, 4068–4080
C_3H_5ClO	1-Chloro-2-propanone. B.p., 121 151, 1107, 1588, 4081–4111
C_3H_5ClO	α-Chloropropionaldehyde. B.p., 86 152
C_3H_5ClO	Epichlorohydrin. B.p., 116.45 82, 153, 533, 606, 1108, 1415, 1589, 2217, 2490, 3333, 4112–4169, 14805–14810, 14819, 14838–14840
$C_3H_5ClO_2$	Methyl chloroacetate. B.p., 131.4 154, 847, 1416, 1590, 1950, 2259, 2491, 2758, 4170–4222, 14534
$C_3H_5Cl_3$	1,1,3-Trichloropropane. B.p., 148 4223, 4224
$C_3H_5Cl_3$	1,2,2-Trichloropropane. B.p., 122 4225–4230
$C_3H_5Cl_3$	1,2,3-Trichloropropane. B.p., 156.85 2058, 2492, 2945, 3515, 4231–4267
C_3H_5I	3-Iodopropene. B.p., 102.0 155, 534, 1109, 1249, 1417, 1760, 2393, 2759, 3275, 3334, 3516, 4268–4296, 14578, 14611, 14612, 14841–14843
C_3H_5N	Propionitrile. B.p., 97 77, 156, 1418, 3335, 4297–4319
$C_3H_5N_3O_9$	Nitroglycerin. 4320
C_3H_6	Cyclopropane. B.p., −31.5 486
C_3H_6	Propene. B.p., −48 487, 506
$C_3H_6Br_2$	1,2-Dibromopropane. B.p., 141 2260, 2494, 2714, 2760, 2928, 2946, 3517, 4112, 4170, 4321–4360
$C_3H_6Br_2$	1,3-Dibromopropane. B.p., 166.9 2424, 2495, 2761, 2947, 3517, 4361–4404
$C_3H_6Br_2O$	2,3-Dibromo-1-propanol. B.p., 219.5 4405–4424
$C_3H_6Cl_2$	1,1-Dichloropropane. B.p., 90 4425, 4426
$C_3H_6Cl_2$	1,2-Dichloropropane. B.p., 97 157, 1419, 3336, 4427–4432
$C_3H_6Cl_2$	1,3-Dichloropropane. B.p., 120.8
$C_3H_6Cl_2$	2,2-Dichloropropane. B.p., 70.4 1110, 1420, 2414, 2496, 3276, 3337, 4436–4452
$C_3H_6Cl_2O$	1,3-Dichloro-2-propanol. B.p., 175.8 848, 1825, 1951, 2948, 3519, 4453–4526, 14843–14847

Formula	Name and System Nos.
C_4H_4S	Thiophene. B.p., 84 187, 617, 1120, 1354, 1442, 1721, 2378, 2909, 3284, 3358, 4594, 4936, 5503, 5913, 5991–6008
$C_4H_5ClO_2$	α-Chlorocrotonic acid. B.p., 212.5 6009, 6010
$C_4H_5Cl_3O$	α,α,β-Trichlorobutyraldehyde. B.p., 164 4233
$C_4H_5Cl_3O_2$	Ethyl trichloroacetate. B.p., 167.2 6011–6016
C_4H_5N	*cis*- and *trans*-Crotonitrile. B.p., 107.5–120.5 188
C_4H_5N	Pyrrole. B.p., 129.8 189, 1601, 2157, 2235, 2272, 2417, 3525, 4118, 4325, 5692, 5790, 6017–6047
C_4H_5NS	Allyl isothiocyanate. B.p., 152.05 709, 1443, 2954, 3526, 5107, 5791, 6048–6058
C_4H_6	1,3-Butadiene. B.p., −4.5 491, 1199, 1228, 1563, 1564, 2053, 2457, 2466, 3359, 5969, 6059–6062
C_4H_6	1-Butyne. B.p., 7 492, 6063, 6064
$C_4H_6Cl_2O_2$	Ethyl dichloroacetate. B.p., 158.1 4782, 6065–6076
C_4H_6O	3-Butyn-1-ol. B.p., 128.9 190
C_4H_6O	Crotonaldehyde. B.p., 102.15 1121, 1263, 1444, 2505, 3360, 5064, 5592, 6077–6087, 14667, 14668
$C_4H_6O_2$	Allyl formate. B.p., 80.0 618, 2379, 2910, 3361, 6088–6091
$C_4H_6O_2$	Biacetyl. B.p., 87–88 191, 710, 1445, 2506, 3362, 5504, 5593, 6092–6094, 14580
$C_4H_6O_2$	Crotonic acid. B.p., 189 22
$C_4H_6O_2$	Methylacrylate. B.p., 80 192, 1446, 3363, 5506, 5594, 6095–6097
$C_4H_6O_2$	Methacrylic acid. 6098
$C_4H_6O_3$	Acetic anhydride. B.p., 138 6099-6107
$C_4H_6O_3$	Methyl pyruvate. B.p., 137.5 2507, 4783, 6108–6132
$C_4H_6O_4$	Methyl oxalate. B.p., 164.45 856, 1659, 1829, 1958, 2060, 2955, 3527, 4234, 4454, 4528, 5108, 5304, 6133–6205, 14844, 14855–14860
C_4H_7Br	*trans*-1-Bromo-1-butene. B.p., 94.70 3364
C_4H_7Br	*cis*-1-Bromo-1-butene. B.p., 86.15 3365
C_4H_7Br	2-Bromo-1-butene. B.p., 81.0 3366
C_4H_7Br	*cis*-2-Bromo-2-butene. B.p., 93.9 3367
C_4H_7Br	*trans*-2-Bromo-2-butene. B.p., 85.55 3368
$C_4H_7BrO_2$	Ethyl bromoacetate. B.p., 158.2 857, 1830, 1959, 2956, 3528, 4326, 4364, 4784, 5109, 6206–6258, 14861–14863
C_4H_7Cl	*trans*-1-Chloro-1-butene. B.p., 68 3369
C_4H_7Cl	*cis*-1-Chloro-1-butene. B.p., 63.4 3370
C_4H_7Cl	2-Chloro-1-butene. B.p., 58.4 3371
C_4H_7Cl	*trans*-2-Chloro-2-butene. B.p., 66.6 3372
C_4H_7Cl	*cis*-2-Chloro-2-butene. B.p., 62.4 3373
C_4H_7Cl	1-Chloro-2-methyl-1-propene. B.p., 68.1 193
C_4H_7ClO	α-3-Chloro-2-butene-1-ol. B.p., 164 194
C_4H_7ClO	β-3-Chloro-2-butene-1-ol. B.p., 166 195

Formula	Name and System Nos.
C_4H_7ClO	2-Chloroethyl vinyl ether. B.p., 108 6259
$C_4H_7ClO_2$	4-Chloromethyl-1,3-dioxolane. B.p., 66/40 196
$C_4H_7ClO_2$	Ethyl chloroacetate. B.p., 143.5 197, 858, 1831, 1960, 2273, 2716, 2766, 2957, 3374, 3529, 4235, 4655, 4785, 5595, 5693, 6133, 6260–6307, 14581, 14864, 14865
$C_4H_7Cl_3O$	Ethyl-1,1,2-trichloroethyl ether. B.p., 172.5 859, 4365, 5305, 6308–6321
C_4H_7N	Butyronitrile. B.p., 118 198, 5596, 6327–6329
C_4H_7N	Isobutyronitrile. B.p., 103 199, 4275, 5507, 5597, 6330, 6335
C_4H_7N	Pyrroline (2,3-dihydropyrrol). B.p., 90.9 711, 1447, 5598, 5991, 6336
C_4H_8	1-Butene. B.p., −6 493, 508, 1200, 1229, 1565, 1566, 2054, 2467, 2640, 5970, 6059, 6337, 14751
C_4H_8	2-Butene. B.p., 1–3.7 510, 511, 1567, 1568, 2468, 2469, 2642, 2648, 5971, 5972, 5977, 6060, 6063, 6064
C_4H_8	2-Methylpropene. B.p., −6 494, 509, 1230, 1569, 2470, 2643, 5973, 6337, 14752
$C_4H_8Br_2O$	Bis(2-bromoethyl) ether. 3530, 5792
$C_4H_8Cl_2O$	Bis(2-chloroethyl) ether. B.p., 178.65 860, 2767, 2959, 3531, 3532, 3861, 3987, 4366, 5110, 5306, 6338–6381, 14572
$C_4H_8Cl_2O$	1,2-Dichloroethyl ether ether. B.p., 145.5 861, 2212, 2508, 2958, 5599, 6048, 6382–6410
$C_4H_8Cl_2O$	1,3-Dichloro-2-methyl-2-propanol. B.p., 172 200
$C_4H_8Cl_2S$	Bis(2-chloroethyl) sulfide. B.p., 216.8 3533, 6411–6419
C_4H_8O	2-Butanone. B.p., 79.6 201, 619, 712, 797, 950, 1122, 1264, 1448, 1722, 1764, 2343, 2380, 2509, 2673, 2884, 2911, 3285, 3376, 3817, 4002, 4595, 4656, 4760, 4786, 4885, 4939, 4969, 5051, 5086, 5508, 5600, 5914, 5940, 5962, 5992, 6420–6460, 14515, 14633, 14648, 14670–14679, 14757, 14760, 14761, 14775, 14829–14832, 14866, 14867
C_4H_8O	1-Butene-3-ol. B.p., 96 202, 6461
C_4H_8O	Butyraldehyde. B.p., 74 203, 713, 951, 4596, 4761, 4937, 4970, 5941, 5993, 6462–6465, 6420, 14680
C_4H_8O	Crotonyl alcohol. B.p., 119 204
C_4H_8O	Cyclopropyl methyl ether. B.p., 44.73 4707
C_4H_8O	Ethyl vinyl ether. B.p., 35.5 3377
C_4H_8O	Isobutylene oxide. B.p., 50 953, 1050, 2344
C_4H_8O	Isobutyraldehyde. B.p., 63.5 620, 714, 952, 1449, 2345, 3378, 3963, 4597, 4734, 4762, 4938, 4971, 6421, 6466–6468, 14681
C_4H_8O	2-Methyl-2-propen-1-ol. B.p., 113.8 6469
C_4H_8O	Tetrahydrofuran. B.p., 65 6470
C_4H_8OS	Ethyl thioacetate. B.p., 116.6 3379, 3434, 4657, 5509, 5601, 6471–6476
$C_4H_8O_2$	Butyric acid. B.p., 162.45 23, 205, 621, 715, 862, 1065, 1602, 1603, 1660, 1723, 1832, 1961, 2148, 2236, 2274, 2381 2510, 2644, 2696, 3970, 4236, 4327, 4367, 4428, 6011, 6065, 6134, 6206, 6260, 6338, 6477–6572
$C_4H_8O_2$	1,2-Dimethoxyethylene. B.p., 102 1450
$C_4H_8O_2$	Dioxane. B.p., 101.32 206, 543, 622, 954, 1123, 1265, 1451, 1604, 1724, 2149, 2382, 2511, 2768, 3246, 3286, 3380, 3535, 4276, 4429, 4598, 4658, 4787, 4886, 5065, 5087, 5482, 5510, 5602, 5694, 6259, 6422, 6573–6611, 14521, 14609
$C_4H_8O_2$	*m*-Dioxane. B.p., 104 207, 6612

Formula	Name and System Nos.
$C_4H_8O_2$	Ethyl acetate. B.p., 77.05 24, 208, 623, 716, 798, 955, 1216, 1266, 1452, 1725, 2162, 2175, 2383, 2697, 2885, 2912, 3381, 4003, 4301, 4940, 4441, 4599, 4659, 4887, 4942, 4972, 4992, 5511, 5603, 5942, 5994, 6423, 6613–6646, 14561, 14584, 14758, 14762, 14776, 14779, 14801, 14794, 14827, 14828, 14833, 14868
$C_4H_8O_2$	Isobutyric acid. B.p., 154.35 209, 544, 717, 863, 1066, 1605, 1833, 1962, 2275, 3944, 4017, 4237, 4328, 4368, 6012, 6066, 6108, 6135, 6207, 6261, 6573, 6647–6719, 14869, 14870
$C_4H_8O_2$	Isopropyl formate. B.p., 68.8 210, 624, 718, 956, 1453, 2886, 2913, 4600, 4763, 4942, 5943, 6424, 6613, 6720–6725
$C_4H_8O_2$	Methyl propionate. B.p., 79.85 211, 625, 719, 799, 957, 1267, 1454, 1726, 2176, 2914, 3382, 4302, 4442, 4660, 4943, 5088, 5512, 5604, 5995, 6425, 6614, 6726–6747, 14760, 14830
$C_4H_8O_2$	Propyl formate. B.p., 80.9 212, 626, 720, 800, 958, 1268, 1455, 1727, 1765, 2177, 2384, 2512, 2915, 3383, 4004, 4303, 4443, 4661, 4944, 5089, 5513, 5605, 5996, 6426, 6462, 6615, 6726, 6748–6777, 14649, 14866
$C_4H_8O_3$	Glycol monoacetate. B.p., 190.9 2960, 3536, 5111, 6136, 6339, 6778–6825
$C_4H_8O_3$	Methyl lactate. B.p., 144.8 213, 864, 1606, 1834, 1963, 2276, 4176, 4238, 5695, 6208, 6262, 6826–6884, 14864
C_4H_8S	Thiophane. B.p., 118.8 545, 1124, 1456, 2518, 2768, 4119, 5483, 5514, 5607, 6885–6896
C_4H_9Br	1-Bromobutane. B.p., 101.5 546, 1004, 1125, 1269, 1457, 1766, 2178, 2426, 2514, 2717, 2769, 3247, 3287, 3384, 3537, 4018, 4120, 4662, 4788, 4888, 5484, 5608, 6574, 6897–6928
C_4H_9Br	2-Bromobutane. B.p., 91.2 801, 1458, 2515, 3288, 3385, 4889, 5515, 5609, 6427, 6727, 6748, 6929–6937
C_4H_9Br	1-Bromo-2-methylpropane. B.p., 91.4 802, 1126, 1270, 1459, 1767, 2179, 2516, 2718, 2770, 3248, 3289, 3386, 3538, 4304, 4601, 4663, 5485, 5516, 5610, 6077, 6428, 6575, 6616, 6728, 6749, 6929, 6938–6965, 8890, 14585
C_4H_9Br	2-Bromo-2-methylpropane. B.p., 73.3 627, 721, 1127, 1271, 1355, 1460, 2517, 2916, 3290, 3387, 4891, 5517, 5611, 5944, 6429, 6617, 6729, 6750, 6966–6975
C_4H_9Cl	1-Chlorobutane. B.p., 77.9 214, 722, 1128, 1272, 1356, 1461, 1768, 2180, 2518, 2887, 3249, 3291, 3388, 4121, 4602, 4664, 4892, 5518, 5612, 5945, 5997, 6088, 6430, 6618, 6730, 6751, 6897, 6976–6997
C_4H_9Cl	2-Chlorobutane. B.p., 68.25 723, 1357, 1462, 2519, 3389, 4603, 4764, 5519, 5613, 5946, 6431, 6619, 6752, 6998–7004
C_4H_9Cl	1-Chloro-2-methylpropane. B.p., 68.8 215, 724, 1129, 1273, 1358, 1463, 2181, 2520, 2888, 3292, 3390, 4005, 4604, 4665, 4735, 4765, 4945, 4946, 5520, 5614, 5947, 6432, 6463, 6576, 6620, 6720, 6731, 6753, 6998, 7005–7022, 14586, 14634, 14650, 14682, 14796, 14834
C_4H_9Cl	2-Chloro-2-methylpropane. B.p., 50.8 725, 1130, 1464, 2645, 2889, 3391, 4605, 4736, 4766, 5450, 5471, 5615, 5774, 5948, 6466, 7023–7030
C_4H_9ClO	1-Chloroethyl ethyl ether. B.p., 98.5 628, 726, 1005, 2385, 3818, 4722, 5998, 6976, 7032–7040
C_4H_9ClO	1-Chloro-2-methyl-2-propanol. B.p., 126.7 216
C_4H_9I	1-Iodobutane. B.p., 130.4 1131, 1274, 1465, 2277, 2427, 2521, 2771, 2961, 3392, 3539, 4122, 4177, 4666, 4789, 5011, 5036, 5112, 5307, 5521, 5616, 5696, 6017, 6109, 6263, 6477, 6647, 6826, 7041–7070
C_4H_9I	2-Iodobutane. B.p., 120.0 1466, 2522, 3393, 5486, 5618, 7071–7074
C_4H_9I	1-Iodo-2-methylpropane. B.p., 120.8 217, 547, 865, 1132, 1275, 1467, 1607, 1769, 2278, 2428, 2523, 2772, 2962, 3394, 3395, 3540, 4123, 4178, 4790, 5012, 5308, 5487, 5522, 5617, 5697, 6322, 6478, 6827, 7075–7100, 14807, 14839
C_4H_9N	Methallylamine. B.p., 78.7 218
C_4H_9N	Pyrrolidine (tetrahydropyrrole). B.p., 88 7101
C_4H_9NO	Morpholine. B.p., 128 7102
$C_4H_9NO_2$	Butyl nitrite. B.p., 78.2 219, 629, 727, 803, 959, 1728, 2182, 2386, 4444, 4606, 4947, 5949, 5999, 6089, 6433, 6621, 6732, 6754, 6938, 6966, 6977, 6999, 7005, 7103–7114

Formula	Name and System Nos.
$C_4H_9NO_2$	Isobutyl nitrite. B.p., 67.1 220, 630, 728, 960, 2356, 4006, 4445, 4607, 4767, 4948, 4973, 4993, 5950, 6000, 6434, 6622, 6721, 6967, 6978, 6970, 7006, 7023, 7115–7142
$C_4H_9NO_3$	Isobutyl nitrate. B.p., 122.9 221, 1608, 2524, 4791, 5698, 7041, 7075
C_4H_{10}	Butane 100, 495, 512, 1201, 1231, 1558, 1570, 1571, 2471, 2646, 2751, 3232, 3320, 3850, 5974, 6061, 14753
C_4H_{10}	2-Methylpropane. B.p., −10 101, 496, 513, 1203, 1232, 1559, 1572, 2472, 2647, 5975, 14754
$C_4H_{10}O$	Butyl alcohol. B.p., 117.75 25, 222, 548, 631, 729, 804, 866, 1276, 1577, 1609, 1699, 1729, 1923, 1928, 1964, 2237, 2279, 2387, 2773, 2917, 2963, 3250, 3293, 3541, 4007, 4019, 4082, 4124, 4179, 4277, 4305, 4329, 4446, 4608, 4893, 4949, 5013, 5066, 5090, 5488, 5699, 6018, 6067, 6095, 6209, 6264, 6323, 6340, 6382, 6435, 6471, 6577, 6623, 6733, 6755, 6828, 6900, 6930, 6939, 6979, 7007, 7042, 7076, 7123, 7143–7246, 14683–14689, 14868
$C_4H_{10}O$	*sec*-Butyl alcohol. B.p., 99.4 223, 549, 632, 805, 961, 1277, 1610, 1730, 2280, 2388, 2698, 3294, 4083, 4125, 4180, 4667, 4894, 4974, 5091, 5619, 5700, 6383, 6472, 6578, 6624, 6734, 6756, 6899, 6931, 6940, 6980, 7008, 7274–7284, 14690–14702
$C_4H_{10}O$	*tert*-Butyl alcohol. B.p., 82.5 224, 550, 633, 731, 806, 962, 1278, 1359, 1611, 1731, 2357, 2389, 3295, 3396, 3819, 4008, 4076, 4126, 4609, 4895, 4950, 4975, 4994, 5092, 5523, 5951, 6436, 6579, 6627, 6735, 6757, 6900, 6941, 6968, 6981, 7009, 7024, 7043, 7285–7315, 14516, 14669, 14682, 14703–14707
$C_4H_{10}O$	Ethyl ether. B.p., 34.5 26, 102, 225, 634, 730, 963, 1051, 1133, 1217, 1360, 1468, 1795, 1934, 2061, 2183, 2390, 2525, 2648, 2674, 2699, 2890, 3233, 3397, 3801, 3820, 3855, 4064, 4077, 4610, 4737, 4768, 4995, 5451, 5472, 5620, 5963, 6062, 6479, 6648, 7316–7332, 14587, 14825, 14826, 14871
$C_4H_{10}O$	Isobutyl alcohol. B.p., 107.0 226, 551, 635, 732, 807, 867, 964, 1006, 1279, 1612, 1732, 1770, 1965, 2150, 2184, 2219, 2238, 2281, 2391, 2774, 2918, 3251, 3296, 3321, 4009, 4020, 4084, 4127, 4181, 4278, 4306, 4330, 4447, 4611, 4896, 4951, 5014, 5067, 5093, 5489, 5621, 5701, 6019, 6096, 6210, 6265, 6324, 6437, 6473, 6580, 6625, 6626, 6758, 6901, 6932, 6942, 6969, 6982, 7010, 7044, 7077, 7124, 7285, 7333–7418, 14525, 14537, 14556, 14708–14722, 14808, 14840
$C_4H_{10}O$	Methyl propyl ether. B.p., 38.9 227, 733, 965, 1052, 1218, 1469, 1470, 2649, 2700, 3398, 3821, 3856, 4612, 4996, 5452, 5775, 7316, 7419–7422
$C_4H_{10}O_2$	Acetaldehyde dimethyl acetal. B.p., 64.3 230, 734, 808, 967, 1471, 2919, 3399, 4010, 4738, 4770, 4952, 4976, 6983, 7011, 7115, 7423–7426, 14538
$C_4H_{10}O_2$	*l*-2,3-Butanediol. 228, 7427
$C_4H_{10}O_2$	*meso*-2,3-Butanediol. B.p., 183 229, 6461
$C_4H_{10}O_2$	1,2-Dimethoxyethane. B.p., 83 231, 5622
$C_4H_{10}O_2$	2-Ethoxyethanol. B.p., 135.1 232, 868, 1067, 1280, 1613, 1835, 1966, 2282, 2719, 2775, 3400, 3862, 4182, 4331, 5015, 5068, 5490, 6020, 6211, 6266, 6829, 7045, 7078, 7125, 7143, 7333, 7428–7514, 14588
$C_4H_{10}O_2$	Ethoxymethoxymethane. B.p., 65.91 233, 966, 1361, 1472, 3401, 4011, 4769, 4953, 6970, 14539, 14589
$C_4H_{10}O_2$	1-Methoxy-2-propanol. B.p., 118 236, 7515
$C_4H_{10}O_2$	2-Methoxy-1-propanol. B.p., 130 236
$C_4H_{10}O_3$	Diethylene glycol. B.p., 245.5 237, 2964, 4405, 5113, 5811, 7516–7597
$C_4H_{10}S$	Butanethiol. B.p., 97.5 552, 1007, 1281, 2776, 4897, 5623, 6021, 6761, 6984, 7598, 7615
$C_4H_{10}S$	2-Butanethiol. B.p., 85.15 7615–7625
$C_4H_{10}S$	Ethyl sulfide. B.p., 92.2 636, 809, 968, 1134, 1282, 1473, 2418, 2526, 2777, 3297, 3402, 4613, 4668, 4722, 4792, 4898, 5524, 5624, 6022, 6438, 6628, 6736, 6759, 6760, 6902, 6943, 7032, 7103, 7144, 7247, 7286, 7598, 7626–7643
$C_4H_{10}S$	2-Methyl-1-propanethiol. B.p., 88 1733, 2392, 4722, 7626, 7644–7666
$C_4H_{10}S$	2-Methyl-2-propanethiol. B.p., 64.35 7662–7666

Formula	Name and System Nos.
$C_4H_{10}SO_4$	Ethyl sulfate. B.p., 208.0 7667
$C_4H_{11}ClSi$	Chloromethyl trimethylsilane. B.p., 97 3403
$C_4H_{11}N$	Butylamine. B.p., 77.8 4614, 6439, 7668–7669
$C_4H_{11}N$	Diethylamine. B.p., 55.9 735, 1474, 2358, 2701, 4615, 4771, 5776, 6440, 7317, 7419, 7423, 7670–7676
$C_4H_{11}N$	Isobutylamine. B.p., 68 1475, 4616, 7678–7684
$C_4H_{11}NO$	2-Amino-2-methyl-1-propanol. B.p., 165.4 7685
$C_4H_{11}NO$	3-Methoxypropylamine. B.p., 116 238
$C_4H_{11}NO_2$	2,2′-Iminodiethanol. B.p., 268 2965, 7686–7689
$C_4H_{12}Si$	Tetramethylsilane. B.p., 26.64 1219
$C_4H_{12}SiO$	Trimethylmethoxysilane. 1476
$C_4H_{12}SiO_4$	Tetramethoxysilane. B.p., 121.8 7690
$C_5H_4O_2$	2-Furaldehyde. B.p., 161.45 239, 869, 1614, 1661, 1836, 1967, 2283, 2458, 2527, 2778, 2966, 3542, 4239, 4332, 4369, 4455, 4793, 5309, 5702, 6049, 6068, 6137, 6308, 6341, 6384, 6480, 6649, 6778, 7046, 7428, 7691–7772, 14855
C_5H_5N	Pyridine. B.p., 115.5 27, 83, 240, 553, 637, 1024, 1135, 1283, 1477, 1615, 2151, 2284, 2528, 2779, 3404, 4128, 4225, 4669, 4794, 5625, 5703, 6099, 6581, 6885, 7047, 7079, 7145, 7248, 7334, 7429, 7599, 7627, 7773–7809, 14723–14733, 14872
C_5H_6	Cyclopentadiene. B.p., 41.0 2650, 4617
C_5H_6O	2-Methyl-3-butyn-2-ol. B.p., 104.4 241
C_5H_6O	2-Methylfuran. B.p., 63.7 242, 736, 1478, 3405, 4708, 4772, 6441, 14540, 14613
$C_5H_6O_2$	Furfuryl alcohol. B.p., 169.35 243, 1068, 1616, 1968, 2720, 2780, 2967, 4370, 5114, 5310, 7691, 7810–7832
C_5H_7N	1-Methylpyrrole (*N*-methylpyrrole). B.p., 112.8 2419, 5626, 5704, 6886, 7033, 7146, 7335, 7628
C_5H_7N	2-Methylpyrrole. B.p., 147.5 7430, 7832
C_5H_7NO	Furfurylamine. B.p., 144 244
C_5H_8	Cyclopentene. B.p., 43 1479, 2651, 4709, 7833
C_5H_8	Isoprene. B.p., 34.3 737, 1480, 1573, 2024, 2652, 2702, 3406, 3802, 3822, 4618, 4710, 4739, 4997, 5453, 5778, 7318, 7420, 7834–7840, 14614, 14820
C_5H_8	3-Methyl-1,2-butadiene. B.p., 40.8 1481, 2653, 2703, 3407, 4619, 5777, 5915, 7319, 7834, 7841
C_5H_8	*cis*-Piperylene (1,3-pentadiene). B.p., 42.5 1482, 2654, 4620, 7833, 7835
C_5H_8O	Cyclopentanone. B.p., 130.65 1617, 2158, 2529, 3863, 4129, 4183, 4226, 4795, 6267, 6650, 6830, 7048, 743 1, 7842–753
C_5H_8O	3-Methyl-3-butene-2-one. B.p., 98.5 245
C_5H_8O	2-Methyl-3-butyne-2-ol. 246
$C_5H_8O_2$	Allyl acetate. B.p., 105 247, 4670
$C_5H_8O_2$	Ethyl acrylate. B.p., 100 248, 1483, 3408, 6097
$C_5H_8O_2$	Methyl methacrylate. B.p., 99.5 249, 1484, 6098
$C_5H_8O_2$	2,3-Pentanedione. B.p., 109 250
$C_5H_8O_2$	2,4-Pentanedione. B.p., 138 5796, 6110, 7853–7864

Formula	Name and System Nos.
$C_5H_8O_3$	Ethyl pyruvate. B.p., 155.5 4797, 6481, 6651, 7865–7892
$C_5H_8O_3$	Levulinic acid (β-acetylpropionic acid). B.p., 252 2968, 5115, 7893–7915
$C_5H_8O_3$	Methyl acetoacetate. B.p., 169.5 1838, 1969, 6309, 6342, 6652, 7692, 7916–7959
$C_5H_8O_4$	Methyl malonate. B.p., 181.5 1662, 1839, 4371, 5311, 7960–8023
$C_5H_9ClO_2$	Propyl chloroacetate. B.p., 162.3 251, 870, 1840, 1970, 2969, 3543, 4798, 5116, 5627, 6482, 7147, 7336, 8024–8045, 14651
C_5H_9N	Isovaleronitrile. B.p., 130.5 1618, 5705, 7049, 8046, 8047
C_5H_9N	Valeronitrile. B.p., 141.3 2285, 5706, 7148, 7432, 8048–8058
C_5H_{10}	Amylenes. 1574, 8059, 8060
C_5H_{10}	Cyclopentane. B.p., 49.4 738, 1053, 1136, 1220, 1285, 1362, 1485, 2185, 2359, 2530, 2655, 2704, 2891, 3234, 3298, 3409, 3803, 4078, 4621, 4711, 4740, 4998, 5005, 5454, 5473, 5525, 5779, 5916, 5933, 5963, 6722, 6762, 7012, 7025, 7116, 7287, 7320, 7337, 7678, 7836, 8061–8066, 14827
C_5H_{10}	2-Methyl-1-butene. B.p., 32 514, 2473, 2656, 4622, 4712
C_5H_{10}	3-Methyl-1-butene. B.p., 21.2 515, 740, 1138, 1223, 1284, 1487, 2025, 2474, 2657, 2752, 3235, 3410, 3805, 3823, 3851, 3857, 4065, 4624, 5008, 5456, 5527, 5786, 5978, 7322, 7838, 8069
C_5H_{10}	2-Methyl-2-butene. B.p., 37.7 516, 539, 969, 1054, 1137, 1221, 1222, 1486, 2475, 2658, 2705, 2892, 3236, 3411, 3412, 3804, 3824, 4741, 4773, 5006, 5007, 5455, 5526, 5623, 5781, 5917, 5965, 7149, 7288, 7321, 7421, 7670, 7837, 7841, 8061, 8067, 8068, 14771, 14773, 14780, 14791, 14800, 14821, 14824, 14825, 14854, 14871
C_5H_{10}	1-Pentene. B.p., 30.2 517, 2476, 2659, 4625, 5782
C_5H_{10}	2-Pentene. B.p., 35.8 518, 1488, 2477, 2660, 4626, 4713, 5783
$C_5H_{10}O$	Allyl ethyl ether. B.p., 63 3413, 14635, 14690
$C_5H_{10}O$	Cyclopentanol. B.p., 140.85 252, 741, 1286, 1619, 2720, 2781, 4085, 4184, 5707, 6023, 6050, 6268, 6343, 6385, 6831, 7050, 7126, 7433, 7853, 8070, 8096
$C_5H_{10}O$	Isovaleraldehyde. B.p., 92.5 253, 554, 638, 1734, 2393, 2531, 3299, 6442, 6629, 6737, 6985, 7629, 8097–8100
$C_5H_{10}O$	3-Methyl-2-butanone. B.p., 94 255, 639, 742, 810, 1008, 1139, 1287, 1489, 1735, 2394, 3414, 4671, 4899, 5069, 5528, 5628, 6001, 6078, 6582, 6944, 6986, 7034, 7104, 7150, 7338, 7630, 7671, 7679, 8101–8110
$C_5H_{10}O$	2-Methyltetrahydrofuran. B.p., 77 254
$C_5H_{10}O$	2-Pentanone. B.p., 102.35 256, 743, 811, 1009, 1140, 1288, 2220, 3415, 4279, 4430, 4672, 5070, 5629, 6079, 6903, 6945 7151, 7339, 7773, 8111–8126
$C_5H_{10}O$	3-Pentanone. B.p., 257 257, 556, 744, 812, 1010, 1141, 1289, 1736, 1771, 2221, 2239, 2532, 3252, 4130, 4280, 4673, 5052, 5071, 5529, 5630, 6080, 6887, 6904, 6933, 6946, 7035, 7152, 7249, 7289, 7340, 7631, 7774, 8097, 8111, 8126–8152, 14533, 14652, 14708, 14789, 14790, 14841–14843, 14852
$C_5H_{10}O$	Tetrahydropyran. 258
$C_5H_{10}O_2$	Butyl formate. B.p., 106.6 259, 813, 1290, 1490, 1772, 2533, 4086, 4281, 5530, 5631, 6905, 6947, 7080, 7153, 7250. 7341, 7775, 8112, 8126, 8153–8169, 14683
$C_5H_{10}O_2$	4,5-Dimethyl-1,3-dioxolane. 260
$C_5H_{10}O_2$	3-Ethoxy-1,2-epoxypropane. B.p., 124 261
$C_5H_{10}O_2$	Ethyl propionate. B.p., 99.15 28, 262, 556, 745, 814, 1291, 1491, 1737, 1773, 1916, 2186, 2534, 3416, 4282, 4307, 4431, 4674, 5632, 6081, 6630, 6906, 6948, 7154, 7251, 7342, 8101, 8113, 8127, 8170–8186
$C_5H_{10}O_2$	3-Hydroxy-3-methyl-2-butanone. B.p., 141 263

Formula	Name and System Nos.
$C_5H_{10}O_2$	Isobutyl formate. B.p., 98.3 264, 640, 746, 815, 1142, 1292, 1492, 1738, 1774, 2535, 2782, 3417, 4283, 4675, 4900, 5094, 5531, 5633, 6583, 6888, 6907, 6949, 7155, 7252, 7290, 7343, 8114, 8128, 8170, 8187–8201, 14709
$C_5H_{10}O_2$	Isopropyl acetate. B.p., 88.6 265, 641, 747, 816, 1011, 1293, 1493, 1739, 1775, 2187, 2395, 3418, 4284, 4425, 4901, 4954, 5072, 5095, 5532, 6443, 6584, 6908, 6950, 6987, 7105, 7156, 7344, 8102, 8202–8215
$C_5H_{10}O_2$	Isovaleric acid. B.p., 176.5 266, 748, 871, 872, 1069, 1620, 1663, 1700, 1841, 1971, 2062, 2286, 2970, 3828, 4240, 4333, 4372, 6212, 7051, 7693, 7960, 8024, 8216–8299, 14873–14877
$C_5H_{10}O_2$	Methyl butyrate. B.p., 162.65 267, 557, 817, 1294, 1494, 1740, 1776, 2240, 2536, 2783, 3419, 4087, 4131, 4285, 4308, 4676, 4902, 5073, 5533, 5634, 6082, 6111, 6585, 6909, 6951, 7081, 7157, 7253, 7345, 7632, 8115, 8129, 8153, 8170, 8300–8313
$C_5H_{10}O_2$	Methyl isobutyrate. B.p., 92.3 268, 642, 817, 1012, 1295, 1495, 1496, 1777, 2537, 2920, 3420, 4286, 4677, 5074, 5096, 5534, 5635, 6910, 6934, 6952, 7158, 7254, 7291, 7346, 7633, 8098, 8103, 8116, 8130, 8187, 8202, 8314–8327
$C_5H_{10}O_2$	Propyl acetate. B.p., 101.6 29, 269, 558, 749, 819, 1013, 1296, 1497, 1778, 1917, 2152, 2163, 2188, 2241, 2538, 2784, 3253, 3421, 4088, 4132, 4287, 4309, 4678, 5075, 5535, 5636, 6112, 6586, 6889, 6911, 6953, 7082, 7159, 7255, 7292, 7347, 7634, 8117, 8131, 8154, 8172, 8188, 8300, 8327–8343, 14562, 14653, 14790, 14842, 14852
$C_5H_{10}O_2$	Tetrahydrofurfuryl alcohol. 8343
$C_5H_{10}O_2$	Valeric acid. B.p., 186.35 873, 1664, 1842, 1972, 2063, 3829, 4334, 4373, 6013, 7916, 7961, 8344–8398
$C_5H_{10}O_3$	Ethyl carbonate. B.p., 126.5 270, 1621, 1973, 2287, 2722, 2785, 2971, 3544, 4133, 4185, 4227, 4799, 6024, 7052, 7083 7127, 7160, 7348, 7776, 7842, 8071, 8399–8422, 14811
$C_5H_{10}O_3$	Ethyl lactate. B.p., 153.9 1843, 1974, 3945, 4241, 6069, 6138, 6213, 6214, 6269, 6386, 7434, 7694, 8072, 8423–8475
$C_5H_{10}O_3$	2-Methoxyethyl acetate. B.p., 144.6 271, 1622, 1844, 1975, 2288, 2539, 2723, 2786, 3545, 3971, 4021, 4134, 4186, 4433, 4800, 5312, 5708, 6139, 6215, 6270, 6387, 6484, 6653, 6654, 6832, 7053, 7084, 7128, 7161, 7349, 7435, 7695, 8070, 8400, 8423, 8476–8530
$C_5H_{10}O_3$	Methyl *β*-methoxypropionate. B.p., 84/100 272
$C_5H_{11}Br$	1-Bromo-3-methylbutane. B.p., 120.65 559, 1025, 1143, 1297, 1498, 1623, 1779, 2189, 2540, 2724, 2788, 2972, 2973, 3254, 3422, 3546, 4135, 4187, 4801, 5016, 5037, 5117, 5313, 5536, 5537, 5637, 5709, 6025, 6326, 6484, 6587, 6655, 7085, 7129, 7162, 7293, 7350, 7436, 7696, 7777, 7843, 8074, 8155, 8216, 8401, 8476, 8533–8557
$C_5H_{11}Br$	1-Bromopentane. B.p., 130.0 8558
$C_5H_{11}Cl$	1-Chloro-3-methylbutane. B.p., 99.4 560, 1026, 1144, 1298, 1500, 1780, 2429, 2541, 2789, 3300, 3423, 4288, 4679, 4802, 4903, 5538, 5638, 5710, 6330, 6588, 6763, 6890, 7163, 7256, 7294, 7351, 8104, 8132, 8173, 8189, 8203, 8301, 8314, 8327, 8559–8571
$C_5H_{11}Cl$	1-Chloropentane. B.p., 108.35 273, 1499, 3424
$C_5H_{11}I$	1-Iodo-3-methylbutane. B.p., 147.65 874, 1145, 1976, 2064, 2430, 2542, 2790, 2929, 2974, 3547, 4022, 4188, 4456, 4803, 5118, 5314, 5639, 5711, 6113, 6140, 6216, 6271, 6485, 6656, 6833, 7164, 7257, 7352, 7437, 7697, 8217, 8344, 8402, 8424, 8477, 8572–8605
$C_5H_{11}I$	2-Iodo-2-methylbutane. B.p., 127.5 8403
$C_5H_{11}N$	Piperidine (hexahydropyridine). B.p., 105.8 274, 1501, 6589, 7778, 8133, 8605–8608, 14872
$C_5H_{11}NO$	Tetrahydrofurfurylamine. B.p., 153 275
$C_5H_{11}NO_2$	Ethyl *N*-ethylaminoformate. 8609, 8611
$C_5H_{11}NO_2$	Isoamyl nitrite. B.p., 97.15 276, 643, 750, 820, 1014, 1299, 1741, 2242, 2396, 4289, 5076, 5097, 6002, 6590, 6913, 6935, 6954, 6988, 8105, 8118, 8134, 8190, 8204, 8315, 8328, 8559, 8611–8624
$C_5H_{11}NO_3$	Isoamyl nitrate. B.p., 149.75 277, 875, 1845, 1977, 4242, 4335, 4374, 4804, 5315, 5712, 6070, 6217, 6272, 6486, 6657, 6834, 7438, 7810, 8425, 8478, 8625–8650

Formula	Name and System Nos.
C_5H_{12}	2-Methylbutane. B.p., 27.6 497, 519, 751, 1146, 1224, 1300, 1502, 2026, 2459, 2478, 2661, 2706, 2753, 3237, 3425, 3806, 3807, 3825, 3858, 4066, 4627, 4715, 5009, 5457, 5474, 5539, 5742, 5784, 5966, 5979, 6487, 7258, 7295, 7323, 7839, 8067, 8069, 8651, 8652, 14792, 14822
C_5H_{12}	Pentane. B.p., 36.15 281, 520, 752, 970, 1056, 1147, 1225, 1363, 1503, 2027, 2190, 2460, 2479, 2662, 2675, 2707, 2754, 3238, 3426, 3808, 3826, 3964, 4067, 4079, 4628, 4717, 4743, 4774, 4999, 5010, 5458, 5475, 5540, 5640, 5785, 5918, 5934, 5952, 7026, 7117, 7259, 7296, 7324, 7353, 7422, 7672, 7680, 7840, 8062, 8068, 8651, 8653, 8654, 14774, 14788, 14823, 14826, 14854, 14871
$C_5H_{12}O$	Amyl alcohol. B.p., 137.8 278, 753, 1624, 2289, 2725, 2791, 2975, 3255, 4089, 4136, 4189, 5713, 6026, 6474, 6836, 7054, 7130, 7439, 7779, 8048, 8404, 8479, 8533, 8655–8679, 14734–14738
$C_5H_{12}O$	*tert*-Amyl alcohol. B.p., 102.25 279, 561, 644, 754, 821, 1301, 1625, 1742, 2191, 2243, 2290, 2397, 2921, 3256, 3301, 4090, 4137, 4190, 4290, 4310, 4629, 4955, 5077, 5098, 5491, 5714, 6027, 6330, 6388, 6475, 6591 6914, 6955, 6989, 7013, 7260, 7780, 8119, 8135, 8156, 8174, 8191, 8302, 8316, 8329, 8480, 8534, 8560, 8653, 8680–8701, 14739–14741
$C_5H_{12}O$	Butyl methyl ether. B.p., 71 1504, 14636, 14691
$C_5H_{12}O$	*tert*-Butyl methyl ether. B.p., 55 280, 1506
$C_5H_{12}O$	Ethyl isopropyl ether. B.p., 54 14637, 14692
$C_5H_{12}O$	Ethyl propyl ether. B.p., 63.6 282, 755, 971, 1148, 1364, 1505, 2360, 2893, 3239, 3427, 4630, 4744, 4956, 4977, 5476, 5541, 5641, 5919, 7001, 7014, 7118, 7673, 8063, 8702–8706, 14638, 14693
$C_5H_{12}O$	Isoamyl alcohol. B.p., 132.05 283, 562, 645, 756, 876, 1015, 1070, 1302, 1626, 1743, 1846, 1979, 2244, 2291, 2398, 2726, 2792, 2922, 2976, 3257, 3428, 3548, 4023, 4091, 4138, 4191, 4243, 4291, 4336, 4957, 5017, 5119, 5316, 5492, 5642, 5715, 6028, 6092, 6218, 6273, 6344, 6389, 6915, 6956, 7055, 7086, 7131, 7354, 7440, 7635, 7781, 7832, 7844, 7854, 8025, 8136, 8157, 8405, 8426, 8481, 8535, 8561, 8573, 8707–8782, 14742–14747, 14817, 14818, 14809, 14811
$C_5H_{12}O$	Isobutyl methyl ether. B.p., 59 14639, 14694
$C_5H_{12}O$	2-Methyl-1-butanol. 8783, 8784
$C_5H_{12}O$	3-Methyl-2-butanol. B.p., 112.9 284, 563, 757, 822, 1303, 1744, 2399, 4139, 5099, 6916, 6957, 8765–8792
$C_5H_{12}O$	2-Pentanol. B.p., 119.3 285, 564, 646, 758, 1304, 1627, 1744, 2292, 2793, 2977, 3302, 4092, 4140, 4192, 4904, 5493, 5716, 6029, 6274, 6592, 6837, 6958, 7056, 7132, 7165, 7441, 7846, 8059, 8137, 8158, 8482, 8536, 8793–8820
$C_5H_{12}O$	3-Pentanol. B.p., 115.4 286, 565, 647, 759, 1305, 1745, 2192, 2400, 2794, 4141, 4193, 5078, 5717, 6476, 6593, 6917, 6959, 6990, 7166, 7782, 8138, 8159, 8175, 8303, 8330, 8821–8837
$C_5H_{12}O_2$	Diethoxymethane. B.p., 87.5 287, 760, 823, 1016, 1507, 1747, 2401, 2543, 3303, 3429, 4631, 4680, 4905, 5100, 5542, 5643, 6003, 6444, 6631, 6738, 6764, 6991, 7106, 7355, 7636, 8106, 8192, 8205, 8317, 8531, 8611, 8680, 14590, 14654
$C_5H_{12}O_2$	1,2-Dimethoxypropane. B.p., 92 288
$C_5H_{12}O_2$	2-Propoxyethanol. B.p., 151.35 289, 877, 1071, 1306, 1628, 1847, 1980, 2293, 2795, 2978, 3258, 3549, 3864, 4375, 4457. 5018, 5120, 5317, 6030, 6071, 6219, 6275, 6345, 6390, 6838, 7087, 7133, 7698, 8075, 8427. 8483, 8537, 8574, 8625, 8707, 8838–8902
$C_5H_{12}O_3$	2-(2-Methoxyethoxy)ethanol. B.p., 192.95 290, 2979, 3550, 3865, 4529, 5121, 5318, 5718, 6779, 7699, 8626, 8903–8967
$C_5H_{12}O_3$	1,1,2-Trimethoxyethane. B.p., 126 291
$C_5H_{12}S$	3-Methyl-1-butanethiol. B.p., 120 8969
$C_5H_{13}ClSiO$	2-Chloroethoxytrimethylsilane. B.p., 134.3 2796
$C_5H_{13}NO$	3-Ethoxypropylamine. 292
$C_5H_{14}SiO$	Ethoxytrimethylsilane. B.p., 75 3430, 8969, 14835
$C_5H_{14}SiO$	Methoxymethyltrimethylsilane. B.p., 83 1508

Formula	Name and System Nos.
$C_6H_3Cl_3$	1,3,5-Trichlorobenzene. B.p., 208.4 2065, 3551, 4458, 8218, 8970–9004
C_6H_4BrCl	*p*-Bromochlorobenzene. B.p., 196.4 1796, 2066, 2981, 3552, 4459, 5122, 6488, 8219, 9005–9028
$C_6H_4Br_2$	*o*-Dibromobenzene. B.p., 181.5 4030
$C_6H_4Br_2$	*p*-Dibromobenzene. B.p., 220.25 2028, 2067, 2980, 3553, 5123, 5319, 5812, 7516, 9029–9105
$C_6H_4ClNO_2$	*m*-Chloronitrobenzene. B.p., 235.5 2982, 3554, 5124, 5813, 7517, 9029, 9106–9130
$C_6H_4ClNO_2$	*o*-Chloronitrobenzene. B.p., 246.0 2983, 3555, 5125, 5814, 7518, 9131–9149
$C_6H_4ClNO_2$	*p*-Chloronitrobenzene. B.p., 239.1 2984, 3556, 5126, 5815, 7519, 7893, 9030, 9150–9179
$C_6H_4Cl_2$	*o*-Dichlorobenzene. B.p., 179.5 2029, 2068, 2797, 2985, 3557, 3866, 4406, 4460, 4530, 4805, 5127, 5320, 6141, 6310, 6346, 6489, 6780, 7700, 7917, 7962, 8220, 8345, 9180–9224
$C_6H_4Cl_2$	*p*-Dichlorobenzene. B.p., 174.4 1072, 1149, 1797, 2030, 2069, 2431, 2544, 2798, 2986, 3558, 3559, 3830, 3867, 4031, 4461, 4531, 4806, 5128, 5321, 6142, 6220, 6311, 6347, 6490, 6658, 6781, 7701, 7811, 7918, 7963, 8221, 8346, 8428, 8609, 8838, 9225–9291
C_6H_5Br	Bromobenzene. B.p., 156.1 878, 1073, 1150, 1798, 1848, 1981, 2031, 2070, 2294, 2432, 2545, 2799, 2930, 2987, 3560, 3831, 3868, 3972, 4244, 4462, 4532, 4807, 5019, 5038, 5129, 5322, 5644, 6031, 6114, 6143, 6221, 6276, 6312, 6348, 6391, 6491, 6659, 6839, 6840, 7167, 7356, 7442, 7702, 7856, 7865, 7919, 7964, 8222, 8347, 8429, 8484, 8627, 8708, 8839, 9180, 9292–9340, 14856, 14857, 14869, 14878–14881
C_6H_5BrO	*o*-Bromophenol. B.p., 194.8 2988, 5130, 6349, 9225, 9341–9366
C_6H_5Cl	Chlorobenzene. B.p., 131.8 293, 648, 879, 972, 1151, 1307, 1509, 2071, 2164, 2295, 2433, 2546, 2727, 2800, 2989, 3431, 3561, 3869, 3973, 4142, 4143, 4194, 4632, 4681, 4808, 5020, 5039, 5131, 5323, 5462, 5543, 5645, 5719, 6032, 6115, 6277, 6392, 6492, 6633, 6660, 6841, 7134, 7168, 7261, 7357, 7443, 7703, 7783, 7812, 7846, 7857, 7866, 8076, 8223, 8406, 8430, 8485, 8655, 8681, 8709, 8840, 9292, 9367–9396, 14503, 14504, 14591, 14815, 14816, 14817
C_6H_5ClO	*o*-Chlorophenol. B.p., 176.8 880, 1849, 1850, 1982, 2990, 3562, 6350, 6493, 8224, 8575, 9181, 9226, 9293, 9397–9431, 14882
C_6H_5ClO	*p*-Chlorophenol. B.p., 219.75 2991, 3563, 5132, 5793, 9031, 9432–9500
C_6H_5F	Fluorobenzene. B.p., 84.9 1152, 1365, 1510, 2547, 2801, 3304, 3432, 4633, 5544, 5646, 5953, 6445, 6632, 6765, 7107, 7169, 7296, 7358, 9501–9505
C_6H_5I	Iodobenzene. B.p., 188.55 1799, 3032, 2072, 2992, 3564, 3832, 3870, 4032, 4407, 4463, 4533, 5133, 5324, 6351, 6494, 6661, 6782, 7444, 7704, 7858, 7920, 7965, 8225, 8348, 8841, 9397, 8501, 9506–9556
$C_6H_5NO_2$	Nitrobenzene. B.p., 210.85 294, 649, 881, 973, 1226, 1511, 1800, 1851, 1935, 1983, 2033, 2073, 2296, 2548, 2993, 3433, 3565, 3871. 4033, 4041, 5056, 5134, 5325, 5816, 6009, 6783, 6918, 6992, 7002, 7170, 7262, 7325, 7520, 7894, 8059, 8652. 8654, 8903. 8970, 9032, 9182, 9294, 9367, 9506, 9557–9640, 14883
$C_6H_5NO_3$	*o*-Nitrophenol. B.p., 217.25 2994, 3566, 5135, 5326, 5794, 5981, 6411, 7521, 9033, 9341, 9557, 9641–9702
C_6H_6	Benzene. B.p., 80.1 84, 295, 566, 650, 651, 761, 824, 974, 1017, 1153, 1308, 1366, 1512, 1748, 1781, 1931, 2193, 2297, 2402, 2461, 2480, 2549, 2708, 2745, 2802, 2894, 2923, 3259, 3305, 3434, 3567, 3872, 3951, 3966, 3974, 4012, 4144, 4448, 4634, 4682, 4723, 4745, 4775, 4809, 4906, 4958, 4978, 5021, 5053, 5101, 5494, 5545, 5647, 5720, 5786, 5920, 5954, 6004, 6083, 6090, 6093, 6332, 6446, 6464, 6467, 6594, 6595, 6634, 6723, 6739, 6766, 6960, 6971, 7003, 7015, 7036, 7101, 7108, 7119, 7171, 7263, 7298, 7326, 7359, 7424, 7445, 7600, 7615, 7637, 7644, 7681, 7784, 8077, 8099, 8107, 8120, 8139, 8160, 8176, 8193, 8206, 8304, 8318, 8331, 8563, 8612, 8656, 8682, 8710, 8785, 8794, 8821, 8831, 8969, 9368, 9502, 9558, 9703–9726, 14541, 14563, 14573, 14592, 14610, 14617, 14640, 14655, 14670, 14695, 14703, 14710, 14739, 14759, 14785, 14802, 14803, 14831, 14835, 14836, 14853, 14866
C_6H_6O	Phenol. B.p., 182 296, 882, 1665, 1852, 1936, 1984, 2074, 2298, 2803, 2931, 2995, 2996, 3568, 3833, 3873, 3988, 4042, 4245, 4337, 4376, 4434, 4464, 4534, 4635, 5040, 5136, 5327, 5721, 5982, 6144, 6352, 6495, 6662, 6784, 6842, 7057, 7172, 7446, 7705, 7813, 7921, 7966, 8078, 8226, 8349, 8431, 8486, 8576, 8657, 8711, 8842, 8904, 8971, 9005, 9034, 9183, 9227, 9295, 9369, 9398, 9727–9859, 14505, 14615, 14748, 14878, 14884

Formula	Name and System Nos.
$C_6H_6O_2$	Pyrocatechol. B.p., 245.9 2997, 3510, 5137, 5817, 7522, 8973, 9035, 9106, 9131, 9150, 9641, 9860–9927
$C_6H_6O_2$	Resorcinol. B.p., 281.4 2998, 3435, 5138, 5818, 9036, 9132, 9151, 9860, 9928–9965
$C_6H_6O_3$	Pyrogallol. B.p., 309 9928, 9966–9971
C_6H_6S	Benzenethiol. B.p., 169.5 2804, 8712, 9228, 9972–9977
C_6H_7N	Aniline. B.p., 184.35 59, 297, 883, 1154, 1666, 1853, 1985, 2299, 2550, 2999, 3571, 3874, 4377, 4535, 5139, 5795, 7173, 7814, 7967, 8060, 8079, 8713, 8843, 8905, 8974, 9006, 9184, 9229, 9296, 9370, 9399, 9508, 9703, 9727, 9978–10067, 14837, 14885–14892
C_6H_7N	2-Picoline. B.p., 134 298, 1155, 2558, 4810, 5722, 7174, 7785, 8080, 8714, 8795, 10068–10073
C_6H_7N	3-Picoline. B.p., 144. 299, 1156, 2552, 4811, 6033, 8715, 9400, 9728, 10074–10076
C_6H_7N	4-Picoline. B.p., 145.3 300, 1157, 2553, 4812, 6034, 9401, 9729, 10077, 10078
C_6H_8	1,3-Cyclohexadiene. B.p., 80.8 302, 652, 762, 975, 1158, 1513, 2554, 3306, 3436, 4636, 4683, 5546, 5648, 5955, 6447, 6635, 7016, 7175, 7299, 7360, 7645, 8683, 8716, 9704, 10079, 10080, 14542, 14593, 14618, 14641, 14656, 14704, 14711, 14723, 14804
C_6H_8	1,4-Cyclohexadiene. B.p., 85.6 301, 653, 1514, 2555, 3437, 5547, 7646, 9705, 14594
$C_6H_8N_2$	*o*-Phenylenediamine. B.p., 258.6 3000, 3572, 5140, 10081–10100
$C_6H_8N_2$	Phenylhydrazine. B.p., 243 303
$C_6H_8O_2$	Vinyl crotonate. B.p., 132.7 304
$C_6H_8O_4$	Methyl fumarate. B.p., 193.25 305, 2075, 5141, 5328, 6785, 7523, 8227, 8906, 9185, 9509, 9730, 10101–10133
$C_6H_8O_4$	Methyl maleate. B.p., 204.05 2076, 3001, 3573, 5142, 5329, 5819, 7524, 9560, 9642, 9731, 10101, 10134–10167
C_6H_9N	1-Ethylpyrrole (*N*-ethylpyrrole). B.p., 130.4 3774, 7176
C_6H_{10}	Biallyl. B.p., 60.2 976, 1159, 1310, 1515, 2361, 2663, 2709, 2895, 3438, 4637, 4746, 4776, 5459, 5548, 5787, 5921, 7027, 7327, 7674, 8064, 8702, 10168, 14543, 14595
C_6H_{10}	Cyclohexene. B.p., 82.75 306, 567, 654, 763, 825, 977, 1160, 1309, 1516, 1749, 2300, 2403, 2556, 2805, 3439, 3575, 4684, 4777, 5549, 5649, 6005, 6448, 6496, 6596, 6636, 6740, 6767, 7017, 7177, 7264, 7300, 7361, 7447, 7647, 8684, 8717, 8786, 8796, 9706, 10079, 10169, 10174, 14544, 14596, 14619, 14642, 14657, 14684, 14705, 14712, 14724, 14802
C_6H_{10}	2,3-Dimethyl-1,3-butadiene. B.p., 68.9 1517
C_6H_{10}	1-Hexyne. B.p., 70.2 3440, 14597
C_6H_{10}	3-Hexyne. B.p., 80.5 3441, 14598
C_6H_{10}	Methylcyclopentene. B.p., 75.85 764, 1518, 3442, 5650, 7301, 10176
C_6H_{10}	4-Methyl-1,3-pentadiene. 307
$C_6H_{10}O$	Allyl ether. B.p., 94.84 4685, 14620
$C_6H_{10}O$	Cyclohexanone. B.p., 155.6 884, 1854, 1986, 2728, 3002, 3875, 3956, 4246, 4378, 4465, 4536, 4813, 5330, 6145, 6278, 6393, 6497, 6597, 6663, 6843, 7706, 7867, 7922, 8228, 8432, 8577, 9297, 9371, 9732, 9980, 10177–10199, 14893
$C_6H_{10}O$	1-Hexene-5-one. B.p., 129 308, 8968
$C_6H_{10}O$	Mesityl oxide (4-methyl-3-penten-2-one). B.p., 129.5 309, 310, 885, 1629, 1987, 2301, 2557, 2729, 2806, 4024, 4145, 4195, 4338, 4814, 4907, 5723, 6035, 6116, 6279, 6844, 7058, 7178, 7448, 7786, 8081, 8407, 8538, 8578, 8718, 8797, 9372, 10200–10217
$C_6H_{10}O_2$	Crotonyl acetate. B.p., 129 311

Formula	Name and System Nos.
$C_6H_{10}O_2$	2,5-Hexadione. B.p., 191.3 3576, 10218–10222
$C_6H_{10}O_2$	Isopropyl acrylate. 1519
$C_6H_{10}O_2$	Propyl acrylate. 1520
$C_6H_{10}O_3$	Ethyl acetoacetate. B.p., 180.4 1667, 1855, 4247, 6313, 6353, 6498, 8229, 8350, 8975, 9007, 9186, 9230, 9298, 9510, 9733, 10223–10283, 14894–14896
$C_6H_{10}O_4$	Ethylidene diacetate. B.p., 168.5 886, 1074, 1668, 2807, 3003, 3577, 5143, 5331, 6222, 6499, 7968, 8230, 8487, 8844, 8907, 9187, 9299, 9734, 10284–10315
$C_6H_{10}O_4$	Ethyl oxalate. B.p., 185.65 1669, 1856, 2078, 3004, 3578, 3579, 3834, 4379, 4466, 4537, 5144, 5332, 5820, 6354, 6786, 7923, 7969, 8231, 8351, 9188, 9231, 9300, 9511, 9735, 9981, 10102, 10223, 10316–10380, 14885–14888, 14897
$C_6H_{10}O_4$	Glycol diacetate. B.p., 186.3 3005, 3580, 5145, 5821, 7970, 8232, 8352, 8908, 9512, 9736, 10103, 10381–10405
$C_6H_{10}O_4$	Methyl succinate. B.p., 195.5 1670, 2077, 3581, 5333, 9008, 9513, 9737, 10134, 10316, 10406–10445
$C_6H_{10}S$	Allyl sulfide. B.p., 139.35 887, 1161, 1311, 1630, 1988, 2558, 2730, 2808, 3006, 3876, 4025, 4093, 4196, 4339, 4815, 5105, 5334, 5724, 6036, 6117, 6280, 6500, 6476, 6919, 7179, 7362, 7787, 8082, 8233, 8408, 8539, 8564, 8658, 8719, 8845, 9301, 9373, 10071, 10074, 10200, 10446–10458
$C_6H_{11}BrO_2$	Ethyl α-bromoisobutyrate. B.p., 178 1857, 6501, 7971, 10459–10462
$C_6H_{11}ClO_2$	Butyl chloroacetate. B.p., 181.9 312, 3582, 5146, 7180, 8720, 9514, 10463–10470, 14685
$C_6H_{11}ClO_2$	Isobutyl chloroacetate. B.p., 174.4 313, 1858, 7363, 9302, 9515, 10471–10480, 14713
$C_6H_{11}N$	Capronitrile. B.p., 163.9 7449, 8083, 8721, 8846, 10481–10487
$C_6H_{11}N$	Diallylamine. B.p., 110.4 314
$C_6H_{11}NO_2$	Nitrocyclohexane. B.p., 205.3 3007, 3877, 5147, 6787, 8909, 9982, 10488–10497
C_6H_{12}	Cyclohexane. B.p., 80.75 85, 315, 568, 655, 765, 826, 978, 1162, 1312, 1367, 1521, 1750, 1782, 2165, 2194, 2302, 2404, 2481, 2559, 2809, 2924, 3307, 3443, 3583, 3878, 4146, 4432, 4449, 4638, 4686, 4718, 4778, 4816, 4908, 4923, 4959, 4979, 5022, 5041, 5054, 5102, 5550, 5651, 5725, 5922, 5956, 6084, 6327, 6333, 6449, 6502, 6598, 6637, 6741, 6768, 6936, 6961, 6972, 6993, 7018, 7037, 7109, 7120, 7181, 7265, 7302, 7364, 7450, 7601, 7616, 7638, 7648, 7668, 7682, 7788, 8084, 8108, 8121, 8140, 8161, 8177, 8194, 8207, 8319, 8332, 8613, 8659, 8685, 8722, 8798, 8822, 8832, 9374, 9503, 9707, 9983, 10080, 10169, 10498–10507, 14545, 14599, 14621, 14643, 14658, 14696, 14714, 14725, 14740, 14755, 14761, 14762, 14797 14799, 14803, 14804, 14832, 14833, 14836, 14851, 14853
C_6H_{12}	Hexene. B.p., 68 1522, 4719, 14671, 14672, 14673
C_6H_{12}	Methylpentene. 14674–14676
C_6H_{12}	Methylcyclopentane. B.p., 72.0 656, 766, 827, 979, 980, 1057, 1163, 1313, 1368, 1523, 1751, 1783, 2195, 2362, 2405, 2482, 2560, 2664, 2710, 2810, 3260, 3308, 3444, 3584, 3879, 4450, 4639, 4687, 4747, 4909, 4960, 4980, 5551, 5652, 5923, 5957, 6006, 6599, 6638, 6724, 6742, 6769, 6973, 7019, 7028, 7110, 7121, 7182, 7266, 7303, 7365, 7425, 7617, 7662, 7669, 7675, 7683, 8141, 8320, 8614, 8686, 8703, 8723, 8799, 9504, 9708, 10508–10510
$C_6H_{12}O$	*trans*-2-Butenyl ethyl ether. B.p., 100.45 3446
$C_6H_{12}O$	*cis*-2-Butenyl ethyl ether. B.p., 100.3 3447
$CH_{12}O$	Butyl vinyl ether. B.p., 93.8 7183
$C_6H_{12}O$	Cyclohexanol. B.p., 160.65 316, 569, 888, 1314, 1671, 1859, 1989, 3008, 3585, 3946, 4147, 4197, 4248, 4340, 4380, 4538, 5148, 5335, 6051, 6146, 6223, 6224, 6281, 6600, 6845, 7707, 7815, 7924, 8026, 8433, 8579, 8628, 8847, 9189, 9232, 9303, 9402, 9516, 9709, 9738, 9984, 10177, 10446, 10481, 10511–10576, 14856, 14858, 14859, 14862, 14879, 14880, 14898
$C_6H_{12}O$	2,2-Dimethyltetrahydrofuran. B.p., 90 317

Formula	Name and System Nos.
$C_6H_{12}O$	Ethyl methylallyl ether. B.p., 76.65 3445
$C_6H_{12}O$	2-Hexanone. B.p., 127 318, 2159, 2811, 4817, 5726, 6118, 6282, 7184, 7185, 7366, 8409, 8800, 10447, 10577–10579
$C_6H_{12}O$	3-Hexanone. B.p., 124 319, 570, 1631, 2812, 4148, 4198, 4818, 5023, 5727, 7059, 7186, 7367, 7451, 7790, 8410, 8540, 10580–10594
$C_6H_{12}O$	Isobutyl vinyl ether. B.p., 83.0 7368
$C_6H_{12}O$	4-Methyl-2-pentanone. B.p., 115.9 320, 768, 828, 1315, 1632, 2245, 2561, 2813, 3261, 4149, 4199, 4819, 5024, 5728, 6920, 7187, 7369, 7452, 7791, 8541, 8724, 8823, 10448, 10498, 10595–10610
$C_6H_{12}O$	2-Methyl-2-pentene-4-ol. 321, 14749
$C_6H_{12}O$	Pinacolone (3,3-dimethyl-2-butanone). B.p., 106 322, 767, 829, 1164, 1316, 2562, 2814, 4150, 5552, 5653, 6601, 6891, 6921, 7267, 7370, 7789, 8162, 8178, 8195, 8305, 8333, 8565, 8615, 9710, 10499, 10610–10618
$C_6H_{12}O_2$	Amyl formate. B.p., 132 323, 8660, 14734
$C_6H_{12}O_2$	Butyl acetate. B.p., 126.2 324, 1633, 1634, 2303, 2563, 2731, 2815, 3009, 3262, 3586, 4151, 4200, 4228, 4820, 5025, 5729, 7060, 7088, 7188, 7371, 7453, 7792, 7847, 7868, 8050, 8085, 8488, 8542, 8661, 8725, 8801, 8848, 9375, 10201, 10449, 10577, 10580, 10619–10635, 14564, 14686
$C_6H_{12}O_2$	*sec*-Butyl acetate. B.p., 112.4 325, 7268
$C_6H_{12}O_2$	Caproic acid. B.p., 205.15 1801, 2034, 2079, 3010, 4381, 5149, 8976, 9009, 9037, 9190, 9233, 9517, 9561, 10104, 10135, 10406, 10636–10693
$C_6H_{12}O_2$	Ethyl butyrate. B.p., 119.9 86, 326, 1317, 1635, 2153, 2304, 2564, 3263, 3587, 4094, 4152, 4201, 5654, 5730, 6639, 7061, 7089, 7189, 7372, 7454, 7793, 8051, 8489, 8543, 8662, 8726, 8802, 9376, 10450, 10581, 10595, 10694–10708, 14810, 14839
$C_6H_{12}O_2$	Ethyl isobutyrate. B.p., 110.1 327, 571, 1318, 1636, 1784, 1918, 2154, 2222, 2565, 3264, 3448, 4095, 4153, 4154, 4292, 4311, 4688, 5026, 5079, 5495, 5655, 5731, 6602, 6923, 7071, 7090, 7190, 7373, 8142, 8163, 8544, 8566, 8803, 9711, 10500, 10596, 10610, 10709–10718
$C_6H_{12}O_2$	4-Hydroxy-4-methylpentanone. B.p., 166 328, 10719
$C_6H_{12}O_2$	Isoamyl formate. B.p., 124.2 329, 1637, 2305, 2566, 2816, 3011, 3588, 4155, 4202, 4821 5027, 5042, 5732, 6037, 6503, 7062, 7091, 7135, 7191, 7374, 7455, 7794, 7848, 7869, 8086, 8411, 8490, 8545, 8663, 8727, 10202, 10451, 10578, 10582, 10619, 10694, 10720–10725, 14743, 14812
$C_6H_{12}O_2$	Isobutyl acetate. B.p., 117.2 330, 572, 1319, 1638, 1990, 2817, 3265, 4096, 4156, 4689, 5028, 5043, 5656, 5733, 6038, 6119, 6603, 7063, 7072, 7092, 7192, 7269, 7375, 7456, 7795, 8052, 8491, 8546, 8728, 8804, 10583, 10597, 10695, 10726–10736, 14715
$C_6H_{12}O_2$	Isocaproic acid. B.p., 199.5 1860, 4382, 7972, 9191, 9234, 9518, 9739, 10136, 10224, 10317, 10407, 10737–10769
$C_6H_{12}O_2$	Isopropyl propionate. B.p., 110.3 331, 10598, 10611
$C_6H_{12}O_2$	Methyl isovalerate. B.p., 116.3 332, 573, 1320, 1639, 2223, 2246, 2818, 3449, 4157, 4312, 5553, 5657, 5734, 6120, 7073, 7093, 7193, 7270, 7376, 7457, 7708, 7796, 8547, 8687, 8805, 10584, 10599, 10696, 10709, 10726, 10770–10777
$C_6H_{12}O_2$	Propyl propionate. B.p., 122.1 333, 1640, 2306, 2561, 2819, 3012, 4158, 4203, 4822, 5658, 5735, 7064, 7136, 7194, 7377, 7458, 7797, 8548, 8729, 10203, 10585, 10620, 10697, 10720, 10778–10780
$C_6H_{12}O_3$	2,2-Dimethoxy-3-butanone. 334
$C_6H_{12}O_3$	2-Ethoxyethyl acetate. B.p., 156.8 335, 1075, 1861, 1991, 3013, 3589, 3975, 4341, 4383, 4435, 4823, 5150, 5336, 5736, 5796, 6225, 6283, 6355, 6394, 6504, 6664, 6846, 7065, 7195, 7378, 7459, 7709, 7816, 7973, 8027, 8234, 8412, 8434, 8580, 8629, 8730, 8849, 9235, 9304, 9740, 10284, 10318, 10381, 10621, 10781–10832
$C_6H_{12}O_3$	Ethyl α-hydroxyisobutyrate. B.p, 150 9741
$C_6H_{12}O$	Isopropyl lactate. B.p., 166.9 6226, 9742, 10511, 10781, 10833–10841

Formula	Name and System Nos.
$C_6H_{12}O_3$	Paraldehyde. B.p., 124 336, 1641, 2307, 2462, 2820, 3590, 4204, 5659, 5737, 6665, 7137, 7196, 7460, 7690, 8087, 8413, 8549, 8664, 8731, 8806, 8850, 9377, 10204, 10512, 10622, 10698, 10721, 10727, 10770, 10842–10850, 14812
$C_6H_{12}O_3$	Propyl lactate. B.p., 171.7 1862, 3014, 4468, 5151, 6227, 6356, 7710, 8851, 9236, 9743, 10178, 10513, 10851–10887, 14845, 14846, 14899, 14900
$C_6H_{12}O_3$	Trioxane. B.p., 114.5 337
$C_6H_{13}Br$	1-Bromohexane. B.p., 156.5 2568, 2821, 3015, 3591, 3835, 4469, 4824, 5152, 5337, 6147, 6228, 6284, 6357, 6395, 6505, 6661, 7197, 7379, 7974, 8235, 8353, 8492, 8630, 9744, 10319, 10514, 10782, 10888–10898
$C_6H_{13}ClO_2$	Chloroacetal. B.p., 157.4 5338, 6052, 6148, 6667, 8435, 9305, 9403, 10179, 10515, 10899–10921, 14881
C_6H_{14}	2,2-Dimethylbutane. B.p., 49.7 2665, 3809, 5924, 5935, 8065, 14827
C_6H_{14}	2,3-Dimethylbutane. B.p., 58.0 769, 981, 1058, 1165, 1321, 1369, 1524, 2196, 2363, 2569, 2666, 2676, 2711, 2896, 3450, 3592, 3827, 4080, 4640, 4690, 4748, 4779, 4961, 4981, 5460, 5477, 5554, 5660, 5788, 5925, 5936, 5959, 5967, 6450, 6640, 6770, 7020, 7029, 7271, 7304, 7328, 7663, 7676, 8066, 8688, 8704, 8732, 10168
C_6H_{14}	Hexane. B.p., 68.95 338, 657, 770, 830, 982, 1059, 1166, 1227, 1322, 1370, 1525, 1752, 1785, 2197, 2308, 2364, 2406, 2570, 2667, 2677, 2712, 2746, 2822, 2897, 2925, 3309, 3451, 3593, 3880, 3965, 4013, 4313, 4641, 4691, 4720, 4749, 4780, 4910, 4924, 4962, 4982, 4983, 5000, 5461, 5478, 5555, 5661, 5789, 5926, 5937, 5959, 6007, 6091, 6451, 6470, 6641, 6725, 6743, 6771, 6974, 6994, 7004, 7021, 7030, 7111, 7122, 7198, 7272, 7305, 7329, 7380, 7426, 7649, 7664, 7677, 7684, 8100, 8122, 8143, 8179, 8196, 8208, 8209, 8321, 8334, 8616, 8665, 8689, 8705, 8733, 8787, 8807, 8824, 8833, 9505, 9562, 9712, 9985, 10171, 10176, 10501, 10408, 10612, 10923–10926, 14546, 14600, 14622, 14644, 14659, 14677. 14697, 14707, 14716, 14783, 14784, 14798, 14834, 14849
C_6H_{14}	2-Methylpentane. B.p., 60.4 80, 5927, 5938, 5960, 7665, 14678
C_6H_{14}	3-Methylpentane. B.p., 63.3 79, 5928, 5939, 5961, 7666, 14679
$C_6H_{14}O$	Amyl methyl ether. B.p., 100 30
$C_6H_{14}O$	*tert*-Amyl methyl ether. B.p., 86 339, 1526, 7273, 8808
$C_6H_{14}O$	*tert*-Butyl ethyl ether. B.p., 73 340, 3452, 7274, 8809, 14645, 14698
$C_6H_{14}O$	2-Ethyl-1-butanol. B.p., 148.9 341, 10927
$C_6H_{14}O$	Ethyl isobutyl ether. B.p., 79 7381
$C_6H_{14}O$	Hexyl alcohol. b.p., 157.85 342, 574, 889, 1323, 1863, 1992, 2309, 3016, 3594, 4159, 4205, 4249, 4342, 4470, 4539, 5153, 5339, 6053, 6072, 6149, 6229, 6285, 6358, 6847, 7066, 7330, 7711, 7817, 8078, 8436, 8493, 8581, 8631, 8852, 9192, 9237, 9306, 9378, 9519, 9563, 9713, 9745, 9986, 10180, 10285, 10452, 10482, 10516, 10783, 10833, 10842, 10852, 10888, 10889, 10928–10981
$C_6H_{14}O$	Isopropyl ether. B.p., 69 31, 343, 983, 1753, 2365, 2407, 2823, 2926, 4314, 4452, 4642, 4984, 5556, 5929, 6008, 6975, 6995, 7022, 7639, 8834, 9714, 10509, 10923, 10928, 14616, 14699
$C_6H_{14}O$	Propyl ether. B.p., 90.7 344, 658, 831, 1018, 1527, 2408, 2420, 2511, 2824, 3310, 3453, 4315, 4643, 4692, 4825, 4911, 5103, 5557, 5662, 5738, 6212, 6336, 6452, 6642, 6744, 6772, 6892, 6924, 6996, 7038, 7112, 7199, 7275, 7306, 7382, 7640, 7798, 8046, 8144, 8164, 8180, 8210, 8306, 8322, 8335, 8567, 8605, 8617, 8825, 9715, 10172, 10502, 10981–10986, 14660
$C_6H_{14}O_2$	Acetal (acetaldehyde diethyl acetal). B.p., 103.6 345, 575, 659, 832, 1019, 1324, 1528, 1754, 2224, 2247, 2572, 3311, 3454, 3595, 4293, 4644, 4912, 5080, 5496, 5558, 5559, 5663, 6453, 6773, 6962, 7200, 7383, 7641, 8145, 8165, 8181, 8197, 8211, 8307, 8323, 8336, 8532, 8568, 8618, 9716, 10173, 10503, 10613, 10710, 10728, 10771, 10987–10994, 14601
$C_6H_{14}O_2$	2-Butoxyethanol. B.p., 171.2 346, 890, 1076, 1642, 1864, 1993, 2310, 2732, 2825, 3017, 3596, 3881, 4384, 4471, 4540, 5154, 5340, 6073, 6150, 6230, 6359, 6788, 6848, 7712, 7818, 8437, 8582, 8632, 9010, 9193, 9238, 9307, 9379, 9520, 9564, 9746, 9987, 10105, 10286, 10320, 10382, 10483, 10517, 10784, 10853, 10889, 10929, 10995–11054

Formula	Name and System Nos.
$C_6H_{14}O_2$	1,2-Diethoxyethane. B.p., 123 347, 7461
$C_6H_{14}O_2$	Ethoxypropoxymethane. B.p., 113.7 348, 3455, 5497, 5664, 8182, 8337, 10711, 14602, 14661
$C_6H_{14}O_2$	Pinacol (2,3-dimethyl-2,3-butanediol). B.p., 174.35 349, 1865, 3018, 3597, 4472, 5155, 5341, 6054, 6151, 8583, 8853, 9239, 9308, 9380, 9565, 9643, 9747, 9988, 10287, 10854, 10900, 11055–11087
$C_6H_{14}O_3$	Dipropylene glycol. B.p., 229.2 4408, 9107, 9152, 9644, 9861, 11088–11110
$C_6H_{14}O_3$	2-(2-Ethoxyethoxy)ethanol. B.p., 261.9 5342, 9748, 9989, 11111–11131
$C_6H_{14}O_4$	Triethylene glycol. B.p., 288.7 350, 5822, 9133, 11132-11156
$C_6H_{14}S$	Isopropyl sulfide. B.p., 120.5 576, 891, 1027, 1167, 1325, 1529, 2160, 2421, 2573, 2733, 2826, 3266, 3456, 4098, 4160, 5343, 5560, 6039, 6122, 6396, 6893, 6925, 7201, 7384, 7799, 8146, 8338, 8550, 10586, 10600, 10699, 10712, 10729, 10987, 11157–11160
$C_6H_{14}S$	Propyl sulfide. B.p., 141.5 1168, 1326, 1994, 2574, 2827, 3882, 4097, 4206, 4826, 5156, 6040, 6055, 6231, 6286, 6397, 6506, 6849, 7138, 7202, 7385, 7462, 7713, 7870, 8053, 8236, 8354, 8734, 8810, 9309, 9381, 10072, 10181, 10623, 11161–11165
$C_6H_{15}BO_3$	Ethyl borate. B.p., 118.6 1643, 4099, 6604, 7094, 7203, 7386, 8551, 8735, 10587, 10700, 10730, 10843, 11166-11169
$C_6H_{15}N$	Diisopropylamine. B.p., 83.86 351
$C_6H_{15}N$	3,3-Dimethyl-1-butylamine. B.p., 112.8 352
$C_6H_{15}N$	Dipropylamine. B.p., 109.2 6094, 6454, 8147, 10588, 10601, 10614, 10981, 10988, 11170–11174
$C_6H_{15}N$	Isohexylamine. 11175–11177
$C_6H_{15}N$	Triethylamine. B.p., 89.4 353, 771, 984, 1530, 2575, 3457, 4426, 4645, 6455, 7331, 8109, 8706, 8835, 9717, 10510, 10924, 10982, 10989, 11178, 11179, 14603
$C_6H_{15}NO$	2-Diethylaminoethanol. B.p., 162 354, 1327, 3019, 7463, 8854, 9718, 9990, 10488, 10995, 11180–11191
$C_6H_{15}NO$	3-Isopropoxypropylamine. B.p., 147 355
$C_6H_{16}SiO$	Ethoxymethyltrimethylsilane. B.p., 102 3458
$C_6H_{16}O_2Si$	Diethoxydimethylsilane. B.p., 114 3459
$C_6H_{18}Si_2O$	Hexamethyldisiloxane. B.p., 100 5976
C_7F_{16}	Perfluoroheptane. B.p., 81.6
$C_7H_5Cl_3$	*α,α,α*-Trichlorotoluene (phenyl chloroform). B.p., 220.9 3020, 3598, 5157, 9038, 9108, 9566, 11192–11217
C_7H_5N	Benzonitrile. B.p., 191.3 3599, 4385, 5344, 8910, 9011, 9240, 9521, 9749, 9991, 10321, 10408, 10996, 11218–11249
C_7H_5NO	Phenyl isocyanate. B.p., 162.8 11250, 11251
$C_7H_6Cl_2$	*α,α*-Dichlorotoluene. B.p., 205.2 2080, 3021, 3600, 6507, 6668, 8237, 9567, 9750, 9862, 10225, 10409, 10636, 11252–11282
C_7H_6O	Benzaldehyde. B.p., 179.2 1672, 1866, 2081, 3022, 3601, 3960, 4386, 4473, 4827, 5158, 6014, 6360, 6508, 6669, 7819, 7925, 8238, 8355, 8855, 9194, 9241, 9522, 9568, 9751, 9992, 10322, 10459, 10489, 10518, 10737, 10785, 10855, 10930, 10997, 11283–11341, 14873, 14901, 14902
$C_7H_6O_2$	Benzoic acid. B.p., 250.5 3023, 4043, 4646, 5159, 8977, 9039, 9134, 9153, 9863, 10226, 11252, 11342–11389
$C_7H_6O_2$	Salicylaldehyde. B.p., 196.7 8356, 10738
C_7H_7Br	*α*-Bromotoluene. B.p., 198.5 2082, 4034, 6509, 6670, 7975, 8239, 8240, 8357, 9404, 9752, 9993, 10106, 10137, 10227, 10410, 10637, 10227, 10410, 10637, 10739, 11390–11412
C_7H_7Br	*m*-Bromotoluene. B.p., 184.3 2035, 2083, 2828, 3024, 3602, 3836, 3883, 4474, 4541, 4828, 5161, 5345, 6152, 6510, 6789, 7976, 8241, 8358, 9523, 9753, 9994, 10107, 10228, 10288, 10323, 10411, 10519, 10740, 11218, 11283, 11413–11432

Formula	Name and System Nos.
C_7H_7Br	*o*-Bromotoluene. B.p., 181.45 1803, 1937, 2036, 2084, 2829, 3025, 3603, 3837, 3884, 4409, 4475, 4542, 4829, 5160, 5346, 6153, 6314, 6361, 6511, 6671, 7714, 7715, 7871, 7977, 8242, 8359, 9405, 9569, 9754, 9995, 10108, 10229, 10289, 10324, 10383, 10412, 10463, 10520, 10638, 10741, 10856, 10931,10998, 11284, 11433, 11219, 11433–11471, 14813, 14882, 14884, 14885. 14889, 14890, 14894, 14897
C_7H_7Br	*p*-Bromotoluene. B.p., 185 1673, 2085, 2830, 3026, 3604, 3838, 4476, 4543, 5162, 5347, 6154, 6512, 7978, 8243, 8360, 9342, 9406, 9755, 9996, 10230, 10324, 10384, 10413, 10521, 10639, 10742, 11285, 11220, 11221, 11285, 11471–11497, 14886
C_7H_7BrO	*o*-Bromoanisole. B.p., 217.7 3027, 5163, 7525, 9040, 9645, 9864, 10640, 11088, 11498–11505
C_7H_7BrO	*p*-Bromoanisole. B.p., 217.7 11506–11508
C_7H_7Cl	*α*-Chlorotoluene. B.p., 179.3 1804, 2086, 2576, 3028, 3605, 3839, 4477, 4544, 4830, 5057, 6155, 6513, 6672, 7716, 7859, 7926, 7979, 8244, 8361, 9407, 9570, 9756, 9997, 10109, 10231, 10290, 10326, 10460, 10522, 10641, 10743, 10857, 10932, 11286, 11433, 11509–11547, 14814, 14845, 14847, 14873, 14875–14877, 14895, 14899, 14901–14905
C_7H_7Cl	*m*-Chlorotoluene. B.p., 162.3 10642
C_7H_7Cl	*o*-Chlorotoluene. B.p., 159.2 1077, 1169, 1805, 1867, 2087, 2577, 2831, 2932, 3029, 3606, 3885, 3976, 4250, 4478, 4545, 4831, 5164, 5348, 6041, 6156, 6232, 6287, 6515, 6673, 7464, 7717, 7872, 7927, 7980, 8029, 8245, 8362, 8438, 8494, 8633, 8736, 8856, 9310, 9408, 9757, 9998, 10182, 10232, 10327, 10523, 10643, 10744, 10786, 10858, 10933, 10999, 11055, 11287, 11548–11570
C_7H_7Cl	*p*-Chlorotoluene. B.p., 163.5 356, 1170, 1868, 2088, 2578, 2832, 3030, 3607, 3840, 3886, 3977, 4387, 4479, 4832, 5349, 6157, 6233, 6315, 6362, 6516, 6674, 6790, 7465, 7718, 7873, 7928, 7981, 8030, 8246, 8363, 8439, 8634, 8737, 8857, 9758, 9972, 9999, 10183, 10233, 10291, 10328, 10471, 10524, 10634, 10745, 10787, 10859, 10934, 11000, 11056, 11222, 11288, 11571–11600
C_7H_7ClO	*m*-Chloroanisole. B.p., 193.3 5350, 5983, 7719, 11601, 11602
C_7H_7ClO	*o*-Chloroanisole. B.p., 195.7 3031, 5165, 5353, 6412, 9759, 11001, 11289, 11603
C_7H_7ClO	*p*-Chloroanisole. B.p., 197.8 3032, 5166, 5984, 9343, 9646, 11604–11611
C_7H_7I	*p*-Iodotoluene. B.p. 214.5 1806, 2037, 2089, 3033, 3608, 4410, 5167, 5352, 8364, 9571, 9647, 9760, 9865, 10645, 11498, 11612–11642
$C_7H_7NO_2$	*m*-Nitrotoluene. B.p., 230.8 3034, 3609, 5168, 5353, 5823, 7526, 7895, 9041, 9109, 9866, 10081, 11192, 11342, 11643–11685
$C_7H_7NO_2$	*o*-Nitrotoluene. B.p., 221.75 3035, 3610, 3887, 4044, 5169, 5354, 5824, 6010, 7527, 7896, 8911, 8978, 9042, 9648, 9867, 10000, 10646, 11089, 11193, 11253, 11343, 11612, 11686–11745
$C_7H_7NO_2$	*p*-Nitrotoluene. B.p., 238.9 3036, 3611, 5170, 5355, 5825, 7528, 7897, 9043, 9110, 9135, 9154, 9868, 9929, 10082, 10647, 11090, 11194, 11344, 11746–11784
C_7H_8	Toluene. B.p., 110.7 87, 357, 577, 660, 772, 892, 985, 1020, 1028, 1171, 1328, 1531, 1644, 1786, 1995, 2198, 2248, 2310, 2408, 2422, 2434, 2463, 2579, 2833, 2933, 3037, 3267, 3312, 3460, 3612, 3978, 4100, 4161, 4207, 4294, 4316, 4480, 4546, 4647, 4693, 4833, 4913, 5029, 5081, 5171, 5356, 5467, 5498, 5561, 5665, 5739, 5826, 6042, 6085, 6158, 6328, 6457, 6517, 6605, 6606, 6612, 6643, 6675, 6774, 6850, 6894, 6926, 7067, 7074, 7095, 7139, 7204, 7276, 7307, 7332, 7387, 7466, 7515, 7602, 7720, 7800, 7849, 7860, 8054, 8088, 8123, 8148, 8166, 8183, 8198, 8212, 8247, 8308, 8324, 8339, 8414, 8440, 8495, 8552, 8558, 8606, 8619, 8666, 8691, 8738, 8788, 8811, 8826, 8858, 9311, 9382, 9572, 9719, 9761, 10001, 10075, 10077, 10205, 10504, 10525, 10589, 10602, 10615, 10624, 10701, 10713, 10722, 10731, 10772, 10778, 10844, 10935, 10983, 10990, 11057, 11157, 11166, 11170, 11175, 11180, 11785–11804, 14547, 14568, 14604, 14622, 14647, 14662, 14667 14717, 14741, 14756, 14819, 14838, 14840, 14850, 14867, 14868, 14906
C_7H_8O	Anisole (methoxybenzene). B.p., 153.85 358, 893, 1869, 1996, 2435, 2580, 2834 3038, 3613, 3888, 3947, 3957, 3979, 4251, 4343, 4481, 4834, 5030, 5357, 5740, 6056, 6123, 6159, 6234, 6288, 6398, 6518, 6676, 6851, 7205, 7467, 7721, 7820, 7874 7929, 7982, 8031, 8248, 8365, 8441, 8496, 8584, 8635, 8739, 8859, 9312, 9762, 10002, 10184, 10234, 10292, 10329, 10526, 10788, 10860, 10901, 10936, 11002, 11058, 11181, 11290, 11548, 11571, 11805–11833, 14870, 14893 14898
C_7H_8O	Benzyl alcohol. B.p., 205.2 359, 1674, 3039, 3614, 4388, 4547, 5058, 5172, 5358, 6413, 6791, 7529, 8912, 8979, 9012, 9044, 9155, 9195, 9242, 9524, 9573, 9649, 9763, 10003, 10138, 11091, 11195, 11223, 11254, 11413, 11434, 11471, 11509, 11613, 11643, 11686, 11746, 11834–11902, 14883, 14891

Formula	Name and System Nos.
C_7H_8O	*m*-Cresol. B.p., 202.2 1675, 1807, 1938, 2090, 3040, 3615, 3616, 3841, 5173, 5359, 5985, 6792, 7527, 7667, 8497, 8980, 9045, 9136, 9196, 9574, 9650, 9764, 10004, 10110, 10139, 10218, 10330, 10385, 10648, 10789, 10861,11003, 11059, 11111, 11224, 11255, 11291, 11435, 11472, 11499, 11614, 11687, 11834, 11903–11972
C_7H_8O	*o*-Cresol. B.p., 191.1 894, 1676, 1808, 1870, 1939, 2091, 3041, 3617, 3889, 3989, 4252, 4389, 4482, 4548, 5174, 5360, 5827, 6793, 6852, 7983, 8249, 8366, 8442, 8498, 8860, 8913, 9344, 9409, 9525, 9575, 9651, 9765, 10005, 10111, 10140, 10235, 10293, 10331, 10386, 10414, 10527, 10649, 10746, 10790, 10834, 10862, 10890, 10937, 11004, 11060, 11112, 11182, 11225, 11256, 11292, 11390, 11414, 11436, 11473, 11510, 11549, 11572, 11603, 11615, 11835, 11903, 11973–12057
C_7H_8O	*p*-Cresol. B.p., 201.7 1678, 1809, 2038, 2092, 3042, 3618, 3619, 3890, 4045, 5059, 5175, 5361, 5797, 5828, 5986, 6794, 7531, 7984, 8367, 8499, 8914, 8982, 9014, 9047, 9198, 9244, 9345, 9526, 9576, 9652, 9766, 10006, 10112, 10141, 10219, 10332, 10387, 10415, 10650, 10651, 10747, 10791, 10835, 10863, 11005, 11061, 11092, 11113, 11226, 11257, 11293, 11391, 11437, 11474, 11616, 11836, 11904, 11973, 12058–12147
$C_7H_8O_2$	Guaiacol (*o*-methoxyphenol). B.p., 205.05 1810, 1940, 2039, 2093, 3043, 3620, 4035, 5176, 5829, 5987, 6795, 8915, 9048, 9447, 9577, 10007, 10142, 10652, 10748, 11196, 11837, 11905, 12058, 12148–12187
$C_7H_8O_2$	*m*-Methoxyphenol. B.p., 214.7 360, 3044, 3621, 5177, 5798, 9049, 9869, 10083, 11345, 12188–12204
C_7H_8S	α-Toluenethiol. B.p., 194.8 12205
C_7H_9N	Benzylamine. B.p., 185.0 8861, 8916, 9578, 9767, 10008, 11006, 11906, 11974, 12059, 12206–12213
C_7H_9N	2,6-Lutidine (2,6-dimethylpyridine). B.p., 144 361, 1172, 2581, 4835, 9410, 9768, 11785, 12214–12217
C_7H_9N	Methylaniline. B.p., 196.25 3045, 3622, 3891, 5178, 5799, 8862, 8917, 8983, 9199, 9245, 9527, 9579, 9769, 10333, 10490, 11007, 11183, 11227, 11258, 11392, 11415, 11688, 11838, 11907, 11975, 12060, 12148, 12218–12245
C_7H_9N	*m*-Toluidine. B.p., 203.1 3046, 3623, 5179, 8984, 9050, 9528, 9580, 9770, 10491, 11438, 11617, 11839, 11908, 11976, 12061, 12149, 12246–12263
C_7H_9N	*o*-Toluidine. B.p., 200.35 3047, 3624, 3892, 5180, 9015, 9051, 9529, 9581, 9771, 10492, 11197, 11228, 11259, 11416, 11439, 11475, 11618, 11840, 11909, 11977, 12062, 12150, 12218, 12264–12287
C_7H_9N	*p*-Toluidine. B.p., 200.55 3048, 3625, 5181, 8985, 9016, 9052, 9530, 9582, 9772, 11260, 11393, 11440, 11476, 11619, 11690, 11841, 11910, 11978, 12063, 12151, 12288–12300
C_7H_9NO	*o*-Anisidine (*ar*-methoxyaniline). B.p., 219.0 3626, 9053, 9111, 9583, 9653, 11620, 11644, 11842, 11979, 12064, 12301–12313
C_7H_{10}	Methylcyclohexadiene. 14726
C_7H_{12}	1-Heptyne. B.p., 99.5 3461, 14605
C_7H_{12}	5-Methyl-1-hexyne. B.p., 90.8 3462
$C_7H_{12}O$	Methylcyclohexanone. B.p., 165.0 2582
$C_7H_{12}O_4$	Ethyl malonate. B.p., 198.9 40, 1679, 3627, 5362, 7532, 8986, 9017, 9531, 9584, 9773, 10113, 10143, 10415, 10653, 10749, 10750, 11229, 11261, 11394, 11477, 11621, 11980, 12065, 12152, 12264, 12314–12349
$C_7H_{13}ClO_2$	Isoamyl chloroacetate. B.p., 195.2 362, 2094, 3049, 3628, 6796, 8250, 8368, 8740, 8918, 10334, 10654, 11008, 11843, 12350–12357, 14744
C_7H_{14}	1,1-Dimethylcyclopentane. B.p., 87.84 3463, 7618, 7650, 14727
C_7H_{14}	*cis*-1,2-Dimethylcyclopentane. B.p., 99.53 3464, 7603, 7651
C_7H_{14}	*trans*-1,2-Dimethylcyclopentane. 3465, 14728
C_7H_{14}	*trans*-1,3-Dimethylcyclopentane. B.p., 90.77 1532, 3466, 7605, 7619, 7652, 14729
C_7H_{14}	Ethylcyclopentane. B.p., 103.45 3467, 7604, 7653, 11786
C_7H_{14}	Heptene. 7206, 12358

Formula — Name and System Nos.

C_7H_{14} Methylcyclohexane. B.p., 101.15
88, 89, 363, 578, 773, 833, 986, 1021, 1173, 1329, 1533, 1755, 1787, 2155, 2199, 2225, 2410, 2583, 2835, 3050, 3268, 3313, 3468, 3469, 3629, 3893, 4102, 4162, 4208, 4295, 4317, 4483, 4549, 4648, 4694, 4836, 4914, 4925, 5082, 5104, 5500, 5562, 5599, 5666, 4571, 6086, 6100, 6329, 6334, 6458, 6519, 6607, 6644, 6745, 6775, 6927, 6963, 7039, 7113, 7207, 7277, 7308, 7388, 7468, 7606, 7642, 7654, 7801, 8124, 8149, 8167, 8184, 8199, 8213, 8309, 8325, 8340, 8443, 8569, 8607, 8620, 8667, 8692, 8741, 8789, 8812, 8827, 8836, 9383, 10009, 10174, 10206, 10505, 10528, 10603, 10616, 10702, 10714, 10773, 10938, 10984, 10991, 11062, 11158, 11167, 11178, 11787, 12359-12362, 14606, 14730, 14843, 14850, 14906

$C_7H_{14}O$ 2,4-Dimethyl-3-pentanone. B.p., 124
4229

$C_7H_{14}O$ Heptaldehyde. B.p., 155
1871, 1997, 3958, 4253

$C_7H_{14}O$ 2-Heptanone. B.p., 149
364, 2584, 3959, 4223, 10792

$C_7H_{14}O$ 4-Heptanone. B.p., 143
365, 895, 1998, 2312, 2734, 2836, 3051, 3894, 4026, 4209, 4344, 6289, 6399, 6677, 6853, 8585, 8668, 8742, 8863, 9384, 10453, 10902, 12363-12375

$C_7H_{14}O$ Isoamyl vinyl ether. B.p., 112.6
8743

$C_7H_{14}O$ 2-Methylcyclohexanol. B.p., 168.5
366, 579, 896, 3052, 4163, 4550, 5363, 6015, 6160, 6235, 6290, 6363, 7722, 7821, 8444, 8586, 8636, 9246, 9654, 9774, 10010, 10185, 10294, 10335, 10793, 10836, 10864, 11009, 11511, 11550, 11573, 11788, 11806, 11981, 12066, 12376-12403

$C_7H_{14}O$ 3-Methylcyclohexanol. B.p., 172
12404

$C_7H_{14}O$ 5-Methyl-2-hexanone. B.p., 144.2
2837, 3053, 4345, 6520, 6678, 7469, 7875, 8445, 8500, 8744, 8864, 10794, 10939, 11161, 12405-12414

$C_7H_{14}O_2$ Amyl acetate. B.p., 148.8
367, 897, 1872, 1999, 2585, 2838, 3054, 3630, 4224, 4346, 5364, 7470, 8501, 8588, 8669, 12415-12421, 14735

$C_7H_{14}O_2$ *sec*-Amyl acetate. B.p., 133.5
368

$C_7H_{14}O_2$ Butyl propionate. B.p., 146.8
369, 1078, 2000, 2735, 3055, 3631, 4347, 6291, 6400, 6854, 7208, 7876, 8865, 11807, 12363, 12405, 12415, 12422-12428

$C_7H_{14}O_2$ Enanthic acid. B.p., 222.0
371, 2040, 3056, 4046, 7898, 9054, 9112, 9137, 9585, 11417, 11512, 11622, 11645, 11691, 11911, 12067, 12429-12453

$C_7H_{14}O_2$ Ethyl isovalerate. B.p., 134.7
372, 898, 1645, 2001, 2313, 2586, 3057, 3632, 4103, 4210, 4348, 4837, 5044, 6124, 6292, 6401, 6856, 7068, 7096, 7209, 7389, 7471, 7850, 7877, 8089, 8415, 8502, 8553, 8589, 8745 8866, 9385, 10207, 10795, 10845, 11162, 12454-12460

$C_7H_{14}O_2$ Ethyl valerate. B.p., 145.45
373, 899, 1873, 3058, 3633, 4349, 4838, 6293, 6857, 8503, 8590, 8746, 8867, 9314, 12364, 12461-12465

$C_7H_{14}O_2$ Isoamyl acetate. B.p., 142.1
374, 900, 1874, 2002, 2314, 2587, 2736, 2839, 3059, 3634, 4104, 4350, 4839, 5045, 5742, 6043, 6125, 6294, 6679, 6858, 7097, 7210, 7390, 7472, 8090, 8504, 8554, 8587, 8747, 9200, 9315, 9386, 9411, 10703, 10796, 10891, 11808, 12365, 12406, 12416, 12461, 12466-12478, 14607, 14745

$C_7H_{14}O_2$ Isobutyl propionate.
375, 901, 1646, 2003, 2315, 2840, 3060, 3635, 4211, 4351, 5743, 6295, 6402, 6855, 7069, 7211, 7391, 7473, 7861, 8055, 8091, 8591, 8748, 8868, 9387, 10208, 10846, 12366, 12407, 12466, 12479-12484

$C_7H_{14}O_2$ Isopropyl butyrate. B.p., 128
4230

$C_7H_{14}O_2$ Isopropyl isobutyrate. B.p., 120.8
376, 1647, 4105, 7098, 7212, 7392, 8555, 11789

$C_7H_{14}O_2$ Methyl caproate. B.p., 149.8
377, 1875, 2004, 3636, 4840, 6859, 7474, 8446, 8593, 8637, 9316, 10186, 10529, 11551, 12486-12490

$C_7H_{14}O_2$ Propyl butyrate. B.p., 142.8
378, 1876, 2005, 2841, 3061, 3637, 3948, 4106, 4352, 4841, 6296, 6403, 6680, 6860, 7213, 7475, 8505, 8592, 8749, 9317, 9388, 10797, 10940, 11809, 12367, 12408, 12417, 12423, 12467 12491-12498, 14865

Formula — Name and System Nos.

$C_7H_{14}O_2$ Propyl isobutyrate. B.p., 133.9
379, 1648, 2316, 2588, 2842, 3638, 4107, 4212, 4353, 6044, 6861, 7099, 7214, 7393, 7862, 7878, 8416, 8594, 8670, 8750, 10209, 10579, 10625, 10847, 12499–12505

$C_7H_{14}O_3$ 1,3-Butanediol methyl ether acetate. B.p., 171.75
380, 1877, 2006, 3063, 3639, 4390, 5182, 5365, 5800, 6236, 6364, 6521, 6681, 6797, 7476, 7723, 7822, 8251, 8369, 8595, 8638, 8869, 9201, 9248, 9318, 9776, 10295, 10336, 10388, 10530, 10941, 11010, 11441, 11574, 11601, 11810, 11982, 12063, 12506–12531

$C_7H_{14}O_3$ 2,2-Dimethoxy-3-pentanone. B.p., 162.5
381

$C_7H_{14}O_3$ Isobutyl lactate. B.p., 182.15
3063, 5183, 8919, 9247, 9532, 9775, 10011, 10493, 11011, 11294, 11418, 11442, 11478, 11513, 11912, 11983, 12069, 12350, 12376, 12532–12551, 14903, 14904, 14907, 14908

C_7H_{16} 2,2-Dimethylpentane. B.p., 79.1
3470, 5930, 7620, 7655, 9720

C_7H_{16} 2,3-Dimethylpentane. B.p., 89.79
3471, 7607, 7621, 7656, 9721

C_7H_{16} 2,4-Dimethylpentane. B.p., 80.8
3472, 5931, 7622, 7657, 9722, 12552

C_7H_{16} 3,3-Dimethylpentane. B.p., 86.0
3473

C_7H_{16} 3-Ethylpentane. B.p., 93.5
3474

C_7H_{16} Heptane. B.p., 98.4
382, 580, 661, 774, 834, 987, 1022, 1174, 1330, 1371, 1534, 1756, 1788, 2200, 2249, 2317, 2411, 2412, 2423, 2589, 2713, 2737, 2843, 2927, 3064, 3270, 3314, 3475, 3640, 3895, 4164, 4296, 4318, 4484, 4551, 4649, 4695, 4915, 4916, 4926, 5031, 5055, 5083, 5500, 5563, 5667, 5744, 6102, 6335, 6459, 6522, 6608, 6645, 6646, 6746, 6747, 6776, 6895, 6928, 6937, 6964, 6997, 7040, 7114, 7215, 7278, 7309, 7394, 7477, 7608, 7623, 7643, 7658, 7802, 8110, 8125,
6997, 7040, 7114, 7215, 7278, 7309, 7394, 7477, 7608, 7623, 7643, 7658, 7802, 8110, 8125,
8150, 8168, 8185, 8200, 8214, 8310, 8326, 8341, 8447, 8570, 8608, 8621, 8693, 8751, 8790, 8813, 8828, 8837, 9389, 9723, 9777, 10012, 10175, 10531, 10590, 10604, 10617, 10704, 10715, 10732, 10774, 10924, 10942, 10925, 10985, 10992, 11063, 11159, 11168, 11179, 11790 12358, 12359, 12485, 14608, 14627, 14680, 14681, 14731, 14867, 14906

C_7H_{16} 2-Methylhexane. B.p., 90.0
1535, 3476, 7609, 7624

C_7H_{16} 3-Methylhexane. B.p., 91.8
1536, 3477, 7610, 7625, 7659, 14732

C_7H_{16} 2,2,3-Trimethylbutane. B.p., 80.87
5932, 7660, 9724, 10506, 12552

$C_7H_{16}O$ Amyl ethyl ether. B.p., 120
383

$C_7H_{16}O$ *tert*-Amyl ethyl ether. B.p., 101
384, 3477, 7278

$C_7H_{16}O$ Butyl isopropyl ether. B.p., 103
5564

$C_7H_{16}O$ 2-Heptanol.
12553

$C_7H_{16}O$ Heptyl alcohol. B.p., 176.15
385, 581, 902, 1079, 1878, 3065, 3641, 4485, 5366, 6074, 6161, 6237, 6365, 6404, 6798, 8032 8596, 9202, 9249, 9319, 9655, 9778, 10013, 10337, 10798, 10837, 10865, 10892, 11012, 11230, 11295, 11443, 11514, 11575, 11791, 11811, 11984, 12219, 12265, 12506, 12554–12573

$C_7H_{16}O_2$ Dipropoxymethane. B.p., 137.2
386, 387, 5668, 7395, 8417, 10454, 10626, 12499, 14663

$C_7H_{16}O_3$ 2-Ethoxyethyl 2-methoxyethyl ether. B.p., 194.2
11913, 12070

$C_7H_{16}O_3$ Ethyl orthoformate. B.p., 195.75
903, 1879, 2007, 2844, 3066, 8506, 9320, 10799, 11812, 12454, 12468, 12574–12580

$C_7H_{16}O_4$ 2-[2-(2-Methoxyethoxy)ethoxy] ethanol. B.p., 245.25
3067, 5184, 5745, 7533, 8920, 9055, 9156, 9586, 11114, 11646, 11692, 11747, 12581–12615

$C_7H_{18}SiO$ Butoxytrimethylsilane. B.p., 124.5
7216

C_8H_6 Phenyl acetylene.
5463

C_8H_7N Indole. B.p., 253.5
3068, 3642, 9870, 12188, 12616–12625

C_8H_7N α-Toluonitrile. B.p., 232.
12626

Formula	Name and System Nos.
C_8H_8	Styrene. B.p., 145 388, 1175, 1331, 1537, 1880, 2008, 2095, 2318, 2436, 2590, 2845, 3069, 3478, 3643, 4213, 4486, 4843, 4917, 5367, 5464, 5465, 5565, 5669, 5746, 5830, 6162, 6238, 6297, 6405, 6523, 6682, 6862, 7217, 7280, 7310, 7396, 7478, 7724, 7930, 7985, 8252, 8448, 8507, 8597, 8639, 8752, 8783, 8814, 8870, 9321, 9779, 10014, 10068, 10236, 10338, 10532, 10800, 10866, 10903, 10943, 11296, 11813, 11985, 12214, 12424, 12455, 12462, 12479, 12491, 12492, 12500, 12574, 12627–12632
C_8H_8O	Acetophenone (methyl phenyl ketone). B.p., 202.05 1811, 2041, 3070, 3644, 3896, 4487, 4552, 5185, 5368, 5801, 6799, 7534, 7986, 8370, 8921, 8987, 9018, 9346, 9412, 9448, 9587, 9656, 9780, 10015, 10144, 10237, 10417, 10655, 10751, 11262, 11395, 11515, 11604, 11844, 11914, 11986, 12071, 12220, 12266, 12288, 12289, 12301, 12314, 12351, 12429, 12633–12665
$C_8H_8O_2$	Anisaldehyde (*p*-methoxybenzaldehyde). B.p., 249.5 7535, 9157, 9871, 11093, 11346, 11748, 12666–12680
$C_8H_8O_2$	Benzyl formate. B.p., 202.3 389, 3071, 3645, 5369, 5831, 7536, 9413, 9449, 9588, 9657, 9781, 10656, 10752, 11198, 11263, 11396, 11845, 11915, 11987, 12072, 12154, 12315, 12633, 12681–12698
$C_8H_8O_2$	Methyl benzoate. B.p., 199.45 390, 2042, 2096, 3072, 3646, 4036, 5186, 5370, 5832, 6800, 7537, 8922, 8988, 9019, 9347, 9450, 9533, 9589, 9658, 9782, 10114, 10145, 10418, 11013, 11264, 11396, 11397, 11623, 11846, 11916, 11988, 12073, 12155, 12316, 12317, 12352, 12581, 12634, 12681, 12699–12727
$C_8H_8O_2$	Phenyl acetate. B.p., 195.7 391, 1680, 2097, 3073, 3647, 5187, 5371, 5833, 6801, 7538, 8253, 8923, 9203, 9348, 9414, 9451, 9534, 9590, 9783, 10146, 10238, 10339, 10389, 10419, 10657, 11014, 11231, 11265, 11398, 11479, 11693, 11847, 11917, 11989, 12074, 12156, 12318, 12635, 12682, 12728–12755
$C_8H_8O_2$	α-Toluic acid. B.p., 266.5 3074, 9056, 9872, 9930, 11749, 12756–12785
$C_8H_8O_3$	Methyl salicylate. B.p., 222.3 3075, 3648, 5188, 5834, 7539, 7899, 8924, 8989, 9057, 9113, 9591, 9659, 11094, 11115, 11199, 11624, 11647, 11694, 11848, 12157, 12302, 12582, 12786–12825
C_8H_9BrO	*p*-Bromophenetole (*p*-bromophenyl ethyl ether). B.p., 234.2 3076, 7540, 9058, 9452, 9660, 9873, 11095, 11200, 12616, 12666, 12826–12835
C_8H_9Cl	*o,m,p*-Chloroethylbenzene. 6524, 7685, 7863, 7931, 8343, 10220, 10719, 10927, 10944, 11015, 11185, 11297, 12553
C_8H_{10}	Ethylbenzene. B.p., 136.15 90, 392, 582, 904, 1176, 1332, 1538, 1649, 2009, 2098, 2161, 2210, 2319, 2591, 2738, 2846, 3027, 3480, 3649, 3897, 3936, 3980, 4027, 4108, 4165, 4214, 4319, 4354, 4488, 4844, 4918, 5372, 5466, 5566, 5670, 5747, 6163, 6298, 6406, 6525, 6683, 6863, 7070, 7140, 7218, 7281, 7282, 7311, 7397, 7419, 7725, 7803, 7851, 7863, 8046, 8254, 8418, 8449, 8508, 8671, 8672, 8694, 8753, 8784, 8791, 8815, 8816, 8829, 8871, 9322, 9390, 9784, 10016, 10069, 10210, 10455, 10591, 10605, 10627, 10705, 10723, 10733, 10779, 10801, 10848, 10945, 11792, 12215, 12368, 12377, 12409, 12456, 12469, 12480, 12501, 12627, 12836–12841, 14569, 14632, 14665, 14718, 14818
C_8H_{10}	*m*-Xylene. B.p., 139 393, 583, 1080, 1177, 1333, 1539, 2010, 2100, 2202, 2320, 2437, 2592, 2739, 2847, 3079, 3271, 3481, 3650, 3898, 3939, 3981, 4028, 4215, 4216, 4355, 4489, 4553, 4696, 4845, 4919, 4927, 5032, 5046, 5189, 5373, 5566, 5671, 5748, 5835, 6045, 6126, 6164, 6299, 6526, 6684, 6864, 7219, 7220, 7283, 7398, 7480, 7726, 7804, 7879, 7932, 8056, 8092, 8255, 8371, 8419, 8450, 8509, 8598, 8640, 8695, 8754, 8817, 8872, 9323, 9391, 9785, 10017, 10070, 10211, 10239, 10296, 10456, 10484, 10533, 10592, 10628, 10802, 10849, 10904, 10946, 11016, 11064, 11163, 11186, 11814, 12216, 12369, 12378, 12457, 12463, 12470, 12481, 12486, 12493, 12502, 12554, 12575, 12628, 12836, 12842–12848, 14530, 14570, 14666, 14748, 14864, 14865
C_8H_{10}	*o*-Xylene. B.p., 143.6 1178, 1334, 1540, 1881, 2011, 2099, 2438, 2593, 2848, 2934, 3078, 3482, 3651, 3899, 3938, 3982, 4356, 4554, 4846, 5033, 5047, 5191, 5567, 5672, 5749, 5836, 6165, 6300, 6527, 6685, 7102, 7221, 7399, 7481, 7727, 8256, 8372, 8451, 8510, 8696, 8755, 8873, 9786, 10018, 10187, 10240, 10297, 10534, 10803, 10905, 10947, 11017, 11298, 11815, 11990, 12370, 12410, 12418, 12425, 12464, 12471, 12482, 12487, 12494, 12629, 12842, 12849
C_8H_{10}	*p*-Xylene. B.p., 138.4 1179, 1541, 2101, 2321, 2322, 2594, 2740, 2849, 3080, 3483, 3652, 3939, 4217, 4357, 4490, 4847, 5569, 5673, 5750, 6301, 6528, 6686, 6865, 7222, 7312, 7400, 7482, 7728, 8093, 8257, 8420, 8452, 8511, 8673, 8756, 8874, 9392, 10019, 10241, 10535, 10629, 10804, 10850, 10948, 11164, 12458, 12472, 12483, 12503, 12841, 12843
$C_8H_{10}O$	Benzyl methyl ether. B.p., 167.8 906, 1882, 2596, 2850, 2935, 3081, 3653, 3900, 4254, 4391, 4491, 4555, 4848, 5374, 6057, 6166, 6239, 6529, 6687, 6802, 6866, 7483, 7729, 7933, 7987, 8258, 8373, 8757, 8925, 9250, 9324, 9787, 10020, 10298, 10340, 10390, 10464, 10536, 10753, 10805, 10867, 10893, 10949, 11018, 11065, 11232, 11299, 11552, 12206, 12379, 12532, 12555, 12850–12861

Formula	Name and System Nos.
$C_8H_{10}O$	*o*-Ethylphenol. B.p., 216.5 12862
$C_8H_{10}O$	*p*-Ethylphenol. B.p., 218.8 3655, 5375, 5988, 6414, 9060, 9114, 9592, 10658, 11300, 11625, 11649, 11849, 12246, 12636, 12786, 12863–12889
$C_8H_{10}O$	*m*-Methylanisole (*m*-methoxytoluene). B.p., 177.2 5376, 7484, 8259
$C_8H_{10}O$	*p*-Methylanisole (*p*-methoxytoluene). B.p., 177.05 1883, 3082, 3654, 3901, 3990, 4392, 4492, 4556, 4849, 5377, 6240, 6688, 7730, 7988, 8374, 8875, 9204, 9251, 9252, 9535, 9788, 10021, 10115, 10242, 10299, 10341, 10420, 10538, 10754, 10806, 10868, 10950, 11019, 11066, 11301, 11444, 12207, 12221, 12380, 12507, 12556, 12890–12911
$C_8H_{10}O$	Phenethyl alcohol (2-phenylethanol). B.p., 219.5 3083, 3656, 5192, 5378, 5837, 6803, 7541, 8926, 8990, 9061, 9453, 9593, 9661, 10084, 11626, 11695, 11751, 11918, 12075, 12158, 12267, 12787, 12863, 12912–12949
$C_8H_{10}O$	Phenetole (ethyl phenyl ether). B.p., 170.4 394, 1884, 2102, 2439, 2851, 2936, 3084, 3657, 3842, 3902, 4255, 4393, 4493, 4850, 5193, 5379, 6167, 6241, 6530, 6689, 7485, 7731, 7824, 7880, 7934, 7989, 8033, 8260, 8375, 8453, 8758, 8876, 9205, 9253, 9415, 9536, 9789, 10022, 10243, 10300, 10342, 10391, 10465, 10472, 10537, 10755, 10807, 10869, 10906, 10951, 11020, 11067, 11233, 11302, 11445, 11516, 11553, 11576, 11992, 12208, 12381, 12404, 12508, 12533, 12557, 12950–12981, 14900
$C_8H_{10}O$	2,4-Xylenol (2,4-dimethylphenol). 210.5 3085, 5380, 5989, 6415, 6804, 9062, 9454, 11480, 11672, 11690, 11919, 12159, 12534, 12637, 12699, 12728, 12864, 12982–12993
$C_8H_{10}O$	3,4-Xylenol (3,4-dimethylphenol). B.p., 226.8 3086, 3658, 3194, 5381, 5838, 6416, 7542, 7900, 9059, 9115, 9158, 9455, 9594, 9662, 9874, 10147, 10659, 11116, 11347, 11500, 11628, 11648, 11697, 11751, 11850, 12247, 12303, 12430, 12638, 12683, 12788, 12826, 12912, 12994–13035
$C_8H_{10}O_2$	*m*-Dimethoxybenzene. B.p., 214.7 3087, 5839, 9063, 9457, 9595, 9663, 10148, 10660, 11201, 11629, 11698, 11851, 11920, 12076, 12160, 12268, 12319, 12684, 12789, 13036, 13048
$C_8H_{10}O_2$	*m*-Ethoxyphenol. B.p., 243.8 13049
$C_8H_{10}O_2$	*o*-Ethoxyphenol. B.p., 216.5 2043, 3088, 3659, 5195, 5840, 6417, 9064, 9458, 9596, 10023, 10149, 10661, 11699, 11852, 12077, 12222, 12248, 12431, 12639, 12790, 12994, 13050–13072
$C_8H_{10}O_2$	2-Phenoxyethanol. B.p., 245.2 4411, 7543, 9065, 11853, 12583, 12791, 12866, 12913, 12995, 13050, 13073–13084
$C_8H_{10}O_2$	Veratrole (*o*-dimethoxybenzene). B.p., 205.5 395, 3089, 3660, 4412, 5382, 7990, 9456, 9597, 9664, 9790, 10024, 10150, 10244, 10343, 10392, 10662, 11630, 11700, 11854, 11921, 11993, 12078, 12640, 12700, 12729, 12865, 13085–13095
$C_8H_{11}N$	*s*-Collidine (2,4,6-trimethylpyridine). B.p., 171 396, 13146
$C_8H_{11}N$	*N,N*-Dimethylaniline. B.p., 194.05 1180, 2597, 3090, 3661, 3903, 5196, 5802, 7825, 8877, 8927, 8991, 9020, 9206, 9254, 9537, 9598, 9791, 10494, 10539, 10952, 11021, 11068, 11117, 11187, 11234, 11266, 11303, 11399, 11419, 11446, 11481, 11517, 11631, 11701, 11855, 11922, 11994, 12079, 12161, 12223, 12382, 12558, 12641, 12890, 12914, 12950, 13051, 13085, 13096–13123
$C_8H_{11}N$	Ethylaniline. B.p., 205.5 3093, 3664, 3905, 5199, 8992, 9066, 9538, 9599, 9792, 10495, 11235, 11267, 11702, 11856, 11923, 11995, 12081, 12162, 12249, 12642, 12867, 12915, 12997, 13052, 13086, 13124–13145
$C_8H_{11}N$	2,4-Xylidine (2,4-dimethylaniline). B.p., 214.0 3091, 3662, 3904, 5197, 9600, 11632, 11703, 11857, 11996, 12080, 12163, 12643, 12916, 12996, 13036, 13053, 13147–13154
$C_8H_{11}N$	3,4-Xylidine (3,4-dimethylaniline). B.p., 225.5 3092, 3663, 5198, 9067, 9601, 11704, 11858, 12917, 13037, 13155–13160
$C_8H_{11}NO$	*o*-Phenetidine (2-ethoxyaniline). B.p., 232.5 3094, 3665, 5200, 7544, 9068, 9116, 9138, 9159, 9665, 9875, 9931, 11650, 11705, 11752, 11859, 12792, 12868, 12918, 12998, 13161–13179
$C_8H_{11}NO$	*p*-Phenetidine (4-ethoxyaniline). B.p., 249.9 3095, 3666, 7545, 9117, 9139, 9160, 9876, 9932, 11348, 11651, 11753, 12999, 13180–13199
$C_8H_{12}O_4$	Ethyl fumarate. B.p., 217.85 3096, 3667, 5201, 5383, 5841, 6805, 7546, 9069, 9459, 9602, 9666, 11652, 11706, 11924, 11997, 12082, 12432, 12584, 12793, 12869, 12919, 12982, 13000, 13038, 13087, 13200–13226

Formula	Name and System Nos.
$C_8H_{12}O_4$	Ethyl maleate. B.p., 223.3 397, 2103, 3097, 3668, 5202, 5384, 5842, 7547, 7901, 9460, 9603, 9667, 9877, 11653, 11707, 11925, 11998, 12083, 12433, 12585, 12794, 12870, 12920, 12983, 13001, 13039, 13054, 13227–13251
C_8H_{14}	Diisobutylene. B.p., 101 398, 14700, 14733, 14872
$C_8H_{14}O$	2-Methallyl ether. B.p., 134.6 399, 6469
$C_8H_{14}O$	2,4,6-Trimethyl-5,6-dihydro-1,2-pyran. 14749
$C_8H_{14}O$	Methylheptenone. B.p., 173.2 1885, 3098, 3669, 4494, 5203, 5385, 6531, 7732, 7935, 7991, 8261, 9255, 9793, 10025, 10245, 10301, 10540, 11069, 11304, 11447, 11518, 11554, 11577, 11999, 12383, 12559, 12850, 12951, 13252–13270
$C_8H_{14}O_2$	Cyclohexyl acetate. B.p., 177.0 2598
$C_8H_{14}O_4$	*meso*-2,3-Butanediol diacetate. B.p., 190 2599, 7427
$C_8H_{14}O_4$	Ethyl succinate. B.p., 217.25 3670, 4047, 5386, 7548, 9070, 9461, 9604, 9668, 11268, 11654, 11708, 12000, 12084, 12434, 13055, 13271–13296
$C_8H_{14}O_4$	Propyl oxalate. B.p., 214 9071, 9605, 10151, 10633, 11269, 11400, 11633, 12320, 12435, 12644, 12701, 13200, 13277 13297–13303
$C_8H_{15}N$	Caprylonitrile. B.p., 205.2 13304
$C_8H_{15}N$	Dimethylallylamine. B.p., 149.0 400
C_8H_{16}	1,1-Dimethylcyclohexane. 3484
C_8H_{16}	*trans*-1,2-Dimethylcyclohexane. 5571
C_8H_{16}	1,3-Dimethylcyclohexane. B.p., 120.7 91, 584, 1181, 1335, 1542, 1650, 1789, 2012, 2323, 2600, 2741, 2852, 3315, 3485, 3671, 4109, 4166, 4218, 4851, 4920, 5048, 5570, 5674, 6127, 6168, 6532, 6690, 7100, 7141, 7223, 7313, 7401, 7486, 7733, 7805, 7853, 8094, 8151, 8311, 8421, 8454, 8512, 8558, 8622, 8674, 8697, 8759, 8818, 8878, 9393, 10026, 10213, 10457, 10541, 10593, 10606, 10618, 10630, 10706, 10716, 10734, 10775, 11172, 11176, 11793, 11794, 12473, 13305, 13306
C_8H_{16}	*cis*-1,4-Dimethylcyclohexane. 3486
C_8H_{16}	*trans*-1,4-Dimethylcyclohexane. 3487
C_8H_{16}	Ethylcyclohexane. B.p., 131.8 2601, 6103, 7487
C_8H_{16}	6-Methyl-1-heptene. B.p., 109 8759
C_8H_{16}	1-Octene. B.p., 121.6 2203
C_8H_{16}	2-Octene. B.p., 125.2 2204
C_8H_{16}	1,1,2-Trimethylcyclopentane. 5572
C_8H_{16}	1,1,3-Trimethylcyclopentane. B.p., 104.9 5573, 5752, 11795
C_8H_{16}	*cis-cis-trans*-1,2,4-Trimethylcyclopentane. 5574
C_8H_{16}	*cis-trans-cis*-1,2,3-Trimethylcyclopentane. B.p., 110.4 11796
C_8H_{16}	*cis-trans-cis*-1,2,4-Trimethylcyclopentane. B.p., 109.3 3488, 11797
C_8H_{16}	2,3,4-Trimethyl-2-pentene. B.p., 116 11798
$C_8H_{16}O$	Allyl isoamyl ether. B.p., 120 401
$C_8H_{16}O$	2-Octanone. B.p., 174.1 1886, 3099, 3672, 4394, 4495, 4557, 5204, 5387, 5803, 6242, 6366, 6533, 7734, 7881, 7936, 8034, 8262, 8376, 9256, 9349, 9794, 10027, 10302, 10542, 10808, 10870, 10907, 10953, 11070, 11305, 11420, 11448, 11519, 11578, 11816, 12001, 12321, 12353, 12384, 12509, 12851, 12891, 12952, 13307–13327

Name and System Nos.

$C_8H_{16}O$ 2,2,5,5-Tetramethyltetrahydrofuran. B.p., 115
402

$C_8H_{16}O_2$ Amyl propionate.
4852

$C_8H_{16}O_2$ Butyl butyrate. B.p., 165.7
403, 907, 1081, 1924, 2013, 2104, 3100, 3673, 5205, 5388, 6075, 6169, 6367, 6534, 6867, 7224, 7735, 7826, 8035, 8455, 8879, 9207, 9257, 9325, 9350, 9795, 10188, 10246, 10303, 10543, 10954, 11022, 11306, 11520, 11555, 11579, 11817, 12852, 12892, 12953, 13307, 13328–13346

$C_8H_{16}O_2$ Caprylic acid. B.p., 238.5
3102, 7902, 9072, 9161, 9606, 9878, 11655, 11709, 11754, 13002, 13201, 13228, 13271, 13347–13348

$C_8H_{16}O_2$ Ethyl caproate. B.p., 166.8
404, 1887, 2105, 5389, 6170, 6692, 7937, 8513, 9258, 9796, 10304, 10809, 11023, 11307, 11521, 11580, 12510, 12560, 13328, 13363–13373

$C_8H_{16}O_2$ 2-Ethyl caproic acid. B.p., 227
11926, 12085

$C_8H_{16}O_2$ Hexyl acetate. B.p., 171.5
1888, 2106, 3103, 4395, 6171, 7992, 8264, 9259, 10305, 10344, 10810, 11024, 11308, 11522, 12511, 12954, 13309, 13374–13377

$C_8H_{16}O_2$ Isoamyl propionate. B.p., 160.3
405, 908, 1082, 1889, 2014, 3104, 3674, 4396, 4496, 5206, 5390, 6076, 6128, 6172, 6535, 6691, 6868, 7736, 7827, 7882, 7938, 8036, 8456, 8514, 8641, 8761, 8928, 9260, 9326, 9797, 10189, 10247, 10306, 10544, 10811, 10908, 10955, 11025, 11523, 11556, 11581, 11818, 12385, 12512, 12561, 12853, 12955, 13329, 13378–13392

$C_8H_{16}O_2$ Isobutyl butyrate. B.p., 156.8
406, 909, 1890, 2015, 2853, 3105, 3675, 5207, 5391, 6173, 6536, 6693, 7737, 7939, 8037, 8263, 8457, 8515, 8599, 8642, 8880, 9327, 9973, 10190, 10545, 10812, 10956, 11026, 11557, 11819, 12513, 13330, 13378, 13393–13397

$C_8H_{16}O_2$ Isobutyl isobutyrate. B.p., 147.3
407, 910, 2016, 3106, 3676, 4256, 4853, 5392, 6243, 6302, 6537, 6694, 6869, 7883, 7940, 8458, 8516, 8600, 8643, 9328, 10546, 10813, 10894, 10957, 11558, 11820, 12386, 12411, 12419, 12488, 12630, 12844, 13398–13401

$C_8H_{16}O_2$ Methyl isoamyl acetate.
2602

$C_8H_{16}O_2$ Propyl isovalerate. B.p., 155.8
408, 1891, 3107, 3677, 4854, 5208, 5753, 6174, 6407, 6695, 6870, 7488, 7738, 7828, 7884, 8459, 8517, 8881, 9329, 10191, 10213, 10547, 10814, 10895, 10909, 10958, 11027, 11559, 11821, 12489, 12576, 12631, 13379, 13402–13412

$C_8H_{16}O_3$ 2,2-Diethoxy-3-butanone. B.p., 163.5
409

$C_8H_{16}O_3$ Isoamyl lactate. B.p., 202.4
3108, 8929, 9021, 9539, 9607, 9798, 10152, 10496, 11118, 11270, 11401, 11421, 11634, 11927, 12002, 12086, 12164, 12322, 12645, 12702, 12703, 12921, 12984, 13003, 13413–13424

$C_8H_{16}O_4$ 2-(2-Ethoxyethoxy)ethyl acetate. B.p., 218.5
410, 3678, 10664, 11028, 11860, 12436, 12646, 12704, 13202, 13425–13435

C_8H_{18} 2,2-Dimethylhexane. B.p., 106.54
3489, 7611

C_8H_{18} 2,3-Dimethylhexane. B.p., 115.8
3490

C_8H_{18} 2,4-Dimethylhexane. B.p., 109.4
5755, 11173

C_8H_{18} 2,5-Dimethylhexane. B.p., 109.4
92, 585, 662, 988, 1182, 1336, 1543, 1790, 2205, 2324, 2413, 2603, 2854, 3109, 3272, 3316, 3491, 3679, 4110, 4167, 4650, 4697, 4855, 4921, 5034, 5501, 5575, 5675, 5754, 5843, 6460, 6609, 6777, 6871, 6896, 6965, 7225, 7284, 7314, 7402, 7489, 7612, 7806, 8152, 8186, 8201, 8215, 8312, 8571, 8623, 8698, 8762, 8792, 10507, 10986, 10993, 11071, 11799, 12360

C_8H_{18} 3,3-Dimethylhexane. B.p., 111.93
7490, 7613

C_8H_{18} 3,4-Dimethylhexane. B.p., 117.9
3492

C_8H_{18} 3-Ethylheptane. B.p., 119.0
3494

C_8H_{18} 3-Ethyl-3-methylpentane.
7491

C_8H_{18} 2-Methyl-3-ethylpentane. B.p., 114
2206

Formula	Name and System Nos.
C_8H_{18}	2-Methylheptane. B.p., 117.2 3493, 11800
C_8H_{18}	4-Methylheptane. B.p., 118 3495
C_8H_{18}	Octane. B.p., 125.75 93, 411, 1029, 1183, 1337, 1544, 1651, 1791, 2107, 2207, 2604, 2855, 3110, 3496, 3680, 3906, 4111, 4168, 4219, 4698, 4856, 4922, 4929, 5576, 5676, 5757, 6046, 6104, 6303, 6538, 6610, 6696, 6872, 7226, 7403, 7492, 7739, 7807, 8265, 8313, 8342, 8518, 8557, 8624, 8699, 8763, 8819, 8882, 9394, 9799, 10028, 10214, 10607, 10631, 10707, 10717, 10724, 10735, 10776, 10780, 10926, 10959, 10994, 11072, 11801, 12838, 13305, 13436–13438, 14629
C_8H_{18}	2,2,3-Trimethylpentane. B.p., 109.8 3497, 5756
C_8H_{18}	2,2,4-Trimethylpentane. B.p., 99.3 1545, 2208, 3498, 5577, 5677, 7404, 7614, 7661, 7808, 8764, 9725, 10073, 12361, 13146, 13436,
C_8H_{18}	2,3,3-Trimethylpentane. B.p., 113.6 3499
C_8H_{18}	2,3,4-Trimethylpentane. B.p., 13.4 3500, 10075, 10078, 11802, 12217
$C_8H_{18}O$	Butyl ether. B.p., 142.6 412, 911, 1184, 2017, 2325, 2440, 2605, 2742, 2856, 2937, 3111, 3681, 3907, 3983, 4220, 4257, 4358, 4857, 5049, 5393, 5758, 6129, 6244, 6304, 6408, 6540, 6697, 6873, 7227, 7228, 7405, 7493, 7740, 7941, 8057, 8095, 8266, 8460, 8519, 8601, 8675, 8765, 8883, 9330, 9395, 9800, 10029, 10215, 10248, 10458, 10548, 10815, 10896, 11029, 11165, 11169, 11309, 11822, 12420, 12426, 12459, 12465, 12474, 12484, 12495, 12504, 12839, 12845, 12849, 13398, 13402 13439, 13440, 14687, 14701, 14719
$C_8H_{18}O$	*sec*-Butyl ether. B.p., 121 413, 14702
$C_8H_{18}O$	2-Ethylhexanol. B.p., 183.5 414
$C_8H_{18}O$	Ethyl hexyl ether. B.p., 143 415
$C_8H_{18}O$	Isobutyl ether. B.p., 122.2 416, 586, 912, 1338, 1652, 2250, 2606, 2857, 3501, 3682, 3908, 4169, 4221, 4858, 5035, 5050, 5578, 5678, 5679, 5759, 6047, 6130, 6476, 6539, 6698, 7142, 7229, 7406, 7494, 7809, 7864 7885, 8047, 8096, 8169, 8422, 8520, 8676, 8700, 8766, 8820, 8830, 8884, 9396, 10030, 10216, 10549, 10608, 10632, 10708, 10718, 10725, 10736, 10777, 10960, 11160, 11174, 11177, 11188, 11803, 12362, 12460, 12840, 13306, 13437, 13438, 13441, 14720
$C_8H_{18}O$	Octyl alcohol. B.p., 195.15 417, 3683, 4397, 4413, 4497, 4558, 5209, 5394, 6016, 6368, 6806, 7741, 7993, 8993, 9073, 9208, 9261, 9351, 9462, 9540, 9608, 9669, 9801, 10031, 10116, 10153, 10221, 10345, 10393, 10421, 10466, 11236, 11271, 11310, 11402, 11422, 11449, 11482, 11525, 11635, 11710, 11928, 12003, 12087, 12165, 12224, 12250, 12269, 12290, 12291, 12323, 12354, 12514, 12535, 12647, 12685, 12686, 12705, 12730, 12846, 12871, 12894, 13004, 13096, 13124, 13147, 13252, 13304, 13413, 13442–13472
$C_8H_{18}O$	*sec*-Octyl alcohol. B.p., 178.7 418, 1083, 1892, 3313, 3684, 4258, 4398, 4498, 4559, 5210, 5395, 6175, 6245, 6369, 6409, 6807, 7994, 8038, 9022, 9209, 9262, 9331, 9352, 9541, 9670, 9802, 10032, 10222, 10249, 10307, 10346, 10394, 10461, 10816, 10871, 10897, 11030, 11237, 11311, 11403, 11423, 11450, 11526, 11560, 11582, 11804, 11929, 12004, 12088, 12225, 12251, 12270, 12292, 12355, 12515, 12536, 12562, 12648, 12847, 12854, 12895, 12956, 13097, 13125, 12353, 13310, 13374, 13380, 13473–13503, 14848, 14892, 14889, 14905, 14907, 14908
$C_8H_{18}O_2$	Acetaldehyde dipropyl acetal (1,1-dipropoxyethane). B.p., 147.7 419, 5680, 14664
$C_8H_{18}O_3$	Bis(2-ethoxyethyl) ether. B.p., 186 420, 3686, 9263, 11930, 12089, 13504, 13505
$C_8H_{18}O.$	2-(2-Butoxyethoxy)ethanol. B.p., 231.2 4414, 5844, 8994, 9074, 11636, 11656, 12795, 12922, 13056, 13161, 13506–13512
$C_8H_{18}S$	Butyl sulfide. B.p., 185.0 2743, 3114, 3909, 3991, 5396, 6316, 6370, 6541, 7742, 7995, 8267, 9264, 9353, 9671, 9803, 10250, 10496, 10550, 10961, 11238, 11250, 11602, 11605, 12005, 12090, 12166, 12537, 12896, 12957, 13254, 13311, 13513–13520
$C_8H_{18}S$	Isobutyl sulfide. B.p., 172.0 2858, 3115, 3910, 5397, 6058, 6246, 6317, 6542, 7743, 7886, 7942, 8610, 9265, 9804, 10251 10872, 10962, 11031, 11239, 11251, 11583, 12006, 13312, 13363, 13381, 13521–13525
$C_8H_{19}N$	Dibutylamine. 421

Formula	Name and System Nos.
$C_8H_{19}N$	Diisobutylamine. B.p., 138.5 10217, 10594, 10609, 11823, 12371, 12412, 12841, 12848, 13441
$C_8H_{19}N$	1,1,3,3-Tetramethylbutylamine. B.p., 140 422
$C_8H_{19}NO$	1-Diethylaminobutane-3-ol. 2607
$C_8H_{20}SiO_4$	Ethyl silicate. B.p., 168.8 1893, 4259, 6176, 9210, 9266, 9332, 9805, 11451, 11561, 11584, 11824, 12007, 12855, 12958, 13331, 13382, 13393, 13403, 13526–13531
C_9H_7N	Isoquinoline. B.p., 240.3 3687, 12827
C_9H_7N	Quinoline. B.p., 237.3 1185, 2608, 3116, 3688, 4859, 5211, 5845, 7549, 7829, 8930, 9075, 9118, 9140, 9162, 9672, 9879, 11032, 11096, 11119, 11501, 11637, 11657, 11711, 11755, 11861, 12189, 12586, 12796, 12872, 12985, 13005, 13506, 13532–13553
C_9H_8	Indene. B.p., 182.4 1186, 2108, 2441, 2859, 3117, 3689, 3911, 4399, 4415, 4499, 4560, 4860, 5212, 5398, 5579, 5681, 5804, 5846, 6177, 6543, 6699, 6808, 7230, 7495, 7744, 7996, 8268, 8377, 8461, 8767, 8885, 8931, 9211, 9267, 9354, 9542, 9806, 10033, 10117, 10252, 10347, 10422, 10551, 10665, 10756, 10963, 11452, 11931, 12008, 12091, 12226, 12271, 12293, 12437, 12538, 12706, 12731, 12897, 12959, 13098, 13255, 13272, 13313, 13332, 13442, 13473, 13504, 13554–13572
C_9H_8O	Cinnamaldehyde (β-phenylacrolein). B.p., 253.5 3118, 3690, 5213, 9163, 9880, 11350, 11756, 12190, 12756, 12828, 13573–13596
C_9H_9N	2-Methylindole. B.p., 268 13597
C_9H_9N	3-Methylindole. B.p., 266.5 3691
$C_9H_{10}O$	Cinnamyl alcohol. B.p., 257 3113, 5214, 9120, 9164, 9609, 9673, 9881, 9933, 11658, 11712, 12617, 12667, 13006, 13073, 13180, 13507, 13573, 13598–13620
$C_9H_{10}O$	*p*-Methylacetophenone (*p*-methylphenyl methyl ketone). B.p., 226.35 3120, 3692, 4416, 5215, 5399, 5847, 9076, 9119, 9463, 9674, 9882, 11202, 11351, 11506, 11659, 11713, 11932, 12092, 12304, 12438, 12797, 12829, 12873, 12923, 12986, 13007, 13162, 13203, 13229, 13273, 13347, 13425, 13532, 13621–13639
$C_9H_{10}O$	Propiophenone (ethyl phenyl ketone). B.p., 217.7 3121, 3693, 4048, 4417, 5216, 5400, 9077, 9464, 9610, 9807, 10666, 11203, 11507, 11638, 11660, 11714, 11862, 11933, 12009, 12093, 12167, 12272, 12294, 12305, 12439, 12798, 12874, 12924, 12987, 13008, 13057, 13099, 13126, 13148, 13204, 13230, 13274, 13640–13650
$C_9H_{10}O_2$	Benzyl acetate. B.p., 214.9 423, 3122, 3694, 4049, 5217, 5848, 7550, 8932, 8995, 9078, 9465, 9612, 9675, 10667, 11204, 11272, 11661, 11715, 11863, 11934, 11935, 12010, 12094, 12168, 12440, 12587, 12649, 12799, 12875, 12925, 12988, 13009, 13040, 13058, 13088, 13205, 13231, 13297, 13426, 13640, 13651–13667
$C_9H_{10}O_2$	Ethyl benzoate. B.p., 212.4 424, 2044, 3123, 3695, 4050, 4750, 5218, 5401, 5849, 6809, 7551, 8996, 9079, 9355, 9466, 9612, 9676, 9726, 10154, 10668, 11205, 11273, 11639, 11716, 11864, 11936, 12011, 12095, 12169, 12324, 12441, 12588, 12650, 12707, 12800, 12876, 12926, 12989, 13010, 13041, 13059, 13089, 13206, 13232, 13275, 13427, 13443, 13641, 13651, 13668–13685
$C_9H_{10}O_2$	Methyl α-toluate. B.p., 213.3 425, 3124, 5219, 11865, 12801, 13668, 13686–13689
$C_9H_{10}O_3$	Ethyl salicylate. B.p., 233.7 3125, 3696, 4051, 5220, 5849, 7552, 7903, 9080, 9121, 9165, 9883, 11097, 11132, 11206, 11352, 11662, 11717, 11757, 12191, 12306, 12589, 12927, 13011, 13074, 13163, 13181, 13233, 13508, 13533, 13621, 13690–13711
C_9H_{12}	Cumene (isopropylbenzene). B.p., 152.8 1187, 1339, 1546, 1894, 2018, 2109, 2442, 2609 2860, 3126, 3502, 3697, 3912, 3984, 4029, 4359, 4500, 4699, 4861, 5221, 5402, 5580, 5682, 5760, 6178, 6544, 6700, 6874, 7231, 7407, 7496, 7745, 7887, 8269, 8462, 8521, 8768, 8886, 9268, 9333, 9808, 10034, 10192, 10348, 10485, 10552, 10817, 10873, 10910, 10964, 11312, 11562, 11585, 11825, 12013, 12372, 12387, 12413, 12427, 12475, 12490, 12496, 12563, 12577, 12960, 13399, 13404, 13439, 13474, 13712, 13713
C_9H_{12}	*m*-Ethyltoluene. B.p., 161.3 8933
C_9H_{12}	*o*-Ethyltoluene. B.p., 165.1 7497, 8934
C_9H_{12}	*p*-Ethyltoluene. B.p., 162.0 8935

Formula	Name and System Nos.
C_9H_{12}	Mesitylene (1,3,5-trimethylbenzene). B.p., 164.6 426, 1188, 1340, 1547, 1895, 2045, 2110, 2326, 2443, 2610, 2861, 2938, 3127, 3503, 3698, 3913, 3985, 4037, 4400, 4501, 4561, 4852, 5222, 5403, 5581, 5683, 5761, 5762, 5851, 6179, 6247, 6318, 6371, 6545, 6701, 6875, 7323, 7408, 7598, 7746, 7888, 7943, 7997, 8039, 8270, 8378, 8463, 8522, 8644, 8769, 8887, 8936, 9269, 9334, 9809, 10035, 10193, 10253, 10349, 10395, 10423, 10553, 10669, 10757, 10818, 10838, 10874, 10965, 11033, 11073, 11527, 11563, 11586, 11826, 11866, 12012, 12227, 12325, 12388, 12516, 12539, 12856, 12961, 13100, 13256, 13314, 13333, 13405, 13444, 13475, 13513, 13521, 13714–13728, 14858, 14860, 14896
C_9H_{12}	Propylbenzene. B.p., 158.9 913, 1189, 1548, 2046, 2111, 2444, 2611, 2939, 3504, 3699, 3914, 3986, 4502, 4863, 5223, 5404, 5582, 5684, 5763, 5764, 5852, 6180, 6248, 6305, 6546, 6703, 6876, 7233, 7409, 7499 7748, 7998, 8040, 8058, 8271, 8379, 8464, 8523, 8645, 8770, 8888, 9335, 9810, 10036, 10254, 10396, 10424, 10473, 10554, 10819, 10911, 10967, 11034, 11074, 11528, 12014, 12326, 12373, 12517, 12578, 12962, 13101, 13257, 13315, 13334, 13365, 13406, 13445, 13476, 13714, 13729–13732
C_9H_{12}	Pseudocumene (1,2,4-trimethylbenzene). B.p., 168.2 1896, 1897, 2112, 3128, 3640, 4260, 4503, 4751, 4864, 5405, 6181, 6547, 6704, 6877, 7234, 7500, 7747, 7944, 7999, 8272, 8465, 8524, 8771, 8889, 8937, 9212, 9270, 9811, 10037, 10194, 10255, 10350, 10425, 10555, 10670, 10875, 10966, 11035, 11075, 11529, 11564, 11587, 12015, 12389, 12732, 12898, 12963, 13316, 13366, 13715, 13733–13739
C_9H_{12}	1,2,3-Trimethylbenzene. B.p., 176.6 8938
$C_9H_{12}O$	Benzyl ethyl ether. B.p., 185.0 3129, 3701, 3843, 3915, 3992, 5224, 5406, 6548, 6705, 6810, 7749, 8000, 8380, 8939, 9023, 9213, 9271, 9356, 9543, 9812, 10038, 10118, 10256, 10351, 10397, 10556, 10671, 10758, 10876, 10968, 11076, 11240, 11313, 11606, 12016, 12209, 12327, 12390, 12518, 12540, 12708, 12733, 13102, 13446, 13477, 13514, 13554, 13740–13747
$C_9H_{12}O$	Mesitol (2,4,6-trimethylphenol). B.p., 220.5 6418, 9467, 13012, 13060, 13534, 13748, 13749
$C_9H_{12}O$	3-Phenylpropanol. B.p., 235.6 3130, 3702, 5225, 5853, 7553, 9081, 9468, 9613, 9677, 9884, 9934, 10085, 11663, 11718, 11758, 12192, 12802, 13013, 13075, 13155, 13164, 13182, 13428, 13574, 13622, 13750–13777
$C_9H_{12}O$	Phenyl propyl ether. B.p., 190.2 427, 3131, 3703, 3916, 5407, 5854, 6549, 7554, 8273, 8381, 9024, 9813, 10039, 10672, 10759, 11404, 11424, 11867, 11937, 12096, 13127, 13447, 13478, 13778, 13779
$C_9H_{12}O_2$	2-Benzyloxyethanol. B.p., 265.2 3132, 11759, 12590, 13183, 13535, 13598, 13750, 13780–13795
$C_9H_{13}N$	*N,N*-Dimethyl-*m*-toluidine. B.p., 203.1 5226
$C_9H_{13}N$	*N,N*-Dimethyl-*o*-toluidine. B.p., 185.3 1898, 3133, 3704, 3917, 5227, 5805, 7830, 8890, 8940, 8997, 9025, 9214, 9272, 9544, 9614, 9814, 10040, 10497, 10557, 10969, 11036, 11120, 11425, 11426, 11453, 11588, 11868, 11938, 12017, 12097, 12170, 12273, 12391, 12564, 12651, 12899, 12964, 13090, 13448, 13479, 13555, 13716, 13729, 13733, 13778, 13796–13806
$C_9H_{13}N$	*N,N*-Dimethyl-*p*-toluidine. B.p., 210.2 3134, 3705, 3918, 5228, 5229, 5806, 8941, 9026, 9082, 9615, 11121, 11719. 11869, 11939, 12018, 12098, 12652, 12877, 12928, 13014, 13061, 13480, 13642, 13807–13812
$C_9H_{14}O$	Phorone (2,6-dimethyl-2,5-heptadien-4-one). B.p., 197.8 3135, 3706, 5230, 5408, 6811, 8382, 8942, 9027, 9545, 9616, 9678, 9815, 10426, 10673, 11314, 11483, 11607, 11940, 12019, 12099, 12171, 12307, 12328, 12709, 12734, 13414, 13449, 13556, 13813–13821
C_9H_{18}	Nonanaphthene. B.p., 136.7 2612
$C_9H_{18}O$	2,6-Dimethyl-4-heptanone. B.p., 168.0 1899, 2613, 2744, 3136, 3707, 3961, 4504, 5231, 6319, 6550, 6706, 7889, 7945, 8274, 8466, 8891, 9273, 9816, 10257, 10558, 10820, 10912, 10970, 11315, 11565, 11589, 12020, 12392, 12519, 13335, 13367, 13384, 13515, 13522, 13822, 13823
$C_9H_{18}O_2$	Butyl isovalerate. B.p., 177.6 428, 1681, 2113, 3708, 5409, 6372, 7750, 8001, 8383, 9817, 10308, 10352, 10398, 11241, 11454, 11484, 11530, 12021, 12100, 12900, 12965, 13481, 13516, 13526, 13740, 13824–13832,
$C_9H_{18}O_2$	Ethyl enanthate. B.p., 188.7 429, 2114, 3137, 3709, 3844, 5410, 9469, 9818, 10353, 11455, 12022, 12101, 13450, 13557, 13833–13835
$C_9H_{18}O_2$	Isoamyl butyrate. B.p., 178.5 430, 1682, 2115, 3138, 3710, 3845, 4505, 4562, 5232, 5233, 5411, 6249, 6551, 6812, 7946, 8002, 8275, 8276, 8384, 8943, 9274, 9357, 9547, 9819, 10258, 10354, 10399, 10821, 11037, 11078, 11242, 11316, 11405, 11456, 11485, 11531, 11590, 11941, 12023, 12102, 12520, 12541, 12857, 12901, 12966, 13258, 13317, 13375, 13482, 13558, 13717, 13741, 13824, 13836–13851

Formula	Name and System Nos.
$C_9H_{18}O_2$	Isoamyl isobutyrate. B.p., 168.9 431, 1900, 2940, 3139, 3711, 4261, 4506, 5234, 5412, 6182, 6373, 6552, 7751, 8525, 9275, 9820, 10259, 10309, 10877, 11038, 11243, 11317, 11457, 11532, 12902, 12967, 13259, 13336, 13483, 13527, 13718, 13822, 13852-13857
$C_9H_{18}O_2$	Isobutyl isovalerate. B.p., 168.7 432, 1084, 1683, 1901, 2116, 3140, 3712, 4262, 4401, 4507, 4563, 5235, 5413, 6250, 6374, 6553, 6813, 7752, 7947, 8003, 8041, 8277, 8944, 9215, 9276, 9336, 9821, 10260, 10310, 10355, 10559, 10822, 10878, 10898, 10913, 10971, 11039, 11077, 11244, 11318, 11319, 11427, 11458, 11533, 11566, 11591, 11827, 12024, 12393, 12521, 12565, 12858, 12903, 12968, 13260, 13318, 13337, 13368, 13484, 13517, 13528, 13559, 13719, 13734, 13823, 13825, 13836, 13852, 13858-13870
$C_9H_{18}O_2$	Methyl caprylate. B.p., 192.9 433, 2117, 3141, 3713, 5414, 10119, 10261, 10356, 10674, 12025, 12103, 12329, 13813, 13871-13873
$C_9H_{18}O_2$	Pelargonic acid (nonanoic acid). B.p., 254 4052, 9083, 9885, 11664, 13874-13889
$C_9H_{18}O_3$	Isobutyl carbonate. B.p., 190.3 434, 1684, 2118, 3714, 4508, 5236, 5415, 5855, 9277, 9470, 9548, 9823, 10427, 10675, 11320, 11406, 11428, 11459, 11486, 11534, 11870, 11942, 12026, 12104, 12330, 12522, 12710, 12735, 12969, 13451, 13485, 13486, 13560, 13720, 13814, 13890-13899
C_9H_{20}	3,3-Diethylpentane. 7501
C_9H_{20}	2-Methyloctane. B.p., 135.2 2614
C_9H_{20}	Nonane. B.p., 150.7 2615, 6105, 7502, 12632, 13712, 14630
C_9H_{20}	2,2,3,3-Tetramethylpentane. 7503
C_9H_{20}	2,2,4,4-Tetramethylpentane. 7504
C_9H_{20}	2,3,3,4-Tetramethylpentane. 7505
C_9H_{20}	2,2,3,4-Tetramethylpentane. 5765
C_9H_{20}	2,2,5-Trimethylhexane. B.p., 120.1 2209
C_9H_{20}	2,4,4-Trimethylhexane. 7506
$C_9H_{20}O_2$	Dibutoxymethane. B.p., 181.8 435, 7236, 14688
$C_9H_{20}O_2$	Diisobutoxymethane. B.p., 163.8 436, 7235, 7410, 8646, 13385, 13407, 14721
$C_{10}H_7Br$	1-Bromonaphthalene. B.p., 281.8 3142, 3715, 5237, 5238, 5856, 7555, 9886, 9935, 11133, 11353, 12591, 12757, 13874, 13900-13913
$C_{10}H_7Cl$	1-Chloronaphthalene. B.p., 262.7 3143, 3716, 5239, 5857, 7556, 9141, 9887, 9936, 10676, 11134, 11207, 11354, 11760, 11943, 12442, 12592, 12668, 12758, 13076, 13184, 13348, 13349, 13509, 13575, 13780, 13875, 13914-13937
$C_{10}H_8$	Naphthalene. B.p., 218.1 41, 437, 1812, 2047, 2119, 2862, 3144, 3717, 3919, 4038, 4053, 4509, 4564, 5240, 5416, 5858, 6183, 6554, 6814, 7557, 7753, 7904, 8004, 8278, 8385, 8945, 8998, 9084, 9122, 9471, 9617, 9679, 9824, 9888, 9937, 10041, 10120, 10155, 10262, 10357, 10428, 10560, 10677, 10760, 11079, 11122, 11208, 11274, 11321, 11355, 11502, 11608, 11665, 11720, 11871, 11944, 12027, 12105, 12172, 12193, 12220, 12252, 12274, 12295, 12308, 12331, 12433, 12593, 12653, 12687, 12711, 12736, 12759, 12803, 12830, 12878, 12929, 13015, 13062, 13077, 13091, 13103, 13156, 13165, 13128, 13207, 13234, 13276, 13298, 13350, 13415, 13452, 13536, 13576, 13599, 13623, 13643, 13669, 13748, 13751, 13781, 13796, 13807, 13876, 13938-13970
$C_{10}H_8O$	1-Naphthol. B.p., 288 3145, 7559, 9938, 10086, 12594, 12760, 13900, 13914, 13971-13989
$C_{10}H_8O$	2-Naphthol. B.p., 290 3146, 9939, 9966, 13901, 13915, 13990-13998
$C_{10}H_9N$	1-Naphthylamine. B.p., 300.8 3147, 5241, 13971, 13999-14002
$C_{10}H_9N$	2-Naphthylamine. B.p., 306.1 13972, 14003, 14004

Formula	Name and System Nos
$C_{10}H_9N$	Quinaldine. B.p., 246.5 3148, 5242, 7558, 9166, 9889, 11098, 12595, 13016, 13510, 14005–14007
$C_{10}H_{10}O_2$	Isosafrole (1,2-methylenedioxy-4-propenylbenzene). B.p., 252.0 438, 3149, 3718, 5243, 5859, 7560, 7686, 9142, 9890, 9940, 10087, 11099, 11135, 11356, 11761, 12194, 12596, 12669, 12761, 13078, 13166, 13185, 13537, 13577, 13600, 13690, 13752, 13782, 13877, 13916, 14008–14024
$C_{10}H_{10}O_2$	Methyl cinnamate. B.p., 261.9 439, 3150, 3719, 5244, 5860, 7561, 9472, 9891, 9941, 11136, 11357, 12597, 12670, 12762, 13578, 13601, 13783, 13902, 13917, 13973, 14008, 14025–14040
$C_{10}H_{10}O_2$	Safrole (4-allyl-1,2-methylenedioxybenzene). B.p., 235.9 440, 3151, 3720, 5245, 5861, 7562, 7905, 9143, 9167, 9473, 9825, 9892, 10088, 11100, 11137, 11358, 11666, 11721, 11762, 11872, 12195, 12444, 12598, 12618, 12671, 12804, 12831, 12930, 13167, 13186, 13208, 13235, 13277, 13351, 13538, 13579, 13602, 13624, 13691, 13753, 13784, 13878, 13938, 14005, 14041–14066
$C_{10}H_{10}O_4$	Methyl phthalate. B.p., 283.2 441, 3152, 3721, 5246, 5862, 7563, 9942, 11138, 12599, 12763, 13903, 13918, 13990, 14067–14076
$C_{10}H_{12}O$	Anethole (*p*-propenylanisole). B.p., 235.7 442, 3153, 3722, 5247, 5863, 7564, 7906, 9474, 9893, 10089, 11101, 11139, 11359, 11873, 12600, 12764, 12832, 12931, 13168, 13187, 13209, 13236, 13352, 13539, 13580, 13625, 13754, 13939, 14041, 14077–14089
$C_{10}H_{12}O$	Estragole (*p*-allylanisole). B.p., 215.6 443, 3154, 3723, 5864, 9085, 10156, 11123, 11209, 11503, 11945, 12173, 13168, 13670, 14090
$C_{10}H_{12}O_2$	Ethyl *α*-toluate. B.p., 228.75 444, 3155, 3724, 5248, 5417, 5865, 7565, 9086, 9168, 9358, 9475, 9680, 9894, 11210, 11764, 11946, 12106, 12445, 12805, 12932, 13017, 13210, 13278, 13353, 13626, 13692, 13755, 13940, 14042, 14091–14109
$C_{10}H_{12}O_2$	Eugenol (4-allyl-2-methoxyphenol). B.p., 255 3156, 3725, 5249, 5866, 9895, 9943, 10090, 11360, 11361, 11763, 12619, 12765, 13540, 13756, 13785, 13879, 13919, 14009, 14025, 14110–14123
$C_{10}H_{12}O_2$	Isoeugenol (2-methoxy-4-propenylphenol). B.p., 268.8 3157, 3726, 5867, 9944, 10091, 12620, 12766, 13581, 13603, 14026, 14124–14135
$C_{10}H_{12}O_2$	Propyl benzoate. B.p., 230.85 445, 3157, 3727, 4054, 5250, 5418, 5868, 7566, 7907, 9087, 9123, 9169, 9359, 9476, 9681, 9896, 11211, 11362, 11667, 11722, 11765, 12107, 12601, 12806, 12879, 12933, 13018, 13237, 13627, 13693, 13757, 13941, 14043, 14077, 14091, 14136–14150
$C_{10}H_{14}$	Butylbenzene. B.p., 183.1 1685, 1813, 2048, 2120, 2445, 2863, 3159, 3728, 3920, 4418, 4865, 4510, 5419, 5583, 5686, 5869, 6184, 6375, 6555, 6707, 6815, 7237, 7567, 7754, 7755, 8005, 8279, 8467, 8892, 8946, 9278, 9360, 9549, 9826, 10042, 10121, 10263, 10358, 10400, 10467, 10561, 10823, 10972, 11040, 11124, 11322, 11429, 11487, 11947, 12108, 12253, 12275, 12394, 12904, 13261, 13319, 13487, 13518, 13815, 13833, 13837, 13858, 13871, 14151–14160
$C_{10}H_{14}$	*sec*-Butylbenzene. B.p., 173.1 8947
$C_{10}H_{14}$	*tert*-Butylbenzene. B.p., 168.5 8948
$C_{10}H_{14}$	Cymene (*p*-isopropyltoluene). B.p., 176.7 1549, 1686, 1814, 1902, 2049, 2121, 2122, 2327, 2616, 2864, 3160, 3505, 3729, 3921, 4039, 4263, 4402, 4419, 4511, 4565, 4866, 5251, 5420, 5584, 5685, 5766, 5870, 6185, 6251, 6376, 6556, 6708, 6878, 7238, 7411, 7507, 7568, 7756, 7948, 8006, 8042, 8280 8386, 8468, 8773, 8893, 8949, 9279, 9550, 9827, 10043, 10264, 10311, 10359, 10468, 10474, 10562, 10678, 10761, 10824, 10879, 10914, 11041, 11080, 11323, 11460, 11488, 11535, 11592, 11874, 11948, 12028, 12109, 12229, 12276, 12332, 12395, 12523, 12542, 12566, 12712, 12737, 12905, 12970, 13104, 13262, 13320, 13338, 13386, 13453, 13488, 13561, 13721, 13735, 13742, 13797, 13838, 13839, 13859, 14151, 14161–14170, 14875
$C_{10}H_{14}$	Isobutylbenzene. B.p., 241.9 14171
$C_{10}H_{14}N_2$	Nicotine. 446, 12833, 14044, 14171
$C_{10}H_{14}O$	Carvacrol (2-*p*-cymenol) B.p., 237.85 3161, 5252, 5871, 7569, 7909, 9088, 9124, 9144, 9170, 9682, 9897, 11364, 11668, 11723, 11766, 12196, 12446, 12621, 12672, 12934, 13157, 13169, 13188, 13238, 13354, 13416, 13541, 13582, 13644, 13694, 13758, 13921, 13942, 14006, 14045, 14078, 14092, 14136, 14172–14189
$C_{10}H_{14}O$	Carvone. B.p., 231 3162, 3730, 5253, 5872, 9089, 9125, 9172, 9477, 9898, 11212, 11363, 11669, 11767, 11949, 12110, 12447, 12807, 12834, 12935, 13170, 13189, 13239, 13604, 13695, 13759, 13943, 14046, 14079, 14093, 14110, 14137, 14172, 14190–14204

Formula	Name and System Nos.
$C_{10}H_{14}O$	Thymol (3-*p*-cymenol). B.p., 232.8 3163, 3731, 4055, 5254, 5873, 7570, 7908, 8999, 9090, 9126, 9145, 9171, 9478, 9618, 9683, 9899, 11213, 11365, 11366, 11670, 11724, 11768, 11875, 12197, 12309, 12654, 12673, 12808, 12936, 13019, 13054, 13063, 13129, 13147, 13149, 13171, 13190, 13211, 13240, 13279, 13299, 13355, 13542, 13583, 13605, 13628, 13645, 13653, 13671, 13696, 13760, 13816, 13880, 13922, 13944, 14007, 14010, 14027, 14047, 14080, 14094, 14138, 14171, 14173, 14190, 14205–14232
$C_{10}H_{14}O_2$	*m*-Diethoxybenzene. B.p., 235.0 447, 3164, 3732, 5255, 5874, 9091, 9479, 9684, 9900, 11367, 12198, 12809, 13212, 13543, 13629, 13761, 14095, 14171, 14206, 14233–14239
$C_{10}H_{15}N$	*N,N*-Diethylaniline. B.p., 217.05 3165, 3733, 3922, 4056, 5256, 7687, 8950, 9092, 9619, 11125, 11214, 11671, 11725, 11876, 11950, 12029, 12111, 12174, 12567, 12655, 12880, 12937, 13020, 13064, 13092, 13455, 13489, 13606, 13630, 13646, 13672, 13762, 13817, 13945, 14048, 14081, 14174, 14192, 14207, 14234, 14240–14255
$C_{10}H_{16}$	Camphene. B.p., 159.6 448, 914, 1190, 1550, 1903, 2123, 2446, 2617, 2865, 3166, 3506, 3734, 3923, 4264, 4512, 4566, 4700, 4867, 5257, 5421, 5585, 5687, 5767, 5875, 6131, 6186, 6252, 6306, 6557, 6709, 6879, 7239, 7412, 7508, 7757, 7890, 7949, 8007, 8043, 8281, 8387, 8469, 8526, 8602, 8647, 8774, 8894, 9280, 9337, 9828, 9974, 10044, 10195, 10265, 10312, 10360, 10429, 10475, 10486, 10563, 10633, 10825, 10839, 10880, 10915, 10973, 11042, 11081, 11189, 11324, 11536, 11567, 11593, 11828, 11877, 12030, 12230, 12333, 12374, 12396, 12476, 12524, 12543, 12568, 12579, 12738, 12859, 12971, 13105, 13263, 13321, 13339, 13369, 13387, 13400, 13408, 13456, 13490, 13523, 13529, 13722, 13730, 13798, 13826, 13840, 13854, 13860, 13890, 14161, 14256–14262, 14879
$C_{10}H_{16}$	Dipentene (*dl*-limonene). B.p., 177.7 2447, 3167, 3926, 4403, 4420, 5258, 6253, 6377, 7765, 7950, 8388, 8895, 8951, 9216, 9551, 10045, 10122, 10266, 10361, 10401, 10469, 10762, 11043, 11082, 11126, 11430, 11594, 12231, 12334, 12397, 12525, 12569, 12972, 13106, 13264, 13322, 13505, 13562, 13743, 13834, 13855, 13872, 13891, 14162, 14256, 14263–14267
$C_{10}H_{16}$	*d*-Limonene. B.p., 177.8 1191, 1551, 1687, 1815, 1904, 2124, 3168, 3507, 3735, 3846, 4265, 4513, 4567, 4701, 4868, 5259, 5422, 5586, 5688, 5876, 6187, 6558, 6710, 6880, 7240, 7413, 7758, 7951, 8008, 8282, 8470, 8775, 9281, 9829, 10046, 10267, 10362, 10430, 10462, 10564, 10679, 10763, 10881, 10916, 10974, 11083, 11325, 11461, 11489, 11537, 11878, 11951, 12031, 12112, 12232, 12335, 12356, 12544, 12688, 12713, 12739, 12973, 13107, 13265, 13280, 13300, 13323, 13340, 13457, 13491, 13563, 13827, 13841, 13861, 13892, 14163, 14268–14274, 14813, 14814, 14837, 14844, 14846, 14847, 14848, 14859, 14874, 14876, 14882, 14884, 14887, 14890–14892, 14894, 14895, 14897, 14899, 14901, 14903, 14905, 14907
$C_{10}H_{16}$	Nopinene (β-pinene). B.p., 163.8 916, 1906, 2125, 3169, 3736, 4514, 4568, 4869, 5260, 5768, 5878, 6188, 6254, 6320, 6559, 6711, 6881, 7241, 7414, 7509, 7760, 8009, 8283, 8389, 8471, 8527, 8603, 8648, 8952, 9217, 9282, 9338, 9830, 10047, 10196, 10268, 10363, 10634, 10680, 10826, 10840, 10882, 10917, 10975, 11044, 11326, 11538, 11568, 11595, 11829, 11952, 12032, 12133, 12233, 12336, 12477, 12526, 12545, 12570, 12580, 12740, 12860, 12974, 13108, 13341, 13388, 13395, 13409, 13458, 13492, 13723, 13731, 13828, 13842, 14164, 14257, 14275, 14276, 14860, 14896
$C_{10}H_{16}$	α-Phellandrene. B.p., 171.5 2126, 4516, 4870, 6189, 6560, 6713, 7952, 8284, 8776, 9831, 9975, 10048, 10269, 10565, 10883, 11327, 11539, 12033, 13493, 14277
$C_{10}H_{16}$	α-Pinene. B.p., 155.8 915, 1552, 1905, 2127, 2618, 3170, 3508, 3509, 3737, 3924, 4222, 4266, 4360, 4404, 4517, 4569, 4702, 4871, 5261, 5587, 5689, 5769, 5877, 6132, 6190, 6255, 6307, 6410, 6561, 6712, 6882, 7242, 7315, 7415, 7510, 7759, 7891, 7953, 8010, 8044, 8285, 8390, 8472, 8529, 8604, 8649, 8701, 8777, 8896, 8953, 9283, 9339, 9832, 9976, 10049, 10123, 10197, 10270, 10313, 10364, 10431, 10476, 10487, 10566, 10635, 10827, 10841, 10884, 10918, 10976, 11045, 11084, 11328, 11329, 11569, 11830, 11879, 12034, 12116, 12234, 12337, 12375, 12398, 12414, 12421, 12428, 12478, 12497, 12498, 12505, 12546, 12975, 13109, 13266, 13301, 13324, 13342, 13343, 13370, 13389, 13396, 13401, 13410, 13440, 13459, 13494, 13524, 13530, 13713, 13724, 13732, 13799, 13829, 13835, 13856, 13862, 13893, 14258, 14263, 14278–14280, 14855, 14857, 14861, 14862, 14863, 14869, 14870, 14878, 14880, 14881, 14893, 14898
$C_{10}H_{16}$	α-Terpinene. B.p., 173.4 1688, 1908, 2128, 2620, 2866, 3171, 3510, 3738, 3925, 4515, 4570, 4872, 5262, 5423, 5588, 5690, 5879, 6192, 6256, 6321, 6562, 6714, 6883, 7511, 7761, 8011, 8286, 8391, 8528, 8897, 8954, 9218, 9284, 9552, 9829, 9833, 10050, 10124, 10198, 10271, 10365, 10432, 10567, 10828, 10885, 10919, 10977, 11046, 11330, 11431, 11462, 11490, 11540, 11570, 11597, 11831, 11880, 11953, 12035, 12115, 12235, 12338, 12399, 12527, 12571, 12714, 12741, 12861, 12906, 12976, 13110, 13267, 13325, 13344, 13371, 13397, 13411, 13460, 13495, 13725, 13843, 13863, 14152, 14165, 14264, 14275, 14278, 14281–14284

Formula	Name and System Nos.
$C_{10}H_{16}$	γ-Terpinene. B.p., 183 3172, 3739, 4518, 4571, 5424, 6193, 6563, 7762, 8287, 8392, 9285, 10051, 10366, 10433, 10568, 11331, 11463, 11491, 11541, 12116, 12689, 12715, 12742, 12977, 13281, 13326, 13461, 13654, 13844, 13864, 14285-14287
$C_{10}H_{16}$	Terpinene. B.p., 181.5 2130, 2131, 6191, 7954, 8012, 8288, 9286, 9553, 9834, 10272, 10569, 11881, 12036, 12117, 12339, 12547, 13496, 14888, 14902, 14904, 14908
$C_{10}H_{16}$	Terpinolene. B.p., 185 1689, 2129, 3173, 3740, 4519, 4572, 4873, 5880, 6194, 6378, 6564, 7763, 8013, 8289, 8393, 8473, 8778, 8897, 9287, 9830, 9835, 9836, 9901, 10052, 10273, 10367, 10434, 10570, 10681, 10829, 11332, 11464, 11492, 11542, 11882, 12037, 12118, 12205, 12236, 12296, 12548, 12907, 13111, 13130, 13497, 13845, 13865, 14153, 14288, 14289
$C_{10}H_{16}$	Terpinylene. B.p., 175 6196, 6565
$C_{10}H_{16}$	Thymene. B.p., 179.7 1192, 1553, 1690, 3174, 3511, 3741, 4520, 4573, 4874, 5589, 5881, 6197, 6556, 6715, 7243, 7416, 7764, 8014, 8290, 8474, 8779, 9288, 9837, 10053, 10368, 10435, 10571, 10682, 11465, 11493, 11543, 11883, 11954, 12038, 12119, 12743, 13112, 13282, 13462, 13498, 14290-14296
$C_{10}H_{16}O$	Camphor. B.p., 209.1 3175, 3742, 5060, 5263, 5425, 5807, 7571, 8954, 9000, 9361, 9480, 9620, 9685, 9838, 10054, 10683, 10764, 11275, 11609, 11726, 11884, 11955, 12039, 12120, 12175, 12254, 12277, 12297, 12340, 12690, 12716, 12990, 13021, 13065, 13113, 13131, 13150, 13213, 13283, 13418, 13463, 13655, 13673, 13800, 13946, 14090, 14208, 14240, 14296-14305
$C_{10}H_{16}O$	Carvenone. B.p., 234.5 3176, 9839, 13172, 13191, 14096, 14139 14175, 14209, 14306, 14307
$C_{10}H_{16}O$	Citral. B.p., 226 13947, 14140, 14241, 14308, 14309
$C_{10}H_{16}O$	Fenchone. B.p., 193 1691, 2620, 3177, 5426, 9554, 9621, 9686, 9840, 10055, 10274, 11333, 11407, 11494, 11610 12040, 12121, 12176, 13114, 13744, 14310
$C_{10}H_{16}O$	Menthenone. B.p., 222.5 14049, 14111, 14176
$C_{10}H_{16}O$	Pulegone. B.p., 223.8 3178, 3743, 4057, 5264, 9093, 9622, 9902, 11508, 11672, 11727, 12122, 12255, 12810, 12938, 13066, 13173, 13214, 13242, 13284, 13656, 13686, 13697, 13948, 14050, 14082, 14097, 14141, 14177, 14210, 14242, 14311-14319
$C_{10}H_{17}Cl$	Bornyl chloride. B.p., 207.5 3179, 6567, 9481, 9623, 10436, 10684, 11728, 12041, 12123, 12341, 12717, 13302, 13419, 13657, 13674, 13675, 13949, 14296, 14311, 14320
$C_{10}H_{18}$	*m*-Menthene-8. B.p., 170.8 1909, 3744, 6198, 7955, 8015, 9841, 9977, 10056, 10275, 10369, 10572, 11408, 11544, 11598, 13736, 13866, 14900
$C_{10}H_{18}O$	Borneol. B.p., 213.4 3180, 3745, 4058, 5265, 5427, 6816, 8955, 9001, 9094, 9482, 9624, 9687, 9842, 10125, 10157, 11276, 11673, 11729, 11769, 11885, 11956, 12042, 12124, 12177, 12237, 12256, 12278, 12298, 12656, 12691, 12718, 12744, 12811, 12939, 13022, 13042, 13067, 13093, 13115, 13132, 13215, 13285, 13429, 13564, 13647, 13658, 13676, 13687, 13698, 13801, 13950, 14051, 14154, 14193, 14211, 14243, 14269, 14279, 14290, 14297, 14308, 14312, 14321-14328
$C_{10}H_{18}O$	Cineole. B.p., 176.35 449, 1085, 1692, 1910, 2132, 3181, 3746, 3927, 4574, 4875, 5266, 5428, 6199, 6257, 6379, 6568, 6716, 6817, 7512, 7766, 7892, 7956, 8016, 8291, 8394, 8899, 8956, 9219, 9289, 9843, 9844, 9845, 10057, 10126, 10276, 10314, 10390, 10437, 10477, 10573, 10765, 10830, 10886, 10978, 11047, 11085, 11102, 11127, 11190, 11245, 11334, 11432, 11466, 11495, 11545, 11599, 12043, 12125, 12210, 12238, 12279, 12400, 12528, 12549, 12572, 12745, 12908, 12978, 13116, 13268, 13327, 13345, 13372, 13376, 13390, 13464, 13499, 13519, 13565, 13737, 13802, 13830, 13846, 13847, 13857, 13867, 13894, 13895, 14155, 14166, 14270, 14277, 14281, 14285, 14291, 14329-14332, 14877
$C_{10}H_{18}O$	Citronellal. B.p., 208.0 3882, 3747, 5267, 6818, 8395, 8957, 9625, 10127, 10158, 10685, 11048, 11277, 11409, 11504, 11730, 11886, 11957, 12044, 12126, 12178, 12657, 12692, 12719, 12746, 12862, 12881, 12940, 13023, 13216, 13243, 13420, 13465, 13659, 13677, 13745, 14156, 14298, 14333-14336
$C_{10}H_{18}O$	Geraniol. B.p., 229.6 3183, 3748, 5268, 8958, 9095, 9483, 9626, 9903, 10159, 11674, 11731, 11770, 11958, 12127, 12179, 12626, 12812, 13079, 13133, 13217, 13286, 13430, 13511, 13631, 13699, 13763, 13808, 13951, 14052, 14098, 14192, 14178, 14194, 14212, 14235, 14244, 14337-14344

Formula	Name and System Nos.
$C_{10}H_{18}O$	Linoloöl. B.p., 199 450, 1693, 3184, 3749, 4521, 5269, 5429, 7767, 8017, 9220, 9484, 9555, 9627, 9846, 10058, 10160, 10371, 10372, 10438, 10478, 11049, 11467, 11496, 11546, 11732, 11959, 12045, 12128, 12180, 12239, 12280, 12342, 12357, 12550, 12658, 12693, 12720, 12747, 12813, 13024, 13117, 13134, 13421, 13466, 13566, 13678, 13726, 13746, 13779, 13803, 13848, 13896, 13897, 13952, 14157, 14167, 14213, 14245, 14259, 14271, 14282, 14292, 14299, 14345-14347
$C_{10}H_{18}O$	Menthone. B.p., 209.5 3750, 5808, 9002, 9628, 9688, 9847, 11278, 11887, 12129, 12240, 12257, 12299, 13135, 13136, 13467, 14179, 14214, 14300, 14321
$C_{10}H_{18}O$	α-Terpineol. B.p., 217.8 3185, 3751, 5270, 5430, 5882, 7572, 8959, 9096, 9485, 9629, 9689, 9848, 10161, 11675, 11733, 11771, 11888, 12046, 12130, 12181, 12258, 12281, 12694, 12814, 12882, 12941, 13025, 13043, 13044, 13118, 13174, 13137, 13218, 13244, 13431, 13544, 13632, 13660, 13679, 13680, 13688, 13700, 13953, 14053, 14083, 14099, 14143, 14168, 14180, 14215, 14246, 14293, 14313, 14372, 14329, 14333, 14337 14348-14354
$C_{10}H_{18}O$	β-Terpineol. B.p., 210.5 3186, 3752, 5431, 6419, 9486, 9630, 9690, 9849, 10059, 11734, 11772, 12047, 12131, 12241, 12259, 12282, 12659, 12721, 12748, 13567, 13661, 13681, 13804, 13954, 14247, 14355-14357
$C_{10}H_{18}O_4$	Propyl succinate. B.p., 250.5 3753, 9945, 11368, 12767, 13881, 13923, 13955, 14011, 14054, 14181, 14216, 14358-14364
$C_{10}H_{19}N$	Bornylamine. B.p., 199.8 9221, 11468
$C_{10}H_{20}$	1-Decene. B.p., 172.0 2210
$C_{10}H_{20}O$	Citronellol. B.p., 224.4 3187, 3754, 5271, 7573, 9097, 9487, 9631, 9691, 9850, 9946, 11676, 11735, 12132, 12674, 12815, 13119, 13138, 13158, 13245, 13432, 13633, 13662, 13701, 13764, 13956, 14055, 14084, 14100, 14112, 14144, 14195, 14217, 14236, 14248, 14334, 14365-14369
$C_{10}H_{20}O$	Menthol. B.p., 216.4 3188, 3755, 4421, 5272, 5432, 5883, 6819, 8960, 9003, 9088, 9632, 9692, 9851, 10092, 10439, 11280, 11640, 11677, 11736, 11773, 11889, 11960, 12048, 12133, 12182, 12242, 12260, 12283, 12300, 12310, 12660, 12695, 12722, 12816, 12942, 13026, 13045, 13068, 13120, 13151, 13175, 13139, 13219, 13287, 13545, 13568, 13634, 13663, 13682, 13689, 13702, 13957, 14085, 14101, 14145, 14158, 14196, 14218, 14249, 14272, 14294, 14301, 14314, 14323, 14335, 14348, 14370-14376
$C_{10}H_{20}O_2$	Capric acid. B.p., 268.8 9904, 9947, 13924, 13958, 14012, 14028, 14377-14381
$C_{10}H_{20}O_2$	Ethyl caprylate. B.p., 208.35 451, 3189, 3756, 5273, 5433, 5884, 6821, 9489, 9693, 10128, 10440, 11410, 11641, 11890, 12049, 12134, 12183, 12723, 12817, 13027, 13069, 13422, 13433, 13468, 13959, 14370, 14382-14384
$C_{10}H_{20}O_2$	Isoamyl isovalerate. B.p., 193.5 452, 1694, 2133, 3190, 3757, 3847, 4522, 4575, 4876, 5275, 5434, 5885, 6200, 6820, 7957, 8018, 8292, 8396, 8961, 9028, 9222, 9362, 9490, 9556, 9852, 10129, 10162, 10277, 10373, 10402, 10441, 10686, 10766, 11246, 11281, 11411, 11469, 11497, 11891, 11961, 12050, 12135, 12343, 12529, 12696, 12724, 12909, 12979, 12991, 13094, 13469, 13569, 13747, 13818, 13873, 13960, 14273, 14286, 14288, 14295, 14330, 14345, 14385-14389
$C_{10}H_{20}O_2$	Methyl pelargonate. B.p., 213.8 453, 3192, 3758, 5274, 5435, 5886, 9099, 9694, 10687, 11737, 11962, 12184, 12661, 13220, 13288, 13648, 14219, 14390
$C_{10}H_{20}O_3$	2,2-Dipropoxy-3-butanone. B.p., 196 454
$C_{10}H_{20}O_4$	2-(2-Butoxyethoxy)ethyl acetate. B.p., 245.3 455, 11369, 13607, 13765, 14029, 14102, 14146, 14391-14394
$C_{10}H_{22}$	Decane. B.p., 173.3 456, 1911, 2134, 3759, 4877, 5770, 5887, 6106, 6717, 7244, 8293, 9853, 10060, 13269, 13738, 14283
$C_{10}H_{22}$	2,7-Dimethyloctane. B.p., 160.1 457, 917, 1193, 1554, 2135, 2621, 2622, 2867, 3193, 3512, 3760, 4267, 4523, 4878, 5436, 5590, 5771, 5888, 6201, 6569, 6718, 6884, 7245, 7417, 7513, 7768, 8019, 8294, 8475, 8530, 8650, 8780, 8900, 9340, 9854, 10061, 10199, 10278, 10374, 10574, 10831, 10920, 10979, 11086, 11335, 11600, 11832, 11833, 12051, 12401, 13391, 13412, 13500, 13727, 13868, 14260, 14280
$C_{10}H_{22}O$	Amyl ether. B.p., 190 458, 2136, 3195, 3762, 3928, 5276, 5437, 6380, 6570, 6822, 7769, 7958, 8020, 8295, 8397, 8677, 8901, 8962, 9223, 9290, 9855, 10062, 10279, 10375, 10403, 10479, 10575, 10767, 11050, 11128, 11247, 11336, 12052, 12136, 12211, 12402, 12530, 13121, 13501, 13570, 13831, 13849 13869, 14159, 14736

Formula	Name and System Nos.
$C_{10}H_{22}O$	Decyl alcohol. B.p., 232.9 3194, 3761, 5277, 8963, 9100, 9633, 9695, 9905, 11678, 11738, 11774, 12818, 12883, 13140, 13176, 13246, 13434, 13512, 13635, 13703, 13766, 13809, 13961, 14056, 14086, 14103, 14147, 14182, 14197, 14220, 14237, 14250, 14338, 14395–14403
$C_{10}H_{22}O$	Isoamyl ether. B.p., 172.6 459, 1086, 1912, 2137, 2138, 2448, 2868, 2941, 3196, 3763, 3929, 3993, 4524, 4879, 5278, 5438, 6202, 6258, 6381, 6571, 6719, 6823, 7514, 7770, 7831, 7959, 8021, 8045, 8296, 8398, 8781, 8902, 8964, 9224, 9291, 9363, 9856, 10063, 10130, 10280, 10315, 10376, 10377, 10404, 10442, 10470, 10480, 10576, 10768, 10832, 10887, 10921, 10980, 11051, 11087, 11103, 11191, 11248, 11337, 11470, 11547, 11963, 12053, 12137, 12212, 12243, 12403, 12531, 12551, 12573, 12750, 12910, 12980, 13122, 13270, 13346, 13373, 13377, 13392, 13470, 13502, 13503, 13520, 13525, 13531, 13571, 13728, 13739, 13832, 13850, 13870, 13898, 14169, 14274, 14276, 14284, 14287, 14331, 14385, 14404, 14746
$C_{10}H_{22}O_2$	Acetaldehyde dibutyl acetal (1,1-dibutoxyethane). B.p., 188.8 460, 7246, 11052, 14689
$C_{10}H_{22}O_2$	Acetaldehyde diisobutyl acetal. B.p., 171.3 461, 7418, 14722
$C_{10}H_{22}O_3$	Isoamyl carbonate. B.p., 232.2 2764
$C_{10}H_{22}S$	Isoamyl sulfide. B.p., 214.8 3197, 5279, 9127, 9364, 9491, 9634, 9696, 9857, 10163, 10688, 10769, 11642, 11739, 11892, 12054, 12185, 12662, 12884, 12992, 13028, 13046, 13070, 13423, 13471, 13819, 13962, 14302, 14320, 14382, 14405–14407
$C_{10}H_{23}N$	Diisoamylamine. B.p., 188.2 12911, 12981, 13572, 14170, 14261, 14266, 14332, 14404
$C_{11}H_{10}$	1-Methylnaphthalene. B.p., 245.1 3198, 3765, 3930, 5280, 5439, 5889, 7574, 7910, 9128, 9173, 9697, 9906, 9948, 10093, 10689, 11140, 11370, 11679, 11740, 11775, 11893, 12199, 12602, 12768, 12819, 12943, 13080, 13177, 13192, 13289, 13356, 13546, 13584, 13585, 13608, 13704, 13767, 13786, 13882, 13899, 13925, 13974, 14013, 14030, 14057, 14087, 14104, 14113, 14148, 14183, 14198, 14221, 14339, 14350, 14358, 14371, 14377, 14395, 14408–14420
$C_{11}H_{10}$	2-Methylnaphthalene. B.p., 241.15 2050, 2139, 3199, 3766, 3931, 4040, 5281, 5440, 5890, 7575, 7911, 8965, 9146, 9174, 9492, 9698, 9907, 9949, 9967, 10064, 10164, 10690, 11129, 11141, 11371, 11680, 11741, 11776, 11894, 11964, 12138, 12200, 12311, 12603, 12769, 12820, 12835, 13081, 13159, 13178, 13193, 13221, 13247, 13290, 13357, 13547, 13586, 13636, 13664, 13705, 13768, 13787, 13883, 13926, 13975, 14014, 14031, 14058, 14088, 14105, 14114, 14124, 14149, 14199, 14222, 14251, 14351, 14359, 14365, 14372, 14378, 14408, 14421–14426
$C_{11}H_{12}O_2$	Ethyl cinnamate. B.p., 272 462, 3200, 3767, 5282, 5891, 7576, 9908, 9950, 11142, 12770, 13609, 13788, 13904, 13927, 13976, 13991, 14067, 14125, 14427–14436
$C_{11}H_{14}O_2$	1-Allyl-3, 4-dimethoxybenzene (eugenol methyl ether). B.p., 255 463, 3201, 3768, 5283, 5892, 7577, 7688, 9909, 9951, 10094, 11104, 11143, 11372, 12201, 12622, 12675, 12771, 13194, 13548, 13587, 13928, 14015, 14032, 14059, 14115, 14223, 14360, 14409, 14437–14443
$C_{11}H_{14}O_2$	Butyl benzoate. B.p., 249.8 464, 3202, 3769, 5284, 5893, 7576, 9147, 9175, 9493, 9910, 11144, 11373, 11777, 12604, 12676, 12772, 13049, 13588, 13610, 13789, 13929, 14016, 14060, 14116, 14184, 14224, 14361, 14410, 14421, 14437, 14444–14446
$C_{11}H_{14}O_2$	1,2-Dimethoxy-4-propenylbenzene (isoeugenol methyl ether). B.p., 270.5 465, 3203, 3770, 5285, 5894, 7579, 9911, 9952, 10095, 11374, 12623, 12677, 12733, 13195, 13589, 13884, 13905, 13930, 13977, 14033, 14068, 14126, 14427, 14428, 14447–14454
$C_{11}H_{14}O_2$	Ethyl β-phenylpropionate. B.p., 248.1 3204, 5895, 11681, 11778, 12744, 13611, 13706, 13769, 13790, 14061, 14391, 14411, 14422, 14455–14457
$C_{11}H_{14}O_2$	Isobutyl benzoate. B.p., 242.15 466, 3205, 3771, 5286, 5896, 7580, 7912, 9148, 9176, 9494, 9912, 11375, 11682, 11779, 12202, 12605, 12678, 13029, 13590, 13612, 13707, 13770, 13963, 14017, 14062, 14089, 14106, 14117, 14185, 14200, 14225, 14306, 14362, 14392, 14396, 14412, 14423, 14438, 1445
$C_{11}H_{16}O$	*p-tert*-Amylphenol. B.p., 266.5 9953, 12624, 13550, 13597, 14118, 14127, 14201, 14413, 14458–14462
$C_{11}H_{16}O$	Methyl thymyl ether. B.p., 216.5 3772, 7581, 9101, 9635, 9913, 10165, 11105, 11376, 11895, 12261, 12344, 12448, 12606, 12697, 12725, 12885, 12944, 13030, 13152, 13141, 13222, 13248, 13291, 13358, 13549, 13771, 14107, 14226, 14252, 14303, 14315, 14324, 14340, 14397, 14463
$C_{11}H_{17}N$	Isoamylaniline. B.p., 256.0 11683, 11780, 12203, 12945, 13772, 14018, 14063, 14119, 14128, 14186, 14202, 14414, 14424, 14439, 14447, 14464, 14465

Formula	Name and System Nos.
$C_{11}H_{20}O$	Isobornyl methyl ether. B.p., 192.2 467, 2140, 3206, 3773, 3848, 3932, 4423, 4525, 5287, 5441, 5897, 6824, 7582, 7771, 8022, 8297, 8966, 9365, 9858, 10065, 10131, 10281, 10378, 10405, 10443, 10691, 11053, 11130, 11249, 11338, 11896, 11897, 12055, 12139, 12213, 12284, 12663, 12751, 13142, 13472, 13805, 13820, 13851, 14160, 14289, 14310, 14336, 14346, 14355, 14386
$C_{11}H_{20}O$	Methyl α-terpineol ether. B.p., 216.2 468, 1816, 2051, 3207, 3774, 4059, 4422, 5288, 5442, 5898, 7583, 9102, 9495, 9636, 9699, 9914, 11106, 11377, 11505, 11742, 11898, 11965, 12262, 12285, 12312, 12345, 12449, 12607, 12821, 12886, 12946, 13031, 13047, 13143, 13223, 13249, 13292, 13359, 13551, 13637, 13665, 13683, 13810, 13964, 14227, 14253, 14304, 14316, 14325, 14326, 14341, 14353, 14356, 14366, 14373, 4383, 14398, 14405, 14466, 14467
$C_{11}H_{22}O_2$	Ethyl pelargonate. B.p., 227 469, 3775, 5289, 13224, 13293, 13708, 13965, 14374
$C_{11}H_{22}O_3$	Isoamyl carbonate. B.p., 232.2 470, 3208, 3776, 4060, 5290, 5443, 7913, 9103, 9129, 9177, 9496, 9915, 11215, 11378, 11684, 11743, 12140, 12822, 12887, 13032, 13250, 13360, 13613, 13638, 13709, 13773, 13966, 14064, 14065, 14108, 14150, 14187, 14203, 14228, 14238, 14307, 14137, 14342, 14367, 14393, 14399, 14415, 14425, 14468, 14469
$C_{11}H_{24}$	Undecane. 6107
$C_{11}H_{24}O_2$	Diamyloxymethane. B.p., 221.6 471, 8678, 14737
$C_{11}H_{24}O_2$	Diisoamyloxymethane. B.p., 210 472, 9004, 9637, 11899, 12346, 12726, 12752, 13144, 13294, 13666, 13684, 14254, 14883
$C_{12}H_{10}$	Acenaphthene. B.p., 277.9 3209, 3777, 3933, 5291, 5899, 7584, 9916, 9954, 9968, 10096, 11145, 11379, 12608, 12775, 13082, 13591, 13614, 13907, 13931, 13978, 13979, 13992, 13993, 13999, 14034, 14069, 14129, 14429, 14448, 14458, 14470–14475
$C_{12}H_{10}$	Biphenyl. B.p., 255.9 3210, 3778, 5292, 5900, 7585, 9178, 9497, 9917, 9955, 9969, 10097, 11146, 11380, 11781, 12204, 12450, 12609, 12776, 12947, 13196, 13552, 13592, 13615, 13710, 13774, 13885, 13932, 13980, 13994, 14019, 14035, 14070, 14120, 14130, 14188, 14229, 14363, 14400, 14416, 14430, 14440, 14444, 14456, 14464, 14476–14481
$C_{12}H_{10}O$	Phenyl ether. B.p., 259.3 473, 3211, 3779, 5293, 5901, 7586, 7689, 9918, 9956, 10098, 11107, 11147, 11381, 11782, 12610, 12625, 12679, 12777, 13083, 13197, 13593, 13616, 13791, 13886, 13933, 13981, 14020, 14036, 14071, 14121, 14131, 14230, 14364, 14379, 14417, 14431, 14441, 14445, 14449, 14457, 14465, 14476, 14482–14487
$C_{12}H_{11}N$	Diphenylamine. B.p., 275 13982
$C_{12}H_{12}$	1-Ethylnaphthalene. B.p., 254.2 11966, 12141
$C_{12}H_{14}O_4$	Ethyl phthalate. B.p., 298.5 474, 3212, 7587, 11148, 14470, 14477, 14482, 14488
$C_{12}H_{16}O_2$	Isoamyl benzoate. B.p., 262.3 475, 3213, 3780, 5294, 5902, 7588, 9919, 9957, 11149, 12611, 12680, 12778, 12888, 13594, 13617, 13792, 13908, 13934, 13983, 14021, 14037, 14122, 14132, 14418, 14432, 14442, 14450, 14468, 14471, 14478, 14483, 14489–14491
$C_{12}H_{16}O_3$	Isoamyl salicylate. B.p., 277.5 3214, 5295, 5903, 7589, 9149, 11108, 11150, 11382, 11783, 12612, 13198, 13553, 13775, 13793, 13909, 13935, 13984, 14038, 14072, 14133, 14433, 14451, 14459, 14479, 14484, 14489, 14492–14494
$C_{12}H_{18}$	1,3,5-Triethylbenzene. B.p., 215.5 2052, 2141, 3215, 3781, 4526, 4576, 5904, 6204, 6572, 6825, 7590, 7772, 7914, 8023, 8298, 8967, 9104, 9498, 9638, 9700, 9859, 9920, 9958, 10066, 10166, 10282, 10379, 10444, 10692, 11054, 11216, 11282, 11339, 11383, 11611, 11744, 11900, 11967, 12056, 12142, 12186, 12244, 12286, 12313, 12347, 12451, 12613, 12664, 12698, 12727, 12753, 12779, 12823, 12889, 12948, 13033, 13071, 13095, 13153, 13179, 13225, 13251, 13295, 13303, 13361, 13424, 13595, 13649, 13667, 13685, 13749, 13806, 13811, 13887, 13967, 14231, 14305, 14309, 14318, 14327, 14343, 14347, 14357, 14368, 14375, 14384, 14387, 14390, 14401, 14406, 14466, 14495, 14496
$C_{12}H_{20}O_2$	Bornyl acetate. B.p., 227.6 476, 3216, 3782, 5296, 5444, 5905, 7591, 9105, 9130, 9179, 9366, 9499, 9701, 9921, 11217, 11685, 11745, 11784, 11968, 12143, 12452, 12824, 12949, 12993, 13034, 13048, 13072, 13226, 13296, 13362, 13435, 13639, 13650, 13711, 13776, 13968, 14066, 14109, 14189, 14204, 14232, 14239, 14319, 14344, 14354, 14369, 14376, 14394, 14402, 14419, 14426, 14469, 14495
$C_{12}H_{20}O_2$	Isobornyl acetate. B.p., 225.8 14262, 14267

Formula	Name and System Nos.
$C_{12}H_{22}O$	Bornyl ethyl ether. B.p., 204.9 3783, 4424, 5297, 5906, 7915, 9639, 10132, 11340, 11412, 11902, 12348, 12665, 12754, 13123, 13154, 13160, 13145, 13821, 13969, 14388, 14496
$C_{12}H_{22}O$	Ethyl isobornyl ether. B.p., 203.8 477, 3217, 3784, 5445, 5990, 9640, 10067, 10133, 10167, 10283, 10380, 10445, 10693, 11131, 11341, 11901, 12057, 12245, 12263, 12287, 12349, 12755, 13812, 14255, 14328, 14389, 14407
$C_{12}H_{22}O_4$	Isoamyl oxalate. B.p., 268.0 3218, 6205, 7592, 9922, 9959, 11151, 11384, 12780, 13618, 13888, 13909, 13936, 13985, 14022, 14039, 14380, 14434, 14452, 14453, 14472, 14480, 14485, 14490, 14497, 14498
$C_{12}H_{24}O_3$	2,2-Dibutoxy-3-butanone. B.p., 228 478
$C_{12}H_{24}O_3$	2,2-Diisobutoxy-3-butanone. B.p., 214 479
$C_{12}H_{26}$	Dodecane. B.p., 216 3785, 5809
$C_{12}H_{26}O_2$	Acetaldehyde diamyl acetal. B.p., 225.3 480, 8679, 14738
$C_{12}H_{26}O_2$	Acetaldehyde diisoamyl acetal. B.p., 213.6 481, 8782, 14747
$C_{13}H_{10}$	Fluorene. B.p., 295 3219, 3786, 5298, 7593, 9923, 9960, 11385, 12781, 13910, 13986, 14460
$C_{13}H_{10}O_2$	Phenyl benzoate. B.p., 315 3220, 3787, 5907, 11152, 14499, 14500
$C_{13}H_{12}$	Diphenylmethane. B.p., 265.6 3221, 3788, 3934, 5299, 5908, 7594, 9924, 9961, 9970, 10099, 11153, 11386, 12614, 12782, 13084, 13199, 13596, 13619, 13777, 13794, 13889, 13911, 13937, 13987, 13988, 13995, 14023, 14040, 14073, 14123, 14134, 14381, 14403, 14420, 14435, 14443, 14454, 14461, 14473, 14481, 14486, 14488, 14491, 14492, 14497
$C_{13}H_{12}O$	Benzyl phenyl ether. B.p., 286.5 3222, 3789, 5909, 7595, 9925, 9962, 9971, 11109, 11154, 11387, 12783, 13912, 14000, 14003, 14074, 14474, 14493, 14501
$C_{13}H_{14}$	2-Isopropylnaphthalene. B.p., 266.5 11969, 12144
$C_{13}H_{28}$	Tridecane. B.p., 234.0 3790, 8299, 9500, 9702, 9926, 9963, 12187, 12453, 12825, 13035, 13620, 13970
$C_{14}H_{12}$	Stilbene (bibenzal). B.p., 306.5 3223, 3791, 5306, 9964, 11155, 11388, 12784, 13989, 13996, 14499
$C_{14}H_{12}O_2$	Benzyl benzoate. B.p., 324 3992, 5910
$C_{14}H_{14}$	1,2-Diphenylethane. B.p., 284 3224, 3793, 5301, 5911, 7596, 9927, 9965, 10100, 11156, 11389, 12615, 12785, 13795, 13913, 13997, 13998, 14001, 14075, 14135, 14436, 14462, 14475, 14494, 14498, 14501
$C_{14}H_{14}O$	Benzyl ether. B.p., 297 3225, 3794, 5302, 5912, 7597, 11110, 14002, 14004, 14076, 14487, 14500
$C_{14}H_{30}$	Tetradecane. B.p., 252.5 3795, 5810
$C_{14}H_{30}O$	Tetradecyl alcohol. B.p., 260.0 11970, 12145
$C_{15}H_{18}$	2-Amylnaphthalene. B.p., 292.3 11971, 12146
$C_{15}H_{33}BO_3$	Isoamyl borate. B.p., 255 14024, 14446
$C_{16}H_{20}$	Diisopropylnaphthalene. B.p., 305 11972, 12147

Bibliography

(1) Adelson and Evans, U. S. Patent 2,500,596 (1950).
(2) Agliardi, *Chimica e industria (Milan)*, **28,** 87 (1946).
(3) Alpert and Elving, *Ind. Eng. Chem.*, **41,** 2864 (1949).
(4) American Cyanamid Co., New Product Bull. **13** (March 1950).
(5) Amick and Harney, U. S. Patent 2,487,086 (1949).
(6) Andrews and Spence, *Ibid.*, 2,061,889 (1936).
(7) *Ibid.*, 2,126,600 (1938).
(8) Anon., *Oil, Paint Drug Reptr.*, **156,** No. 18, 4 (Oct. 4, 1949).
(9) Aston, Kennedy, and Messerly, *J. Am. Chem. Soc.*, **63,** 2343 (1941).
(10) Atkins, *J. Chem. Soc.*, **117,** 218 (1920).
(11) Babcock, U. S. Patent 2,049,486 (1936).
(12) *Ibid.*, 2,461,191 (1949).
(13) Bahr and Zieler, *Z. angew. allgem. Chem.*, **43,** 286 (1930).
(14) Baker *et al.*, *Ind. Eng. Chem.*, **31,** 1260, 1263 (1939).
(15) Bakowski and Treszczanowicz, *Przemysl Chem.*, **22,** 211 (1938).
(16) Bancelin and Rivat, *Bull. soc. chim.*, (4) **25,** 552 (1919).
(17) Baney, U. S. Patent 2,425,220 (1947).
(18) Barrett Division, Allied Chemical and Dye Corp., *Chem. Inds.*, **33,** 513 (1933).
(19) Baud, *Bull. soc. chim.*, (4) **5,** 1022 (1909).
(20) Beduwe, *Bull. soc. chim. Belg.*, **34,** 41 (1925).
(21) Benning, U. S. Patents 2,450,414–15 (1948).
(22) Benning and Park, *Ibid.*, 2,384,449 (1945).
(23) Berg and Harrison, *Trans. Am. Inst. Chem. Engrs.*, **43,** 487 (1947).
(24) Berg and Harrison, U. S. Patent 2,442,229 (1948).
(25) *Ibid.*, 2,477,715 (1949).
(26) Berg, Harrison, and Montgomery, *Ind. Eng. Chem.*, **38,** 1149 (1946).
(27) Berthelot, *Compt. rend.*, **57,** 430 (1863).
(28) Birch, Collis, and Lowry, *Nature*, **158,** 60 (1946).
(29) Bishop and Denton, *Ind. Eng. Chem.*, **42,** 883 (1950).
(30) Bloomer, U. S. Patent 2,381,996 (1945).
(31) Bludworth and Flower, *Ibid.*, 2,381,032 (1945).
(32) Bonner, Bonner, and Gurney, *J. Am. Chem. Soc.*, **55,** 1406 (1933).
(33) Bonner and Wallace, *Ibid.*, **52,** 1747 (1930).
(34) Bouillon, *Compt. rend.*, **230,** 1290 (1950).
(35) Bouzat and Schmitt, *Ibid.*, **198,** 1923 (1934).
(36) Bozza and Gallarati, *Giorn. chim. ind. applicata*, **13,** 163 (1931).
(37) Bramer *et al.*, U. S. Patent 2,090,652 (1937).
(38) Brandon, *Ibid.*, 2,459,410 (1949).
(39) Brant, *J. Am. Chem. Soc.*, 64, 2224 (1942).
(40) Bremner, Jones, and Coats, Brit. Patent 592,919 (1947).
(41) Briner and Cardoso, *Compt. rend.*, **144,** 911 (1907).
(42) Britton, Nutting, and Horsley, *Anal. Chem.*, **19,** 601 (1947).
(43) Broick, Dept. of Commerce, OTS Rept., **PB 76303.**
(44) Bromiley and Quiggle, *Ind. Eng. Chem.*, **25,** 1136 (1933).
(45) Brooks, U. S. Patent 2,436,286 (1948).
(46) Brown, *J. Chem. Soc.*, **35,** 547 (1879).
(47) Brown, U. S. Patent 2,286,056 (1942).
(48) Brunjes and Furnas, *Ind. Eng. Chem.*, **27,** 396 (1935).
(49) Buchheim, Ger. Patent 616,596; *Chem. Zentr.*, **1935,** II, 3703.
(50) Buell, U. S. Patent 2,382,603 (1945).
(51) Burgin, Hearne, and Rust, *Ind. Eng. Chem.*, **33,** 385 (1941).
(52) Bushmakin, Begetova, and Kuchinskaya, *Sintet. Kauchuk*, No. **4,** 8 (1936).
(53) Bushmakin and Kuchinskaya, *Ibid.*, No. **5,** 3 (1936).
(54) Bushmakin and Voeikova, *J. Gen. Chem. (U.S.S.R.)*, **19,** 1615 (1949).
(55) Bylewski, *Roczniki Chem.*, **13,** 322 (1933).
(56) Cadbury, *J. Chem. Education*, **12,** 292 (1933).
(57) Calder and Fleer, U. S. Patents 2,401,335–6 (1946).
(58) Calices and Hannotte, *Ing. chim.*, **20,** 1 (1936).
(59) Calingaert and Wojciechowski, *J. Am. Chem. Soc.*, **72,** 5310 (1950).
(60) Campbell and Dulmage, *Ibid.*, **70,** 1723 (1948).
(61) Carbide and Carbon Chemicals Corp., Catalog, 12th ed., 1945.
(62) Carbide and Carbon Chemicals Corp., "Cellosolve and Carbitol Solvents," Jan. 1, 1947.
(63) Carbide and Carbon Chemicals Corp., *Chem. Inds.*, **33,** 521 (1933).
(64) Carey and Lewis, *Ind. Eng. Chem.*, **24,** 882 (1932).
(65) Carley and Bertelsen, III, *Ibid.*, **41,** 2806 (1949).
(66) Carnell, U. S. Patent 2,430,388 (1947).
(67) Carpenter, Davis, and Wiedeman, *Ibid.*, 2,404,163 (1946).
(68) Carlson, *Ibid.*, 2,381,876 (1945).

(69) Celanese Chemical Corp., New Product Bull. **N-08-1.**
(70) Ceslak and Karnatz, Brit. Patent 580,048 (1946).
(71) Chavanne, *Bull. soc. chim. Belg.*, **27,** 205 (1913).
(72) Churchill, Collamore, and Katz, *Oil Gas J.*, **41,** 33 (Aug. 6, 1942).
(73) Claiborne and Fuqua, *Anal. Chem.*, **21,** 1165 (1949).
(74) Clark, U. S. Patent 2,385,610 (1945).
(75) Clough and Johns, *Ind. Eng. Chem.*, **15,** 1030 (1923).
(76) Colburn, *Trans. Am. Inst. Chem. Engrs.*, **40,** 333 (1944).
(77) Coles and Popper, *Ind. Eng. Chem.*, **42,** 1434 (1950).
(78) Conner, Elving, Benischeck, Tobias, and Steingiser, *Ibid.*, **42,** 106 (1950).
(79) Conner, Elving, and Steingiser, *Ibid.*, **40,** 497 (1948).
(80) Cornish, Archibald, Murphy, and Evans, *Ibid.*, **26,** 397 (1934).
(81) Coulson, Brit. Patent 585,108 (1947).
(82) Coulson and Jones, *J. Soc. Chem. Ind.* (*London*), **65,** 169 (1946).
(83) Coulter, Lindsay, and Baker, *Ind. Eng. Chem.*, **33,** 1251 (1941).
(84) Craig, paper presented before Div. of Organic Chemistry, 104th Meeting AM. CHEM. SOC. Buffalo, N. Y., 1942.
(85) Cretcher, Kock, and Pittenger, *J. Am. Chem. Soc.*, **47,** 1173 (1925).
(86) Daudt, U. S. Patent 2,390,518 (1945).
(87) Davidson, *Ibid.*, 2,506,858 (1950).
(88) Deansley, *Ibid.*, 1,866,800 (1932).
(89) *Ibid.*, 2,290,636 (1942).
(90) De Mol, *Ing. chim.*, **22,** 362 (1938).
(91) Denyer, Fidler, and Lowry, *Ind. Eng. Chem.*, **41,** 2726 (1949).
(92) Dominik and Wojciechowska, *Przemysl Chem.*, **23,** 61 (1939).
(93) Dow Chemical Co., unpublished data.
(94) Drake, U. S. Patent 2,170,854 (1939).
(95) Dunlop and Trimble, *Ind. Eng. Chem.*, **32,** 1000 (1940).
(96) Engel, U. S. Patent 2,363,159 (1944).
(97) *Ibid.*, 2,376,870 (1945).
(98) *Ibid.*, 2,404,167 (1946).
(99) *Ibid.*, 2,445,944 (1948).
(100) *Ibid.*, 2,481,734 (1949).
(101) Engs, Wik, and Roberts, *Ibid.*, 2,414,639 (1947).
(102) Ernst and Kaufler, Ger. Patent 486,492 (1926).
(103) Evans, Brit. Patent 579,675 (1946).
(104) Evans, U. S. Patent 2,140,694 (1938).
(105) Evans and Edlung, *Ind. Eng. Chem.*, **28,** 1186 (1936).
(106) Evans and Hass, U. S. Patent 2,442,589 (1948).
(107) Evans, Morris, and Shokal, *Ibid.*, 2,372,941 (1945).
(108) *Ibid.*, 2,426,821 (1947).
(109) Eversole, *Ibid.*, 2,160,064 (1939).
(110) Ewell and Welch, *Ind. Eng. Chem.*, **37,** 1224 (1945).
(111) Ewell and Welch, *J. Am. Chem. Soc.*, **63,** 2475 (1941).
(112) Fairborne, *J. Chem. Soc.*, **1932,** 1965.
(113) Farchan Research Laboratory, Data Sheet B, February 1949.
(114) Feldman, Julian, private communication.
(115) Field, U. S. Patent 2,212,810 (1940).
(116) *Ibid.*, 2,265,939 (1941).
(117) Fisher, *Ibid.*, 2,341,433 (1944).
(118) Fisher and Fein, *Ibid.*, 2,438,278 (1948).
(119) Fordyce and Simonsen, *Ind. Eng. Chem.*, **41,** 104 (1949).
(120) Fowler and Hunt, *Ibid.*, **33,** 90 (1941).
(121) Fredenhager and Kerck, *Z. anorg. allgem. Chem.*, **252,** 280 (1944).
(122) Frey, U. S. Patent 2,322,800 (1943).
(123) Frey *et al.*, *Ibid.*, 2,186,524 (1940).
(124) Friedel, *Bull. soc. chim.*, (2) **24,** 160, 241 (1875).
(125) Fritzsche and Stockton, *Ind. Eng. Chem.*, **38,** 737 (1946).
(126) Fritzweiler, *Angew. Chem.*, **45,** 605; **46,** 241 (1933).
(127) Fuchs, *Chem. Ztg.*, **51,** 402 (1927).
(128) Fuqua, U. S. Patent 2,481,211 (1949).
(129) Gautier, *Ann. chim. et phys.*, (4) **17,** 191 (1869).
(130) Geckler and Fragen, U. S. Patent 2,316,126 (1943).
(131) Ghysels, *Bull. soc. chim. Belg.*, **33,** 57 (1924).
(132) Gibson, U. S. Patent 2,347,317 (1944).
(133) Giguere and Maass, *Can. J. Research*, **18B,** 181 (1940).
(134) Goldblum, Martin, and Young, *Ind. Eng. Chem.*, **39,** 1474 (1947).
(135) Gomberg, *J. Am. Chem. Soc.*, **41,** 1414 (1919).
(136) Gordon and Benson, *Can. J. Research*, **24B,** 285 (1946).
(137) Gordon and Bright, U. S. Patent 2,171,549 (1939).

(138) Gowing-Scopes, *Analyst*, **39,** 6 (1914).
(139) Greenburg, U. S. Patent 2,313,536 (1943).
(140) *Ibid.*, 2,405,300 (1946).
(141) Greene, *Ibid.*, 2,480,919 (1949).
(142) Gresham, *Ibid.*, 2,395,265 (1946).
(143) *Ibid.*, 2,479,068 (1949).
(144) Gresham and Brooks, *Ibid.*, 2,449,470 (1948).
(145) Griswold and Ludwig, *Ind. Eng. Chem.*, **35,** 117 (1943).
(146) Guinot, U. S. Patent 2,316,860 (1943).
(147) Guinot and Chassaing, *Ibid.*, 2,437,519 (1948).
(148) Hammond, *Ibid.*, 2,356,785 (1944).
(149) Hands and Norman, *Ind. Chemist*, **21,** 307 (1945).
(150) Hannotte, *Bull. soc. chim. Belg.*, **35,** 85 (1926).
(151) Hansley, U. S. Patent 2,452,460 (1948).
(152) Harney and Amick, *Ibid.*, 2,454,447 (1948).
(153) Harrison and Berg, *Ind. Eng. Chem.*, **38,** 117 (1946).
(154) Hatch and Ballin, *J. Am. Chem. Soc.*, **71,** 1039 (1949).
(155) Haywood, *J. Phys. Chem.*, **3,** 317 (1899).
(156) Heldman, *J. Am. Chem. Soc.*, **66,** 661 (1944).
(157) Hennion and Groebner, *Ibid.*, **70,** 426 (1948).
(158) Herold, Wustrow, and Wetzel, U. S. Patent 2,091,636 (1937).
(159) Herz and Rathmann, *Chem. Ztg.*, **36,** 1417 (1912).
(160) Hicks-Bruun and Bruun, *J. Research Natl. Bur. Standards*, **8,** 525 (1932).
(161) Hill, *J. Chem. Soc.*, **101,** 2467 (1912).
(162) Holley, *J. Am. Chem. Soc.*, **24,** 448 (1902).
(163) Holley and Weaver, *Ibid.*, **27,** 1049 (1905).
(164) Holst and Hamburger, *Z. physik. Chem.*, **91,** 513 (1916).
(165) Homfray, *J. Chem. Soc.*, **87,** 1441 (1905).
(166) Hopkins, Yerger, and Lynch, *J. Am. Chem. Soc.*, **61,** 2460 (1939).
(167) Horsley, *Anal. Chem.*, **19,** 508 (1947).
(168) *Ibid.*, **21,** 831 (1949).
(169) Houston, *J. Am. Chem. Soc.*, **55,** 4131 (1933).
(170) Howe and Hass, *Ind. Eng. Chem.*, **38,** 251 (1946).
(171) Huntress, "Organic Chlorine Compounds," p. 588, 1038, New York, John Wiley & Sons, 1948.
(172) Huntress and Sanchez-Nieva, *J. Am. Chem. Soc.*, **70,** 2813 (1948).
(173) Hyatt, U. S. Patent 2,176,500 (1939).
(174) Izard, *Ibid.*, 2,061,732 (1936).
(175) Jackson and Young, *J. Chem. Soc.*, **73,** 922 (1898).
(176) Janecke, *Z. physik. Chem.*, **164,** 401 (1933).
(177) Jensen, U. S. Patent 2,360,685 (1944).
(178) Johnson and Spurlin, *Ibid.*, 2,459,433 (1949).
(179) Jones, Schoenborn, and Colburn, *Ind. Eng. Chem.*, **35,** 666 (1943).
(180) Kaplan and Monakhova, *J. Gen. Chem. (U.S.S.R.)*, **7,** 2499 (1937).
(181) Karpinski and Swietoslawski, *Compt. rend.*, **198,** 2166 (1934).
(182) Karr, U. S. Patent 2,463,629 (1949).
(183) Kellogg and Cady, *J. Am. Chem. Soc.*, **70,** 3986 (1948).
(184) Kimberlin, U. S. Patent 2,275,151 (1943).
(185) Kireev, Kaplan, and Zlobin, *J. Applied Chem. (U.S.S.R.)*, **7,** 1333 (1934).
(186) Kireev and Monakhova, *J. Phys. Chem. (U.S.S.R.)*, **7,** 71 (1936).
(187) Kireev and Sitnikov, *Ibid.*, **15,** 492 (1941).
(188) Kireev and Skvortsova, *Ibid.*, **7,** 63 (1936).
(189) Kleinert, *Z. angew. allgem. Chem.*, **46,** 18 (1933).
(190) Kodak Ltd., Brit. Patent 501,927 (1939).
(191) Konowaloff, *Ann. Physik.*, (2) **14,** 34 (1881).
(192) Kretschmer, Nowakowska, and Wiebe, *J. Am. Chem. Soc.*, **70,** 1785 (1948).
(193) Kretschmer and Wiebe, *Ibid.*, **71,** 1793 (1949).
(194) *Ibid.*, p. 3176.
(195) Kuenen, *Z. physik. Chem.*, **24,** 667 (1897).
(196) *Ibid.*, **37,** 485 (1901).
(197) Lacher, Buck, and Parry, *J. Am. Chem. Soc.*, **63,** 2422 (1941).
(198) Lacher and Hunt, *Ibid.*, **63,** 1752 (1941).
(199) Lacourt, *Bull. soc. chim. Belg.*, **36,** 346 (1927).
(200) Lake, U. S. Patent 2,432,771 (1947).
(201) Lake and McDowell, *Ibid.*, 2,456,561 (1948).
(202) Lake and Stribley, *Ibid.*, 2,439,777 (1948).
(203) *Ibid.*, 2,477,303 (1949).
(204) Lange, "Handbook of Chemistry", 5th ed., p. 1386, Sandusky, Ohio, Handbook Publishers, Inc., 1944.
(205) Lebo, *J. Am. Chem. Soc.*, **43,** 1005 (1921).
(206) Lecat, *Acad. roy. belg., Classe sci., Mem.*, **23,** 8 (2) (1943–44).

(207) Lecat, *Ann. chim.*, (12) **2,** 158–202 (1947).
(208) Lecat, *Ann. soc. sci. Bruxelles*, **45,** I, 169 (1925).
(209) *Ibid.*, **45,** I, 284 (1925).
(210) *Ibid.*, **47B,** I, 21 (1927).
(211) *Ibid.*, p. 63.
(212) *Ibid.*, p. 108.
(213) *Ibid.*, **47B,** II, 39 (1927).
(214) *Ibid.*, p. 87.
(215) *Ibid.*, **47B,** I, 149 (1927).
(216) *Ibid.*, **48B,** I, 13 (1928).
(217) *Ibid.*, **48B,** II, 54 (1928).
(218) *Ibid.*, p. 113.
(219) *Ibid.*, p. 1.
(220) *Ibid.*, p. 105.
(221) *Ibid.*, **49B,** I, 17 (1929).
(222) *Ibid.*, p. 109.
(223) *Ibid.*, p. 28.
(224) *Ibid.*, p. 119.
(225) *Ibid.*, **50B,** I, 21 (1930).
(226) *Ibid.*, **55B,** 253 (1935).
(227) *Ibid.*, **56B,** 41 (1936).
(228) *Ibid.*, p. 221.
(229) *Ibid.*, **60,** 155 (1940–46).
(230) *Ibid.*, p. 163.
(231) *Ibid.*, p. 169.
(232) *Ibid.*, p. 228.
(233) *Ibid.*, **61,** 63 (1947).
(234) *Ibid.*, p. 79.
(235) *Ibid.*, p. 148.
(236) *Ibid.*, **61,** pp. 153–62.
(237) *Ibid.*, pp. 255–62.
(238) *Ibid.*, **62,** 55–60 (1948).
(239) *Ibid.*, pp. 93–9.
(240) *Ibid.*, pp. 128–40.
(241) *Ibid.*, **63,** 58–65 (1949).
(242) *Ibid.*, p. 111.
(243) Lecat, "Azeotropisme," Brussels, Lamertin, 1918.
(244) Lecat. *Bull. classe sci. Acad. roy. Belg.*, **29,** 273–89 (1943).
(245) *Ibid.*, **32,** 351–62 (1946).
(246) *Ibid.*, **33,** 160–83 (1947).
(247) *Ibid.*, **35,** 484 (1949).
(248) Lecat, *Compt. rend.*, **217,** 242 (1943).
(249) *Ibid.*, **222,** 733 (1946).
(250) *Ibid.*, pp. 733, 882, 1488.
(251) *Ibid.*, **223,** 286 (1946).
(252) Lecat, *Rec. trav. chim.*, **45,** 620 (1926).
(253) *Ibid.*, **46,** 240 (1927).
(254) *Ibid.*, **47,** 13 (1928).
(255) Lecat, "Tables azéotropiques," Brussels, l'Auteur, July 1949.
(256) Lecat, *Z. anorg. allgem. Chem.*, **186,** 119 (1929).
(257) Lepingle, *Bull. soc. chim.*, **39,** 741, 864 (1926).
(258) Liberman, Parnes, and Kursanov, *Bull. acad. sci. U.R.S.S., Classe sci. chim.*, **1948,** 101.
(259) Licht and Denzler, *Chem. Eng. Progress*, **44,** 627 (1948).
(260) Lidstone, *J. Chem. Soc.*, **1940,** 241.
(261) Litkenhous, Van Arsdale, and Hutchison, *J. Phys. Chem.*, **44,** 377 (1940).
(262) Loder, French Patent 814,838 (1937); U. S. Patents 2,135,447–60 (1938).
(263) McCarty, *J. Am. Chem. Soc.*, **71,** 1339 (1949).
(264) McDermott, F. A., private communication.
(265) McDonald and McMillan, *Ind. Eng. Chem.*, **36,** 1175 (1944).
(266) McKinnis, U. S. Patent 2,388,429 (1945).
(267) McMillan, *J. Am. Chem. Soc.*, **58,** 1345 (1936).
(268) Magnus, *Ann. Physik.*, **38,** 488 (1836).
(269) Marschner and Cropper, *Ind. Eng. Chem.*, **38,** 262 (1946).
(270) *Ibid.*, **41,** 1357 (1949).
(271) Marshall, *J. Chem. Soc.*, **89,** 1351 (1906).
(272) Matuszak and Frey, *Ind. Eng. Chem., Anal. Ed.*, **9,** 111 (1937).
(273) Merriman, *J. Chem. Soc.*, **103,** 1790, 1801 (1913).
(274) Morton, "Laboratory Technic in Organic Chemistry," p. 66, New York, McGraw-Hill Book Co., 1938.
(275) Munter, Aepli, and Kossatz, *Ind. Eng. Chem.*, **39,** 427 (1947).

(276) Murray, *J. Council Sci. Ind. Research*, **17**, 213 (1944).
(277) Nadeau and Fisher, U. S. Patent 2,165,293 (1939).
(278) Natta, *Ibid.*, 2,308,229 (1943).
(279) Naumann, *Ber.*, **10**, 1421, 1819, 2099 (1877).
(280) Navez, *Bull. soc. chim. Belg.*, **39**, 435 (1930).
(281) Nelson and Markham, *J. Am. Chem. Soc.*, **72**, 2417 (1950).
(282) Noyes and Warfel, *Ibid.*, **23**, 463 (1901).
(283) Oblad, U. S. Patent 2,440,414 (1948).
(284) Oddo, *Gazz. chim. ital.*, **41**, II, 232 (1911).
(285) Othmer, *Ind. Eng. Chem.*, **35**, 614 (1943).
(286) Othmer, U. S. Patent 2,050,234 (1936).
(287) *Ibid.*, 2,170,834 (1939).
(288) *Ibid.*, 2,395,010 (1946).
(289) Othmer and Josefowitz, *Ind. Eng. Chem.*, **39**, 1175 (1947).
(290) Othmer and Morley, *Ibid.*, **38**, 751 (1946).
(291) Othmer and Savitt, *Ibid.*, **40**, 168 (1948).
(292) Othmer, Savitt, Krasner, Goldberg, and Markowitz, *Ibid.*, **41**, 572 (1949).
(293) Othmer, Schlechter, and Koszalka, *Ibid.*, **37**, 895 (1945).
(294) Padgitt, Amis, and Hughes, *J. Am. Chem. Soc.*, **64**, 1231 (1942).
(295) Pahlovouni, *Bull. soc. chim. Belg.*, **36**, 533 (1927).
(296) Patterson, U. S. Patent 2,407,997 (1946).
(297) Patterson and Ozol, *Ibid.*, 2,386,058 (1945).
(298) Petry, *Ibid.*, 2,411,106 (1946).
(299) Pfann, *J. Am. Chem. Soc.*, **66**, 155 (1944).
(300) Pearce and Gerster, *Ind. Eng. Chem.*, **42**, 1418 (1950).
(301) Pennington and Reed, *Chem. Eng. Progress*, **46**, 464 (1950).
(302) Picon and Flahaut, *Compt. rend.*, **230**, 1954 (1950).
(303) Pierre, *Ibid.*, **74**, 224 (1872).
(304) Pierre and Puchot, *Ibid.*, **73**, 599 (1871).
(305) Piret and Hall, *Ind. Eng. Chem.*, **40**, 661 (1948).
(306) Plate and Tarasova, *Bull. acad. sci. U.R.S.S., Classe sci. chim.*, **1941**, 201; Universal Oil Products Library, *Bull.* **17**, 145 (1942).
(307) Popelier, *Bull. soc. chim. Belg.*, **32**, 179 (1923).
(308) Prahl and Mathes, *Angew. Chem.*, **47**, 11 (1934).
(309) Pratt, Preprint, *Trans. Inst. Chem. Engrs. (London)* (March 1947).
(310) Pryanishnikov and Genin, *J. Applied Chem. (U.S.S.R.)*, **13**, 140 (1940).
(311) Quiggle and Fenske, *J. Am. Chem. Soc.*, **59**, 1829 (1937).
(312) Rabcewicz-Zubkowski, *Roczniki Chem.*, **13**, 193 (1933).
(313) *Ibid.*, p. 334.
(314) Räder, *Z. anorg. allgem. Chem.*, **130**, 325 (1923).
(315) Ray, U. S. Patent 2,498,928 (1950).
(316) Reed, *Ibid.*, 2,511,993 (1950).
(317) Reeves and Sadle, *J. Am. Chem. Soc.*, **72**, 1251 (1950).
(318) Rehberg, *Ibid.*, **71**, 3247 (1949).
(319) Rehberg, U. S. Patent 2,406,561 (1946).
(320) Rehberg and Fisher, *J. Am. Chem. Soc.*, **66**, 1203 (1944).
(321) Reid, U. S. Patent 2,070,962 (1937).
(322) Reinders and Minjer, *Rec. trav. chim.*, **59**, 207, 369 (1940).
(323) *Ibid.*, **66**, 552, 564, 573 (1947).
(324) Ricard and Guinot, U. S. Patent 1,915,002 (1933).
(325) Richards and Hargreaves, *Ind. Eng. Chem.*, **36**, 805 (1944).
(326) Riethof, U. S. Patent 2,383,016 (1945).
(327) *Ibid.*, 2,412,649–51 (1946).
(328) Robinson, "Elements of Fractional Distillation," p. 230, New York, McGraw-Hill Book Co., 1930.
(329) Robinson, Wright, and Bennett, *J. Phys. Chem.*, **36**, 658 (1932).
(330) Rohm and Haas Co., Bull. on *tert*-octylamine (1949).
(331) Rohm and Haas Co., "Physical Properties of the Methylamines," 1949.
(332) Roscoe, *Ann.*, **116**, 203 (1860).
(333) Roscoe and Dittmar, *Ibid.*, **112**, 327 (1859).
(334) Ryland, *Am. Chem. J.*, **22**, 390 (1899); *Chem. News (London)*, **81**, 15, 42, 50 (1908).
(335) Sakuyama, *J. Soc. Chim. Ind. Japan*, **44**, 266 (1941).
(336) Sandberg and Patterson, U. S. Patent 2,428,815 (1947).
(337) Sastry, *J. Soc. Chem. Ind. (London)*, **35**, 450 (1916).
(338) Sauer, *J. Am. Chem. Soc.*, **66**, 1707 (1944).
(339) Sauer, U. S. Patent 2,381,139 (1945).
(340) Sauer and Hadsell, *J. Am. Chem. Soc.*, **70**, 4258 (1948).
(341) Sauer and Patnode, *Ibid.*, **67**, 1548 (1945).
(342) Sauer and Reed, U. S. Patent 2,388,575 (1945).
(343) Sauer, Scheiber, and Hadsell, *J. Am. Chem. Soc.*, **70**, 4254 (1948).

(344) Scatchard and Raymond, *Ibid.*, **60**, 1278 (1938).
(345) Scatchard, Wood, and Mochel, *Ibid.*, **61**, 3206 (1939).
(346) Scatchard, Wood, and Mochel, *J. Phys. Chem.*, **43**, 119 (1939).
(347) Schelling and Anderson, U. S. Patent 2,422,802 (1947).
(348) Schopmeyer and Arnold, U. S. Patent 2,350,370 (1944).
(349) Schichtantz, *J. Research Natl. Bur. Standards*, **18**, 129 (1937).
(350) Schreinmakers, *Z. physik. Chem.*, **35**, 459 (1900).
(351) *Ibid.*, **39**, 485; **40**, 440; **41**, 331 (1902).
(352) *Ibid.*, **47**, 445; **48**, 257 (1904).
(353) Schumaker and Hunt, *Ind. Eng. Chem.*, **34**, 701 (1942).
(354) Schutz and Mallonee, *J. Am. Chem. Soc.*, **62**, 1491 (1940).
(355) Senkus, U. S. Patent 2,406,713 (1946).
(356) Shawinigan Chemical, Ltd., Dept. Chem. Development, "Report on Vinyl Crotonate."
(357) Shell Chemical Corp., "Allyl Alcohol," 1946.
(358) Shell Chemical Corp., "Methyl Ethyl Ketone," 1938.
(359) Shell Chemical Corp., "Organic Chemicals Manufactured by Shell," 1939.
(360) Shell Development Co., Data Sheet, 1946.
(361) Shell Development Co., unpublished data.
(362) Shostakovskiĭ and Prilezhaeva, *J. Gen. Chem.* (*U.S.S.R.*), **17**, 1129 (1947).
(363) Simonetta and Barakan, *Gazz. chim. ital.*, **77**, 105 (1947).
(364) Simonetta and Mugnaini, *Chimica e industria* (*Milan*), **30**, **73** (1948).
(365) Smith, *Ind. Eng. Chem.*, **34**, 251 (1942).
(366) Smith, U. S. Patent 2,385,546 (1945).
(367) Smith and Bonner, *Ind. Eng. Chem.*, **41**, 2867 (1949).
(368) Smith and Wojciechowski, *J. Research Natl. Bur. Standards*, **18**, 461 (1937).
(369) Smyth and Engel, *J. Am. Chem. Soc.*, **51**, 2646 (1929).
(370) Snyder and Gilbert, *Ind. Eng. Chem.*, **34**, 1519 (1942).
(371) Société des usines chimiques Rhône-Poulenc, Brit. Patent 595,738 (1947).
(372) Soday and Bennett, *J. Chem. Education*, **7**, 1336 (1930).
(373) Speck, U. S. Patent 2,449,152 (1948).
(374) Speier, *J. Am. Chem. Soc.*, **70**, 4142 (1948).
(375) Spicer and Kruger, *Ibid.*, **72**, 1855 (1950).
(376) Stasse, U. S. Patent 2,363,157 (1944).
(377) *Ibid.*, 2,363,158 (1944).
(378) Steel and Bagstor, *J. Chem. Soc.*, **97**, 2607 (1910).
(379) Steinhauser and White, *Ind. Eng. Chem.*, **41**, 2912 (1949).
(380) Steitz, U. S. Patent 2,500,329 (1950).
(381) Stengel and O'Loughlin, *Ibid.*, 2,315,139 (1943).
(382) Stockhardt and Hull, *Ind. Eng. Chem.*, **23**, 1438 (1931).
(383) Streiff *et al.*, paper presented before Div. of Petroleum Chemistry, 110th Meeting AM. CHEM. Soc., Chicago, 1946.
(384) Stribley and Lake, U. S. Patent 2,463,919 (1949).
(385) Sullivan, *Ibid.*, 2,265,220 (1941).
(386) Sutherland, *Ibid.*, 2,290,654 (1942).
(387) Swietoslawski *et al.*, *Roczniki Chem.*, **12**, 48 (1932).
(388) Swietoslawski and Kopczynski, *Ibid.*, **11**, 440 (1931).
(389) Swietoslawski and Wajcenblit, *Compt. rend.*, **193**, 664 (1931).
(390) Swinehart and Shenk, "Boron Fluoride and Its Addition Compounds," Harshaw Chemical Co., 1946.
(391) Tarbutton and Deming, *J. Am. Chem. Soc.*, **72**, 2086 (1950).
(392) Taylor and Horsley, U. S. Patent 2,293,317 (1942).
(393) Teague and Felsing, *J. Am. Chem. Soc.*, **65**, 485 (1943).
(394) Teter and Merwin, U. S. Patent 2,388,507 (1945).
(395) Thayer, *J. Phys. Chem.*, **3**, 36 (1899).
(396) Timmermans and Delcourt, *J. chim. phys.*, **31**, 98 (1934).
(397) Tomassi, *Roczniki Chem.*, **21**, 108 (1947).
(398) Tomkins, Wheat, and Stranks, *Can. J. Research*, **26F**, 168 (1948).
(399) Tongberg and Johnston, *Ind. Eng. Chem.*, **25**, 733 (1933).
(400) Treybal, Weber, and Daley, *Ibid.*, **38**, 817 (1946).
(401) Trillat and Cambies, *Compt. rend.*, **118**, 1277 (1894).
(402) Tuda, Oguri, and Hukusima, *J. Pharm. Soc.* (*Japan*), **61**, 74 (1941).
(403) Tuerck and Brittain, U. S. Patent 2,405,471 (1946).
(404) Tyerman, Brit. Patent 590,713 (1947).
(405) Tyrer, *J. Chem. Soc.*, **101**, 81, 1104 (1912).
(406) Usines de Melle, French Patent 844,000 (1939).
(407) Van de Walle, *Bull. soc. chim. Belg.*, **34**, 10, 399 (1925).
(408) Van Klooster and Douglas, *J. Phys. Chem.*, **49**, 67 (1945).
(409) Wade and Finnemore, *J. Chem. Soc.*, **85**, 938 (1904).
(410) Wade and Merriman, *Ibid.*, **99**, 997 (1911).
(411) Walker and Carlisle, *Chem. Eng. News*, **21**, 1250 (1943).

(412) Wallace and Atkins, *J. Chem. Soc.*, **101**, 1179 (1912).
(413) *Ibid.*, p. 1958.
(414) Walls and Dean, U. S. Patent 2,371,860 (1945).
(415) Welling, *Ibid.*, 2,376,104 (1945).
(416) *Ibid.*, 2,386,375 (1945).
(417) *Ibid.*, 2,401,282 (1946).
(418) Wentworth, *Ibid.*, 2,038,865, 2,041,668 (1936).
(419) White and Rose, *J. Research Natl. Bur. Standards*, **17**, 943 (1936).
(420) *Ibid.*, **21**, 151 (1938).
(421) Willert, U. S. Patent 2,445,738 (1948).
(422) Williams, *Trans. Am. Inst. Chem. Engrs.*, **37**, 157 (1941).
(423) Williams and Meeker, *Anal. Chem.*, **20**, 733 (1948).
(424) Williams, Rosenberg, and Rothenberg, *Ind. Eng. Chem.*, **40**, 1273 (1948).
(425) Wood, *J. Am. Chem. Soc.*, **59**, 1510 (1937).
(426) Woods, *J. Soc. Chem. Ind. (London)*, **66**, 26 (1947).
(427) Wuyts, *Bull. soc. chim. Belg.*, **33**, 178 (1924).
(428) Wuyts and Bailleux, *Ibid.*, **29**, 55 (1920).
(429) Wuyts and Docquier, *Ibid.*, **44**, 297 (1935).
(430) Young, *J. Chem. Soc.*, **81**, 707 (1902).
(431) Young and Fortey, *Ibid.*, **81**, 739 (1902).
(432) *Ibid.*, **83**, 45, 68, 77 (1903).
(433) Young and Fortey, *J. Chem. Soc., Trans.*, **81**, 717 (1902).
(434) Young and Nelson, *Ind. Eng. Chem., Anal. Ed.*, **4**, 67 (1932).
(435) Yu and Hickman, *J. Chem. Education*, **26**, 207 (1949).
(436) Zhdanov, *J. Gen. Chem. (U.S.S.R.)*, **11**, 471 (1941).
(437) Zmaczynski, *Roczniki Chem.*, **11**, 449 (1931).

Vapor-Liquid Equilibrium Diagrams of Alcohol-Ketone Azeotropes as a Function of Pressure

E. C. BRITTON, H. S. NUTTING, and L. H. HORSLEY

The Dow Chemical Co., Midland, Mich.

Pressure has a marked effect on the azeotropic composition and vapor-liquid equilibrium diagrams of alcohol-ketone systems (*1*). This is due to the fact that the slopes of the vapor pressure curves of alcohols are appreciably greater than for ketones; it results in an unusually larger change in the relative boiling points of the components of an alcohol-ketone system with change in pressure.

As a result of the study of these systems, it has been found that the methanol-acetone azeotrope exhibits the unusual phenomenon of becoming nonazeotropic at both low and high pressures—that is, below 200-mm. pressure the system is nonazeotropic with methanol as the more volatile product, while above 15,000 mm. the system is nonazeotropic with acetone the more volatile component.

Some of the equilibrium data for this system and two other alcohol-ketone azeotropes are shown in Figures 1 and 2 on the following pages.

The similarity of the diagrams for the different systems at suitable pressures is of interest. For example, the diagram for methanol-acetone at 10,000 mm. corresponds approximately to the diagram for methanol–methyl ethyl ketone at 1000 mm. and for ethanol–methyl propyl ketone at 100 mm.

Literature Cited

(1) Britton, E. C., Nutting, H. S., and Horsley, L. H. (to Dow Chemical Co.), U. S. Patent 2,324,255 (July 13, 1943).

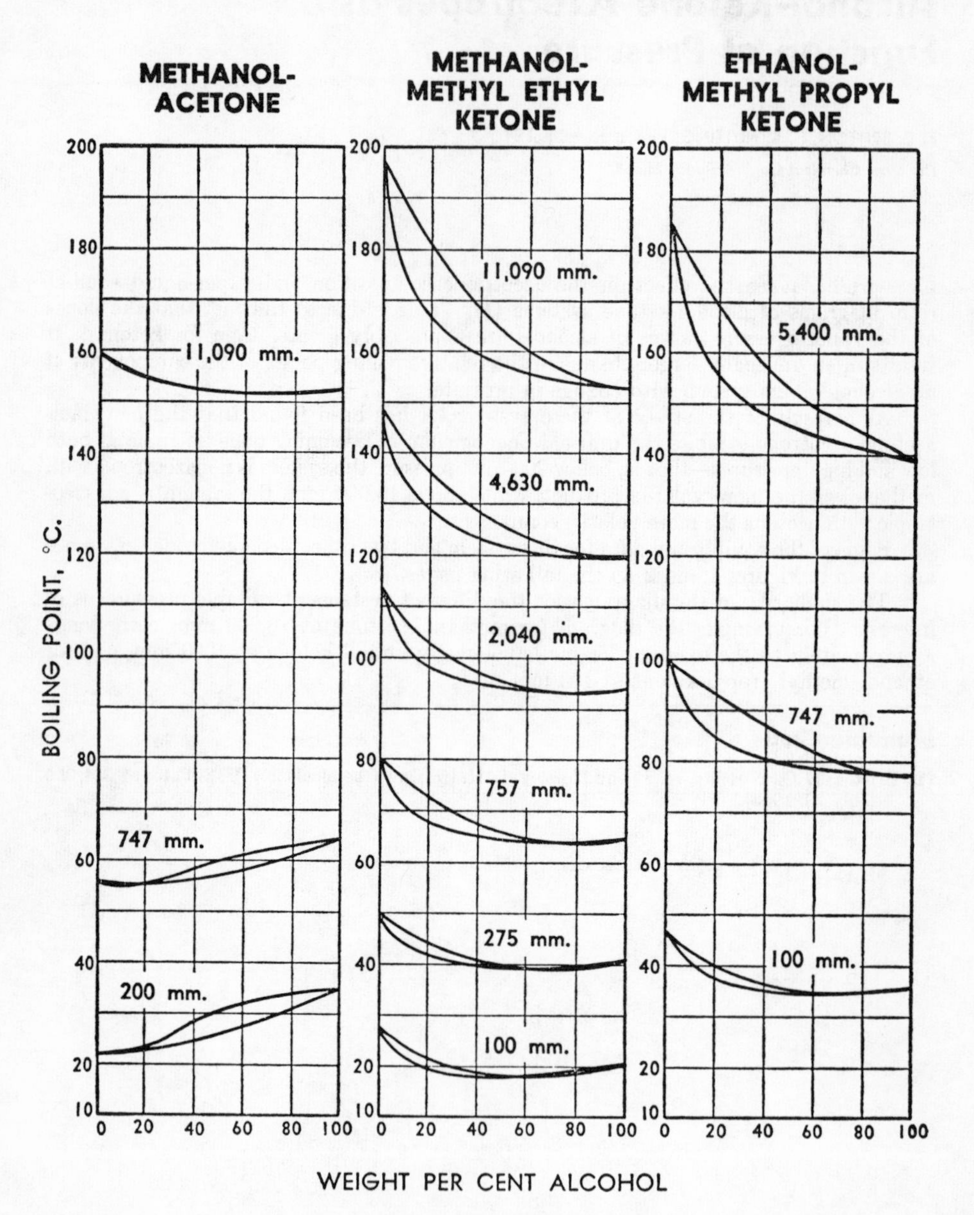

Figure 1. Vapor-Liquid Equilibrium Diagrams of Alcohol–Ketone Systems at Various Pressures

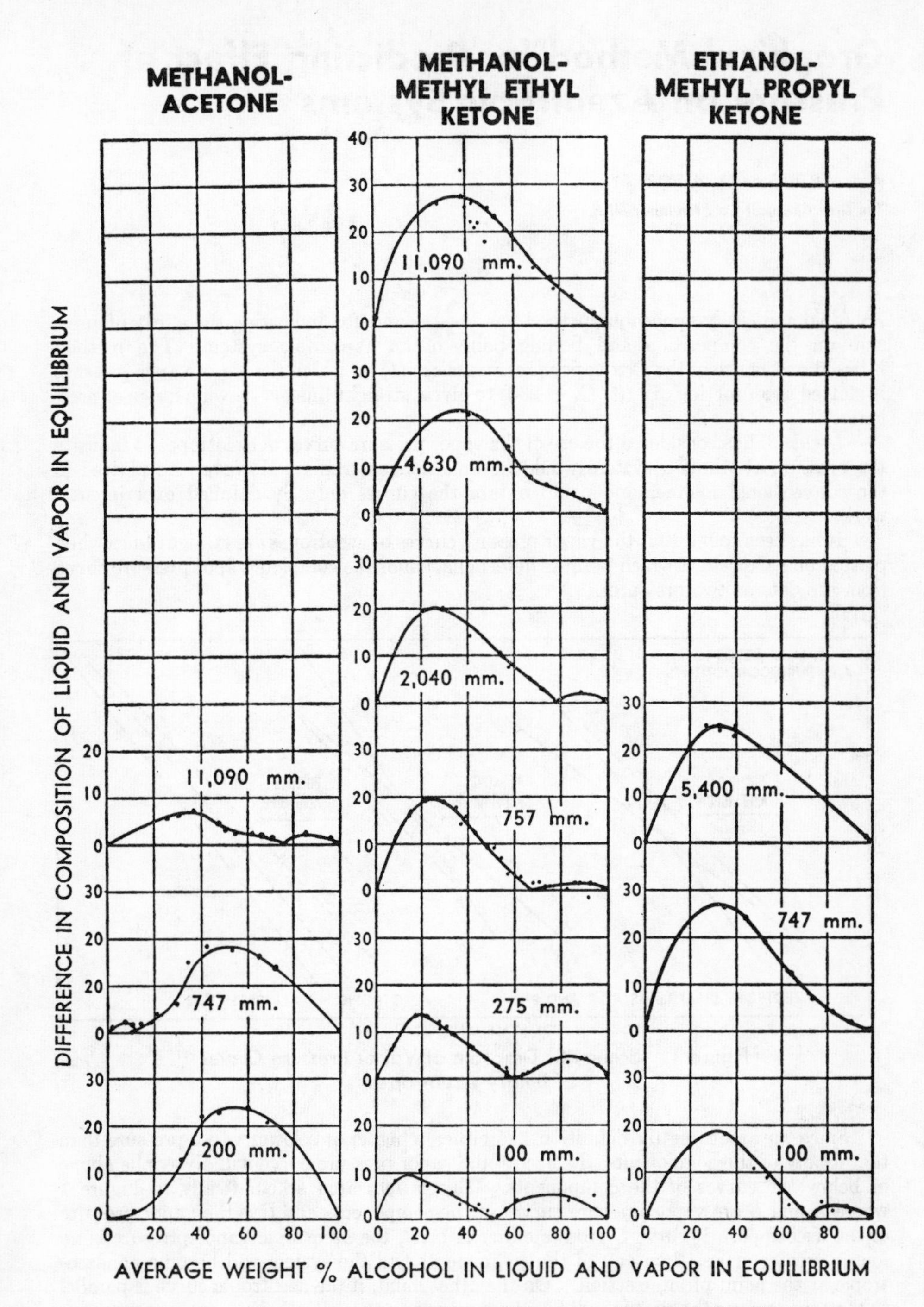

Figure 2. Difference in Composition of Vapor and Liquid in Equilibrium

As a function of corresponding average composition of vapor and liquid for alcohol-ketone systems

Graphical Method for Predicting Effect of Pressure on Azeotropic Systems

H. S. NUTTING and L. H. HORSLEY

The Dow Chemical Co., Midland, Mich.

A rapid and easily applicable method has been found for indicating the effect of pressure on the composition and boiling point of an azeotropic system. The method is based on the use of the Cox vapor pressure chart (*1*) on which the log of vapor pressure is plotted as a function of $1/(t° \text{ C.} + 230)$ to give a straight line over a wide range of pressures.

Lecat (*2*) has considered the use of the vapor pressure curves of azeotropes to indicate the pressure at which a system would become nonazeotropic. However, he plotted in the conventional manner and could obtain the curves only by detailed experimental work.

It has been found that the vapor pressure curves of azeotropes are straight lines when plotted on a Cox chart which permits determination of the complete vapor pressure curve from the data at two pressures.

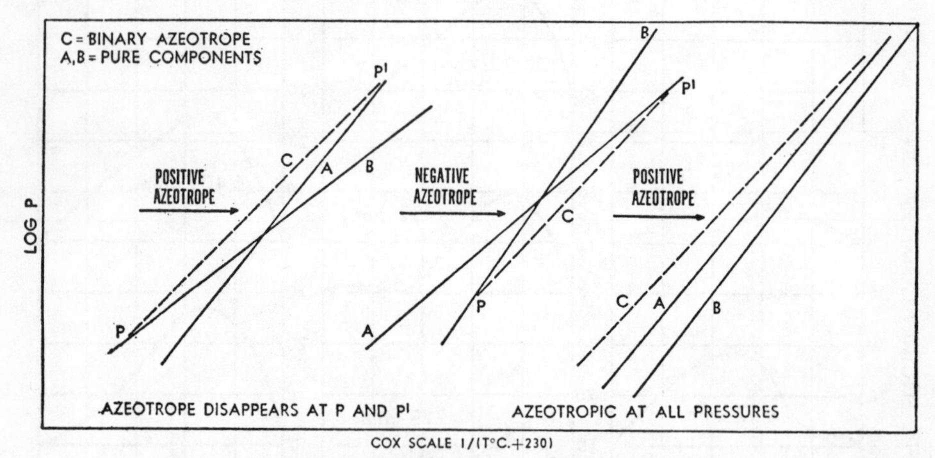

Figure 1. Schematic Diagram of Vapor Pressure Curves of Binary Azeotropes

Since an azeotrope by definition has either a higher or a lower vapor pressure than that of any of the components, the azeotropic vapor pressure curve will always lie above or below the curves of the components. This is indicated schematically in Figure 1 where *A* and *B* are vapor pressure curves of the components and *C* is the vapor pressure of the azeotrope. If curve *C* crosses either *A* or *B*, the azeotropic vapor pressure is no longer greater or less than any of the components and the system will become nonazeotropic at the point of intersection. On the other hand, if the azeotropic curve is parallel to the other curves the system will be azeotropic up to the critical pressure.

The method has been successfully applied to numerous systems, four of which are shown in Figure 2. The azeotrope methanol–methyl ethyl ketone became nonazeotropic

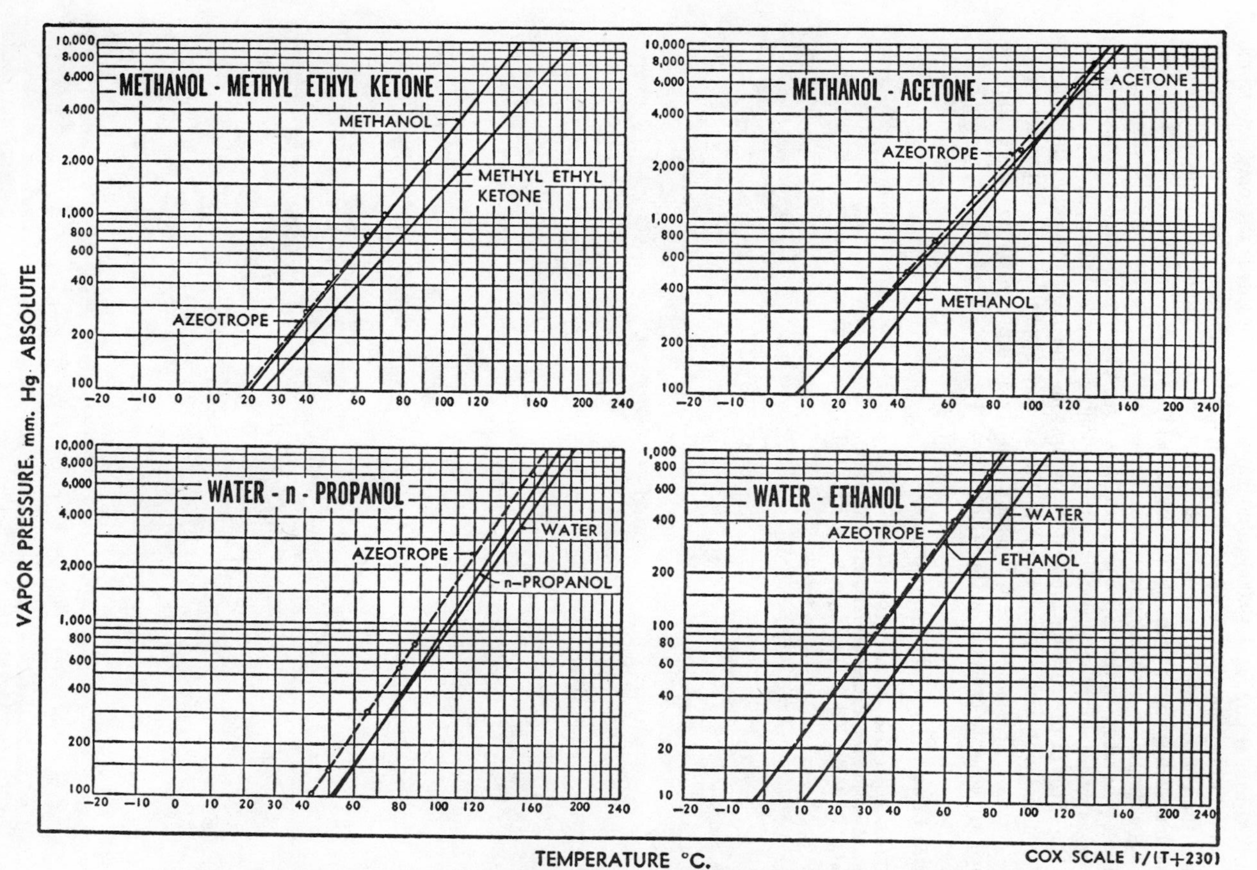

Figure 2. Azeotropic Vapor Pressure Curves of Methanol–Methyl Ethyl Ketone, Methanol-Acetone, Water–*n*-Propanol, and Water-Ethanol

at 3000 mm. of mercury after it was predicted that this would occur at 2000 to 4000 mm. The azeotrope methanol-acetone was studied in detail after it was predicted that the azeotropism would disappear at both low and high pressures. This system is nonazeotropic below 200 mm. of mercury and above 15,000 mm. compared to predicted limits of 200 to 500 mm. and 10,000 to 20,000 mm. While this is the only azeotropic system known to become nonazeotropic at both low and high pressures, there are indications that the phenomenon occurs in several other systems, contrary to the conclusions of Lecat that such systems probably do not exist (*3*).

Caution should be used in extrapolating curves to very low pressures because of the possibility of curvature in the vapor pressure lines over a manyfold range of pressures.

In cases where only the normal azeotropic boiling point is known, it is possible to predict the effect of pressure on the system by drawing the azeotrope curve through the normal boiling point with a slope equal to the average slopes of the component vapor pressure curves. This procedure will permit a fairly accurate prediction of whether the azeotrope will cease to exist below the critical pressure.

Literature Cited

(1) Cox, *Ind. Eng. Chem.*, **15,** 592 (1923).
(2) Lecat, *Ann. soc. sci. Bruxelles*, **49B,** 261–333 (1929).
(3) Lecat, "Traité de Chimie Organique," Vol. 1, p. 139, Paris, Grignard, Mason et Cie., 1935.

Graphical Method for Predicting Azeotropism and Effect of Pressure on Azeotropic Constants

L. H. HORSLEY
The Dow Chemical Co., Midland, Mich.

Lecat (*2*) has devised an analytical method for determining azeotropic boiling points and compositions for certain related groups of binary systems. The method is based on the fact that the composition and boiling point of an azeotrope are related to the relative boiling points of the two components.

Lecat thus obtained a series of equations of the form

$$\delta = a + |\Delta|b + \Delta^2 c$$
$$C = d + \Delta e + \Delta^2 f$$

where Δ = (boiling point of component A) − (boiling point of component B)
$|\Delta|$ = difference in boiling point of A and B (absolute value of Δ)
C = azeotropic composition in weight per cent A
δ = difference in boiling point of azeotrope and the lower boiling component
$a, b, \ldots f$ = constants for a given series of related azeotropes such as methanol-hydrocarbons

Note that Δ may be positive or negative; $|\Delta|$ is always positive.

From a practical standpoint, for determining the azeotropic constants of a system, the plots of the above equations have been found more useful and are given in Figures 1 to 5 for forty-five systems for which data are available. Up to this time only the curve for ethanol–halide hydrocarbons has been published (*1*).

Another use for this set of curves is for estimating the azeotropic boiling point and composition at pressures other than atmospheric. Consider the azeotrope methanol-benzene. Since the vapor pressure curves of methanol and benzene are known, the difference in boiling point, Δ, can be obtained at any pressure. From this value of Δ and the C-Δ curve for methanol-hydrocarbons the azeotropic concentration C at that pressure can be determined. For example, the effect of pressure on the methanol-benzene azeotrope is shown in Table I.

Table I. Effect of Pressure

Pressure, Mm. Hg	Boiling Point, ° C.		Δ, ° C.	Azeotropic Boiling Point, ° C.		C, Weight %	
	Methanol	Benzene		Calcd.	Found	Calcd.	Found
200	35	43	−8	23	26	30	34
400	50	61	−11	39	42	33	36
760	65	80	−15	55	57	39	40
6,000	130	162	−32	125	124	54	55
11,000	153	193	−40	150	149	64	63

A plot of Δ as a function of C from this table is shown in Figure 6. The experimental data are represented by the five points while the smooth curve is identical with the methanol-hydrocarbon curve in Figure 1.

Similar curves and data for other systems over the pressure range indicated are also shown. In each case the curve is the same as the general curves of Figures 1 to 5, while the experimental points are for the particular system and for the pressure range indicated.

In the same way, the δ-$|\Delta|$ curves of Figures 1 to 5 can be used to determine δ and the azeotropic boiling point at any pressure from the value of $|\Delta|$ at that pressure.

While the agreement between predicted and experimental values is far from perfect, the method has served as a valuable guide in estimating effect of pressure on azeotropic systems.

It is recognized that it would be more convenient to be able to plot pressure instead of Δ as a function of C and δ. However, this would require a separate curve for each azeotrope, whereas the above method permits use of a single curve for a large group of systems.

Literature Cited

(1) Lecat, *Ann. soc. sci. Bruxelles*, **55B**, 43 (1935).
(2) Lecat, *Compt. rend.*, **183**, 880 (1926); **184**, 816 (1927); **189**, 990 (1929); *Ann. soc. sci. Bruxelles*, **47B**, 39, 87 (1927); **48B**, 1, 105 (1928); **49B**, 28, 119 (1929); **55B**, 43, 253 (1935); **56B**, 41 (1936); *Atti accad. nazl. Lincei*, (6) **9**, 1121 (1929); *Z. anorg. allgem. Chem.*, **186**, 119 (1930).

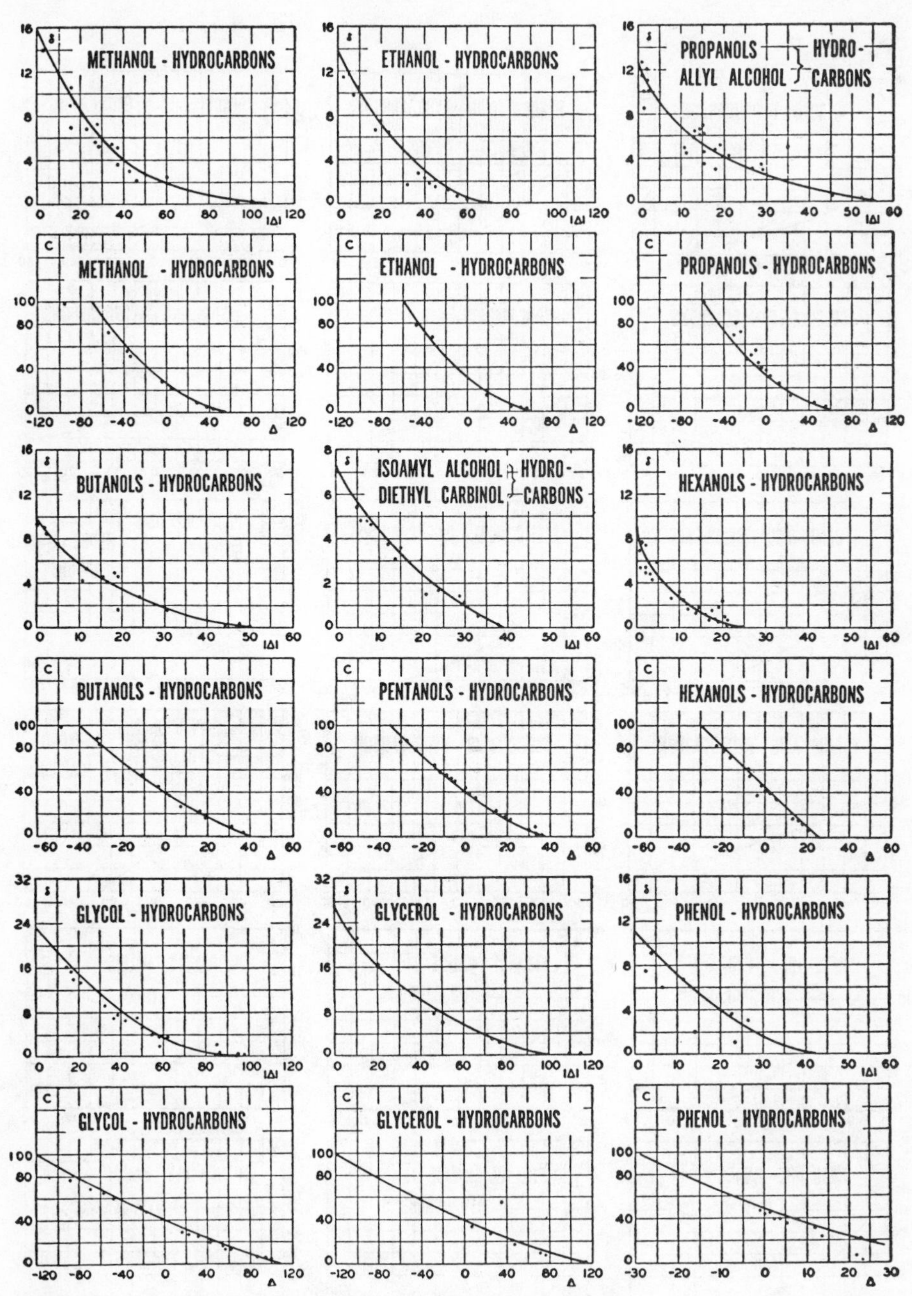

Figure 1. C-Δ and δ-|Δ| Curves for Alcohol-Hydrocarbon, Glycol-Hydrocarbon, and Phenol-Hydrocarbon Systems

C. Azeotropic composition in weight % first component
δ. Boiling point of lower boiling component minus azeotropic boiling point
|Δ|. Absolute difference in boiling points of components
Δ. Boiling point of first component minus boiling point of second component

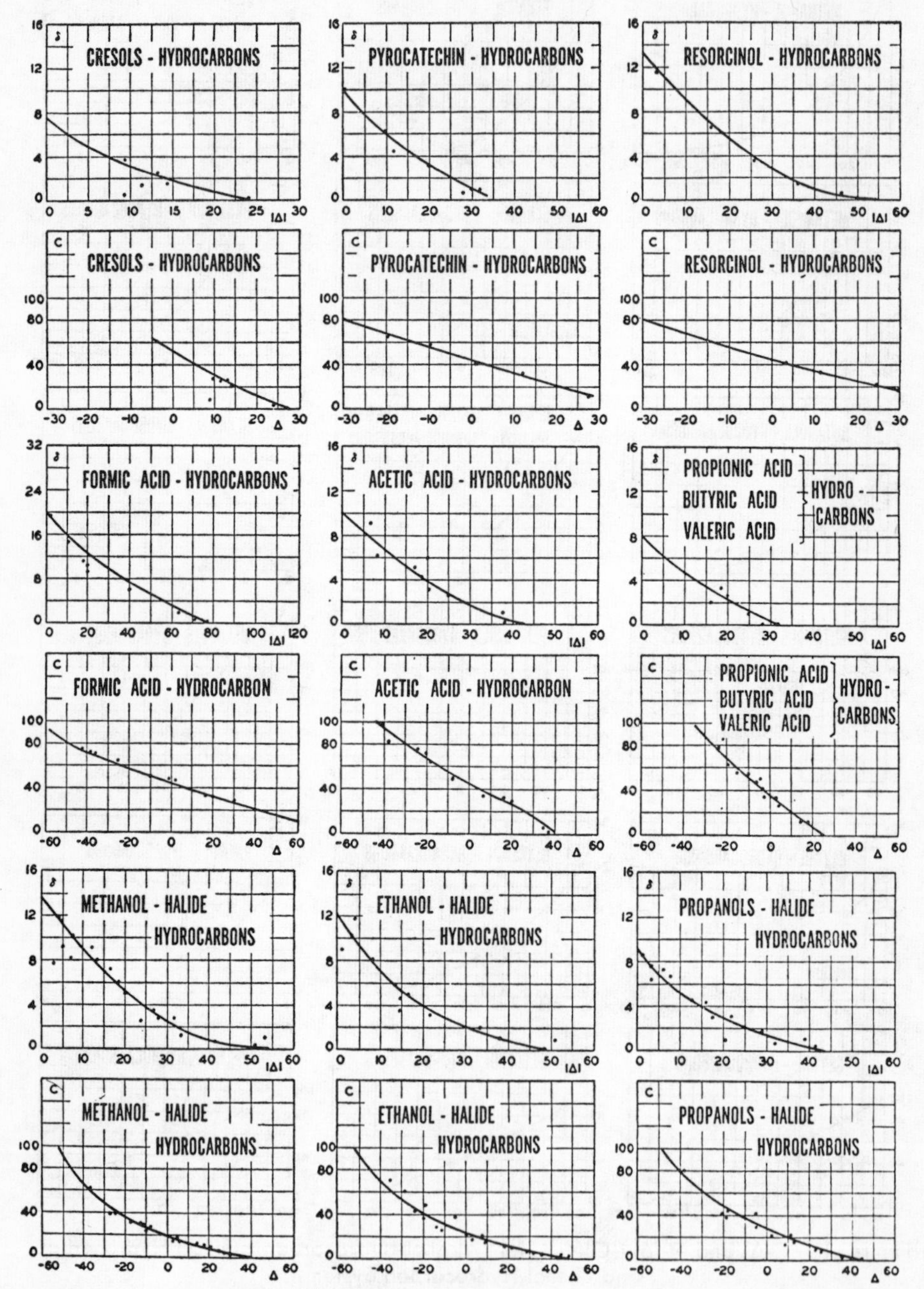

Figure 2. C-Δ and δ-|Δ| Curves for Phenol-Hydrocarbon, Acid-Hydrocarbon, and Alcohol–Halide Hydrocarbon Systems

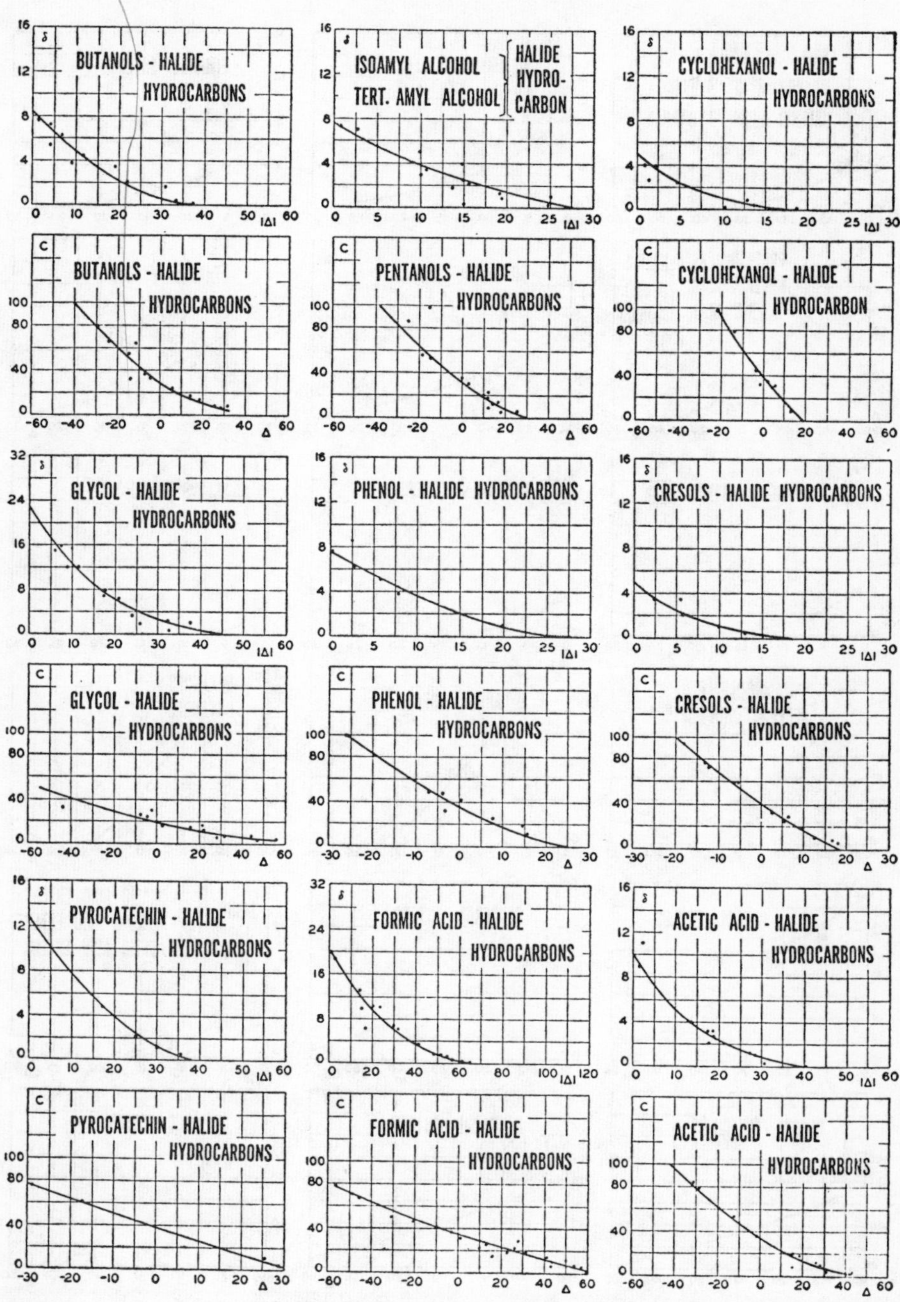

Figure 3. C-Δ and δ-|Δ| Curves for Alcohol–Halide Hydrocarbon, Glycol–Halide Hydrocarbon, Phenol–Halide Hydrocarbon, and Acid–Halide Hydrocarbon Systems

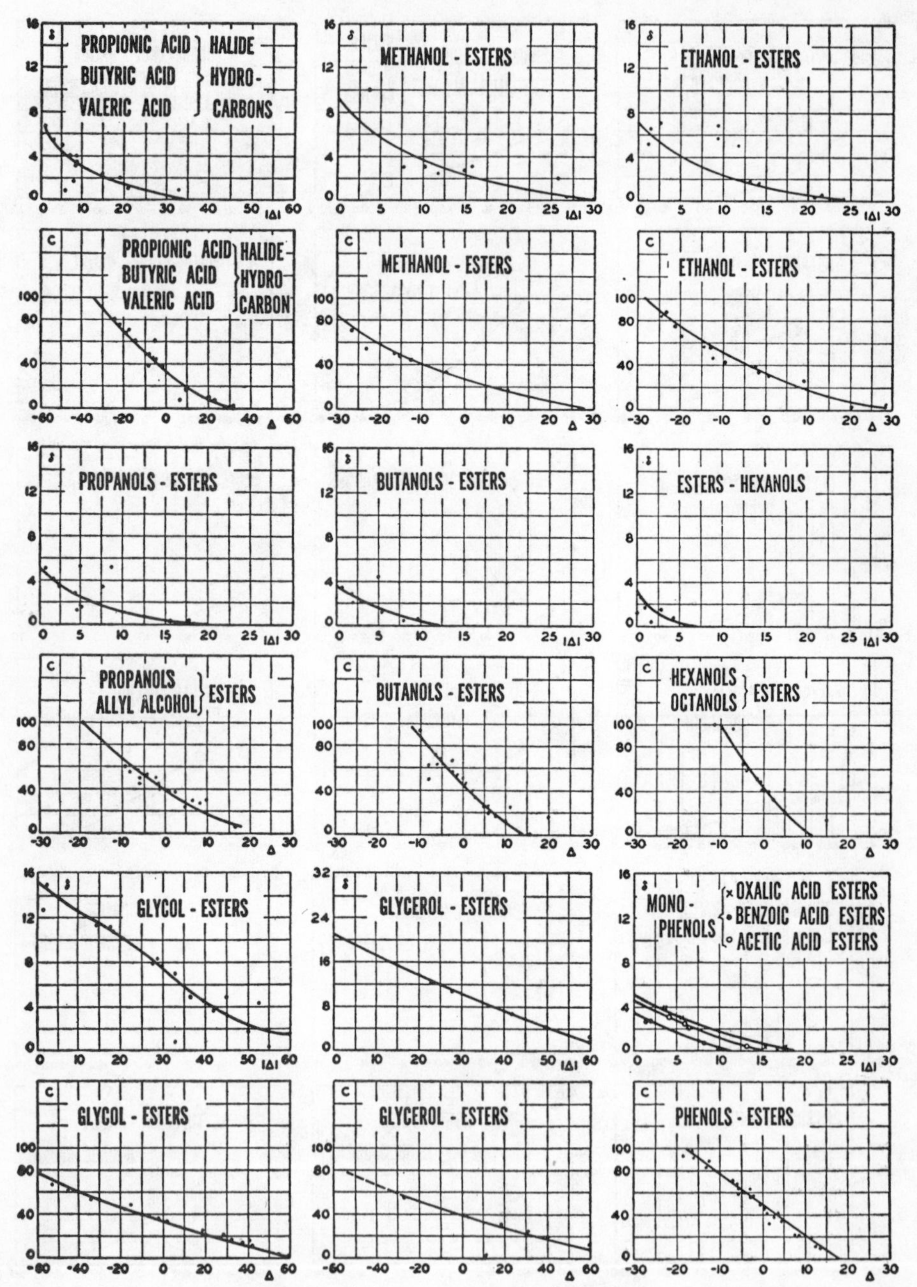

Figure 4. C-Δ and δ-|Δ| Curves for Acid–Halide Hydrocarbon, Alcohol-Ester, Glycol-Ester, and Phenol-Ester Systems

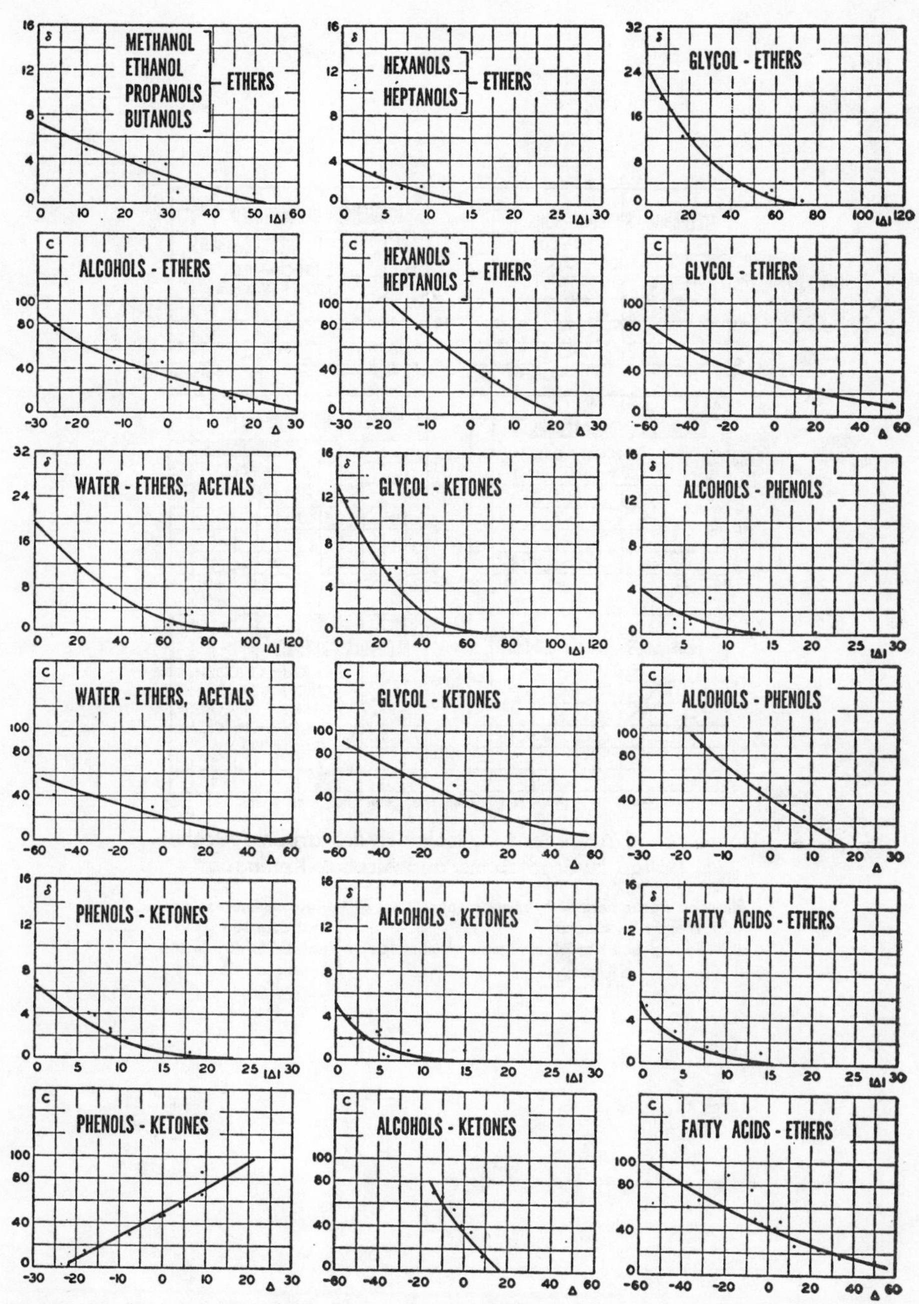

Figure 5. C-Δ and δ-|Δ| Curves for Alcohols-Ethers, Glycols-Ethers, Water-Ethers, Acids-Ethers, Alcohols-Ketones, Glycol-Ketones, Alcohols-Phenols, and Phenols-Ketones

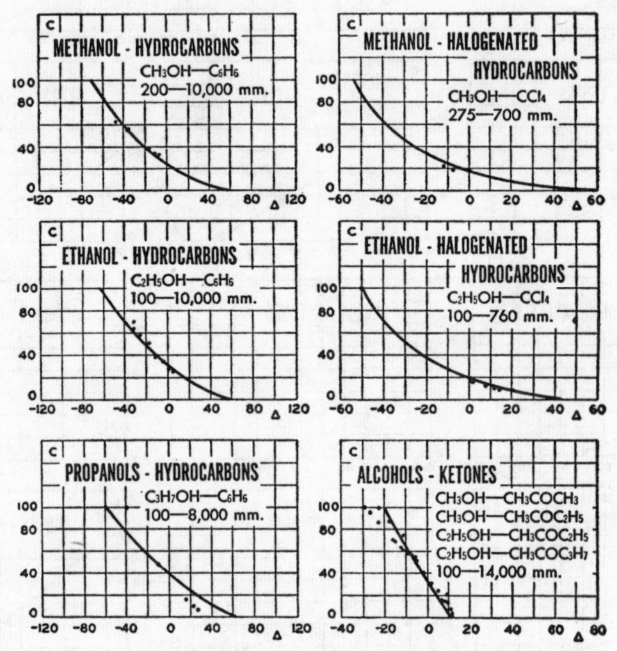

Figure 6. C-Δ Curves for Alcohol-Hydrocarbons, Alcohol–Halide Hydrocarbons, and Alcohols-Ketones

Showing agreement with experimental data at various pressures

C. Weight % alcohol

Δ. Boiling point of alcohol minus boiling point { hydrocarbon / halide hydrocarbon / ketone }